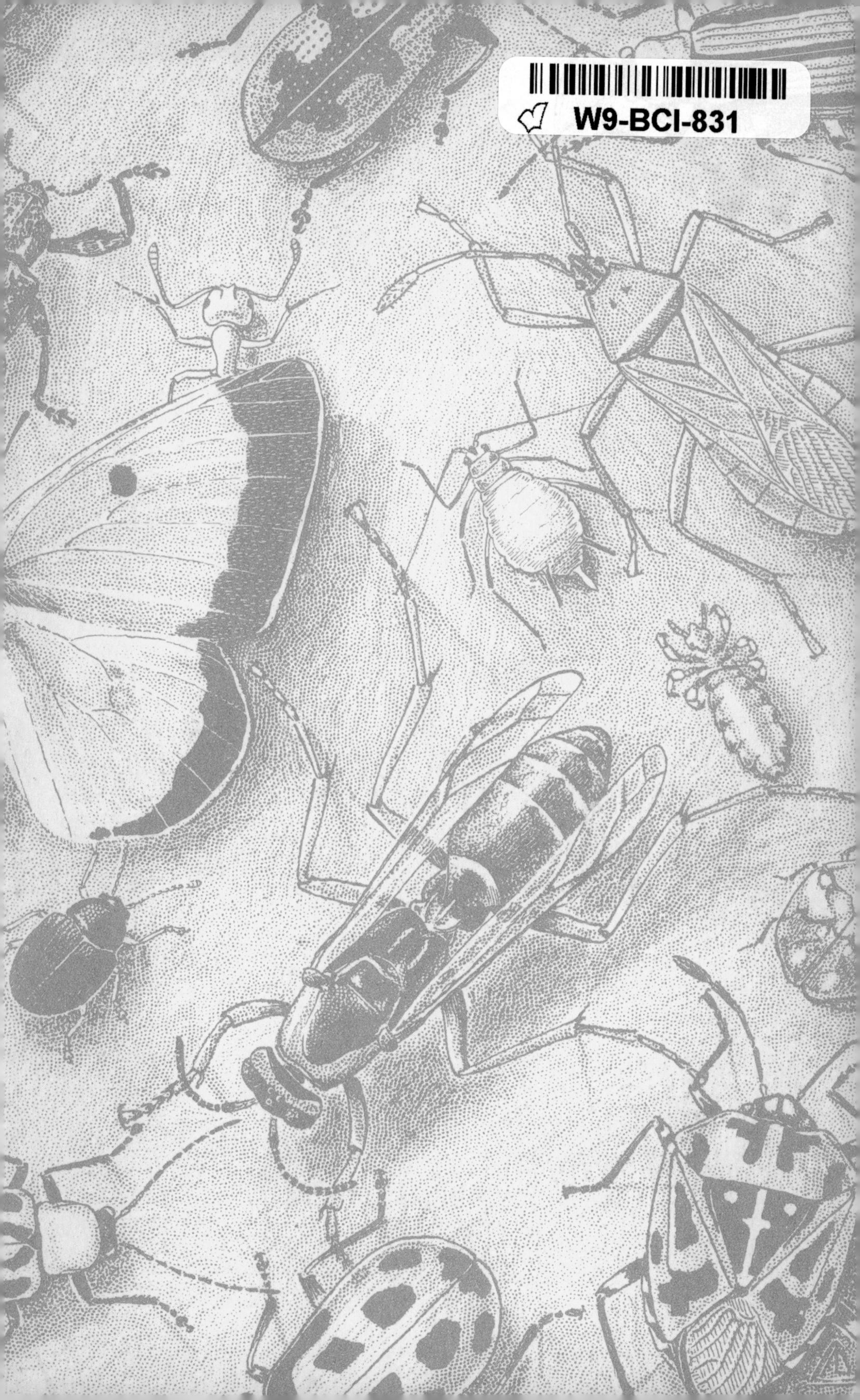

82d Congress, 2d Session, House Document No. 413

The Yearbook of Agriculture

1952

For sale by the Superintendent of Documents, Washington 25, D. C. - Price $2.50

Insects

THE YEARBOOK OF AGRICULTURE 1952

United States

Department

of Agriculture

Washington, D. C.

UNITED STATES GOVERNMENT PRINTING OFFICE

The Yearbook Committee

Bureau of Entomology and Plant Quarantine	F. C. BISHOPP, *chairman*
	G. J. HAEUSSLER
	H. L. HALLER
	W. L. POPHAM
	B. A. PORTER
	E. R. SASSCER
	J. S. WADE
Bureau of Animal Industry	BENJAMIN SCHWARTZ
Bureau of Plant Industry, Soils, and Agricultural Engineering	KARL S. QUISENBERRY
Office of Experiment Stations	E. R. MC GOVRAN
Office of Information	ALFRED STEFFERUD, *editor*

Foreword

THIS PRACTICAL BOOK GIVES farmers and many other persons a great deal of information about the useful insects, as well as the harmful ones which are estimated to cost us four billion dollars a year.

It is a timely book. In helping us combat our insect enemies it helps us produce more food, feed, fiber, and wood, all of which we need more than ever before.

It is also a disturbing book—and that, to me, is one of its virtues. Although the science of entomology has made great progress in the past two decades, the problems caused by insects seem to be bigger than ever. We have more insect pests, although we have better insecticides to use against them and better ways to fight them. Effective though our quarantines are against foreign pests, some of them are slipping through and require vigorous attention. Many aspects need to be considered in the control of insects. We must stop the destruction of our crops and forests, but the insecticides we use must leave no dangerous residues on foods, destroy no beneficial wildlife, and do no damage to our soils.

We thought we had some of the problems solved when we got such good results from the new insecticides. DDT, for example, made medical history in 1943 and 1944 when an outbreak of typhus in Naples was controlled in a few weeks by its use. Entomologists hoped then that DDT could end all insect-borne diseases and even eradicate the house fly. In less than a decade, however, DDT was found to be a failure against the body louse in Korea, and the specter of typhus hung over that area. DDT and the insecticides substituted for it failed to control mosquitoes in some places. In 1952 the house fly was no longer controlled in many places by any of the residual-type insecticides in use, and it seemed likely that other pests (those of agricultural, as well as medical, importance) in time would develop resistance.

The answer, like the challenge, is clear.

We dare not think of any knowledge—least of all knowledge of living things—as static, fixed, or finished. We need to push on to new horizons of thinking and investigation and, reaching them, see newer horizons. We need a longer view in research and an appreciation that it can have two goals: First, practical, everyday results that can be expressed in terms of definite methods, tools, and advice, and, second, fundamental, basic knowledge, on which the applied science rests.

A book like this and the long research that made it possible exemplify the first goal. But if we are to progress further in this vital work, we need to keep the second goal always before us, remembering that science and knowledge are ever-growing and ever-changing.

CHARLES F. BRANNAN, *Secretary of Agriculture.*

Preface

INTO THIS YEARBOOK HAVE GONE the results of nearly 100 years of the study of insects. The Bureau of Entomology and Plant Quarantine, which was responsible in large measure for the book, traces its origins that far back. The century has seen great changes in farming methods, the intensiveness and extent of agriculture, transportation, and crops. All have affected profoundly our relationships with insects. We hope this Yearbook will be a contribution to the general understanding of those relationships and to the efficiency and well-being of American farming and living.

Insects takes its place in the new Yearbook series that began in 1936 and has dealt successively with plant and animal genetics, soils, nutrition, economics, climate, livestock diseases, developments in agricultural sciences, grass, trees, and the processing of farm products. Some of those volumes can be bought from the Superintendent of Documents, Government Printing Office, Washington 25, D. C. He will quote the prices on request. No person in the Department of Agriculture has copies for general distribution.

Some of them are out of print—that is, they cannot be bought from the Government Printing Office. (They are available in nearly every public library in the country, however, and used copies are not very hard to come by.)

Sometimes we are asked why we do not reprint the old books. We give several reasons. Although the information in them remains basically correct, recent scientific developments would make certain revisions necessary. Even small changes and additions very likely would mean new plates for many pages, and the cost of the second edition might be the same as that of the first. Also, many subjects of great importance to farmers and other citizens are waiting to be treated in Yearbooks. Among them, for example, are plant diseases, marketing of farm goods, the farm home, the small farm, and water. We look upon the published and the projected Yearbooks all together as an inclusive, authoritative agricultural library. We select the Yearbook subjects (two or three years in advance) on the basis of need and interest, as indicated in communications and comments from farmers and others, as well as the availability of research findings and writers. We try to avoid duplicating material to which farmers have easy access elsewhere.

A number of persons contributed greatly to this book. C. F. W. Muesebeck and A. M. Vance, of the Bureau of Entomology and Plant Quarantine, gave valuable advice and help on a number of technical matters.

Arthur D. Cushman, also of that Bureau, made most of the color illustrations, many of the line drawings, and the end papers. Edwin Way Teale took seven of the eight photographs. The eighth was supplied by Frank M. Carpenter.

ALFRED STEFFERUD, *Editor of the Yearbook.*

Contents

Introducing the Insects

How To Know an Insect

Insects as Helpers

Warnings as to Insecticides

Resistance to Insecticides

Fumigants

Quarantines

Other Controls

Economic Entomology

Insects, Man, and Homes

Insects on Cotton

Insects and Vegetables

Insects on Fruit

Insects on Field Crops

Pests on Ornamentals

Livestock and Insects

Forests, Trees, and Pests

Insects and Wildlife

Bibliography and Appendix

Some Important Insects

Some Important Insects

970134°—52——2

Insects

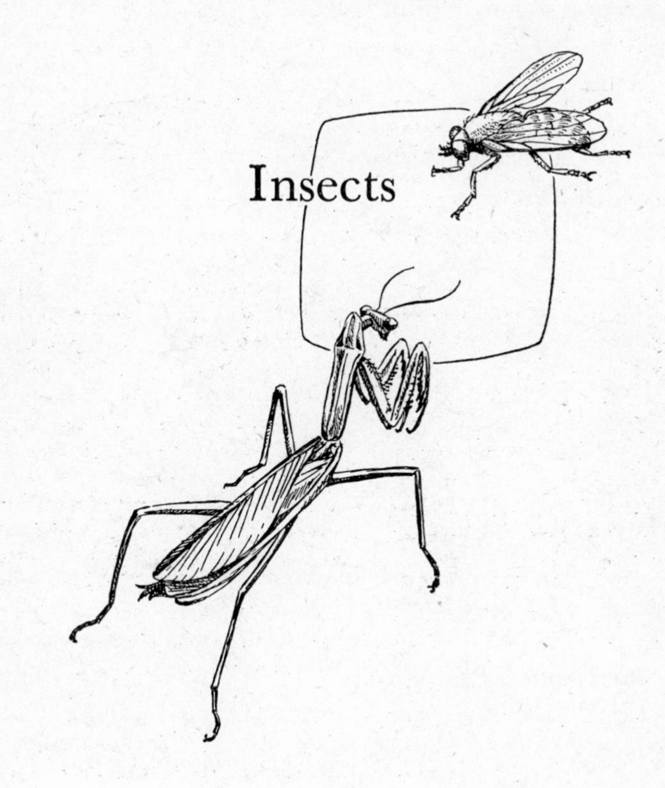

Introducing the Insects

How Many Insects Are There?

Curtis W. Sabrosky

When people ask, "How many insects are there?" they usually want answers to two different questions: How many *kinds* of insects are there? What is the total number of *individual* insects in the world? An honest answer to both is: Nobody knows exactly.

The number of kinds, or species, is so great that entomologists cannot keep an accurate count, except for small groups. The number of kinds that have already been described and named is estimated by various scientists at 625,000 to 1,500,000. No one can even guess when the big tally will be finished. For such huge groups as beetles and flies, an exact count may never be possible, although generally the numbers of the smaller groups can be tallied more accurately.

Workers in the division of insect identification of the Department of Agriculture estimate that by the end of 1948 approximately 686,000 different species of insects had been described and named for the entire world. In addition were some 9,000 species of ticks and mites, which are not true insects but look like insects to the lay person.

About two-fifths of the known kinds of insects are beetles. Moths and butterflies, ants, bees, wasps, and true flies comprise another two-fifths.

For North America, north of Mexico, the latest figures show nearly 82,500 kinds of insects, plus 2,613 kinds of ticks and mites. Just as for the world, beetles far outnumber other kinds of insect life, with ants, bees and wasps, and the true flies having a good share. The moths and butterflies, which run second to beetles in the world as a whole, are in fourth place in our area, with 10,300 species. The true bugs are not far behind, with 8,700 species. The remaining 5,400 species belong to the other 19 orders.

Not all 82,500 kinds live in the same locality or even in the same region. The mountains and the plains, the great swamps of the Everglades and peaks of the Sierras, the deserts of the Southwest and the northern forests—each has its own particular insects. Some kinds live only on the very top of a mountain or two. Others are found in many States.

How many species can we expect to find in any one State? For most States we have no totals. A few tabulations, made in various years, are available:

	Total insects	*Flies*
Connecticut	8,869	1,565
Michigan	......	3,233
New England	......	3,304
New Jersey	10,385	1,661
New York	15,449	3,615
North Carolina	11,094	2,111

From them we can deduce that States of average topography, climate, and vegetation might have 10,000 to 15,000 kinds; there might be fewer species in the smaller States and more in the larger ones that have wide ranges of growing seasons, types of plants, elevation, and so on.

How many insects are injurious to man? Entomologists estimated some years ago that approximately 6,500 species of insects in the United States were important enough to be called public enemies. Today the number is probably closer to 10,000.

How do the numbers of insects compare with those of other animals? In current books on zoology, estimates of the total number of described species of animals range from 823,000 to 1,115,000. If the number of kinds of insects is between 625,000 and 900,000, probably 70 to 80 percent of all the known kinds of animals are insects. That proportion has held quite steady in the estimates of many zoologists for the past century or more.

The starting point of our modern system of naming animals is 1758. In that year the names, pedigrees, and descriptions of all the animals then known were printed in one book of only 824 pages, the *Systema Naturae* by the great Swedish naturalist, Carolus Linnaeus. He listed 4,379 kinds of animals, of which 1,937 were insects. From that beginning, knowledge has expanded greatly as scientists explored the lesser known parts of the earth from pole to pole and the crannies of the better known places, their own back yards. Within 100 years, nearly 100,000 kinds of insects had been identified. By 1900 the total was about 300,000. It has more than doubled since then. Each year now about 6,000 or 7,000 kinds of insects are described and named for the first time.

Today a mere list of the scientific names of the known insects (based on a conservative estimate of the total number), without one word of description or anything else, in a book with two columns to a page and print fine enough for 100 lines in each column, would fill a volume of 3,300 pages. To say it in another way: If the names were printed one to a line in an 8-page, 8-column newspaper of average size, without headlines and pictures, more than 8 weeks, including Sundays, would be needed to print only the names of the insects that are already known in the world.

WHAT IS THE REAL TOTAL? So far, we have been considering the number of different species of insects that have been described and named. But how many kinds would there be if all were known and named? No one can say for sure, but the question has provoked a good deal of speculation. Recent guesses vary from 2,500,000 to 10,000,000 different kinds.

Maybe there are not quite so many as some people think, however. For example, a listing in 1949 of the termites of the world recognized 1,717 distinct species, even though some previous estimates ranged as high as 2,600 species. For North America, north of Mexico, there are 41 distinct species, compared to 59 in earlier lists, because further study showed that some proposed names applied only to subspecies or color varieties or were simply synonyms, that is, duplication of names for the same species. That experience in a small and intensively studied group may be repeated to an even greater extent in some of the larger groups. Even so, many really new and hitherto unknown kinds of insects are being found and described every day somewhere in the world, and their number should far exceed any decrease caused by duplication of names. The final roll call may be far short of 10 million but it seems sure to be somewhere in the millions.

THE NUMBER of individual insects, the second part of our question, is a tremendous problem in itself. No one dares to guess the answer for the world, or a country, or a State. Even for smaller areas, such as acres or square miles, any figures are only approximations based on square-foot samples or similar measures. In any given area, the population of insects will not only depend on such things as the soil and the plants, but it will vary from season to season and even from one minute to the next. Still, samples will give us some ideas of the normal population.

Sometimes insects break out of their usual population by swarming or migrating or by sudden bursts of thousands or millions of individuals that cover sidewalks or lay waste mile after mile of grain fields or strip leaves from thousands of trees. Then we can make special counts or estimates of the size of the crowd. Many other figures are also available for such concentrations of insects as occur in beehives, ant nests, and termite colonies. Let us look at a few of the many facts that are known about the numbers of insects.

Great reproductive capacity is common among insects. One example: In one summer season from April to August, the descendants of one pair of house flies, if all lived and reproduced normally, would make a total of 191,000,000,000,000,000,000. But fortunately reproduction usually does not go on at full speed. Other insects, birds, diseases, insecticides, and weather take a toll of the eggs that are laid and the young that are born.

Many calculations have been made for aphids, or plant-lice, because they have many generations in a season. Glenn W. Herrick found that the cabbage aphid, which had an average of 41 young per female, had 16 generations between March 31 and October 2 in New York State. If all lived, the descendants of one female aphid would amount to 1,560,000,000,000,000,000,000,000 by the end of the season. Such related kinds as the melon aphid or the cotton aphid will have twice as many offspring per female and more generations per year in the South.

Not all kinds of insects are so prolific. Some have very few young, some have only one family each year, and some take years to grow from egg to adult. But even such insects, if common enough, may be very numerous. Consider a slow breeder like the famous periodical cicada, or 17-year locust; the swarms that result when one of its broods emerges from the ground after a 17-year childhood will always be remembered by those who have seen them. As many as 40,000 cicadas may emerge from the ground under a large-sized tree. Sometimes the emergence holes are so close together that 84 of them can be counted in a square foot of soil surface.

Some insects lay eggs continuously over long periods. Especially is that true among the social insects, those that are organized into societies such as nests, hives, or colonies. Ant queens have been known to lay as many as 340 eggs a day. Honey bee queens can lay 1,500 to 2,000 eggs a day. Termites, the so-called white ants, hold the record: The queen is a specialized machine for turning out eggs day after day. Alfred E. Emerson, an authority on termites, has stated that a capacity of 6,000 to 7,000 eggs a day is not unusual for specialized termite queens, which may live from 15 to 50 years. Many years ago, in four different queens of an East African termite, *Macrotermes bellicosus*, Karl Escherich observed an egg-laying rate of one egg every 2 seconds, or 43,000 a day. We do not know, of course, how long eggs are laid at such record rates. Under natural conditions the daily number may vary a good deal. But in large colonies and under good conditions, egg production is certainly a highly developed big business.

A remarkable method of reproduction in some insects is polyembryony, a process whereby two or more young result from a single egg. In its simplest form, one egg divides into two, just as identical twins originate in the higher animals. But some insects do not stop there. The parts of the original egg may keep on dividing. In some species as many as 1,500 to 2,500 insects finally result from a single egg. L. O. Howard, in his book *The Insect Menace,* said he found that nearly 3,000 small parasitic wasps emerged from a single caterpillar in which probably no more than a dozen eggs had been laid. Polyembryony occurs in parasitic insects, a fact of obvious importance to man when he uses them to fight his insect battles for him.

Swarms or outbreaks of insects—the spurts or surges of numbers that attract attention—are the natural result of such potential powers of reproduction. They may be a normal part of the life of the insect, such as mating flights or swarms of honey bees. Or they may occur when something happens to tip the balance of nature and give a head start to some insect with great powers of reproduction.

Probably everyone has seen such a swarm or outbreak—a great flight of mayflies, whose dead bodies wash up on the shores of lakes in large windrows, the swarming of honey bees, the flights of ants and termites, the migrations of locusts and butterflies, armyworms, periodical cicadas, or chinch bugs on the march into corn fields. A fantastic number of individual insects might be in such a mass outbreak, and their damage could be almost beyond belief—whether the earth is scorched by swarms of locusts and grasshoppers or the destruction caused by less conspicuous insects. In Canada in 1919 and 1920, for example, an outbreak of the spruce budworm destroyed a volume of wood said to be equal to a 40-year supply for all the pulp mills then operating in Canada.

Tremendous swarms of locusts, such as described in the Bible as a plague on the Children of Israel in Egypt, are reported in many parts of the world. We have figures for outbreaks in Africa and the Near East. For the Moroccan locust, workers found as many as 6,000 egg pods per square yard, with an average of 30 to 35 eggs in a pod. During a campaign against migratory locusts in western Turkey, collectors gathered 430 tons of eggs and 1,200 tons of locusts in 3 months.

The most spectacular examples in the United States are the migrating swarms of Rocky Mountain grasshoppers in the Great Plains in the 1870's. The locusts are said to have left fields as barren as if they had been burned over. Only holes in the ground showed where plants had been. Trees were stripped of their leaves and green bark. One observer in Nebraska recorded that one of the invading swarms of locusts averaged a half mile in height and was 100 miles wide and 300 miles long. In places the column, seen through field glasses and measured by surveying instruments, was nearly a mile high. With an estimate of 27 locusts per cubic yard, he figured nearly 28 million per cubic mile. He said the swarm was as thick as that for at least 6 hours and moved at least 5 miles an hour. He calculated that more than 124 billion locusts were on the move in that one migration.

Not always is the occurrence of large numbers of insects harmful. In the mountains of California and elsewhere, lady beetles (or ladybirds) overwinter in masses in sheltered places. Two men working together can sometimes collect from 50 to 100 pounds of beetles in a day. Judging by the average weight of each beetle, one can figure that such collections contain 1,200,000 to 2,400,000 beetles. It is thus possible to gather large numbers of these insect-eating beetles and later release them in places where they will attack insects that are feeding on crops.

Migrations of butterflies are especially striking. Millions of butterflies may fly for days and as far as 2,000 miles, and the migrating swarm may be several hundred miles in width. Such flights apparently are more common in other parts of the world, but some have been recorded in the United States. The monarch butterfly (or common milkweed butterfly) is a regular commuter. Each fall, individuals of this species fly south, and some of them may make the return trip of 1,000 miles or so the following spring.

In Texas in the summer of 1921, C. H. Gable and W. A. Baker recorded a migration of snout butterflies, *Libytheana bachmanii,* which were so numerous that an average of about 1,250,000 of them per minute flew across a front 250 miles wide. At the main observation point the migration continued at the same level of intensity for 18 days.

THE NORMAL POPULATION of insects, not counting swarms or unusual increases, has been studied for some situations and some species. The best figures we have are for insects living in the soil, probably because it is easier to get practically complete samples of the population. Even so, the data are hard to compare because the studies are so different: Different kinds of soil or time of year, samples taken down to different depths, and treated in different ways that might or might not find such small things as mites and springtails. Because those two kinds far outnumber all other animals in most soils and forest litter, a small difference in technique could make a difference of millions per acre in the number of insects reported.

Studies of grassland insects in England, in which the top 9 to 12 inches of soil was examined, disclosed totals for insects and mites that ranged up to several hundred million per acre.

Even for specific kinds of insects, the estimates may be unbelievably high. For example, certain wireworms, such as the larvae of *Agriotes* beetles, have been found in numbers calculated to be from 3 million to 25 million per acre. In most of the reports, mites and springtails formed two-thirds or more of the total; in some, the number of springtails was nine-tenths of the total for insects.

The population of arthropods (jointed-legged invertebrate animals—insects, mites, centipedes, and such) in the forest litter and humus also has been studied. From samples taken to a depth of 5 inches in oak and pine stands on stony clay and sandy soils in North Carolina, A. S. Pearse calculated that there were approximately 124 million animals per acre. Of these, nearly 90 million were mites, 28 million springtails, and 4.5 million other insects. In a scrub oak area in Pennsylvania with apparently a richer forest litter, C. H. Hoffmann and his coworkers found an average of 9,759 arthropods per square foot of surface in 2 inches of litter and 1 inch of humus. That figures out to 425 million per acre. As in Pearse's study, the mites were the most abundant kind of animal, averaging 294 million per acre. Springtails averaged 119 million, with only 11 million for all other arthropods. The number per acre is an estimate based on the average of square-foot samples. It may be smaller in some parts of an area and much larger in others.

A CENSUS OF COLONIES of social insects is easy compared to the difficulties of counting or estimating the general insect population. Many figures have been published for ants, termites, bees, and wasps, some being actual counts and some estimates based on samples.

Ants differ greatly in the size of their colonies, from small nests with a dozen workers to large and populous nests with several hundred thousand. E. A. Andrews calculated that an ant colony in Jamaica had 630,000 individuals, nine-tenths of them workers. Large nests of *Formica* in Europe are generally agreed to contain an average of 150,000 to 200,000 ants. In a 10-acre study area in Maryland, E. N. Cory and Elizabeth Haviland found 73 mounds of various sizes of the Allegheny mound ant. In two mounds studied, they found 41,000 and 238,000 ants. From these figures, and the approximate relation between size of mound and number of ants, they calculated an average of about 27 ants for every square foot of the 10 acres.

Colonies of termites vary in size as much as ant nests do. Some have a few hundred individuals at most, but others may have several million. The colonies are relatively small in the United States, and a nest with a quarter of a million termites is a very large one. The records for size go to the tropical species, especially those that build large nests in the soil. Alfred E. Emerson found 3 million termites in a colony of the South American *Nasutitermes surinamensis*. F. G. Holdaway and his colleagues recorded from 750,000 to 1,806,000 termites in several

Known Species of Insects and Other Animals

Group	*Common names*	*Estimate by Metcalf and Flint (1939, 1951)*	*Estimate by Ross (1948)*
Insecta	Insects	640, 000	900, 000
Other Arthropoda	Spiders, centipedes, crawfish, etc	73, 500	50, 000
Mollusca	Clams and other shellfish, snails	80, 000	80, 000
Chordata	Mammals, birds, fish, reptiles, etc	60, 000	38, 000
All other animals	Sponges, corals, worms, etc	62, 500	47, 000
Total		916, 000	1, 115, 000

Number of Described Species of Insects, Ticks, and Mites at the End of 1948

Order	*Common names*	*World*	*North America, north of Mexico*
Anoplura	Sucking lice (true lice)	250	62
Coleoptera	Beetles, weevils, twisted-winged insects.	277, 000	26, 676
Collembola	Springtails	2, 000	314
Corrodentia	Booklice, barklice	1, 100	120
Dermaptera	Earwigs	1, 100	18
Diptera	Flies, mosquitoes, gnats	85, 000	16, 700
Embioptera	Embiids	149	8
Ephemeroptera	Mayflies	1, 500	550
Hemiptera	True bugs and Homoptera (cicadas, leafhoppers, aphids, scale insects).	55, 000	8, 742
Hymenoptera	Ants, bees, wasps	103, 000	14, 528
Isoptera	Termites ("white ants")	1, 717	41
Lepidoptera	Butterflies and moths	112, 000	10, 300
Mallophaga	Biting lice (bird lice)	2, 675	318
Mecoptera	Scorpionflies	350	66
Neuroptera	Lacewings, ant-lions, dobsonflies	4, 670	338
Odonata	Dragonflies, damselflies	4, 870	412
Orthoptera	Grasshoppers, crickets, roaches, mantids, katydids.	22, 500	1, 015
Plecoptera	Stoneflies	1, 490	340
Protura		90	29
Siphonaptera	Fleas	1, 100	238
Thysanoptera	Thrips	3, 170	606
Thysanura	Bristletails, "silverfish"	700	50
Trichoptera	Caddisflies	4, 450	921
Zoraptera		19	2
Total		685, 900	82, 394
Acarina	Ticks	440	113
	Mites	8, 700	2, 500

mounds of *N. exitiosus* in Australia.

Honey bees have long been the subject of insect censuses. Jan Swammerdam in 1737 counted the cells and bees of three Dutch straw hives. In 1740 René de Réaumur counted 43,008 bees in a large swarm.

Strong colonies in modern beehives contain about 55,000 bees. As many as 30,000 may leave a hive in a swarm.

A good colony with a vigorous queen should produce about 200,000 bees in a year. The normal egg production during the lifetime of a queen bee has been estimated to be as high as 1,500,000, but probably it does not usually exceed 500,000.

Some wild species of bees may also have large colonies. In the South American stingless bees (*Trigona*), 50,000 to 100,000 individuals may be in a single nest. The largest known nest of a tropical bee, *Trigona postica,* had 27 combs with about 64,000 cells and 70,000 to 80,000 adult bees.

The social wasps and hornets have rather small colonies. The largest nests range from a few hundred individuals to several thousand.

How many insects are there? And how many kinds of insects? Maybe we shall never know. But wherever we go and whether we see them or not, we are surrounded by countless millions of insects. Every forest, every field, every back yard, every roadway is a gigantic insect zoo. A wide world of endless variety and interest is open to all who will do a little investigating on their own.

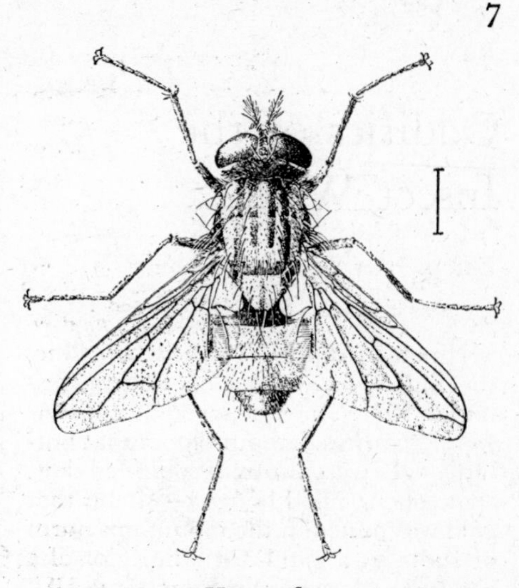

House fly.

CURTIS W. SABROSKY *has been a specialist in Diptera (flies) in the division of insect identification of the Bureau of Entomology and Plant Quarantine since 1946. He was instructor and assistant professor of entomology for 8 years in Michigan State College and has served with the United States Public Health Service on studies of malaria mosquitoes. He is the author of numerous publications on the classification of flies and on rules governing the scientific names of animals.*

For further reading on insect populations, Mr. Sabrosky recommends Malcolm Burr's The Insect Legion, *published by James Nisbet & Co., London, in 1939; C. B. Williams'* The Migration of Butterflies, *Oliver and Boyd, Edinburgh, 1930; and the following articles in periodicals:*

E. A. Andrews: Populations of Ant Mounds, *Quarterly Review of Biology, volume 4, pages 248–257. 1929.*

F. S. Bodenheimer: Population Problems of Social Insects, *Biological Reviews of the Cambridge Philosophical Society, volume 12, pages 393–430. 1937.*

Royal N. Chapman, Kenneth M. King, Alfred E. Emerson, Samuel A. Graham, and Harry S. Smith: Symposium on Insect Populations, *Ecological Monographs, volume 9, pages 259–320. July 1939.*

E. N. Cory and E. E. Haviland: Population Studies of Formica exsectoides Forel, *Annals of the Entomological Society of America, volume 31, pages 50–57. March 1938.*

C. H. Gable and W. A. Baker: Notes on a Migration of Libythea bachmanni Kirtl., *Canadian Entomologist, volume 54, pages 265–266. 1922.*

Glenn W. Herrick: The "Ponderable" Substance of Aphids, *Entomological News, volume 37, pages 207–210. July 1926.*

C. H. Hoffmann, H. K. Townes, H. H. Swift, and R. I. Sailer: Field Studies on the Effects of Airplane Applications of DDT on Forest Invertebrates, *Ecological Monographs, volume 19, pages 1–46. January 1949.*

F. G. Holdaway, F. J. Gay, and T. Greaves: The Termite Population of a Mound Colony of Eutermes exitiosus Hill, *Journal of the Council for Scientific and Industrial Research, volume 8, pages 42–46. 1935.*

Z. P. Metcalf: How Many Insects Are There in the World? *Entomological News, volume 51, pages 219–222. October 1940.*

A. S. Pearse: Observations on the Microfauna of the Duke Forest, *Ecological Monographs, volume 16, pages 127–150. April 1946.*

Oddities of the Insect World

Edwin Way Teale

Nineteen centuries ago, when Pliny the Elder was writing his natural history in Rome, men believed that insects were creatures without blood, that butterfly eggs were drops of solidified dew, that echoes killed honey bees, and that gold was mined in the mountains north of India by a giant ant "the color of a cat and as large as an Egyptian wolf."

"This gold," Pliny assured his readers, "is extracted in the winter and is taken by the Indians during the heats of summer while the ants are compelled by the excessive warmth to hide themselves in their holes. Still, however, on being aroused by catching the scent of the Indians, they sally forth and frequently tear them to pieces, though provided with the swiftest camels for the purpose of flight, so great is their fleetness, combined with their ferocity and their passion for gold."

Today, nobody credits Pliny's story of wolf-size ants with a passion for gold any more than they believe in his oriental locusts that grew to such size that their hind legs were dried and used for saws. These traveler's tales, the product of imagination or misunderstanding, have been long discredited. Imaginary wonders, in fact, are less needed in dealing with the insects than with any other group of living creatures. The truth is odd and dramatic enough.

In 1857, when Alfred Russel Wallace landed on the Kei Islands of the Malay Archipelago to collect natural-history specimens, he soon noticed that each time he entered a deep damp forest glade he found the air filled with a fragrance that reminded him of attar of roses. For a long time he tried to trace the perfume to flowers. Finally he discovered that its source was not a flower but a beetle, the green and purple and yellow tiger beetle, *Therates labiatus*. It inhabited the damp and gloomy glades and fed mainly on insects that visited the flowers. Its perfume, Wallace concluded, aided it in attracting small nectar gatherers to the spot.

At least three species of oriental praying mantids use color instead of perfume to aid them in securing their food. These insects, like the mantid native to the southern part of the United States, imprison their prey within the spined traps formed by their forelegs. By having parts of their bodies expanded into thin plates which are brightly tinted on the under side, the oriental insects resemble flowers on the bushes where they hunt. When climbing to a favorable position, the mantid keeps the bright-colored under sides of the plates hidden. However, when it finds itself among flowers to its liking, it turns the colored plates uppermost and remains motionless until a victim alights close by.

One British naturalist reports seeing a mantid in India climb laboriously to the tips of three branches before it found flowers in bloom. On the first two times, when it found buds, it slowly retraced its steps and began again. Attaining the flowers, it took its position among them and exposed the under side of its pink, petallike plates. Some oriental mantids have plates that are blue, some mauve, some purple. Still others have pure white plates, that have a surface that is glistening and waxy, like the petals of real flowers.

In a number of instances, the orthoptera of the Tropics are ingeniously camouflaged by nature to escape the notice of their enemies. For example, the long-horned grasshopper, *Metaprosagoga insignis*, possesses wings which not only resemble leaves but which are equipped with irregular patches that look as though the leaf tissue had been eaten away by an insect, leaving only a network of veins visible. Another tropical leaf-grasshopper has brownish wings that suggest dried leaves. The resemblance is heightened by the fact that markings near their extremities give the impression that they are cracked or torn. Then there is a mantid of the Orient, *Brancsikia aeroplana,* which has curled-up brownish edges to its wings, thus heightening their resemblance to dry brown leaves. On the wings of a katydid from Venezuela, which William Beebe once showed me, imitation dewdrops and fungus spots increased the effectiveness of the insect's camouflage.

Probably the most famous camouflaged insect in the world is *Kallima,* the dead-leaf butterfly of the Far East. In *The Malay Archipelago,* Alfred Russel Wallace tells of his first meeting with this remarkable butterfly. At the time he encountered it he was collecting in Sumatra, beating the bushes for insects and examining his net carefully for poisonous snakes, which were often dislodged from the branches, before extracting the insects he had caught.

"When on the wing," he writes of the dead-leaf butterfly, "it is very conspicuous. The species is not uncommon in dry woods and thickets and I often endeavored to catch it without success, for, after flying a short distance, it would enter a bush among dry or dead leaves and however carefully I crept up to the spot where the butterfly settled and though I lost sight of it for some time, I at length discovered that it was close before my eyes but that in its position of repose it so closely resembled a dead leaf attached to a twig as almost certainly to deceive the eye even when gazing full upon it.

"A very closely allied species, *Kallima inachis,* inhabits India where it is very common. No two are alike but all the variations correspond to those of dead leaves. Every tint of yellow, ash, brown, and red is found here and in many specimens there occur patches and spots formed of small black dots, so closely resembling the way in which minute fungi grow on leaves that it is almost impossible at first not to believe that fungi have grown on the butterflies themselves!"

Walkingstick insects, in the Tropics, also present some amazingly realistic instances of insect camouflage. One of the most remarkable bears the scientific name of *Achrioptera spinosissima.* About half a foot in length, its green and brown body is decorated with spines that are tinted bright red like thorns. The insect looks for all the world like a broken piece of briar moving along on six legs. Another tropical walkingstick, *Palophus reyi,* is almost a foot long. The outer skin of its body is roughened into an amazingly close approximation of dry bark on a dead twig.

Such resemblances benefit the insect by making it inconspicuous amid its surroundings. But what benefit those brownie bugs of the insect world, the *Membracidae,* obtain from the fantastic adornments they possess is often difficult to see. Again, it is in the Tropics that the most spectacular examples are found. Nature seems to have run riot, designing oddities just for the sake of originality. In some species of treehoppers, the prothorax is drawn out into hornlike adornments; in others, it rises in a high, curving crown; in others, it forms spears or balls. Oftentimes these are brightly colored. While American treehoppers are less extravagantly formed than those in the Tropics, some species are among our oddest-appearing insects. All are small, and the strangeness of their forms frequently is unappreciated without the aid of a magnifying glass.

When Charles Darwin was crossing the Atlantic in 1832, at the start of his famous voyage in the Beagle, the ship dropped anchor at desolate St. Paul's Island, 540 miles from the coast of South America. "Not a single plant," Darwin writes, "not even a lichen, grows on this islet; yet it is inhabited by several insects and spiders." Most of them were parasites on the boobies and other sea birds that landed on the barren rocks and one was a small brown moth belonging to a genus that feeds on feathers.

The bleak cluster of volcanic rocks

that form St. Paul's Island is but one of many strange places where insects are able to survive. Oceanic water striders skate over the waves hundreds of miles from shore. They lay their eggs on floating sea-bird feathers and other bits of refuse and often live their whole lives without ever seeing land. In Ecuador, butterflies are found among the crags of the Andes 16,500 feet above sea level, while explorers, scaling the flanks of the Himalayas, have encountered a praying mantid almost as high.

Snow-white and blind insects live deep beneath the earth's surface in caverns. Springtails skip across snowbanks during February thaws in Northern States. Certain flies breed in the brine of the Great Salt Lake and a number of insects make their homes in the dangerous confines of insectivorous pitcher plants. One curious little larva spends its early days swimming about in pools of petroleum, breathing through a tiny tube which it thrusts above the surface. And another insect is able to live in the mud of hot springs where the water reaches a temperature of 120° F.

At the opposite extreme is the so-called ice-bug, or alpine rock crawler, which inhabits cold mountain recesses, usually at elevations from 5,400 to 8,600 feet above sea level. It prefers temperatures of about 38° F., temperatures at which most insects are dormant. If the mercury rises to 80°, the ice-bug seems to suffer heat prostration.

Two insects that spend their early days under curious conditions are familiar to most parts of the United States. They are the rat-tailed maggot and the froghopper, the immature form of the Cercopidae. The former inhabits stagnant water, caught in knotholes, or other waste fluids. It feeds on the bottom and breathes air through an extensible tube that forms its tail. Thus, like a diver obtaining oxygen through an air hose while working on sea bottom, the fly larva is able to remain submerged as long as it desires.

By surrounding itself with bubbles, the little froghopper produces its own climate. In spring and summer, small masses of froth often appear on grass stems and weeds. They are the foam castles of the cercopids. A kind of bicycle pump, formed of overlapping plates beneath its abdomen, which provide a chamber into which air is drawn and expelled, permits the insect to produce bubbles in excess sap, which it has sucked from the plant. Within this bubble mass, sheltered from the direct rays of the sun and kept moist by the foam, the immature insect spends its early days. For millions of years, it has been employing its own primitive form of air conditioning.

One of the classic studies of the French entomologist, J. Henri Fabre, concerned the aerial journey of the wingless larva of the oil-beetle. Hatching from eggs deposited by the female insect close to flowering plants, the minute larvae slowly ascend the stems and lurk among the petals until a wild bee alights in search of pollen or nectar. Quickly the young beetle attaches itself to the hair on the bee's back and goes sailing through the air as a passenger when the winged insect flies back to its nest. Here the larva lets go. It has found its proper home, a place where it will be supplied with ample food until it transforms into an adult beetle. Not all larvae attach themselves to the right insects, but enough do to carry on the species by means of this ingenious stratagem.

Even more remarkable is the sequence of seemingly unrelated events that transport to their destination the eggs of the human bot fly. The female fly makes no effort to lay her eggs on the ultimate victim. Instead, she visits swampy lowlands where mosquitoes are emerging. There, she overtakes a mosquito, grasps it, and swiftly deposits minute eggs on the under side of its abdomen. Then she releases it and flies away. Her work is done. The mosquito—or, at least, some of the mosquitoes thus burdened with bot fly eggs—eventually lands on a human being.

The eggs are on the under side of the insect where they come in contact with the skin of its victim. Thus heated, the eggs hatch while the mosquito is sucking blood and the tiny larvae burrow into the skin of their unwilling host.

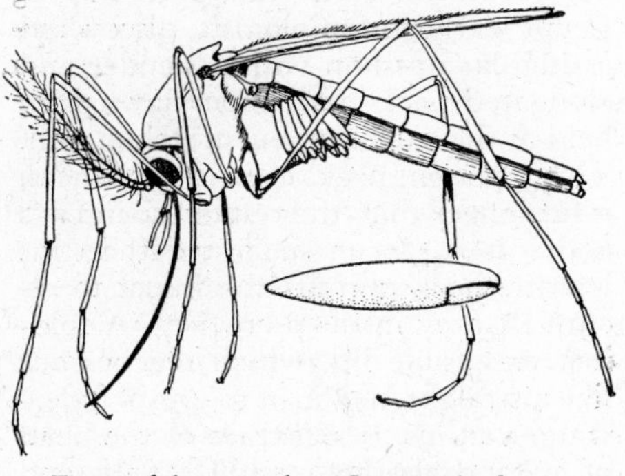

Eggs of human bot fly attached to a mosquito.

Another instinctive stratagem is employed by an ant queen found in Tunis. She alights, after the nuptial flight in which she is fertilized by a male of her own species, near the nest of a larger species of ant. Workers seize her and drag her into the underground chambers. There she takes refuge on the back of the queen and remains unmolested. Using her opportunity, she eventually decapitates the rightful queen and is accepted as the new queen by the workers. Her eggs develop workers of her own species and, in the end, the colony is made up of the smaller ants.

William Morton Wheeler, in his *Ants, Their Structure, Development and Behavior,* tells of a carnivorous butterfly larva that lives in the nests of an Australian ant where it feeds upon the young. An especially tough outer shell protects it from attacks by adult ants. In Queensland this remarkable butterfly, *Liphyra brassolis,* was studied by F. P. Dodd in the early years of the present century. The adult butterfly, emerging in the nest, is covered by fugitive scales, which save its life because the loose scales come off in the mandibles of the ants. In describing his observations, Dodd writes:

"Directly the ants encounter the scales they are in trouble. They fasten on to their feet and impede their movements, or, if their antennae or mandibles come in contact with any part of the butterfly, the scales adhere thereto, so that the ant is soon in a bad way and has quite enough to do in attempting to free herself of her incumbrances without taking any further interest in the butterfly. It is exceedingly ludicrous to observe the ants endeavoring to free themselves, their legs move awkwardly and their mandibles open and close in evident annoyance and perplexity, and they are also much concerned about the state of their antennae, for the obnoxious scales will not be shaken off, and they seem to become very low-spirited."

A number of insect oddities reveal their peculiar characteristics in defending themselves against attack. The blister beetle of southern Europe is equipped with a caustic fluid that protects it from its enemies. In olden times, such insects were ground up to form blistering ointments and plasters. A number of common insects, such as the familiar lady beetle, have weak places at the joints of their legs, which rupture to let out drops of disagreeable fluid when they are attacked. The monarch butterfly, noted for its seasonal migrations, is said to possess blood disagreeable to birds, thus reducing its chances of being attacked.

As the polecat, among animals, relies on an offensive smell to repel its enemies, so a number of insects protect themselves by exuding disagreeable odors. Stink bugs are familiar to everyone. The lacewing, a pale-green, filmy little insect with golden eyes that lays stalked eggs from which hatch the aphis-lions that devour hordes of plant-lice, is another skunk of the insect world. Handle one and the disagreeable fluid it exudes clings to your hands for hours.

Incidentally, the plant-lice that are preyed upon by the immature lacewings are reported to employ a surprising method of defense occasionally when they are approached by the sickle-shaped, sucking jaws of an aphis-lion. The plump aphids produce, in addition to honeydew, a waxy secretion that collects at the ends of two tubes projecting backward from their abdomens. Before its enemy can use its jaws, an aphid sometimes will back quickly toward it, pushing the waxy blobs into its face. This sticky material halts the attack while the aphis-lion stops to clean away the wax.

The bluish-backed bombardier beetle, *Brachinus fumans,* gains time by a different ruse. When it is pursued by an enemy, it emits a little cloud of offensive gas. This gas attack takes the pursuer by surprise. It stops and the momentary pause is often sufficient to permit the beetle to escape.

These are active forms of defense. Other insects employ passive forms. They feign death to escape death. Otto Plath, in his *Bumblebees and Their Ways,* records an instance in which a robber fly was fighting with a bumble bee in a glass jar. Getting the worst of the battle, the fly suddenly fell on its back as though stung to death. It lay there, apparently lifeless, until Plath shook both insects out of the jar. Then the "dead" robber fly sprang into the air and darted away. Ambush bugs, lady beetles, monarch butterflies, and a long list of other insect opossums feign death. Some walkingsticks will become rigid and apparently lifeless when alarmed. In one instance, a walkingstick feigned death for 6 hours, remaining as rigid as a twig all during that time.

Giants and dwarfs among the insects cover a wide range. The great atlas moth of India, with a wingspread of a foot; an East Indian walkingstick 15 inches in length; the Hercules beetle of Africa, which drones over the countryside at evening with a sound like an approaching airplane—those are some of the giants. Among the pigmies are the microlepidoptera, the minute beetles so small they can literally creep through the eye of a needle, and the fairy flies, which are built on such a miniature scale that, although they are perfect in all their parts, they measure only one-hundredth of an inch from head to tail.

In addition to oddities of size among the insects, there are innumerable oddities of form. Near the pyramids in Egypt early entomologists discovered a singular ant-lion with a slender and elongated neck. Its caliper jaws seem held at the end of an outstretched arm. This pipestem neck, in many instances, is far longer than the rest of the insect's body. It has been suggested that this lengthy neck permits the insect to secure its prey in deep crevices. A folding, extensible lip, which reaches out like a straightened arm to grasp underwater victims, is a feature of the head of every dragonfly nymph. At the end of the lip are grasping hooks, by means of which the nymph pulls its captive back into its mouth.

Enormous forelegs, more than twice the length of the rest of its body, are the characteristic of a black wood beetle discovered by Alfred Russel Wallace in the Moluccas. This beetle, *Euchirus longimanus,* covers a space of 8 inches with all its legs extended. Another insect curiosity of the Malay Archipelago is an antlered fly. Various species have protuberances on their heads that suggest the horns of deer, elk, and moose in miniature.

Even more remarkable is a stalk-eyed fly of South Africa, *Diopsis apicalis.* Like the hammerhead shark, it has its eyes extending out from the sides of its head. The stalks to which they are attached, however, are drawn out to such surprising length that the measurement from eye to eye is one-third more than the length of the body from head to tail.

An abdomen that has amazing powers of distention is a characteristic of the nymph of the bloodsucking *Rhodnius.* In a few minutes, one of these nymphs can distend itself with blood up to 12 times its original weight. As the huge meal is digested, the abdomen contracts smoothly like a deflating balloon. Similarly, the abdomens of the honey ants of the Southwest possess the ability to expand enormously. Certain members of the colony act as storage vessels for the honeydew gathered by the workers. They never leave the nest. With abdomens so swollen they cannot walk, they cling to the roof of their underground chamber, regurgitating food to the workers when it is needed.

Various other ants must be numbered among the insect oddities. In *Ant-Hill Odyssey,* William M. Mann tells of collecting a species that is known to Brazilian natives as "The Terrible Ant." Fully an inch in length, it is said to produce a serious fever by its sting. A hundred years ago, when Henry W. Bates was collecting in the Amazon basin, he encountered villages that had been deserted because of an invasion of fire ants. These small red insects have stings like red-hot needles. Then there are the army ants that march in long lines in the jungle, the slave-making ants that raid other colonies for pupae, the tree ant of India, *Oecophylla smaragdina,* that uses its larvae as a means of sewing leaves together into a nest, passing the silk-producing grubs back and forth from one leaf edge to another to provide a solid bond. Within these leaf sheds, the ants keep smaller insects that produce honeydew, the sweet fluid upon which the ants feed.

Honeydew is so universally relished by ants that it has been described as their "national dish." Other insects have a taste for varied and often surprising things. That goat of the insect world, the drug-store beetle, is known to consume 45 different substances, including the poisons aconite and belladonna. Other beetles feed on cigarettes, mustard plasters, and red pepper. Ants have shown themselves resistant to cyanide. Termites are able to digest cellulose in wood because of the aid of minute organisms within their intestines. In the case of some insects, a reduced diet slows down growth. Some wood-boring grubs, such as those of the cerambycid beetles, sometimes live in house timbers or furniture for years after they have been put in place. In one instance, an adult beetle emerged from a porch post that had been standing for 20 years. The dried timber lacks the nutritive qualities of the living tree and the growth of the grub is arrested, so long periods pass before it reaches maturity. Underground, the nymph of the periodical cicada spends more than a decade and a half tunneling through darkness in the soil before it emerges into its brief life as an adult.

In the mating and reproduction activities of the insects, we find some of the strangest habits of all. The deathwatch beetle, that stand-by of ghost stories laid in old castles, bumps its head on the top of its wooden tunnel to send a kind of telegraphic message to its mate. To attract the attention of the females at mating time, the males of certain flies blow shining little bubbles of froth. Some chalcidflies which parasitize caterpillars, have the faculty of laying self-multiplying eggs. More than 2,000 larvae may be produced by the depositing of a single chalcid egg in the body of a victim. During the lifetime of a termite queen, in the Tropics, as many as 10 million eggs may come from the insect's bloated body.

L. C. Miall, in *The Natural History of Aquatic Insects,* tells of a minute fly found in England under the bark of poplar, willow, and beech trees. It produces viviparously small larvae "which escape by tearing open the body of their parent and in turn produce other larvae after the same fashion."

These seem fantastic creatures and bizarre habits. But to one who views with fresh eyes the old, taken-for-granted, commonplace habits of even the most familiar insects—the everyday butterflies and grasshoppers and ants we see about us—there is in the events of their lives much that is a source of astonishment and wonder. A century ago, this amazing strangeness of the familiar insects was eloquently expressed in describing the metamorphosis of a moth in the early pages of

970134°—52——3

the pioneer entomology by William Kirby and William Spence.

"Were a naturalist to announce to the world," they write, "the discovery of an animal which first existed in the form of a serpent; which then penetrated into the earth, and weaving a shroud of pure silk of the finest texture, contracted itself within this covering into a body without external mouth or limbs, and resembling, more than anything else, an Egyptian mummy; and which, lastly after remaining in this state without food and without motion . . . should at the end of that period burst its silken cerements, struggle through its earthly covering and start into day a winged bird—what think you would be the sensation excited by this strange piece of intelligence? After the first doubts of its truth were dispelled, what astonishment would succeed! Amongst the learned, what surmises!—what investigations! Even the most torpid would flock to the sight of such a prodigy."

EDWIN WAY TEALE *is a past president of the New York Entomological Society and the author of numerous books on insects, including* Grassroot Jungles, The Boys' Book of Insects, Near Horizons, The Golden Throng, *and* North With the Spring. *His books have appeared in British, Spanish, French, Swedish, Finnish, and Braille editions.* Near Horizons *was awarded the John Burroughs Medal for distinguished nature writing. In 1949, Mr. Teale edited a one-volume omnibus of the writings of Fabre, entitled* The Insect World of J. Henri Fabre.

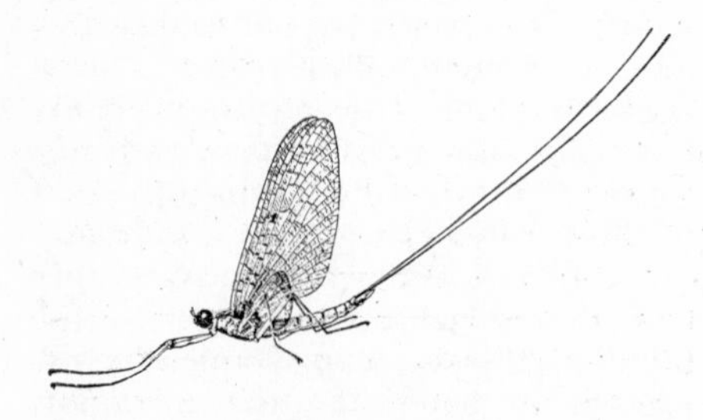

Stenomema canadense, a common mayfly.

Fossil Insects

Frank M. Carpenter

Written in the rocks of Colorado, Kansas, Oklahoma, and many other places is the story of insects in the ages before man appeared on earth.

The insects were trapped, caught in mud or sticky resin, and thereby left a permanent record—as did dinosaur, mollusk, and plants—that broadens our knowledge of their evolution. About 12,000 species of fossil insects have been described. Countless thousands of specimens have been collected.

Fossil insects are not found in as many deposits or localities as most other invertebrates. Like other organisms, insects are preserved as fossils by a sequence of events that results in their burial in a suitable medium. Immediate burial is necessary to preserve the whole insect; otherwise the body parts soften and fall apart, and only the wings remain. The wings decompose more slowly and therefore can be preserved under less favorable conditions. That is the reason why many specimens of fossil insects consist of wings alone. When conditions were good for preserving insects, large numbers of fossils usually occur.

An example of such abundance is provided by the Tertiary shales at Florissant, Colo., which have yielded upwards of 60,000 specimens. The shale originated about 40 million years ago in a shallow lake, extending into several narrow valleys and rimmed by granitic hills. Several neighboring volcanoes frequently erupted and scattered ashes and debris over a wide area. Whatever insects were flying or were being blown over the lake at those times were forced into the water by the falling ashes and were promptly buried.

Fossil insects have been found at

nearly 150 localities in various parts of the world. About nine-tenths of the specimens have been collected at 12 of these deposits. The remainder has come from less productive rocks. Some of the latter are important because of their geological position, however. One of them is the Commentry shales of central France. These were deposited by a deep fresh-water lake, which existed during the Upper Carboniferous period some 250 million years ago. About 1,500 specimens have been found in the shales. They are well preserved and are almost the oldest insects known.

Another deposit, notable for the abundance of fossils as well as their ages, is the Elmo limestone in eastern Kansas. The rock, fine-grained and nearly white, was deposited by a shallow fresh-water lake inhabited by aquatic insects, crustaceans, and small king crabs. A collector who carefully breaks the limestone, after it has been dug up and dried, may get as many as 50 good insects a day. Most of the fossils are strikingly well preserved. Some show even the coloration and minute hairs on the wings. About 10,000 specimens so far have been collected there.

A similar but more extensive limestone formation was discovered in 1940 in northeastern Oklahoma. It originated in a shallow, saline lake, barren of life except for algae and bivalve crustaceans (Conchostraca). Most of the insects preserved there were presumably carried to the lake by floods.

The lithographic limestone of Bavaria, famous for such fossil vertebrates as the flying reptiles and the earliest birds, is not nearly so important for its insects. Several thousand specimens have been found there, but fewer than one-tenth of them are well preserved.

The richest of all deposits is the Baltic amber from Germany. The material is itself the fossil resin from an extinct pine tree (*Pinites succinifera*). The Amber Pine Forest existed for several million years during the early Tertiary period, and extended from about the site of Bornholm and Rügen in the south to that of the White Sea and Ural River in the east. The northern and western borders are uncertain because those regions are covered by the ocean. At any rate, the local accumulation of the amber along the coast of East Prussia is the result of the washing out of the flooded forest. Insects and other small invertebrates, which were caught in the resin on the tree trunks, are preserved in great detail and perfection. At least 150,000 insects have been found in the amber.

The earliest geological record of the insects is still uncertain. Fragments of small arthropods, which have been recovered in a Devonian chert in Scotland, have been determined by some entomologists as Collembola (springtails), but the identity will remain doubtful until more is known about them. The oldest unquestionable insects have been found in rocks of early Upper Carboniferous age, about 250 million years ago. Only three of these fossils are known—one each from Czechoslovakia, Germany, and Pennsylvania—and each consists of a single wing. Whatever else may be inferred from the specimens, it is certain that insects with fully developed wings existed then.

Insects are much more abundantly represented in the later Upper Carboniferous rocks than in the earlier ones, so that we have at least a working knowledge of the insect fauna of the time. Six orders of insects have been recognized, all but one of them extinct. The most interesting was the Palaeodictyoptera, which were of medium size and resembled mayflies. Since some of the Palaeodictyoptera were more generalized than any of the other winged insects known, the group as a whole is usually considered to be the ancestral stock from which all other winged insects have been evolved. As far as we know, all species of the order had a pair of membranous lobes on the first thoracic segment. The lobes appear to be homologous with the functional wings of the other two thoracic segments and are regarded as indicating the steps by which functional wings arose. Unfortunately nothing is known about the immature stages of the Palaeodictyoptera. The order reached its maximum development in the Carboniferous period but persisted through the Permian period.

The most spectacular insects of the Carboniferous and Permian were the Protodonata. They resembled dragonflies. Their chewing mouth parts were powerful, and their legs, like those of true dragonflies, were covered with strong spines. They were undoubtedly predaceous, catching their victims in flight and devouring them while resting on tree ferns or other ancient plants. All of the Protodonata were large and some were veritable giants, having a wing expanse of 30 inches and a body length of 15 inches. Specimens of such large species have been found in rocks in France, Kansas, and Oklahoma. Since birds and other flying vertebrates did not exist at that time, these huge insects presumably ruled the air. Their nymphs have not been found, but they were probably aquatic and like those of true dragonflies or damselflies.

The only living order or group of families of insects known to have existed in Carboniferous time is the Blattidae, or cockroaches. Their remains make up a high percentage of insects of that period, but that is probably due partly to the favorable conditions prevailing in the Carboniferous swamps that produced the deposits. Some formations of that period, such as the coal beds of Pennsylvania, have yielded no insects except roaches. The average size of the Carboniferous roaches was somewhat greater than that of living species, but none of the fossil forms exceeds in size certain living species of the Tropics. The difference between the ancient roaches, existing some 250 million years ago, and those of today is exceedingly slight, involving chiefly position of wing veins.

By the beginning of the Permian period, about 50 million years after the appearance of the first insects, a marked change had taken place in insects. Although the several extinct orders which arose in the Carboniferous still existed, several living orders besides the roaches were represented. Along with the giant dragonflies were minute barklice, only one-eighth of an inch across the wings. Altogether, the lower Permian insect fauna was very diverse—more so, in fact, than any other insect fauna known. There was about equal representation of the extinct orders of the Carboniferous and relatively specialized existing orders. Also adding to this diversity were several other extinct orders, known only from Permian strata. One of them, the Protelytroptera, included beetle-like insects, having well-developed elytra, but they were closely related to the roaches and had no affinities with the Coleoptera. The living orders that appeared in early Permian time include such types as the Odonata (dragonflies), Ephemeroptera (mayflies), Corrodentia (barklice), Hemiptera (bugs), Neuroptera (lacewings), and Mecoptera (scorpionflies). The lacewings and scorpionflies are especially noteworthy because the living species have com-

Geological Ages of Existing Orders of Insects

Name of order	*Earliest geological record*
Collembola	Devonian [?].
Entotrophi	Middle Tertiary.
Thysanura	Jurassic.
Odonata	Lower Permian.
Ephemeroptera	Lower Permian.
Plecoptera	Upper Permian.
Orthoptera	Triassic.
Orthoptera (Blattidae).	Upper Carboniferous.
Isoptera	Lower Tertiary.
Dermaptera	Jurassic.
Embioptera	Lower Tertiary.
Corrodentia	Lower Permian.
Mallophaga	[No fossils known.]
Hemiptera	Lower Permian.
Anoplura	Quarternary.
Thysanoptera	Upper Permian.
Mecoptera	Lower Permian.
Neuroptera	Lower Permian.
Trichoptera	Jurassic.
Diptera	Jurassic.
Siphonaptera	Lower Tertiary.
Lepidoptera	Lower Tertiary.
Coleoptera	Upper Permian.
Strepsiptera	Lower Tertiary.
Hymenoptera	Jurassic.

plete metamorphosis. Coleoptera and Plecoptera are first found in late Permian strata, but they probably existed earlier in the period.

With the beginning of the Mesozoic era, the insect fauna changed even more markedly. In fact, the contrast between the archaic fauna of the Permian and the relatively modern one of the Triassic is as great as that between the faunas of the Triassic and the Recent periods. None of the extinct orders remained after the beginning of the Mesozoic, but a few living families occur in Triassic strata. Among the notable insects of that period were certain Australian species related to the Orthoptera, which had a large stridulatory apparatus on the wing. This constitutes the earliest record of sound production in the insects. Because at the time these insects lived there were no birds or other vertebrates that produce the ordinary animal sounds of forests or woodlands, it is quite possible that these stridulating insects and their relatives were the noisiest creatures then in existence.

The Jurassic insect fauna was much like that of the Triassic except that more existing families occur. In fact the appearance of this fauna is so modern that if we had a collection of Jurassic species pinned in the usual way, it would not look very different from our present-day collections, except that there would probably be no flower insects, such as the bees and syrphid flies. This is a great contrast to the condition of the vertebrate fauna of the time, which included the dinosaurs, flying reptiles, and toothed birds. By the beginning of the next period, the Cretaceous, the flowering plants had become established and in all probability the types of insects associated with these plants promptly followed. Unfortunately our knowledge of the Cretaceous insects is insignificant because of the lack of adequate specimens.

Early Tertiary strata have yielded a higher percentage of living genera than the Jurassic, especially of flies, beetles,

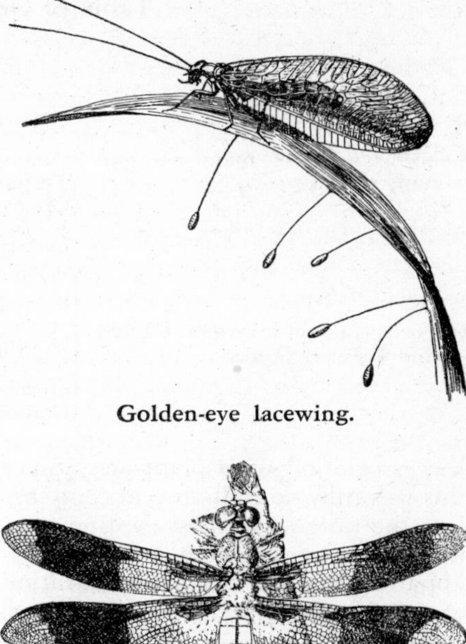

Golden-eye lacewing.

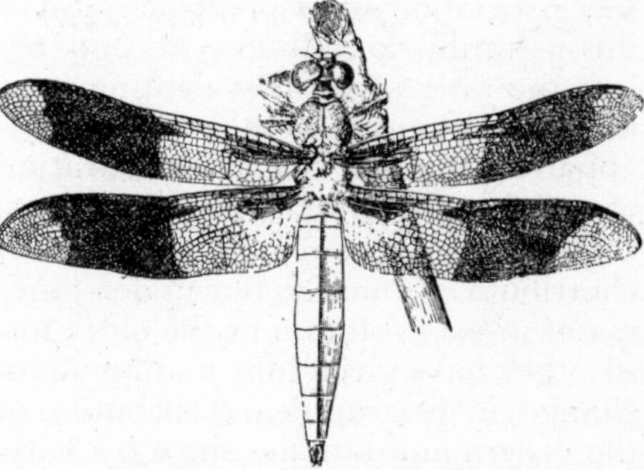

Plathemis lydia, a dragonfly.

dragonflies, and true bugs. The insects in the Baltic amber, which is now regarded as of early Tertiary age, are especially important in enabling accurate comparisons with living genera and species. Studies of families of amber insects have shown that the amount of evolution that has taken place since the early Tertiary has varied for different families. The Baltic amber ant fauna, for example, includes 43 genera, of which 24, or 55 percent, still exist, whereas all but one of the genera of bees in the amber are extinct. In this connection, it is noteworthy that William Morton Wheeler, who made an extensive study of the amber ants, found eight species of them which he could not distinguish from living species. Furthermore, he also found that the social habits of the amber ants were about as highly organized as those of the living forms, with caste differentiation, polymorphic workers, and even

Table of Geologic Periods

Era	Period		Approximate time (in millions of years): Duration of period	Since beginning of period
Cenozoic (age of mammals and man)	Quaternary		1	1
	Tertiary		69	70
Mesozoic (age of reptiles)	Cretaceous		50	120
	Jurassic		35	155
	Triassic		35	190
Paleozoic (age of invertebrates and primitive vertebrates)	Permian		25	215
	Carboniferous	Upper	35	250
		Lower	50	300
	Devonian		50	350
	Silurian		40	390
	Ordovician		90	480
	Cambrian		70	550

the association with plant-lice. Since this was fully 50 million years ago, before the time when most existing families of mammals were evolved, it is apparent that the social organization of ants is a much older one than ours.

Although Tertiary insects do not contribute so much to our understanding of insect evolution as the older fossils, they have given information about changes in geographical distribution of the genera and families since the early Tertiary. Many genera and families which have been found in the Baltic amber are now entirely absent from Europe, and some are known to occur only on such distant land masses as Australia and South America. The same is true of Tertiary insects of other parts of the world. The Florissant shales (middle Tertiary) in Colorado have yielded several species of lacewings of the family Osmylidae, a group now absent from North America. Hundreds of instances of this sort can be cited. The significance of such changes in distribution is not clear and will not be until more evidence has been accumulated and correlated with the fossil record of other groups of animals and plants.

A detailed study of the geological history of the insects, which I have only sketched, yields evidence of certain progressive changes in structure and development which confirm conclusions on insect evolution reached by morphological and embryological investigations. Although this is still a highly controversial subject, we have enough evidence at hand, derived from these three sources, to indicate the main steps in insect evolution. There is, however, no fossil evidence bearing on the question of insect origin; the oldest insects known show no transition to other arthropods. On the other hand, morphological and embryological studies carried out mainly since 1935 have pointed to the probable origin of the insects from some terrestrial arthropod, related to the existing Symphyla. The time of that origin is pure conjecture, but judging from the fossil record we can only conclude it was at least as far back as the Lower Carboniferous (Mississippian).

Morphological studies of existing insects prove that the first true insects were wingless (Apterygota), like the Thysanura (silverfish) and Entotrophi, combining the generalized characteristics of both of these groups.

The development of winged insects (Pterygota) was the first great evolutionary step within the insect line. The origin of wings is by no means clear; they probably were developed from lateral flaps, like those on the first thoracic segment of the Palaeodictyoptera. These primitive flying insects, termed the Palaeoptera and exemplified by the Odonata, Ephemeroptera, and several extinct orders, were unable to flex their wings over the abdomen at rest.

The second main evolutionary

change was the development of an articulation that made it possible for the wings to be held over the abdomen when the insect was not in flight. All living Pterygota except the Odonata and Ephemeroptera belong in this category, which is termed the Neoptera. The acquisition of this wing-flexing mechanism was an important change, for it enabled the insects, in adult as well as the immature stages, to hide in debris or under stones or logs. The first neopterous types had a simple or direct type of postembryonic development and are usually termed the hemimetabolous Neoptera.

The third main evolutionary step was the attainment of the more complex type of metamorphosis, with larval and pupal stages, resulting in the holometabolous Neoptera.

The fossil record of the insects, though incomplete, has given us a general idea of the time of occurrence of the three events. The existence of two orders of insects (Mecoptera and Neuroptera) with complete metamorphosis in lower Permian rocks can only mean that this step was attained at least by late Upper Carboniferous time. Similarly, the presence of species with wing-flexing abilities in the early Upper Carboniferous shows that the hemimetabolous Neoptera arose in the Lower Carboniferous. Unfortunately, since no insects have been found in strata older than those of the Upper Carboniferous period, we have no actual record of the existence of Palaeoptera before these Neoptera; nor, for that matter, is there any Paleozoic record of the Apterygota. Because all evidence derived from other sources indicates the primitive nature of these two categories, however, we can infer that the Palaeoptera preceded the Neoptera, and therefore that they existed in the early part of the Lower Carboniferous. Similarly, we can infer that the Apterygota, which must have preceded them, arose still earlier in the Lower Carboniferous or, more likely, in the Devonian. The conclusion to be drawn from the record, at any rate, is that all three of the main steps in insect evolution took place before the end of the Carboniferous period, about 250 million years ago. Nothing nearly so important has happened to the insects since then.

Another contribution that fossil insects have made to our understanding of the evolution of the group pertains to the progressive increase in the relative numbers of species having complete metamorphosis in the geological periods since the lower Permian. Starting from the beginning of the Permian, during which only about 10 percent of the known species had complete metamorphosis, there has been an increase up to 88 percent at the present time. The most rapid change (10 to 40 percent) seems to have taken place in the interval of the Permian period. Although there is a possibility that such a marked shift in the insect population did actually take place in that time, the more probable explanation is that complete metamorphosis arose further back in the geologic time than the lower Permian, and that the change was more gradual.

Those are two examples of the way in which the study of fossils has contributed to our understanding of insect evolution. There is every indication that the insects have been as numerous on earth as they are now for at least the time since the Jurassic period, about 150 million years; and also that the insect fauna of our time is but a small part of the total parade of insect life that has lived on the earth during the past 250 million years. It is not surprising, therefore, that our understanding of insect evolution depends to a large extent on a knowledge of this extinct population.

FRANK M. CARPENTER *is professor of entomology, Alexander Agassiz professor of zoology, and curator of fossil insects in the Museum of Comparative Zoology at Harvard University. He joined the staff of Harvard in 1932 and has done research on fossil insects, insect evolution, and the taxonomy of Mecoptera and Neuroptera.*

How Insects Live

E. O. Essig

For some 250 million years insects have been able to flourish on land and water, in arctic barrens and tropic jungles, in deserts and grassy prairies because they have developed special and wonderful adaptations to meet all the varied conditions of this earth. Not just a few but literally thousands of species, representing practically every order, live together in nearly every ecological niche.

They have survived so long without being greatly altered in size and form or reduced in numbers. In direct competition with all other higher forms of life on land, they stand supreme in numbers of species and individuals. Only some lower microscopic forms like bacteria may outnumber them.

It is easier to describe the remarkable adaptations of insects than it is to explain the reasons for them. It is difficult to know whether the body structures and complicated life histories or the environmental factors were the most important. Many other factors may have entered into the long, slow process of change and adjustment.

Consider first as a factor of survival the dominant position of the female insect. She is the foundation, the perpetuation, the multiplication of the species. In many species she is the all; males do not exist. The termite queens of the fungus-feeding tropical species may live for a half century. Certain Australian queen termites may lay as many as 360 eggs in an hour, 8,640 in a day, 3,153,000 in a year. She may continue without interruption for 25 to 50 years.

Parthenogenesis, or reproduction without fertilization of the female, is not unusual among insects. The most common examples are among the aphids. Certain species have in their life cycle both parthenogenetic and sexual forms. In the tropical and warmer regions no males appear, however, and the females continue year after year producing only their own sex. A similar phenomenon occurs among coccids, or scale insects, and among many weevils, sawflies, gall wasps, bethylid wasps, certain bees, and hymenopterous parasites. Among honey bees, unfertilized females may produce only males. In certain parasites, one species may produce only males and another only females. A South African race of the common honey bee is said to produce parthenogenetically not only males and workers but even queens. Some ants also reproduce by unfertilized eggs. Thus we find that parthenogenetic reproduction results only in males in many of the insects although females are not uncommon, while among aphids and coccids only females are produced.

Polymorphism is a condition in which there are adults of two or more distinct forms of the same sex. There also are polymorphic larval forms. To illustrate, in the aphid genus *Periphyllus* there are as many as 17 distinct recognizable forms, some of which are so different from the others that they have been mistaken for separate species. Among social insects, especially among termites and ants, polymorphism reaches its peak in the insect world. As many as 12 distinct series of castes and forms occur in the species of *Eutermes*.

Among the many qualities of insect fitness are the hard, elastic, tough exoskeleton with its powers of renewal and its resistance to corrosive chemicals; the many protective devices, such as rugosities, hairs, spines, and scales, as well as the folded wings; the many legs; the ability to lose and even to regenerate certain appendages without greatly interfering with life and reproductive processes; the protective coloration and devices for mimicry; the excretion of protective waxes, resins, and offensive glandular materials; poisonous body fluids and gases; stinging hairs and other devices; the specially constructed living quarters in plant tissues, in water, soil, debris; the enveloping and protecting cases of wood, earth, waxes, paper; the webs, cocoons, spittle, nests, galls; the internal parasitic habits on other hosts; the innumerable other means of protection and of escaping natural enemies through the complicated processes of development; the methods of escape by protective coloration and mimicry, death feigning, jumping, snapping, and flight; the aggressiveness exemplified by ants, mosquitoes, bees, wasps; the ability to bite and sting; the ability to reproduce in such numbers as to overcome almost every opposing factor, even including larger animals and human beings.

Those are the weapons with which insects counter man's inroads on forests and native vegetation and other habitats of insects, the cultivation of onetime grasslands, the draining of aquatic breeding places, and the devices of chemical and biological control. That is why insects are rarely exterminated. In fact, many species, benefited by the immense acreages of special farm crops, have actually increased because of man's agricultural activities.

As I said, insects generally have occupied only land surfaces and freshwater areas. On land, they occupy all areas except the permanent arctic and antarctic icecaps. They live in the soil, in fresh and brackish water, and in and on all conceivable kinds of animal and plant materials. Insects, even the aquatic forms, are always associated with the flora and fauna of every region. The associations may be somewhat detrimental to plant and other animal life, or they may be mutually beneficial to both the hosts and the insects; despite the damage by locusts, armyworms, weevils, and other serious pests, plants have not been greatly hampered by them. On the other hand, it is difficult to ascertain to what degree plants may be benefited by insects. Assuredly, we do know that the pollination of many plants can only be accomplished by certain ants, bees, butterflies, moths, flies, beetles, and other insects.

Not all insects are plant feeders. Fleas, lice, gnats, midges, mosquitoes, and some bugs, beetles, thrips, neuropterons, strepsipterons, ants, wasps, and parasitic forms prey on animals. As carriers of diseases to man and to domestic and wild animals, they are of great concern and have spread death and misery over the world through the ages.

The varying conditions of topography, climate, and other forms of life with which they are associated and upon which they subsist undoubtedly also have influenced their variability of structure and habits. Although the ancestors of insects are thought to have been aquatic, many entomologists believe insects first evolved on land. Another general belief is that insects did not arise until after plants appeared on earth. R. J. Tillyard has said that the earliest fossils have been found in the lower part of the Upper Carboniferous period in North America, and that at a somewhat higher horizon, in the upper part of the Upper Carboniferous, insects occurred abundantly both in North America and in Europe. These insects were aquatic and terrestrial. If insects were ever oceanic, they did not remain so because up to now, at least, they have never invaded the ocean to any extent. Few, if any, truly oceanic aquatic insects feed, for instance, on the abundance of aquatic plants along the shores of all the great oceans. This warehouse of plant food appears not to have been the objective of insect adaptability.

In fresh water, insects are quite at home and often develop in tremendous numbers, as, for example, the mayflies in certain of the Great Lakes. The abundance of dragonflies, stoneflies, caddisflies, water bugs, water beetles, mosquitoes, gnats, and other insects testify to their perfect conformity to an aquatic life. Many of the land and aerial forms also have remarkable aquatic adaptations, such as walking on water and swimming with the wings that ordinarily they use for flight. An example is certain minute hymenopterous species, which parasitize the eggs of water insects.

Probably many more years of study will be needed to explain all of the complex adaptations and interrelations of insects to other insects and animals, plants, and lower organisms. The more general relationships have been known for many years, but only in recent times has the relationship of insects to viruses and other micro-organisms been revealed.

Small size is not the only important asset of insects in their struggle to survive. Their varied methods of locomotion are admirably adapted to their needs. The younger stages of all insects and all stages of many species are wingless. Thus early in life they learn to walk, crawl, run, jump, and hop. Except among the more primitive wingless forms, flying is attained in the mature stages. In some, like aphids, wingless (apterous) and winged (alate) forms appear in the same generations. Then the alates are the dispersing and migrating forms, and the apterae remain more or less fixed in the immediate surroundings of their birth. Among many other insects, only one of the sexes (the male in some coccids and aphids, for example) may be winged. Throughout practically the whole insect group we find both the winged and wingless condition in the adult forms, as exemplified by such well-developed groups as ants, parasitic hymenoptera, flies, moths, and beetles. In the lower orders, Protura, Thysanura, Aptera, and Collembola, all stages are wingless. Nevertheless, representatives of nearly all of them occur throughout the whole world. Among the higher insects, all members of the orders Mallophaga, Anoplura, and Siphonaptera are wholly apterous. In nearly all the other orders, wingless adults occur.

The remarkable thing is the phenomenal degree of variation from any definite standard in their anatomical, physiological, and ecological constitution.

Practically all insects walk or crawl. Six legs enable the adults to move along at a rather even and rapid rate. Certain of the running forms, such as silverfish, cockroaches, psocids, bird lice, bugs, many beetles, flies, and ants may move very fast.

The larvae may be legless (apodous) or have either the normal three pairs of legs, or these and additional prolegs, as among caterpillars, sawflies, and horntails. Larvae of weevils, flies, and other members of the order Diptera and some other specialized parasitic forms are apodous. Many of the weevil larvae appear to get about as easily as caterpillars; for them, pseudopods serve as legs.

Certain running insects, like silverfish, cockroaches, and ants, travel almost like lightning and are gone in a flash. Other forms move with a slow and often wobbly gait. Insects that are more or less attached to the host plant, like wingless aphids, move about slowly and depend upon the winged forms for dispersal.

Such forms as the female armored scales can crawl only in the first stage of development. Males eventually develop into fully legged and also winged adults, which seek out and mate with the immobile females.

Many insects jump. Those that do usually also walk and run. Jumping may be a means of locomotion and of escaping from enemies, as exemplified by springtails, crickets, grasshoppers, leafhoppers, fleas, and others.

Aquatic insects are efficient swimmers. They may maneuver with all their legs or with only the hind legs as oars. Dragonfly nymphs expel water through the terminal abdominal opening with such force as to propel them forward, slowly or in a rapid darting motion. Whirligig beetles swim under water and also gyrate in rapid, fantastic movements on the surface. Several families of bugs, including water striders and many gnats and flies, run rapidly on the water. Many spiders and other arthropods can do that, too.

Small size and light weight keep insects from flying as fast as some birds, but in maneuverability insects probably exceed all other animals.

Only adults have wings. There may be only a single pair in the true flies, in certain mayflies, and in male coccids or scale insects, but ordinarily there are two pairs. They are membranous with simple or complicated venation and are naked or covered with hairs and scales. The scales and hairs may be beautifully colored and arranged in more or less definite color patterns, as in the butterflies, moths, dragonflies, flies, caddisflies, and others. In the whiteflies and the coniopterygids, they are covered with a white, powdery wax.

At rest, the wings may remain extended at right angles to the body, as in the dragonflies and many true flies, but they are more often folded together above the dorsum or flat over the back or somewhat around the body.

The flight of insects is remarkable almost beyond belief even though rarely have we noted closely the leisurely floating of butterflies, the tireless movements of honey bees from flower to flower, the aimless whirl of grasshoppers on a hot day, the determined buzzing of mosquitoes, flies, and gnats. The plump and lazy-looking bot fly is believed to be the fastest flier and may attain a speed of 40 or 50 miles an hour; the large dragonfly is about the most agile flier of the animal kingdom. These so-called hawkers capture their insect prey on the wing and remain almost constantly in the air, going forward and backward, remaining poised in a fixed position, and then darting faster than the eye can follow—only to reappear in almost the same spot. They have been observed great distances from water during migration flights.

Hummingbird moths get their name from their resemblance to hummingbirds and their habit of collecting food from flowers in a manner so like that of the real hummingbirds that they are often mistaken for them. While the adults are beneficial, because, by means of their excessively long rostrum, they pollinate many flowers which cannot be fertilized by any other natural means, yet the large caterpillars, like the tomato and tobacco worms and other species, do considerable damage to crops.

MANY SPECIES MIGRATE long distances on the wing. Locusts have become an international problem because they may breed in one country and migrate to devastate another country often 100 miles or more away. Butterflies and moths and many other insects have regular yearly seasonal migrations.

Most insects have dispersal flights. Often during the spring, summer, and fall certain species take to wing, and the air may be filled with flying thrips, aphids, termites, crickets, beetles, flies, ants, and others. The flights may be for relatively short distances and for only a few hours or days, but altogether the insects may gradually move across vast areas of cultivated and natural vegetation in seeking new feeding grounds. Such flights follow a rather definite pattern year after year. There are, for example, the regular flights of insects that winter over as adults and young in the southern parts of the United States and Mexico and move northward as spring and summer advance. Therefore there may be an even and sometimes excessive and rapid distribution of a given species to all the available hosts in a large region.

Insects may be carried in other ways. Winds and air currents pick up the minute wingless and winged forms alike and carry them far. Such fragile forms as aphids, scale insects, thrips, and tiny caterpillars may have means of supplementing their weak flight by spinning waxy filaments and silken threads or balloons, which increase their buoyancy and carry them long distances. An example is the winged individuals of a spruce aphid, *Lachnus piceae,* which have been observed in large numbers on the fresh snow of the icecap of Northeast Land, Spitsbergen, 800 miles from the Kola Peninsula, Russia, from which the insects were believed to have been carried. This aphid is often abundant in the coniferous forests of northern Russia and is carried by strong winds into regions in which it cannot exist naturally. It may also be carried by more favorable air currents to new and desirable forested areas. Insects may also be transported by water, host animals, birds, and other insects. Quarantine laws cannot completely prevent the unusual natural migrations and movements of insects, which have been going on over long periods of time.

Wing beats of insects, according to L. E. Chadwick, vary with the species and may be as rapid as 350 strokes a second. Even among the different individuals of a species the wing beats, as in *Drosophila,* may vary from 9,000 per minute to about 13,000. Wing beats for the large yellow swallowtail butterfly average about 6 a minute, for the sphinx moth 90, for the honey bee from 160 to 220, for the bumble bee 240, and for the house fly about 160.

Many insects have complicated life histories. In fact, the entire life cycle of most species is still imperfectly known. Even the common insect pests that have been under constant observation for years may present biological puzzles. As we advance in our understanding of some of the more complex life histories of species, such as the parasitic and social forms, the more are we forced to go back and review the exact development of common forms that have been generally considered to be simple and thoroughly understood. In that way, many new and unsuspected facts have been learned that were overlooked by previous students and investigators.

The entomologist regards every individual insect he encounters as only one phase of a simple or complex stage in the development of the insect from birth to adult. Between the beginning and end of this cycle, few (3 or 4) or many (6 to 17) different stages or types of individuals may appear. To know these for more than a few groups is beyond the capacity and experience of most entomologists. It is possible to recognize all the types of individuals in a genus or possibly even in more than one family, however.

Let us consider briefly the more generalized types of transformation in certain of the representative orders.

Primitive or ametabola (unchangeable):

In this type there is little difference in the general appearance of the various stages throughout the entire life of the insect. The condition is evident in certain so-called primitive insects such as silverfish, bristletails, springtails, campodids, and japygids.

Metabola (change or metamorphosis):

1. Paurometabola (small or slight change)—having gradual or direct metamorphosis, in which anatomically the various stages look much alike, but there are usually marked changes in color and size and often in the acquisition of wings. Representatives are earwigs, grasshoppers, katydids, crickets, phasmids, mantids, cockroaches, termites, booklice, barklice, embiids, thrips, sucking animal lice, biting bird lice, and bugs and their relatives (fulgorids, delphacids, cicadids, treehoppers, leafhoppers, spittlebugs, psyllids, aleyrodids or whiteflies, plant-lice or aphids, phylloxeras, and chermes).

2. Hemimetabola (incomplete changes)—in which the aquatic young or nymphs differ from the adults by having accessory organs for aquatic respiration while the free-living adults are winged (mayflies, dragonflies, damselflies, stoneflies, and salmonflies).

3. Holometabola (complete change)—metamorphosis in higher insects, which pass through complete and complex changes having larvae, pupae, and adult stages (dobsonflies, dustywings, lacewings, ant-lions, owlflies, mantispids, raphidiids, scorpionflies, caddisflies, moths, butterflies, beetles,

weevils, ants, bees, wasps, gall wasps, horntails, parasitic hymenopterons, flies, and fleas).

Just how these simple and complicated methods of development affect the physiology and instincts of insects is not fully known, but, according to William Morton Wheeler, the insects, like ants, that have the most complicated metamorphoses and most highly developed reflexes manifest "in addition to these reflexes . . . more complicated trains of behavior, the so-called instincts; and both these and the reflexes may be affected with a certain modifiability or plasticity which, in its highest manifestations, has been called intelligence."

It is interesting to ask and difficult to answer a question often brought up: "Do insects display intelligence?" Although entomologists and biologists disagree on the point, it is important to remember that such a phenomenon as instinct, bordering on intelligence, exists among insects and must exert a considerable influence upon their attainment of their present conspicuous status in the life of the world.

T. D. A. Cockerell, an authority on bees, discussing bumble bees, remarked: "Although we have emphasized the dominance of instinct in the affairs of these insects, it must be admitted that ordinary memory and what we must call intelligence have a part."

The late William Morton Wheeler, an authority on ants, said this:

"Many attempts have been made to define instinct, but it is evident that none of these could be completely successful, because instinct transcends intelligence and has its mainspring in the depths of the life process itself. Perhaps as good a formal definition as I am able to give is the following: An instinct is a more or less complicated activity manifested by an organism which is acting, first, as a whole rather than as a part; second, as the representative of a species rather than as an individual; third, without previous experience; and fourth, with an end or purpose of which it has no knowledge. This definition will satisfy the person of scholastic mind, but to the biologist it is a mass of obscurities; for it is certain that the man lives not who can tell where the whole begins and the part leaves off in a living organism, or can frame a satisfactory definition of a living individual or a species; and the intellect abdicates when it is called upon to grasp an activity that is unconsciously purposeful."

Then, too, there are so many interesting facts concerning the developmental patterns of growth of both lower and higher categories of insects that it is almost impossible to grasp more than a few fragments as to what it all means. The course of the life history of a simple insect, such as a maple aphid of the genus *Periphyllus,* which gives rise to at least 17 different kinds of progeny from egg to true sexual males and females, is only one example. The phenomenon is further complicated by the fact that only the eggs survive the winters and every year the full complement of different types of individuals regularly appear and disappear in cyclic order.

In contrast to this somewhat lowly member of the insect world, there are extremely highly developed life cycles and interrelations among the members of different castes with their guests, ectoparasites and endoparasites, and with plants, with other food-producing insects, like aphids and coccids, and with all the environmental factors surrounding each species. Other activities of ants, such as slave making, and the toleration and uses of permanent social parasites, all indicate the ability of these insects to hold their own and to thrive along with literally a million other species of insects in what appears to be a world already overrun with their own kind.

Aside from their remarkable anatomical and physiological characters, insects have developed special traits, devices, and means of protection, such as running, jumping, snapping, flying, swimming, death feigning, motionless attitudes, and protective mimicry to their surroundings and of many natural objects. They also protect themselves by spinning silken webs and cocoons; by constructing earthen and other types of coverings, cells, or nests; by excreting wax or protective and often offensive fluids and gases; by a covering of stinging hairs; or by using stings for defense or for procuring food for their young. Eggs are protected by inserting them into plant tissues, such as wood, fruit, or seeds; by placing them in cells or cases in the soil; or in the nests of aggressive and protecting ants. Larvae protect themselves by working as leaf miners, gall makers, or as parasites in or on other insects or higher animals.

Many insects are luminous. Wonderful indeed are the fireflies, which are beetles belonging to the family Lampyridae; the fire beetles belonging to the elaterid genus, *Pyrophorus;* beetles belonging to the families Lycidae, Phengodidae, Drilidae, Cantharidae, Carabidae (*Physodera*); the springtail genera *Anurida, Achorutes,* and *Onychiurus;* and certain midges and gnats, including the remarkable cave-inhabiting New Zealand glowworm. The larvae of the North Carolina fungus gnat, *Platyura fultoni,* glow at either end, and the adults of the European midge, *Chironomus plumosus,* are luminous. Luminescence appears to be associated with insects living in damp or moist locations or during the rainy seasons and may also be associated with mating reactions.

The New Zealand glowworm is unique. R. B. Goldschmidt wrote: "[Its] very successful adaptation cannot function without all of the following acquisitions: (1) The tendency of the larva to live in dark, moist places. (2) The development of a continuously shining organ of luminescence out of the Malpighian tubules. (3) The ability to build a tent. (4) The ability to build the trapping threads and to insert on them the special sticky droplets. (5) The carnivorous habit with all its physiological adjustments. (6) The ability to choose the proper habitat where the prey breeds in large quantities. (7) The instincts needed for the feeding process. (8) The adaptation of the entire cycle to the ecological features." Such a complicated and specialized life with its adaptations must have required a very long time for development.

In order to survive the heat of summer and cold of winter and unusual periods of drought, insects can assume an inactive condition for short or long periods. The periods usually conform to ordinary seasonal conditions, but some extremes occur during the regular growing periods of spring and summer.

Some insects, like aphids, may have as many as 10 or more generations a year; cicadas may require 2 or 3 to 17 years to develop a single generation. Aphids usually live exposed on the plant and reproduce in almost unbelievable numbers. Conversely, their rather close relatives, the cicadas, require much longer periods of development, and this may be made possible because the larval period is spent in the soil where much greater protection is afforded from natural enemies and from unfavorable weather.

The term "aestivation" refers particularly to quiescence and cessation of growth and development during the summer. Usually during this period the insect may not be fully fed. Examples of aestivating insects occur in many of the higher orders. One of the most remarkable cases is the aphid belonging to the genus *Periphyllus.* The insect overwinters as an egg, which hatches in the spring. After two generations of apterous parthenogenetic females and a third generation of similar apterae and alates, tiny wingless individuals, called dimorphs, also appear. The dimorphs continue to appear along with three or more succeeding generations of normal apterous and winged individuals. The dimorphs are flat and disclike and so small as to be barely visible to the unaided eye. They settle on the surfaces of the leaves and are so closely appressed and so near the color of their immediate surroundings that they often are overlooked even by entomologists studying the other forms of the species. From the end of May to nearly the middle of August, there is no noticeable growth in size or change in their appearance. By then, they are the only surviving form of the aphid. Then, with the approach of fall, the most suitable time for going into aestivation, these minute dimorphs begin to grow and finally assume normal size and form. When fully mature they give birth to apterous and alate parthenogenetic forms. These in turn give rise to the sexuales, which disappear after laying the overwintering eggs. The important thing in this life history is the fact that the minute, delicate, aestivating dimorph is the only survivor of the species during the midsummer period.

Many weevils, including the vegetable weevil, introduced into the west coast of North America from South America, aestivate in California. The Colorado potato beetle aestivates during the dry season in the Tropics and hibernates in central and northern United States and in Europe.

Some insects can live in a quiescent condition for long periods in various stages of their development. I have referred to the 17-year larval and pupal periods of the cicada. A South American root-infesting coccid, *Margarodes vitium,* is reported to have lived 17 years without food in the dry, unnatural condition of an insect collection. Adults of the wood-infesting *Buprestis aurulenta* have remained in structural timbers for 10 to 26 years before finally emerging.

Aestivation is particularly adapted to insects living in arid and desert areas where the summers are dry and hot. During the more unfavorable periods many insects hide themselves in the soil at suitable depths and under all available protective objects. In these areas many other animals feed upon them, but the remaining insects survive despite all obstacles.

Hibernation means passing the winter in an inactive and quiescent condition. In this phase the insect, in whatever stage of development, may or may not be fully fed, but nevertheless is in condition to withstand the rigors of the cold season in the temperate and arctic regions. Hibernation is almost universal among insects in those areas. The winter may be spent as an egg, in which the tiny first-stage larva may often be fully developed by late summer or fall and awaiting the coming of spring to emerge. It may be spent as a larva, as an active nymph, as a pupa, or as an adult. Because insects can withstand very low temperatures, they normally suffer no serious losses during the winter within their normal range. Hibernation by rather fragile forms like mosquitoes and butterflies in sheltered, relatively dry places out of doors therefore is quite common and successful. Somewhat more difficult to comprehend is the successful hibernation of butterflies in low shrubbery, where they may be completely enveloped in snow and ice for 3 to 4 months.

Methods of hibernation are varied. Some insects prepare for hibernation by constructing such shelters as silken nests or cocoons. Others seek hiding places above or below ground which may be suitable for the condition of the particular insect.

Insects are highly efficient in using every available source of food. They consume every kind of plant product, including the entire living and dead plant from root to top. Plants that may be poisonous to other animals or to some insects are acceptable to other kinds of insects. Insects feed on all animals, including insects themselves. Only the stripped bones devoid of all digestible matter resist their hunger.

How, therefore, can plant and animal life exist on the earth and escape destruction by all the multitudinous insect destroyers? The answer lies with the insects themselves. Among all the varied species, they maintain a reasonable balance, which permits normal and sometimes even excessive populations to survive, but at a low enough level so that plants continue to propagate in what we may consider to be a normal manner. Of course this so-called balance may have been determined between insects and other related natural factors ages ago. Think of what would happen if all insects were completely wiped out! The interrelations between the plant-feeding insects and the predacious and parasitic forms are exceedingly intricate and unrelenting.

Parasitism by other insects invades every species of insect—the plant and animal feeders and even the parasitic ones themselves. All forms of the host from egg to adult are subject to destruction by predators and parasites. The degree of parasitism or hyperparasitism may be fourfold or more. The development of many young from a single egg or embryo also occurs among the parasitic forms: Not only is there competition among several species of parasites within a single host, therefore, but there is a struggle for survival among many individuals from a single egg of the same species within the body of a single host.

Some of the relationships between insects and plants have become so complicated that in most instances neither insect nor plant could long exist apart.

Similar relationships exist between insects and other animals and between certain insects and others of their own kind, yet their basic existence depends on the vegetable kingdom. Although millions of insects derive their subsistence from plants, they seem not to interfere greatly with the natural development of the plant world. It is true that in special situations insects might even exterminate a species of plant in a given location, and we know too well that they are responsible for tremendous losses to crops almost everywhere. However, it appears that plants have actually occupied as much of the earth's surface as is possible despite their insect dependents.

The ability to create a specialized type and supply of food is not uncommon among many groups of insects. Such modifications may affect other animal and especially insect hosts, as in the case of parasites, but are more often conspicuous in plant hosts. Chief among these latter are galls, produced by the dipterous gall midges or gall flies belonging to the family Itonididae, and the gall wasps of the hymenopterous family Cynipidae. Members of other orders, including certain species of thrips, lace bugs, psyllids, aphids, coccids, beetles, weevils, sawflies, trypetid flies, and possibly still others also produce plant galls in which the larvae develop. The galls formed by these various insects may also be inhabited by many other kinds of insects that feed upon the gall itself and by predators and parasites that prey upon all the various insects associated with the galls. Complicated biological relationships thus are associated with insect galls. The development of galls of different insects may vary somewhat, but generally it appears to be caused by excretions of the developing larvae or nymphs and to follow a more or less definite pattern for a given species or group of closely related species. Thus, the shape, vestiture, sculpturing, and color may be characteristic of a species or variety and may thus aid in recognizing them.

The galls of a Chinese aphid, *Melaphis chinensis*, are artificially reared on *Rhus semialata* in China in commercial quantities as a source of dye and tannin and for medical purposes. The host plants are carefully cultivated so as to enable the aphids to produce a maximum crop of galls. Quantities of the galls have been shipped to the United States and other countries.

Host specificity is illustrated among the cynipid gall flies. In general, about 90 percent of the galls are produced on species of oaks, 5 percent on species of roses, and 5 percent on different genera of the composites. Among the aphids and coccids, a species is usually associated with a distinct genus or even species of plant.

Certain insects cultivate specialized types of plants, especially fungi. This type of propagation attains its highest development among subterranean and mound-building termites, which also have highly developed caste systems. Their termitaria may be entirely underground or they may extend to the surface or rise many feet above it, in which case they are formed of thick, earthen walls hardened by the salivary excretions used in their construction. The termitaria may vary from a foot in height and diameter for some species to great mounds, pillars, or chimneys 15 to 30 feet high and almost as great in diameter. The fungus gardens are distributed throughout the central portions of the mound in a somewhat irregular manner. Termitaria of these types are constructed by rather small tropical or subtropical termites that reach their highest development in tropical Africa, South America, south India, and Australia. The termites are nocturnal foragers and prey on various types of vegetation, which is comminuted and mixed with excreta. This forms the food for rearing the fungi upon which the termites subsist.

Leaf-cutting ants of the tribe Attii also cultivate fungi in much the same way as termites but feed only on the fungus hyphae. The so-called ant gardens of the Amazonian ants in the genera *Azteca* and *Camponotus* are prepared and planted and the crop utilized for food.

Harvester ants play an important part in the accidental distribution of seeds by collecting, carrying, and storing them for food in their nests.

As INSECTS HAVE BEEN UPON this earth millions of years longer than human beings it is to be expected that they have acquired specializations and adaptations not wholly understood by us. The degree of development among insects is extremely variable and difficult to measure by human standards. There has been much speculation concerning the faculties of insects. It is well known that many species of ants, bees, and wasps, especially those that have communal tendencies, show a high degree of differentiation and efficiency in organization and labor. They may be likened to living machines motivated by some unexplainable power defined as instinct, if not powers of reasoning and intelligence. Yet insects display many remarkable traits not wholly understood by man.

The high degree of organization and caste systems of social insects (termites, ants, bees, wasps) have been investigated by entomologists, but there is still a great deal to be learned about them. Much has been written about the highly specialized attainments of ants, in particular, concerning their ability to build nests; their social organizations, caste systems, and slave making; their means of communication; methods of collecting, storing, and growing food; their art of defense and selection and procedure in producing queens; and their maintenance and tolerance of an assemblage of nurses, guests, satellites, commensals, paupers, scavengers, kidnappers, murderers, and assassins somewhat after the pattern of our human society.

E. O. ESSIG *is professor of entomology, entomologist in the experiment station, and former chairman of the division of entomology and parasitology in the College of Agriculture, University of California, Berkeley. He has been a member of that institution since 1914. Following graduation from Pomona College in 1909, he has devoted most of his life to agriculture and especially to entomology, on which subject he has written more than 1,000 papers and four books. His specialty in that field is the taxonomic and economic study of aphids, which insects have recently come into prominence in agriculture because they are among the worst insect vectors of plant virus diseases.*

Readers can find more information on how insects live in W. V. Balduf's The Bionomics of Entomophagous Coleoptera, *published by John S. Swift Company in 1935; R. J. Tillyard's* The Insects of Australia and New Zealand, *Angus and Robertson (Sydney, Australia), 1926.*

970134°—52——4

Life Processes of Insects

Frank H. Babers, John J. Pratt, Jr.

A study of insect physiology can tell us a great deal about the phenomenon of life and help entomologists in their fight against insect pests.

Of especial interest is nutrition, for the digestive systems of insects are as diverse as the insects themselves and the kinds of food they eat. When all the evidence on that complex subject is in we will be that much closer to the solution to some mysteries that still confront the biologist, physiologist, and biochemist.

Some species eat almost anything, but some have a restricted diet. Some have been given more than one common name because they customarily feed on more than one plant: Bollworm, tomato fruitworm, and corn earworm, for instance, are one insect.

The influence of diet on the growth is illustrated by the honey bee. Larvae that are to become queens are fed on a diet of royal jelly. Other larvae destined to become workers are fed on royal jelly for only 2 days and for the rest of their larval life receive honey and pollen.

Several factors or vitamins are necessary for normal growth. The fat-soluble factors so important in mammalian physiology, except for cholesterol, apparently are not required by a number of insects. The water-soluble factors do play an important role. Most species need the B vitamins. Vitamin C does not seem to be required, but at least one insect, the cockroach, synthesizes vitamin C. Symbionts are bacteria that are transmitted hereditarily from parent insect to offspring. Apparently these bacteria are essential in the nutrition of many insects. Sometimes the insects provide specialized structures, called mycetocytes, for the bacteria to live in.

A vinegar fly, *Drosophila melanogaster,* has been reared under sterile conditions on a definite chemical medium. It is the first multicelled organism to be raised in the absence of micro-organisms on a diet whose chemical composition was exactly known.

Certain insects, such as mealworms, require little water because they can derive metabolic water from carbohydrates.

The ability to utilize sugars varies considerably. Mannose is used by blow flies and vinegar flies but not by bees. Only aphids are able to use arabinose. Vinegar flies can survive for long periods on a diet of pure sucrose, raffinose, or melezitose.

To grow, insects must have proteins or their equivalent. Some mature insects can survive a long time on a protein-free diet, but they either undergo no further development in their adult stages or utilize food materials already stored in the body. Certain amino acids, the building blocks of proteins, seem to be essential for proper growth and development; the German cockroach requires at least five, valine, tryptophane, histidine, arginine, and cystine.

Ectoparasites such as lice seem to develop better on vitamin-deficient rabbits than on well-fed ones. When human volunteers were fed for several months on a diet deficient in certain vitamins and then infested with lice, however, the lice developed just as well as they did on humans that had a complete diet. On the other hand, it seems true that various insects often develop better and in greater numbers on plants with nutritional deficiencies than on well-fed plants. Powder-post beetles cannot digest cellulose. If allowed to choose among pieces of oak sapwood of different starch content, the female almost always chooses the wood with the highest starch content in which to lay her eggs.

Metabolism is the sum of all the chemical and physical processes by which living organized substance is produced and maintained. The subject obviously is complex and in only a few instances has the metabolism of an ingested food been followed completely.

What happens to the blood pigment hemoglobin after it is ingested by bloodsucking arthropods has been investigated. In most of the insects studied the bulk of hemoglobin seems to be broken down in the gut to hematin, which is then excreted unchanged. In mosquitoes and fleas, no pigment seems to be absorbed. In all the other forms, pigment in varying amounts is absorbed and circulates in the hemolymph. In the louse the absorbed pigment is further broken down to the bile pigment, biliverdin, and in other species bilirubin is also found.

During metamorphosis, the period during which the insect changes from an immature stage to an adult, the dehydrogenase enzyme activity in the blow fly falls rapidly at first, reaches a minimum at about the halfway point of the pupal period, then rises rapidly and continuously until metamorphosis is completed. The acidity of the pupal fluid follows a somewhat different course, becoming strongly acid soon after the beginning of metamorphosis, and reaches a maximum at about the same time the dehydrogenase activity is lowest. The acidity then decreases until the time for emergence, when the fluids are almost neutral. In the Japanese beetle, the changes in fat and glycogen content during metamorphosis may indicate that the insect synthesized glycogen from fat.

The metabolism of iodine by vinegar flies was studied by the use of radioactive iodine (I^{121}). When it was fed to larvae, the iodine was concentrated mostly in the protein of the skeletal parts of the larvae. If the pupae formed from larvae fed radioactive iodine were removed from the food before emergence, the adult insects did not contain radioactive material.

The amount of oxygen consumed by tissues during metabolism is an indication of the activity of the metabolic processes. The oxygen consumption of cockroach muscle is about the same as that of pigeon-breast muscle, which heretofore has been considered the most active tissue known.

Besides the usual waste products of metabolism, many insects excrete materials like wax and silk, which they use for various purposes. Other substances, such as the fetid material excreted by stink bugs, are used for protection. Still others, such as the venom of the wasp, are used in obtaining food.

Radioactive amino acids have been injected into the giant silkworm and apparently radioactive silk was obtained. The studies will help explain the chemical structure of silk.

The naturalist Athanasius Kircher in 1643 recommended music as an antidote for tarantula bites. Different treatments are used today for insect bites, but often they are no more effective than Kircher's. We know little about the nature of insect venom. In some ants it is formic acid; in others, toxic protein. Bee venom is made up of several toxic constituents, the chief of which is apitoxin. When it is injected by the sting of the bee, enzymes in the toxin cause a breakdown of cell protoplasm and the liberation of histamine. It is this chemical that is responsible for many of the symptoms of bee sting. Since early times bee venom often has been recommended for the treatment of arthritis, neuritis, and rheumatism.

Another mystery is the nature of the salivary gland secretion of various mosquitoes and flies. A toxic arrow poison used by the Bushmen of the Kalahari Desert in South Africa is obtained from the larva of the beetle *Diamphidia locusta*.

Insects do not have blood vessels. The circulating fluid flows freely throughout the body cavity except while it is being moved by the dorsal vessel or heart. It corresponds to both blood and lymph and is called hemolymph. In some insects it is clear and colorless. In others it is yellow or green. The volume varies greatly between species and individuals of one species. The hemolymph does not contain respiratory pigments such as hemoglobin or hemocyanin. Many analyses of hemolymph have been made, but the function of only a few of the many components has been determined.

Insect hemolymph contains more free amino acids than does human blood, which averages about 6 milligrams per hundred milliliters. Insect blood may contain as high as 385 milligrams per hundred milliliters. At least 24 compounds with the chemical properties of amino acids that occur free in the hemolymph of insects have been identified by the use of paper chromatographic methods. Several of them have not been identified yet as constituents of proteins.

In most insects the hemolymph contains a much higher percentage of potassium than does mammalian blood. Among phytophagous, or plant-feeding insects, the sodium-potassium ratio is less than 1; among carnivorous insects, the ratio is greater than 1. Some species of insects apparently have some sort of sodium-potassium regulatory system, because the ratio in the body fluid is not dependent on the ratio in food. In the silkworm larva, the sodium concentration in the body fluid seems to be in simple diffusion equilibrium with ingested sodium. Silkworm pupae and adults contain almost no sodium. It therefore must be selectively excreted.

Insect hemolymph contains a number of cells, or hemocytes. Their most obvious activity corresponds to that of the leucocytes, or white blood corpuscles, of the vertebrates in that they ingest any small particles of solid matter set free in the blood. Ten classes and 32 types of cells have been found in the blood of the southern armyworm, and 8 classes and 23 types of cells in the blood of the mealworm.

When removed from the insect, the hemolymph of some species clots rapidly and in others more slowly or not at all. The process of coagulation is not comparable to that of mammalian blood and varies between insect species. Hemolymph from Japanese beetle grubs coagulates by a gelation of the plasma, while that from the wax moth coagulates by agglutination of the cells. The coagulation of the hemolymph from these two species may be greatly retarded by exposing the larvae to sublethal intensities of ultrasonic waves. None of the chemicals normally used to prevent the clotting of mammalian blood has a similar effect on insect blood.

Twenty or more species of insects have developed resistance to insecticides following exposure to insecticides under natural conditions. Resistant strains have been developed in the laboratory by exposing many insects to concentrations of insecticide that killed 90 percent of them. Eggs from the survivors were used to maintain a colony. The process was repeated with each generation. In a short time the offspring showed considerable tolerance for the insecticide used in the selective process and also, usually, for many chemically unrelated compounds.

The control of the wild resistant insects has become a serious problem—DDT, after a few years of use, often has failed to control house flies and mosquitoes. Apparently no external differences exist between susceptible and insecticide-resistant flies. Scientists have tried to find out whether there are physiological differences. They have yet found no significant difference in vigor between susceptible and resistant strains: Resistance is not due simply to the failure of the insecticide to penetrate the cuticle of the insect, because the insects are also resistant when the insecticide is injected directly into the body cavity.

The enzyme cholinesterase rapidly destroys actylcholine, a chemical of important function in the transmission of nerve impulses across the nerve-cell junctions of several animal species. In insects the role of cholinesterase has not been determined, but because of the high concentration of the enzyme in insect nerve tissue, it is of interest in the physiology of resistance to insecticides.

The cholinesterase activity of the heads of resistant flies is less than that of normal flies. DDT applied externally to house flies apparently is first absorbed and then metabolized. One DDT-resistant strain was more able to metabolize DDT than were normal flies. By the use of large amounts of piperonyl cyclonene, the conversion of DDT to the metabolic product by the resistant flies was largely prevented. Another strain of DDT-resistant flies also rapidly metabolized DDT that had been absorbed. The main product of metabolism was DDE (1,1-dichloro-2,2-bis-(*p*-chlorophenyl) ethylene). A small amount of DDA (bis-(*p*-chlorophenyl) acetic acid) was also identified. Only small amounts of the metabolites were excreted and large amounts were retained in the body. In contrast to that strain, the normal, or DDT-susceptible, flies could metabolize only a negligible amount of DDT in 24 hours; neither DDE nor DDA was a product of the metabolism.

Cytochrome oxidase, an enzyme found in cells, is of great importance in the metabolic processes. The activity of the enzyme was much greater in one strain of resistant flies than in a normal strain.

We do not know whether the physiological differences between resistant and susceptible strains are due to the resistance. They may be variations in strain, due to differences in rearing procedures or some other factor.

The rate of loss of tolerance to insecticides following cessation of exposure also seems to vary tremendously between strains. Some strains, whose resistance was developed either in the field or laboratory, revert rapidly to nonresistant insects. Others retain resistance over many generations once they have acquired it. Resistance seems to be inherited, but the method of genetic transmission is still in doubt.

Colors of insects are as varied as those of the rainbow and are frequently due to complex mixtures of pigments. Most of the insect pigments were once thought to be simple end products of metabolism without physiological function. We now know that this is not always correct. Before the physiological function of the pigments was established, many were of commercial importance. Carminic acid from the cochineal insect was used as a wool dye from early times until azo dyes were discovered.

The term melanin is loosely applied to denote what is probably a group of pigments with varying composition. The pigments appear to be derived from tyrosine, an amino acid, by a series of enzymatic reactions. The darkening of insect blood on exposure to air is also generally due to melanin formation; the blood does not darken in the insect because of the inhibition of the enzymes by some unknown factor, possibly by a low oxidation-reduction potential. The biochemistry of pigment formation has thrown considerable light on the action of genes, the units in the chromosomes that carry the hereditary characters. Evidence has been presented that the process of melanin formation in mammalian tissues follows a similar pattern to that of insects.

The presence of hemoglobin in insects is an interesting point because it does not ordinarily function in its traditional role of oxygen carrier. In midge larvae (Tendipedidae), such a function seems doubtful, even when the oxygen tension is reduced greatly. The active group of the hemoglobin found in bot fly (*Gasterophilus*) larvae is the same as that in the hemoglobin of horse blood, but the protein part of the complex is different. Its molecular weight is about 34,000, compared to about 67,000 for human hemoglobin. Its affinity for carbon monoxide is much less than horse hemoglobin, but it has a high affinity for oxygen. Its functional significance, however, is obscure.

The metabolism of chlorophyll, the green pigment in plants, has been studied in the silkworm, potato beetle, squash bug, and a few other species. Many of the pigments in the squash bug are the results of the breakdown of chlorophyll, the site of breakdown apparently being the ventriculus, or functional stomach.

Insects do not always produce their own pigments. Sometimes the colors are the result of hereditary symbiotic bacteria found in insect tissues.

The wing pigments of the Pieridae, a common family of butterflies, were first studied by F. G. Hopkins in 1889. He concluded that they were waste metabolic products whose only physiological function is ornamental. The pigments mostly are now classified chemically as pterines. We have evidence that they are not just ornamental. The pterine ring may be considered a derivative of riboflavin, which is usually present in the Malpighian tubes of insects, for example. Thus there is a possible connection with the metabolism of vitamin B_2. The pterine ring is also found in the folic acid molecule, which has been shown to be an essential metabolite for the larva of the yellow-fever mosquito and the mealworm.

The walkingstick *Dixippus* is dark-colored at night and light-colored by day. Its color may be changed by illuminating the insect at night or placing it in a dark place by day. The color of other species, such as the cabbageworm, *Pieris brassicae,* is influenced by the illumination of the larva as it rests before pupation.

Hormones are chemical substances produced in an organ and liberated into the blood stream. Other organs then become excited by this hormone and functional activity results. Much light has been shed on many phases of invertebrate endocrinology, which science includes the hormones, since Stefan Kopec of Jagellonian University, Poland, in 1922, demonstrated the effect of a hormone on insect development. In insects, periods of great cell activity are followed by a process called molting during which time the insect sheds its old skin and is fitted with a new and larger one. Kopec showed that the molting process is controlled by hormones that are species-nonspecific. Blood taken from an insect at the proper time and injected into an insect of another species will cause molting, although the injected insect is not normally ready for the process. The hormones, which have so many varied functions, are secreted by at least 11 organs in insects. Physiological functions which are hormone-regulated are often influenced by temperature and humidity or other environmental factors.

It has not been determined whether sex hormones comparable to those found in the vertebrates are present in insects. There are present in insects physiologically active substances that participate in the development of hereditary characters. Because of their similarity to hormones, they are called gene hormones.

Developmental hormones in the immature stages are not always found in similar organs in all species, but they are secreted by at least three glands, all located in the head of the insect: The corpus allatum; the ring gland, or Weismann's ring; and some glandlike cells of the brain. In adult insects, one or more hormones secreted by the corpus allatum are important in reproduction. Color changes are also apparently due to the action of hormones.

Some hormones cause metamorphosis. By the injection of material from larvae ready to pupate, very young larvae have been made to undergo metamorphosis. But if a large larva is divided into two sections by ligaturing about 12 hours before time for normal pupation, only the forward half will pupate, although the rear half will remain alive for many days.

In the *Cecropia* silkworm, as in many other insects, metamorphosis is interrupted by a long diapause period that begins soon after the formation of the pupa. Diapause is characterized by cessation of cellular growth. It apparently is caused by the destruction of enzymes involved in the cytochrome system. Following the liberation of a growth hormone by cells in the pupal brain and the stimulation by this hormone of the prothoracic gland, the cytochrome system again begins to function and cell growth occurs.

The outer covering of insects, the integument, is both skeleton and skin. As in all arthropods, the integument consists of an epidermis, one cell layer in thickness, and a hard cuticular membrane. During their intermittent periods of activity, the epidermal cells secrete the circular membrane, commonly called the cuticle, over the surface of the animal. Entomologists used to believe that the characteristic component of cuticle was chitin, a hard, insoluble compound found in varying proportions in most insect cuticles. It was thought that the chitin formed a framework in the interstices in which other components of the cuticle were deposited. Scientists now believe that proteins rather than chitin are the fundamental constituents of cuticle. It might be (as suggested by the interpretation of X-ray diffraction data) that the cuticle consists of alternating layers of protein and chitin.

The cuticle may be rigid, flexible, or elastic. It also is waterproof; it has to be, because the integument keeps a proper water balance in the insect. The epicuticle, the thin outer membrane that is the most important in waterproofing the cuticle, is a complex structure of several layers. The first to be deposited is the innermost or cuticulin layer, believed to consist of a lipoprotein, which perhaps is denatured, condensed, and finally tanned along with other proteins present in the outer layers. Then a thick viscous fluid is discharged, and on top of that a wax layer. The wax layer is then topped with a hard cement layer, which is thought to consist of tanned proteins combined with lipids. The cement layer is secreted by some of the dermal glands whose openings are scattered over the surface of the integument.

Throughout the cuticle, running vertically from the cells, are the pore canals, of unknown function. In the cuticle of flesh fly larvae (Sarcophagidae), 15,000 of these were found per square millimeter.

The cuticle cannot grow and, in the rigid parts of the insect, cannot be stretched. As the insect grows, therefore, the cuticle is shed and is replaced by a larger cuticle. That process, molting, follows a period of great cell activity. When first laid down, the new cuticle is soft and often colorless, but it rapidly hardens and assumes its normal color.

The blow fly has been a favorite experimental insect because its larval cuticle is not shed before pupation, but rather is converted into the hard puparium. In the flesh fly (*Sarcophaga barbata*) the formation of the hard puparium from the soft larval cuticle is by the following process: Phenols are oxidized enzymatically by polyphenol oxidase to orthoquinone. The orthoquinone combines with the protein present and hardens it by a tanning process, during which the integument, which may have been colorless for a short period after the molt, becomes colored brown or black. The colors due to tanning, however, are not the basis for the brilliant iridescent or metallic colors of some insects. Such colors are due usually to the interference in the reflection of light from the multiple thin plates or scales that some insects have.

The shell, or chorion, of an insect's egg is like cuticle in many ways, but is even more complex. The shell of the egg of the assassin bug, *Rhodnius prolixus,* consists of seven layers, none of them waterproof. A cement layer is added to the outside of the egg when it is laid. Waterproofing is effected by a thin wax layer on the inside of the chorion, similar to the one that waterproofs the cuticle of most adult forms. The wax is secreted by the maturing egg and is attached securely to the innermost layer of the chorion. The other layers are modifications of various proteinlike materials somewhat like those in the cuticle.

The development of high-speed

cameras, with which many exposures per second are possible, and cathode-ray oscilloscopes, by which small changes in electrical potential can be accurately recorded, has aided the study of the physiology of insect flight. When certain insects are held so that their feet are in contact with a movable platform, the insect will rest quietly. If the platform is removed, the insect moves its wings as in flight and many experiments can be done while the insect is actually suspended in air under simulated flight conditions. If small electrodes are inserted among the flight muscles, potential changes can be measured and correlated with wing movement. Some butterflies move their wings at a leisurely 5 beats a second, but certain midges attain about 1,000 wing beats a second. The vinegar fly is capable of flights lasting up to 2 hours. At the start, wing beats are about 300 per second but at the end, when fatigue becomes evident, they are about 100 a second. Among the insects with slow frequencies of wing beats, the wing movements are completely synchronous with nerve impulses, but when the frequency of wing beat increases there is no synchrony.

Insects, like the vertebrates, have highly developed, specialized sensory receptors that can be stimulated by chemicals. The chemical senses of insects may be roughly classified as taste, smell, and the common chemical sense of vertebrates whereby response is made to such irritants as ammonia and chlorine. The structure of the organs of taste and smell of insects differ greatly from that of the vertebrates, but a striking similarity exists in the physiological behavior toward many compounds and in the way in which stimulation is brought about. As among the vertebrates, however, the distinction between taste and smell is based on unsatisfactory evidence. We cannot yet relegate either taste or smell in insects to specific areas of the body; areas of contact chemoreceptors have now been found on the mouth parts, tarsal leg segments, antennae, and ovipositors of various species, although the actual organs are not always known.

In seeking materials that will attract and repel insects, research workers have investigated the mechanical response of insects to thousands of compounds that vaporize at body temperatures. Many of the compounds are synthetic; many are natural materials of unknown composition.

One such is a substance secreted by the female gypsy moth. It will attract male gypsy moths over long distances.

The method by which the worker honey bees inform other bees of the location of a new food supply has been described by Karl von Frisch, of the University of Munich. It has long been known that worker bees returning to the hive often performed a kind of dance on the comb, but the reason for the dance was obscure. Von Frisch found that by the direction and duration of their movements, during the dance, the worker bees transmitted to other workers the direction and distance from the hive to the new-found food. He observed the antics in the darkness of the hive by the use of red light, to which the bees are insensitive. He found that he could predict the distance to about 100 yards. Direction was accurate to about 3°. The system worked for any distance up to about 3.7 miles. For direction, the bees use the sun as an orienting point. They also are apparently sensitive to polarized light, which they can use to get their bearings, because they can fly accurately whether or not the sun is visible.

Dr. von Frisch's discoveries, like others we have discussed, throw new light into the mysteries of nature. More such discoveries will come. They will give us a better understanding of insect physiology, of better controls of insects, and, indeed, of all life processes, including our own.

Frank H. Babers, *a biochemist, is in charge of a project that deals with the mode of action of insecticides and physiology of insects. He is a grad-*

uate of the University of Florida and Princeton University. He joined the Department of Agriculture in 1936. From 1946 to 1948 he was in charge of the chemical section of the Orlando, Fla., laboratory of the Bureau of Entomology and Plant Quarantine.

JOHN J. PRATT, JR., *joined the research staff of the Bureau of Entomology and Plant Quarantine upon receiving his doctor's degree from Cornell University in 1948. His work concerns the study of the mode of action of insecticides, the development of resistance to insecticides by insects, and insect physiology.*

Suggested for further reference are Bee Venom Therapy; Bee Venom, Its Nature, and Its Effect on Arthritic and Rheumatoid Conditions, *by Bodog F. Beck, D. Appleton-Century Co., New York, 1935;* Physiologie de l'Insects, *by Remy Chauvin, Institute National de la Recherchie Agronomique, Paris, 1949;* Bees; Their Vision, Chemical Senses, and Language, by Karl von Frisch, *Cornell University Press, Ithaca, N. Y., 1950;* Bibliography of Animal Venoms, *by R. W. Harmon and C. B. Pollard, University of Florida Press, Gainesville, 1948;* The Principles of Insect Physiology, *by V. B. Wigglesworth, Methuen and Company, London, 1950; and the following articles in periodicals:*

V. G. Dethier and L. E. Chadwick: Chemoreception in Insects, *Physiological Reviews, volume 28, pages 220–254. 1948.*

Hubert and Mabel Frings: The Loci of Contact Chemoreceptors in Insects—a Review With New Evidence, *American Midland Naturalist, volume 41, pages 602–658. 1949.*

Aaron Bunsen Lerner and Thomas B. Fitzpatrick: Biochemistry of Melanin Formation, *Physiological Reviews, volume 30, pages 91–125. 1950.*

William Trager: Insect Nutrition, *Biological Reviews of the Cambridge Philosophical Society, volume 22, pages 148–177. 1947.*

V. B. Wigglesworth: The Fate of Haemoglobin in Rhodinius Prolixus (Hemiptera) and Other Blood-Sucking Arthropods, *Proceedings of the Royal Society (London), series B, volume 131, pages 313–339, 1943; and* The Insect Cuticle, *Biological Reviews of the Cambridge Philosophical Society, volume 23, pages 408–451. 1948.*

Carroll M. Williams: Biochemical Mechanisms in Insect Growth and Metamorphosis, *Federation Proceedings, volume 10, pages 546–552, 1950.*

J. Franklin Yeager: The Blood Picture of the Southern Armyworm (Prodenia Eridania), *Journal of Agricultural Research, volume 71, pages 1–40, 1945.*

How Insects Choose Their Food Plants

Charles T. Brues

All forms of animal life need organic materials in order to exist, grow, and reproduce. Some subsist on living, dead, or decaying plants. Others get the foods they require from living or dead animals.

Many kinds, including some of the insects, live on a mixed diet of both plant and animal materials. Civilized man has almost endless variety in his diet: Bacteria, yeasts, fungi, roots, berries, fruits, and foliage of plants furnish vegetable food; he eats the flesh of many invertebrate animals such as crustaceans and mollusks, although fish, birds, and mammals commonly furnish his main protein requirements.

No insect selects food in such variety, but a few insects are omnivorous in the sense that they may consume many kinds of plant and animal materials. Most of the more specialized kinds restrict their diet to a limited range—particularly the forms that develop as parasites within the bodies of host animals, which almost invariably are other insects.

Such parasitic ones, which are called entomophagous parasites, generally are very specific in the selection of their hosts. They usually lay their eggs on or directly within the body of the host insect and continue from generation to generation to confine their attacks to the same species of hosts.

Predatory insects, which capture living prey just as do the carnivorous birds and mammals, confine their diet to animals smaller or less active than themselves. Quite frequently they also select particular kinds of prey: Some consistently capture aphids, some devour caterpillars, some feed on scale insects, and a few are addicted to a diet of snails. On the other hand, groups like the praying mantids and ant-lions accept and relish a wide range of flesh. Because predators subsist largely on other insects, they depend mainly on the vegetarian kinds, which are the most abundant source of suitable prey.

Parasitic and predatory insects reduce the abundance of plant-eating insect life. Nevertheless, under the conditions that have prevailed in nature for millions of years, their influence has not kept the vast hordes of vegetarian insects from maintaining populations at a high level. Neither has it curtailed their evolutionary differentiation, because they have developed innumerable adaptations in structure and in habits to their environment. Some of the most striking features in this respect relate to the instinctive behavior that determines the selection of food plants.

Farmers always have known that many species of insects feed only on a particular crop or series of crops. They appear season after season and evince an unvarying predilection for the plants that nourished their forebears. There is great variation in the number and variety of food plants they select, but there is a fixity of purpose in their behavior that is far beyond their dietary requirements.

In a search for the causes underlying such selection, we shall consider mainly those species—about half of the living species of insects—which feed on the flowering plants, particularly those of economic importance, since we have more accurate knowledge of them than we do of most of the insects that are associated with wild plants.

Common in home and market gardens are cabbage, cauliflower, radish, kohlrabi, brussels sprouts, turnips, and collards. These members of the family Cruciferae have a pungent odor and taste because of the presence of chemicals known as mustard oils, which the tissues of the plants secrete. The chemicals attract a series of generally unrelated insects to the plants, on which they may lay their eggs.

Thus, the cabbage butterfly seeks out the cabbage patch in the garden to deposit its eggs. The caterpillars that hatch from the eggs eat and grow to maturity on the plants selected by the parent butterfly. If they are placed on other plants to which they are not accustomed, they go on a hunger strike, doggedly refusing to eat, and finally perish miserably in the midst of plenty. Only if sap of the food plant or mustard oils are smeared on the strange foliage will they recover their appetites and resume feeding. There is a close correlation between the choice made by the butterfly and the fondness of its caterpillar offspring for the kind of food that has been chosen for them.

In some insects, the adult and larval stages feed on the same plants, but the adult cabbage butterfly, like other butterflies and moths, sucks the nectar of various flowers and the laying of its eggs on the larval food plant is not a response to its adult appetite. Any failure of the butterfly to select plants acceptable to its offspring would spell disaster, because the young caterpillars cannot go foraging in search of plants other than those upon which they find themselves. Similar peculiarities prevail among the great variety of diverse insects that restrict their feeding to specific plants.

The sense of smell in adult insects is so much more acute than that of humans that we cannot appreciate its action. In the developmental, growing stages of the higher insects, such as caterpillars and grubs, it is far less acute but equally discriminative, and it is commonly associated with the refusal of any food that lacks the specific stimulus to which their olfactory apparatus is attuned. It is as if a human would eat corn pone only, or cabbage, or onions, or cottage cheese, and never venture a baked potato, hot dog, or ice-cream cone to vary the monotony.

Another example of the association of insects with specific kinds of host plants is the Colorado potato beetle, which spread northward from its native home in Mexico, following its native food plant, a common weed of the potato family. Now widely distributed in the United States, it confines its feeding almost entirely to the foliage of the potato plant. Sometimes it appears on tomato and eggplant, which are related members of the family Solanaceae. Grow a few potatoes in the garden, and the potato beetles will find them sooner or later—sooner if your neighbors harbor them, and later if a long journey is required.

The Mexican bean beetle feeds only on the foliage of various sorts of garden beans, cowpeas, soybeans, and related legumes. In recent decades it has extended its range into the northern parts of the United States; wherever it goes, it always seeks out beans. It is hard for humans to appreciate this point, for we cannot perceive anything special about the odor of potato or bean foliage.

The bean beetle is a black sheep of the large family of lady beetles, whose other representatives, eminently predatory, feed voraciously on plant-lice and scale insects, both as larvae and adults. This small group may have become vegetarians in the geological past, for it has had time since to spread around the world and to develop a number of species, each restricted to special plants, such as members of the cotton family in Africa, potatoes in the Orient, and legumes in Europe.

Another American species, the squash beetle, feeds on the foliage of native gourd vines and on several other garden cucurbits. The squash beetle has never reverted to a meat diet; it may well be that its vegetarian habits represent a sudden shift of instinct comparable to the structural mutations that occur sporadically in nature or as the result of experimental techniques.

Of the wild plants, consider the milkweed, which has a milky sap, or latex. The familiar monarch butterfly always lays its eggs on milkweed, which is the only food that its caterpillars will accept. Also on the leaves of milkweed are commonly seen rather large, black-spotted red beetles, which eat the foliage as adults and bore in the roots as larval grubs. Like the monarch butterfly, they are addicted to milkweed and would be starved out of existence without it. In the scheme of nature, they are fortunately provided for by the mother insect, whose unvarying instinct leads her to lay her eggs in the proper site.

An insect that restricts its feeding to a single species of plant is the boll weevil. The larvae of this snout beetle burrow within the flower buds and immature bolls of cotton. It is native to the New World Tropics, whence cotton came into cultivation, and has extended its range into the cotton fields of our Southern States since the beginning of the present century. Thorough search has failed to find any other acceptable food plants, which is a very striking point because another insect, a caterpillar known as the bollworm, similarly bores into the green bolls of cotton but also likes other succulent fruits and vegetables. It can be so abundant in the ripening ears of corn as to rank as a major pest of corn.

Another pest of corn, the European corn borer, now widely naturalized in our country, is a still more general feeder. It bores into all above-ground parts of the plant. It does not stop at that, however, as it appears equally fond of many plants as diverse as dahlias, smartweed, and hemp.

We can group the insects I have mentioned and others as well into three categories. The first group includes the feeders that exercise little choice, depending largely on availability, abundance, texture of foliage, succulence, and the like. Nearly all of them have preferred food plants, however. Thus, the gypsy moth caterpillar feeds on the leaves of a variety of deciduous forest trees, but it is most abundant on oak and on birch, avoids ash, and refuses chestnut, while the older caterpillars in a pinch will consume even tough pine needles after their jaws have become big and strong enough to cope with such material. The common cecropia moth seems to prefer willow leaves, but its diet includes a great variety of our common deciduous trees and shrubs.

Many grasshoppers range over a wide variety of low plants. Such insects are known as polyphagous because they accept plants in considerable variety.

The second group, the insects that restrict their feeding to a small and discrete number of usually similar plants, are termed oligophagous. No clear-cut line can be drawn to separate them from the polyphagous forms, but they obviously represent a distinct specialization in food selection, especially when their food plants have some characteristics in common, which we can demonstrate through our own senses or by laboratory methods.

Members of the most highly specialized series, the third group, are referred to as monophagous; that is, they are restricted to a single species of food plant. They are comparatively few in number; indeed, some entomologists believe that none exists in the strictest sense. But to all intents and purposes the boll weevil, whose habits have been minutely studied, falls into this category, and several other insects appear to be just as precise in their tastes. All in all, the vegetarian insects form a vast series in which more or less indiscriminate choice of food becomes more and more restricted and sometime may reach a stage of absolute dependence on a single species of plant.

Such a succession appears to be an evolutionary process, but by no means is it a single progression of changes, as the restriction of food plants appears time and time again in unrelated groups. Rather, it is the indication of an inherent tendency in insects (undoubtedly engendered by their delicate sense of smell) that leads them to live in a world of odors.

Up until a few decades ago plausibly enough it was customary to attribute the unerring selection of food plants by oligophagous insects to a sixth botanical sense that enabled them to recognize the natural relationships of plants without recourse to treatises on systematic botany.

Such a supposition clarifies the behavior of some of the insects I have mentioned, but it has flaws. An example is the cabbage butterfly, which commonly restricts its feeding to plants of the cabbage family although its caterpillars sometimes appear on other dissimilar and unrelated plants. One is the nasturtium. The explanation is that nasturtium leaves have the same pungent odor and taste due to an essential oil similar to that in cabbage. A Dutch entomologist, E. Verschaffelt, who studied the behavior of the butterflies and caterpillars with reference to mustard oils, concluded that the presence of those chemicals was the factor that determined their choice. Other entomologists, particularly Vincent G. Dethier, have extended such studies to a large number of other insects and their food plants, and have found that some specific chemical (or more than one in combination) commonly forms the tie that binds them to an invariably constant diet.

It is evident now that odors, recognizable to the acute and discriminative chemical sense of the insects, are the main factors involved in the selection of food plants by oligophagous insects. But knowledge of the multitude of chemical substances elaborated by plants is still too fragmentary to permit any broad generalization. Some species of less fastidious tastes will accept considerable variety, but may evince a dislike for some chemical to which they are not accustomed, even when it is combined with one that is highly attractive when not thus contaminated. That is not the whole story, however.

We must approach some other considerations with caution, as their meaning is not yet clear. They relate more directly to instinctive behavior.

Among the aphids, or plant-lice, there occurs quite commonly an alternation of generations, whereby the aphids migrate during the course of the seasonal cycle from one kind of plant to another and then return to the original host plant after the period of winter dormancy. These aphids frequently have a small series of acceptable plants, and one or both of the alternate food plants may not include more than a single botanical species. Early in the summer, several generations of wingless females rapidly succeed one another on the summer food plant, followed by a generation of winged females, which then migrate to another species of plant known as the alternate food plant. There they give rise to a generation of aphids of both sexes, which produce eggs that overwinter. The next spring these give rise to a brood of winged females that migrate back to the summer food plant, after which the cycle repeats itself.

With some minor variations, that is the fundamental pattern—two very different food plants are selected alternately. Thus the migrating aphids are conditioned to two diverse plants at different times, and we cannot attribute their attraction to a single specific chemical stimulus. Other factors obviously enter the picture, but they cannot be singled out further than to note that the appearance of the winged migrants and sexual phases is correlated with the season. This is a phenomenon similar to photoperiodism in plants, where vegetative growth and flowering are often closely related to seasonal variations in the duration of the daylight period. We cannot state definitely whether chemical changes in the plants may elicit a differential response by the aphids as the season progresses.

More surprising still is the relationship that exists among some gall-making insects. Many diverse insects induce the formation of abnormal growths or of highly modified specific structures. They are known as galls and are developed by the plant under some stimulus from the insects that lay their eggs in the tissues of the plant and undergo their growth feeding within the developing gall. The nature of the stimulus is not yet understood, but it is highly specific, as the galls produced by each species are always alike in form and structure.

The gall insects are quite uniformly oligophagous or monophagous. One group, the gall wasps, are small, wasplike insects in some hundreds of species. Nearly all of them produce galls on oaks. They are highly specific for particular kinds of oaks—each lays its eggs in some restricted part of the tree, whether leaves, twigs, buds, or roots. Furthermore, some species of gall wasps undergo an alternation of generations, whereby one generation induces galls on some aerial part of the plant and the next goes underground to induce a root gall, returning in the succeeding generation again to the previous location above ground.

In the gall wasps, the restriction of choice to particular food plants is similar to the one I outlined among the aphids, but the matter is further complicated by the fact that the response of the plant is an essential requirement for the maintenance of the relationship.

So we see that an insect's selection of food plants depends primarily on an acute and discriminative chemical sense, which enables it to recognize by smell and taste many essential oils and other less pungent substances in particular plants. As the presence of each such chemical is usually confined to some natural group of plants, they are the ones to which the insects are attracted. When the same chemical attractant appears sporadically in unrelated plants, they also may be chosen. This basic conception is supported by observations of the behavior of insects in nature and by the application of some experimental techniques. It explains the puzzling "botanical sense." It has already opened up a promising field for the study of attractants and repellents that should have great practical value.

The insect's selective appetite, so far as we can see at present, is purely an instinct to do thus and so, whether or no. Such instincts are innate and unalterable attributes of all insect behavior which excite our wonderment and captivate our curiosity because we can go no further than to catalog their manifestations.

Some matters relating to the correlation that exists between the larval appetite and the consistent choice of acceptable food plants on which to lay the eggs are amenable to analytical treatment. Even in insects that shift to another type of food when they reach the adult reproductive stage, we may assign some form of memory or nostalgia to account for the return of the gravid butterfly to a cabbage head after a round of sipping the nectar of sweetly scented flowers. That may seem a bit farfetched, but it is obvious that once it has been incorporated into the sphere of instinct, an identical response will inevitably be called forth. At this stage, any transgressions will be quickly eliminated through the most rigorous action of natural selection whereby any butterfly that failed to select a proper food plant is unable to pass on to posterity her careless or vacillating tendencies. That such aberrations of instinct do occur, although rarely, is attested by actual observations of insects under natural conditions. Any such mutation of instinct may conceivably persist if compatible with the appetite of the larva and capable of weathering the competitive pressure imposed by the living environment.

In yet another way may memory have a part in the differential choice of food plants by insects that normally accept a variety of host plants. Where we cannot detect chemical attractants in common, it appears that memory of the larval food might lead the adult to prefer it to other acceptable plants. There are many cases where such strains, races, or clones appear to be established in nature. Experimental proof so far has been inconclusive, but it seems probable that when varied food plants are readily acceptable such strains do exist. We might even compare them to those racial or geographic components of our human population that consistently evince a preferential fondness for cabbage, garlic, red pepper, baked beans, macaroni, curry, or some other item of food.

CHARLES T. BRUES *is professor of entomology emeritus in Harvard University, where he taught and engaged in research on various phases of entomology for 37 years. He has devoted much time to studies on the food habits of insects, a subject on which he has published extensively. A graduate of the University of Texas, he served as field agent for the Bureau of Entomology and later as curator at the Milwaukee Public Museum, before joining the biological staff of Harvard in 1909.*

For accounts of the life histories and food habits of some of the insects mentioned in his article, Dr. Brues suggests his article in Psyche, Food Preferences of the Colorado Potato Beetle, *volume 47, pages 38–43, 1940; and the following publications of the Department of Agriculture:*

Bulletin 250, Food Plants of the Gipsy Moth in America, *by F. H. Mosher, issued in 1915; Farmer's Bulletin 1548,* The European Corn Borer, *by D. J. Caffrey and L. H. Worthley, 1927; Technical Bulletin 77,* The Host Plants of the European Corn Borer in New England, *by Benjamin E. Hodgson, 1928; and Bureau of Entomology Bulletins 50,* The Cotton Bollworm, *by A. L. Quaintance and C. T. Brues, and 51,* The Mexican Cotton Boll Weevil, *by W. D. Hunter and W. E. Hinds, both issued in 1905.*

For information about the factors concerned in food selection he suggests his articles, The Selection of Food-Plants by Insects, With Special Reference to Lepidopterous Larvae, *in the American Naturalist, volume 54, pages 313–332, 1920;* The Specificity of Food-Plants in the Evolution of Phytophagous Insects, *American Naturalist, volume 58, pages 127–144, 1924;* Aberrant Feeding Behavior Among Insects and Its Bearing on the Development of Specialized Food Habits, *Quarterly Review of Biology, volume 11, pages 305–319, 1936; and articles by:*

V. G. Dethier: Gustation and Olfaction in Lepidopterous Larvae, *Biological Bulletin, volume 72, pages 7–23, 1937; and* Chemical Factors Determining the Choice of Food Plants by Papilio Larvae, *American Naturalist, volume 75, pages 61–73, 1941.*

M. Raucourt and B. Trouvelot: Les principes constituants de la pomme de terre et le Doryphore, *Annales des Épiphyties et de Phytogénétique, volume 2, pages 51–98. 1936.*

Also recommended for further reading are Insect Dietary: An Account of the Food Habits of Insects, *by Dr. Brues, published by the Harvard University Press, 1946, and* Chemical Insect Attractants and Repellents, *by Vincent G. Dethier, The Blakiston Co., Philadelphia, 1947.*

How To Know an Insect

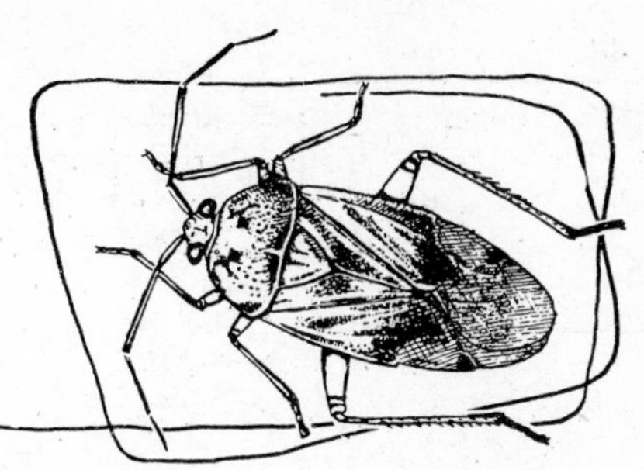

What Kind of Insect Is It?

C. F. W. Muesebeck

The Animal Kingdom is made up of a number of major divisions, or phyla.

One of them, the Chordata, includes man and the other mammals, birds, reptiles, fish—in fact, all the vertebrates, the creatures that have backbones.

By far the largest division from the standpoint of the number of different kinds, or species, it comprises is the Arthropoda. At least 80 percent of all known animals are arthropods. This phylum comprises invertebrate (backboneless) animals that have a segmented body, jointed appendages, and a hard outer covering, or exoskeleton. It is in turn divided into a number of groups called classes, each of which differs in some fundamental characteristics from the others. One of these classes, known as Hexapoda, or Insecta, contains all the insects. Various members of other classes of Arthropoda, especially such organisms as mites, ticks, spiders, scorpions, millipedes, centipedes, and sowbugs, however, are so commonly regarded as insects that it seems advisable to indicate the basic distinctions between these several classes in a simple key.

A key is based on the process of elimination. In the key that follows, for example, one considers (as in entry number 1) the number of legs of the creature he wishes to identify. If it has five or more pairs, he consults entry 2 (as given at the right); if it has three or four pairs, he skips to entry 4. And so on.

Key to the Principal Classes of Arthropoda

1. With five or more pairs of legs...... 2
   With three or four pairs of legs..... 4
2. Body wormlike; head not merged with the thorax and provided with one pair of antennae or with none 3
   Body not wormlike; head merged with the thorax and provided with two pairs of antennae...........
   Crustacea (crabs, lobsters, shrimp, sowbugs, etc.) (figure 1, next page)
3. Body segments each with only one pair of legs....................
   Chilopoda (centipedes) (figure 2)
   Most of the body segments each with two pairs of legs................
   Diplopoda (millipedes) (figure 3)
4. Body composed of two main divisions, the cephalothorax (fused head and thorax) and abdomen; four pairs of jointed legs; wings and antennae lacking ....
   Arachnida (spiders (figure 4), scorpions (figure 5), mites, ticks, etc.)
   Body composed of three main divisions, the head, thorax, and abdomen; only three pairs of jointed legs; wings usually, antennae always, present...................
   Insecta (all insects)

For purposes of orderly classification and to facilitate identification, each of these classes is divided into a number of orders, an order is broken down into families, a family is divided into genera, and each genus is composed of related

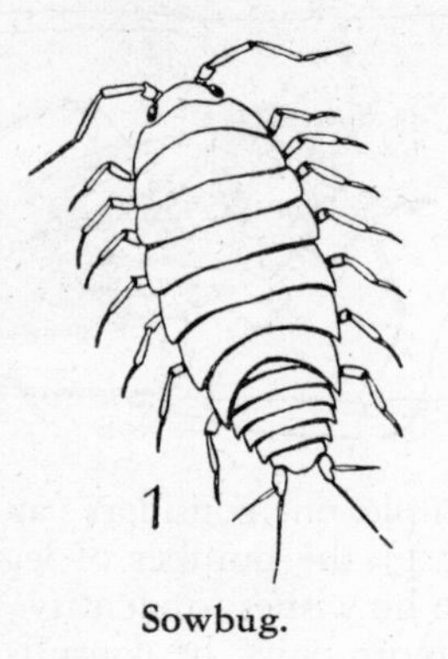

Sowbug.

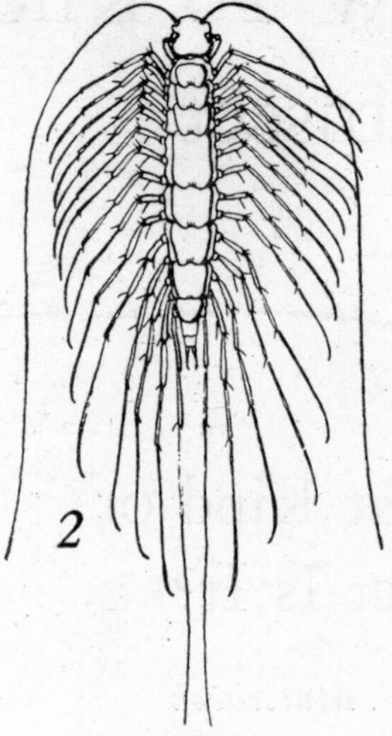

Centipede.

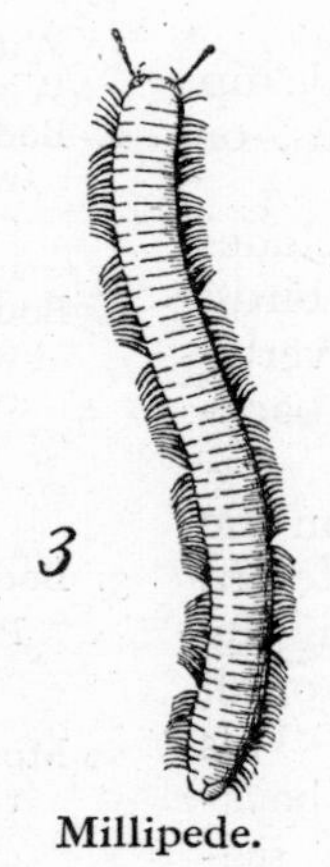

Millipede.

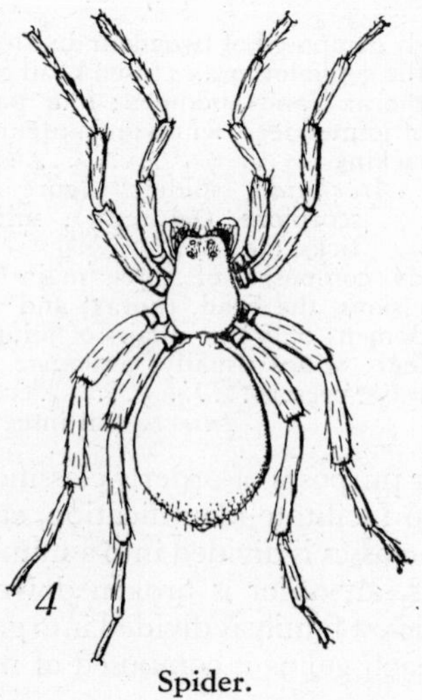

Spider.

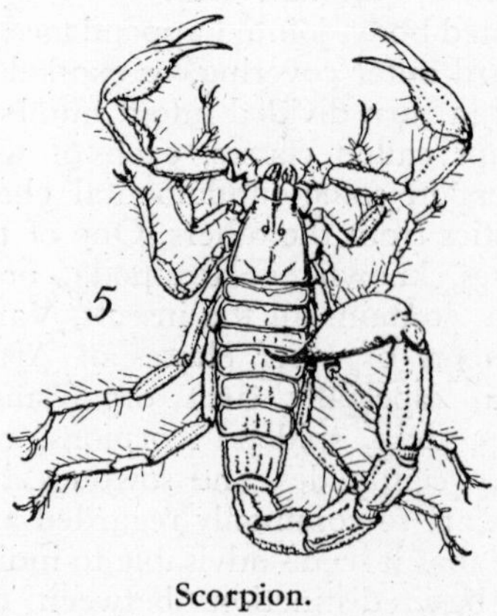

Scorpion.

A froghopper producing its protecting mass of bubbles. Within, it is sheltered from the direct rays of the sun and kept moist by the foam.

The lacewing is one of the polecats of the insect world. It exudes a disagreeable smelling fluid when it is touched.

After 17 years of tunneling in the darkness of the earth, a periodical cicada nymph begins transforming into the adult cicada.

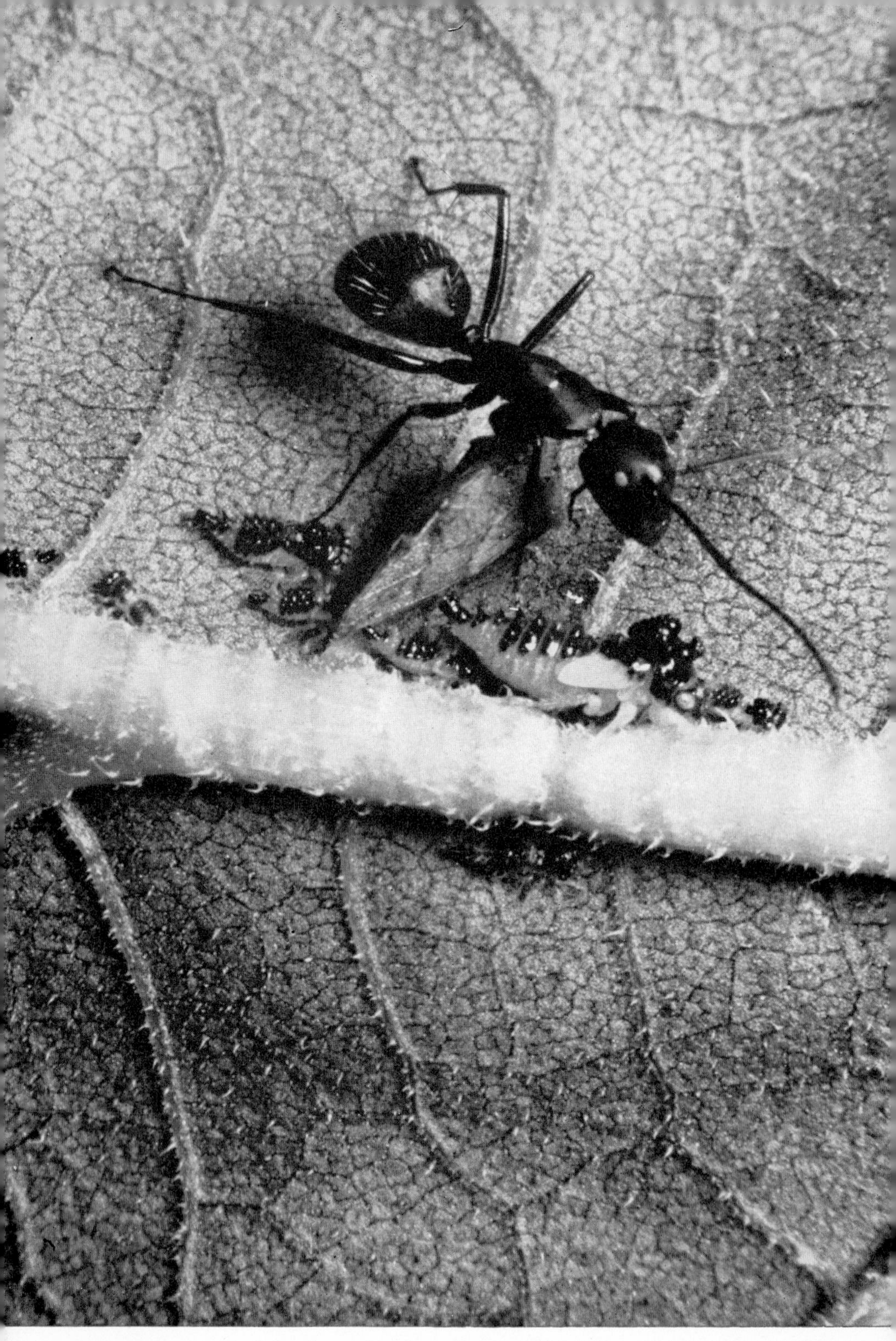

A carpenter ant obtaining honeydew from the nymphs of the treehopper, *Entylia sinuata.*

One of the American walkingstick insects. In the Tropics, such insects assume their largest and their oddest forms.

The dragonfly. The nymphs of these insects live under water and are equipped with extensible lower lips that can shoot out to grasp prey.

Face of a robber fly, which sometimes feigns death to escape its enemies. The foregoing photographs are by Edwin Way Teale. (See page 8.)

This dragonfly, preserved in the limestone of Solnhofen, Bavaria, lived millions of years ago. (See page 14.)

species. Thousands of species of insects have thus far been described. Obviously each species must have a distinct name, and because many species are cosmopolitan the same name must be used for the same species everywhere. When the present system of naming animals was established about 200 years ago, most scientific books were written in Latin, and Latin was considered the universal language of science. The scientific names of animals, therefore, are in Latin or in Latin form. The name of each species consists of two words, the name of the genus to which the species belongs and a word, often an adjective, that stands for the species.

The generic name begins with a capital letter; the specific (i. e., the species) name is written in lower case and may be followed by the name, or an abbreviation of the name, of the person who originally proposed the scientific name and described the species. Thus, the name of the house fly is written *Musca domestica* L. The "L." is an abbreviation for Carolus Linnaeus, the Swedish scientist who described this species.

Under the International Rules of Zoological Nomenclature, a generic name may not be duplicated anywhere in the animal kingdom. The same specific name may be used repeatedly but only for one species in any one genus. The rules assure a distinctive name for each kind, or species, of animal and make it possible to record information about any species under a designation that will be universally understood.

As SHOWN in the foregoing key to the major classes of arthropods, insects have only three pairs of legs, never more. This is the most distinctive characteristic of the class Insecta. Insects also have three separate body divisions, head, thorax, and abdomen. There is always one pair of antennae.

Wings are usually present. When they occur, wings alone will serve immediately to identify an arthropod as an insect, for they are found in no other class of this phylum. Many insects, however, are wingless. In all the major orders, some wingless forms occur. In a few of the smaller orders, such as the Thysanura (silverfish), Collembola (springtails), Siphonaptera (fleas), Mallophaga (biting lice), and Anoplura (sucking lice), all the species are wingless. The winged or wingless condition, the texture or covering of the wings, their shape, their number (whether two or four), the manner in which they are held when at rest, and the peculiarities of their system of veins furnish characters that help one recognize a given insect as belonging to a particular order. Examples of wings of different kinds are noted in the sketches of insects that are used to illustrate the key to the principal insect groups. Other structures, in which significant differences occur that are useful in the definition of orders or families, are the mouth parts and the antennae.

For the identification of genera, and eventually of species, a great array of characteristics must be studied, including minute details of sculpture, arrangements of hairs or bristles, shape and proportional measurements of various parts of the body and appendages, and even details of the reproductive organs that can be demonstrated only by preparation on microscope slides after dissection. Details of every kind that tend to be distinctive of group or species need to be used and the range of variation in all of them must be determined.

Many of the insects commonly collected or observed doing damage are in the immature stages. During this period they may bear no resemblance whatever to the adults of the same species. The members of the Orthoptera (grasshoppers, roaches, crickets, mantids) and the Hemiptera (bugs), among others, develop by gradual change after hatching from the eggs, and the young are similar in general form to the adults, differing principally in size and in the lack of wings. The young of other large orders, however,

970134°—52——5

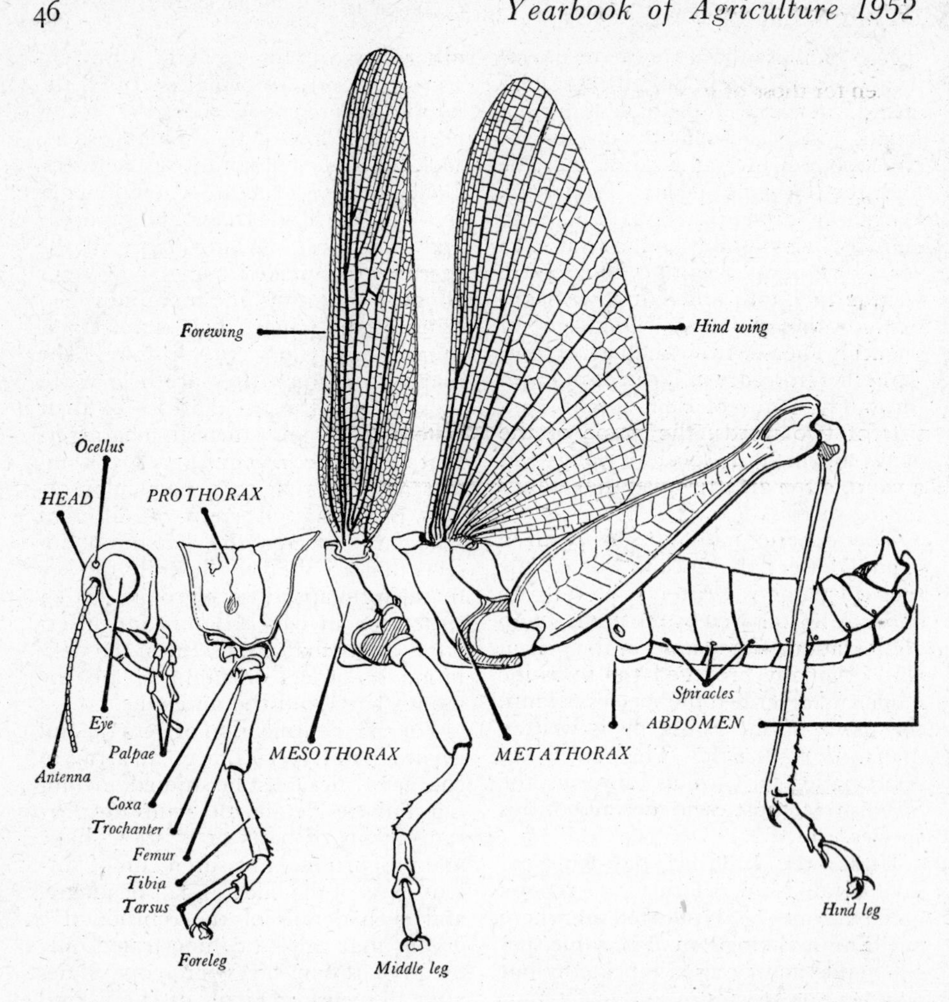

such as the Coleoptera (beetles), Diptera (flies), Lepidoptera (moths and butterflies) and Hymenoptera (sawflies, bees, wasps, and ants), are wholly unlike the adults. The eggs hatch into larvae, some of which are commonly called grubs, maggots, or caterpillars. These represent the feeding stage, during which all growth occurs. When development is complete, the larva changes into a pupa, which is the resting, inactive stage, and then the remarkable transformation to the adult insect takes place. Most of the commonly encountered larvae belong to the four orders just mentioned and may be distinguished by the following characteristics:

The larvae of moths and butterflies have a pair of jointed legs on each of the first three body segments and, in addition, short, fleshy, unjointed legs (called prolegs) on some of the other segments. The head is distinctly set off.

Beetle larvae resemble those of the moths and butterflies in usually having a pair of jointed legs on each of the first three body segments and also in the distinct head, but they are at once distinguished by lacking prolegs.

The maggots of flies are completely legless, the body tapers noticeably toward the anterior end, and the head is usually not distinctly set off from the rest of the body.

Larvae of sawflies (a section of the

order Hymenoptera) are often mistaken for those of moths and butterflies because they are provided with both jointed legs and prolegs and are found in similar situations, but they may be recognized by the presence on each side of the head of a dark-colored eyespot, which is lacking in larvae of the other group. They also are usually not hairy whereas larvae of Lepidoptera are often conspicuously so.

Adult insects, even those of the same order, often differ so much in appearance that they are not thought to be related, and it is impossible to construct a key by which every insect may be correctly placed. The simplified key that follows, however, will aid one with little knowledge of insects to recognize the more common types in the adult stage. Often even such group recognition will suffice to indicate what should be done in a practical case that seems to demand prompt action. It should be easily possible, for example, for anyone with no entomological training to distinguish an ant from a termite. Most persons consider termites to be a type of ant, distinguishable only by an expert, but actually termites and ants belong in widely separated orders and structurally are quite unlike.

Key to Major Groups Containing Common Insects

1. Wings present, the front wings often in the form of hard, leathery or horny, wing covers 2
   Wings absent or represented only by minute pads 43
2. With only one pair of wings, these always membranous 3
   With two pairs of wings, the front pair often represented by hard wing covers beneath which the hind wings are concealed in repose 8
3. End of abdomen with two or three slender but conspicuous, backwardly projecting filaments . . . 4
   End of abdomen without such filaments . . . .
   Order Diptera (mosquitoes, midges, flies) 5
4. Wings with a network of veins, including many cross veins . . . .
   Order Ephemeroptera (mayflies), in part (figure 6, below)
   Wings with very few longitudinal veins and no cross veins . . . .
   Hemiptera, in part (males of scale insects or Coccidae)
   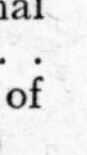
5. Antenna very short, usually three-segmented, the last segment the longest and provided with a conspicuous, long bristle or with a number of rings or annulations . . 6
   Antenna longer and composed of many segments; body generally slender; wings narrow . . . . .
   (Midges, crane flies, mosquitoes) (figure 7)

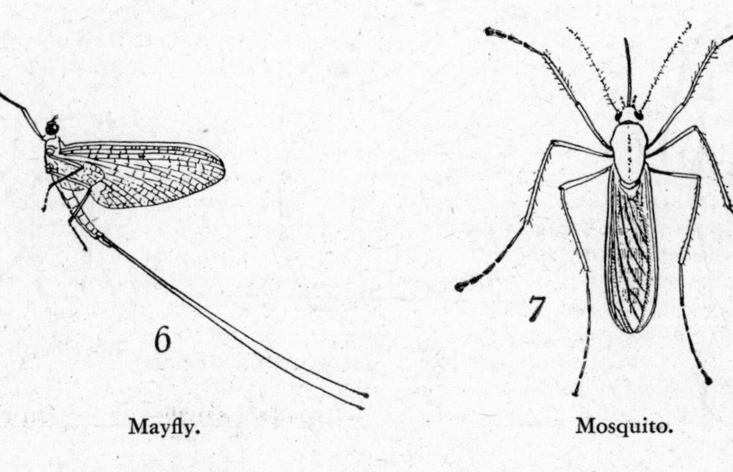

Mayfly. Mosquito.

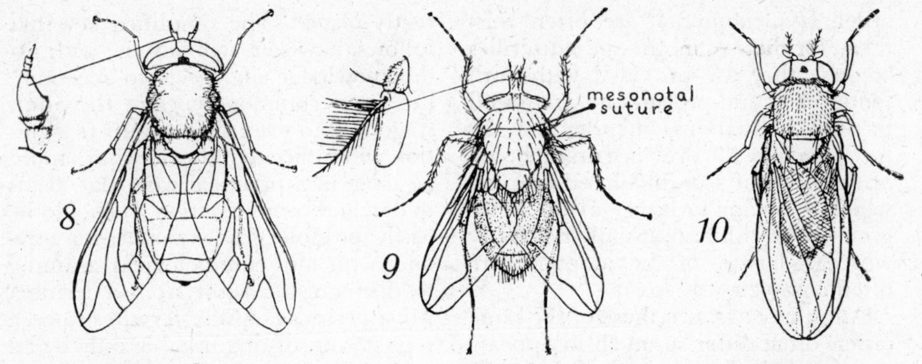

Horse fly. Blow fly. Pomace fly.

6. Last segment of antenna ringed or annulated and without a conspicuous long bristle (arista) at base . . . .
   (Bee flies, robber flies, horse flies) (figure 8)

   Last segment of antenna with a long bristle (arista) on upper side at base 7

7. Calypter (scalelike structure behind base of wing) large and conspicuous; mesonotal suture complete; larger flies . . . .
   Calypterate Muscoidea (house flies, blow flies, flesh flies and their relatives) (figure 9)

   Calypter small and inconspicuous; mesonotal suture incomplete; mostly small flies, much smaller than house fly . . . .
   Acalypterate Muscoidea (eye gnats, pomace or vinegar flies, fruit flies) (figure 10)

8. Front wings horny, rigid, opaque, without veins, meeting in a line over middle of body and concealing the membranous hind wings . 9

   Front wings usually membranous although often covered with scales or hairs; if leathery, with the veins distinct, and not meeting along a line over middle of body 16

9. Tip of abdomen with a pair of prominent forceps-like appendages; front wings (wing covers) very short . . . .
   Order Dermaptera (earwigs) (figure 11)

   Tip of abdomen without such appendages; front wings (wing covers) usually covering most or all of abdomen although sometimes short . . . .
   Order Coleoptera (beetles) . 10

10. Front of head produced into a beak . . . .
    Family Curculionidae (weevils) (figure 12)

    Front of head not produced into a beak 11

11. Wing covers very short, leaving last five or more of the abdominal segments exposed . . . .
    Family Staphylinidae (rove beetles) (figure 13)

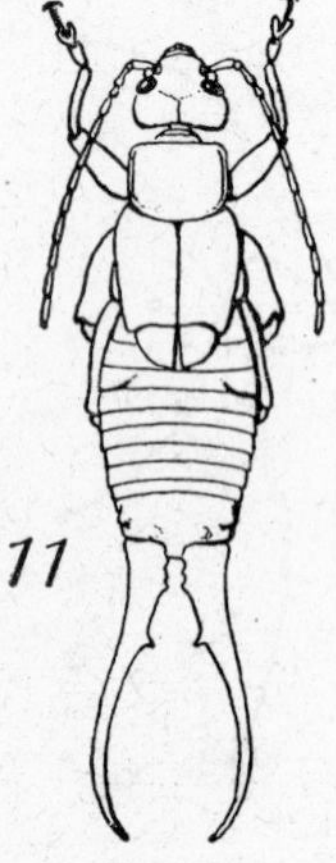

Earwig.

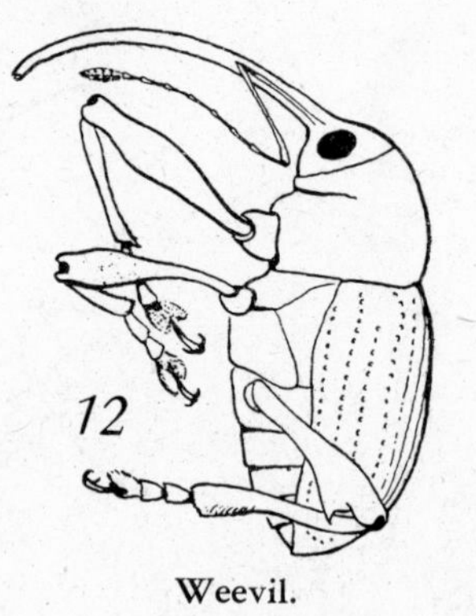

Weevil.

13

Rove beetle.

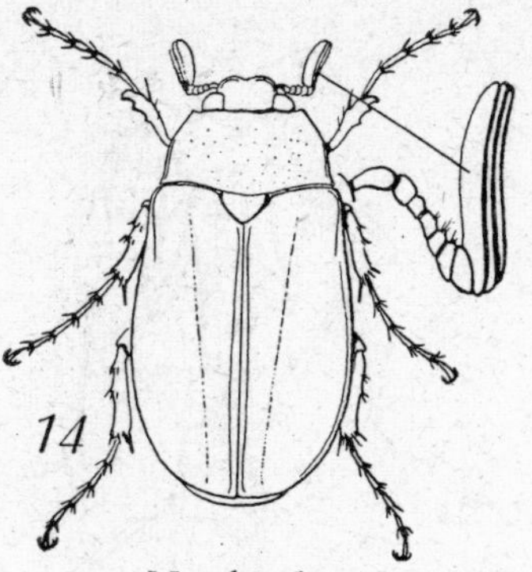

May beetle.

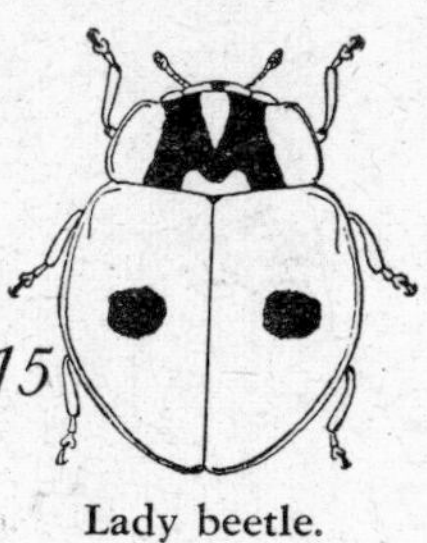

Lady beetle.

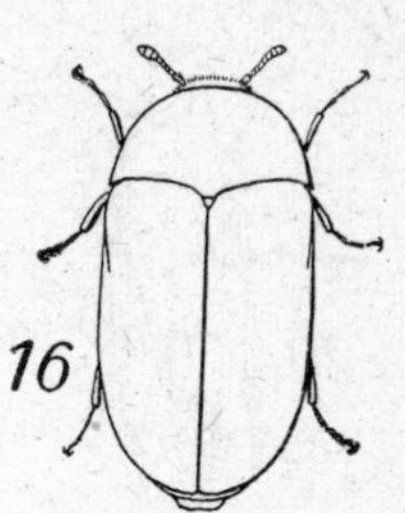

Larder beetle.

Wing covers extending to or near tip of abdomen, rarely leaving three segments exposed 12

12. Antennae enlarged toward tips . . . 13
 Antennae not enlarged toward tips, slender, sometimes longer than the body 15

13. Antennae lamellate (segments composing the club in the form of leaflike plates) . . . .
 Family Scarabaeidae (May beetles, Japanese beetle, rose chafer, etc.) (figure 14)
 Antennae not lamellate 14

14. Tarsi apparently three-segmented .
 Family Coccinellidae (lady beetles) (figure 15)
 Tarsi four-segmented . . . .
 Family Dermestidae (larder beetles, carpet beetles) (figure 16)

15. Tarsi five-segmented, the third segment not enlarged; antennae much shorter than body . . . . .
 Family Carabidae (ground beetles) (figure 17)
 Tarsi apparently four-segmented, the third segment greatly enlarged and deeply cleft concealing the very small fourth segment; antennae usually longer than body . . . .
 Family Cerambycidae (longhorned beetles) (figure 18)

16. Front wings more or less leathery or parchment-like 17
 Wings membranous 23

17. Mouth parts in the form of a piercing and sucking beak . . . . . .
 Order Hemiptera, in part . . 18
 Mouth parts fitted for chewing . . .
 Order Orthoptera 19

18. Front wings leathery only at base, the apical third or more abruptly membranous and overlapping; beak arising from front part of head . . . .
 Suborder Heteroptera (true bugs) (figure 19)
 Front wings of same thickness throughout and usually sloping rooflike over the body . . . . . .
 Suborder Homoptera, in part (leafhoppers and their allies) (figure 20)

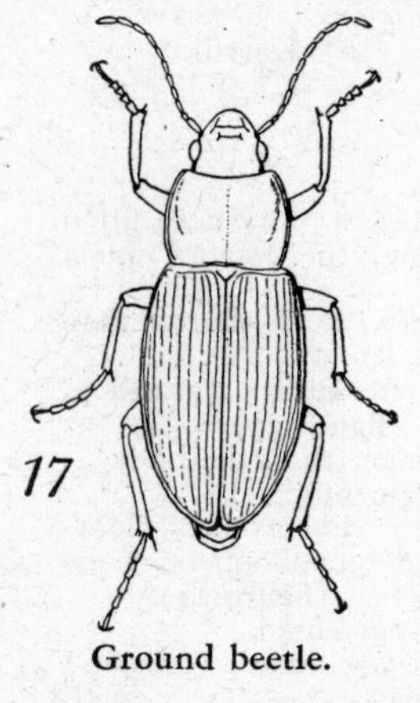

Ground beetle.

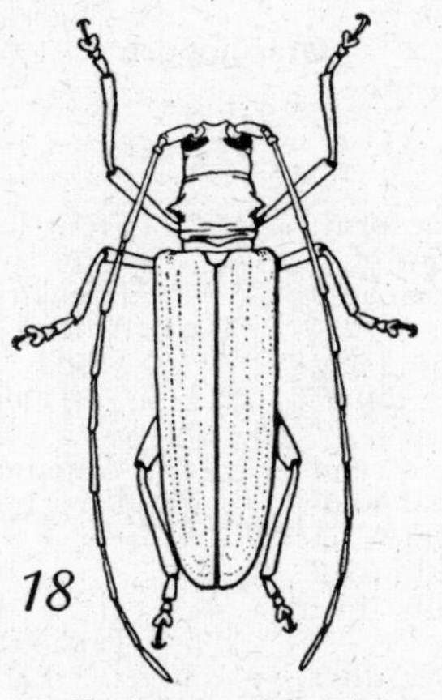

Longhorned beetle.

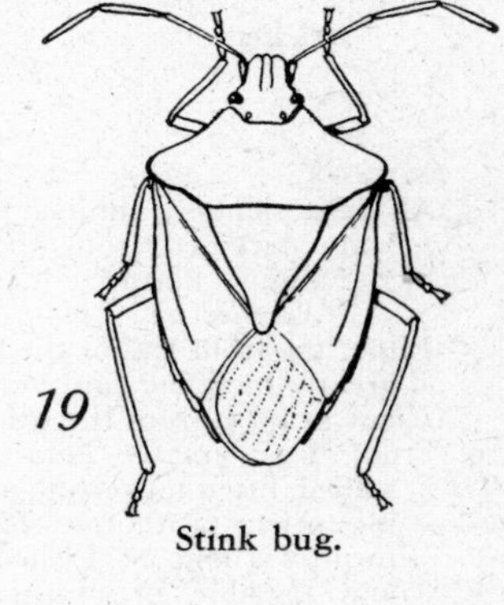

Stink bug.

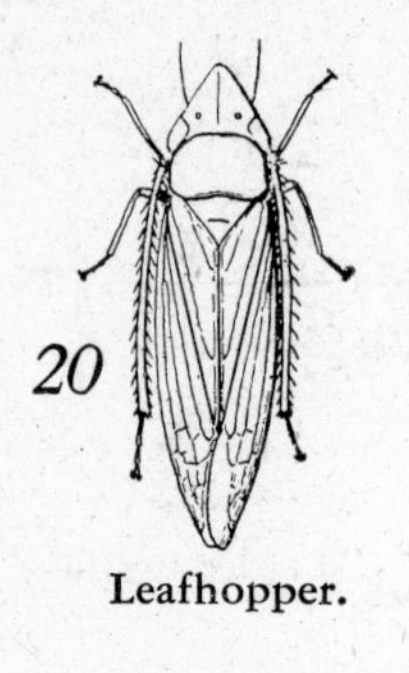

Leafhopper.

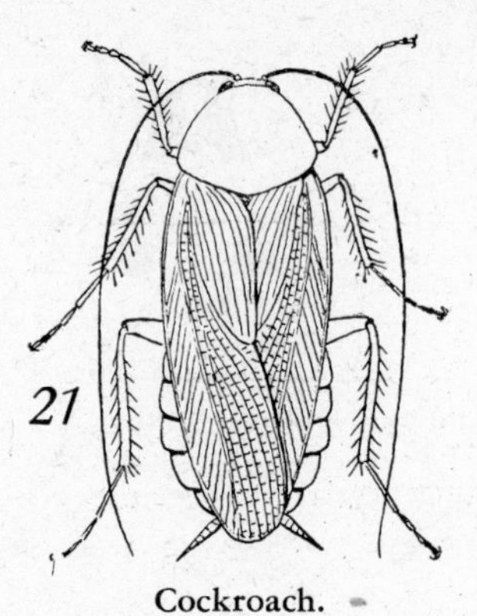

Cockroach.

22

Praying mantid.

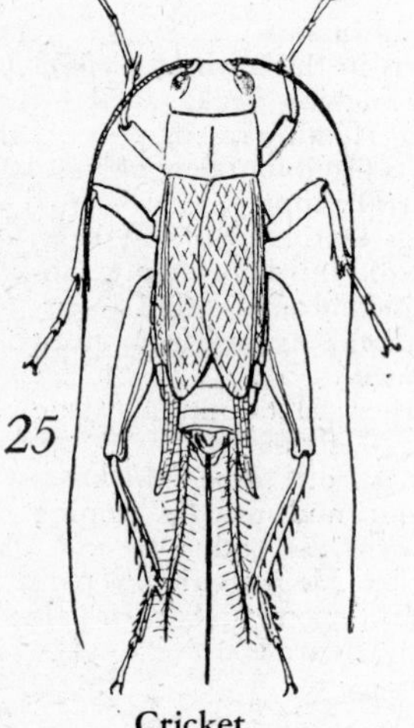

Cricket.

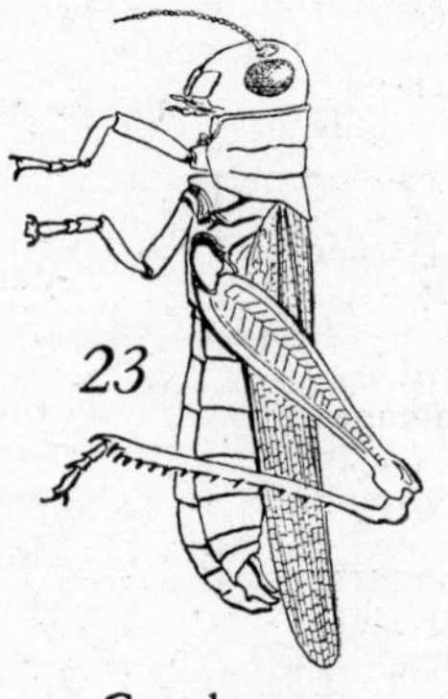

Grasshopper.

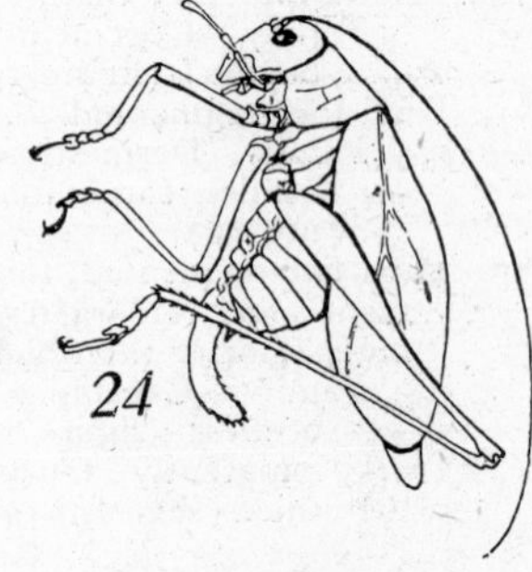

Katydid.

19. All legs slender, similar in form; body flattened from above . . .
    Family Blattidae (roaches) (figure 21)

    Either the front legs or the hind legs greatly modified and very different in form from the others . . . 20

20. Front legs greatly enlarged and spined, fitted for seizing and holding prey; prothorax slender, in form of a long neck; head broad and capable of unusually free movement . . . .
    Family Mantidae (mantids) (figure 22)

    Front legs normal; hind legs fitted for jumping, the femora much enlarged 21

21. Antennae short, much shorter than body . . . .
    Family Acrididae (grasshoppers) (figure 23)

    Antennae longer than the body . . 22

22. Tarsi four-segmented . . . .
    Family Locustidae (long-horned grasshoppers, katydids, etc.) (figure 24)

    Tarsi three-segmented . . . . . .
    Family Gryllidae (crickets) (figure 25)

23. Wings covered with minute overlapping scales, often in beautiful color patterns . . . .
    Order Lepidoptera (moths and butterflies) 24
    Wings not covered with scales . . . 26
24. Antennae usually threadlike or feathery, not enlarged at tips; wings, in repose, held rooflike over body; body very hairy. Mostly night-flying insects . . .
    Suborder Heterocera (moths) (figure 26)
    Antennae enlarged at tips; wings, in repose, usually held in a vertical position, or the forewings erect and the hind wings more or less horizontal; body not especially hairy. Mostly day-flying . . . .
    Suborder Rhopalocera (butterflies and skippers) 25
25. Extreme tips of antennae recurved or hooked . . . .
    Family Hesperiidae (skippers) (figure 27)
    Extreme tips of antennae knobbed .
    Family Papilionidae and allies (butterflies) (figure 28)
26. Wings very narrow, bladelike and fringed with long bristles; tarsus ending in a large bladderlike structure . . . .
    Order Thysanoptera (thrips) (figure 29)
    Wings not bladelike; tarsus without such a bladderlike structure . . . 27
27. Mouth parts in the form of a beak fitted for piercing and sucking . .
    Hemiptera, in part 28
    Mouth parts fitted for chewing . . . 29
28. Front wings lacelike, horizontal and overlapping in repose; small, flattened insects . . . .
    Family Tingidae (lace bugs) (figure 30)
    Front wings not lacelike, usually sloping and not overlapping in repose . . . .
    Families Cicadidae (cicadas) (figure 31), Aphidae (plantlice) (figure 32), and their relatives

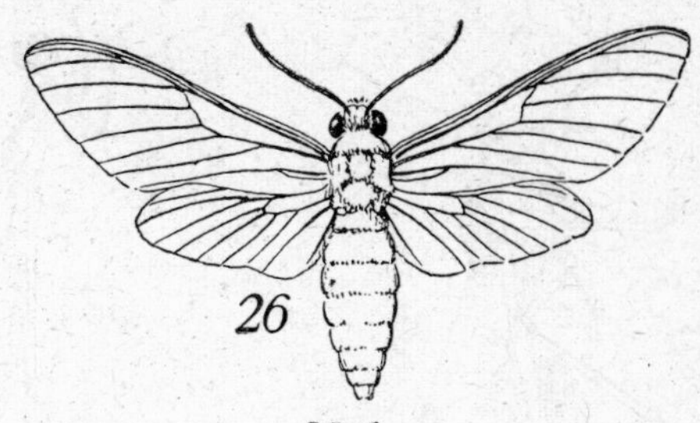

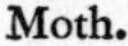
Moth.

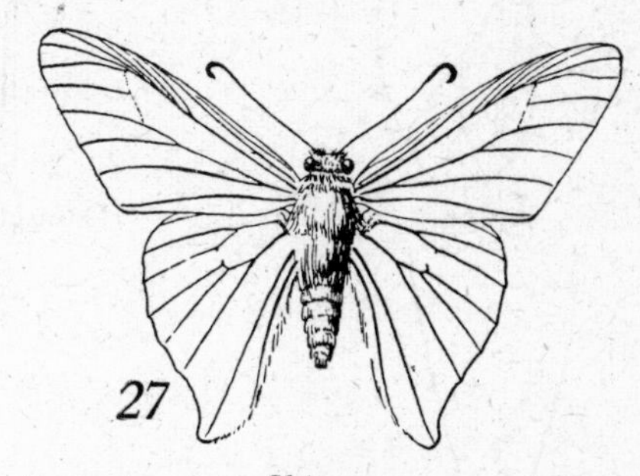

Skipper.

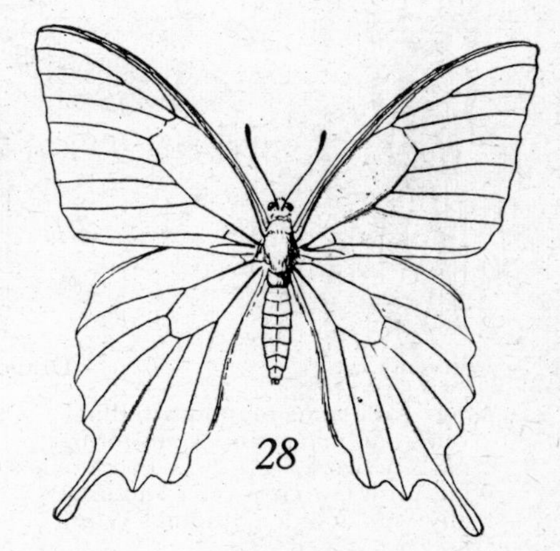

Butterfly.

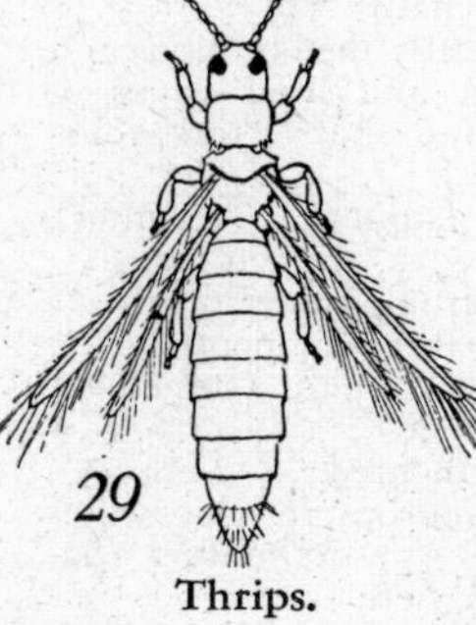

Thrips.

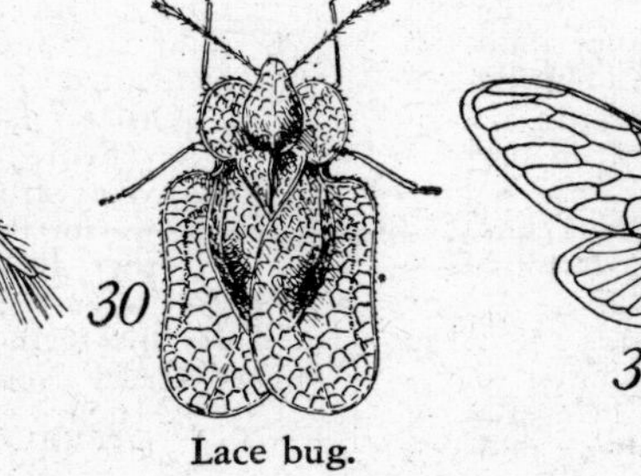

Lace bug.

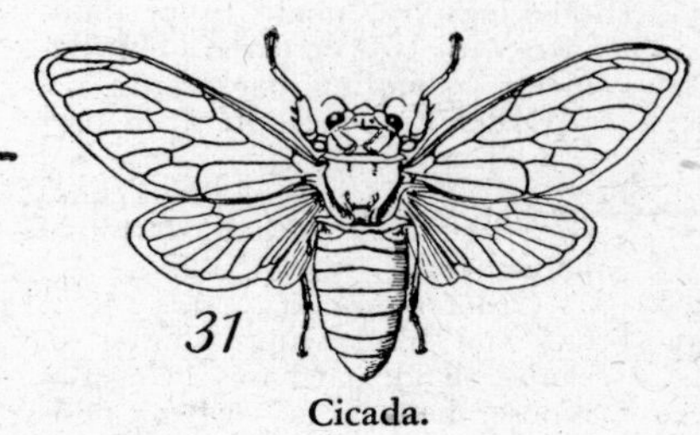

Cicada.

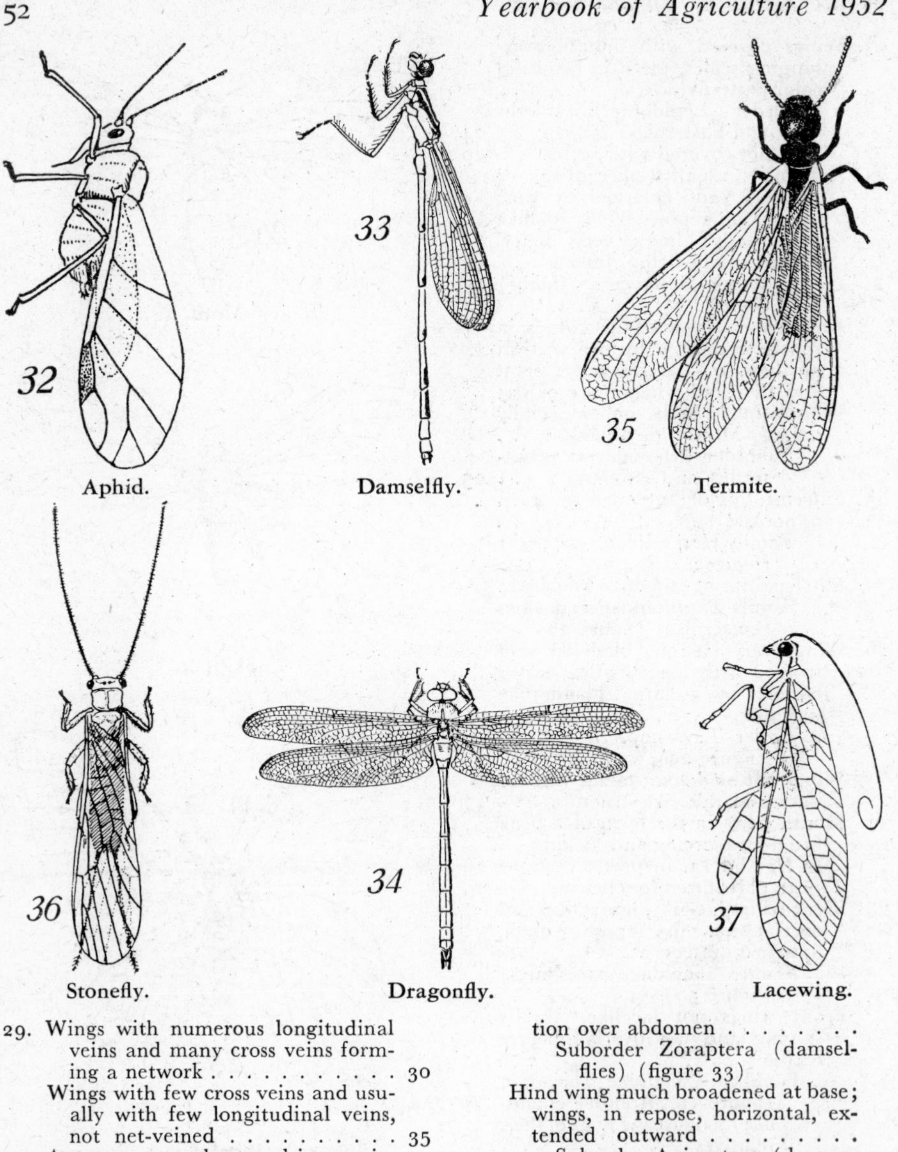

Aphid. Damselfly. Termite.

Stonefly. Dragonfly. Lacewing.

29. Wings with numerous longitudinal veins and many cross veins forming a network 30
    Wings with few cross veins and usually with few longitudinal veins, not net-veined 35
30. Antennae very short and inconspicuous, composed of few segments . 31
    Antennae conspicuous, composed of many segments 33
31. Hind wings very small; tip of abdomen with two or three long filaments extending backward . . .
    Order Ephemeroptera, in part (mayflies)
    Front and hind wings of about equal size; abdomen without terminal filaments . . . .
    Order Odonata 32
32. Front and hind wings similar in shape, slender at bases; wings, in repose, held in a vertical position over abdomen . . . .
    Suborder Zoraptera (damselflies) (figure 33)
    Hind wing much broadened at base; wings, in repose, horizontal, extended outward . . . .
    Suborder Anisoptera (dragonflies) (figure 34)
33. Wing veins mostly membranous and faint; front and hind wings of same size and shape; tarsi four-segmented . . . .
    Order Isoptera (termites) (figure 35, winged form)
    Wing veins strongly developed . . . 34
34. Tarsi two- or three-segmented . . .
    Order Plecoptera (stoneflies) (figure 36)
    Tarsi five-segmented . . . .
    Order Neuroptera (lacewings (figure 37) dobsonflies (figure 38), etc.)

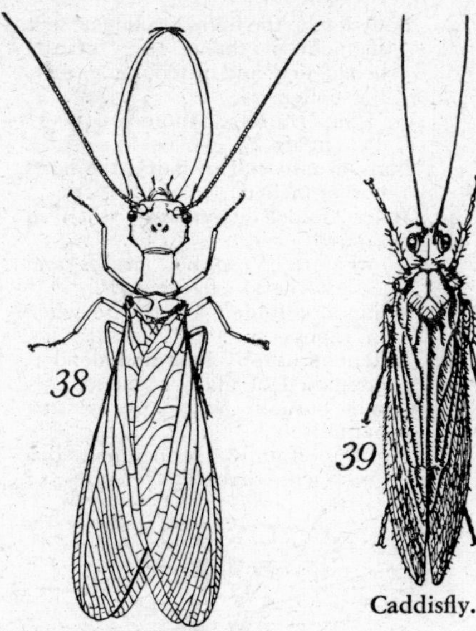

Dobsonfly.

Caddisfly.

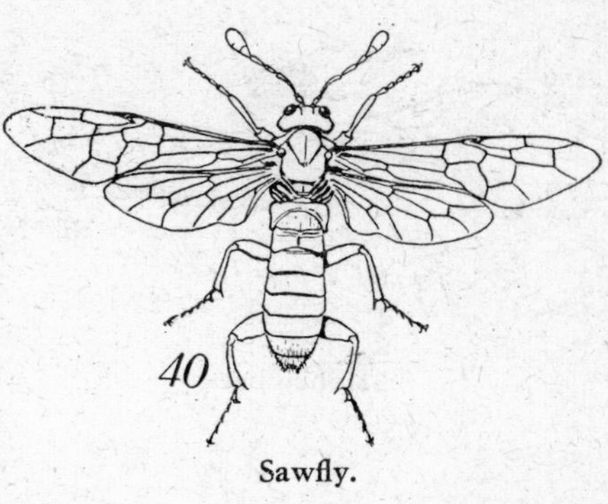

Sawfly.

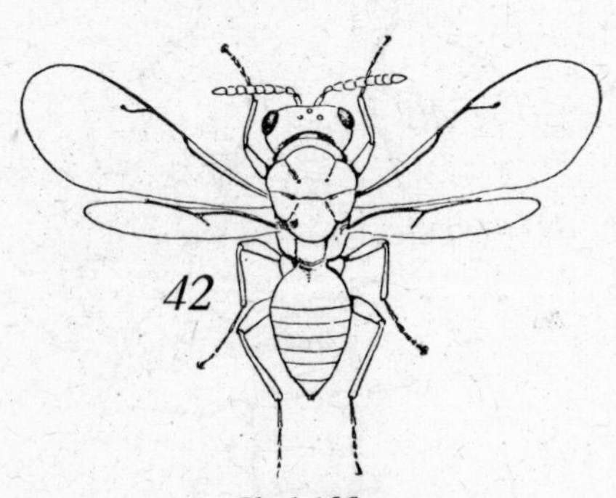

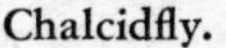

Chalcidfly.

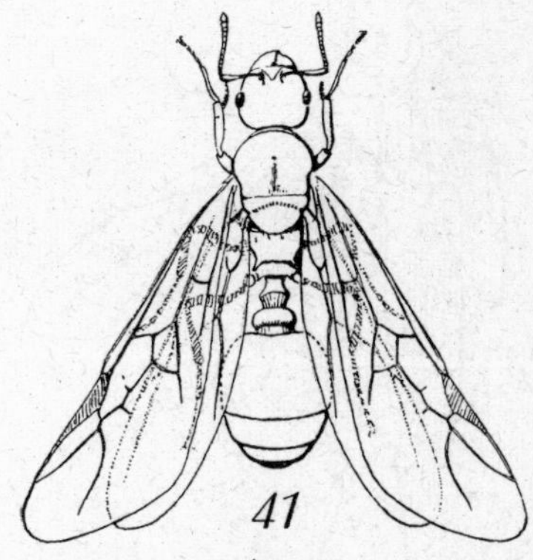

Ant.

35. Tarsi five-segmented 36
    Tarsi two- or three-segmented . . .
        Order Corrodentia (psocids)
36. Wings covered with fine long hair and held rooflike over abdomen, in response . . . .
        Order Trichoptera (caddisflies) (figure 39)
    Wings transparent, not covered with long hairs, not held rooflike over abdomen in repose . . . .
        Order Hymenoptera 37
37. Abdomen broadly joined to the thorax . . . .
        Suborder Symphyta (sawflies, wood wasps) (figure 40)
    Abdomen more or less constricted at base 38
38. Petiole of abdomen (basal part by which abdomen is attached to thorax) composed of a single vertical platelike segment or of two narrow segments that are conspicuously set off from the remainder of the abdomen . . . . .
        Family Formicidae (ants) (figure 41, winged form)
    Petiole of abdomen not as above . . 39
39. Front wing without a stigma (a more or less triangular, opaque, often discolored spot behind middle of front margin) . . . .
        Superfamily Chalcidoidea, etc. (chalcidflies and their relatives) (figure 42)
    Front wing with a stigma 40

Honey bee.

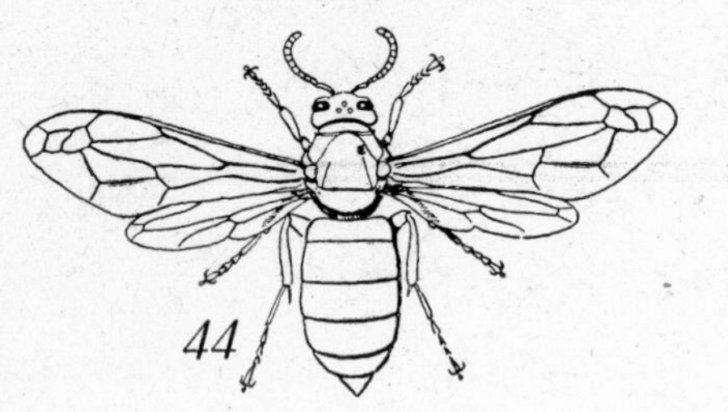

Hornet.

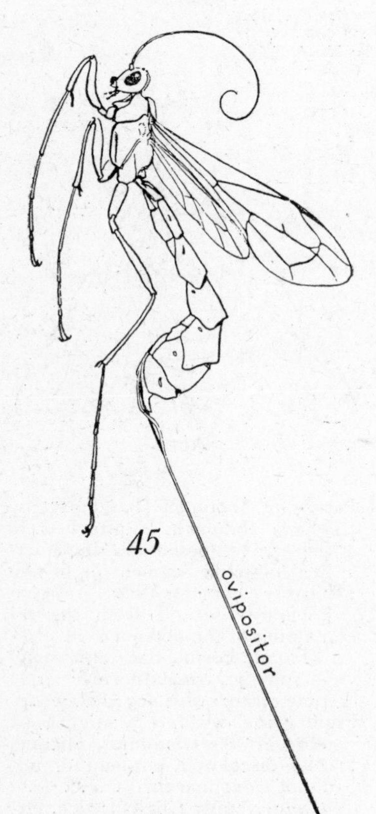

Ichneumonfly.

40. Body hairy, the hairs branched; first segment of tarsus often greatly broadened and fitted for gathering pollen . . . .
    Superfamily Apoidea (bees) (figure 43)

    Body usually not so hairy, the hairs not branched 41
41. Wings folded lengthwise when in repose . . . .
    Family Vespidae (wasps and hornets) (figure 44)

    Wings not folded lengthwise when in repose 42
42. Antennae usually long and slender, composed of many segments; female usually with a projecting ovipositor . . . .
    Superfamily Ichneumonoidea (ichneumonflies) (figure 45)

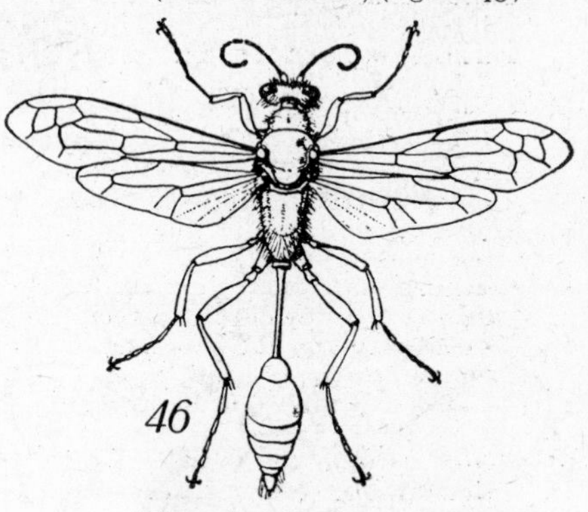

Thread-waisted wasp.

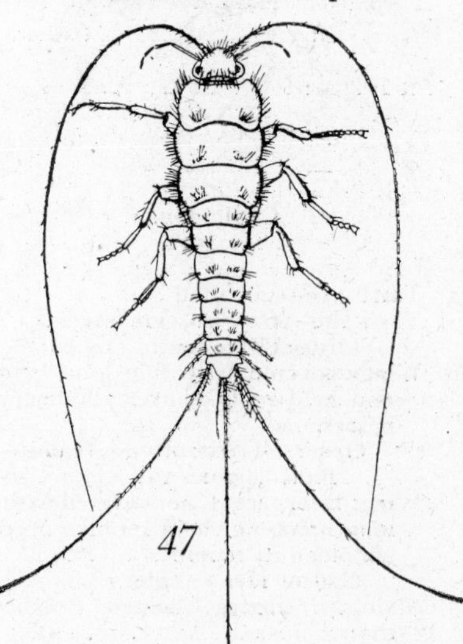

Silverfish.

Antennae short, composed of 12 or 13 segments; female without a projecting ovipositor . . . . . . Superfamily Sphecoidea (thread-waisted wasps) (figure 46)

43\. Tip of abdomen with two or three long appendages directed backward 44
Tip of abdomen without such appendages 45

44\. Abdominal appendages thick, rigid, in the form of forceps . . . . . . Order Dermaptera, in part (earwigs)
Abdominal appendages delicate, flexible, antenna-like . . . . Order Thysanura (silverfish, etc.) (figure 47)

45\. Tarsus composed of only one to three segments 46
Tarsus composed of four or five segments 50

46\. Antennae conspicuous, projecting in front of head 47
Antennae very short, inconspicuous, not projecting in front of head . 49

47\. Antennae composed of three to six segments 48
Antennae with more than six segments; very tiny insects that sometimes occur by the thousands in damp houses . . . . Corrodentia (psocids) (figure 48)

48\. Mouth parts in the form of a distinct beak; body greatly flattened . . . . Order Hemiptera, Family Cimicidae (bed bugs) (figure 49)
Mouth parts not in the form of a beak; body not flattened . . . . Order Collembola (springtails) (figure 50)

49\. With biting mouth parts . . . . . . Order Mallophaga (biting lice) (figure 51)
With piercing and sucking mouth parts . . . . Order Anoplura (sucking lice) (figure 52)

50\. Antennae prominent 51
Antennae inconspicuous, not projecting 52

51\. Body noticeably constricted at base of abdomen, antennae elbowed, the basal segment very long; tarsus five-segmented . . . . . . Order Hymenoptera, Family Formicidae (ants) (figure 53, wingless form)
Body not constricted at base of abdomen; antennae not elbowed, basal segment short; tarsus four-segmented . . . . Order Isoptera (termites) (figure 54, wingless form)

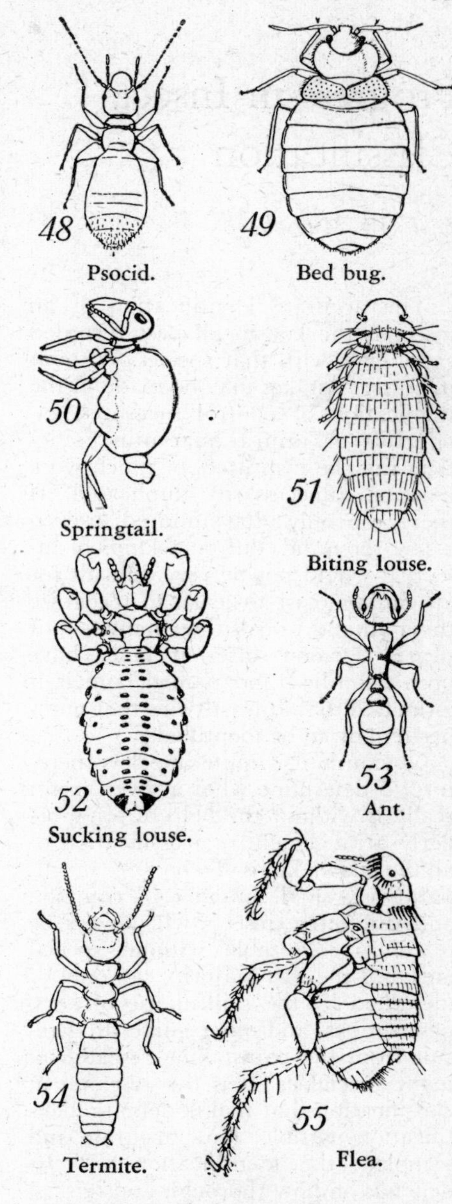

Psocid. Bed bug. Springtail. Biting louse. Sucking louse. Ant. Termite. Flea.

52\. Body strongly compressed from the sides; abdomen distinctly segmented; coxae very large and strongly flattened; legs fitted for jumping . . . . Order Siphonaptera (fleas) (figure 55)
Body not compressed; abdomen not distinctly segmented; legs not fitted for jumping . . . . Order Diptera, in part; wingless forms (sheep-tick and its relatives)

Progress in Insect Classification

C. F. W. Muesebeck

The accurate identification of an insect is the key to all past recorded experience with that species. Without it, costly mistakes may be made in the application of control measures, ineffective or unjust quarantine practices may be instituted, or much work may be unnecessarily duplicated. If there were only a few hundred, or even a few thousand, different kinds of insects it would not be very difficult for an entomologist to learn to recognize them all and to call their names—but nearly 700,000 different kinds have been described and named, and it is estimated that at least twice that number remain to be identified.

Obviously it is quite hopeless therefore to determine what a given insect really is without the help of some orderly arrangement or classification of all the known kinds. To be sure, a comparatively small number of common and distinctive insects will always be readily recognizable without special aids, but the vast majority can only be identified by the skillful use of keys, descriptions, and other guides that result from the painstaking research of many specialists. It is this research in classification that makes definite identification possible. How accurate and complete the identification will be depends on how thorough and critical the research has been.

Classification of living things is an effort to interpret nature. It attempts to bring together the kinds that are alike and closely related and to separate those that are unlike and unrelated. The earliest classifications of insects were based largely on habits and habitats and on certain gross anatomical features that contribute to define the facies, or general aspects, of the different kinds. They were trial classifications and were naturally extremely artificial. They brought together things that were in no sense related and separated widely forms that belonged close together. With the growth of knowledge about insects and the rapid increase in the number of known kinds, however, the search for new characters usable in the development of more satisfactory classifications was intensified. Methods and concepts are improving steadily; the result is that insect taxonomists gradually are producing in their classifications an interpretation of insect life that is much closer to existing facts than any of the arrangements previously developed.

In the efforts to attain the goal of having classifications in accord with the natural relationships of insects, one has to take into account not only anatomical characteristics but also facts pertaining to the physiology, biology, distribution, ecology, and sometimes cytology, of the species. Sometimes, indeed, anatomical distinctions are lacking or at least are not evident, although conspicuous differences have been observed in the life habits of the insect populations in question—differences in time of appearance, food preferences, method of hibernation, or even in reaction to certain insecticides.

Such facts, when known, are usually indicators of fundamental distinctions between forms that at first appeared to be identical. They suggest that a restudy of series of specimens may reveal structural differences formerly overlooked, and often it does. That was so with the screw-worm flies, the European spruce sawflies, and the California red scale and the yellow scale of citrus, among others. The two screw-worm flies were long regarded as a single species that fed sometimes as a true parasite on warm-blooded animals, including man, and sometimes as a scavenger upon dead animals. These differences in feeding habits led taxonomists to a comparative study of flies reared from larvae of the two habit types, and to the discovery that the flies from the two sources could, after all, be distinguished on the basis of anatomical differences and represented two entirely different species.

That information resulted in an abrupt change in control procedure against the parasitic form. With the spruce sawflies it was a cytological study that established the distinctness of two species long regarded as one. In the case of the red and yellow scales of citrus, differences in susceptibility to attack by certain parasites and differences in location on infested trees eventually led to the discovery of structural differences by which the two species could be identified.

By the utilization, then, of all available information, taxonomists are attempting to correlate behavior and other life characteristics of insects with anatomical features, since it has come to be realized that only in this way can sound, natural classifications be developed. In the formation of keys, which are the guides to identification and which reflect the judgment of taxonomists with respect to relationships, however, it is necessary to depend on the use of physical characteristics of the insects. Only those are always definitely determinable from the specimens themselves. Therefore the principal efforts of the research taxonomist are necessarily directed toward the search for physical peculiarities, however small, that seem likely to be relatively constant and more or less distinctive. That that is no simple task must be obvious from the enormous number of known kinds and the continued addition to that number of 10,000 or more new species annually. A key that will infallibly lead the user to the correct name for a given insect can rarely be constructed even for a comparatively small group of insects. Few characteristics are absolutely fixed, and the extent and direction of the variation are themselves extremely variable. *Bracon hebetor,* an abundant and widely distributed parasite of certain pests of stored products, ranges in color from completely yellow to wholly black.

On the other hand, all the moths of all the species in the genus *Rupela* are without exception entirely white. One individual may be five times as large as another fully matured specimen of the same species. In another species, perhaps a closely related one, the specimens may be of rather uniform size. Details of sculpture or of wing venation may be strikingly constant or may vary widely. It is important to determine the range of variability in each instance, but that requires large numbers of specimens and these are not always to be had. Seldom, therefore, can a character that is employed in a key be considered absolute, and no key can be regarded as more than a temporary guide to identification. It will inevitably require modification, or even complete recasting, as knowledge of the particular group involved increases; its usefulness will depend to no small extent on the aptitude, experience, and perhaps even intuition of the user.

Dimorphism among adult insects of the same species is a common phenomenon. It is often a cause of serious difficulty in the development of classifications. The winged sex forms in termites and ants, for example, bear little resemblance to the wingless workers of the same species; in the mutillid wasps, which are popularly and inaccurately known as velvet ants, the winged males are so unlike the wingless females that their identity can only be established by biological association. That is true also of the cankerworm moths, in which the female is a grublike egg sac but the male is a normal winged moth. Such striking caste or sexual dimorphism occurs in various sections of all the major insect groups. Furthermore, since the biological association of conspicuously different castes or sexes of the same species may be difficult and slow, it sometimes happens that the male and female of a single species are long treated as two distinct things and are known under different names. Only field observations or biological studies can establish the facts in such cases.

More often than not it is in the larval stage that an insect is destructive. Because it is harmless and is seldom seen, the adult may be unknown to the grower whose crop is being damaged. In order that the right control measures may be applied, the insect has to be identified in its larval stage. For practical reasons, then, it has become essential, in the case of various insect groups, to supplement classifications founded on adults with keys to the larvae. The development of such keys is particularly difficult and slow because the identity of the larvae must first be definitely established. Otherwise, however good the key might be, it would not lead the user to the available information on habits and control of the pest. The name originally proposed for the adult insect is the clue, and the larva must be identifiable by the same name. For definite association of the larva with the adult, however, field or laboratory studies must usually be conducted, and these often demand facilities not readily available. Accordingly, the number of different kinds of insects for which this type of association has been worked out is very small and grows slowly. Even in the Lepidoptera (moths and butterflies) and the Coleoptera (beetles), where more work on immature forms has been done than in the other major groups of insects, fewer than 3 percent of the described species are known in the larval stage. Since about 1910, however, a great deal of progress has been made in this field of taxonomic work, and because emphasis has naturally been placed on the injurious species, most of the major pests are now identifiable in the immature stages.

Although, as I have indicated, the normal course is to base names on the adults and to develop the original and principal classifications from adult characteristics, there is one conspicuous exception. That involves the important group of plant pests comprising the family Aleyrodidae, the members of which are known as whiteflies. They are tiny insects that are not collected abundantly in the adult stage but are commonly seen fixed on leaves of infested plants when they are in the pupal stage. The family, which contains such devastating pests as the citrus blackfly, was long ignored, and most of the present knowledge concerning its classification has been accumulated during the past 50 years, the first significant and basic work being done by American taxonomists. Good characters upon which to base a classification were discovered in the pupae, and nearly the whole classification of the whiteflies is founded on this stage. In fact, it is rarely possible to identify adults in this group because adults have been definitely associated with the immature forms in only a few instances.

In keeping with its growing complexity, taxonomy has gradually become increasingly specialized, until now a worker usually confines himself to a single limited field, as, for example, aphids, or fleas, ants, biting lice, cutworm moths, leafhoppers, scale insects, termites, thrips, weevils, certain sections of the wasps or bees, grasshoppers, gall flies, or mosquitoes.

Such specialization is essential for thoroughly competent and authoritative work in the identification and classification of insects. Even to keep abreast of the taxonomic literature in any one of the restricted fields cited is a time-consuming task, for taxonomy—the description, nomenclature, and orderly classification of organisms—is international, and a taxonomist must take into account everything that is published in his specialty throughout the world. Furthermore, new approaches and more refined techniques must be sought continually in dealing with problems involving the classification of so complex a group of variable and evolving organisms as the insects have been found to be. Final decision as to identity often rests on features of certain internal structures that must be dissected out and mounted on slides after more or less elaborate preparatorial treatment. Indeed, such meticulous preparation of slides, which usually involves staining the tissues, is now a routine prerequisite for the study and identification of the whole insects of many groups, including aphids, whiteflies, scale insects, thrips, fleas, and lice.

The very recognition of the difficulties and complexities that have been outlined here is itself evidence of significant progress in classification research. More and more emphasis is being placed on fundamentals, and greater caution is practiced in making identifications. Today the taxonomists tend increasingly not to venture specific identifications in groups that have not been thoroughly studied and revised, although a generation or two ago, when the problems involved were not so well understood, determinations, often inaccurate, were freely made in the same groups. With the increase in knowledge about any group of insects, identification has grown more difficult but it has, at the same time, become more accurate and precise.

The recent history of taxonomic research in the mosquitoes is a good example of the progress that is being made as the result of intensive, specialized study of one family of insects. At the same time it indicates rather clearly how vast the task of the insect taxonomist is. From the time of the discovery of the transmission of malaria, yellow fever, and dengue by mosquitoes, this family, which now contains approximately 2,000 species, was studied actively. It soon became one of the best known insect groups of comparable size. The basic classification, after going through a period of great instability in the first two decades of the twentieth century, had reached a high degree of stability, thanks largely to the efforts of H. G. Dyar in the United States and F. W. Edwards in England. This taxonomy was based on both adult and larval characters, which greatly enhanced its strength. Large revisionary works had been published for the mosquito faunas of most of the regions of the world, and it seemed possible to make definite determinations rather readily for mosquitoes from anywhere. With the outbreak of the Second World War, when rapid recognition of the mosquitoes encountered in remote parts of the world was important, however, it became evident that much of what had been done on the classification of this family was out of date and that many species could not be determined satisfactorily.

Under that demand, intensive study of the family was undertaken by many taxonomists, and comprehensive keys were prepared to the anophelines (malaria vectors) of the world, as well as keys to other mosquitoes of medical importance occurring in certain crucial areas. The presence of military entomologists in the war theaters made possible the extensive and careful collection of specimens, many of the adults being individually reared and associated with larval and pupal forms. Such material was studied in the field laboratories and in the museums where the specimens were finally deposited; a flood of papers describing new species and revising genera and species groups resulted. Much was learned about the taxonomic relationships of species, and many new characters usable for distinguishing the different species were discovered. The study of mosquitoes in the pupal stage was given a great impetus, and the results are proving fruitful in the continuing attempts to improve the classification of the family. Although the gaps in the knowledge of mosquitoes are being filled in rapidly, however, much remains to be done. That is even truer of other insect groups, including the scale insects, ants, fleas, lice, aphids, grasshoppers, and certain small families of moths and beetles which have been rather intensively studied because of their conspicuous economic importance.

If this, then, is the situation in the relatively small groups that have received special attention because of their unusual importance to man's welfare, it must be evident that an immense amount of work will need to be done before the many larger groups that have had comparatively little study are thoroughly investigated and classified.

Thus, in 200 years since Linnaeus, during which time the number of known species of insects has increased from fewer than 2,000 to approximately 700,000, insect classification has become an elaborate and complex activity. At first it consisted essentially of the mere sorting of specimens into a series of figurative pigeonholes on the basis of differences that were often purely superficial. Gradually it has had to take into consideration many factors that have increased immeasurably the difficulty of the work. These include variation in all its aspects, dimorphism, the correlation of biological characteristics with structural peculiarities insofar as knowledge of biology will allow, and the identification of immature insects. The last virtually is a separate field in itself, because it is concerned with forms utterly unlike the adults with which they belong.

Insect classification is now recognized as a task that is never finished. Adjustments or complete revisions of the classifications of all groups become necessary as more new species are discovered and new information is accumulated about those already known.

C. F. W. MUESEBECK, *who received his academic training in entomology at Cornell University before joining the Bureau of Entomology in 1916, has been in charge of the division of insect identification since 1935. In recognition of his service, the Department of Agriculture awarded him a distinguished service medal in 1951. Before he joined the Department, Mr. Muesebeck spent several years in Europe in search of specific parasites of some injurious insect pests that had been introduced into the United States.*

Values of Insect Collections

Clarence E. Mickel

The pleasure and challenge of taking part in one vital scientific activity can be his who makes a collection of insects.

He starts for the fun of it, the joy in the endless variety of form, color, behavior, and universality of insects. Before long he wants to know the correct scientific names of the specimens he has and to expand his collection to include examples of other species. His interest grows with his collection and both may attain considerable size. Whatever his age and schooling he is a scientist then, one of a group whose work has great economic value to farmers and everybody else.

He will discover the basic value of a collection of correctly identified specimens—that the correct scientific name of a species is the key to all published information about that species, its habits, and the damage or good it does. He will also discover that there is still a great deal to be learned about all insects and that his own careful observations are of value in adding to the store of knowledge about them.

His collection may be small, from twenty to several hundred specimens, with examples of the orders and principal families of insects. Or it may in time embrace thousands of specimens and be restricted to certain groups of insects, such as a family or a genus.

He may prefer to make what we call a general collection. His aim then is to accumulate representative specimens of the common insects in his own neighborhood so that he can enjoy their beauty of color and form or use them to learn to recognize the insects or simply to satisfy his instinct for collecting. The scope and size of his collection will depend on him and the breadth of his interest. He may limit himself to specimens he finds in his own back yard or he may include those of his town or county.

In any event, as he attempts to identify the specimens he has collected, he will discover much about the methods of science—the need for proper mounting and preservation of specimens, lest parts of a specimen be damaged and lost and thereby make impossible its correct identification, the need for the minute examination of the specimen as it is being identified, the difference between learning for its own sake and learning with a practical application in mind (in this instance the control of harmful insects), and the scientist's deep concern for orderly classification and naming.

He will do well to get all the stages of life of the insects he collects, particularly if his aim is to know all the pests of plants, animals, stored products or buildings around his home. Before long, he will gain information on where, when, and how insects live and the names of the orders and families of the specimens he has collected. Such details he will get from reference works, including the chapter "What Kind of Insect Is It?" on page 43.

Anyone can make such collections. He must have some technical knowledge, but that he can acquire as his collection is made and grows. Mounting equipment and supplies, storage boxes for insects, and a few reference books will require some monetary outlay, but the amount will not be excessive. If he owns this Yearbook he will have many of the facts he wishes to know, but if he seriously expects to identify insect specimens he will require some additional technical works. Collecting insects is as inexpensive a hobby as anyone can have. His collection may or may not have scientific value, but it can have tremendous personal value to him: It teaches him a great deal about the insect world and about all living things. The chances are that anybody, boy or man or girl or woman, who makes a general collection gets an intense interest in insects that will last his lifetime and expand into other branches of natural science.

Another kind of collection is the one a biologist or entomologist may make on his own. Occasionally a person with training in biology becomes interested in the problems of the classification of a limited group of insects, such as a family or genus. He may do research on the classification of the group and, if he is not associated with some entomological research institute, he may have his personal collection of the group. Actually, some professional entomologists own private collections of the group of insects in which they are interested and on which they conduct taxonomic research.

They take more pains than beginners do with mounting and preserving specimens: Each specimen bears a label stating the locality where the specimen was collected, the date, the name of the collector, and any other biological information that can be printed on a small label. Each specimen also bears a second label giving the correct scientific name, the name of the scientist who made the identification, and the year the identification was made. The first or locality label is important—no specimen has scientific value without it. The owners of such collections often are competent entomologists and their colleagues regard their work highly. The results of their researches are published in the professional journals. It follows, therefore, that private collections may be of great scientific value; in fact, they may be of as great scientific value as any professional collection in a museum or entomological research institute. The owners may describe new species and genera of insects and the specimens from which they make their descriptions become valuable as reference specimens.

When an entomologist, amateur or professional, publishes the results of his research in a professional journal, his description of a new species and the data regarding the specimens on

970134°—52——6

which it is based become public property, but the specimens themselves are still in private hands. Often the publication is adequate for the identification of specimens collected thereafter, but sometimes an accurate identification cannot be made without reference to the original specimens. In such cases it may be necessary that an entomologist other than the original describer examine the specimens from which the description was made. It is vital then that the original specimens are properly taken care of and that they be available for examination by competent investigators.

Collections built up, financed, and taken care of by an individual should remain his property as long as he is engaged in research, of course, but collections of scientific value belong to the entomological research world as soon as their usefulness to the owner is finished. Many collections are given or sold to research institutions, where they are cared for and maintained for the use of all entomologists, but it has happened that fine collections have been so neglected that the specimens have become damaged or lost. One example is the collection of the famous American entomologist, Thomas Say, which upon his death in 1834 was lost or destroyed by pests—one of the most valuable of all the early insect collections was lost because no provision was made for its care.

Professional insect collections are maintained by institutions for reference, research, and teaching.

The reference collection is systematically arranged so that any series of specimens representing a single species can be consulted to verify the identification of new specimens. The number of specimens in a series need not be large, although it should include specimens of both sexes, of the immature stages, and of the injury caused by the insect of economic importance. Because of the differences in methods of preservation, adult specimens often are maintained separately from immature specimens, and both may be maintained separately from the specimens of insect injury.

The scope of the reference collection depends on the institution sponsoring it. A city, county, or State institution may often elect to limit the collection to the insects found within its boundaries, but large museums and a few universities maintain reference collections that are almost world-wide in scope.

When a specimen is sent to the institution for identification, it can be compared with already named material by a specialist who is intimately familiar with the group, and a decision made as to whether it is the species it is thought to be. The name must be correct, because all published information regarding the insect is indexed under the scientific name; once that is available, all the known facts about the insect can be assembled in a short time, and, if the insect is doing or can do damage to crops or trees, men who are working to control it know with what sort of thing they have to deal. Thus an extensive reference collection is of inestimable value in the correct naming of new specimens and is indispensable to Federal and State agencies charged with the duty of research on the control of injurious insects.

Because hundreds of thousands of species have been described, a complete representative collection of all species would be next to impossible. No collection in the world includes representatives of all of the described species. Some important collections contain a few thousand, but some contain specimens of many thousands of species.

A considerable number of specimens submitted for identification can be routinely identified without difficulty. There still remain, however, thousands of undescribed species of insects, and many which have been so poorly described, or are so little known, that identification of specimens is of great technical difficulty. A research collection is necessary to study and solve such problems of classification, and it differs from a reference collection in the number of specimens of each species included—the research collection having long series of specimens of a species whenever possible, while the reference collection will have only a few. Thus research collections often have a tremendous amount of unidentified material which, because of technical difficulties, can only be identified after much study and research. Obviously, extensive reference and research collections require the services of a specially trained curatorial staff, the larger collections requiring a correspondingly large staff.

The number and variety of species of insects make their systematic arrangement or classification a highly technical procedure. The scientific study of the similarities and differences among species of animals is known as taxonomy; the systematic arrangement of the species based on such studies is known as their classification. As new and undescribed species of insects are discovered and studied, the classification is bound to become more difficult and complex. The naming and identification of insect specimens consequently depends on how well the group has been studied and described. Some groups are well known and can be identified easily, but many are poorly known and their identification is difficult and laborious. There is a great need therefore for taxonomic research on them to facilitate their identification. The reserves of unidentified insect specimens in research collections provide a reservoir of material that can be drawn upon when opportunity offers for the intensive study of some insect group.

Reference and research collections help the entomologist who works to reduce the economic injuries of insect pests. They also are useful to other biological scientists. Animal physiologists, animal ecologists, geneticists, plant pathologists, cytologists, and others carry on research in which they use insects as experimental animals, or insects impose themselves upon the experiments in some way or other. It is necessary for scientific accuracy that these scientists know the correct names of the insects with which they are dealing. Usually only the insect taxonomist can supply this information, and to do that efficiently he must have an adequate research and reference collection at his disposal.

When an insect taxonomist describes a new species, he customarily draws up the description from a single specimen. When he does that, he calls the specimen a holotype. If he has available a specimen of the other sex and has to give it a separate description from the holotype, he describes and designates it as an allotype. If the taxonomist has a series of specimens at the time he makes the description, all the remaining specimens are designated as paratypes. His purpose in all this is to provide an indisputable specimen of the species which he intends to describe.

The apparent structural differences between some insect species are exceedingly slight. It has happened often that a man has described a new species from a series of several specimens only to have some other person years later find that the series consisted of several species. Then the question arises: To which species in the series does the name belong which the original author gave? It is to prevent situations such as this that the practice of designating a holotype has come into being. Types (holotypes, allotypes, and paratypes) have served this purpose so well that insect taxonomists have come to depend on them. They have great scientific value and should be well cared for. In insect taxonomy no specimen is of any greater value than the holotype. Most reference and research collections include a considerable number of type specimens and the more type specimens an insect collection contains, the greater its value.

Primarily then, the reference and research collections are of the greatest value to the insect taxonomist. They are the indispensable material with which he works. They are of value to workers in the future who find in them a reservoir of material for study and comparison. Indirectly they are of great importance to the public, because all the information the public receives about insects is associated with the name. If the name is incorrect the public will be misinformed, and misinformation about insects may result in economic loss, in personal discomfort, in sickness, and even loss of life.

Among the large research and reference collections in the United States and Canada are the National Museum in Washington, D. C.; Canadian National Collection in Ottawa, Ontario; American Museum of Natural History, New York; Museum of Comparative Zoology, Cambridge, Mass.; Academy of Natural Sciences of Philadelphia; Illinois Natural History Survey, Urbana; California Academy of Sciences, San Francisco; Carnegie Museum, Pittsburgh; Chicago Museum of Natural History; Cornell University, Ithaca, N. Y.; University of Minnesota, St. Paul; Ohio State University, Columbus; University of Kansas, Lawrence; and the University Museum, University of Michigan, Ann Arbor.

THE UNIVERSITIES OR COLLEGES that have no reference or research collections often have collections that are used in courses in entomology and zoology. Teachers have found it needful to have enough specimens so that each student can have a specimen to study and examine under a microscope. A student can learn the orders and families of insects only by handling specimens and attempting to identify them; he must make a collection of his own or the teacher must furnish the specimens, both adult and immature, and samples of the injury the insect has caused. Sometimes, as a substitute or if the teaching is informal, the specimens are arranged in a permanent exhibit for use by more than one individual.

Another type of teaching collection is that arranged by extension workers and other entomologists who find small portable exhibits useful in acquainting the public with insect pests.

Sometimes—when a private collection is offered for sale, say, or an inventory has to be made of an institutional collection—it is necessary to put a monetary value on a collection. Some of the factors then involved are: The actual cost of obtaining specimens, including the collector's time and expenses, or the purchase price; the cost of the technical materials used in preparation of the specimens, such as pins, labels, trays, cork, storage cabinets, microscope slides, and chemicals; the labor in preparing the specimens; the number of holotype or type specimens in the collection; the rareness of the specimens; and the physical condition of the collection. No financial estimate, though, can place a value on the usefulness of collections that permit ready identification and so promptly unlock the store of existing knowledge about any species; neither can a financial estimate adequately assess the educational, cultural, and scientific values of collections. Those values are indeed high.

CLARENCE E. MICKEL *is chief of the division of entomology and economic zoology in the University of Minnesota, which he joined in 1922. In 1930 he studied in Europe on a fellowship. He was secretary-treasurer of the Entomological Society of America in 1936–44 and President of the society in 1944–45. He was chosen President of the International Great Plains Conference of Entomologists in 1946.*

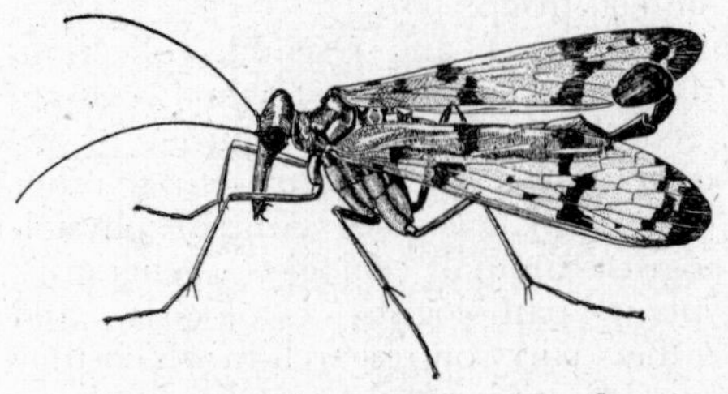

Panorpa rufescens, a scorpionfly.

How To Collect and Preserve Insects for Study

Paul W. Oman

The equipment used in collecting insects is simple and inexpensive. The average collector usually will need only a few items: Nets, killing bottles, suction bottle, tweezers, scissors, small brushes, and insect pins. Many collectors prefer to make most of their own equipment even though most items may be purchased from commercial supply companies.

The insect net is essentially a cloth bag hung from a loop that is attached to a handle. The size, shape, and material of the net depend on its use.

The beating net (fig. 1) must be strong enough to stand rough use. A handle of straight-grain hickory or ash, such as a hoe handle, fitted at one end with a metal ferrule (fig. 1, C) about an inch in diameter to hold the wire loop in place, is recommended. The handle should be about 1⅜ inches in diameter and 3½ to 4½ feet long.

The wire loop (fig. 1, A) should be of No. 12 steel wire (0.189 inch in diameter), although even heavier wire is sometimes preferred. After the loop is shaped, it can be tempered so that it will spring back into shape if it is bent when it is used.

For the bag, 6-ounce drill, heavy muslin, or light canvas is recommended. It may be made as shown in figure 1, D. The four lobes form the rounded bottom of the bag when sewed together. The details of the double-thickness hem as it hangs on the wire loop are shown in figure 1, E. This type of construction is advisable because that part of the bag gets the most wear. For a lightweight bag, the entire top band may be made of a stout material and the bag sewed to it. The final step is to complete the bag by sewing together the two ends of the material and the margins of the cut lobes.

This beating net is not satisfactory for the capture of moths, butterflies, flies, wasps, and other swift-flying or fragile insects. For them, the nets described in the next three paragraphs are useful.

The general-purpose net should have a loop 12 inches in diameter and a bag of unbleached muslin or of coarse or medium-mesh brussels. It should be tapered more toward the bottom than the beating net, but it should not come to a point. The handle need not be so stout as that for the beating net.

The butterfly net is like the general-purpose net, but the bag is of good-quality marquisette or fine netting, and the handle is a little longer and of lighter weight. This net is also useful in capturing dragonflies and other large-winged insects.

The fly net should have a loop 8 inches in diameter and a bag of medium-mesh brussels or fine netting. The handle should be short and light. The wire loop need not be so heavy as that for the beating net. This net is also good for collecting bees and wasps.

The aquatic net, for collecting insects that live in or on water or on aquatic plants, should not have a circular loop, but should be either square (with the handle attached to one corner) or about semicircular (with the side opposite the handle straight). The bag should be shallow (about as deep as the length of the straight side in the semicircular net) and should be made of heavy scrim with a canvas band for the wire loop.

The bag for any of the nets I have described may be made of silk bolting cloth, which is durable and has meshes of various sizes but is more expensive. Nylon may also be used. The bag for any net, excepting the water net, should be long enough so that the tip may be flipped over the rim of the wire loop to form a pocket from which the netted insects will not escape.

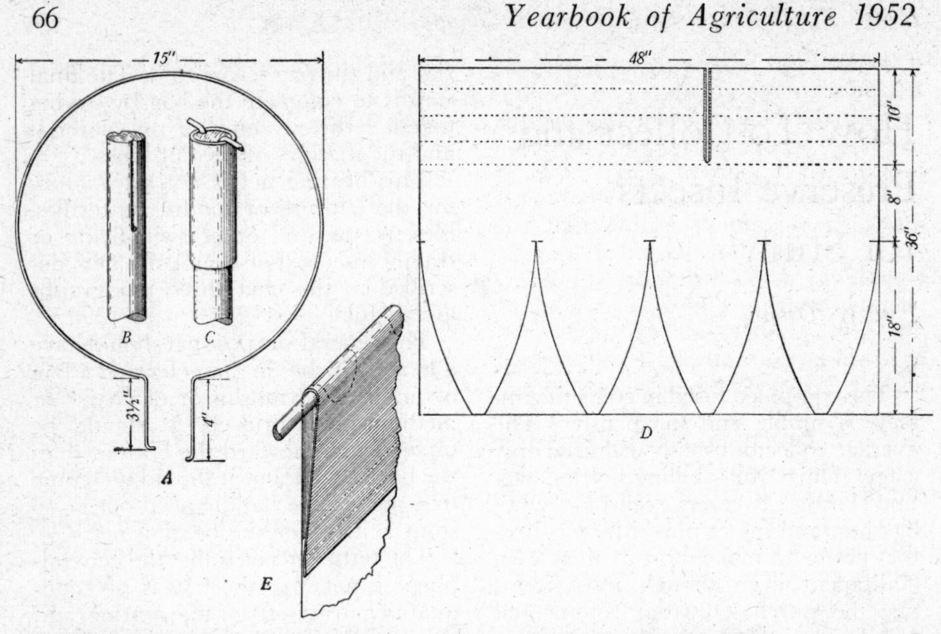

1. The construction of a beating net: A, Steel wire loop 15 inches in diameter; B, end of net handle showing grooves and holes into which the arms of the wire loop fit; C, net handle with metal ferrule to hold net in place; D, how to cut a single piece of cloth to make a round-bottom bag; E, details of top part of net fitted over a section of the wire loop.

Nets should be kept dry. A wet net damages the specimens and dampness causes the fabric to rot quickly. Aquatic nets should be thoroughly dried after use.

A KILLING BOTTLE may be made from any fairly heavy glass jar or vial with a wide mouth. The collector should have several bottles of various sizes (fig. 2, A, B). Empty pickle jars, olive jars, and the like will furnish an assortment of larger bottles. Smaller ones may be made from test tubes or shell vials 1 to 1½ inches in diameter. These should be supplied with tight-fitting corks. Figure 2, C illustrates a convenient adaptation of a screw cap for a jar to keep bees, grasshoppers, and other lively insects from escaping from the killing bottle when it is opened for putting in other specimens. This cap is made by soldering an incomplete metal cone to a screw cap with the top cut out. A metal tube about 1 inch in diameter is then soldered inside the cone.

Calcium cyanide, potassium cyanide, or sodium cyanide may be used as the killing agent in the bottle. Wrap some granular cyanide (a heaping teaspoonful for small bottles, larger amounts for large bottles) in cellucotton, or place it in a "nest" in cellucotton or a little cloth bag, and put this in the bottom of the bottle. Over this place a plug of several layers of cellucotton or a layer of dry sawdust. If the bottle is more than 1½ inches in diameter, a quarter-inch layer of plaster of paris should be poured in and allowed to harden for a few hours before the bottle is corked. If the bottle is a small one, several disks of clean blotting paper, cut to fit the bottle snugly, may be used in place of the plaster of paris.

Cyanide is a deadly poison and should be handled with great care. All bottles should be conspicuously labeled *poison* and should be kept away from persons who do not realize the deadliness of the chemical. The bottom of a cyanide bottle should be taped so that if the bottle is broken the cyanide will not be scattered about.

To make a killing bottle in which to use ethyl acetate (acetic ether), pour a half inch or more of plaster of paris into the bottom of a suitable jar or vial, allow it to set, and dry it thoroughly in an oven. After the plaster of paris is completely dry, saturate it with ethyl acetate, pouring off any excess fluid. The killing bottle is then ready for use and will last for months if kept tightly corked. When it becomes ineffective it can be dried in the oven and recharged. Insects may be preserved in such bottles for an indefinite time without becoming brittle if they receive an occasional moistening with ethyl acetate. Ethyl acetate is relatively easy to obtain, and the killing bottles have the advantage of being comparatively safe to use.

The killing bottle will last longer and give better results if the following simple rules are observed:

1. Before using the cyanide bottle, put in a few strips of soft paper, such as ordinary toilet paper. This will help keep the bottle dry and will prevent the specimens from mutilating one another. Change these strips whenever they become soiled or slightly moist. Wipe out the bottle if it becomes moist.

2. Keep a special bottle for moths and butterflies. The scales from these insects will stick to other insects and spoil them.

3. Never mix small or delicate insects with large insects like grasshoppers and large beetles. Beetles are hard to kill

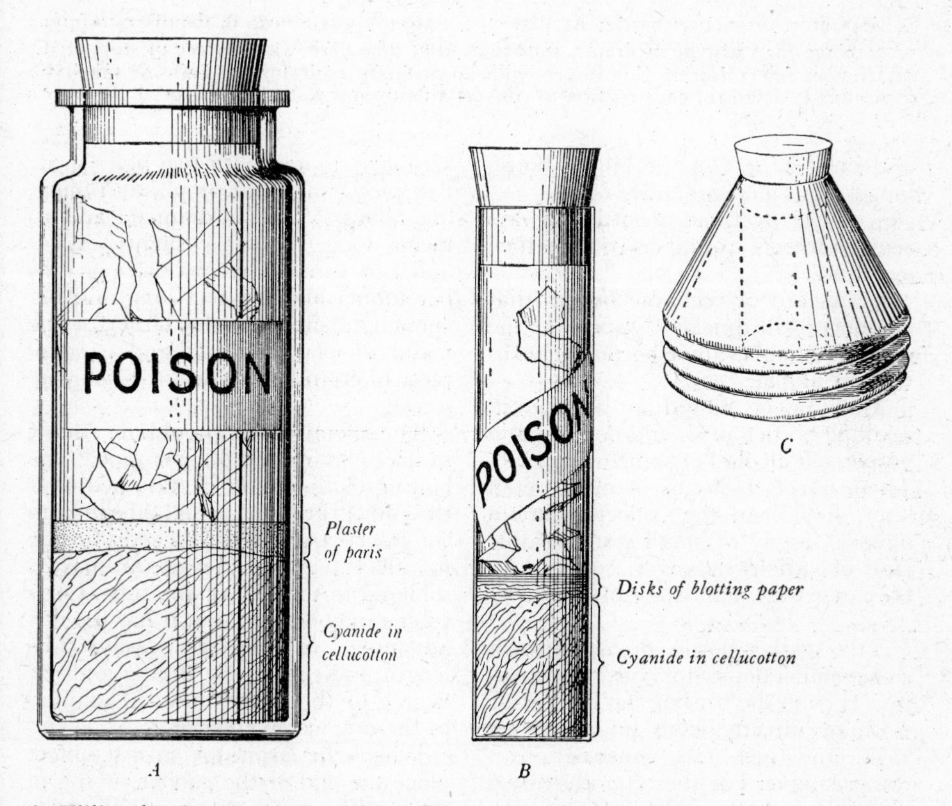

2. Killing bottles: A, Large, wide-mouth cyanide bottle for large insects; B, vial-type cyanide bottle for small insects; C, screw-cap top for large cyanide bottle showing a convenient arrangement to prevent the escape of active specimens.

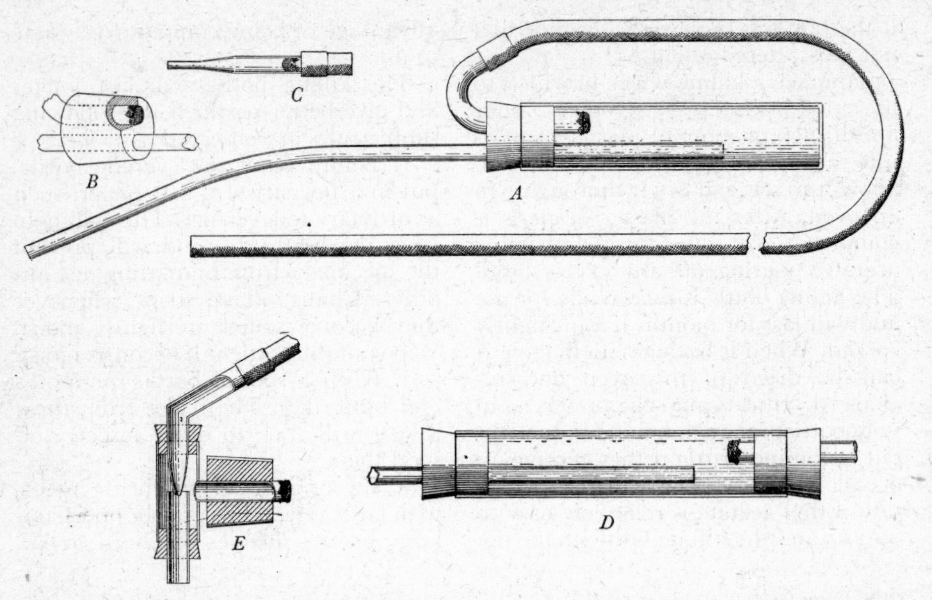

3. Aspirator, or suction bottle: A, Vial-type aspirator assembled; B, details of stopper assemblage for vial-type aspirator, showing outlet tube flush with surface of stopper; C, attachment for collecting tiny insects with an ordinary aspirator; D, body of tube-type aspirator; E, details of construction to convert an aspirator to the blow type.

and must be left in the killing bottle longer than most other insects.

4. Never overload a bottle. Always remove insects from it as soon as they are dead.

5. Discard or recharge bottles that no longer kill quickly. Dispose of the contents of old cyanide bottles by burning or burying.

Many insects should not be killed in a killing bottle but should be placed in 70 percent alcohol or some other fluid. These insects I discuss in more detail later. For them the collector should have a supply of small homeopathic vials of various sizes with corks to fit. He can get them at drug stores.

THE suction bottle, or aspirator, is a convenient device for collecting small insects from the beating net or beating cloth or directly from under stones, bark, and such. Its construction is rather simple. For the type illustrated in figure 3, A, the following materials are needed: A glass vial 1 to 1½ inches in diameter and about 4½ inches long; a rubber stopper with two holes in it; two pieces of metal or plastic tubing, one about ¼ inch in diameter and 10 inches long, the other slightly larger and 4 or 5 inches long; a piece of rubber tubing about 3 feet long and big enough to slip onto the larger of the metal or plastic tubes; and a small piece of bolting cloth or fine-mesh wire screen.

The metal tubes should fit snugly in the holes in the rubber stopper. The bolting cloth should be fastened over the end of the larger metal tube to keep the insects from being sucked into the mouth. If wire screen is used it may be soldered to the end of the tube. Glass tubing may be used, but it has the disadvantage of breaking easily. The length and size of the tubing and the degree of the bends may be adapted to the user's convenience.

When the aspirator is assembled, place the end of the rubber tubing in the mouth, aim the longer tube of the aspirator at a small insect, and suck sharply. The air current will pull the insect into the vial. With a little practice it is possible to collect small insects much more quickly and in better condition this way than by almost any other method.

A convenient attachment for collecting thrips, small flies, tiny beetles, and other minute insects normally killed in liquid is illustrated in figure 3, C. A piece of fine-mesh bolting cloth, inserted in the glass tubing near the large end, keeps the tiny insects from going on into the aspirator. They can then be blown out into the vial of liquid in which they are to be preserved.

Some collectors prefer the tube-type aspirator, the body of which is illustrated in figure 3, D. Either the tube-type or the vial-type aspirator may be converted to a blow-type collecting bottle by substituting for the shorter tube, to which the rubber tubing is attached, the attachment illustrated in figure 3, E. This piece of equipment makes use of an air current to create a partial vacuum; with it in use in the assembled aspirator the same result is obtained by blowing instead of sucking through the rubber tubing. This type of attachment is essential if the aspirator is to be used to collect insects that emit disagreeable odors.

Many insects spend all or part of their lives in ground litter and leafmold. They cannot be captured by ordinary collecting methods. Because they are too active to be caught by hand or feign death when disturbed, a sifter should be used.

Almost any container with a wire-mesh bottom will serve as a sifter. The size of the meshes in the screen will depend upon the size of the insects sought. For general purposes a screen with eight meshes to the inch will be satisfactory. The screen may be fastened to a wooden frame to make a box-shaped sifter, or it may be attached to a wire hoop, which is then sewed to one end of a cloth sleeve about 12 inches in diameter. In the latter type of sifter it is convenient to have a wire hoop of the same size at the other end of the cloth sleeve to hold it open.

Place the leafmold or ground litter in the sifter and shake it gently over a piece of white oilcloth spread flat on the ground. As the insects fall into the cloth they may be easily captured with an aspirator or tweezers. Many insects feign death and are not easily seen until they move, so the debris on the cloth should not be discarded too quickly. The sifter is especially useful for collecting in winter.

THE COLLECTOR who wishes to get large numbers of the small insects that are usually found in ground litter will find it advantageous to construct a separator (usually called a Berlese funnel by entomologists) for use instead of the sifter. Fundamentally, the separator consists of a funnel over which a sieve containing leafmold or other litter may be placed. The funnel leads into a receptacle containing a liquid preservative, into which the insects fall when driven from the material in the sieve by the progressive drying with a light bulb or some other source of mild heat.

Collecting around lights, especially on warm, humid nights, frequently permits the collector to obtain in abundance insects that are captured rarely or not at all by other methods. The use of light traps as a means of obtaining insects for the collection is not recommended because specimens are too frequently damaged. Insects for the collection should be selected and captured by attending the light continuously while it is in operation.

Although any reasonably bright light will serve, more insects are attracted to blue lights than to other kinds. A convenient method of collecting at a light is to hang up a white sheet so that the light shines upon it; the lower edge is turned up to form a trough into which some of the insects will fall. The specimens are collected as they come to the sheet. Many insects may also be collected around street lights and lighted store windows.

Baits of many kinds are valuable aids to the collector. One of the best known uses for baits is in sugaring for moths. For sugaring, make a mixture of molasses or brown sugar, a little asafoetida, and stale beer or fermenting fruit juices, and daub it on tree trunks along a route that can be conveniently visited with a lantern or flashlight. As with light collecting, this method is most productive on warm, humid nights. The bait should be applied about dusk and may be visited at intervals all that night and frequently will be found to be attractive to insects on succeeding nights.

Insects that are attracted to sweet substances or decaying meat may be captured in simple jar traps. Bait the jar (an olive bottle or a fruit jar will do) with an appropriate bait and bury it with the open top flush with the surface of the ground. It is frequently desirable to set these traps under loose boards or stones lying on the ground.

An assortment of tweezers and brushes should be available as an aid in collecting and handling the specimens after they are dead. Such equipment may be purchased at small cost from most biological supply houses. A few small camel's-hair brushes, sizes 0 to 2, are handy for picking up small insects that might be crushed if handled with tweezers. Moisten the tip of the brush on the tongue or in the liquid preservative, touch the specimen with the brush, and you can transfer it safely to the collecting vial.

Rearing is one of the best methods of obtaining good specimens. It has the added advantage of permitting observations on the life history of the species and enables the collector to get examples of the various immature stages.

To rear specimens successfully, the natural conditions under which the immature insects were found should be simulated as closely as possible in the rearing cages. Insects that feed on living plants may be caged over potted plants or fed frequently with fresh material from their host plant. With a little ingenuity a suitable cage can be prepared. The important thing is to have it tight enough to keep the insects in and yet provide for sufficient ventilation so that the container will not sweat. Some loose, slightly moist soil or sand and ground litter should be provided in case the insect is one that pupates in or on the ground. Insects that feed on decaying animal matter should also have the cage provided with slightly moist soil or sand.

Insects that infest seeds and those that cause plant galls may be reared merely by enclosing the seeds or galls in a tight container. Such material should not be permitted to become too dry; neither should it be kept moist, else the material and the specimens will mold. It is a good plan to insert the open end of a glass vial through a hole in the container; then, if the container is dark, when the specimens emerge they will be attracted to the light, enter the vial, and can be easily removed and killed. Tiny parasitic wasps may be reared from their hosts in this manner. A cardboard ice-cream container is excellent for this type of rearing.

Adult moths, butterflies, beetles, and many other insects may be obtained by collecting chrysalids or pupae and caging them until the specimens emerge. In this way the best specimens of moths and butterflies may be secured. Always permit the reared specimen to harden and color completely before killing it, but do not leave it in the cage so long that it will damage itself in trying to escape. Cages should always be placed where they will be safe from ants.

Bark and wood are often infested by boring insects, such as beetles. Often these insects can be collected during the winter, the period of effective field collecting being thus extended. If they are placed in glass or metal containers, excellent specimens of the adults may be obtained.

The method of killing and preserving to be used depends upon the kind of insects involved. No one method is satisfactory for all specimens. Frequently it is desirable to kill in liquid any specimens that will later be pinned. The best general liquid killing and preserving agent, which should always be used unless some other preservative is especially recommended, is 70 to 75 percent grain (ethyl) alcohol. Formalin, which is frequently used as a preservative for biological specimens, is not recommended as a preservative for insects because it hardens the tissues and makes the specimens difficult to prepare for study. In the discussion that follows, alcohol, unless otherwise indicated, means 70 to 75 percent grain alcohol.

Detailed instructions for killing and preserving the various kinds of insects are given later, but if the material is not readily recognized, the following rule of thumb may be followed.

Use alcohol to kill ants, aphids, beetles, bugs, fleas, lice, mayflies, silverfish, springtails, and termites.

Use a killing bottle for bees, butterflies, crickets, damselflies, dragonflies, flies, grasshoppers, moths, roaches, and wasps.

Use boiling water to kill insect larvae, such as cutworms, grubs, and maggots, and transfer the specimens to alcohol after a few minutes.

Insects killed in alcohol but later mounted dry should first be dehydrated in 100 percent alcohol (200 proof, also called absolute alcohol). That takes 1 to 24 hours, depending on the size of the specimens. They should then be degreased in xylene (xylol) or benzene (benzol). This requires about the same length of time as the dehydration. They should be dried and mounted.

Specimens killed dry, in a killing bottle, and containing considerable fatty tissue, should be degreased before being mounted. Soak the specimens in a bath of commercial sulfuric ether until the fluid ceases to become yellow from the dissolved oils; change the fluid if necessary. Complete degreasing may take a day to a week, depending on the size and number of specimens, their fat content, and the volume of ether used. A wad of absorbent tissue or filter paper should be placed in the bottom of the container to absorb waste that accumulates and might otherwise cling to the specimens.

Ether is highly inflammable and must be used with great care. Other solvents are chloroform, benzene, xylene, and diethyl carbonate. If chloroform is used, the specimens must be held submerged by a wire screen. After being degreased, specimens should be transferred to a clean pad of absorbent tissue and their appendages arranged. When they are dry enough they may be mounted.

Specimens that contain little fatty tissue may be mounted without further preparation. Pinned specimens that have become greasy because of the decomposition of body fats may be degreased by being put in an ether or chloroform bath for a few hours.

THE FOLLOWING OUTLINE gives instructions for killing and preserving the commoner types of insects and indicates the usual method of mounting for study.

Anoplura (sucking lice): Kill and preserve in alcohol. Mount on slides.

Coleoptera (beetles): Kill in alcohol or ethyl acetate vapor. Mount on pins.

Collembola (springtails): Kill and preserve in alcohol. Mount on slides.

Corrodentia (booklice): Kill and preserve in alcohol.

Dermaptera (earwigs): Kill in cyanide, ethyl acetate vapor, or alcohol. Mount on pins.

Diptera (flies): Kill in cyanide, except minute forms, such as eye gnats and fungus gnats, which may be killed in alcohol. Mount on pins.

Ephemeroptera (mayflies): Kill and preserve in alcohol.

Hemiptera (true bugs and their allies): Kill in cyanide, ethyl acetate vapor, or alcohol, except the immature stages, aphids, scale insects, and Aleyrodidae (whiteflies). Mount on pins. Nymphs should be killed in alcohol and mounted on pins. Aphids should be killed in alcohol and mounted on slides.

Scale insects and whiteflies on host material should be preserved dry, but if they are not on host material they should be preserved in alcohol. Mount on slides.

Hymenoptera (bees, wasps, ants, etc.): Kill in cyanide, except ants, gall wasps, and small parasitic forms, which may be killed in alcohol. Mount on pins.

Isoptera (termites): Kill and preserve in alcohol.

Lepidoptera (moths and butterflies): Kill in cyanide. Mount on pins.

Mallophaga (biting lice): Kill in alcohol. Mount on slides.

Mecoptera (scorpionflies): Kill in cyanide. Mount on pins.

Neuroptera (lacewings, ant-lions, etc.): Kill in cyanide. Mount on pins.

Odonata (dragonflies): Kill in cyanide. Mount on pins.

Orthoptera (grasshoppers, crickets, roaches): Kill in cyanide. Mount on pins.

Plecoptera (stoneflies): Kill and preserve in alcohol.

Siphonaptera (fleas): Kill in alcohol. Mount on slides.

Thysanoptera (thrips): Kill in a liquid made of 8 parts 95 percent alcohol, 5 parts distilled water, 1 part glycerin, and 1 part glacial acetic acid. Mount on slides.

Thysanura (silverfish and their allies): Kill and preserve in alcohol.

Trichoptera (caddisflies): Kill in cyanide. Mount on pins.

Larvae of insects should be killed in boiling water and allowed to remain in the water from 1 to 5 minutes according to size, then preserved in alcohol.

Centipedes, millipedes, mites, spiders, ticks, and other small arthropods should be killed and preserved in alcohol. The smaller forms are usually mounted on slides.

It is frequently impracticable to mount all collected specimens soon after they are killed, and some method of caring for them so they will not be broken must be used. Specimens collected in liquid may be preserved in it indefinitely without injury, the only precaution being to keep plenty of fluid in the container. Specimens killed in the ethyl acetate bottle and intended for the ether bath may also be preserved indefinitely in a container with just enough ethyl acetate to keep them from drying.

Specimens that are killed in cyanide and are to be mounted without further treatment will soon become dry and brittle. They should be placed in paper pill boxes between layers of cellucotton cut to fit the box and packed tightly enough so that the specimens will not shift about, but not pressed down enough to flatten or distort them. Cotton should not be used, as legs and

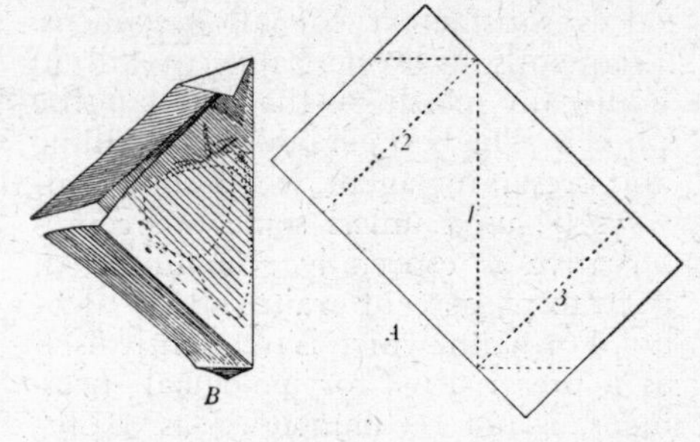

4. Method of folding a rectangular piece of paper to form a triangular envelope for large-winged insects: A, Correct shape of unfolded paper, showing where the folds should be made and the sequence of the first three folds; B, "triangle" almost completely folded, showing correct position of the enclosed butterfly.

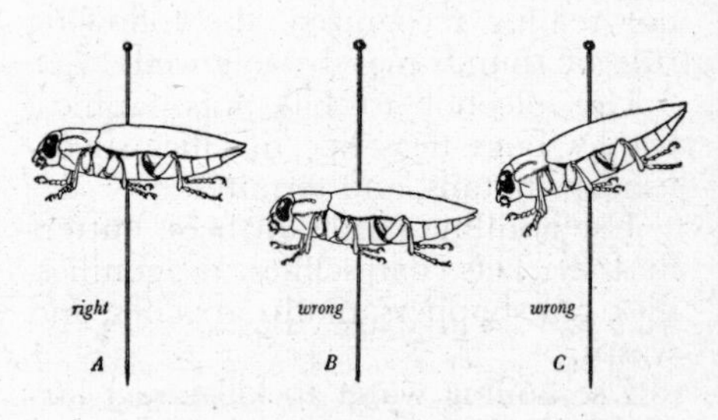

5. Illustration of right and wrong methods of pinning: A, Correct height and position of specimen; B, insect too low on the pin; C, insect tilted on the pin.

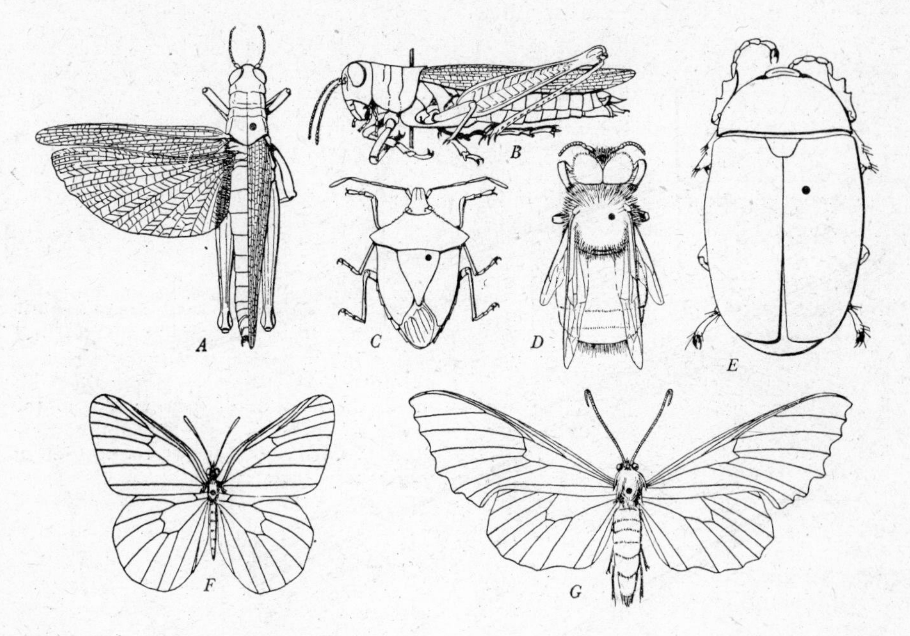

6. Examples of correct pinning methods for common insects; the black spots show where the pins should go. A, Grasshopper and related Orthoptera, showing how wings should be spread; B, side view of a grasshopper, showing position of legs and antennae; C, a stink bug, an example of the order Hemiptera, showing method of pinning large bugs; D, a bee, order Hymenoptera, to show where bees, wasps, and flies should be pinned; E, a May beetle, order Coleoptera, showing method of pinning beetles; F, G, butterfly and moth, order Lepidoptera, showing location of pin and position of wings and antennae.

antennae catch on the fibers and are apt to be broken off. Medium-size and small Lepidoptera should be packed one specimen to a layer. Large Lepidoptera, Odonata, and other insects with large wings and relatively small bodies should be placed in envelopes or folded "triangles" (fig. 4), which may then be packed between layers of cellucotton.

Specimens are mounted to facilitate handling and study. Their value increases with the convenience with which they may be examined. Some insects, such as scale insects, aphids, lice, thrips, and other minute forms, can be satisfactorily studied only after they are mounted on a microscope slide. The proper preparation of slide mounts is a task requiring considerable equipment and experience, and slide preparations should not be attempted without the aid of specific instructions, which are usually different for different groups of insects. For the usual larger insects, standard pinning practices have been developed, designed to avoid injury to the specimens and to expedite study.

Medium and large insects should be pinned vertically through the body. Figure 5 illustrates some right and wrong pinning practices. The height of the specimen on the pin will depend somewhat on its size. There should be enough room at the top of the pin so that it may be handled without letting the fingers touch the specimen (fig. 5, A), but it should not be so low that proper labels cannot be placed beneath the specimen.

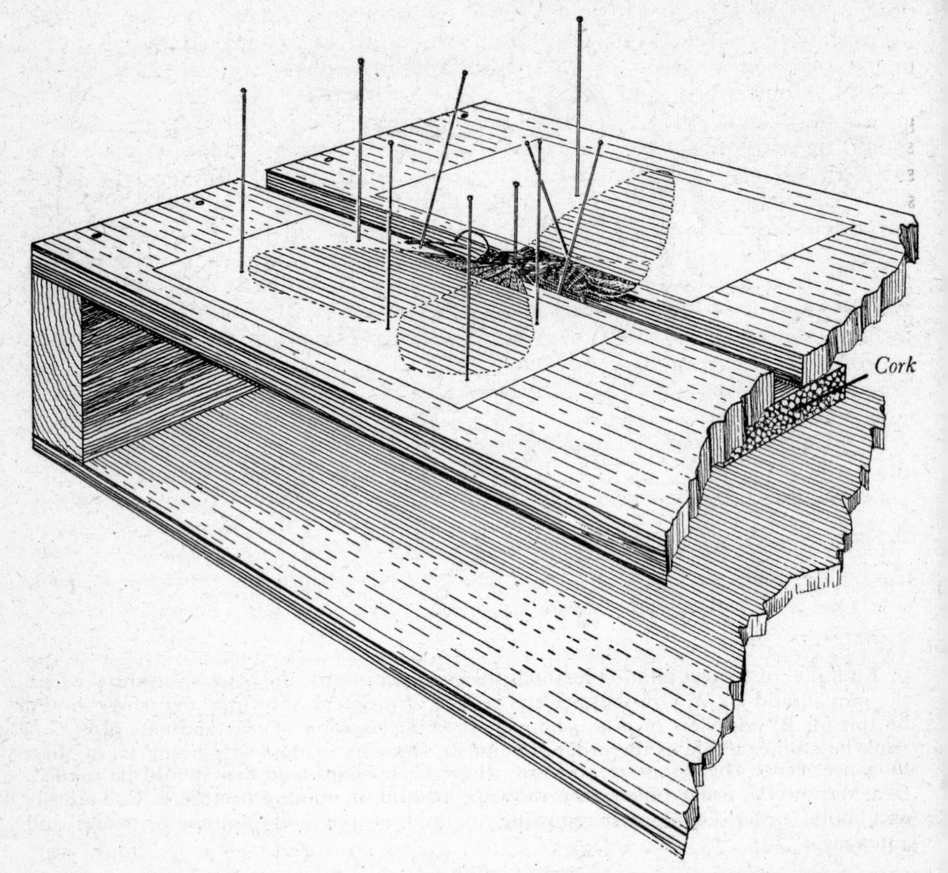

7. Portion of a spreading board, showing construction of the board and steps in the process of spreading the wings and arranging the abdomen and antennae of a butterfly, order Lepidoptera.

The standard methods for pinning the commoner kinds of insects are:

1. Grasshoppers, katydids, etc.: Pin through the back part of the thorax to the right of the middle line (fig. 6, A).

2. Stink bugs and other large Hemiptera: Pin through the scutellum to the right of the middle line (fig. 6, C).

3. Bees, wasps, and flies: Pin through the thorax between or a little behind the bases of the forewings and to the right of the middle line (fig. 6, D).

4. Beetles: Pin through the right wing cover near the base (fig. 6, E).

5. Moths, butterflies, dragonflies, and damselflies: Pin through the middle line of the thorax at the thickest point or between or a little behind the bases of the forewings (fig. 6, F, G).

Before the specimen is permitted to dry (or after being thoroughly relaxed if already dried) the legs, wings, and antennae should be properly arranged so they are visible for study, as shown in figure 6. With many insects, such as beetles, bugs, flies, and bees, it is only necessary to arrange the legs and antennae and they will stay in place. It is usually necessary to pin specimens of grasshoppers close to the edge of a box so that other pins to hold the legs in place may be thrust into the sides of the box at various angles. With some specimens, such as wasps and long-legged flies and bugs, the legs and abdomen may be kept in place until dry by pushing a piece of stiff paper up on the pin beneath them.

Moths, butterflies, and sometimes grasshoppers, dragonflies, and cicadas, should have the wings on one or both sides spread. A spreading board such as shown in figure 7 is useful for this purpose.

The collector will find it advantageous to have several boards with the middle grooves of different widths to accommodate insects of various sizes, but for general purposes a board made from the following materials will be satisfactory:

1. A hardwood base, ¼ by 4 by 12 inches.
2. Two hardwood end pieces, ½ by ¾ by 4 inches.
3. Two softwood top pieces, ⅜ by 1⅞ by 12 inches.
4. One flat strip of cork, ¼ by 1 by 11 inches.

When assembled as illustrated, the softwood top pieces leave a groove ¼ inch wide. On the under side of these, a cork strip is glued so that it covers the space between the top pieces.

Specimens must be thoroughly relaxed for spreading; otherwise they will be broken. Figure 7 shows the wings on the left side of the specimen spread in the proper manner. The first step in spreading the wings, after pinning the specimen in the groove at the proper height, is shown on the right side of the board in figure 7. To complete the process, hold the strip of semitransparent paper covering the wings gently with the fingers of one hand and pull the wings forward with an insect pin until the hind margin of the forewing is at right angles to the body of the insect. The hind wing should then be brought forward until its front margin is just under the hind margin of the forewing. Pin both wings in place with plenty of pins arranged around them, not through them. The abdomen and antennae should also be held in place by pins. The paper strips holding the wings in place should be of fairly thin, not stiff, paper.

Specimens should be left on the spreading board until thoroughly dry. For large insects this requires 2 or 3 weeks. Smaller specimens will dry in less time. During this time they should be stored in pestproof containers. Do not forget the collection-data label, which should be associated with the specimen at all times.

Small insects that cannot be pinned directly through the body with regular insect pins should be mounted on card points or on special pins known as minuten nadeln.

Card points are slender triangles of paper. These are pinned through the broad end with a regular insect pin (No. 2 or 3), and the specimen is glued to the point, as illustrated in figure 8, A. Card points may be cut with scissors from a strip of paper ⅜ inch wide, but a punch, obtainable from supply houses, makes better and more uniform points. A good-quality linen ledger paper should be used; "substance 36" is recommended. Ordinary glue is not recommended for fastening the specimen to the point because it tends to become brittle. Some of the clear acetate cellulose cements, such as Ambroid, which may be purchased in small amounts at variety stores, are more satisfactory. An adequate supply may be made by dissolving a transparent resin toothbrush handle in a small amount of banana oil (amyl acetate). Pure white shellac is also fairly satisfactory. Whatever adhesive is used, it should not be permitted to get so thick that it "strings," and only a small amount should be used.

To mount most insects, the tip of the card point should be bent down at a slight angle so that when the insect is in an upright position the bent tip of the point fits against the side of the insect (fig. 8, B). Only a very small part of the point should be bent; a little practice will make it easy to judge how much of the point should be bent and at what angle to fit the particular specimen that is being mounted. Most insects that are mounted on points

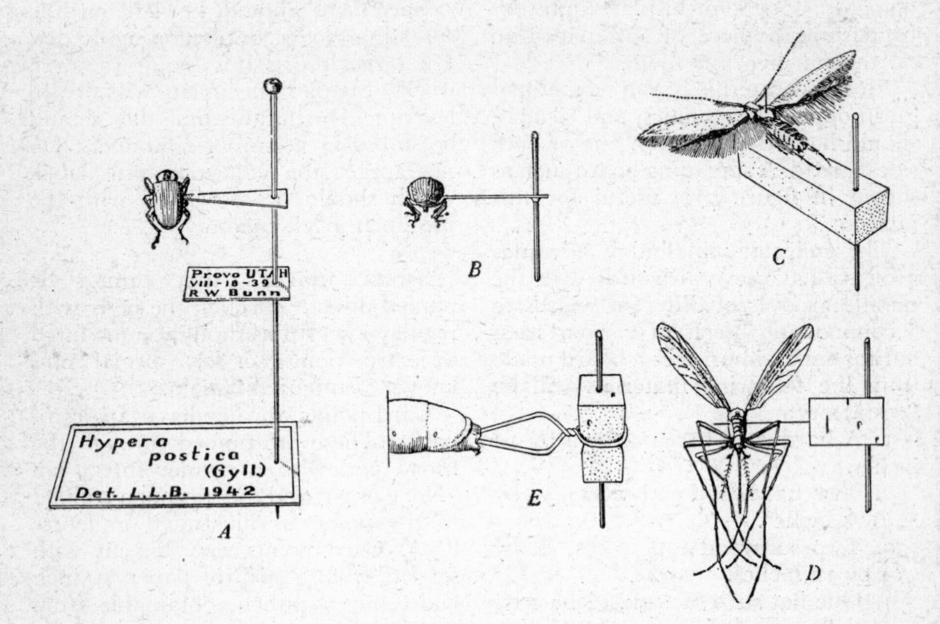

8. Double mounts for small insects: A, Position of card point and labels on the pin; B, details of attachment of specimen to card point; C, small moth, order Lepidoptera, pinned with a "minuten nadeln" to a block of pith on a regular insect pin; D, a mosquito, order Diptera, pinned with a "minuten nadeln" to a block of cork on a regular insect pin; E, method of attaching an inflated larva to a regular insect pin by twisting fine wire around a block of cork.

should be attached by the right side, although there are a few exceptions to this rule. A convenient method is to arrange the insects on their backs or left sides with their heads toward the worker; then, with the pin held in the left hand, touch a bit of adhesive to the bent point and apply it to the right side of the insect. If the tip of the point can be slipped between the body of the insect and an adjacent leg, a stronger mount will result. The insect should be attached to the point by the side of the thorax, not by the wing, abdomen, or head.

Some insects, too heavy to be held on the point by the adhesive and not large enough to be pinned with regular pins, may be attached to card points by puncturing the right side at the place where the card point would normally be placed and inserting in this puncture the tip of an unbent card point with a little adhesive on it. For puncturing specimens, a needle ground to make a small, sharp scalpel is best.

Minuten nadeln are very small steel pins without heads. They are used to pin small insects on a piece of cork or pith, which is then pinned on a regular insect pin, as illustrated in figure 8, C, D. They should never be used for hard-bodied insects (beetles, bugs).

As with direct pinning, insects mounted on double mounts should be prepared according to standard practices. For the commoner groups these are:

1. Beetles, bugs, leafhoppers, etc.: Mount on card points with the tip bent down and attached to the right side of the specimen (fig. 8, A, B).

2. Small parasitic wasps: Mount on unbent card points with the adhesive applied to the left side of the specimen and the feet toward the pin.

3. Small moths: Mount on minuten nadeln thrust through the middle of the thorax from above and with the abdomen of the specimen toward the insect pin (fig. 8, C).

4. Small flies and mosquitoes: Pin with minuten nadeln through the side of the thorax with the right side of the specimen toward the insect pin (fig. 8, D). Some workers prefer small flies fastened directly to regular insect pins by a bit of adhesive applied to the right side of the specimen.

Insects that have dried after being killed in a cyanide bottle must be relaxed before they are mounted. This can easily be done in a relaxing jar made as follows: Into a wide-mouth jar or can with a tight cover put an inch or two of clean sand; saturate the sand with water to which a few drops of phenol (carbolic acid) have been added to keep mold from growing; cover the sand with a piece or two of cardboard cut to fit the jar, and it is ready for use. Specimens must not come in direct contact with the water and should not be left in the relaxer too long or they will be spoiled. From 1 to 3 days is usually enough. A relaxer should not be left where it will get too warm, or it will sweat on the inside.

Temporary labels giving essential information as to date and place of collection should be attached to specimens during preparation and mounting. Before they are put away in the collection, they should be given permanent labels, placed on the pin or in the vial. These labels are small, and the data on them must be restricted to the most important information. Additional information about the specimen or specimens may be kept in field notes, associated with the proper material by means of lot numbers or some other convenient system. When specimens are sent for identification they should always be accompanied by all available information.

The following information should be given on the label or labels for each specimen: Locality (usually a place shown on a good map); the day, month, and year when collected; the name of the collector; and, if known, the host, food plant, or material attacked.

Permanent labels should be on good-quality paper, heavy enough so that it will stay flat when the labels are cut out, of a texture that it will not come loose on the pin, and with a surface that can be written on with a fine pen. The ink should be permanent and should not run if the labels are placed in jars containing liquid preservative.

The size of the pin labels will depend somewhat on the insects for which they are intended. Very small labels, necessary for small specimens mounted on points, are not suitable for large moths, butterflies, cicadas, etc., because they cannot be easily read when pinned below these large-bodied insects. Large labels, suitable for the larger insects, take up too much room in the collection if used for small specimens. Labels printed with 4-point type or diamond type will be found suitable for most purposes. Labels may also be made any size by printing a few of them in strips in large type, having an etching made at the desired reduction, and printing the desired number of labels from the etching.

Labels should be attached so that they are balanced with the mounted specimen. Figure 8, A illustrates how to pin labels for specimens mounted on points; for pinned specimens the long axis of the label should coincide with the long axis of the specimen, and the left margin of the label should be toward the head of the specimen. The label may be run up on the pin to the desired height by using the pinning block; the middle step will usually give about the right height.

Standard equipment for housing the collection assures uniformity of containers when additions are necessary. It is obtainable from any of several reliable supply houses.

970134°—52——7

Material preserved in liquid need receive no attention other than replacement of preservative and corks. Vials should be examined periodically to be sure the specimens do not become dry. Small vials may be stored in racks in such a way that the corks are not in constant contact with the liquid; this also expedites arrangement and examination of the material. Vials that cannot be inspected frequently should have the corks replaced with cotton plugs and be placed upside down in a jar large enough to hold several vials, and the jar partially filled with the preservative.

Pinned specimens should be housed in pestproof boxes. Standard insect boxes, called Schmitt boxes, are recommended. If other boxes, such as cork-lined cigar boxes, are used, they must be examined frequently for evidence of pest damage and fumigated periodically. Even pestproof boxes should be fumigated occasionally, lest a pest gain entrance and damage all the specimens. Most entomological institutions store their collections in glass-top drawers fitted with cork-lined trays of various sizes which can be shifted and arranged without the necessity of repinning specimens.

A few simple precautions against museum pests, such as carpet beetles, are a necessary part of the care of material not preserved in liquid. Naphthalene, in the form of ordinary moth balls or flakes, is inexpensive and satisfactory as a repellent, but it will not kill pests once they have gained access to the collection. To kill pests it is necessary to use some fumigant such as paradichlorobenzene (PDB), carbon disulfide, ethylene dichloride, or carbon tetrachloride. Carbon disulfide is probably the most widely used and is effective, but it is inflammable and explosive when mixed with air in certain proportions, it has an unpleasant odor, and it will stain insect boxes.

A small amount of naphthalene or paradichlorobenzene may be included in each box of specimens, either in a cloth bag or a small box with a perforated top firmly pinned in the corner. Naphthalene in the form of moth balls may be pinned in the box by attaching the ball to an ordinary pin. To do this, heat the head of the pin, force it into the moth ball, and permit it to cool. Liquid fumigants may be used without the danger of staining the boxes by saturating a cotton plug and placing it in a short, wide-mouthed vial pinned in the corner.

Adult insects intended for a collection or submitted for identification (to Federal, State, or county entomological authorities, for example) should not be shipped alive without a permit from the United States Department of Agriculture.

Pupae or larvae sent for rearing should be enclosed in tight containers, such as tin salve boxes or mailing cases. Pupae preferably should be packed loosely in moist (but not wet) moss. Larvae should be packed with enough food material to last until they arrive at the destination.

Bulky insects, or pieces of host plants bearing insects such as scale insects, should be partly or completely dried before being placed in a container or should be packed in a container that will permit drying to continue after closure.

Mounted insects should be firmly pinned in a box securely lined with cork or some other suitable material.

Vials should be wrapped separately in strong paper and then packed in a mailing case or strong box with cotton or cellucotton around them.

Do not put loose naphthalene or paradichlorobenzene in either pill boxes or insect boxes that are being shipped. Never send insects in ordinary envelopes.

PAUL W. OMAN *received his academic training at the University of Kansas and the George Washington University. He joined the division of insect identification of the Bureau of Entomology and Plant Quarantine in 1930. He began a period of military duty in 1950.*

Insects as Helpers

Insect Friends of Man

F. C. Bishopp

We must spend some time in our gardens watching insects at work to appreciate how they cooperate in giving us food, flowers, and comfort and to know that insects are not all bad.

Some insects improve soil. Air penetrates the soil through the burrows of ants, grubs, beetles, and wild bees.

These burrowing hordes also bring earth to the surface from the deeper soil layers and thus aid in improving its physical condition and in burying decaying vegetable matter. The grubs, or larvae, of many wood-inhabiting beetles, ants, termites, and minute insects (like the springtails) are constantly at work, tearing to pieces leaves, twigs, and trunks of fallen trees so that they may be returned to the soil to provide nutrients for other plant growth.

Insects hasten the decay of animal bodies and their return to the soil. Thus they figure in the endless cycle that involves all life. Not that the insects engaged in soil-forming activities are wholly beneficial. Some, like white grubs and cicadas, in their young stages may damage plants by feeding on the roots and (as adults) by attacking the stems, twigs, leaves, or fruit. Others, such as blow fly maggots, after they have done their work of carrion disposal and soil penetration may become disease-bearing flies.

Some other helpful insects we call predators and parasites.

The predators are the lions and tigers of the insect world. Some devour a large part or all of their prey. Others, such as the ant-lions, merely suck the body fluids.

The predatory insects of greatest economic importance are the dragonflies, damselflies, aphis-lions, ground beetles, lady beetles, and syrphid flies. Among the many other predators are the ant-lions or doodle-bugs, robber flies, snipe flies, tiger beetles, and wasps and ants.

Dragonflies and damselflies are interesting and familiar. There are about 2,000 known species, 300 of which occur in the United States. The gauzy-winged, brilliantly colored creatures called dragonflies, devil's-darning-needles, or mosquito hawks live around ponds, lakes, and swamps. Their enormous eyes, made up of as many as 20,000 sight units, or facets, occupy a large part of the head and are so curved as to permit the insect to see in all directions at once. A network of veins covers the two pairs of large, rigidly extended wings.

Its highly developed eyes and speedy flight enable the dragonfly to catch in flight the mosquitoes and other small insects that are its only food. In flight the legs form a sort of basket into which the small insects are scooped. The dragonfly, while still on the wing, promptly devours the insects with its stout jaws, which work sidewise. Among our dragonflies is the big green darner, *Anax junius*.

The dragonflies are fast fliers and may travel far. Some of the larger species commonly hunt several miles from their breeding grounds. They migrate long distances when swamps dry up. Migrations from Australia to Tasmania, 200 miles away, have been recorded.

The damselflies are smaller and more delicate than the dragonflies, flit about more leisurely, and fold the wings on the back when at rest. They prey on small, soft-bodied insects.

The young of dragonflies and damselflies, known as nymphs or naiads, destroy mosquitoes and other insects in the water. These strange-looking creatures live among the debris of stones on the bottom of streams and ponds. They have an odd, jointed extension of the under lip, or labium, which folds over the mouth parts but can be suddenly extended to grasp prey with its two powerful hooks.

The tiny naiads usually grow to full size, 1 to 2 inches long, in several months, but some species may spend 3 or 4 years in this stage. When it is grown, the naiad crawls out of the water on a stick or stone. When it has dried off, the skin splits down the back, and the head, thorax, netted wings, legs, and finally the long abdomen are drawn out. Soon the beautiful wings are spread, the metallic colors appear, and the new predatory life begins.

The aphis-lions are among the most helpful insects of prey. There are 15 families in this group of nerve-winged insects. All are predaceous. Among them are the dobsonflies; the ant-lions, or doodle-bugs; and the aphis-lions, or golden-eyed lacewings.

The aphis-lions are in gardens everywhere. They destroy many kinds of destructive insects, the eggs of many caterpillars, all stages of plant-feeding mites, scale insects, aphids, and mealybugs.

Aphis-lions are the young, or larvae, of delicate, gauzy-winged insects with rather long antennae and beautiful golden eyes. These lacewings often are seen crawling about on the leaves or flying rather clumsily from plant to plant. The many species have similar habits and general appearance. Some are pale green. Others are brownish. The adult lacewing usually lives 4 to 6 weeks. In that time the female may lay several hundred eggs.

To keep the ravenous little aphis-

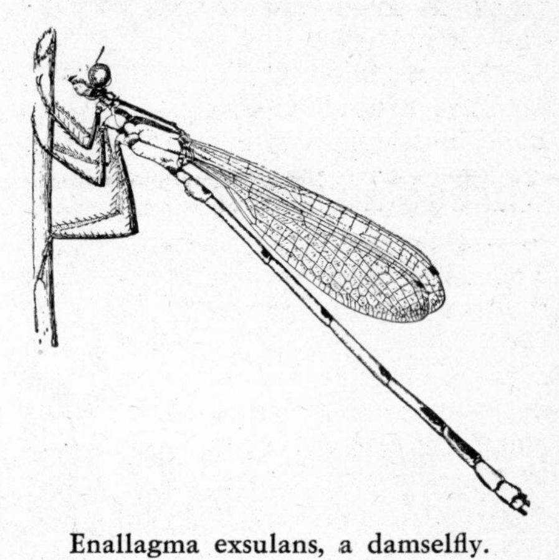

Enallagma exsulans, a damselfly.

lion that first hatches from devouring its brothers and sisters before they hatch (and perhaps to give protection from other enemies), the mother lacewing lays each oval egg on the top of a delicate stalk projecting from the surface of a leaf or twig. The incubation period is 6 to 14 days. The larvae are odd, grayish-brownish creatures. They have a rather broad abdomen and conspicuous curved jaws, which extend forward from the head. With its pincerlike jaws the larva seizes its prey and sucks out its body juices.

When the larvae attain full growth, in 2 or 3 weeks, they spin oval, yellowish-white pea-sized cocoons on a leaf. The larva in its spinning operations tops off each cocoon with a circular cap, which the pupa pushes off when it is ready to become an adult. The change to the adult stage takes 1 to 3 weeks in warm weather.

Praying mantids are odd-looking relatives of the grasshoppers. The name comes from the attitude they assume as they rest on twigs or stalk their prey.

The Chinese mantis is 4 inches long

and can capture, hold, and devour large insects. Since it came into the United States about 1896, it has spread through much of the East. Like all members of its family, it lives on insects in its nymphal and adult stages. The mantid is cannibalistic. The female devours the male with which she mates and often eats her own young.

The eggs, laid in rather large masses, are firmly attached to twigs of trees. Each mass contains 50 to 400 eggs. A female often deposits 3 to 6 masses. Winter is passed in the egg stage. There is usually only one generation a year. The young resemble the adults except that they have no wings.

LADY BEETLES have habits that are anything but ladylike. Both the young and adult beetles kill and greedily eat various soft-bodied insects. Most familiar are the bright reddish-yellow species, which has black spots on the wing covers, or elytra, and the black species, which has red spots. Less well known are the numerous minute black species. Not many persons associate the rather clumsy-looking dark-colored larvae with the bright-colored adults. Neither do gardeners, familiar with the Mexican bean beetle and the squash beetle and their depredations, recognize them as lady beetles gone astray. Many of the lady beetles are native to the United States. Their combined action in destroying the eggs and young of destructive aphids, scales, and other soft-bodied plant-feeding insects is of great value to those who raise crops and flowers.

Sometimes they are called lady birds, as in the old rhyme: "Lady bird, lady bird! Fly away home! Your house is on fire, your children do roam."

The eggs of lady beetles are oval and yellow or orange. They are laid in small masses, usually on the under side of leaves, and hatch in a few days. The young larva, with its six long legs and tubercle-covered body, starts in search for soft insects. It devours one aphid after another. In about 20 days it becomes full-grown and is about one-fourth inch long. It then attaches itself to a leaf or stem by the tip of its abdomen, draws itself up, and pupates. The cast skin often remains more or less over the pupa. The adult splits the pupal skin and crawls forth to make further inroads on the fast-multiplying aphids. Some species congregate in great masses in the fall and spend the winter in that way in some protected place.

The vedalia, the small, reddish-brown Australian lady beetle, has done yeoman service against the cottony-cushion scale on fruit trees in the United States, Hawaii, New Zealand, and other countries into which it was imported to do just that. We tell more about the vedalia on page 380.

Syrphid flies help in the pollination of crops. The sluglike larvae of many species are effective killers of various plant pests, especially aphids. The flies usually are brightly colored. Some have banded bodies and buzz loudly in flying, so they are often mistaken for bees. The eggs are laid on the leaves near aphid colonies. Even the newly hatched larvae capture and destroy aphids.

Adults and larvae of many other groups of the true flies prey upon other insects and are of value in reducing pest damage.

THE PARASITIC INSECTS are less spectacular in their work than the predatory ones but are more interesting and helpful to man. Several groups of insects contain species that are parasitic on other insects. The most abundant and important of these are two-winged flies and the wasps.

Parasites attack insects of all types in all stages of development. The host is not killed at once. Usually the larva of the parasite enters the body of its host and feeds on its tissues until it is nearly grown; then the host dies. The parasite may then pupate within the dead body or emerge and pupate on or nearby the remains of the host insect.

Tachinid flies resemble large, bristly house flies. The many species prey on a wide variety of insects, especially caterpillars. The flies are seen frequently about flowers, feeding on the nectar. Most of the species lay eggs, but some deposit maggots. The eggs are usually attached to the skin of the host. On hatching, the maggot penetrates the skin. A caterpillar may be killed by a single fly larva, or it may serve as host for a dozen or more.

Some species lay their eggs on the soil, and newly hatched maggots seek a host, penetrate its body, and develop within it. The troublesome European earwig is heavily parasitized by a fly of this type. Other species oviposit on the leaves of plants. When a caterpillar eats the leaf, the small eggs are swallowed, the maggots hatch, bore through the wall of the digestive tract, and develop in the body cavity.

Compsilura concinnata, a fly imported from Europe to combat the gypsy moth and brown-tail moth, inserts its young into the caterpillar. The fly has been found to develop in the larvae of about 100 different species of destructive caterpillars, which it checks effectively.

The flesh flies are a large family. Some are small and some are rather large and gray. They have varied habits. Some are parasites of warm-blooded animals. Others are scavengers. Many are parasitic on many kinds of insects, some of which are serious crop pests. All flesh flies deposit living young.

The grasshopper maggot, a parasite of grasshoppers, is a member of this family. The adult fly emerges in spring from the soil where it has spent the winter as a pupa, soon mates, and begins depositing its maggots on grasshoppers, usually while the grasshopper is in flight. The fly darts at a hopper in the air and attaches one of its minute sticky maggots to its host. The larva bores in; when it is fully developed, the host dies. The large maggot then crawls out and enters the soil to pupate.

Wasps feed mostly on other insects. The yellow-jackets eat vegetable matter, such as overripe fruit, and soft-bodied insects, the juice of which they feed to their young. Both yellow-jackets and the larger wasps, reddish to mahogany in color and known as *Polistes,* kill such destructive caterpillars as the corn earworm and armyworm. The yellow-jackets build large, globular, enclosed paper nests on buildings, in trees or shrubs, or in underground cavities. The *Polistes* build flat, open nests in similar situations. They can be a nuisance about houses because they sting viciously when they are molested. The benefits derived from the predacious habits of the *Polistes* outweigh their objectionable traits.

These wasps are social. Their families are made up of males, females, and sterile workers. Usually the fertilized females of *Polistes* pass the winter in protected places like attics while the yellow-jackets overwinter in protected places out of doors. In the spring they start a small paper nest, lay eggs in its cells, and rear a small number of workers, which continue to build more cells and largely take over the care of the young. During a season a *Polistes* nest may become 6 to 8 inches in diameter and house several hundred wasps; the yellow-jacket family may reach several thousand.

The mud daubers, thread-waisted wasps, and digger wasps are not social. The mud daubers construct nests of mud in buildings or other protected places and store them with soft-bodied insects or spiders, upon which the young feed. The other two groups of wasps I mentioned make individual nests in the soil or in logs and store them with insects or spiders. In this group are the so-called tarantula killers and horse guards. Horse guards do much good by catching horse flies, horn flies, and stable flies on livestock.

The parasitic wasps help man by combatting destructive insects of practically all kinds. Like other parasitic and predatory insects, however, they do not confine themselves to injurious insects. Some direct their attack against other parasitic insects and are called secondary parasites.

The appearance, host relations, and

other habits of the parasitic wasps are varied beyond the possibility of generalizing about them. Typically, the adults have four wings, usually clear, with various types of veins. The body color is mostly brown or black. The wasps differ greatly in size. Some are so small that several may develop within an insect egg no larger than a pinhead. Others have a body length of 2 inches or more.

Lysiphlebus testaceipes ovipositing in an aphid.

Among the parasitic wasps are diverse types of reproduction and host relations. Females of some species in several families reproduce generation after generation without males. Others have both sexes in certain generations. In general, virgin females produce female offspring. Among the wasplike parasites two to a dozen or more individuals may develop from a single egg—a phenomenon known as polyembryony. It occurs in several families of this group. Their reproductive capacity often is enormous. A number of species deposit several hundred eggs a day and lay a total of 1,000 to 1,500. In some species the developmental cycle may be completed in 5 to 10 days. If suitable hosts are present, therefore, the number of offspring of a single female might reach millions in one season.

Certain species of parasitic wasps attack only one species of insect or are restricted to closely related species as hosts. Many, though, will attack a great variety of hosts. Some species of parasites lay their eggs in the egg of the host, and the larvae do not complete development until the host has reached larval maturity or has pupated.

Lysiphlebus testaceipes, a useful and readily observed parasite, is a slender but industrious little insect that destroys millions of aphids. It becomes very active on sunny days. Then it scurries about among the aphids on a leaf and stops here and there to tap an aphid with its antennae. Afterwards, it thrusts its ovipositor into the aphid with a quick motion and deposits an egg within. The aphid shows no ill effects for about 3 days, when it stops reproducing. Soon the rapidly developing parasite larva devours the vital organs of the aphid.

The minute egg parasites are extremely numerous and of great economic importance. One of these, *Trichogramma minutum,* which destroys the eggs of many of our most injurious pests, such as the cotton leafworm, bollworm, codling moth, and sugarcane borer, has been propagated and released by the millions in infested fields and groves. There is doubt, however, as to the degree of control these parasites can achieve.

Insects are indispensable as pollinizers of plants. Many insects serve us in this way—thrips, butterflies, ants, beetles, flies, wasps, and bees.

The chapters that follow give details of this vital subject, but it is hardly

Trichogramma minutum female stinging a moth egg and placing its own egg within it.

amiss to give some of the main points here, too.

Some 50 seed and fruit crops depend on honey bees or yield more satisfactorily because of their presence. Some, such as red and white clover, onions, most varieties of apples, sweet cherries, and plums, would be barren without insect pollinators.

A strong colony of honey bees may contain 60,000 or more workers. An estimated 37,000 loads of nectar are required to make a pound of honey; the bees in a colony, each making 10 field trips a day, would visit 300,000 flowers a day. Thus honey bees are more important in fertilizing crops than in producing honey—even though 200 million pounds of honey and 4 million pounds of wax are produced each year in the United States.

Beeswax, extensively used in industry and the arts, is secreted as thin scales or flakes by glands on the under side of the abdomen of the worker bee. The bee uses wax to make the comb, in which honey is stored and the young reared. The artistry and engineering ability of the bee can be appreciated by noting the perfection of the hexagonal cells and the evenness of their delicate walls in a section of comb honey.

In every colony there are three forms, the queen or female, drones or males, and workers. The workers, imperfectly developed females, are most numerous and do all the work. The drones are somewhat larger than the workers, devoid of stings, and few in number. They appear most plentifully in the early summer at swarming time, after which the workers drive them out of the hives.

The queen is much larger than the worker bees and her sole duty is to lay eggs. During the 2 or 3 years of her existence she may lay as many as a million eggs. These are placed in the bottom of newly cleaned and polished cells and hatch into minute white, legless grubs, or larvae, in 3 days.

The cells are capped by the workers, and the larvae spin their cocoons and pupate. In this quiet stage the larva transforms to the winged insect in about 12 days. Thus the development from egg to adult takes 21 days. Drones require 24 days and queens only 16. The worker bee, on reaching maturity, cuts out the cell cap and crawls out. For a time it is relatively inactive. Then it becomes a nurse or house bee and helps care for its sisters. Later it takes up the work as a field bee. Some field bees gather nectar. Others collect pollen, which is tucked into the pollen baskets formed of hairs on the outside of the tibia of the hind legs.

The place of bees in agriculture is coming to be recognized, and more attention is being given to the use of honey bees in the replacement of wild bees as crop pollinizers. Intensive cultivation of land and the general use of insecticides are rapidly eliminating native pollinating insects. Increasing the number of hives of honey bees and the numerical strength of those colonies is a means of overcoming this deficiency in our agriculture.

An example of the unusual relations of insects to plants—the delicate balance between plants and their pollinators—is that of the minute fig wasp and the Smyrna fig. The fig is a fleshy, hollow, pear-shaped growth, which contains hundreds of minute flowers lining the interior surfaces of a cavity. The cavity has a tiny opening at the apex, the free end. The Smyrna fig produces only female flowers and no pollen. Before 1900 the Smyrna figs produced in the United States were inferior to those grown in Asia Minor. An investigation revealed that this was due to the absence in California of the minute, wasplike insects that serve as pollinators of the Asiatic figs, their sole agent of pollination. The insects develop in wild inedible figs known as caprifigs, which produce only male flowers with an abundance of pollen and which are the parent stock of our edible figs. The male insects are wingless and never leave the fruit in which they develop. They find a female still in a gall-like formation within the fig, puncture this cell, and fertilize the female. She then gnaws her way out and in escaping from the fig becomes covered with pollen. She is winged and flies about seeking a place to lay her eggs. She enters Smyrna figs as well as caprifigs if they grow near each other. The Smyrna figs are not suitable for the development of the fig wasp, but pollen from her body accomplishes fertilization of the fig flowers and the development of a delicious fruit.

Repeated efforts to introduce the fig wasps from Asia Minor into California were finally successful. Recently these wasps began causing trouble by carrying a disease, brown rot, from the wild figs to the Smyrnas. This was met by rearing the fig wasps by millions in incubators free from the disease and liberating them in the fig orchards.

MOST SCALE INSECTS are injurious because they suck the juices from many of our cultivated plants. Some, however, have been turned to our benefit.

The lac insect, *Laccifer lacca,* is one. It lives on trees of the fig family, commonly in the East Indies, Malay, and India. The minute young lac insect, or crawler, finds a suitable place on a twig, or branch, inserts its beak into the plant tissue, grows, and secretes a resinous material, which ultimately covers it. The thousands of crawlers settle side by side, and the resinous secretion builds up around them and completely encases the twig. Most of the crawlers develop in about 3 months into females, which occupy small cavities in the resinous mass and from which they never escape. The males emerge and fertilize the females through the small openings which extend to the surface of the encrustation. As the eggs develop in the body of the female, she assumes a saclike, bright-red appearance. The red pigment is the source of the lac dye of commerce. The female dies, the eggs hatch, the crawlers escape and move to a nearby uninfested part of the twig, and the process is repeated.

The largest yields of lac and dye are obtained by harvesting the infested twigs while the females are still living. That is done twice a year, about June and November. The encrusted twigs are known as stick lac. About 40 million pounds of the material are harvested each year. The stick lac is ground, largely in crude mortars. The resulting granular lac is called seed lac; the fine particles are molded into toys and ornaments, and the wood is used for fuel. The seed lac is then washed, melted, spread out in a thin layer, and dried, thus forming the shellac of commerce. Many people of India depend upon the lac industry for a living.

The red dye from the lac insects is little used today. It is made by evaporating the water in which the seed lac is washed.

A dye formerly widely used in industry, known as cochineal, is made from the dried, pulverized bodies of an insect related to the lac insect. It lives on a cactus or pricklypear. Cochineal is used mainly in cosmetics, as a coloring for beverages, and in decorating cakes and pastries. It used to be prized as a dye for textiles because of its permanence.

Cochineal is produced mainly in Honduras, the Canary Islands, and Mexico. The insects are kept over winter on cactus plants in houses. In spring the females are transferred to cacti outdoors and can be harvested in 3 months. About 70,000 insects are required to make a pound of dye.

GALLS are peculiar growths produced by a number of insects. They usually damage somewhat the plants they attack, but some kinds are used as a source of dyes and tanning materials and for medicines.

The Aleppo gall, or gallnut, produced by a wasplike insect on several species of oaks in western Asia and eastern Europe, has been used for centuries as a tonic, astringent, and antidote for certain poisons. The early Greeks used it for dyeing wool, mohair, and skins.

Other galls have been used for dyeing fabrics and as a tattoo dye. The Aleppo gall is used for preparing a permanent type of ink. It has been specified in formulas for ink by the United States Treasury and the Bank of England.

SILK originates in the spittle of an insect. In China and Japan, thousands of families care for silkworms as a part of their daily activities during the summer months.

The silk industry began in China, where the source of silk was kept a secret for more than 2,000 years. Attempts to take silkworm eggs out of the country were punishable by death. A few eggs were smuggled out of China about A. D. 555 and taken to Constantinople. Since that time commercial production has sprung up in some of the warmer countries, but the industry has been confined largely to China, Japan, India, and the Mediterranean region.

Sericulture has been attempted in the United States and interest in it is considerable. Silkworms can be raised and mulberry trees grown successfully here, but a tremendous amount of hand labor is involved and Americans must compete with the low labor costs in China, Japan, and India. Silk also must now compete in price with synthetic fibers, which can be produced at relatively low cost. Men in the Department of Agriculture conducted experiments with silk culture in 1884–91 and 1902–8. That work and many commercial undertakings in different parts of the country proved the impracticability of silk culture in the United States.

The silkworm is the larva, or caterpillar, of the moth *Bombyx mori.* Man has taken care of it so long that it has become thoroughly domesticated. The ashy-white moth has a fat body and a wing expanse of about 2 inches. It takes no food and seldom attempts to fly. After mating, the female deposits 300 to 400 round, yellow eggs, which soon become gray or lilac and paler as hatching time approaches.

At summer temperatures, the eggs hatch in 10 days. The larval stage requires 30 to 40 days, during which four molts occur. The baby worms are one-eighth inch long, and the full-grown caterpillar is fully 3 inches long. It is grayish or creamy in color and hairless. It has a hump behind the head and a spinelike horn at the tail. When full-grown, the larvae become restless and, if they are given a suitable place, such as dried brushy plants, they soon begin to spin their cocoons. The operation takes about 3 days of constant motions of the head from side to side at the rate of about 65 a minute. The cocoon is formed from a secretion from two large glands that extend along the inside of the body and open through a common duct on the lower lip. As the clear viscous fluid is exposed to the air it hardens into the fine silk fiber. The filament forming a cocoon is continuous and ranges in length from 800 to 1,200 yards. The cocoons are oval and vary in color, according to strain or race, from white to a beautiful golden yellow.

The larva pupates within the cocoon. In about 2 weeks the moth escapes through an opening in the end of the cocoon. The cocoons from which the moths emerge are called pierced cocoons. They are of low value because they cannot be reeled, but they are carded and made into thread.

For rearing moths, the cocoons are usually strung on a thread and hung in a cool, dark place until the moths emerge. The males and females are then put on cheesecloth, where they mate and where the eggs are deposited and adhere lightly to the cloth.

The race of silkworms most commonly used produces only one generation of worms a year, but other races produce two and still others produce several. The eggs are held in cold storage until they are to be hatched. An ounce of eggs will produce 30,000 to 35,000 worms, which will yield 100 to 120 pounds of fresh cocoons. The cocoons produce 10 to 12 pounds of raw silk.

Mulberry leaves are used almost entirely as food for silkworms. The white mulberry, *Morus alba,* is the preferred species. Foliage of Osage-orange has been used as a substitute. Lettuce leaves are sometimes used when the larvae are small.

The rearing of silkworms is laborious. The larvae are kept in a rearing house on trays in constant shade at a temperature between 65° and 78° F. They are first fed on chopped mulberry leaves supplied about eight times a day. After 4 or 5 days, fresh leaves are put in a tray with bobbinet bottom. On it is placed the tray that contains the larvae. They soon crawl up onto the fresh food. As they grow, the larvae are transferred frequently to fresh leaves on clean trays. They consume a surprising quantity of leaves, which must always be dry. Wet leaves or other adverse conditions favor the development of certain diseases which often take a heavy toll of the silkworms.

For reeling silk, the cocoons are gathered about 8 days after spinning begins, and the pupae are killed, usually with heat, and thoroughly dried. They are assorted and are ready for reeling. Reeling also involves much hand work, although recently developed reels work largely automatically. The cement holding the fibers together is loosened by putting the cocoons into boiling water. After the loose strands have been removed by a revolving brush the cocoons are put in warm water and the filament from four or five of them is caught up and twisted into a thread which is wound on a reel. This raw silk is removed from the reel in 2-ounce hanks, which are weighed and baled.

INSECTS do not feed entirely on plants we are interested in growing. Many kinds feed on weeds. Certain species of this sort have been introduced with beneficial results into regions where some plant has become a serious nuisance.

The control of pricklypear by insects in Australia is an example of what can be accomplished in this way at low cost. About 1787 cactus plants were taken to Australia by Capt. Arthur Phillip for culturing cochineal insects for dye. Various species of cacti escaped later from gardens so that by 1925 some 20 different kinds were found growing wild. In the absence of natural enemies the pricklypears spread rapidly. By 1925 about 60 million acres were affected, half of it so densely covered as to make the land useless.

Australia established a Commonwealth Prickly Pear Board in 1920 and sent entomologists to America, the original home of these cacti, to study the insect enemies and methods of rearing and shipping them to Australia. This work was continued in North and South America in cooperation with American entomologists from 1920 to 1937, during which time more than a half million insects of 50 different species were dispatched to Australia. Several were successfully established, including cochineal insects, a large plant bug, a moth borer, and a spider mite. The insects checked the new growth of cactus and reduced the density of the plants so that some grass was returning. It was not until 1930, however, when 3 billion eggs of a moth, *Cactoblastis cactorum,* from Argentina had been released throughout the territory, that the hope of controlling the pest began to be realized. Seven years after the first introduction of this moth the last dense growth of pricklypear was destroyed and the land reclaimed and opened to settlement and livestock production.

The total cost was about £168,600, or a fraction of a penny an acre—a modest figure as compared with £10 per acre for the much less satisfactory chemical and mechanical procedure previously used.

F. C. BISHOPP, *a native of Colorado, has been conducting or directing research in the Bureau of Entomology and Plant Quarantine on insects since 1904. Since 1941 he has been assistant chief of the Bureau.*

Honey Bees as Agents of Pollination

George H. Vansell, W. H. Griggs

Plants have sexes somewhat as animals do. Many plants carry both the male and female elements on the same individual. Other plants have the sex organs in separate plants—that is, a plant may be strictly male or female. In any case, pollen from the male part of the plant must come in contact with the female element if seed is to result.

Reproduction is the sole function of a flower. In a typical flower the essential female parts, regardless of their variable form and number, are ovary, style, and stigma. The ovary, the basal part, becomes the fruit. The style is a column of tissue arising from the top of the ovary. The expanded or otherwise modified tip of the style is the stigma. In many plants the surface of the stigma has a sticky secretion to which the pollen adheres. In a typical male part of the flower, the anther simply produces pollen, which is the functional male sex element.

Pollination is the transfer of pollen from the anther to the stigma or the distribution of pollen. Pollination must be accomplished before fertilization (the union of the male germ cell, contained in the pollen grains, with the female germ cell or egg in the ovary) and eventual reproduction can take place.

If pollen is transferred from an anther to the stigma of the same flower or to the stigma of another flower on the same plant, self-pollination is said to have taken place. The transfer of pollen from an anther to the stigma of a flower of another individual plant is spoken of as cross-pollination. Those are botanical definitions and do not consider the varietal factor, which is of such great importance to fruit production. Self-pollination, as used in fruit production, also includes the transfer of pollen from the anthers of a flower of one variety to the stigma of a flower of the same variety. Cross-pollination, in the horticultural sense, refers to the transfer of pollen from the flower of one variety to a flower of a different variety.

Charles Darwin, the English naturalist, concluded from his observations and exhaustive experiments with many plant families that plants resulting from cross-pollination generally had greater vigor, weight, and height and produced flowers earlier than those resulting from self-pollination. It has since been shown that the advantages of cross-pollination and the disadvantages of self-pollination are not always so decisive as Darwin supposed. Nevertheless, there is a long list of species and varieties of plants that are self-sterile and require cross-pollination; the advantages of hybrid vigor in some modern cropping practices also is well established.

Darwin listed several ways in which plants are constructed to avoid self-pollination and insure cross-pollination:

1. By the separation of the sexes, in which staminate and pistillate flowers are borne on separate plants, as in the hemp, willow, holly, and date.

2. By a difference in the time of maturity of the pollen and stigma in the same flower, as in the red clover, beet, plantain, and avocado.

3. By special mechanical contrivances that prevent self-pollination or that favor insect pollination, as in many orchids, legumes, and mints.

4. By producing different forms of flowers on the same plant with different lengths of stamens and pistils, as in the Chinese primrose.

5. By complete or partial sterility of the flowers to their own pollen or the prepotency of pollen from another individual or variety over the plant's own pollen, as in lobelia, mignonette, mullein, and many varieties of apple, pear, cherry, plum, and almond.

No difficulty is encountered in the

Honey bee on comb.

pollination and fertilization of some self-fertile plants because both sexual elements develop so close together that pollen is directly deposited on the stigma. Wheat illustrates such a situation—it is self-pollinating and at the same time self-fertile. Self-fertile plants exist, however, which are wholly or partly incapable of fertilizing themselves without the aid of a transferring agent. Cantaloup is a prime example of this condition.

Other plants cannot fertilize themselves following self-pollination by a transferring agent even though both sexual parts mature at the same time. Varieties of sweet cherry and almond illustrate this situation; pollen from some other variety is required to effect fertilization. Not only are all the varieties of these fruits self-unfruitful; there are instances as well of interincompatible varieties.

Varieties of certain fruits, such as the apple, pear, and plum, produce some fruit as a response to self-pollination but not enough for a profitable crop. Such varieties are said to be partially self-fruitful. In such instances agents for the transfer of pollen between different varieties are essential for commercial production.

Even in many cases of self-fruitfulness, like the French prune, the activity of insects on the blossoms greatly increases fruit production through better pollen distribution. French prune trees, enclosed in tents, gave sets of 19.0 percent when bees were present and 0.34 percent when bees were absent. Similar results were obtained when trees of the self-fruitful sour cherry Montmorency were caged in Michigan.

It is perhaps significant that because California has such a large population of honey bees the yield of fruit, lint, and seed from many plants, such as plums, cotton, alfalfa, Ladino clover, onions, carrots, cantaloups, lima beans, and white mustard, often is outstanding.

A NUMBER OF AGENTS may be necessary for the distribution of pollen from plant to plant, because some pollens are dry and light and others are moist and heavy. The commonest agents of pollen distribution are gravity, wind, and insects. For example, corn pollen drops from the tassel to the silks. Date palm pollen is a fine dust, which floats away like fog. Pine pollen, with its bladderlike wings, is readily carried by wind. Deciduous fruit pollens are rather gummy and generally must be transferred by insects. The huge pollen grain of cotton is thickly dotted with sticky fluid, which makes it far too heavy to be carried by the wind but adapts it well to sticking to the hairs that cover the bodies of pollinating insects. Pollination may sometimes also be accomplished by rain, birds, and artificial means devised by man.

Even among many plants designated botanically as pollinated by wind and gravity, insects are sometimes a factor in the collection and distribution of pollen. For example, the pollens from bee colonies often contain liberal quantities from corn, oak, pine, walnut, ryegrass, Sudangrass, Canary

Island palm, date palm, juniper, cypress, elm, or redwood. Few of those plants, if any, produce visible nectar for the attraction of insects to the male blossom parts; therefore they are probably visited only by the pollen-collecting insects.

Fruits develop in many plants without pollination and fertilization or the subsequent development of seeds. A number of our cultivated plants regularly bear such parthenocarpic—seedless—fruits. Among them are seedless raisin grapes, English forcing cucumbers, navel oranges, bananas, pineapples, and some varieties of pears, figs, and Japanese persimmons. Sometimes mere pollination without subsequent fertilization may be sufficient to start fruit development. The application of synthetic plant hormones to the flowers and leaves has also been found to stimulate parthenocarpy in tomatoes, Smyrna figs, holly, pears, and others.

NATIVE WILD BEES (bumble bees, leaf-cutting bees, alkali bees, carpenter bees) are specially adapted for gathering pollen and nectar from flowers. Many other insects also do so—some beetles, flies, moths, thrips. In fact, any of the thousands of insects that visit flowers purposely or accidentally can be agents for carrying pollen grains from the anther to the stigma. But of all of them the most important by far is the honey bee, *Apis mellifera,* whose existence depends on pollen and nectar from plants. We estimate that bees accomplish more than 80 percent of the pollination by insects. Yields of fruits and legumes and vegetable seed often have been doubled or trebled simply by providing adequate numbers of bees.

THE HONEY BEE was introduced into the United States from Europe. Unlike the native wild bees, it is a colonial insect throughout the year and therefore is available in force at any season. Semidomestication in man-made hives makes it available for placement wherever needed for pollination service. (The native bumble bee is also colonial in summer, but only the queen survives the winter to establish a new colony in spring.)

Honey bees have a complete metamorphosis—they pass through egg, larva, pupa, and adult stages. Each colony has three types of individuals, the queen, a handful of drones, and many thousands of workers. The queen bee is the true female whose primary function is egg production. The drone, or male bee, has no function except to provide sperm when a young queen is mated. That done, the workers may drive him out of the hive. The mature workers are not sexual forms, although in the egg and early larval stages there is no difference between them and a queen. The kind of food and care given them causes them to develop into workers or queens. It is the worker that is familiar to all as the proverbial busy bee in orchards, gardens, and fields.

Honey bees require carbohydrates, proteins, fat, vitamins, and other elements for food. The carbohydrates are derived largely from the plant nectar, which is a liquid containing three kinds of sugars. Water is carried into the hive in quantity from various sources. The other requirements are met largely by plant pollens. Bees also sometimes seek out salt and possibly other minerals.

Pollen primarily is utilized for rearing and maturing young bees through the larval and early-adult phases. The food of the mature field bees is largely honey or the nectar from which honey is elaborated. In seeking those foods from blossoms, a bee inadvertently fulfills the required distribution of pollen so necessary to reproduction in plants.

AN INDIVIDUAL BEE usually visits one plant species to collect either pollen or nectar—a fortunate provision of nature, because a pollen from one species is not effective in completely fertilizing another kind of plant. For instance, pear pollen is of no use in setting fruit on a plum tree.

Various investigators watched individual bees and found that each one visited only a small area to collect a load of pollen or nectar. After the trip back to the hive, the bee repeatedly returned to the same area.

G. Bonnier one day marked all bees working on a strip of buckwheat, 3 by 16 feet in area, and found only marked bees there the next day. A. Minderhoud studied an area where bees were working clover, dandelion, and other plants. After marking all bees on areas of approximately a square yard, he recorded their movements on squared paper. The bees repeatedly returned to the same square or within a radius of 10 yards of it. C. N. Buzzard noted that bees working *Cotoneaster horizontalis* covered an area of only 2 square yards. From 15 observations of marked bees during the next 5 days, he concluded that the same bees returned to the same bush and strayed only where the branches intertwined.

Sardar Singh noted the honey bee's liking for a small area of alsike clover, birdsfoot trefoil, aster, dandelion, goldenrod, white sweetclover, and apple in New York State. Some individual bees devoted whole visits to a single apple tree and returned for later visits to the same tree. Other bees worked between adjacent trees. The ratio of observed exchanges of bees between trees 10 feet apart to trees more than 15 feet apart worked out at 2:1. Five bees (out of 66 observed) rambled over three to five trees.

In England, C. G. Butler, E. P. Jeffree, and H. Kalmus found that visitation areas on *Epilobium* were usually less than 5 yards across. C. R. Ribbands showed that foraging bees working in a garden with five different sorts of flowers usually attached themselves to a particular area of the most suitable crop found. The size of the foraging area varied considerably. He noted that bees changed their attachment from a pollen crop to a nectar crop, but never vice versa.

Karl von Frisch has reported in several publications that the scout bees, after locating a source of pollen or nectar, transmit their knowledge to other bees through an intricate system of "dances" within the colony.

Since foraging bees usually attach themselves to one species, bee pellets usually contain but one kind of pollen grain. However, A. D. Betts in England analyzed 915 pollen loads and found 3 percent were mixtures. Only seven of the loads showed distinct segregation of the grains into two separate areas. When pellets from trapped pollen were sorted out in the western United States, only a few segregated mixtures were apparent among many thousands examined.

It is presumed that the exhaustion of a source with advancing time of day may be a factor in obtaining segregated mixtures. For example, an orchard morningglory blossom opens at sunrise and closes before midday during bright, warm weather. On the other hand, redmaids (*Calandrinia ciliata*) unfold in late forenoon and are at their height during the heat of late afternoon. In this case a shift by a partially loaded bee from morningglory to redmaids would be expected. Colonies in the same apiary evidently choose different pollen sources or visit different areas because the trapped supply from one colony is frequently unlike that from another.

The abundance of pollen or its state of exhaustion in a source may greatly influence the rate of collection. Many bees have been seen to get full loads of pollen from one pistachio catkin. The number of visits reported to dandelion heads for a pollen load varied from 8 to 100 when dandelions were scarce and colonies numerous. Ribbands reported 47 foraging trips by 1 bee to Shirley poppy flowers during 1 day—indicating easy and rapid collection.

The legs of a honey bee are modified for handling pollen. An eye brush occurs on the inner surface of the front tibia. The large first tarsal joint is covered with long unbranched hairs, forming a body brush. At the base of the first tarsal joint is an instrument for cleaning the antennae. The hind legs of the worker bear the organs with which it transports two large loads of pollen from the flower to the hive. The inner surface of the large basal segment of the hind tarsus is covered with sharp, stiff spines closely arranged in transverse rows. They are particularly employed for taking the pollen from the middle tarsi and holding it until it is transferred to the pollen basket. As a bee pushes in among the anthers of a flower even for nectar, the body becomes literally covered with pollen grains.

Nectar is the sweet fluid secreted in plant blossoms. Its function presumably is to attract insects to the flowering parts. When an insect gathers nectar from a blossom, its body becomes coated with pollen grains, which are transferred later to other blossoms.

Nectars of different plants have a variable sugar content and aroma. Such factors result in visitation of different kinds of insects to the various plants. The blossom nectar of firethorn (*Pyracantha*) evidently has low attractiveness to honey bees although blow flies feed on it greedily. The peculiar odor may influence both insects—that is, repel the one and attract the other. Dermestid beetles are common on yarrow blossoms, but a honey bee is seldom seen on them.

The sugar concentration of the nectar is an important factor in plant visitation by bees. The nectar of oranges has about 16 percent sugar as the petals unfold. During a humid day, when the nectar continues at that concentration or is diluted with fog moisture along the southern California coastal belt, the honey bee displays little interest in it. Then they busily gather the scanty mustard nectar, which has a much higher sugar content. When the day is dry enough for evaporation of water to about 25 percent sugar, they collect the orange nectar. Before concentration increases to 40 percent, bees become so numerous that the blossoms are sucked dry. Then as humidity conditions change back to give little evaporation, bee activity on orange blossoms practically ceases.

At Davis, Calif., apricot nectar may be completely ignored for several days while honey bees are busy working almond blossoms. Under such conditions the apricot nectar contained less than 10 percent sugar when the almond had 35 percent or more. During a dry north wind, the apricot nectar lost water rapidly and then it, too, was collected by many bees.

Since sugar concentration of nectar affects bee activity, it likewise influences the pollination potential. In plum varieties a wide variation in the quality and quantity of nectar has been found, and the bees have been observed to prefer some plum varieties over others. Eight varieties growing in the same orchard at Davis had nectar averages ranging from 10 to 28 percent sugar. Three other varieties had no collectible nectar. The Kelsey, a notably shy bearer at Davis, was one of these.

A POLLEN GRAIN is somewhat like a plant seed in that it germinates to send out a rootlike projection, which is called a pollen tube. On the stigma of a flower the tube penetrates down the style into the ovary, where union with the egg cell occurs. Each seed produced requires one pollen-grain germination tube. In a many-seeded fruit like a watermelon, numerous pollen grains must be applied to the stigma. Fertilization could be effected in an almond blossom with one pollen grain.

Wide differences exist in the length of the style of flowers and in the time for growth of the pollen tube down it. An alfalfa pollen tube grows down the pistil and enters the ovule in a day. In some oaks the time is almost a year in growing one-eighth inch. With Indian corn the distance from the stigma at the end of the corn silk to the attachment of the silk to the young corn grain may be a foot or more, yet fertilization is effected within a few days. In the latter case the large pollen grain carries much starchy food material which makes possible the great length to which the tube grows.

The pollen grains of various plants vary greatly in size, shape, and surface structure. Some flowers produce an abundance of pollen which is fully exposed. Others produce only a scanty amount which is tightly enclosed. These differences undoubtedly affect its collection by bees. The food value also varies. Some pollen grains are evidently too sticky for easy manipulation and others are too dry. In any event, trapped pollen supplies indicate the bee's preference for some types. For example, a trap operated in a California cotton field failed to yield pollen from the cotton although it was abundant on the plants. In an almond orchard a large supply of almost pure almond pollen was readily trapped in spite of wildflower sources. Under a condition of scarcity, bees will even collect a pollen substitute like dry mash from a chicken feeder. Also, in a greenhouse they have been observed to collect tomato and beet pollens, which are ordinarily ignored outdoors. The rather omnivorous habit of honey bees of collecting pollen from so many plants, especially under stress for a supply, is radically different from that of many other bees, which require a special kind of pollen.

To a plant breeder the variety of pollen and the resulting seed within the species is a salient factor, as it is also to a grower in the case of certain self-unfruitful varieties. In many fruits, like apples, a nearly full complement of seeds is needed to produce a shapely product. To commercial cotton producers the lint is the chief thing, but there again the production of seed is important for two reasons—the production of normal lint depends upon fertile seeds, and such seeds are the source of cottonseed oil.

Producers of package bees make use of the early and abundant supplies of pollen in deciduous fruit orchards. Where that trade is established, many colonies are regularly rented to orchardists. The possibility of getting much honey from deciduous fruit blossoms is limited by their early blossoming. The quality of this honey also is generally low; for example, almond honey is bitter and prune honey readily ferments.

On the other hand, several of the summer-blossoming species of legumes, including alsike clover, white clover, sweetclover, hairy vetch, birdsfoot trefoil, and alfalfa, are sources of high-quality honeys. Red clover is usually not even considered a source of honey in the United States. Except for alfalfa, all these legumes are medium to good sources of pollen.

The chief supply of pollinators in the country is maintained by the beekeeping industry. In the past its size and extent have been based largely on the ability of the beekeeper to make a living from the production and sale of honey. There are about 6 million colonies in the United States—one-third are in the South, one-third west of the Mississippi, and the rest in the Northeast. Properly distributed, the supply of pollinators probably would be adequate to meet the needs of agriculture. In areas having concentrated plantings of specialty crops, such as deciduous fruits and small-seeded legumes, the growers must draw upon the bee industry to meet their great requirements for pollinators during blossoming time. Maintaining the industry in a healthy condition is essential to our agricultural economy.

A hive and all its bees can be moved readily by screening the entrance after the field workers come in for the night. It should be taken at least a mile and a half from the old location—otherwise many of the bees would return to the former location and thus be lost. During hot weather a ventilating wire screen may have to be substituted for the regular cover. Commercial beekeepers frequently move colonies without closing the entrance, but the novice should not attempt to do so.

After a colony is moved, the bees reorient themselves by flying close to the hive until they become familiar with their new surroundings. The habit may be made use of in pollina-

970134°—52——8

tion practice. Bees brought into an orchard at blooming time tend to work the nearby trees first, but often it may be necessary to move the colonies in ahead of the bloom. For example, an almond orchard in the West may be almost impassable from the beginning of the winter rains to the end of blossoming in early spring. Bees are ordinarily placed in such orchards following harvest in the fall because colonies are moved from the river bottoms and the mountains at that time.

Throughout the country in deciduous-fruit areas, especially where apples, sweet cherries, and plums are grown, it is common practice to rent commercial bees for pollination during blooming time. Many colonies going to fruit orchards are of local origin but some long hauls are necessary. For example, bees are moved long distances to Wenatchee, Wash., Hood River, Oreg., the Shenandoah Valley in Virginia, and the apple districts of Pennsylvania. The colonies frequently come from the neighboring States.

Developments in the small-seeded legume industry since 1945 have shown the advantage of providing more bees than are normally present. Colonies are rented and often brought in from distant places. To the seed district around Delta, Utah, with about 30,000 acres in alfalfa, 10,000 to 15,000 colonies are brought each year. Beekeeping in the area is not feasible the year around, and most of the colonies are removed to southern California after the alfalfa season, a distance of 500 miles or more. Some colonies were moved more than 1,000 miles from southern California to Colorado for alfalfa-seed pollination in 1950. A similar situation occurs in the clover-seed area of Jefferson County in Oregon, where a large acreage is grown and some 15,000 colonies were moved in in 1950. Many of the colonies came from the Sacramento Valley in California, 500 miles away. A substantial income, either from a good honey crop or from rental fees, is required to take care of the high cost of such moves.

Bees are often moved by truck in lots of approximately 100 two-story hives—perhaps 4 million potential pollinators. The truck is loaded in the evening and goes nonstop to its destination. On arrival the colonies are placed in or near the fields.

Growers of cucumbers and some other plants in greenhouses have found it necessary to supply bees for pollination. The business is rather extensive. In the production of some hybrid seeds, cages supplied with bees are in use. Colonies depreciate rapidly in both greenhouses and cages, and frequent replacement is necessary.

When a beekeeper engages his bees for pollination service he faces special problems: Extra expenses for moving and caring for the colonies, shortage of feed, and insecticidal poisoning. Ordinarily he can expect no honey in orchards, and little or no surplus honey is obtained by the large number of colonies frequently used for alfalfa. It may even be necessary to feed the colonies. The grower should make sure that enough bees are provided during the blooming period to produce the maximum set of fruit or seed.

Bee-collected pollen pellets can be obtained readily with a pollen-collecting trap consisting of a screen grid which scrapes pollen from the legs of bees as they go through it to enter their hives.

Quantities of pollen of apple, almond, cherry, plum, and pear have been collected in that way at the California Agricultural Experiment Station. During favorable periods the yields per trap approached 2 pounds daily. More than 50 pounds have been obtained from one colony in a year.

Bees add substances to the pollen to form it into pellets. Sugar—nectar or honey—is one such substance, as shown by the higher content of sugar in bee-collected pollen than in hand-collected pollen. The viability of deciduous-fruit pollen from freshly gathered bee pellets is high, but at room temperature it rapidly loses its ability to germinate. Pollen taken from the anthers by hand, however, remains viable for a longer period. The exact reason for the difference is not known.

In testing the viability of bee-pellet pollen, one can enhance germination by dispersing the pellets in a 15-percent cane sugar sirup immediately before plating on the agar medium. Smearing the dispersed grains on the plate separates them so that they may be readily counted in determining the percentage of germination.

Storage at low temperature greatly prolongs the viable life of the pollen from the pellets of honey bees as well as hand-collected pollen. Bee-collected apple pollen, removed from the trap at 30-minute intervals, frozen with dry ice, and placed in a freezing compartment in 1949, remained highly viable for a year. In the spring of 1950 the pollen was used to hand-pollinate apple blossoms in the orchard from which it was collected in 1949. Subsequently fruits were set and matured. This demonstration of stability should assure future progress in the use of bee-collected pollen in artificial pollination.

Some beekeepers trap bee-collected pollen and dry and store it for feeding their bees when pollen is scarce. The trapped pollen is sometimes shipped from areas with mild winters to Northern States where long winters make supplementary feeding necessary. Perhaps bee-collected pollen might also be valuable for medicinal purposes or as a source of vitamins. Honey contains numerous pollen grains—the age-old belief that honey is healthful may have its basis in that fact. The pollen pellets might also be beneficial in the diet of baby chicks. We believe that these and other potential uses should be investigated.

CONTROLLED ARTIFICIAL POLLINATION has been used for many years in plant-breeding work and in studies to determine the pollination requirements of our cultivated plants. The usual practice is to emasculate the blossoms of the mother variety, apply the desired pollen to the stigma, and bag the flowers to exclude insects which might bring unwanted pollen. Many superior varieties of fruit, vegetable, and field crops have been developed in this way. The method also has been used in breeding varieties of forest trees, particularly pines.

Commercial hand-pollination of dates has been practiced since ancient times. The cluster of male or staminate flowers—the spadix—is removed from the male date palm and shaken gently over the flower clusters of the female tree.

L. H. MacDaniels and A. J. Heinicke in 1929 suggested using hand-pollination as a temporary expedient in apple orchards consisting of solid blocks of self-unfruitful varieties. They also thought such pollination might be worth while in years of unfavorable weather conditions even in apple orchards well provided with pollinizing varieties. Later MacDaniels put the method on a commercial basis and developed carriers for diluting the pollen for more economical use.

About that time the pollination problem had become acute in the apple-producing sections of Washington because of the heavy spray program, which practically eliminated pollinating insects, and the removal of less profitable varieties in favor of Delicious and Winesaps, both of which are self-unfruitful. Winesap produces mostly nonviable pollen and is therefore an ineffective pollinizer for Delicious.

Washington apple growers quickly adopted the methods suggested by MacDaniels and Heinicke. By 1937 hundreds of acres of Delicious orchards were hand-pollinated in the Wenatchee and Yakima districts. More recently the trend has been to provide means for cross-pollination by insects by grafting over some Winesap and Delicious trees to pollinizing varieties, interplanting pollinator trees, and providing more bees. Most growers now make sure that their new plantings contain adequate pollinizing varieties.

Pollen for hand-pollination is obtained by gathering flowers from a variety known to be a good pollinizer for the variety in question and removing the anthers by rubbing the flowers over 8-mesh hardware cloth. Blossoms should be gathered when most of them are in the balloon stage, just before the petals open. The pollen can be cured by holding the anthers in shallow trays at room temperature for about 2 days. The cured pollen should be placed in bottles stoppered with cotton and held in a dry, cool place until it is used.

Materials such as lycopodium spores, wheat flour, cornstarch, egg albumen, and powdered milk have been used to dilute the pollen in order to reduce the cost of hand-pollination. Lycopodium spores generally have proved to be the most satisfactory carrier, although tests have shown definite promise for powdered milk and egg albumen, which cost less than lycopodium.

To hand-pollinate an apple tree in good bloom, the usual practice is to touch the stigmas of one flower in every fourth or fifth cluster. A size 4 pig-hair brush, the rubber end of a pencil, a cork, or the bare finger can be used. The pollen should be applied 1 to 3 days after the flowers open because the flowers are no longer receptive to pollination when the tips of the styles turn brown. A skilled operator can pollinate a 20-year-old apple tree in about an hour. It would take much longer to hand-pollinate a fruit tree like the sweet cherry, in which a much higher percentage of the blossoms must set fruit in order to give a commercial crop.

Regardless of how the pollen is obtained or how much it is diluted, hand-pollination is laborious and costly—especially in light of the relatively low cost of pollination by bees. One argument in favor of hand cross-pollination is that it will greatly reduce the amount of fruit thinning needed to obtain good size where natural pollinating agents are not available. According to John C. Snyder, however, the idea of reducing thinning costs does not justify the permanent use of hand-pollination as a substitute for pollinizer varieties and honey bees.

Many labor-saving methods for applying pollen have been developed and tested. Dust and liquid mixtures of pollen have been applied from airplanes and conventional spray and dusting equipment. Bombs and shotgun shells containing pollen have been used for rapid distribution of pollen. Under controlled experimental tests conducted by R. M. Bullock and F. L. Overley, however, these rapid methods have failed to give significant increases in fruit set. They concluded that hand-pollination is the most satisfactory method of artificial pollination.

A semiartificial method of cross-pollination involves pollen dispensers designed to force honey bees to pass through prepared pollen as they leave the hive. The idea is that the bees will pick up the pollen and spread it through the orchard. Overley and W. J. O'Neill tested two types of pollen dispensers and reported that their value was questionable.

During 1951 we supplied hives of bees with pollen dispensers for almond and sweet cherry trees, which were caged to exclude outside insects. Only a few fruits were set on the trees even though the dispensers were kept supplied with viable pollen throughout the blooming period and the bees actively worked the blossoms. Satisfactory fruit sets were obtained on branches of the trees to which the same pollen was applied by hand.

A PERSON COLLECTING pollen by hand can usually gather only enough green anthers from fruit blossoms in an 8-hour day to produce 3 to 5 ounces of cured pollen. But bee-collected pollen can be obtained readily in almost unlimited quantities by the use of pollen traps. The pollen pellets of the common fruit species are readily distinguished by their color. Although all bees of a colony do not visit the same species, one can get a nearly pure sample by careful selection of the time and place of trapping.

Experiments at Davis, Calif., during 1948 showed that the percentage of viability of freshly trapped pellet-pollen is approximately the same as that of hand-collected pollen. It also gave fruit sets that compared favorably with those effected by hand-collected pollen when it was applied by hand with small brushes. Diluting the bee-pollen with an equal amount of lycopodium spores hardly reduced fruit set. Although viability of this pollen is rapidly lost at room temperature, it can be maintained for several days in ordinary cold storage at about 32° F., and for a much longer period at extremely low temperatures. If handled properly, therefore, the pollen in freshly trapped pollen pellets of honey bees may serve as well as hand-collected pollen in hand-pollination.

Various methods of rapid application of the pellet-pollen have been tested. The pellets have been dispersed in water and in salt and sugar solutions. The resulting mixtures have been sprayed on almonds, sweet cherries, plums, apples, and pears. The various pellet-pollens also have been applied as dusts after they were mixed with various carrying powders. Thus far commercial fruit sets have not been obtained from such rapid methods of application. J. C. Kremer suggested that bee-collected pollen from early blooming apple varieties could be mixed with lycopodium spores and stored under dry conditions at 34° to 36°. The mixture could then be used later in pollen dispensers inserted at the entrance of bee colonies for the cross-pollination of varieties that blossom late in the spring. This method failed to give satisfactory fruit sets when tested on caged almond and sweet cherry trees at Davis during the blossoming period of 1951.

THERE IS MUCH MORE to getting results in pollination than an adequate supply of bees. The blossoms must be attractive to the pollen distributors for either pollen or nectar. For best results the specific blossoms must be more attractive than their competitors. For the self-unfruitful varieties compatible sources of pollen must be at hand. In producing seed from male-sterile varieties the same is true. The varieties providing pollen and those needing it must flower at the same time. Even after all other factors are taken into account, bad weather can cause failure by preventing insect activity. Some of those factors are brought out in the following paragraphs about some plants that need the help of insects for pollination.

Many commercial fruit varieties are propagated asexually. From the viewpoint of pollination, therefore, an orchard of a single variety is one tree, so to speak. Self-unfruitfulness in such a case creates a pollination problem that requires special consideration in the planting of an orchard.

THE ALMOND is an interesting example of self-unfruitfulness. Almonds were planted in California in 1853, but the yields of the early orchards were low and variable. The eventual failure of the first plantings was due largely to a lack of knowledge of pollination requirements and other factors of successful culture. California had 100,000 acres of almonds in 1952. According to W. P. Tufts, the pollination problem with the almond was recognized and recorded as early as 1885, when A. T. Hatch of Suisun noted that Languedoc trees growing near seedlings always produced heavier crops than those planted in solid blocks—the only plausible explanation for the many instances of crop failure was lack of cross-pollination. Tufts' early studies indicated the self-incompatibility of some varieties. Later investigations showed that all varieties were self-unfruitful and that a few pairs of varieties were interincompatible. For example, Nonpareil and I. X. L., Languedoc and Texas, and Jordanolo and Harpareil are interincompatible pairs. Combinations of those varieties therefore should be planted without putting a pollinizer with them.

The eventual recommendation was to plant the proper varieties with specific reference to pollination requirements.

Almonds may bloom from the end of January to the end of March. They may be classed as early or later in the time of blossoming. The following list gives varieties in the usual sequence of blooming from the earliest to the latest (Nonpareil is included in both groups because it occupies a position about midway): *Early*—Harriott, Jordanolo, Jordan, Ne Plus Ultra, Harpareil, King, California, Lewelling, I. X. L., Peerless, Princess, Nonpareil. *Late*—Nonpareil, Drake, Eureka, Languedoc, Texas, Reams.

Except in the instances we noted of the interincompatibility, any varieties listed as early or late will usually serve as a satisfactory pollinizer for any other variety in the same list. The blossoming periods of very early blooming varieties as Harriott and Jordanolo, however, may not overlap sufficiently in some seasons to insure adequate cross-pollination with Nonpareil. Many almond growers have planted only Jordanolo and Nonpareil because of their greater commercial value. From a pollination standpoint, however, that combination is often poor.

Because almond trees blossom early when the weather may be too cool for maximum insect activity, more bees and more trees of the pollinizing variety are needed than for later blossoming fruits. There should be at least one row of pollinizers for every three rows of the main variety. In adverse seasons it would pay to have two rows of the main variety and then two rows of the pollinizer. Two or three strong colonies of bees should be supplied per acre.

Almost all varieties of the European pear are self-unfruitful. A few (Doyenné du Comice, Flemish Beauty, Beurré Hardy, Howell) are usually self-fruitful, but even they generally will produce better crops when they are cross-pollinated. In some localities in California, Bartlett, Colonel Wilder, Beurré d'Anjou, Seckel, and Beurré Clairgeau may range from partly to completely self-fruitful in some years.

The Bartlett (or Williams' Bon Chrétien) is a widely grown variety. California had more than 36,000 acres of Bartletts in 1952. It is self-unfruitful in the East. Bartlett is said to be usually self-fruitful under interior valley and coastal conditions in California, but should not be planted without pollinizers in the Sierra Nevada foothills. Hand cross-pollination has given greatly increased fruit sets over self-pollination or open (natural) pollination, regardless of location or whether the trees were planted in solid blocks or provided with pollinizers.

Except for a few very early and late blossoming varieties, the blooming periods of most of the commonly grown pears overlap well enough for cross-pollination. Bartlett has a long, mid-season blooming period that overlaps those of nearly all the other important varieties with the possible exception of the very early Le Conte, Forelle, Kieffer, and Clairgeau.

Winter Nelis has proved to be the most satisfactory pollinizer for Bartlett under most conditions in California. In the East and Northwest, Bartlett blooms several days before Winter Nelis. In California, however, following the warmest winters, the blossoming period of the Winter Nelis may be past before the Bartlett blossoms have opened.

Nectar-collecting honey bees usually prefer flowers of other plants to those of pears. That undoubtedly is because some pear flowers provide a relatively small amount of nectar, low in sugar concentration. Bees do work pear blossoms for pollen, which most varieties produce in abundance. If the concentration of bees is great enough, therefore, effective cross-pollination will undoubtedly result in orchards that have enough pollinizing varieties. Orchardists who desire a heavier fruit set probably should provide two or three colonies of bees instead of one, as is usually recommended.

Nearly all of the commercially important pears in the United States produce viable pollen and will effectively cross-pollinate each other. Only the combination of Bartlett and Seckel has proved to be interincompatible. Other unfruitful combinations have been reported among closely related varieties. Several European varieties produce mostly nonviable pollen and therefore cannot be used as pollinizers.

CHERRIES are of three groups—sweet cherries, sour or pie cherries, and Duke cherries, which are hybrids of the other two.

Most of the sweet cherries grown in the United States are produced in the Pacific Coast States. California produces the bulk of the crop. Small commercial plantings of sour cherries are in western Oregon and Washington, although the main production is in the Northeast. Duke varieties are of little commercial importance anywhere in the country.

All varieties of sweet cherries are self-unfruitful and must be cross-pollinated for satisfactory yields. Not all combinations of varieties are fruitful. Examples of variety combinations that are interincompatible and therefore will not produce crops when planted together (unless other effective pollinizing varieties are provided) are: Early Purple and Rockport; Advance and Rockport; Windsor and Abundance; Napoleon (Royal Ann), Bing, and Lambert; Black Tartarian, Knight's Early Black, and Early Rivers. (Some strains of Black Tartarian may be interfruitful with Knight's Early Black and Early Rivers.)

All important sweet cherry varieties produce good, viable pollen. Most variety combinations should be interfruitful therefore if their blooming periods overlap enough.

As to pollination, there are evidently different strains of certain cherry varieties, perhaps because seedlings that now exist are so similar to the original varieties that they cannot be distinguished from their parents. One should therefore select trees of strains that he knows can fertilize the desired variety.

Varieties bloom at different times. One should select varieties that have overlapping blooming periods and are interfruitful. The average blooming period for most sweet cherries is about 2 weeks. Weather conditions just before and during bloom markedly influence the length of the period of bloom as well as the dates of blooming, but varieties keep approximately the same order of blooming each season. A list of most of the varieties grown in California in order of earliness of blossoming is: *Early*—Burbank, Chapman, California Advance, Black Heart, Knight's Early Black, Early Purple Guigne, Black Republican, Black Tartarian. *Late*—Napoleon (Royal Ann), Windsor, Parkhill, Early Rivers, Rockport, Bing, Pontiac, Abundance, Bush Tartarian, Noir de Schmidt, Giant, Lambert, Saylor, Long Stem Bing, Gil Peck, Deacon.

The blossoming periods of the varieties within each group will usually coincide well enough for effective cross-pollination. The blossoming periods of Black Tartarian and Black Republican generally overlap well enough with those in the late group for satisfactory cross-transfer of pollen.

In the East the blooming periods of the main varieties usually coincide well enough for cross-pollination.

In general, only sweet cherries should be planted for cross-pollination of sweet cherries. Sour cherries usually bloom too late to be satisfactory pollinizers for sweet cherries, and the percentages of fruit set are low. Duke cherries are unsatisfactory pollinizers for sweet cherries, although the blooming periods of the Duke cherries coincide with those of the late sweet cherries.

The commercially important varieties of sour cherries (Early Richmond, Montmorency, Dyehouse, and the Morello group) are self-fruitful if enough pollinizing insects are available. Better crops can be expected, however, if a sour cherry orchard contains more than one variety. Almost any variety of sour cherry will serve as an effective pollinizer for the other sour varieties. The later blooming sweet cherries will also satisfactorily cross-pollinate the sour varieties if their blooming periods overlap enough. The pollen of Duke cherries usually does not give satisfactory fruit sets on sour cherries.

Some of the Duke varieties, such as Royal Duke and May Duke, may be partly self-fruitful, but cross-pollination is essential for commercial crops. Duke cherries will generally set heavier crops when cross-pollinated by either sweet or sour cherries than when other Duke varieties are used as pollinizers for them. The pollen of Duke cherries gives low percentages of germination in laboratory tests. The low order of viability of their pollen undoubtedly explains why Duke cherries serve as poor pollinizers for sweet and sour cherries as well as other Dukes. Sweet cherries in the late-blossoming group make satisfactory pollinizers for such earlier blossoming Duke cherries as Olivet, Reine Hortense, and May Duke. But the sour cherry varieties may best serve as pollinizers for the later blooming Dukes, Late Duke, Royal Duke, and Abesse d'Oignies.

KEEPING BOXES of honey bees in the home apple orchard was a common practice even before the development of the movable frame beehive. The need for cross-pollination was not appreciated, however, until the growers started standardizing and limiting their orchards to a few varieties. Undoubtedly the decline in the activity of native wild pollinating insects also was a factor.

A few varieties (Baldwin, Early Harvest, Grimes Golden, Oldenburg, Rome Beauty, Wealthy, Yellow Transparent, Yellow Newtown) are considered to be self-fruitful in certain favorable locations. Some others (Ben Davis, Esopus Spitzenburg, Golden Delicious, Jonathan, Red Astrachan, Wagener, and York Imperial) produce varying amounts of a commercial crop when self-pollinated. It is generally agreed, however, that all varieties should be interplanted and that honey bees be put among them during the blooming periods to insure good yields.

The following are unusually good pollinizers and generally effect excellent sets of fruit on most other varieties: Ben Davis, Delicious, Fameuse, Golden Delicious, Grimes Golden, Jonathan, McIntosh, Northern Spy, Rome Beauty, Wagener, Wealthy, Winter Banana, Yellow Transparent, and York Imperial.

Others, including Arkansas, Baldwin, Gravenstein, Rhode Island Greening, Stark, Stayman Winesap, Thompkins King, and Winesap, produce mostly infertile pollen and consequently are ineffective as cross-pollinizers.

Most other commercial varieties grown in this country usually serve as satisfactory pollinizers.

Interunfruitful combinations are rare except among closely related varieties and those having infertile pollen. Parent varieties are ineffective as cross-pollinizers for their color sports or bud mutations, and the mutations, in turn, are of no value as cross-pollinizers for the parent variety. For example, Delicious is interincompatible with any of its color sports, such as Redwin, Richared, Starking, and Shotwell Delicious.

An exception is Grimes Golden, which is ineffective as a pollinizer for Arkansas but an excellent pollinizer for other varieties. Presumably it is unrelated to Arkansas.

According to present evidence, based mainly on orchard observations, color mutations of apple varieties have the same pollination requirements and value as cross-pollinizers as their parent varieties.

The blooming periods of two varieties must overlap if cross-pollination is to be accomplished. According to W. H. Chandler and others, apple trees require more chilling before their buds will open evenly in the spring than most other fruits. Mild winters may widen the gap between the blooming dates. The relative order of blooming, however, is usually the same for any one locality. High spring temperatures following winters cold enough to meet the chilling requirements tend to shorten the blooming periods of all varieties. Under those conditions, all but the very early- and late-blooming varieties will overlap sufficiently for pollination. On the other hand, cold spring weather will tend to cause the blooming periods of the early and late varieties to be much more widely separated. In most years, however, midseason varieties would overlap with the early- and late-blooming ones sufficiently to provide an adequate pollen supply.

THE POLLINATION REQUIREMENTS of plums have been studied at the California Agricultural Experiment Station for more than 40 years. Beginning in 1916, A. H. Hendrickson made a series of reports showing self-unfruitfulness of many varieties of European and Japanese plums. He also showed that bees must be provided in plum orchards for commercial crops even though the varieties are highly self-fruitful. Since then, work in England, New York, Michigan, and California has shown that the European plums may be classified as usually self-fruitful, partly self-fruitful, or self-unfruitful. The self-unfruitful varieties outnumber those that may be listed as partly or completely self-fruitful. Apparently no interincompatible pairs or groups of European plum varieties exist among those grown commercially in the United States. Because most varieties produce a high percentage of viable pollen, any variety should be effective in cross-pollinating another, provided their blossoming seasons overlap sufficiently.

The blooming season of the European plums in the East usually overlaps well enough to provide cross-pollination. In California the varieties are classed as either early or late blossoming.

Most of the Japanese plums are self-unfruitful. A few varieties, such as Beauty, Climax, Methley, Red Rosa, and Santa Rosa, are partly self-fruitful, but, like the others, these five varieties will generally set much better when interplanted with other varieties for cross-pollination. Some of the earlier blossoming Japanese varieties are deficient in pollen production, and several varieties produce pollen that is low in viability. Other varieties, like Burbank, Duarte, Elephant Heart, Red Rosa, Redhart, Santa Rosa, and Wickson, are satisfactory pollinizers. The blossoming season of Tragedy, a European plum, coincides with several of the late Japanese varieties. Tragedy is also a moderately effective pollinizer for several Japanese plums, but it does not set fruit following cross-pollination by them. Certain American plums are also effective pollinizers for several Japanese varieties.

The necessity of finding a specific pollinizer is emphasized in the case of Elephant Heart. It is attractive and one of the largest of the Japanese plums. It has high quality and is a good shipper. It would undoubtedly be an important late-season plum except for its shy bearing habit. Between 1936 and 1948, workers at the California station tried 21 varieties as pollinizers for Elephant Heart. Finally in 1948, Myrobalan 5Q, a selected Myrobalan seedling and one of 47 varieties of pollen tested as pollinizers for Elephant Heart that year, gave a satisfactory fruit set. Extensive tests in 1949 proved that Elephant Heart can produce heavy crops with this source of cross-pollination. But the fruit of Myrobalan 5Q has no commercial value and the search for a suitable pollinizer was continued. In 1950 it was discovered that a promising new Japanese variety, Redheart, developed in breeding work, will also bring about heavy fruit sets on Elephant Heart.

SEED PRODUCTION is the object of pollination of legumes. The most familiar large-seeded legumes such as peas and beans are generally self-pollinated, but many of the small-seeded ones require insect pollination. Even with the self-fertile legumes, cross-pollination is desirable because greater vigor results. The seedling plants in a legume field are of mixed heredity; that is ideal for true crossing and is different from orchard trees, which are propagated asexually.

Some of the self-fertile species of legumes require tripping—release of the staminal column—by insects before they will set seed. In the process, cross-pollination is readily accomplished. An orchard presents a relatively small number of blossoms, and only some of them are required to give a commercial crop. But a legume field has a tremendous number of blossoms, and it is desirable to set the greatest possible number of pods. The orchardist may accomplish his aim with one colony to the acre, but in some legume fields five or more colonies may be needed to set maximum crops.

Alfalfa has become our leading legume hay crop. Adapted varieties are grown extensively even in the Middle West, where early attempts at production failed. The Intermountain States, particularly Utah, used to be the important producers of alfalfa seed. Since 1925, however, their yields gradually declined from 8 to 10 bushels an acre to as low as 1 bushel. Injurious insects may have been a factor, but the reduction in the number of wild bees is considered to be one of the main causes of the lowered yields.

Alfalfa blossoms require tripping (forcing the pistil out of the keel) and cross-pollination by insects for high-yields of seed. Native wild bees, notably leaf-cutting bees and alkali bees, took to alfalfa as a favorite source of pollen and nectar; where they are still abundant, tripping proceeds apace and high seed yields are maintained.

As a rule, the pollen collectors are more efficient in tripping than the nectar collectors. The presence of more easily worked pollen sources within flight range, such as mustard, sweetclover, birdsfoot trefoil, and star-thistle, attracts the pollen-collecting bees away from alfalfa. For example, pollen trapped in the Cache Valley of Utah, which has other good pollen sources, contained little or no alfalfa pollen. A high proportion of alfalfa pollen was obtained in traps at Delta, Utah, where more attractive sources of pollen were limited.

The use of honey bees to pollinate alfalfa blossoms has increased greatly. California, which has many bee colonies, has been making rapid strides in seed production. The State produced 15 million pounds in 1949; many yields ranged from 500 to 1,000 pounds or more of seed an acre. The 1950 yield was 33 million pounds. A survey by workers at the experiment station indicated that a production of 150 to 200 pounds of seed per acre per colony of bees was not uncommon. In one instance, a 132-acre field was supplied with bees during the flowering season at the rate of 5 or 6 colonies an acre. It was inspected daily for 2 months. Almost no wild bees were seen. Only limited amounts of pollen were collected by honey bees, but nectar-collecting bees were numerous. The field averaged 896 pounds of recleaned seed to the acre. Tripping was continuous but relatively slow in comparison to the rapid tripping by wild bees or pollen-collecting honey bees, as noted in some favored areas of other States.

In earlier years bees were usually placed in large apiaries outside the field to be pollinated. The practice has been growing of scattering the colonies in small apiaries along drives crossing the field. Field experiments in 1949 and 1950 showed an increase in the rate of tripping around newly established groups of colonies—indicating the superiority of the newer arrangement.

Until recently the honey bee has not been considered an effective pollinator of red clover because measurements have shown that the length of the corolla tube of the floret exceeds the length of the honey bee's tongue.

The longer-tongued bumble bees have often been given credit for being the important pollinators of red clover because they collect nectar and pollen from this plant in preference to many others. If bumble bees are numerous, no particular difficulty is experienced in setting seed, but they are becoming scarce in many areas.

W. E. Dunham reported that of the insects responsible for red clover pollination in Ohio several years ago, 82 percent were honey bees, 15 percent were bumble bees, and 3 percent other insects. An acre of red clover is said to contain some 216 million individual florets. A bee takes about 30 minutes to visit 346 florets to get a load of pollen.

R. G. Richmond showed that red clover caged with honey bees in Colorado produced 61.5 seeds per flower head and only 0.49 seeds per head when pollinating insects were excluded. He stated that first-cutting red clover set a good seed crop when conditions were inviting to honey bees.

A 27-acre field of Kenland red clover in the Sacramento Valley produced 616 pounds of clean seed to the acre in 1950. The field was planted that spring and no hay was cut. A large acreage of seed alfalfa was growing in the adjoining field. Honey bee colonies were in scattered groups in all fields. The grower stated that the bees worked the clover and the alfalfa about equally well.

Pollination of red clover is accomplished by the honey bee in this way: The bee approaches the floret over the keel and forces its head down directly between the keel and the standard petal. The fore and middle pairs of legs clutch and claw at the wings of the floret to spring them and the keel away from the standard, thus tripping the flower. Tripping exposes the stigma and anthers, which touch the bee on the underneath side of the head where it joins the thorax. Pollen is thus accumulated and carried to the next blossom.

White clover also needs pollination by insects for seed production. The several varieties, among them British, Dutch, and Ladino, are freely worked by honey bees. White clover is a leading source of honey in the North Central and Northeastern States, but Ladino clover (giant white) from Italy does not equal the Dutch clover (small white) in honey production. Because those two types readily cross, stands grown for seed must be far enough apart so insects cannot fly from one field to the other.

In Oregon, from Ladino plants in cages where no insects could reach them, H. A. Scullen harvested 300 seeds from a sample of 100 heads; 100 heads just outside the cages yielded 14,900 seeds. At Thornton, Calif., where three colonies of bees per acre were placed for pollinating alfalfa and red clover, heads from stray Ladino plants averaged 276 seeds each, or a total of 27,600 seeds in 100 heads.

The sweetclovers grown in the United States include many varieties, both yellow and white. Some are self-pollinating and self-fertile; others are self-fertile but require insect pollination, and still others are self-sterile and require cross-pollination. As a source of both nectar and pollen, sweetclover is highly attractive to honey bees. Variation among plants is increased by cross-pollination effected by the large number of bees that visit the plants. Increased yields of sweetclover seed have been demonstrated many times by providing at least one colony of bees to the acre.

Crimson clover, of the true clovers, is the most important winter annual cover crop in the United States. The different varieties are self-fertile, but their florets are not self-tripping, and insect visitation is required for heavy seed crops. Growers of crimson clover seed have become increasingly conscious of the benefits from introducing colonies of honey bees into their fields.

Observations in the lower Sacramento Valley disclosed that relatively few bees are required for pollination of all Ladino clover florets, compared to the numbers required for pollination of alfalfa. New flower buds do not open until the middle of the morning, and a concentration of two or three bees to the square yard can work all of them repeatedly in one afternoon. Following pollination, the florets turn down on the stem and close permanently at nightfall. Nectar is not secreted for 3 to 6 hours after a bud opens. In June and July the bees generally work the blossoms for pollen.

Alsike clover depends upon pollination by honey bees and also to some extent on wild insects for seed production. Alsike produces an enormous number of individual florets, all of which must be cross-pollinated for heavy yields of seed. Field experiments in Ohio demonstrated that honey bees increased seed yields from a 10-year average of 1.6 bushels an acre to 8 bushels an acre. Yields as high as 20 bushels an acre were found to be possible with maximum insect pollination.

Alsike bloom produces a relatively poor supply of nectar in some years. If the concentration of bees is heavy enough to pollinate the crop adequately under such conditions, very little honey will be produced.

Birdsfoot trefoil is becoming an important permanent pasture crop. Apparently it does well on many soils where clovers and alfalfa do poorly. As it is self-sterile, seed formation depends upon cross-pollination by insects. On caged insect-free plots in Oregon, H. A. Scullen obtained no seeds on either birdsfoot or big trefoil while similar plants exposed to bees seeded freely. The flowers of trefoil have great attraction for bees as a source of nectar and pollen. Bees were observed to leave a flowering alfalfa field near Davis, Calif., and fly 1 mile to gather trefoil pollen. Exceptionally heavy seed yields have been obtained where there were many bee colonies.

Many vegetables do not require pollination to produce an edible crop, but of these, carrots, radishes, turnips, cabbage, celery, and many others require insect pollination for seed production. Both pollination and seed formation are essential in the production of the edible part of the pickling cucumber, cantaloup, and watermelon.

Pollination of all sections of the compound ovary is evidently necessary for proper shape and quality of melons, as the deformed part of an incompletely pollinated cantaloup not only lacks seed but is also poor in sweetness and flavor. Honey bees are employed in the commercial production of the seed and fruit of several vegetable crops.

Varietal crossing is generally undesirable in producing seeds for the propagation of vegetable crops. Hence the Department of Agriculture regulations require that in the production of seed of many vegetables the plots of the different varieties must be at least one-fourth mile apart. An even greater distance would be safer because pollen grains are always found on the honey bee and its flight range exceeds one-fourth mile.

Cucumbers, muskmelons, watermelons, pumpkins, and squash have similar floral structures. The group—cucurbits—generally is characterized by having male and female blossoms on different parts of the same plant. Such an arrangement obviously requires insects for the transfer of pollen, as the plants are not wind-pollinated. Most varieties of cucurbits are self- and interfertile when pollinated by hand.

Honey bees are widely used in greenhouse and field production of cucumbers. Because the individual flowers are open for only a short time, a heavy concentration of bees is advisable whether the cucumbers are grown for the fresh market, for pickling, or for seed.

Watermelons and muskmelons often produce bisexual or complete flowers, instead of separate pistillate and staminate flowers. The complete flowers, however, do not fertilize themselves, and honey bees are as essential in their pollination as in the pistillate flowers.

Cabbage and the closely related cabbagelike plants as cauliflower, broccoli, and brussels sprouts require cross-pollination by insects for good seed yields. Varieties of cabbage display various degrees of self-incompatibility. Cross-incompatibility is also common.

Bees are effective agents in cross-pollination. Attempts to bring about self-pollination have had little success. Besides honey bees, cuckoo bees, leaf-cutting bees, mining bees, bumble bees, and bee flies are attracted to cabbage flowers. Some are said to work at lower temperatures than the honey bee. Because cabbage for seed production is often grown in a cool location or during cool weather, some of these insects may be individually more effective than the honey bee in its pollination. The optimum temperature for pollen germination, however, is about 68° F., and bees are active in the field at temperatures as low as 60°.

ENGLISH HOLLY trees bear their pistillate and staminate flowers on separate plants. Although a small percentage of the pistillate flowers on some trees develop parthenocarpic berries, facilities for cross-pollination are required for commercial crops. The seeded berries resulting from cross-pollination are larger, less subject to premature dropping, earlier maturing, and more resistant to withering after cutting. Bees are attracted to both staminate and pistillate holly flowers to such an extent that, when they are abundant, only one male tree is needed for pollinating 50 pistillate trees. The pollinizers should be selected for their foliage quality as well as their capacity to produce an abundance of viable pollen when the pistillate trees are blooming.

POLLINATION BY HONEY BEES has thus become an essential factor in producing many crops, along with the factors that are taken for granted, such as the preparation of the soil, the supplying of moisture, and cultivation, pruning, and thinning. Because beekeeping is a specialty, just as fruit growing or the production of seeds are specialties, most growers will find it advantageous to rent bees rather than to keep their own. Cooperation between grower and beekeeper thus becomes important and is mutually advantageous.

GEORGE H. VANSELL, *an apiculturist in the Department of Agriculture, is stationed at Davis, Calif. He has studied in the University of Kansas, Harvard and Stanford Universities, and the University of California. He has taught in the Universities of Kentucky and California. The activity of bees in collecting nectar and pollen, especially as agents of pollen distribution, has been his chief interest for many years.*

W. H. GRIGGS *is assistant professor of pomology in the University of California at Davis. He has charge of investigations into the pollination of fruits and nuts. He received his training in pomology in the University of Missouri and the University of Maryland. Dr. Griggs was assistant professor of pomology in the University of Connecticut in 1946 and 1947.*

For further reference:

E. C. Auchter and H. B. Knapp: Orchard and Small Fruit Culture, *John Wiley & Sons. 1937.*

A. D. Betts: The Constancy of the Pollen Collecting Bees, *Bee World, volume 16, pages 111–113. 1935.*

G. Bonnier: Sur la Division du Travail chez les Abeilles, *Academie des Science, Paris, Comptes Rendus, volume 143, pages 941–946. 1906.*

R. M. Bullock: Is Artificial Pollination Practical? *American Fruit Grower, pages 14–15, May 1948;* Handling and Application of Pollen to Fruit Trees, *with F. L. Overley, Proceedings of the American Society for Horticultural Science, volume 54, pages 125–132, 1949.*

C. G. Butler: The Behavior of Bees When Foraging, *Journal of the Royal Society of Arts, volume 93, pages 501–511, 1945;* The Behavior of a Population of Honey Bees on an Artificial and a Natural Crop, *with E. P. Jeffree and H. Kalmus, Journal of Experimental Biology, volume 20, pages 65–73, 1943.*

C. N. Buzzard: Bee Organization, *Bee World, volume 17, pages 133–135, 1936;* De l'Organisation du Travail chez les

Abeilles, *Société d'Apiculteur des Alpes-Maritimes, Bulletin 15, pages 65–70, 1936.*

J. W. Carlson: Alfalfa-Seed Investigations in Utah, *Utah Agricultural Experiment Station Bulletin 258. 1935.*

D. B. Casteel: The Behavior of the Honey Bee in Pollen Collecting, *U. S. D. A. Bureau of Entomology Bulletin 121. 1912.*

W. H. Chandler, M. H. Kimball, G. L. Philp, W. P. Tufts, and George P. Weldon: Chilling Requirements for Opening of Buds on Deciduous Orchard Trees and Some Other Plants in California, *California Agricultural Experiment Station Bulletin 611. 1937.*

M. B. Crane and A. G. Brown: Incompatibility and Sterility in the Gage and Dessert Plums, *Journal of Pomology and Horticultural Science, volume 17, pages 51–66. 1939.*

M. B. Cummings, E. W. Jenkins, and R. G. Dunning: Sterility in Pears, *Vermont Agricultural Experiment Station Bulletin 408. 1936.*

Charles Robert Darwin: The Effects of Cross and Self Fertilisation in the Vegetable Kingdom, *D. Appleton & Co. 1877.*

W. E. Dunham: Insect Pollination of Alsike Clover, *Gleanings in Bee Culture, volume 66, page 425, 1938;* Insect Pollination of Red Clover in Western Ohio, *Gleanings in Bee Culture, volume 67, pages 486–488, 1939.*

R. E. P. Dwyer and F. T. Bowman: Pollination of Williams (Bartlett) Pear in New South Wales. Part I. Investigations at Bathurst Experiment Farm, 1928–34, *New South Wales Department of Agriculture Scientific Bulletin 62. 1938.*

Olav Einset: Experiments in Cherry Pollination, *New York Agricultural Experiment Station (Geneva) Bulletin 617. 1932.*

S. W. Fletcher: Pollination of Bartlett and Kieffer Pears, *Annual Report of Virginia Polytechnic Institute Agricultural Experiment Station for 1909, pages 213–224. 1910.*

K. von Frisch: Die Sprache der Bienen und ihre Nutzenwendung in der Landwirtshaft, *Experientia, volume 2, pages 397–404. 1946.*

V. R. Gardner: A Preliminary Report on the Pollination of the Sweet Cherry, *Oregon Agricultural Experiment Station Bulletin 116. 1913.*

J. H. Gourley and F. S. Howlett: Modern Fruit Production, *The Macmillan Co. 1941.*

W. H. Griggs and George H. Vansell: The Use of Bee-Collected Pollen in Artificial Pollination of Deciduous Fruits, *Proceedings of the American Society for Horticultural Science, volume 54, pages 118–124, 1949;* The Germinating Ability of Quick-Frozen Bee-Collected Apple Pollen Stored in a Dry Ice Container, *with J. F. Reinhardt, Journal of Economic Entomology, volume 43, page 549, 1950.*

R. A. Grout: Pollination—An Agricultural Practice, *Dadant & Sons, Inc. 1949.*

Q. A. Hare and George H. Vansell: Pollen Collection by Honey Bees in the Delta, Utah, Alfalfa-Seed Producing Area, *Journal of the American Society of Agronomy, volume 38, pages 462–469. 1946.*

A. H. Hendrickson: The Common Honey Bee as an Agent in Prune Pollination, *California Agricultural Experiment Station Bulletin 291, 1918;* Plum Pollination, *California Agricultural Experiment Station Bulletin 310, 1919;* Further Experiments in Plum Pollination, *California Agricultural Experiment Station Bulletin 352, 1922.*

George E. King and A. B. Burrell: An Improved Device to Facilitate Pollen Distribution by Bees, *Proceedings of the American Society for Horticultural Science, volume 29, pages 156–159. 1933.*

Paul Knuth: Handbuch der Blütenbiologie, *5 volumes, Wilhelm Engelemann, Leipzig, Germany, 1898.*

J. C. Kremer: Traps for the Collection and Distribution of Pollen in Orchards, *Michigan Agricultural Experiment Station Quarterly Bulletin 31, No. 1, pages 12–21. 1948.*

C. I. Lewis and C. C. Vincent: Pollination of the Apple, *Oregon Agricultural Experiment Station Bulletin 104. 1909.*

L. H. MacDaniels: The Possibilities of Hand Pollination in the Orchard on a Commercial Scale, *Proceedings of the American Society for Horticultural Science, volume 27, 370–373, 1931;* Pollination and Other Factors Affecting the Set of Fruit With Special Reference to the Apple, *with A. J. Heinicke, Cornell Agricultural Experiment Station Bulletin 497, 1929.*

R. E. Marshall, S. Johnson, H. D. Hootman, and H. M. Wells: Pollination of Orchard Fruits in Michigan, *Michigan Agricultural Experiment Station Special Bulletin* 188. 1929.

W. J. Middlebrooke: Pollination of Fruit Trees, 1904–12, *Journal of the Board of Agriculture, London, volume 22, pages 418–443. 1915–16.*

A. Minderhoud: Untersuchungen Über Das Betragen Der Honigbiene Als Blütenbestäuberin, *Gartenvauwissenschaft, volume 4, pages 342–362. 1931.*

A. A. Moffett: Chromosome Number and Pollen Germination in Pears, *Journal of Pomology and Horticultural Science, volume 12, pages 321–326. 1934.*

F. L. Overley and R. M. Bullock: Pollen Diluents and the Application of Pollen to Tree Fruits, *Proceedings of the American Society for Horticultural Science, volume 49, pages 163–169. 1947.*

O. H. Pearson: Observations on the Type of Sterility in Brassica Oleracea var. Capitata, *Proceedings of the American Society for Horticultural Science, volume 26, pages 34–38, 1929;* Breeding Plants of the Cabbage Group, *California Agricultural Experiment Station Bulletin 532, 1932.*

G. L. Philp: Cherry Culture in California, *California Agricultural Extension Circular 46, revised. 1947.*

F. W. Rane: Fertilization of Muskmelon, *Society for the Promotion of Agricultural Science, Report of the 19th Annual Meeting, pages 150–151. 1898.*

A. J. Pieters and E. A. Hollowell: Clover Improvement, *Yearbook of Agriculture 1937, pages 1190–1214.*

C. R. Ribbands: The Foraging Method of Individual Honey Bees, *Journal of Animal Ecology, volume 18, pages 47–66. 1949.*

R. G. Richmond: Red Clover Pollination of Honey Bees in Colorado, *Colorado Agricultural Experiment Station Bulletin 391. 1932.*

A. N. Roberts and C. A. Boller: Pollination Requirements of the English Holly, Ilex Aquifolium, *Proceedings of the American Society for Horticultural Science, volume 52, pages 501–509. 1948.*

R. H. Roberts: Better Cherry Yields in Wisconsin, *Wisconsin Agricultural Experiment Station Bulletin 344. 1922.*

J. T. Rosa: Fruiting Habit and Pollination of Cantaloupe, *Proceedings of the American Society for Horticultural Science, volume 21, pages 51–57, 1924;* Pollination and Fruiting Habit of the Watermelon, *Proceedings of the American Society for Horticultural Science, volume 22, pages 331–333. 1925.*

C. W. Schaefer and C. L. Farrar: The Use of Pollen Traps and Pollen Supplements in Developing Honey Bee Colonies, *Bureau of Entomology and Plant Quarantine Circular E–531. 1941.*

J. S. Shoemaker: Cherry Pollination Studies, *Ohio Agricultural Experiment Station Bulletin 422. 1928.*

C. E. Shuster: Pollination and Growing of the Cherry, *Oregon Agricultural Experiment Station Bulletin 212. 1925.*

Sardar Singh: Behavior Studies of Honey Bees in Gathering Nectar and Pollen, *New York Agricultural Experiment Station Mem. 288. 1950.*

F. W. L. Sladen: How Pollen Is Collected by the Social Bees, and the Part Played in the Process by the Auricle, *British Bee Journal, volume 39, pages 491–494. 1911.*

John C. Snyder: The Pollination of Tree Fruits and Nuts, *Washington State College Extension Bulletin 342, reprint. 1947.*

F. E. Todd and O. Bretherick: Composition of Pollens, *Journal of Economic Entomology, volume 35, pages 312–317. 1942.*

W. P. Tufts: Almond Pollination, *California Agricultural Experiment Station Bulletin 306, 1919; and California Agricultural Experiment Station Bulletins 346,* Almond Pollination *(1922), 373,* Pear Pollination *(1923), and 385,* Pollination of the Sweet Cherry *(1925), with G. L. Philp.*

Pollination by Native Insects

George E. Bohart

The earliest flowering plants in the fossil record were related to the magnolias, which to this day depend for pollination on the visits of beetles. Beetles, which comprise the order Coleoptera, were the most abundant and adaptable insects during the dawn period of flowering plants and thus, quite naturally, were the first pollinators. The flies and the sawflies and wasps were present but poor in variety and primitively developed. In the ensuing ages, however, their adaptation to the products of flowers became a dominant feature of their structure and habits. The moths and butterflies, which first appeared in the early days of flowers, soon adapted themselves completely to floral offerings. Now nearly all of them are highly developed for taking nectar from flowers.

While the insects were thus becoming specialized to take advantage of flowers, plants were likewise becoming specialized to make more efficient use of insects. Certain flowers developed characteristics limiting them to pollination by certain types of insects, which in turn become highly adapted to these specialized flowers. Today we have many plants so constructed that only a few specially adapted insects can visit them successfully. Figs, orchids, Spanish-bayonet, and monkshood are examples.

The so-called hawk-moth orchids (in the genera *Habenaria, Angraecum,* and others) exemplify the many intricate modifications possessed by orchids to insure pollination by specific kinds of insects. In these flowers the nectar, lying at the bottom of a long narrow tube, is accessible only to the long-tongued hawk moths. While probing for nectar, the moth brings each eye against a sticky disk to which a mass of pollen is attached, and flies away, carrying the masses on its eyes. The masses (called *pollinia*) then bend forward on their stalks in such a way that, when the moth inserts its proboscis into the next flower, they fit perfectly against the stigma and adhere to it. From the presence in Africa of an orchid of this type, with a nectar tube 12 inches long, there is inferred the existence in that region of a hawk moth with a tongue equally long.

In most acts of pollination the insect has no interest in the plant beyond its store of nectar or pollen, pollination on its part being an accident. It is the plant which, by its offering of nourishment and by the arrangement of floral parts, insures that such "accidents" will occur.

The yucca moth, which is the sole pollinator of yucca (Spanish-bayonet), is a unique exception and provides a good example of symbiotic relationships between plants and animals. It is no mere nectar sipper. At first, operating somewhat in the manner of the fig wasp, the female stabs the ovary of the yucca flower with her ovipositor and inserts an egg. That is commonplace insect behavior, but her next acts, though instinctive, seem to display careful planning and an uncanny knowledge of botany. She mounts a stamen, scrapes together a wad of pollen, carries it back to the pistil containing her egg, and thrusts it into the funnel-shaped stigma. She takes neither nectar nor pollen for herself but performs the only act that will guarantee the proper food for her offspring, the developing ovules of the plant. The yucca plant in its turn may lose a few seeds to the young worms—surely a small price to pay for such perfect pollination service.

Some years ago, scientists argued hotly whether insects or flowers became specialized first or whether it was simultaneous. Voluminous papers attempted to explain why and how the process of mutual adaptation developed, but the subject finally became so controversial and unproductive that it was all but dropped. Recently, however, technical advances in agriculture have demanded that progress on problems of pollination keep pace. Knowledge gathered by the early workers in defense of their philosophical arguments is now being put to work in the applied field, but many of the old challenging questions of insect-flower evolution remain unanswered.

Granting the influence of pollinating insects on biological history, what would happen if they should suddenly disappear? It would certainly not mean the end of the flowering plants, because many important plant types have secondarily become adapted to pollination by other agents than insects. The great family of the grasses depends upon cross-pollination by wind or automatic self-pollination within closed flowers. Most of the nut and acorn trees have become adapted to pollen transfer by wind. Even many species within the family of legumes, which is highly specialized for pollination by bees, have come secondarily to depend mainly upon automatic self-pollination within the young blossoms. Peas and beans are familiar examples.

It is likely, therefore, that man could carry on without insects for pollination. The grasses and self-pollinating legumes could form the basis of his agricultural economy. Many of the insect-pollinated plants could be maintained by vegetative propagation, although most of them would be barren of fruit. Tomatoes and potatoes he would still have, but he would have difficulty finding substitutes for clover and alfalfa, and he would have to get along with reduced yields of a variety of crops ranging from cotton to onions. Perhaps the most drastic effects would be in uncultivated areas where a large share of the soil-holding and soil-enriching plants would die out. Furthermore, it would be a bleak springtime if no gay-colored flowers were to grow in the forest glens and open hillsides.

So much for what did not happen and is not likely to happen. Let us examine what has happened or may happen in the future. Probably the insect pollinators will not disappear, and we can go right on eating apples and finding pieces of okra in our vegetable soup.

When the first settlers arrived in America they found no honey bees but there were flowers, fruits, and vegetables in the forests and fields. Furthermore, they were able to produce native American and introduced European crops of many kinds for more than 50 years before honey bees were well established. Native insects were still abundant enough to pollinate the native and introduced insect-pollinated plants. Honey bees were colonized in North America before 1638, but for several decades they were probably more important as honey producers than as pollinators. So long as cultivated areas were composed of small fields surrounded by wild land, native insects were able to handle the pollination job without help from foreign labor. Inevitably, however, as the plow turned under large tracts of sod the native beneficial insects began to disappear. At the same time the available pollinators were spread more thinly over the ever-enlarging orchards and seed fields.

Our native pollinators have suffered the same fate as other forms of wildlife. Certain species have been able to persist and even increase in cultivated areas by taking advantage of road cuts, outbuildings, eroded areas, and the like for nesting places. But most species have had to retreat into fence rows, stream gullies, wood lots, and waste fields to maintain themselves. In recent years, as clean cultivation and intensive land utilization have become the rule, such havens are fast disappearing within flight range of the crops that need insects for pollination.

The logical question at this point is: How important or necessary are native pollinators to our agricultural set-up now that honey bees can be brought in large numbers to any field or orchard? There is no single answer to such a question. An estimated 80 percent of the insect pollination of our commercial crops is performed by honey bees—but that figure, which is only an estimate, does not tell us which crops are involved in the 20 percent pollinated by native insects and whether the whole 100 percent is adequate.

Honey bees, unlike most of our native pollinators, collect nectar or pollen or both from a wide assortment of plants. Consequently, there are few crops, whose blossoms are attractive to any insects, that do not hold some attraction for honey bees. Besides, honey bees can be increased and moved about easily. Nevertheless, in the forests and ranges many herbs, shrubs, and trees will always have to depend on native insects for their reproduction. Likewise, many forms of wildlife and range stock depend in whole or in part for food upon the plants or the seeds and fruit that the native pollinators make possible. Bee for bee, various native species are more efficient pollinators of certain crops, such as alfalfa, red clover, and sometimes even fruit, than honey bees. About that, more later; first let us look at the insects themselves.

Thousands of species of insects assist in the pollination of our entire fauna of insect-pollinated plants. They are distributed principally among the bees and wasps, the butterflies and moths, the flies and gnats, and the beetles. Even minute thrips may be important in the self-pollination of certain plants like carrots and some of the composites, which have tiny, closely aggregated flowers. The order Hymenoptera, even without the honey bee, is by far the most important order of insects in the pollination of commercial crops. Flies probably rank next in importance although the moths, which are very abundant, may do more pollinating under cover of darkness than they are given credit for. However, the value of moths and butterflies as pollinators is more often than not offset by the dam-

970134°—52——9

age they do as larvae. Flies, likewise, are frequently harmful as larvae and many species are carriers of disease as adults.

Among the Hymenoptera, bees, which comprise the superfamily Apoidea, are the most useful pollinators. Some other members of the order, such as the thread-waisted wasps, visit many flowers to partake of nectar, but theirs is a supplementary role on commercial crops and it is difficult to conceive of methods for making better use of them.

THE WILD BEES (after the honey bee) have rightfully received most of the attention accorded to our insect pollinators.

At least 5,000 species of bees probably exist in North America, many of them still undescribed by the taxonomists. Most of the species are important only to wild plants, but at least several hundred take part in the pollination of cultivated crops. For example, more than 100 species have been reported as visitors to flowers of alfalfa alone.

All but a few of our many species can be grouped in families thus: Colletidae, obtuse-tongued bees; Halictidae, sweat bees and their allies; Andrenidae, mining bees; Megachilidae, thick-jawed bees; Anthophoridae, flower-loving bees; Xylocopidae, carpenter bees; Apidae, honey bees and bumble bees.

The first three families are commonly called short-tongued bees and the last four long-tongued bees, although that is not an invariable distinction.

Wild bees have great diversity in habits and habitats. Biological information has been published on fewer than 5 percent of the species. We do not even know where many of our more important pollinators nest. Reasonably complete biological studies have been made in this country for fewer than a score of species. By piecing knowledge of species in this country with the more complete knowledge of their European relatives, however, we have a ground work on which to build.

Bees are characterized by the habit of providing a store of honey and pollen for their offspring, although many species, cuckoolike, preempt the stores of their more industrious relatives.

Most wild bees are solitary. Each female constructs, provisions, and lays eggs in her own nest without help from her neighbors. Each cell in the nest is sealed up as soon as it is provisioned and provided with an egg, and there is no further contact between parent and offspring. A number of species of the family Halictidae have advanced to the stage where the overwintered mother bee remains with her daughters and assists them by guarding the communal nest entrance and laying fertilized eggs.

Many of the so-called solitary bees are gregarious to a greater or lesser degree. Highly gregarious species may dig their burrows in the soil only an inch or two apart and cover acres with their bee towns. Populations in such sites are sometimes comparable to those of moderate-size apiaries of honey bee colonies. A nesting site of alkali bees in Utah was estimated to contain 200,000 nesting females. This site and another large one nearby provided good pollination for the alfalfa-seed fields within a radius of at least 2 miles.

Most bee species are strictly solitary, showing no tendency toward neighborliness and often nesting in well-hidden places. In order to persist in effective numbers as pollinators, such species must have extensive areas suitable for their nesting. The recent experience of alfalfa-seed growers in Saskatchewan is a case in point. Their alfalfa is pollinated principally by leaf-cutting bees, which nest in beetle burrows in the forest timber. A few acres of seed surrounded by forest usually had plenty of leaf-cutting bees and good seed crops, but when the same area was given over to extensive cultivation, only a few seed fields next to the wild country were adequately pollinated.

Social life is a striking but rather uncommon attribute of bees. The true social habit, involving division of labor and cooperation between parents and offspring, reaches its culmination in the complex society of the honey bee, but the glimmerings of social behavior are exhibited by several divergent stocks in various parts of the world. Among our native forms, bumble bees have the most complex society but their hive is a humble and untidy affair compared to that of the honey bee. The bumble bee, like the honey bee, belongs to the family Apidae, most of whose members are social. In the Tropics are many species of small stingless Apidae which, in some regards, are as highly developed socially as the honey bee. They are the most abundant bees in many tropical areas and have been used by the Indians of South America for honey production, but attempts to colonize them in this country have failed.

Nesting places are nearly as varied as the bees themselves. The bumble bees choose well-protected cavities, which may be above ground or subterranean, depending upon the species. Carpenter bees (*Xylocopa*) and representatives of many genera of the Megachilidae nest in beetle burrows in wood or chisel their own tunnels. The small carpenter bees (*Ceratina*) and again many representatives of the Megachilidae nest in the natural channels of hollow or pithy-stemmed plants. Broad-tongued bees, sweat bees, mining bees, and flower-loving bees almost invariably construct burrows in the ground.

Some of the less common environments chosen by certain species include abandoned snail shells, small limb crotches, burrows of other bees, nests of mud-dauber wasps, and cavities in porous types of rock. Various megachilids are especially prone to develop tastes for unusual nesting places.

Most bees nest in the soil. Depending upon the species, the soil may be moist or dry, loose or packed, or even solid rock. The surface may be bare or vegetated, flat or vertical. Few species nest in rich organic soil or in densely shaded places. Most seem to like soil that packs firmly, at least at the level of the brood cells.

Nests of solitary bees in the soil are usually in the form of burrows with short or long branches containing brood cells. Some species make their tunnels only an inch or two long, but

The large mountain carpenter bee and a series of brood cells tunneled in cedar.

others drive the main shaft down for 2 or 3 feet. Some have vertical and others have horizontal cells. Some have several cells in a linear series, and others have only one. Some have cells in tight clusters like bunches of grapes, and others have them at the ends of short, horizontal branches along the main vertical shaft. Each genus of bees usually has a distinctive plan of architecture, but plenty of leeway is left for one species to differ from another. Above the generic level, basic architectural patterns are discernible in some cases (for example, in all halictid nests the entrance tunnel is wider than the branch tunnels) but in some families, like Megachilidae, the diversity of nest types defies satisfactory classification.

Bees, like all insects that undergo complete metamorphosis, pass through four principal life-history stages, the egg, larva, pupa, and adult. The egg is always laid within a brood cell. Bumble bees and honey bees generally lay it in an empty cell, and the young larva is fed progressively by nurse bees in the hive. In this country all other bees lay their eggs on, within, or under

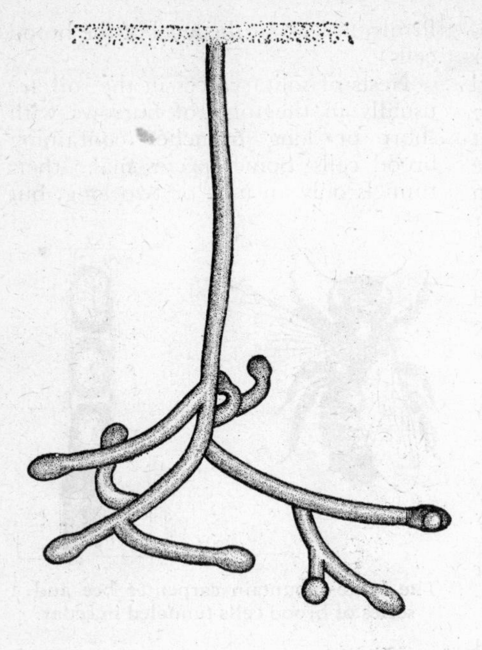

Nest of Andrena subaustralis, exterior view (one cell cut open).

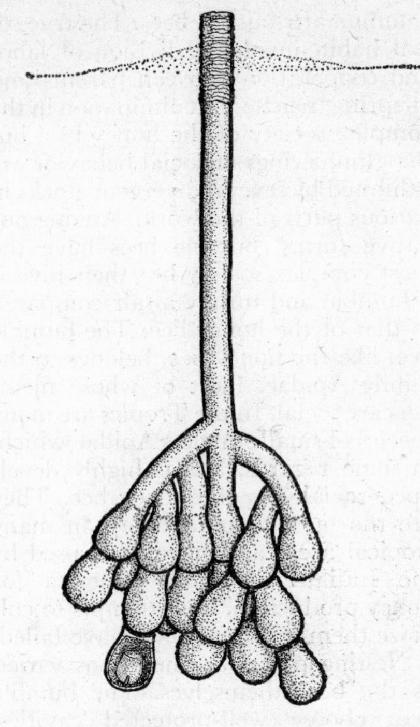

Nest of Diadasia enevata, exterior view (one cell cut open).

a mass of honey-moistened pollen, which becomes the sole nourishment of the growing larva. After laying the egg, the mother bee seals the cell. The eggs and developing larvae of most bees dry out readily. Consequently some sort of seal coat is applied to the inner walls of the cells by the mother bee. Megachilid larvae, which are less delicate, usually are not protected in such a fashion, although some of them are protected by cells lined with sections cut from leaves (leaf-cutting bees), with plant fibers (cotton bees), or with pitch (resin bees).

As I mentioned, the young of all bees are fed a combination of honey and pollen. Larvae of the honey bee are also fed a gland-secreted material called royal jelly. Queens particularly are fed large amounts of the material. Royal jelly or its equivalent may be added to the food of the solitary bees, but this has not been actually observed.

The eggs of solitary bees, being relatively few in number, are much larger than those of honey bees and perhaps contain substances that are provided for honey bee larvae in royal jelly.

The beebread, as the store of food is often called, is prepared in a variety of ways. *Hylaeus,* which is generally considered one of the most primitive bees, does not collect pollen on her body but takes it into her honey stomach with the nectar. This distinctly liquid material is regurgitated into transparent waxen envelopes. The egg floats on the liquid in the envelope. The halictids fashion a flattened or egg-shaped ball of pollen, to which a small amount of nectar is added just before the egg is laid. This pellet of food material is measured exactly to serve the needs of the larva, and none is ever left over. The andrenids make a similar but more spherical ball. Sometimes different species within a genus may be dis-

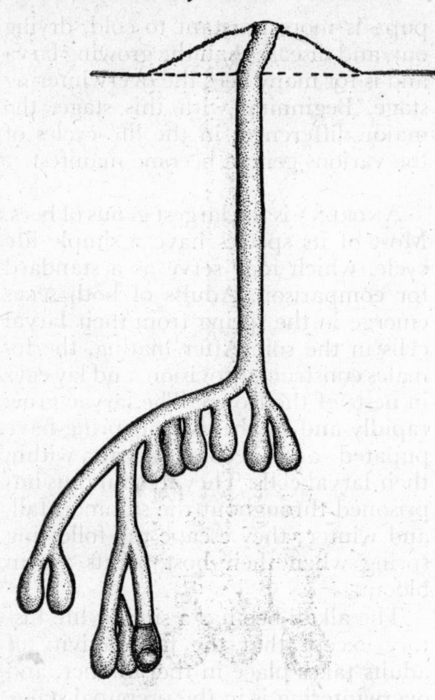

Nest of Nomia melanderi, exterior view (one cell cut open).

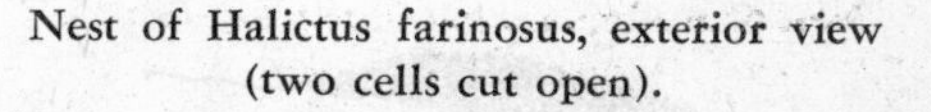

Nest of Halictus farinosus, exterior view (two cells cut open).

tinguished by the shape of the pollen loaf. Size and shape of the egg and its method of placement also vary widely.

The eggs generally hatch within 2 or 3 days, and the larvae attain full growth within from 1 to 3 weeks, molting and usually eating their cast skins twice during the process. There follows a period of several days during which the great quantities of pollen in the digestive tract are absorbed and waste materials are discharged as fecal strips or pellets. Most bees, like the honey bee, maintain sanitary quarters during the feeding period. Among honey bees, at least, the midgut does not communicate with the hindgut until the feeding period is over. In the large family of megachilids, however, the larvae may begin defecating when only one-third grown. Abandoned nests can often be identified by the type and manner of placement of the feces. Many of the megachilids use their pellets as building blocks in the construction of their cocoons.

Some bee larvae spin cocoons in which they pupate. Some do not. Honey bees and bumble bees, which are supposed to be at the top of the evolutionary scale, spin cocoons as do most of the megachilids, which are also thought of as advanced forms. Cocoon formation is scattered throughout the anthophorids, which are considered intermediate in the evolutionary scale. It is rare among the more lowly halictids and andrenids, and absent among the most primitive of bees, the colletids. As bees are supposed to have developed from hunting wasps, most of which spin well-made cocoons, one would expect the evolutionary trend, if any, to be away from rather than toward the cocoon-spinning habit.

Mature bee larvae, after defecating and perhaps spinning a cocoon, become nearly motionless prepupae. The pre-

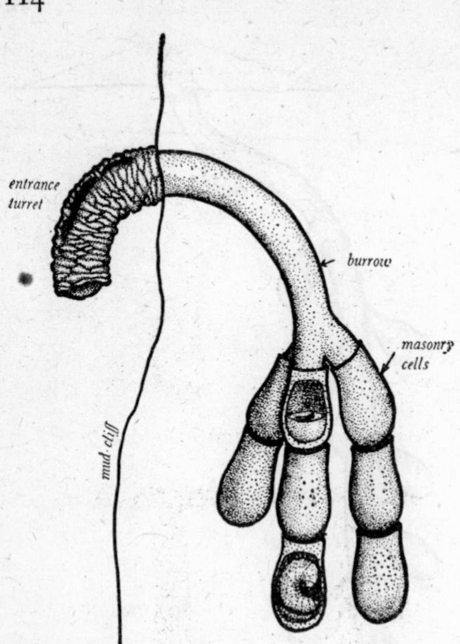

Nest of Anthophora occidentalis, exterior view (two cells cut open).

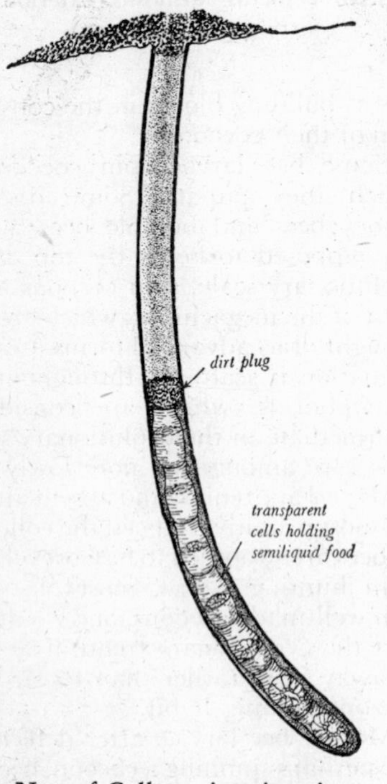

Nest of Colletes, interior view.

pupa is more resistant to cold, drying out, and disease than the growing larva and is for many bees the overwintering stage. Beginning with this stage, the major differences in the life cycles of the various genera become manifest.

ANDRENA is the largest genus of bees. Most of its species have a simple life cycle, which may serve as a standard for comparison. Adults of both sexes emerge in the spring from their larval cells in the soil. After mating, the females construct, provision, and lay eggs in nests of their own. The larvae grow rapidly and by the end of spring have pupated and become adults within their larval cells. They remain thus imprisoned throughout the summer, fall, and winter; they escape the following spring when their host plants are in bloom.

The alkali bee has a similar life history except that the first activity of adults takes place in the summer, and overwintering is in the prepupal stage. In most localities, a second brood of adults appears in the late summer. It is composed predominantly of females. The scarcity of males at this time may account for the high percentage of males usually occurring in the overwintering generation since males develop from unfertilized eggs.

This life-history pattern, allowing for variation in time of adult activity and number of generations in the active season, is the predominant one for wild bees. It is safe to say that most genera of bees pass the winter in the prepupal stage.

Halictus is a large and familiar genus of ground-nesting bees. Many of the species show a tendency toward social behavior. They are not related to bumble bees, but their life cycle is similar in several ways. Many *Halictus* have a life history somewhat as follows: In the spring, overwintered females leave their hibernation burrows to construct and provision brood nests. Within a month or 6 weeks their progeny, all females, make their nests in the form of side burrows of the parental nest, or else dig new ones of their own. Their progeny, being unfertilized, develop into males. The development of males from unfertilized eggs (parthenogenesis) is a general but not infallible rule among Hymenoptera. The old, overwintered female continues to lay eggs, this time on pollen balls of her daughters. These develop into females, which emerge in the summer and mate with the males, of which there is a large crop. The males soon die and the females dig themselves into hibernation burrows for the winter. Some species produce a third generation in the late summer composed of both males and females.

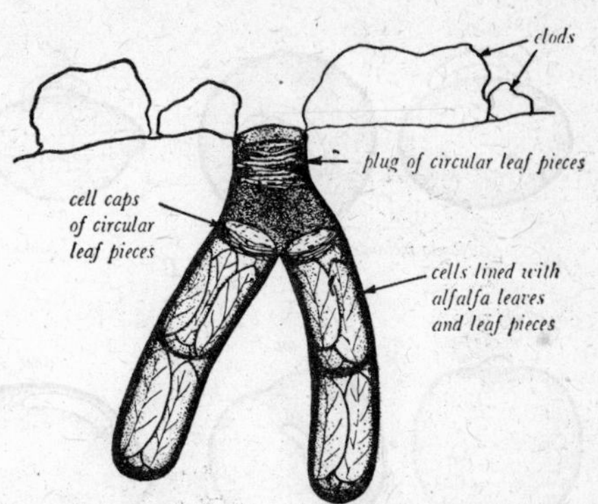

Nest of Megachile dentitarsis, interior view.

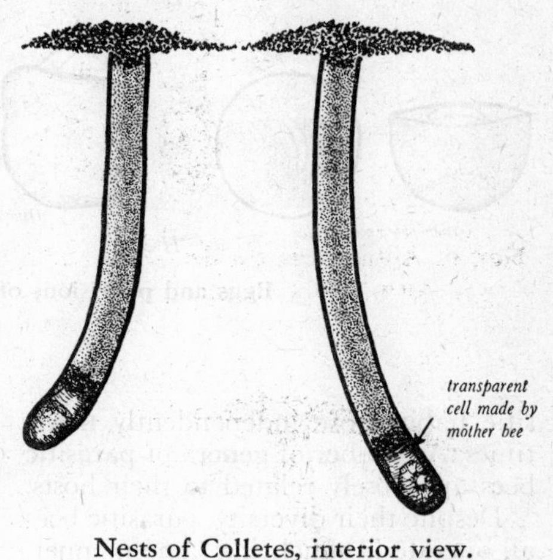

Nests of Colletes, interior view.

Bumble bees carry this pattern to a higher social level. The mated, overwintered females are large individuals known as queens. In the spring the queen leaves her hibernation quarters and spends considerable time feeding and searching for a nesting place. After finding one, she prepares a small bed of woolly material in which she constructs a ball of pollen and a waxen cup or two filled with honey. She then lays a group of eggs in a cavity in the pollen and feeds the young larvae honey, increasing the pollen supply as needed. This progressive feeding is a step forward in social development.

Bumble bees have the birdlike habit of brooding on the eggs and young larvae. The queen's first brood generally develops into four to eight small worker bees. The workers are females with small bodies and poorly developed ovaries, apparently resulting from a limited food supply in the larval stage. Shortly after emerging, the worker bees take over the field and hive duties. The queen then retires to a life of egg laying.

Successive broods of workers tend to become larger as there are increasing numbers of bees to feed them in the larval stage. By the middle of the summer a large share of the larvae are fed a maximum diet and develop into queens. At the same time the males (drones) begin to appear. Some of the males may come from unfertilized eggs laid by the queen, but apparently most of them are the progeny of laying workers. The queens mate with males outside the nest, and after a few days or weeks of freedom they dig into sod or other material for hibernation. In the early fall, when no more female eggs are being laid by the exhausted old queen, the proportion of males increases and the colony gradually dies out. During the senescent period, scavenging larvae of moths and beetles rapidly destroy the nest.

Many genera of bees have become specialized as social parasites—they live not on the tissues but on the food of their hosts. They are parasitic on other bees in all cases and, since they belong to various branches of the bee family tree, it is apparent that the para-

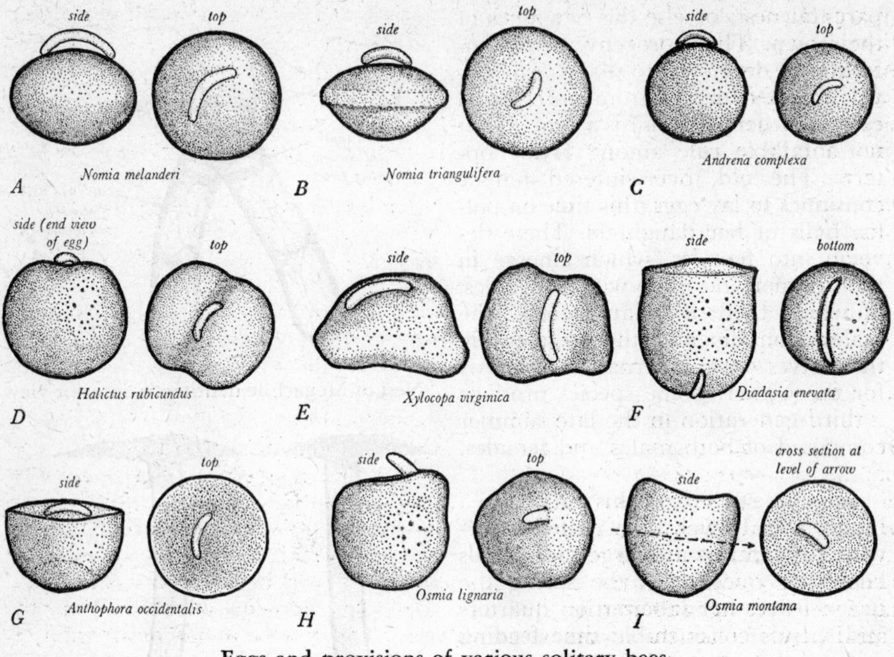

Eggs and provisions of various solitary bees.

sitic habit arose independently many times. A number of genera of parasitic bees are closely related to their hosts.

Despite their diversity, parasitic bees all operate in much the same manner. The female spends most of her time searching for nests of her host. When she finds one, she waits for a propitious moment to slip in and place an egg on a completed pollen ball before the cell is sealed. Apparently the host bee then seals the cell without recognizing that one of the eggs is not her own. The parasite is well protected with heavy armor and a long sting in case the foraging host returns and finds her in the nest. The young larva of the parasitic bee has long jaws adapted for piercing the egg or young larva of the host. When this is accomplished, the intruder develops on the stored food just as if it were the rightful progeny of the host.

Let us now consider the usefulness of wild bees in the pollination of specific crops. Although wild bees supplement the activities of honey bees in the pollination of many crops such as sweetclover and most of the fruits and cruciferous vegetables, honey bees are apparently at least as efficient and need only be supplied in reasonable numbers to handle the job alone.

Red clover was recognized by Charles Darwin as a plant that requires bumble bees for satisfactory seed production. The flowers have a deep corolla tube and tend to produce little nectar. Consequently honey bees often find it difficult or unprofitable to take nectar from red clover. They can obtain pollen from it readily but more desirable sources of pollen in the vicinity may satisfy their needs. In New Zealand, where red clover is well adapted, seed production was almost nil until the end of the nineteenth century, when several species of bumble bees were successfully introduced and established. Bumble bees have longer tongues than honey bees, and most species regard red clover with special favor as a source of nectar and pollen. Apparently they have declined drastically in numbers in the United States since 1900. In only a few districts are they adequate for the pollination of red clover; even there they are unreliable because of yearly fluctuations in numbers. Fortunately in most regions honey bees, in sufficient numbers and properly managed, can be induced to pollinate red clover. Undeniably, however, a general increase in bumble bees in the red clover seed areas would be a boon.

Alfalfa presents a different problem. It is a favorite source of nectar for honey bees, especially in the West, but is not a preferred source of pollen. Honey bees pollinate most kinds of flowers equally well when gathering nectar or pollen, but in the case of alfalfa the nectar gatherer is able to "steal" nectar from the flower without tripping a special mechanism involved in the pollination process. Nectar gatherers accidentally trip a small percentage of the flowers they visit, but for effective pollination they must be present in great numbers—greater, in fact, than the beekeeper is generally willing to supply when a honey crop is his primary goal. In some places the seed growers have largely overcome this difficulty by paying beekeepers to overstock the alfalfa fields with honey bees, but this does not seem to work equally well everywhere. It also involves difficult problems in financial arrangements between seed growers and beekeepers and in maintenance of colony strength. In some areas, where 5 to 25 percent of the honey bees visiting alfalfa collect pollen, the problem is much less acute, and overstocking is practiced only for exceptionally high yields.

Many kinds of native bees visit alfalfa and most of them pollinate it efficiently, because they work it primarily for pollen, and trip the majority of the flowers they visit. Some species even seem to prefer alfalfa to neighboring pollen sources. Despite the variety of bees that visit alfalfa, however, there are not enough of them in most seed fields to provide adequate pollination—especially when the fields are large or an entire district is given over to seed production. The alkali bee is one of the few species that can build up sufficient numbers on small pieces of wasteland to pollinate extensive acreages of alfalfa. In a new seed district near Yakima, Wash., alkali bees are responsible for most of the pollination on thousands of acres of high-yielding alfalfa-seed fields. This bee is an important pollinator in localized areas in most of the States west of the Great Plains. In Canada leaf-cutting bees (Megachilidae) are generally credited with most of the pollination of alfalfa, although they can do a good job only on small acreages surrounded by much wild land. An important future development in pollination by wild bees may be in the production of foundation and registered seed stocks which require isolation in order to maintain their purity.

Fruit trees are pollinated principally by honey bees in this country. In most districts, however, various vernal species of wild bees have a supplementary role. Even syrphid flies and blow flies are important in some localities, notably in pear orchards. Honey bees are generally satisfactory pollinators of fruit except in parts of New England and eastern Canada where weather unfavorable for honey bee activity is customary during the apple-blossoming season. When they are present there, bumble bees and a few other species active at cooler temperatures are more satisfactory.

Tomatoes, peas, and string beans are examples of automatically self-pollinated crops. The principal existing varieties are highly self-fertile and apparently receive no benefit from the cross-pollination accomplished by insects. Various wild bees are more attracted than honey bees to those crops. For example, bumble bees collect pollen readily from tomatoes. Leaf-cutting bees are strongly attracted by certain varieties of peas. It is possible that wild bees could be important in the development of a hybrid-seed industry for several such vegetable crops.

Several small species of sweat bees appear to be the only bees that visit the flowers of beets in Utah. Beets are generally considered to be wind-pollinated, but insects are known to assist in the transfer of beet pollen. In Utah, where hybrid seed of sugar beets is being produced on experimental plots by planting alternate rows of male-sterile and pollen-parent varieties, the set of seed on the male-sterile lines is greatly enhanced by the presence of sweat bees. Such isolated experiences indicate that more seed crops are benefited by wild bees than is generally recognized.

Any attempts to conserve wild bees must be based on a knowledge of their habits and on a knowledge of the natural and man-made factors that operate against them.

Even in environments undisturbed by man, wild bees fall prey to an assortment of natural enemies. Philanthinid wasps store them as food for their larvae. Robber flies pounce on them in the air and drain them of blood. Ambush bugs and crab spiders lie in wait on the flowers for a meal of bee blood. Back at the nests, conopid flies perch on spears of grass and seize passing bees for long enough to force an egg between their abdominal segments, an egg that soon develops into a fat maggot occupying the entire body cavity of the host bee. Cuckoo bees lurk about the nesting sites and seize an opportunity when the mother bee is foraging to slip in and lay an egg in the cell being provisioned. Bee flies hover over the nest entrances and spray them with minute eggs. The eggs develop into hordes of spiny little maggots, which work their way into the bee cells before they are sealed and remain there until the bee larvae are full-grown. Only one maggot develops on a bee larva, but its persistent sucking gradually transfers the semiliquid contents of the bee larva into its own growing body and leaves only a dried-up husk. Toward the end of the nesting season, wingless velvet ants crawl over the ground in the late afternoon, searching for any evidence of a nest. Once they find it, they force their way in, chew a hole through the host cocoon, and deposit an egg on the prepupa within. The invader then repairs the hole in the cocoon with salivary material and covers up the nest, leaving her offspring to fatten on its cell mate in security.

In general, the gregarious species, more than the strictly solitary ones, are seriously harmed by parasites. *Anthophora occidentalis,* a large western bee that nests gregariously in clay banks, is parasitized in Utah by a chalcid wasp, three meloid beetles, a clerid beetle, a velvet ant, two parasitic bees, and a bee fly. Total parasitism in some sites runs as high as 50 percent. The alkali bee, which nests by thousands in flat, alkaline ground, is parasitized in Utah by one parasitic bee, one meloid beetle, one conopid fly, and one bee fly. The first three are of minor importance, but the bee fly (*Heterostylum robustum*) nearly wiped out several large aggregations in Cache Valley in 1947; since then it has held them down, with parasitism as high as 90 percent. Strangely enough, this same fly occurs in the large nesting areas of central Utah, but only a few maggots have been found in thousands of cells examined.

Diseases are found among wild bees just as they are among honey bees. Infections resembling the foul broods of honey bees have not been observed among the native species, but very likely they exist. Certainly, larvae in their cells in the ground are frequently seen to sicken and die. Probably the development of organisms on the stored food is more serious to the wild bees. Various types of mold attack the pollens and some invade the bodies of the bee larvae, although that may usually be secondary after the larva is weakened on account of the moldy food supply. On the wet soil used by the alkali bee the pollen balls may suddenly liquefy, in which case the larva quickly dies. In some sites this has been observed in as many as one-quarter of the cells. Diseases of adults are not often seen but would usually be difficult to observe or evaluate. In California in the spring of 1934 a large population of *Andrena complexa* gathering food from buttercups became infested with a fungus (probably *Empusa* sp.) and most of them died, still clinging to their host plants.

The impression should not be gained that predators, parasites, and diseases are so serious that wild bees have no chance to increase. In central Utah the many kinds of insects and pathogens attacking brood of the alkali bee prevented only 30 percent from emerging over a period of 3 years. During this period the known nesting sites increased in size and several new sites were founded.

Predators and parasites of wild bees will probably prove difficult to control. The life history of many of them is so tied to that of their hosts that selective control measures may be impossible.

Spoilage of the stores and molding of the larvae have been seen to increase following rain during the active nesting period of several species that nest in the soil. It is obvious that irrigation and floodwater over the nests would be harmful then. Even during the dormant season, standing water would cause trouble, depending on the soil type and the species of the bees.

The principal limiting factor in numbers of wild bees appears to be available forage. Particularly is that true in wild or thinly settled land. The close association between species of bees and particular genera of flowers was probably developed as a response to competition for forage; the less aggressive types had to specialize to survive.

Competition has similarly forced many bees to restrict their season of activity to avoid periods of drought. In desert areas most bees can remain dormant for several years, if necessary, until there is enough moisture for blossoming of their host plants.

Forage for bees is not generally abundant in densely timbered territory, in deserts, or in open prairies. It is more often suitable for large populations of bees in transitional zones at the edges of deserts or forests, in hilly country, or in abandoned agricultural areas that are reverting to forest. Forage and bees are also usually abundant for limited periods in semiarid country where rain falling during a restricted season gives rise to short but intense periods of bloom. Some cultivated areas are highly productive of forage; a common condition is for flowers to be produced in greater quantity but lesser variety than before cultivation.

For bees to build up sufficient numbers of overwintering forms for a good emergence the following year, there must be a continuity of bloom during the season of foraging activity. The interrupted bloom common to most agricultural areas is thought to be largely responsible for the small existing populations of wild bees. For example, it has been stated that wild bees will increase in alfalfa-seed-producing areas when the cutting schedule allows for a constant supply of bloom. Applied to wild bees in general, the statement is based on an oversimplified notion of their life histories. It would apply best to leaf-cutting bees, most of which, in Utah at least, have activity periods involving two to three generations, which last through the blossoming period of alfalfa. Good forage and weather conditions in the spring before alfalfa blooms are probably more important for bees like honey bees, bumble bees, and sweat bees, which have a long season. Bees like *Nomia,* which do not appear until late summer, or *Osmia,* which disappear shortly after the first blooming of alfalfa, would be benefited more by a single cutting designed to achieve the maximum bloom at the proper time.

The value of spring forage for bees with a long season is illustrated by events in an isolated alfalfa-seed district near Fredonia, Ariz. Bumble bees were abundant in the summer of 1949 and provided excellent pollination for the alfalfa. An unprecedented drought in the area in 1950 prevented any spring bloom and, although queens were seen in the spring, there were no workers in the summer for pollination. It is likely in this instance that a few irrigated acres of an early-blooming crop like vetch would have allowed the bumble bees to increase as usual.

More than half of our species of bees have a short season of activity. In most cases the timing of emergence of such bees with the first blooming of their natural host plants is remarkable. In the Sacramento Valley of California, where a nesting site of two species of *Andrena* was under observation, emergence of the bees and the first appearance of willow blossoms took place on the same day. Bad weather during the short period of activity of such bees is apt to be their most serious hazard.

The presence of permanent and suitable nesting sites may be as important as abundant forage for the maintenance of effective numbers of wild pollinators. The decline in populations of wild bees in agricultural areas has probably been brought about at least as much by destruction of nesting sites as by destruction of forage. In this connection it is interesting to speculate upon the probable history of populations of the alkali bee in central Utah. In view of the fact that common, introduced plants like alfalfa, sweetclover, and Russian-thistle are almost the sole forage plants for these bees in the area, it appears that they must have actually increased following the appearance of white settlers. Many statements from the older farmers in the region attest to their abundance in the early days of alfalfa-seed growing. However, as cultivation increased, the nesting sites, although generally in poor soil, were plowed up and planted to alfalfa. Now only scattered areas are close enough to remaining nesting sites to be benefited. The best seed district in Utah from the standpoint of pollination by alkali bees is adjacent to many acres of permanent saltgrass pasture that furnishes plenty of suitable land for nesting.

Intensification of land utilization has played havoc with the nesting sites of wild bees. The old rail fences provided sites for many timber-inhabiting bees like leaf-cutting bees and *Osmia* and provided a network of areas of undisturbed ground for nesting and of wild plants for forage. The clean cultivation now practiced to destroy weeds and soil-inhabiting insects is wiping out many of these last sanctuaries. It may soon become necessary to determine in each area how valuable the wild bees are for the pollination of crops and whether nesting sites can be reserved for them in a manner compatible with good agriculture.

Destruction of harmful organisms together with conservation of beneficial ones should be our aim. Too often the ravages of the destructive forms are so conspicuous that we lose sight of the value of the beneficial forms. This is clearly evident in the use of insecticides. The necessity for insecticidal control for many insect pests is unquestioned. But it is becoming increasingly apparent that the simple question, "Will this application provide economic control of the pest concerned?" must be expanded to, "Will this application fit into a general program calculated to control all important pests without presenting a hazard to health or seriously affecting beneficial parasites, predators, and pollinators?"

Conservation programs for wild bees have never been tried or even formulated on an area-wide basis. Although it is encouraging to know that a few seed growers are taking steps to protect known nesting sites, it is disheartening to know that most farmers do not appreciate the value of wild bees and are unlikely to take readily to conservation measures involving setting aside pieces of land and complicating the cropping procedures.

The following general measures should tend to conserve and even increase the numbers of many kinds of wild bees. Details for carrying them out would depend upon many local factors; local conditions would probably call for certain additional measures.

1. Apply insecticides to blossoming plants only when there is no other way to control the harmful insects. Such applications should be made between 7 p. m. and 7 a. m. and should contain only toxaphene, methoxychlor, or other toxicants demonstrated to be relatively safe for bees when used at the proper strength.

2. Provide a continuous supply of bloom throughout the season. Forage crops such as vetch, clover, and alfalfa make a good series lasting from late spring through summer. Fruit trees, maples, hawthorns, elderberries, and other hedgerow plants generally provide needed spring forage. Of course, each area would be best served by the plants suited to its own climate and agricultural needs.

3. Establish and maintain hedgerows around agricultural fields and along roadways, ditch banks, and canals. Pithy-stemmed plants such as elderberry, sumac, and tree-of-Heaven should be encouraged in such hedgerows. Light browsing would make them more suitable for nesting than if they were left undisturbed.

4. Hollow-stemmed plants such as milkthistle, wild parsnip, canebrake, and teasel should be broken over after the stalks are well developed. These will provide nesting places for leaf-cutting bees and harbor many hibernating species.

5. Establish and protect areas of bunch-type perennial grasses, especially along the tops of banks. They will provide nesting places for bumble bees and tend to stabilize and shelter the banks. Banks so protected, especially if nearly vertical, are ideal nesting places for many kinds of bees.

6. Preserve known nesting sites of gregarious bees from being cultivated, flooded, trampled, or encroached upon by dense vegetation. Expand the available nesting ground if necessary, and establish new areas with the same conditions as populated sites. In the past few years many nesting sites of the alkali bee have been discovered by alfalfa-seed growers. Once apprised of their value, the growers have usually been willing and even anxious to keep them in an unaltered state. Several and perhaps most of the gregarious species of bees migrate in large groups to newly prepared areas. If other conditions for population increase are favorable, it should not take long for new areas to be populated.

Another approach to the problem is through better utilization of available populations of native pollinators. The following principles should apply to many crops.

1. Grow the crop in areas where native pollinators are known to be abundant. In most cases such areas will be adjacent to or surrounded by untilled land.

2. Limit the acreage of the crop in bloom at one time to that which the native pollinators can handle.

3. Reduce competitive sources of pollen and nectar.

4. Time the blooming of the crop with the period of greatest natural abundance of the pollinator. (In general, only forage crops would be concerned here.)

GEORGE E. BOHART, *a member of the division of bee culture of the Bureau of Entomology and Plant Quarantine, is in charge of the pollination studies in connection with the production of legume seed, conducted at the Legume Seed Research Laboratory in Logan, Utah.*

The attention of the reader is directed to the section of color drawings in which appears a drawing of an alkali bee (Nomia sp.) tripping an alfalfa blossom and the nesting sites and life stages of the bees. Opposite the drawing is a description of the life history and pollination activities of alkali bees.

Breeding Bees

Otto Mackensen, William C. Roberts

Because honey bees produce honey and beeswax and help pollinate many plants, improving them through breeding benefits beekeepers and farmers.

Man has kept bees for ages, but selective breeding of bees has lagged far behind that of other domesticated animals and plants. The main reasons therefor stem from the social nature of honey bees, the mating of the queen and drone away from the hive, and a lethal mechanism that may kill a large percentage of eggs and brood.

Honey bees will not mate, reproduce, or survive in isolated pairs as nonsocial insects do. Each colony consists of a fertile queen and her many infertile daughters, the worker bees. All contribute to the performance of the colony. The colony rather than the individual is the unit upon which the selection of breeding individuals must be based. After a superior colony has been chosen, one can only use as breeding individuals the virgin queens that are sisters to the workers and the drones that are sons of the queen.

The breeding quality of a colony can be obscured by environmental factors. A colony's large honey crop might be the result of its robbing activities rather than its industry in bringing in nectar from the field. A queen might have a high egg-production potential, but the actual number of eggs she lays each day depends on the size of the population of the colony, its food, and space.

The drone, which develops from an unfertilized egg, is haploid—he carries only a single set of chromosomes and genes, the tiny elements of heredity. The sperms he produces are all genetically identical; they carry the same genes as the drone himself. The queens and workers, developed from fertilized eggs, are diploid; they carry a double set of chromosomes and genes. In the production of eggs, the genes segregate, so that each egg carries a sample half of the genes of the queen. A queen may mate with one or more drones, but after her mating period she does not mate again.

The sperms are stored in the queen in a spherical structure called the spermatheca, and released a few at a time as the eggs are laid. If a queen is mated to one drone, all the workers of the hive receive identical genes from the drone and all the genetic variability comes from the queen. The same is true of queens reared from the colony. If the queen mates with two or more drones, there will be greater variability in the workers.

The control of parentage obviously is essential to breed improvement. In this the honey bee presents a special problem because the queen leaves the hive to mate. She returns in about 15 or 20 minutes, bearing evidence of having copulated, but how and where mating takes place is still a debated point. Attempts to mate queens in confinement have failed.

Of the various methods employed to control mating, two have proved most practical: Isolation, by placing colonies containing the breeding individuals (virgin queens and drones) in a location far away from other bees; and artificial insemination, by taking semen from one or more drones and injecting it into the queen by means of special instruments.

Each method has advantages and disadvantages and a place in breeding programs.

At a mating station several types of virgin queens can be mated at once and in large numbers. Only one type of drone can be allowed to fly there at one time, however. Because stray swarms may drift into the area unnoticed, one can never be certain that isolation is entirely effective, even when requirements of distance have been met. Individual matings cannot be distinguished because many queens mate more than once.

With instrumental insemination, on the other hand, control of parentage can be absolute. Many types of drones can be used simultaneously in the same queen yard and individual- or multiple-drone matings can be made at will. Because the operation is time-consuming, however, only a limited number of inseminations can be made.

THE DISTANCES required for complete isolation at a mating station under various conditions have not been determined fully. In some experiments, virgin queens did not mate when the nearest source of drones was 6 miles away. A shorter distance may be all right when enough drones of the desired type are provided or when the location is geographically isolated, as by mountains or a body of water.

For 2 years the division of bee culture of the Bureau of Entomology and Plant Quarantine maintained a mating station at Grand Isle on the marshy coast of Louisiana. It was 20 miles from other bees and was adequately isolated. Queens and drones of a highly selected yellow strain that were mated there showed no evidence of having mated with strange drones. Kelleys Island, Ohio, 4.5 miles from the mainland in Lake Erie, has been used since 1948 as a mating station for the mass production of hybrid queens. It also is adequately isolated. Virgin queens did not mate during a complete lack of drones on the island although mainland colonies 5 or 6 miles away contained drones. Islands, marshy coasts, and desert areas probably offer the best locations for isolated mating stations.

INSTRUMENTAL INSEMINATION can be learned by anyone, but because expensive equipment is needed and it takes so much time, few beekeepers have made use of it.

The principal instruments needed are a stereoscopic microscope, a device for administering carbon dioxide as an anesthetic, and the insemination apparatus itself (the manipulating stand, holding hooks, queen holder, and syringe). The procedure, as we practiced it in 1952 and the results to be expected are given in the paragraphs that follow.

The queen is allowed to back into the queen holder tube until the end of her abdomen projects. She is secured by means of a stopper, through which carbon dioxide is flowing, and placed in the manipulating stand. Then the chitinous plates at the tip of the abdomen are separated with the holding hooks to expose the genital opening. Semen is taken into the syringe from the drone and injected into the genital opening of the queen. The operation takes about 5 minutes.

The drone penis is relatively large and in copulation turns inside out, bringing the semen to the end of the everted penis. In artificial insemination, partial eversion is brought about by exposure to chloroform fumes and completed by pressure. The semen appears at the end of the everted penis as a cream-colored fluid accompanied by a white mucus. After a little practice, the operator can easily take the semen into the syringe.

A tonguelike structure, the valve fold, obstructs the opening to the oviduct. The fold must be pulled aside to permit the end of the syringe to pass. The semen must be deposited in the oviduct for successful insemination. The complete or partial failure of early investigators was probably due in large part to ignorance of this structure or disregard for it. From the oviducts, the sperms migrate into the spermatheca.

During the insemination operation, carbon dioxide is allowed to flow through the queen holder. It acts as an anesthetic and it also stimulates early oviposition. Properly used, it reduces the average age at initial oviposition from about 40 days after emergence in untreated queens to 11.5 days, which is about the age of initial oviposition after natural mating. Three exposures of 10 minutes' duration are given at 1-day intervals. With or without insemination, this will stimulate egg production in queens. Other anesthetics and electric shock have the same effect.

By using a counting chamber slide to count samples of sperm with a microscope, we found that the spermathecae of naturally mated queens contained an average of 5.73 million sperms and those of queens inseminated with sperm from a single drone contained an average of 0.87 million. About 2.5 cubic millimeters can usually be taken from three drones. The average number of sperms reaching the spermatheca when this amount was given one, two, three, and four times were 2.97, 4.11, 4.85, and 5.52 million, respectively. The number varied greatly in individual matings, but the variation was not so great when the amount of semen and number of injections increased. When three and four inseminations were given, the variation was less than that of naturally mated queens. Two inseminations of about 3 to 4 cubic millimeters have given excellent results. Queens so inseminated have performed as well as naturally mated queens of the same parentage.

Queens that lay unfertilized eggs in worker cells, where they intend to lay fertilized eggs, are called drone layers. With single-drone inseminations, a few queens will be partial or complete drone layers at the start and others will later become drone layers. Some have performed satisfactorily in small hives for a year or more, however. When larger inseminations are given, drone layers are rarely found at the beginning of egg laying.

The percentage of good laying queens obtained varies with the stock and rearing conditions. The results we got in two lines during the 1950 season give an idea of what might be expected. Of 38 queens inseminated in one line, 36 (95 percent) started laying; 33 (87 percent) were considered good queens. In another slightly inbred line, 32 queens were inseminated; 25 (78 percent) started laying and 22 (69 percent) were considered good queens. All in both groups produced good worker brood.

Several men have made noteworthy contributions. Lloyd R. Watson, of Alfred, N. Y., developed a workable syringe and was the first to demonstrate (in 1926) a successful technique that could be used by others. W. J. Nolan, of the division of bee culture, developed the basic manipulating apparatus and queen holder. Harry H. Laidlaw, of the University of California at Davis, made a detailed anatomical study of the reproductive organs of bees and pointed out the importance of the valve fold.

We have been striving to improve the instrumental insemination apparatus and technique since 1935. We found that semen could be collected more quickly from the completely everted penis than from the seminal vesicles or dissected parts of the partially everted penis, as earlier workers had done.

The greatest improvement in apparatus was that made in the syringe. A glass syringe tip was constructed that tapered at the end to an outside diameter under 0.3 millimeter (0.012 inch) so that it could be inserted into the oviduct, which usually has a diameter of 0.33 millimeter. The plunger barrel had an inside diameter of 0.41 millimeter; that was large enough to give the syringe a capacity of about 3 cubic millimeters, or the amount of semen

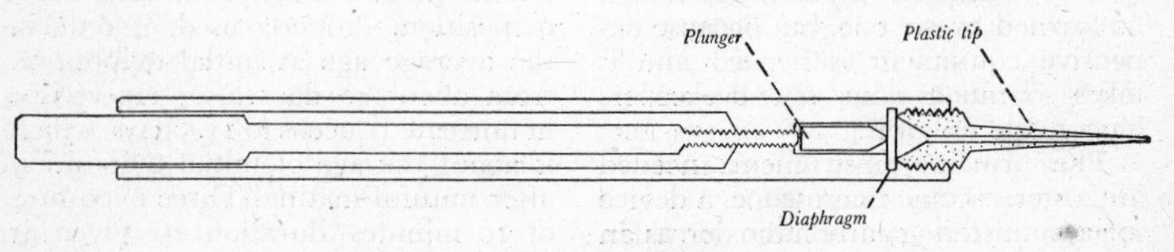

Sketch of section through syringe.

usually obtained from three to four drones. Later a less breakable tip of the same type was made of plastic.

A syringe was finally designed that does away with the troublesome tight-fitting plunger. It employs a rubber diaphragm. The base of the tip fits against the diaphragm and has a cone-shaped depression into which the diaphragm is pushed by a plunger activated by a screw. In use, the tip is first filled with water, then some of the water is pushed out, and semen taken up in its place. This tip has a main barrel of 0.025 inch (inside diameter) and then tapers 0.156 inch to an inside diameter of 0.006 inch. The outside diameter at the end is 0.010 inch (the average oviduct diameter is 0.013 inch).

A LETHAL MECHANISM in bees complicates breeding. To clarify this mechanism some preliminary explanations are necessary.

We have explained the location of the hereditary determiners, the genes, in linear order on chromosomes and how they are inherited in bees. When genes are paired as in the diploid queen, and one member has a different action than the other, each gene is called an allele of the other. Individuals in the population may carry still other alleles at the same locus on the chromosomes, and there may be a large series, each having a slightly different action. Fertilization may bring together various combinations of these alleles.

Genes have various effects. Some have detrimental effects. In some instances this effect is so great that the gene kills the individual inheriting it. Such a gene is called a lethal.

The lethals we are concerned with are members of a series of alleles which we have designated as *a, b, c, d,* et cetera. Females (queens and workers) are always heterozygous—that is, they contain two of these alleles that are different, as, for example, *a* and *b*. A queen of this composition produces eggs one-half of which are *a* and one-half are *b*. Since the drones develop from unfertilized eggs, one-half of the sons are *a* and produce only *a* sperm, and the other half are *b* and produce only *b* sperm.

When an egg such as *a* is fertilized by a sperm carrying a different lethal allele such as *b*, a queen or worker having the composition *a/b* results. If it is fertilized by a sperm carrying a similar allele (*a*), this homozygous combination (*a/a*) causes the individual to die before maturity, usually in the egg stage. When a queen (*a/b*) is mated to a single drone carrying a different lethal allele such as *c*, then all the progeny resulting from fertilized eggs will have lethal alleles dissimilar (*a/c, b/c*) and will be viable—able to live to maturity. Efficiency in the brood nest will be high, and a populous colony will result. If, on the other hand, she is mated with a single drone having a similar lethal allele such as *b*, then one-half of her progeny resulting from fertilized eggs will be *a/b* and viable, and one-half will be homozygous (*a/a*) and will die. Because most of the dying eggs are not removed until hatching time, 3 days after they are laid, efficiency is low in such a brood nest, and a weak colony will result.

Failure of selection to eliminate the lethals indicates that a nonlethal gene does not exist at this locus. Inbreeding reduces the number of lethals in the population and increases the chances of similar lethals meeting to produce low viability. Outbreeding brings new lethals into the population and this increases the frequency of high viability.

A similar series of lethals in a related insect *Bracon hebetor,* better known to geneticists as Habrobracon, has been studied by P. W. Whiting, of the University of Pennsylvania. In that insect a definite association with sex has been established. Such an association has not been proved in the honey bee, where promotion of outbreeding may be justification enough for the existence of such a wasteful lethal mechanism.

As long as individual matings are made, the percentage of viable fertil-

970134°—52——10

ized eggs will either be near 100 percent or near 50 percent. Of course, there may be a small percentage of deaths from other causes. If mated naturally, many queens will mate twice and often intermediate viabilities will result, depending on the composition of queen and drone and the proportion of types of sperm reaching the spermatheca. The same is true when several drones are used in artificial insemination.

By a series of individual matings something can be learned of the opposing lethal alleles in a given cross. If all the progenies are highly viable, then the opposing lethal alleles are different; if some of the progenies are poorly viable, however, then some of the opposing alleles are similar.

Lethal alleles can be identified most easily when we cross lines that contain only two alleles each. Crosses by individual matings between such lines will then fall into one of three classes: (1) All progenies of low viability, showing that the alleles are the same; (2) all progenies highly viable, showing the alleles to be different; and (3) one-half the progenies highly viable and one-half poorly viable, showing that the two lines have one allele in common. This procedure has been used to establish two-allele tester lines with definitely identified alleles for use in determining the alleles of any untested breeding stock.

Two-allele lines can be readily established in one of two ways: (1) By making individual matings and breeding from a low-viability progeny or (2) by mating unfertilized queens to their own sons. The second way is done by inducing virgin queens to lay by exposure to carbon dioxide, rearing drones from them, and mating these drones back to their mothers. As the virgin queen can contain only two lethal alleles, there are only two alleles in the line established.

Lethal alleles therefore are important in bee breeding. Matings that involve similar alleles cause low viability of the brood and lower colony population. This in turn reduces productivity of the colony. Selection for such qualities as honey production, which is profoundly influenced by colony population, is inefficient unless the lethal-allele conditions are comparable in all colonies. Because the lethals cannot be eliminated by selection, some form of controlled hybridization seems most promising.

THE EARLY BEE BREEDER raised virgin queens from his best colonies and thus controlled the female parent. He attempted to control male parentage by stimulating certain queens (colonies) to produce great numbers of drones. Thus he increased the chances that his selected queens would mate with these selected drones. Some mass selection thus has been practiced since early times. Progress was made in selecting for body color, type, and temperament, but we doubt whether much improvement was made in less easily measured characteristics, such as honey production and vigor. In fact, continuous selection for color, type, and temperament has resulted in lower vigor and honey yield, as exemplified by the golden bees developed in the United States. They looked beautiful but were inferior in productivity.

Seeing no real improvement through mass selection, the American bee breeder sought new stock from other beekeepers in this country or through the importation of races and strains from abroad. In mixing them with his own stock, he intentionally or unwittingly was hybridizing two races or strains. The superiority of the first few generations was inaccurately accredited to the new stock. Hybrids, of course, do not breed true, and it was impossible to maintain the superiority in later generations. As inbreeding progressed, low viability due to the mating of similar lethal alleles became more and more frequent.

The precepts of breed improvement successfully used by early plant and animal breeders included such ideas as *like produces like or the likeness of some ancestor, inbreeding produces prepotency or refinement,* and *breed the best to the best.* The development of all breeds of livestock has included some inbreeding to produce uniformity within the breeds.

If the beekeeper follows in the footsteps of the animal breeder and tries to fix characteristics by inbreeding or line breeding, he immediately runs into difficulties. These systems of breeding will almost invariably increase the proportion of low-viability matings by reducing the number of lethal alleles in the line. What the beekeeper gains in uniformity and fixation of desirable characteristics, therefore, might be more than nullified by increase in mortality.

In order to produce uniform colonies with high-viability brood, one has to cross races and strains that are likely to contain different lethal alleles or specially selected lines of known lethal-allele composition.

Hybrid breeding seems to be the bee breeders' best solution to their special problems. Plants and animals have frequently been improved by crossing. Hybrid plants are generally taller than their parents, larger in size, more vigorous, longer lived, and more resistant to diseases. When it comes to heredity, animals behave as plants do. The effects of hybridizing chickens, mice, guinea pigs, and rabbits are the same as in plants. The superiority of hybrid corn is attested by the fact that 81 percent of all corn planted in the United States in 1951 was hybrid seed. Hybrid bees therefore appear to offer the surest and fastest method of producing superiority in production, egg viability, and performance.

Inbreeding, followed by crossing, has been the successful method employed by plant and animal breeders. Inbreeding is the mating of closely related individuals such as parent-offspring, brother-sister, or cousins. After several generations, each inbred line becomes constant and uniform within itself but distinctly different from other inbred lines. Inbred lines go through a purification process such that only those individuals that possess much of the best that was in the original stocks in the beginning can survive. Although these inbred lines themselves will be inferior, they have possibilities as parents. By crossing inbred lines, one can gather together again the best qualities that have been distributed to the several inbred lines and create a new variety. Size, vigor, fertility, and viability can be fully restored in the hybrid with the advantage of real improvement through the elimination of undesirable characters.

Crosses among certain inbred lines have shown a combination of desired characters that are definitely superior to those of the stocks from which the inbreds originated. This superiority could not have been reached as readily in the original stock by selection alone.

To produce hybrid bees, the breeder may cross different races, strains, or inbred lines of bees. Unless the races or strains are homozygous for the desired characters, the hybrids will be variable. Furthermore, the hybrids produced the following year or from other crosses of the same races or strains will differ from each other. The only sure method of having uniform hybrids is to cross strains or inbred lines that are homozygous for the desired characters.

To produce inbred lines, the bee breeder must know which matings to make to obtain the desired inbreeding with the least expense of time and labor. Because of the mating habits of bees, it is an economic necessity that all inbreeding matings be made by artificial insemination. The first chart shows the percentage of inbreeding in successive generations by several systems of inbreeding possible in bees. The percentage of inbreeding is the percentage of heterozygous loci in the original selected individuals that become homozygous by inbreeding. Inbreeding has no effect on genes already homozygous in the line so we are only concerned with those loci that are originally heterozygous. Since the bee breeder cannot know which genes were

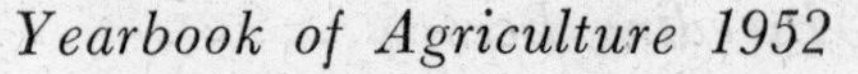

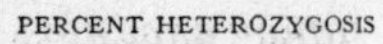
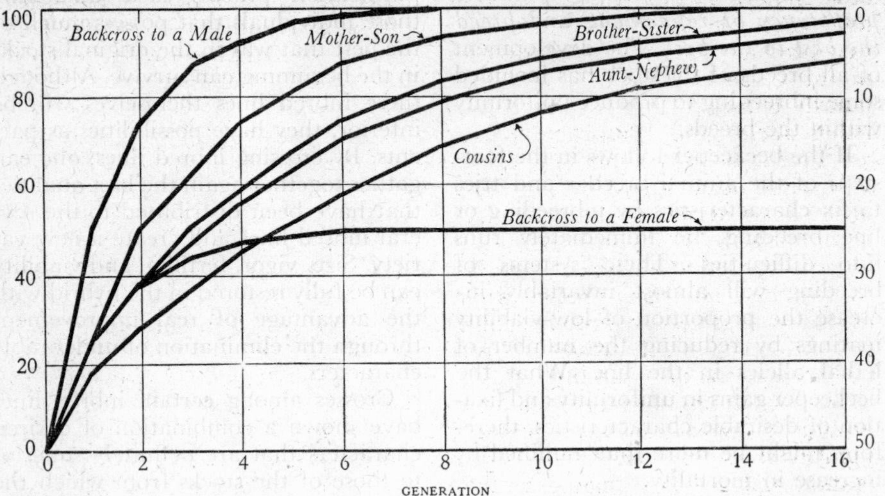

1. The percentage of inbreeding and the percentage of heterozygosis (assuming the initial value to be 50 percent) in successive generations of various systems in inbreeding in honey bees.

originally heterozygous and what effect each gene has, he can only measure the relative purity of the stocks by the percentage of inbreeding.

The two systems of inbreeding that increase homozygosis fastest (backcross to a male and mother-son matings) are not advisable economically. Loss of breeding individuals and consequently loss of inbred lines is high when these systems are followed exclusively. The third most rapid method of increasing homozygosis is brother-sister matings. This is the most practical system. Because drones mature more slowly than queens, backcrossing to a female for the first two generations produces inbreeding 37.5 percent faster, in time consumed per generation, than do the brother-sister matings, as illustrated in the first two generations in the second chart. Thus a combination of backcrossing to the original selected queen for the first two generations, followed by brother-sister matings in all future generations, is recommended for the production of inbred lines in the shortest period of time. Since all matings in this system can be multiple-drone matings (all drones of each mating are sons of one queen), success in producing and maintaining inbred lines is insured.

The bee breeder should know what inbreeding will do to his stocks. If he starts an inbred line by backcrossing for two generations and then makes brother-sister matings, he should expect that each line will become more and more uniform as inbreeding progresses. Most noticeable, however, for the first few generations will be the quality of the brood.

If queen B, a daughter of A, is mated to several drones (sons of A), the brood viability of queen B will average 75 percent. A daughter queen C is then mated to sons of queen A and will have brood viability that will average either 75 or 50 percent. If it is 50 percent, the line has been reduced to two lethal alleles and the brood of queens D, E, and F will also be 50 percent if mated as shown in the diagram. If brood of queen C is 75 percent viable, then that of D may also be 75 percent but somewhere not far from E or F in the diagram the viability will probably drop to 50 percent and all future generations will remain at that level. However, by selection it is possible to keep viability at 75 percent but the breeder would be reducing the effectiveness of inbreeding slightly by selection for heterozygosity of lethal alleles and other genes linked to these. It is probably advisable to select the matings that produce 50 percent viable brood in the C or D generation and thus quickly reduce all inbred lines to two lethal alleles and consequently have 50-percent viability in all inbred lines. If this is done, an analysis of the lethal alleles in all inbred lines is more readily accomplished. By test crossing to identify the lethal alleles in each line, the breeder can then predict which crosses will give high brood viability in hybrids and which crosses will give intermediate or low viability.

In one season of inbreeding it is possible to get as far as producing a number of sister queens of the D generation and get these mated to their brothers (drones produced by their mother queen C). These queens will be wintered, and the following year the breeder can make test crosses while continuing to inbreed the lines by brother-sister matings. It is advisable to test the inbred lines at the E generation of queens (50-percent inbred). One generation of brother-sister mating should be made each year after the first season. This insures continuing the inbred lines until they are selected in hybrid combinations.

The bee breeder can accomplish very little by selection while inbreeding. He can surely select queens and drones in each generation for color and general appearance. In a sense he can progeny-test each generation by measuring such qualities in the workers as tongue length, wing length, color, or temper—but the economic value of bees is measured by the total productivity of the entire colony.

Thus very little selection can be made by testing inbreds as inbreds mated to drones of the same line. Since viability of brood in two-allele lines is only 50 percent, colonies headed by inbred queens lacking in vigor do not develop sufficient populations to accurately evaluate such economically important characteristics as honey production, swarming tendencies, and wintering qualities. This selection in inbreds as inbreds is supplemental rather than substitutable for selection between inbred lines when in crosses with other inbred lines.

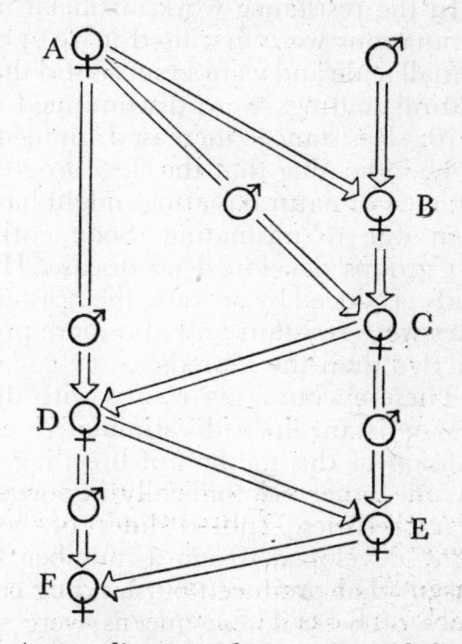

2. Arrow diagram of a recommended system of mating for inbreeding in bees. After two generations of back-crossing to a selected queen the line is continued by brother-sister matings.

The division of bee culture undertook bee breeding in earnest in 1937 when a program for development of disease-resistant strains was initiated. Earlier work had been limited largely to control of mating, introduction of races, and studies of the characteristics of races.

The program was begun in cooperation with the State experiment stations of Iowa, Texas, Wisconsin, and Wyoming. Work in Iowa had shown that some stocks were more resistant than others. Each year colonies headed by daughters of highly resistant queens of the previous year were tested. The queens were mated at isolated mating stations. In the three principal lines carried until 1945, one showed definite increase in resistance, another less increase in resistance, and a third line apparently little or no increase. The lines became stabilized at characteristic levels considerably below complete resistance. Selection of negative colonies (showing no disease after inoculation) was more effective than selection of recovery colonies (recovered from disease produced in inoculation).

In the resistance work, artificial inseminations were first used in 1943 on a small scale and were so successful that natural matings were discontinued in 1946. Resistance increased immediately, indicating that the slow progress with use of natural matings might have been due to mismating. Soon entire test groups developed no disease. Hybrids produced by crossing the resistant lines were resistant and also more productive than the inbreds.

These encouraging results with disease-resistant hybrids stimulated expansion of this method of breeding to include other economically important characteristics. Inbred lines of bees were developed from a number of queens that produced outstanding colonies of bees. These queens were selected because their colonies not only produced large crops of honey but possessed other desired qualities such as gentleness, vigor, high egg production, or nonswarming tendencies. After the lines were inbred, they were crossed and tested in various hybrid combinations. Artificially inseminated queens were tested for honey production for the first time in 1943. As expected, differences between various hybrid combinations were apparent early in the breeding and testing program.

It soon became obvious that testing of hybrids under a wide range of climatic and environmental conditions was desirable. The Department of Agriculture, division of bee culture, therefore entered into an agreement with the nonprofit Honey Bee Improvement Cooperative Association. Through this agency a large number of hybrid queens of various types were distributed and tested by beekeepers throughout the United States. The queens are produced on Kelleys Island in Lake Erie. As the island is isolated, one can control matings. All hybrid queens are allowed to mate naturally to the drones produced by other unrelated hybrid queens. Thus the test colonies are headed by single-hybrid queens and the workers in these colonies are double hybrids. Having only one such isolated mating station, the various types of single-hybrid queens must all be mated to drones of a single type of hybrid. Some of the queens are tested at the various bee culture laboratories of the Department of Agriculture. The Department also is continuing to test other hybrids that are artificially inseminated.

Beekeepers who have obtained test queens have been favorably impressed by the superiority of certain double hybrids, which have produced as much as 50 percent more honey than comparable commercial lines. The hybrids also have shown greater uniformity, more brood per colony, and brood of higher viability than the commercial lines.

We have seen that the problems involved in breeding bees are too great for the individual breeder to go far in improving his own stock. He can do little more than avoid the mating of closely related individuals, select for high brood quality, and outcross to unrelated strains whenever low brood viability becomes too frequent.

Breeding and testing have shown that hybridization can produce superior bees. The best solution is thus a hybrid-breeding program such as only State or Federal research organizations, widely supported cooperative organizations, or large commercial firms can conduct. The ultimate objective of such programs is a number of four-way hybrids adapted to different regions or systems of management. The research agencies can then supply the foundation stock for the production of large numbers of these hybrids.

Otto Mackensen *is in charge of the bee breeding work of the division of bee culture, Bureau of Entomology and Plant Quarantine. He has specialized in bee breeding and artificial insemination research since 1935, when he joined the staff of the Southern States Bee Culture Laboratory, which is maintained in cooperation with the Louisiana State University at Baton Rouge. Dr. Mackensen, a native of Texas, holds degrees from Texas Agricultural and Mechanical College and Texas University.*

WILLIAM C. ROBERTS, *an apiculturist in the Bureau of Entomology and Plant Quarantine, has been associated with the North Central States Bee Culture Laboratory and the University of Wisconsin since 1943. Dr. Roberts, a native of Louisiana, is a graduate of the Universities of Louisiana and Wisconsin. Between 1935 and 1943 he worked at the Southern States Bee Culture Laboratory at Baton Rouge, and was an instructor in apiculture at Louisiana State University. His present work in bee breeding includes supervision of the Kelleys Island, Ohio, hybrid queen production project.*

Suggested for further reading:

Harry H. Laidlaw, Jr.: Artificial Insemination of the Queen Bee (*Apis mellifera* L.), Morphological Basis and Results, *Journal of Morphology, volume 74, pages 429–465, 1944;* Development of Precision Instruments for Artificial Insemination of Queen Bees, *Journal of Economic Entomology, volume 42, pages 254–261, 1949.*

Otto Mackensen: Effect of Carbon Dioxide on Initial Oviposition of Artificially Inseminated and Virgin Queen Bees, *Journal of Economic Entomology, volume 40, pages 344–349, 1947;* A New Syringe for the Artificial Insemination of Queen Bees, *American Bee Journal, volume 88, page 412, 1948;* Viability and Sex Determination in the Honey Bee (*Apis mellifera* L.), *Genetics, volume 36, pages 500–509, 1951;* A Manual for the Artificial Insemination of Queen Bees, *with W. C. Roberts, Bureau of Entomology and Plant Quarantine, ET–250, 1948.*

William C. Roberts: The Performance of the Queen Bee, *American Bee Journal, volume 86, pages 185–186, 211, 1946;* Breeding Improved Honey Bees, *with Otto Mackensen, American Bee Journal, volume 91, pages 292–294, 328–330, 382–384, 418–421, 473–475, 1951.*

P. W. Whiting: Multiple Alleles in Sex Determination of Habrobracon, *Journal of Morphology, volume 66, pages 323–355, 1940;* Multiple Alleles in Complementary Sex Determination of Habrobracon, *Genetics, volume 28, pages 365–382, 1943.*

Insecticides and Bees

Frank E. Todd, S. E. McGregor

Bees are so important in agriculture and so important to so many of us that we cannot afford to destroy them along with the harmful insects.

Two-thirds of the 5,600,000 colonies of bees in the United States are east of the Mississippi River. About one-half of them are in the Southern States. Of the 1,946,000 colonies west of the Mississippi, the Plains States have about 30 percent, California 24 percent, and the Intermountain and the Southwestern States 20 percent each. Six percent are in the Pacific Northwest. Although 500,000 persons keep bees in the United States, 80 percent of the colonies belong to about 50,000 beekeepers, about 1,000 of whom depend on bees for their livelihood. The latter group controls about two-fifths of the colonies.

But the extensive use of insecticides has driven beekeeping out of many localities. In apple-growing areas, for example, growers have to pay rental fees to entice beekeepers into the areas during blossom time to insure pollination, and growers of legume seed are beginning to follow this practice. In many cotton-growing areas, spreading arsenical dusts by airplane has nearly wiped out the bee industry.

About three-fourths of the annual honey crop comes from cultivated alfalfa, buckwheat, clovers, cotton, and oranges. The honey crop is the beekeeper's source of livelihood, and unless it covers his expenses he cannot stay in business. A widespread abandonment of beekeeping in turn would reduce the supply of pollinators for agricultural crops. Although bees visit most of the flowering plants to obtain food for colony maintenance, few species contribute enough nectar to make a honey crop. Apple blossoms, for example, contribute pollen and nectar for colony maintenance, but apple honey is unknown on the market.

Dandelion, mustard, goldenrod, and gum weeds are examples of important sources of food for maintenance only; their elimination by weed spraying may limit the amount of beekeeping an area can support. Native bees depend on weeds even more than honey bees do. Their foods must be obtained locally. Often their survival requires a continuity of sources, usually weeds. Spraying grain fields in the Sacramento Valley of California to remove weeds has caused the near disappearance of star thistle honey from the market. Herbicides are also being applied along roadsides for sweetclover and mesquite, both important sources of the honey crop. Bees are not killed by weed sprays, but food sources may be seriously reduced by their widespread use.

Controlling harmful insects on agricultural crops is often beneficial to beekeeping. Almost always can insecticides be applied so as not to harm bees—but control programs that disregard bees usually are followed by an acute bee poison problem.

The problem began in the early 1870's. A strange malady appeared then among colonies of honey bees. In the spring dead bees piled up around the hives, colonies failed later to recover strength, and many died outright. The malady and the use of paris green to control codling moth on apples and pears appeared at the same time; the use of paris green spread rapidly and so did the sickness among bees. Beekeepers soon learned the source of trouble: The trees were being sprayed while they were in bloom.

C. M. Brose, of the Colorado Agricultural Experiment Station, in 1888 reported finding arsenic in dead bees fed london purple and paris green in sirup. He found no arsenic in the stored honey. A. J. Cook, of the Michigan Agricultural Experiment Station, reported that bees died soon after they fed on sirup or water containing london purple at the strengths used in spraying. He strongly advocated laws to prohibit the spraying of fruit trees in blossom.

Beekeepers made vigorous complaints. In 1891 the Association of Economic Entomologists appointed a committee to find an answer to the question: "Will arsenical sprays applied to flowering fruit trees kill honey bees?" The chairman was F. M. Webster, of the Ohio Agricultural Experiment Station.

In 1892 Webster made the committee's first report. He sprayed a flowering plum tree with paris green and then caged it, enclosing a colony of bees. An analysis of the dead bees showed arsenic, before and after they were washed to remove external contamination. Experiments on apple trees in the open were less convincing. His second report in 1895 covered more detailed work. He found arsenic in dead bees taken from sprayed apple trees and in bees taken from a colony that had died shortly after the apple orchard in which it was located had been sprayed. That evidence convinced everybody. Research gave proof also that bees do not injure fruit (although they may suck juices from overripe fruit after it is punctured by birds and yellow-jackets) and that honey bees are an economic necessity as pollinators.

About 1920 two new factors arose—the development of the cheaper calcium arsenate dust and the use of the airplane to apply insecticides.

THE BOLL WEEVIL had become established in the South, but repeated applications of calcium arsenate reduced its damage. The land of cotton covered more territory than the fruit areas; calcium arsenate was just as toxic as the sprays used in orchards; consequently losses of bees were more extensive. Not uncommonly did beekeepers lose 500 colonies in a season. The choice was to move the bees or go out of business. Moving often meant transporting several truck loads of hives 100 miles or more to strange and less profitable honey locations; besides, the beekeeper often would not know whether insecticides were being applied in the locality until he saw a dusting plane or found an apiary already poisoned. Beekeeping in cotton areas declined. Most beekeepers quit, some moved to distant areas, and a few developed specialties, such as rearing queens away from the cotton areas.

Arsenicals applied on crops elsewhere caused corresponding losses of bees, even though the crops (such as tomatoes, potatoes, or lettuce) were unattractive to bees. The reason was that the dust was drifting onto plants attractive to bees along the borders or outside the treated fields. Analyses disclosed that, regardless of place or method of application, all arsenicals were highly toxic to bees—about one-third of a part per million of the bee's body weight was enough to cause death. Furthermore, any arsenical carried into the hive with pollen on the bee's legs and stored for future food remained poisonous for months.

One would expect that some of the enormous quantities of insecticides applied on cultivated crops would show up in honey. That is not the case. Nectar is carried in the honey sac, a specialized part of the alimentary tract. When the nectar contains poison, the carrier is quickly affected. Instead of returning to the hive, the bee attempts to throw off the effect of the poison and becomes lost or dies in the field. Should the bee return with a load of poisoned nectar, there is a second safety factor. Every drop of nectar is rehandled by the hive bees, which are exposed to poison longer than the field bees. Hive bees tend to leave the colony when poisoned, carrying with them the poisoned nectar. It is therefore unlikely that poisons would ever be stored with honey. Chemical analysis of honey stored in the brood nests of colonies affected with arsenical poisoning has failed to reveal any trace of arsenic.

Calcium arsenate was used in increasing amounts until 1946. Other materials were below it in volume or toxicity. The arsenicals are some 50 times more toxic to bees than cryolite. Large amounts of sulfur were used, but as applied to field crops it is safe for bees. Several plant derivatives—nicotine, pyrethrum, sabadilla—were applied, but losses were minor as they are safe for bees within a few hours after application.

Since 1946 the synthetic insecticides have brought new problems. They differ in relative killing powers and affect colonies differently. Some, like the arsenicals, cause a large number of bees to die near the hive entrance. Others, like chlordane, cause the bees to die in the field away from the hive. Benzene hexachloride causes bees from affected colonies to be furiously mean. DDT causes slight stupefaction. Lethal effects from exposure to dieldrin may continue for a week and from parathion (less toxic than dieldrin but very dangerous) for 2 to 4 days. Losses from applications of toxaphene may be negligible.

Toxaphene, the least dangerous to honey bees, gives good control of a number of harmful insects. Applied to such crops as alfalfa, the protected crop produces more flowers—actually a benefit to the honey bees. That consideration led to the establishment by the Department of Agriculture of a laboratory at Tucson, Ariz., in 1949 to study the effects of insecticides on bees.

Insecticides that kill colonies quickly or remain in their stores of food for long periods, such as the arsenicals, are most damaging to beekeeping. Several of the synthetic insecticides kill only the field force that comes in contact with the material, and the affected colony recovers its strength in time. In areas with such concentrated plantings as cotton or alfalfa grown for seed, however, repeated exposure may steadily reduce the field force so that the honey crop fails and the colony may die from a weakened condition or lack of food. Up to now no synthetic insecticide used on a commercial scale has caused as much damage to beekeeping as the arsenicals have.

Many organic insecticides have been tested against bees in the laboratory and in the field. In the laboratory most of them have been found to be toxic as stomach poisons, by contact, or both. Some have been classified as to their relative effect on bees when applied to flowering plants, as follows: *May be used with safety*—toxaphene, methoxychlor, sulfur. *Safety questionable, experience variable*—DDT, chlordane. *Unsafe*—BHC, lindane, aldrin. *Very destructive*—parathion, dieldrin, arsenicals.

The organic insecticides tested generally can be used safely on plants not in flower. With one exception, fields treated while they are in flower are safe for bees within 48 hours after an application. Fields treated with dieldrin are not safe for bees for a whole week. Insecticides applied during the hours bees are visiting the field are much more damaging than those applied at night when no bees are present. Insecticides that kill more than 10 percent of bee visitors to the field are considered unsafe for use on plants while they are in flower.

Beekeepers have experimented with various means of resolving the problem of bee poisoning. When it was confined to the fruit-producing areas, legislation was sponsored to prohibit the spraying of fruit trees in bloom. Such laws were passed by Ontario in 1892, Vermont in 1896, New York in 1898, Michigan in 1905, Nebraska and Colorado in 1913, Kentucky in 1915, Utah in 1919, and Prince Edward Island, Canada, in 1920. The laws provided no special enforcement agency and low penalties and soon proved they were not the solution.

Losses because of insecticides spread by airplane brought some lawsuits, several of which resulted in judgments in favor of the beekeeper. The right to own bees as personal property has been recognized. The law will protect bees as it will any other form of property. The principle has been sustained that a person may not use his property in such a manner that damage to his neighbor is a foreseeable result. The principle has been recognized that the dusting of growing crops to prevent the inroads of insects is frequently necessary and a legitimate operation, but it must be conducted at a time and manner so as not to endanger other legitimate industries, such as apiculture.

In California, where airplane dusting affects several industries and the county agricultural commissioners are organized for thorough enforcement, county ordinances are used. The ordinances require the pest-control operators to obtain permits and to operate under strict conditions set up by the commissioners. Although burdensome to operator and commissioner, the method has reduced the poisoning of bees, but only because of the close supervision made possible by the California system of enforcing agricultural statutes.

A community approach was made in Arizona. In 1945 a survey revealed that an estimated 10,000 colonies were killed as a result of dusting programs. In 1946 leaders of the insecticide trade and the operators of airplane dusters reached an agreement whereby the sale and use of an arsenical as an insecticide was practically discontinued and DDT or other materials were substituted. As a result, in the following 5 years, severe losses from bee poisoning were largely eliminated, relations improved, and better crops were produced.

In Millard County, Utah, beekeepers suffered honey-crop failures in 1946 because alfalfa-seed crops were dusted with DDT while they were in full bloom. Research workers had developed a program of bud-stage dusting, which adequately controlled lygus bugs. Growers had difficulty estimating lygus bug populations on their fields, and so they were also dusting alfalfa in the bloom stages, with consequent danger to honey bees. To improve the situation, the county supervisors and the growers agreed to finance jointly the services of an entomologist. His duties were to make surveys of insect populations and recommend control measures to the growers, giving due consideration to the protection of bees. The savings in insecticides his advice made possible exceeded his salary and expenses, and damage to beekeeping was practically eliminated.

As long as insecticides are used, bee poisoning probably will continue to be a problem. Although the bee industry is still absorbing greater losses from insecticide poisoning than it should, there is a growing spirit of cooperation between growers and beekeepers. In that lies the best chance of solution.

FRANK E. TODD *is apiculturist in charge of the Southwestern States Bee Culture Laboratory of the Department of Agriculture in Tucson, Ariz.*

S. E. MCGREGOR, *apiculturist with the division of bee culture of the Bureau of Entomology and Plant Quarantine, has been in bee work since 1925 in Texas, Arkansas, Louisiana, New York, Wisconsin, and Arizona.*

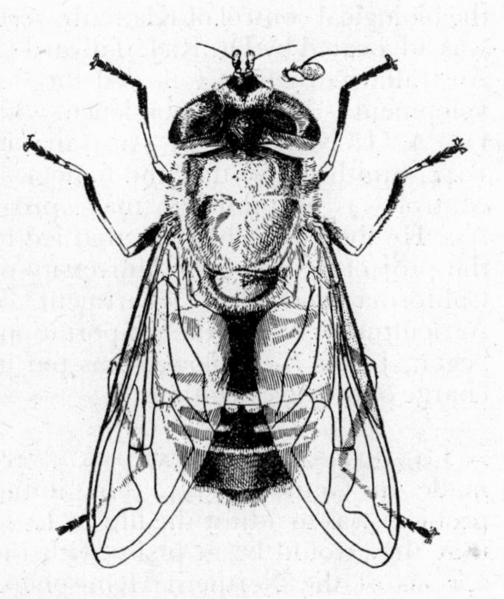

The drone fly closely mimics the honey bee in color, size, and actions.

Insects To Control a Weed

James K. Holloway, C. B. Huffaker

Over many square miles of western range lands millions of pea-sized, bright, metallic-colored beetles are destroying a common weed that for years has caused huge economic losses.

The weed, *Hypericum perforatum,* has a number of common names. In California it is called Klamath weed because it was first reported, about 1900, in northern California in the vicinity of the Klamath River. In many of the Western States it is sometimes referred to as goat weed. The recognized common name in Europe, original home of the weed, is St. Johnswort because, according to legend, it blooms on June 24, the day of St. John the Baptist.

It has invaded extensive temperate regions throughout the world. It is considered a noxious weed in the range lands of Australia, New Zealand, Canada, and the United States. The infested areas in California are estimated at 400,000 acres. Oregon, Washington, Idaho, Nevada, and Montana also have many thousands of infested acres.

Klamath weed causes losses by displacing desirable range plants. It is poisonous to livestock, but death as a result is rare. Animals that eat much of it become scabby, sore-mouthed, and unthrifty. It causes the white parts of the skin to become photosensitive and, when exposed to sunlight, blisters form on the unpigmented skin areas. Cattle are more sensitive to it than sheep.

In some localities in California the grasses dry rapidly in the spring, and the most abundant remaining green plant is Klamath weed. In those localities cattle are usually moved from the ranges before the condition arises. But on occasion unavoidable delays do occur, and the animals may then consume damaging quantities of the weed. The ingested plant causes cattle to become irritable so that they are difficult to corral; sometimes it is almost impossible to load them into trucks and it may be necessary to confine them and give them other feed for a day or two, until the effects of feeding on the weed wear off.

Many attempts have been made to control the weed, a perennial, with chemicals—borax, 2,4-D, and others. But the materials are expensive and the land to be treated is mostly extensive and inaccessible.

Control of the weed by insects has been under consideration for several years. The general method was successful in other countries, notably Australia, but its use in this country is a recent development.

The Commonwealth of Australia first began a search for insect enemies of St. Johnswort in 1920 in England. Early in 1935, after the insects imported from Britain proved apparently unsuccessful in Australia, the search was transferred to southern France. The early work in Europe comprised tests by starvation and breeding of many insects on 42 species of economic plants, representing 19 botanical families, to determine whether the insects could feed and breed on them.

At the satisfactory conclusion of the tests in Europe, the species that had shown neither feeding nor reproduction upon the test plants in Europe were shipped to Australia. Before they could be liberated, however, additional tests had to be made on plants that had not been tested in Europe.

About 8 years after two species of the leaf-feeding beetles, *Chrysolina*, were released in Australia, encouraging results were reported. Subsequently men at the University of California who had watched the experiments with great interest were authorized by the Department of Agriculture to import *Chrysolina hyperici*, *C. gemellata*, and a root borer, *Agrilus hyperici*. The stipulation was made that feeding tests be made on sugar beet, flax, hemp, sweetpotato, tobacco, and cotton.

A project for the importation, testing, and colonization of the three species was then set up by the Bureau of Entomology and Plant Quarantine and the University of California.

The war made it impossible to collect the insects in Europe. It was learned, though, that abundant material was available in Australia and would be transported to California by the United States Army Air Transport Command. The Australian Council for Scientific and Industrial Research offered to collect and ship the material.

Leaders in those activities were Frank Wilson and Harry S. Smith. Wilson was sent to southern Europe in 1935 when the first shipments of the natural enemies of *Hypericum perforatum* from England to Australia failed to progress satisfactorily. Wilson had been associated with the work in England and he continued it in France until 1940. Professor Smith, who was head of the division of biological control in the University of California until his retirement in 1951, is regarded as one of the world's foremost proponents of biological control. Ever since the biological control of Klamath weed was advocated by Dr. R. J. Tillyard of Australia in 1926 he followed the developments. In correspondence with Dr. A. J. Nicholson of Australia in 1944, Smith found that the biological control was beginning to make progress. He then took the steps that led to the project between the University of California and the Department of Agriculture. When the importations began, James K. Holloway was put in charge of the investigations.

THE FIRST IMPORTATIONS were made in October 1944. The initial problem was to adjust the life cycles so that they would be in phase with the seasons of the Northern Hemisphere. The specimens of the root borer (*Agrilus hyperici*) were received as mature larvae in roots. Some of them were retarded in cold storage, but others were forced to emerge upon arrival. Neither method proved satisfactory, and further importations were curtailed until the work in Europe could be resumed.

The two species of *Chrysolina* were occasionally shipped as mature larvae, which would emerge as adults upon arrival, feed, and enter summer dormancy about 3 weeks later. Most of the shipments, however, consisted of summer-dormant adults. Either way, the problem was to bring the adults out of aestivation into the egg-laying phase. By subjecting the adults to fine sprays of water each day, a state similar to normal winter moisture conditions was reproduced in the laboratory, and the beetles came out of aestivation, mated, and began producing fertile eggs within 2 to 3 weeks.

During the first year of importations, enough *C. hyperici* were received to conduct the feeding tests. The tests were completed in May 1945. No feeding had taken place on any of the test plants, and four colonies were released late in the season.

In January 1946 the feeding tests with *C. gemellata* were completed. Permission was obtained to release 13,650 adults that were being retained in quarantine. They were divided into two colonies of 5,000 each, one colony of 2,000, and one of 1,650.

The experimental releases of both species were made in the Coastal Range, northern Sacramento River Valley, and the Sierra foothills—localities considered representative of the grazing areas in which the weed occurs in California.

A total of 330,000 adults of *C. hyperici,* shipped from Australia, was released in 1947 at 66 sites in 15 counties of California. Two experimental colonies of 5,000 each were released in Oregon through the cooperation of the Oregon Agricultural Experiment Station.

Both species of *Chrysolina* were well established by 1948, and we did not need to import more. Two of the original releases of *C. gemellata* had shown a remarkable increase, and from them we collected 212,000 adult beetles, which we placed in 52 new locations in 16 counties of California. Three other releases were made in Oregon and two in Idaho. Initial releases of *C. hyperici* were made in Washington, Idaho, and Montana in 1948 through the cooperation of the State experiment stations. The Forest Service joined the project in 1949 in Oregon, Washington, Idaho, and Montana. In May of that year 140,000 adult *C. hyperici* were collected and shipped to those areas in units of 5,000 each, making 28 new locations in the Northwest.

C. gemellata was so numerous and widespread in California by 1950 that redistribution became a local problem. Perhaps 3 million adult beetles were collected and redistributed in May 1950.

The success of *C. hyperici* has been limited. It has become established in other localities, but an increase comparable to that of *C. gemellata* has been restricted mainly to the coastal mountains in California.

The effectiveness of the leaf-feeding beetles in controlling Klamath weed is associated with their life cycles and their weed host. The balance between the propagative ability of the weed and that of its insect enemy is determined by factors of soil condition, climate, and the influences of interrelated plants and animals.

The two species of weed-feeding beetles differ slightly in their environmental requirements. Yet that small difference means that one species reproduces abundantly and the other's reproduction is curtailed under California conditions.

C. gemellata starts reproducing quickly when the fall rains come. Consequently its progeny have enough time to make the necessary growth before the dry season arrives in late spring and early summer—conditions that are hazardous to pupal development. Also, the egg-laying period is longer, and greater numbers of eggs are deposited.

But *C. hyperici* reacts slowly to moist conditions in the fall and under average California conditions deposits most of its eggs so late that there is insufficient time to complete the necessary phases of development before dry weather sets in.

The life history of the more successful species is attuned to the phases of weed growth and to local climatic conditions. The adult beetles issue from their pupal cells just beneath the surface of the soil in April and early May. They feed voraciously during May and June on the foliage of the plants, which then are flowering. By late June and early July the beetles have completed preparation, by feeding and sunning, for their summer sleep. This inactive, dry-season stage is spent beneath debris, under small stones, and in crevices of the soil.

The beetles spend 4 to 6 months in this inactive condition without food or water. During this period the weed, too, enters a relatively dormant phase. It develops and ripens its seed crop but drops most of its leaves and becomes hard and woody.

The larvae feed actively in warm periods in winter and spring. Their intensive feeding keeps the plant stripped of leaves over a long period when its food reserves are at a low ebb. Thus the root system and the plant die of starvation. Adult feeding, voracious as it is, does not last long enough to produce wholesale death of the plants without the previous feeding by the larvae.

The rains in fall and early winter reactivate weed and beetle. The weed sends out vigorous, prostrate, leafy shoots in rosettes at the base of the flowering stalks. The beetles mate, and many eggs are placed on the leafy growth. The larvae from the eggs and the host weed grow during the winter in relation to the temperatures. All stages of the beetles can survive heavy snows and cold. By midwinter and early spring in favorable locations the larvae reach a half-grown to nearly mature grub stage.

From then on the weed suffers progressive destruction of its foliage by the larvae. The fully mature larvae enter the soil to pupate at about the time the plant begins to develop the shoots that become the flower-bearing stalks. The appearance of the adult beetles completes a single cycle, which covers a year.

The beetles can move in effective numbers into new areas, but enough of both sexes must be present to assure fertility of the eggs. About 3 years generally are required to give local control in a remote area where only a few thousand beetles have been released. In the third reproductive year the numbers reach a level at which they can exert controlling pressure on the weed.

Local dispersion is normally accomplished by the crawling adult beetles, which often are seen moving in great numbers across roads or ravines from centers of overpopulation where the weed has been cleared. Dispersion by flight is less commonly observed but occurs under conditions of high beetle density, complete depletion of the food supply, and hot, sunny weather. Colonies have appeared which apparently are the results of single or repeated flights from production centers as far as 3 miles distant.

Through its natural powers of dispersion, plus a supplemental influence from establishment of secondary initial colonies in the area, *C. gemellata* has now spread and effected general control of the weed over hundreds of square miles in southern Humboldt County, California.

The same species has cleared an open range area in Placer County and moved from that limited infestation through small, isolated patches of weed to points up to 3 miles away in various directions. No additional releases were made anywhere in the area. A second and younger colony in Placer County was located in an area notably unfavorable as to climate, yet it cleared that field of the weed within 3 years.

C. hyperici, though poorly adapted to the California conditions generally, brought under control 4 to 5 square miles in an upland area of Humboldt County, where retention of soil moisture late in the season has operated to its advantage.

Ranchers and farm workers attest to the complete destruction of the weed by the beetles. They have seen how the hungry insects have removed the weed from a large area near Blocksburg, Calif.

The beetles also can locate and destroy small, isolated stands of weeds that were missed in previous years. The appearance of the seedling weeds in cleared fields is common, but so far enough beetles are present in the area to find them. These scattered reinfestation spots and plants in the edges of heavily wooded borders (less preferred by the beetles) maintain the general distribution of the beetles in an area after the weeds cease to be a range problem. That fact may assure the return of the beetles in effective numbers quickly enough to take care of reinfestations before they can reach serious proportions.

THE CONTROL OF A WEED by the biological method involves several aspects of ecology. Klamath weed is primarily a pest in range areas where soil moisture is ample from winter to early summer but deficient later in the year. Overgrazing fosters its spread. Under such conditions, its deep root system enables it to overcome even the sturdiest grass competitors, particularly when grazing has been so heavy that seed production by the more vigorous perennial grasses is curtailed.

An insect may control weeds by more subtle means than direct destruction. If its action is such as to remove the competitive advantage of the weed host over desirable plant species, the weed may then be overcome by plants that cannot alone compete with it. That does not explain the control of Klamath weed, but the pressure of the beetles on the weed at a time when vigorous competing range plants occupy the area may be enough to prevent the return of the weed in such fields under proper grazing management.

Several investigators believe that three-fourths of the land south of Mount Shasta and from the coast to the Sierra foothills in California was originally covered with perennial bunchgrasses. Annual plants now make up most of the forage there. Their replacements by perennials would be impossible (and not necessarily desirable) everywhere in the region.

It therefore seems probable that with the destruction of Klamath weed the predominant annual-plant cover characteristic of the region may regain the land under normal conditions. That has happened in the areas where the weed has been cleared for three successive seasons. In Placer County, annual grasses, dominated by soft chess (*Bromus hordeaceus*), legumes such as birdsfoot trefoil, clovers, and lupines, and desirable forbs such as filaree, have returned as thickly as they are in neighboring range lands that have remained free of Klamath weed.

The success of the beetles in Humboldt County is attended by circumstances favorable to return of a forage cover of maximum value. In the areas most heavily infested with the weed (indicative of a favorable soil and site), the main perennial bunchgrass of earlier years (*Danthonia californica*) has managed to survive along animal trails and about the edges of seepage areas, which were too wet for Klamath weed in winter. The destruction of the dense stands of the aggressive weed has permitted a gradual return of this fine range plant. Although its distribution in the original beetle-release remained spotty for some years, it soon began to develop a vigorous cover that spread slowly over new ground.

At the end of a 50-acre field that had been cleared of weed by the beetles for 3 years, a rather complete stand of the hardy bunchgrass developed. Over the whole field—most of which had been weed-free only 2 years—*Dan-*

thonia increased from 9.2 percent of the total plant cover in 1947 to 23.4 percent in 1950. By considering soft chess (*Bromus hordeaceus*), *Danthonia,* and desirable legumes together, one gets a general picture of the total forage improvement due to the beetle action. The three desirable types increased from 14.8 percent in 1947 to 43.4 percent in 1950. Klamath weed was reduced from predominance (57.6 percent) to complete absence. Thus the position of the weed and the position of the three desirable plants was practically reversed.

The *Chrysolina* beetles have become a permanent part of the natural fauna. Their future success will depend mostly on how closely the life processes of the beetles and their host coincide with changes in weather, for on that synchronization depends how fast the beetles multiply and how intensive is their action on uninvaded weed stands and reinfested fields.

Indications are that the beetles can duplicate throughout the Northwest the success they have had in California. It would be an economical, self-perpetuating way to combat a serious pest, now that the first intensive research and exhaustive explorations are completed.

JAMES K. HOLLOWAY *is an entomologist in the Bureau of Entomology and Plant Quarantine, the division of foreign parasite introduction, and specialist in biological control in the University of California College of Agriculture. He has been engaged in research in biological control since 1927 and has had responsibility for carrying forward the project on the biological control of Klamath weed in this country since its inception in 1944. He studied at Mississippi State College and Ohio State University.*

C. B. HUFFAKER, *an entomologist and ecologist, has been engaged in ecological research since 1940. In 1946 he was appointed assistant entomologist in the division of biological control of the University of California, where he has been particularly interested in the population complexes of insects and the weeds attacked by them as components of a natural range environment. Dr. Huffaker holds degrees from the University of Tennessee and Ohio State University.*

The authors suggest for further reading Bio-Ecology *by Frederic E. Clements and Victor E. Shelford, published by John Wiley & Sons, Inc., in 1939, and the following publications:*

Australian Council for Scientific and Industrial Research—Bulletin 169, The Entomological Control of St. John's Wort (*Hypericum perforatum* L.) . . ., *by Frank Wilson, 1943; and Pamphlet 29,* The Possibility of the Entomological Control of St. John's Wort in Australia—Progress Report, *by G. A. Currie and S. Garthside, 1932.*

California Agricultural Experiment Station Bulletins—615, The Chemical Control of St. Johnswort, *by R. N. Raynor, 1937; and 503,* St. Johnswort on Range Lands of California, *by Arthur W. Sampson and Kenneth W. Parker, 1930.*

California Forest and Range Experiment Station Technical Note 21, Standards for Judging the Degree of Forage Utilization on California Annual-Type Ranges, *by A. L. Hormay and A. Fausett, 1942.*

In Ecology, The Return of Native Perennial Bunchgrass Following the Removal of Klamath Weed (*Hypericum perforatum*) L.) by Imported Beetles, *by C. B. Huffaker, volume 32, pages 443–458, 1951.*

In the Journal of Economic Entomology, The Role of *Chrysolina gemellata* in the Biological Control of Klamath Weed, *by J. K. Holloway and C. B. Huffaker, volume 44, pages 244–247, 1951.*

In the Proceedings of the Entomological Society of Washington, Biological Control of Weeds in the United States, *by H. S. Smith, volume 49, number 6, pages 169–170, 1947.*

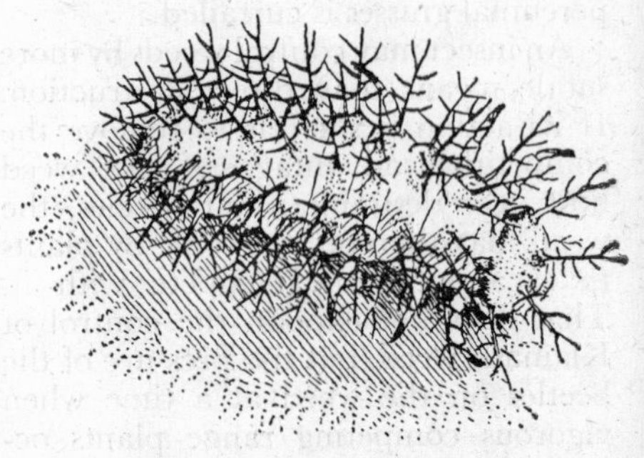

Mexican bean beetle larva.

Insects as Destroyers

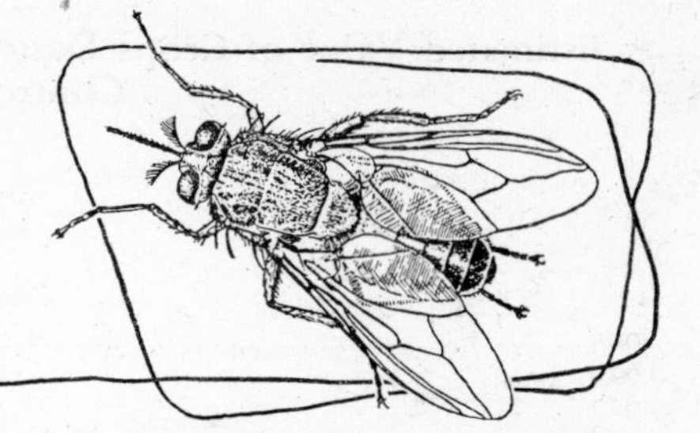

Losses Caused by Insects

G. J. Haeussler

Every minute of the day and night billions of insects are chewing, sucking, biting, and boring away at our crops, livestock, timber, gardens, homes, mills, warehouses, and ourselves.

How much damage they do is hard to say. Many variables and complicating factors are involved. The damage by one kind of insect to a crop differs from year to year and from one area to another. Pests cause losses in uncounted ways.

The infestations reduce the yield of crops, lower the quality, increase the cost of production and harvesting, and require outlays for materials and equipment to apply control measures. The products must be screened or washed to remove insects or insect fragments; washed, brushed, trimmed, or otherwise treated to remove insecticide residues; and graded to eliminate or otherwise allow for injury. Livestock pests lower the production of meat and milk and the value of hides.

Mosquitoes, house flies, ticks, and fleas exact a toll in human diseases and in efficiency and money—time lost from work, the cost of screens on homes, interference with the cultivation or harvesting of crops, the loss of business at resort places.

Insects cause direct losses to timber production. They also cause indirect ones: The fire hazards of insect-killed trees in the forest, the effect on conservation, spoiling of beauty in parks and other scenic areas and on streets and properties in towns and cities.

Food and homes suffer. Insects attack grains while they are in farm storage and in transit and while they are stored in elevators. Others infest dried fruits during and after the drying process. Clothes moths, carpet beetles, pantry pests, and termites invade homes, infest food, ruin clothing, damage the timbers of houses.

A compilation of estimated losses due to 60-odd insects in the United States was made in 1938 by J. A. Hyslop, of the Department of Agriculture. He set the total damage, including the cost of control measures, at $1,601,527,000 annually. His estimates were based on prices far lower than those of today and did not take into account all injurious insects.

We can be more specific now about losses to certain crops and commodities.

The European corn borer, one of our insect immigrants, has been one of the farmers' worst enemies. Surveys to determine its distribution, abundance, and damage show how the losses increased as the corn borer spread throughout the Corn Belt. In 1949, when conditions were especially favorable, the damage reached an all-time high. Fortunately weather conditions unfavorable to the borer and other natural factors sometimes check its ravages, as they did in 1950. Practical methods are now available for controlling it in field corn, sweet corn, and seed corn, but by no means has it been eliminated.

970134°—52——11

Estimated Value of Crops Destroyed by Grasshoppers and Saved by Control Measures

Year	States	Estimated value of crops	
		Destroyed by grasshoppers	Saved by control measures
	Number	Dollars	Dollars
1925	20	10, 484, 904	
1926	21	9, 757, 851	
1927	21	10, 506, 901	
1928	20	12, 818, 951	
1929	21	15, 688, 194	
1930	22	20, 516, 174	
1931	23	34, 073, 351	
1932	23	41, 968, 578	
1933	23	58, 403, 961	
1934	23	35, 765, 862	
1935	18	14, 753, 080	5, 540, 803
1936	14	102, 029, 061	25, 817, 848
1937	20	65, 836, 215	102, 288, 178
1938	24	83, 841, 727	176, 442, 672
1939	24	48, 811, 430	128, 483, 225
1940	22	24, 087, 117	44, 568, 833
1941	23	23, 822, 713	35, 583, 136
1942	20	14, 016, 475	29, 307, 683
1943	19	13, 217, 884	6, 891, 461
1944	21	13, 486, 060	22, 712, 485
1945	23	12, 671, 604	29, 708, 832
1946	20	22, 743, 328	41, 150, 436
1947	20	22, 342, 835	50, 368, 599
1948	19	36, 826, 624	67, 586, 232
1949	20	27, 376, 479	72, 077, 868
1950	18	19, 333, 402	25, 327, 876

Losses Caused by Vegetable and Truck Crop Insects

Insect	Crops affected	Area involved	Period	Estimated annual losses Dollars
Mexican bean beetle	Beans	New Mexico, Arizona, Colorado, and eastern United States except Michigan.	1944	5, 502, 000
Beet leafhopper	Sugar beets, tomatoes, beans, cantaloups.	Western United States.	1930's	2, 430, 000
	Beets, sugar and table.	Intermountain region.	1944	3, 676, 000
	Beans, dry	Idaho, Oregon	1944	2, 446, 000
Cabbage caterpillars	Cabbage and cauliflower.	United States	1928–32	5, 433, 000
		Southern States and California.	1944	7, 663, 000
Onion thrips	Onions	United States	1944	14, 500, 000
Pea aphid	Peas, canning and market.	United States	1944	3, 969, 000
Aphids	Potato	Northern States, except Idaho.	1944	66, 467, 000
Sweetpotato weevil	Sweetpotato	Gulf Coast States	1944	5, 031, 000
Tobacco hornworm	Tobacco	Southern States	1944	84, 073, 000
Celery leaf tier	Celery	California and Florida.	Outbreak years.	1, 000, 000

Grasshoppers damage a variety of crops and range plants. More than 75 years ago C. V. Riley estimated that the grasshoppers caused crop losses amounting to 200 million dollars in a number of Western States from 1874 to 1877. Hyslop recorded that entomologists in 23 Western and Midwestern States estimated the average annual value of crops destroyed by grasshoppers from 1925 to 1934 at about 25 million dollars. The losses remain high, especially in outbreak years, but control campaigns and better control methods have meant great savings of crops. Now that practical, effective materials are available to the individual farmer, grasshoppers should never again be allowed to cause such losses as those in the 1930's.

Cereal and forage crops are attacked by many other pests. Among them are the corn earworm, hessian fly, chinch bug, velvetbean caterpillar, lygus bugs, and greenbug.

Among the many kinds of insects that attack vegetable and truck crops are aphids, leafhoppers, sucking bugs, beetles and weevils, caterpillars, thrips, spider mites, cutworms, wireworms, and mole crickets. Many cause direct injury. Certain aphids and leafhoppers and some others cause indirect damage by transmitting diseases to potatoes, sugar beets, and similar plants. No attempt has ever been made to bring together estimates of all these losses, but one of the tables gives some idea of them.

As for the fruit insects: Yearly losses in our apple crop because of the codling moth from 1940 to 1944 were set at about 15 percent of the crop value, or $25,245,000. That did not include the cost of measures to combat the pest, which cost an estimated 25 million dollars more. DDT has been used extensively and effectively against the codling moth, so that the average annual losses from codling moth from 1944 to 1948 were about 4 percent of the crop value, or $9,176,000.

The citrus crops of California are said to have suffered losses of about 10 million dollars in 1943–1944 because of the California red scale. In 1943 and 1944 losses to peach growers east of the Rocky Mountains because of the plum curculio and the cost of applying control measures have been estimated at nearly 8 million dollars a year. The peach tree borer is another serious pest over much of the eastern two-thirds of the country. If not controlled, infestations of the borers weaken and often kill peach trees. The extent of the damage is difficult to determine, but the annual cost of applying control measures alone was estimated at $3,200,000 in 1943 and 1944.

The boll weevil takes a big bite out of our cotton crop each year. The cut in production from 1909 to 1949 in the 13 States in which the boll weevil occurs meant an estimated average loss of cotton and cottonseed of more than 203 million dollars annually. The loss was more than 500 million dollars in each of 5 years, between 400 million and 500 million dollars 1 year, and between 300 million and 400 million dollars in each of 3 years. It was 200 million to 300 million dollars in each of 6 years. The estimated loss was below 100 million dollars in only 16 of the 41 years. The value of the cotton was computed at the seasonal average price received by farmers and does not consider what they might have received had the yield not been reduced by insects. To those losses must be added the damage caused by other insect pests. One of them, the bollworm, is estimated to have destroyed cotton in Texas alone to the extent of 85 million dollars in some years.

Robert C. Jackson, of the National Cotton Council, cited estimates of the Bureau of Agricultural Economics that insects destroyed 15.1 percent of the 1946 cotton crop and drew these conclusions: Besides the lint, there was lost 613,000 tons of cottonseed, or, based on the season's average price, more than 44 million dollars worth. The 613,000 tons of cottonseed that was destroyed would have produced 179 million pounds of refined cottonseed oil, which

Estimated Losses to Livestock, 1940–44

Pest	*Animals affected*	*Average annual loss Dollars*
Cattle grubs	Cattle	160, 000, 000
Horn flies, stable flies, deer flies	Cattle, horses, mules	100, 000, 000
Screw-worms and blow flies	Cattle, horses, hogs, sheep, goats	15, 000, 000
Lice	Cattle, goats, hogs, sheep	30, 000, 000
Ticks	Cattle, sheep, horses	6, 500, 000
Lice, mites, fleas, ticks	Poultry and eggs	85, 000, 000

Estimated Savings from Control of Livestock Pests, 1949

Animals and pests	*States reporting Number*	*Animals treated Number*	*Estimated savings Dollars*
Cattle treated for grubs	29	3, 889, 344	14, 643, 708
Cattle treated for flies	28	13, 769, 846	47, 245, 628
Cattle treated for lice	28	6, 469, 493	14, 083, 966
Sheep treated for ticks and related pests	27	3, 540, 922	3, 568, 173
Hogs treated for mites and related pests	29	4, 538, 256	5, 781, 720
Poultry treated for lice and related pests	25	43, 482, 013	7, 056, 915

Estimates of Losses to Corn Caused by the European Corn Borer

Year	*Areas known to be infested*		*Areas included in estimate*		*Estimated value of crop loss*		
	States	*Counties*	*States*	*Counties*	*Corn harvested for grain*	*Sweet corn*	*Total loss*
	Number	*Number*	*Number*	*Number*	*Dollars*	*Dollars*	*Dollars*
1939	20	455	16	285	1, 846, 335	2, 130, 791	3, 977, 126
1940	20	479	19	258	4, 140, 479	2, 539, 348	6, 679, 827
1941	20	556	18	258	4, 260, 248	675, 742	4, 935, 990
1942	22	661	18	308	15, 211, 895	1, 817, 181	17, 029, 076
1943	23	791	20	337	27, 800, 740	5, 562, 778	33, 363, 518
1944	26	883	22	400	20, 185, 153	2, 528, 770	22, 713, 923
1945	26	913	22	398	32, 846, 459	3, 918, 106	36, 764, 565
1946	28	959	22	446	26, 679, 552	2, 061, 237	28, 740, 789
1947	28	1, 053	22	806	93, 532, 296	3, 238, 495	96, 770, 791
1948	29	1, 169	25	892	99, 107, 000	4, 129, 000	103, 236, 000
1949	29	1, 314	26	1, 001	349, 635, 000	....	349, 635, 000
1950	36	1, 405	26	1, 001	84, 911, 000	....	84, 911, 000

Losses Caused by Cereal and Forage Crop Pests

Insect	*Crops affected*	*Area involved*	*Period*	*Estimated annual losses*
Corn earworm	Corn	United States	1945	$140, 000, 000
Hessian fly	Wheat	United States	1944	47, 400, 000
			1945	37, 000, 000
Chinch bug	Corn	United States	1934	27, 500, 000
	Wheat, barley, rye, oats.	United States	1934	28, 000, 000
Velvetbean caterpillar.	Peanuts and soybeans.	Southeastern States	1946	5, 000, 000
Pea aphid	Alfalfa	United States	1944	30, 580, 000
Lygus bugs	Alfalfa seed	United States	1944	15, 800, 000
Vetch weevil	Hairy vetch seed	United States	1944	2, 290, 000
Greenbug	Oats and wheat	Kansas, Oklahoma, Texas.	1907	[1] 50, 000, 000
	Wheat	Oklahoma	1950	[1] 22, 000, 000
	Oats	Oklahoma	1950	[1] 2, 000, 000
	Barley	Oklahoma	1950	[1] 800, 000

[1] Bushels.

might have provided the total minimum edible fat requirements for more than 8 million persons. The oil would have made 200 million pounds of margarine, which is more than one-third the amount consumed in the United States in 1946. The 613,000 tons of cottonseed would have turned out 276,000 tons of high-protein meal and 152,000 tons of cottonseed hulls. The meal would have provided enough protein to produce 178 million additional pounds of beef, or to take care of enough cows to produce 690 million gallons of milk—enough to provide every individual in this country with 19 quarts of milk.

Estimates prepared by the National Cotton Council placed the value of cotton lint and seed destroyed by insects in the United States in 1950 at $907,884,000, the highest in history.

As in the case of insect pests of other crops, losses to cotton caused by insects vary greatly from area to area and even from field to field. Moreover, the loss in quality of lint and seed is sometimes serious even though no great reduction in yield occurs. Applications of insecticides to control sucking bugs, especially in the Southwestern States, often pay dividends because of the resulting improvement in the grade or quality of the lint.

Livestock pests each year cost this country about 500 million dollars, mostly in wasted feed, lower production of meat and milk, and damaged hides. Cattle lose energy and weight when they have to fight off attacks of horn flies, stable flies, and horse flies, which also rob cattle of blood. The combined loss of energy and blood represents a great waste of food and forage. Animals protected from horn flies may gain one-half pound in weight a day more than unprotected animals. Horn flies can cut milk flow as much as 10 to 20 percent. Heel flies cause such annoyance when they are laying their eggs that milk flow suffers and beef animals fail to put on finish normally. The total annual loss in cattle hides and calfskins due to injury by cattle grubs has been estimated at more than 2 million dollars.

A few examples of estimated losses to livestock, taken from published records, are given in a table. They were considered conservative at the time they were made; later increases in the values of livestock and livestock products have made the losses even more alarming.

Some estimates of the amount of savings resulting from control of insects and related pests of livestock in 1949 were assembled and summarized by the Extension Service. They are given in an accompanying table. They pertain to fewer than 30 States, but they give an indication of the savings ranchers and stockmen make when they control insect pests.

IN A REPORT in 1950, Lyle F. Watts, Chief of the Forest Service, wrote: "Insects and diseases rank with fire as destroyers of forests. Ordinarily the damage caused by these pests is less conspicuous. But they are at work every year, and no forest area is entirely free from them. Their total effect probably exceeds that of fire."

The actual amount of loss insects cause to forests is hard to measure, but a few estimates have been made. An outbreak of the spruce budworm from 1910 to 1920 in balsam, fir, and spruce forests of Minnesota and Maine killed about 70 to 90 percent of the mature stand. The loss of timber was estimated at about 4.5 million dollars annually during that period. The Engelmann spruce beetle, in an outbreak in 1940 to 1946, destroyed about 20 percent of the Engelmann spruce timber in Colorado. The average yearly loss amounted to about 500 million board feet, valued at about 1 million dollars. The outbreak continued in 1951. An outbreak of the mountain pine beetle caused an estimated annual loss of 60 million board feet of lodgepole pine in Wyoming in 1946 and 1947. Some 15 million feet of ponderosa pine was destroyed by the Black Hills beetle in South Dakota in 1947.

An outbreak of the Douglas-fir tussock moth on more than 400,000 acres of forest near Moscow, Idaho, was brought under control in 1947 by DDT sprays applied from airplanes. The insect had defoliated the stands in 1946 and had killed the timber on about 16,000 acres. An estimated additional 1,518,856,000 board feet of timber, valued at $84,328,000, might have been killed had no steps been taken to prevent further defoliation.

Insects cause an average annual loss of at least 5 percent of the rice, corn, wheat, barley, oats, grain sorghums, and similar crops after they are harvested and while they are in storage on the farm, in elevators, or in warehouses. Much of this loss comes right on the farm and is more severe in the southern parts of the country where in the warmer temperatures the weevils, beetles, and moths breed and feed through most of the year. The actual amount of grain lost annually because of these pests has been estimated at 300 million bushels, worth more than 500 million dollars at 1951 prices. In the fall of 1947, entomologists estimated from samples of wheat taken from untreated bins in a Midwestern State that the farmers there and then were giving 380 billion insects free board and lodging in their grain bins.

Processed foods and packaged goods of various kinds get their share of insect damage, although such contamination is far less today than it was in our grandparents' time. One recalls the barrels of flour and cornmeal and the open boxes of dried prunes common in the local store not many years ago. How often, in buying these products, did one carry home meal infested with weevils and prunes covered with the excrement of the worms that infested them? Today if the housewife finds a sign of an insect in a package it goes back to the dealer. Our food and drug laws now insist that our food be free from insect contamination. Despite the advances, the meal and flour moths and the flour, grain, rice, and cigarette beetles still cause great damage to some processed foods and packaged goods. The annual loss in this country from those pests was estimated at 150 million dollars between 1940 and 1944. The estimate includes the destruction caused by the pests in processing plants, warehouses, retail stores, and homes.

Every now and then a housekeeper has to discard a partly used package of cereal, meal, nuts, dried fruit, or other food which, forgotten on the pantry shelf, has become infested by moths, worms, or weevils—the pantry pests. Suppose each family in the United States discarded only 50 cents worth of infested products a year: The loss would be about 20 million dollars.

The losses to clothing, rugs, furniture, and other furnishings by clothes moths, carpet beetles, and similar pests are estimated by entomologists to be from 200 million to 500 million dollars annually.

Such figures should give us pause. They are figures for fewer than 100 of the 600 or more injurious species of insects of primary importance that are known to occur in North America. They emphasize that everyone is affected in many ways by many insects, even though he might go for months without even seeing or noticing an insect or any signs of insect damage. Losses caused by all insects in the United States add up to a staggering amount, whether we regard it in terms of dollars, lost food and fiber, or time and materials used in combatting them. That amount, in the opinion of entomologists, is at least 4 billion dollars for an average year—4 billion dollars.

G. J. HAEUSSLER *is head of the division of truck crop and garden insect investigations in the Bureau of Entomology and Plant Quarantine. From 1944 to 1951 he was in charge of the division of insect survey and information. A graduate of the University of Massachusetts, he joined the Department in 1925. He was engaged for 16 years in investigations on the biological control of fruit insects.*

Carriers of Human Diseases

F. C. Bishopp, Cornelius B. Philip

Through the centuries people have been plagued by insects and have died by the millions from diseases carried by them. Man is gradually gaining mastery over them, but the battle is long and expensive, the burden is too heavy for the poor in many parts of the world, and we still have much to learn about these agents of death.

Probably 10,000 kinds of mites, ticks, and insects infect man directly or indirectly with disease. Most of them are only occasional and accidental carriers. Many spread diseases among livestock and wildlife and carry them from the animal reservoirs of infections back to persons.

INSECTS TRANSMIT DISEASE in many complex ways.

First, their mere presence or attack, without the transfer of germs, may produce a disease or harmful condition. Itch mites and screw-worms that invade the tissues are of this type. Some insects cause accidental injury to sense organs. Others produce intense itching and allergies, such as are caused by body lice, bee stings, and bites of chiggers and ticks. Some persons have idiosyncrasies that intensify their reaction to such attacks.

A fly or other insect that walks over and feeds on filth and then deposits the germ-laden contaminants on food by crawling over it, vomiting on it, or defecating on it is spoken of as a mechanical carrier. An insect, such as a horse fly, is also a mechanical carrier when it picks up germs by biting a diseased animal or person and then carries the germ on its beak until it bites a healthy individual.

More complex is the relationship among insect, disease, and man when the disease germ multiplies in the insect but does not change greatly in form. That occurs in fleas when they ingest plague organisms with the blood of a plague-stricken rat.

The most complex relationship is illustrated by anopheline mosquitoes in transmitting malaria. The malaria organisms in the blood of man at times produce male and female cells. The mosquito ingests the cells when it bites. The cells mate in the mosquito's stomach and develop into active ookinetes, which penetrate the stomach wall of the mosquito and thereon form cysts. Cell division takes place in the cysts, and hundreds of small, spindle-shaped sporozoites are formed.

The greatly enlarged oocyst then bursts open within the insect's body cavity. The active sporozoites swarm out, soon reach and penetrate the salivary glands, and are ready to pass into the blood stream of the next person the mosquito bites. This cycle, which takes 7 to 10 days, is called the essential or sexual cycle. Upon entering the blood stream, the minute malaria organisms—the sporozoites—enter such organs as the liver. In a few days they attack the red blood cells, in which they go through another cycle of growth and multiplication. Some ultimately become sexually mature, ready for other mosquitoes to ingest, and so repeat the sexual cycle in the insect.

Many variations occur in this method of disease transmission, which is called obligatory or cyclic because the disease organism is dependent on an insect for its continued natural transmission.

INSECTS CARRY DISEASE ORGANISMS of many types, among them microscopic viruses, bacteria, and protozoa and the larger roundworms and tapeworms. Ways by which disease organisms are kept alive in higher animals and insects and are passed from one generation to another frequently are very complex. Unraveling them has often required great scientific imagination and patient skill. We give some examples later. Sometimes disease organisms are carried from one stage of an insect host to another, with the intermediate stage or stages not transmitting infection or even living as parasites. In many instances the disease agents pass through the egg from one host generation to the next.

The disease cycle can be broken by destroying the insect vector, by using drugs to kill or suppress the disease organisms in the human host, or by immunization. Most successful usually is a combination of the three, plus isolation of infected persons (to prevent the insect vector from acquiring the disease organism) and such sanitary measures as screening to protect healthy persons.

Does the disease make the insect sick or kill it? Sometimes the infected insect is not injured in any way—apparently it has become tolerant. Sometimes its life span may be shortened. Occasionally it may be killed—when that happens, that particular kind of insect is not a usual or well-adapted carrier of those particular disease germs.

INSECTS OF THE ORDER DIPTERA, or two-winged flies, perhaps are responsible for more human illness and death than any other group. They may rank with the world's top killers of man. Mosquitoes inhabit practically all parts of the earth except the polar regions. They alone carry malaria, yellow fever, dengue, and bancroftian and malayan filariasis. They also carry certain types of encephalitis and may be involved occasionally in the mechanical transfer of tularemia and anthrax.

Malaria, the great disabler, prevails throughout the Tropics and much of the temperate regions. Outbreaks have occurred in Canada and as far north as Archangel in Soviet Russia. Species of dapple-winged *Anopheles* mosquitoes are the carriers of human malaria.

Large areas of the United States once were malarious, but as the swamps were drained and the land tilled and people got into screened houses, the malady was pushed southward. There the mild climate and abundant water areas gave opportunity for mosquitoes to breed in numbers during the long summer. The malaria parasites also developed in the mosquitoes and people were more exposed, because they spent more time outside during the warm evenings. Poorly built and unscreened houses sometimes permitted infection to occur even indoors. Since 1943 the disease has been further reduced by the use of DDT. There is little malaria now in the United States.

About a dozen species of *Anopheles* mosquitoes occur in the United States, but only one in the Eastern and Southern States has been important in transmitting malaria. Likewise in the Pacific States a single species, but a different one, is the natural carrier. Scores of different kinds of *Anopheles* exist in various parts of the world. Their varying breeding and biting habits determine which control measures are instituted in any area. Some carry malaria. Others have no part in infecting man.

Yellow fever, or yellow jack, periodically put terror in the hearts of our people, especially in the South in the early days. When Reed, Carroll, Lazear, and Agramonte proved in 1901 that a semidomestic mosquito, now known as the yellow-fever mosquito, was the vector, some of the terror disappeared. But although we know how to control or eradicate the mosquito, and although a protective vaccine has been developed, the disease is still regarded as a serious threat to this country and to many other warmer parts of the world. A deadly virus disease, it still lurks in the jungles of South America and Africa. To start serious trouble, the virus needs only to be transferred by jungle species of mosquitoes from an infected monkey to a man, who in turn may infect the yellow-fever mosquito in a populous area. Indeed, this insidious disease has suddenly flared up since 1950 in the jungles of Panama and Costa Rica, where it was thought to be stamped out, resulting in somewhat hysteric, unfounded reports even in Mexico.

The yellow-fever mosquito lives close to humans. It breeds in water in old tin cans, flower vases, and discarded tires. It is seldom found more than a quarter of a mile from a house. Only female mosquitoes bite. Females of the yellow-fever species slip out of hiding places at twilight, find exposed ankles or arms, and dart away at the slightest motion.

The Nobel Prize in Medicine for 1951 was awarded Max Theiler for development of a vaccine of living, attenuated virus, which has not only protected thousands of exposed civilians and troops but has undoubtedly been instrumental in keeping this dread disease out of the Far East, despite the increase in travel by air.

Dengue, or breakbone fever, also carried by the yellow-fever mosquito, is a painful and debilitating but not fatal virus disease that strikes occasionally. In an epidemic in 1922, Texas had more than a half million cases. For short periods it incapacitated large numbers of our troops on Guam and other Pacific islands during the Second World War.

ENCEPHALITIS, caused by several kinds of viruses that attack the central nervous systems of vertebrates, is transmitted by several species of mosquitoes. One species may be a vector of one virus strain and not of another. An outbreak of the so-called St. Louis type of encephalitis in 1933 is thought to have been carried by the northern house mosquito. A strain of the disease that has caused several hundred cases of human encephalitis each year is carried primarily by *Culex tarsalis*. Several species of mosquitoes can transmit the serious "Japanese B" encephalitis, which has caused serious epidemics in Japan and adjacent areas. Two types of equine sleeping sickness that have killed thousands of horses in the United States also cause illness in man and are probably transferred by a number of our common species of mosquitoes. Some infected parasitic bugs and bird mites have been found in the wild.

Elephantiasis, a disfiguring malady of people in the Tropics and subtropics, is carried by mosquitoes. The extremities and genitals often become greatly swollen because of small roundworms that establish themselves in the lymph glands. Into the blood stream the worms discharge eggs, which, after developing to active embryos known as microfilariae, are picked up by mosquitoes when biting. Some strains of the young worms swarm in the blood near the surface of the body at the time of the day or night when the favored species of mosquito is likely to bite.

Upon reaching the stomach of the mosquito, the young worms wiggle out of their saclike sheaths in an hour or so. They work through the stomach wall and into the thoracic muscles. There they grow for 2 or 3 weeks. Then they migrate to the beak of the mosquito, curl up, and await a chance to gain entrance to the skin of a person when the mosquito again bites. The worms, about one-twentieth inch long, burrow into the skin, reach the capillaries, and are carried in the blood stream to a lymph gland, where they develop to maturity. The female worms are 3 to 4 inches long. The males are about half that size. The cycle is complete when mating takes place and production of microfilariae begins.

Elephantiasis does not necessarily follow infestation from an infected mosquito bite, but skin irritation and fever are often manifest. Infection by these little worms is called filariasis. The malady occurred a number of years in the vicinity of Charleston, S. C., but it appears to have died out. No other endemic foci are known in the United States, although the carrier, the southern house mosquito, is widely distributed in the South.

The development and use of various ways to control mosquitoes are discussed on page 476.

Indians gave the name *no-see-ums* to the tiny mottled winged gnats that can readily crawl through a fine screen. They are also called punkies or sand flies (although they are not the same as *Phlebotomus,* discussed later), and are known scientifically as *Culicoides.* Their bites can be extremely irritating. Often they produce delayed reactions. The 20 species in North America differ greatly in breeding habits, but all develop in water or moist places. The larvae of the most troublesome kinds develop in the mud on salt marshes and in rot holes in trees where decaying leaves and water are held. The insects, however annoying, are not known to carry human disease in this country. They were mistakenly accused of causing "sand-fly fever" in American troops in New Guinea. They are an intermediate host of certain roundworms (nematodes) in Africa and elsewhere in the Tropics. These roundworms in the blood of man apparently do not cause illness.

Installing dikes and tide gates to protect salt-marsh areas, clearing and deepening the margins of ponds and streams, and filling tree holes are steps that reduce breeding. Insecticidal sprays and fogs protect communities against the adults. Painting screens with 5 percent DDT in kerosene, the use of close-woven bed nets, and the application of repellents to exposed parts of the body give some relief.

Black flies, of the family Simuliidae, are annoying pests to lumbermen, campers, fishermen, and others in the north woods. These rather small, hump-backed gnats are not confined to the north country, however. Some 75 species exist in the United States. Many others occur in other countries. All breed in flowing water. Some kinds live only in fast mountain streams. They lay their eggs on sticks and rocks projecting from the water. The larvae cling to objects in the water, from which they gather food with a set of motile brushes around the mouth. They spin weblike pockets under the water and pupate in them.

As carriers of human diseases, black flies are not serious in this country, although many persons get severe dermatitis or allergic reactions from the bites. In Mexico, Central America, South America, and Africa, some species are hosts for early stages of a roundworm, which they transfer from one person to another. The worms form nodules under the skin, principally on the head and upper part of the body which cause so-called onchoceriasis. Some get into the eyes and may produce blindness.

The larvae of black flies can be killed by adding small amounts of DDT to the infested stream. Dosages required to control larvae will not injure fish, but care should be taken not to apply excessive amounts, which will kill fish. DDT fogs applied from the air or ground help to destroy these gnats. Damming streams to eliminate rapids has some merit. Repellents are not entirely satisfactory.

Sand flies are annoying bloodsuckers and carriers of at least two serious diseases, although none of the half dozen species of this group (*Phlebotomus*) that occur uncommonly in this country is a disease carrier. The dangerous verruga or Oroya fever, which occurs in Peru, Ecuador, Bolivia, and other South American countries, is carried by sand flies. They also transmit pappataci, sand-fly, or 8-day fever of the Mediterranean region, Near East, southern China, Ceylon, and India. It is a mild febrile disease of man.

Kala azar, a leishmaniasis endemic in the Mediterranean area, Iraq, southern Russia, India, and China, is carried by sand flies, as is a repulsive skin disease, Oriental sore, in that general area.

The insects breed in damp animal and vegetable wastes and in crevices in rocks and walls. A spray of DDT in kerosene in corners of sleeping quarters, around the base of houses, and their other breeding and resting places controls the sand flies and stops infections.

Close relatives of sand flies are other moth flies that have no thirst for blood. Some of them breed in sewage filters. Often they emerge from the sewer beds in large numbers and invade nearby houses. They are not attracted to food, but occasionally get on it or on dishes and utensils, which they undoubtedly contaminate. The larvae on the stones in the filter beds require much oxygen and may be killed simply by flooding the beds with a few inches of quiet water or sewage. Insecticides (such as DDT emulsions) are also effective but may destroy other organisms that aid in keeping the filters open.

HORSE FLIES AND DEER FLIES are serious pests of livestock but usually are less troublesome to man. These aggressive bloodsuckers will also attack man. Their bites are painful. Bathers and picnickers on beaches near salt marshes along the Atlantic seaboard are often driven away by attacks of "greenhead" horse flies. Outdoorsmen in the north woods are familiar with swarms of the flies.

Deer flies often attack man. In the summer of 1935, 170 young men of the Civilian Conservation Corps were preparing a game refuge on salt marshes near Bear Lake, Utah. The deer flies were very annoying; 30 men contracted tularemia, or rabbit fever, in 2 weeks, and the camp had to be closed.

The flies carry tularemia on their beaks. Occasionally anthrax germs also are carried in that way by horse flies and deer flies between diseased and healthy animals and sometimes to man.

In tropical West Africa, deer flies of two or more species are hosts of the filarial parasite (*Loa loa*) of man. The parasite lodges in the connective tissues under the skin and often invades the eyes.

One can combat horse flies and deer flies in several ways. Drainage of marshy breeding areas is frequently impractical. Spraying in early summer with DDT solution of marshes and swamps where the flies breed has some value. Because of the danger of injuring wildlife, the use of insecticides should be under the direction of an experienced person. Repellents to protect livestock have so far not proved very practical.

TSETSE FLIES carry African sleeping sickness, a deadly disease caused by minute, single-cell organisms, the trypanosomes. One form, Gambian sleeping sickness, is carried mainly by a fly, *Glossina palpalis,* which resembles the stable fly. Another kind, which brings death more rapidly, is Rhodesian sleeping sickness. It is carried principally by *G. morsitans.* Besides these diseases of humans, tsetse flies carry several related diseases of livestock and wildlife. The disease organisms are taken up by the fly in the blood meal, pass through developmental stages, and multiply in the digestive tract. They invade the salivary glands when mature and at a subsequent feeding of the fly they gain entrance to another animal host.

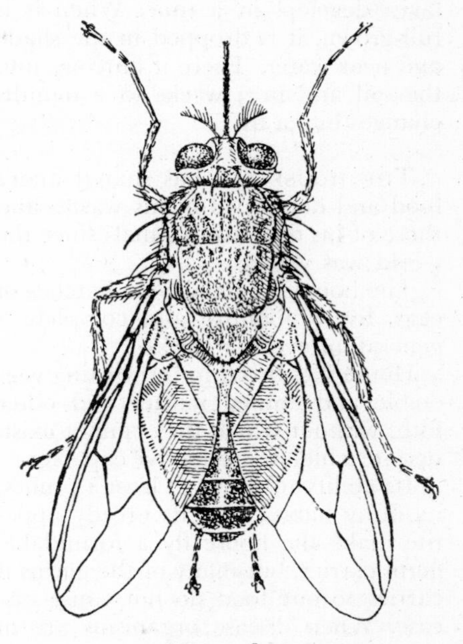

Tsetse fly.

These dangerous flies are confined to tropical and subtropical Africa, where they hinder settlement and development.

Tsetse flies live 3 to 6 months. They can travel considerable distances, although *G. palpalis* stays close to the banks of lakes or the timber along streams. The insects differ from most flies in that the eggs hatch and the larvae develop in a uterine pouch within the body of the mother fly. One larva develops at a time. When it is full-grown, it is dropped in the shade and near water. There it burrows into the soil and in 3 weeks to 2 months changes into a fly.

THE HOUSE FLY has shared man's food and developed in his wastes and those of his domestic animals since the world was young.

The house fly may lay 21 batches of eggs, live 5 months, and complete a generation every 2 weeks.

House flies breed in fermenting vegetable and animal matter and other filth, without which they cannot exist, despite a high reproductive capacity.

Its ability to travel at least 13 miles, its filthy habits, and its greedy appetite make the house fly a formidable germ carrier, but many of the germs it carries to our food do not cause disease. When disease organisms are in the wastes, however, the house fly carries them. In earlier days, many cases of typhoid were clearly chargeable to it and some still are. Dysentery, diarrhea, and other digestive troubles are often due to contamination of foods and utensils by flies. House flies are believed to have a part in spreading the germs of cholera, yaws, trachoma, and tuberculosis. They also transport certain parasitic worms.

After the Second World War, DDT—applied as a residual or long-lasting spray to walls and ceilings of buildings—made the house fly almost a rarity for a time. But in line with nature's defenses to perpetuate a species regardless of man's wishes, strains of flies resistant to the effects of DDT began to appear in 1947 in various parts of the world; those strains became more resistant and widespread in the next years.

Other insecticides, somewhat like DDT chemically, were found to have the same residual killing effect, but were less persistent. Among them were benzene hexachloride, lindane, methoxychlor, TDE, chlordane, toxaphene and dieldrin. No doubt others will be discovered, but the house fly has demonstrated its ability to develop resistance to each of the materials after a number of generations have been exposed to them. To help meet the situation, the old and safe pyrethrum has been brought back more fully into use, alone and in mixtures. Unlike DDT, it is a quick killer.

Screens and other means of excluding flies from buildings and food are of great value and will undoubtedly continue to be necessary for protection against the house fly, mosquitoes, and other troublesome and dangerous insects. Sticky fly paper, traps, and electrocuting devices are also useful in destroying flies that breed despite rigid sanitation.

BLOW FLIES, often called green bottle flies and blue bottle flies, are of many kinds. They have life cycles and habits somewhat like those of the house fly, but they breed mainly in carcasses of dead animals and in meat in garbage. They are seldom so numerous as house flies but carry many of the same disease-producing organisms.

Laboratory studies have incriminated field-collected blow flies in the conveyance of poliomyelitis virus, although their role in causing human infection is still a moot question. The habits of blow flies would seem to give opportunity for them to transmit that disease and many others.

The larvae of blow flies also develop in wounds or natural openings of the body. Such attacks are called myiasis. Some species, true parasites, develop in the tissues of living animals. Other species, when accidentally ingested as eggs or young maggots, may continue to grow in the digestive tract and produce severe irritation, nausea, vomiting, and diarrhea.

The true parasites may suck blood, as the human-infesting Congo floor maggot does, or they may invade wounds or inflamed nasal passages, as the screw-worm does. Screw-worms, if not promptly killed and removed, may destroy enough tissue to produce disfigurement or death of the victim.

Some other insects that customarily live as parasites in livestock occasionally attack man. The sheep bot fly sometimes darts at the eye of a person and deposits in it a droplet containing a number of minute, active, spiny larvae. The larvae crawl over the eyeball and cause inflammation. Shepherds in North Africa are said to be blinded by repeated attacks. Horse bot flies and cattle grubs in the first stage of their development occasionally get into the skin of people working around livestock. The horse bots burrow about in the skin, producing what is likened to creeping eruption. The cattle grubs penetrate deeper and usually work upward as they do in cattle. Often they come to the surface on the neck or head and produce a boil-like swelling, from which they can be removed. They sometimes cause severe illness.

Dermatobia is a fly that produces serious losses to livestock in the tropical Americas. Often it infests man and has therefore been called the human bot fly. The larvae develop in pockets beneath the skin and maintain an opening through which to get air. To get its larvae to a suitable host, the fly catches a mosquito or other bloodsucking insect, attaches eggs to its body, and then releases it. When the mosquito bites a warm-blooded animal, the little maggots pop out of the eggs and burrow into the skin.

FLEAS, like the biting flies, are among the higher insects that have complete metamorphosis. They have developed highly specialized parasitic habits in the adult stage only. The wingless adults have laterally compressed bodies and strong, spiny legs, which help them move rapidly among the hairs or feathers of their hosts. Their mouth parts are fitted for piercing and sucking. All species, as far as we know, are parasites of higher vertebrates. Fleas have astonishing strength in proportion to their small size. The human flea can jump 13 inches.

Some persons attract fleas more than do others under the same exposure. In one person, an area of inflammation immediately surrounds the bite; in others, a delayed irritation occurs. *Pulex irritans* is thus an appropriate name for the human flea, which has adapted itself to residence in folds of man's clothing as a substitute for the fur of the lower animals. Their eggs are dropped promiscuously and are not fastened to clothing or hair as are those of lice. The maggotlike larvae live on organic waste about the premises.

Other species that may become annoying in human abodes are the rat, cat, and dog fleas, which do not have so restricted a host preference as do some of their cousins on various rodents in the field.

The chigoe is an especially irritating kind of flea to man and animals in the Tropics. The females bury themselves in the skin, particularly of the feet, and cause persistent, ulcerlike craters, from which the fleas have to be removed before the wound can heal. This flea is not a known disease carrier.

Of greater concern are the species that carry the serious and widely occurring rodent infections, bubonic plague and murine typhus, to man. They live everywhere in warm climates. One of the authors during the Second World War watched the pests jump in all directions from the wrinkles in the pantaloons of Arabs while he was studying the effects of DDT in Egypt; boil up into his clothes from the straw in abandoned pillboxes and from cave floors occupied by refugees in Sicily, where he was investigating mosquitoes and sand flies; and emerge by thousands from the ground litter of a small, abandoned native village along a mountain stream in the Philippines. Regardless of locality, race and color, they were after human blood.

Bubonic plague is by all odds the most serious of the human diseases attributed to the flea. Think of the ravages of the Black Death in the Middle Ages, particularly among the populations of port cities. Plague still stalks the earth. In military operations in the Tropics we may have unavoidably spread the disease to new areas through beachhead or landing operations when it was not possible to use safeguards, like collared anchor cables and inspection, which are observed in peacetime to restrict the emigration of rats and their rat fleas into new ports and settled areas.

One of us lived in 1930 in a West African port city where people regarded the annual human death rate of about 600 as not unusual.

The disease waxes and wanes in the Tropics, but the antibiotics developed since 1940 give promise of relief if they are available. No one now need die of this once dreaded disease if diagnosis is made early enough and suitable drugs are available. Experimental data indicate that a combination of streptomycin and aureomycin is the treatment of choice.

The ecology of the so-called "sylvatic plague" in the western half of the United States has been quite obscure. There the infection continues to wipe out whole populations of field rodents locally with only an occasional human case. The disease has not affected rats in cities to any great extent. The special fleas of the affected ground squirrels, prairie dogs, and rabbits are less prone to bite human beings than are the oriental and the northern rat fleas.

Murine typhus, or endemic typhus, is much like the louse-borne type, which in numbers of cases, but not in virulence, outweighs plague as a world-wide human disease. The spread of murine typhus from man to man by lice, after establishment from fleas, has been reported in Mexico and Manchuria. New laboratory techniques and careful diagnosis are required to verify such reports.

Murine typhus occurs widely in tropical and temperate climates. Treatment with antibiotics has been effective, but preventive measures are still the most important. Constant vigilance is required against the spread of rat fleas by domestic rats from foreign ports. In endemic localities DDT or other toxicants are used in rat runways to reduce existing flea populations on rats. Another weapon is rat poisons, which have been spectacularly improved in recent years; one of them is the comparatively safe warfarin.

ALMOST EVERYONE has been stung by bees, wasps, and ants. Some have suffered the more painful sting of a velvet ant, the "cow-killer." All these insects use their stings merely in self-defense, but the pain is none the less severe. The effects generally do not last long, but some persons who are allergic to the poison that the insect injects may be seriously affected or even killed, particularly when they get many stings.

The material that causes the pain and the stinging mechanism vary among the different insects. The venom is usually a complex protein material. Among ants, formic acid is partly responsible for the pain of the bite or sting. Most insects can sting more than once, but a honey bee loses its life when it stings. The barbed sting holds fast in the flesh, and the tip of the abdomen and the two poison glands are torn off. The muscles that operate the stinging organ keep contracting for a few minutes, force the sting deeper into the skin, and pump the venom into the wound. The sting therefore should be removed quickly. That is best done by scraping the sting off with a knife or the fingernail; pulling it out with the fingers might squeeze more venom in.

CATERPILLARS do not carry human diseases, but often they cause painful injuries. The hairs or spines on the bodies of the larvae are mainly responsible. The hollow spines, connected at their bases with poison glands, contain poisonous materials. They are broken off in the skin of man when a sensitive part of the body comes in contact with the caterpillar or its shed skin.

The spines help protect the caterpillar against its predatory enemies, but they do not prevent its destruction by parasitic flies and wasps, which kill a high percentage of them.

Several species in seven or eight families of moths can sting in that way. Some of the worst, such as the puss caterpillar, look quite innocent, but many ugly and dangerous-appearing caterpillars, such as the hickory horned devil, are harmless.

Some urticating caterpillars are crop or forest pests, such as the brown-tail moth in New England, the flannel moth of the Northern States, the io moth, the saddleback caterpillar, and the puss caterpillar. The last named occasionally strips the leaves from elms, hackberries, and other shade trees in the South.

The hairs of the brown-tail moth retain their poison for a long time and, when the insects are numerous, may irritate the skin and eyes of many people. The sting of most of the species, although painful, does not last long. The puss caterpillar can have a more lasting, severe sting, which can give persons the symptoms of paralysis.

Before they reach full growth, the caterpillars can be controlled by spraying the infested shade trees or shrubbery with arsenate of lead or DDT. The likelihood of a person coming in contact with them is increased when the caterpillars are crawling around seeking a place to pupate. There is no specific remedy for the sting, although packs of bicarbonate of soda and cooling lotions are advised.

BEETLES of the family Meloidae have in their body fluids a poisonous substance, cantharidin, which blisters the skin. The beetles are collected and dried and the cantharidin is extracted and sold as a drug. Of the many species of blister beetles, one is widely known in this country as the old-fashioned potato beetle.

Some of the rove beetles (family Staphylinidae) also can cause blisters, which are often slow to heal. The so-called toddy disease among natives in the Marshall Islands is supposedly caused by rove beetles that get into palm pulp, which is fermented to make an alcoholic drink. The poison in the beetle is extracted by the alcohol and causes symptoms when the liquid is imbibed.

TO THE ENTOMOLOGIST the term "bug" refers specifically to an order of insects, the Hemiptera, which includes the wingless bed bugs of various species, and the winged, biting, or blood-sucking insects known as "kissing bugs," assassin bugs, conenoses, and their relatives.

Few insects have been more often maligned and less confirmed as carriers of disease than the bed bug or its close relative in the Tropics and subtropics, the Indian bed bug. Some other species of the bed bug family that are customary parasites of poultry, swallows, or bats may invade houses on occasion but cause little complaint among human inhabitants. An infestation of bed bugs is considered a sign of filth and uncleanliness in houses and hotels, but the bugs are seen sometimes in public conveyances so that any person might take one home. A few persons are sensitive to their bites and may develop a temporary rash, local swelling, or irritation following such attacks. The bugs are nocturnal. In daytime they retreat into mattresses, joints of wooden bedsteads, cracks, and other hideouts in bedrooms. Their flat bodies can edge into tight crevices. They have a distinctive, pungent odor. All active stages are parasitic from the time they hatch from eggs, which are laid in their hiding places. Adults can live a year without a meal of blood but will usually migrate during such a starvation period.

No one so far has proved that bed bugs are the actual, natural vectors of any important human disease. The causative agents of several diseases, including those of kala azar of Asia, Chagas' disease of South America, relapsing fever, infectious jaundice, lymphocytic choriomeningitis, tularemia, and also plague, have been shown experimentally to persist some times in the bodies of the bugs. They also have been reported as vectors of Rocky Mountain spotted fever in Brazil. From earlier experimental work in Poland similar conclusions were drawn, but such experimental results have not been found by other investigators.

Certain of the conenoses, sometimes called kissing bugs, of the family Triatomidae have been shown to be the natural carriers of trypanosomiasis in the American Tropics and even in temperate parts of South America. Chagas' disease, named for a Brazilian investigator, causes high mortality among children in some localities. The disease is caused by minute organisms, trypanosomes, which multiply in human organs and pass through a definite developmental cycle in bugs that have fed on persons having them in their blood. Some 40 species of the triatomids have been found naturally infected, but fewer than 12 are of any importance in human transmission. Several species habitually pass excrement while biting or soon thereafter. Transmission probably occurs through fecal contamination of the bite wounds and other abrasions or of the mucous membranes of the victim, rather than through direct inoculation by the mouth parts of the feeding bug. A number of native and domestic animals are reported to be reservoirs.

Several species of the bugs occur in various parts of the Southern States, where they infest rodent nests and other animal habitations. They may invade human dwellings or camps and attack man himself. Natural infection of trypanosomes in wood rats, and in their parasites, *Triatoma protracta* or *T. uhleri,* has been reported in a few localities. Human infection in this country has been suspected only on serological evidence. Triatomids were found naturally infected with western equine encephalomyelitis virus in Kansas, but it is doubtful whether they are of importance in either human or equine transmission.

Assassin bugs prey on other insects but are not parasitic on animals. If annoyed or accidentally touched, some species can inflict severe and painful "stings" with their beaks.

Bed bugs are controlled with preparations of DDT. The conenoses are susceptible to the new insecticides, but the delayed action of DDT and their ability to fly and quickly reinfest premises complicate the problem of control. DDT can be applied as a 10-percent dust or a 5-percent solution in deodorized kerosene to the hiding places of the bugs.

COCKROACHES are the only members of the grasshopper group (order Orthoptera) that are involved in the contamination of food. Crickets often enter houses and occasionally eat holes in clothing but are not attracted to food.

Of the many species of cockroaches, only five are common house inhabitors. They are the large American, oriental, and Australian cockroaches and the smaller German cockroach, or "water bug," and the brown-banded roach. Their habits are similar. They prefer secluded, warm, damp places, as behind sinks, around drain pipes, and in furnace rooms. They lay their eggs inside a pod. The German cockroach carries the egg capsule attached to the tip of the abdomen until a day or two before the eggs hatch. The young insects resemble the adults except in size and lack of wings. Cockroaches grow slowly. The American cockroach usually takes a full year to develop from egg to adult. Then and later the filthy pest at night or on dark days busily runs about, sampling filth and foods and imparting to infested areas his fetid, roachy smell.

People have long assumed that cockroaches must be carriers of various enteric diseases and tuberculosis. Now we know that certain disease organisms

(*Salmonella*) were still alive when passed 10 to 20 days after being fed to three common kinds of household roaches. The germs remained infective in the fecal pellets for more than 199 days afterward. These insects furnish one of the important sources for spread of intercurrent salmonellosis in laboratory animals.

Cockroaches can be controlled by thorough sanitation, elimination of breeding and hiding places, and insecticides. Sodium fluoride dust (at least 50 percent) has been used in this way. Chlordane, applied as a 2-percent spray or a 5-percent powder to restricted areas where the insects hide has given good results. A 5 percent DDT spray or 10 percent DDT powder is also recommended but is less effective than chlordane. Pyrethrum sprays are recommended in situations where foods might be contaminated with chlordane or DDT. Pyrethrum must be reapplied frequently because it loses its effectiveness in a few days.

OF THE TWO KINDS OF LICE, we are concerned here with the sucking lice (Anoplura). The biting lice (Mallophaga) are chiefly parasites of birds.

Three kinds of sucking lice commonly infest man, the head, body, and crab lice.

Crab lice, also called pubic lice, prefer hairy parts of the human body in the pubic region and armpits. In severe infestations they may be found in the eyebrows and lashes. They may cause intense itching but have no known effect on the health of the host.

The other lice have greatly influenced human history. They have affected the outcome of many military campaigns because they spread epidemic typhus. This disease, the "red death" of the Middle Ages, has been the scourge of soldiers and displaced peoples during times of their greatest misery, when they were least able to exercise customary habits of sanitation.

No insect has shown greater adaptation to the habits of its human host than has the body louse. It alone of all the members of its order has forsaken the fur of its host and found refuge in man's inner garments, on which its eggs are fastened and to which it clings except while feeding. An adult may feed as often as six times a day. The longer the garments are worn next to the skin, the better the body louse thrives.

The head louse is related to the body louse, but it is slightly smaller and darker in color and is found only among hairs of the head. The more luxuriant the head adornment of natives, the greater opportunity is provided for lice to develop.

Adult lice may survive up to 5 days without a meal of blood. The younger stages must feed oftener than once a day to stay healthy. A person's first exposure means little or no discomfort, but a sensitivity occurs after a week or 10 days, when the average person develops an intense itching from the feeding of the lice. A tolerance is later developed by constantly infested peoples, who take little notice of their presence. Infestations of head lice are not uncommon in the United States; occasionally they occur among school children.

Louse-borne typhus, like plague, has been one of the historic scourges of vermin-infested mankind. Like malaria, on the other hand, it is one of the few serious insect-transmitted diseases in which man himself serves as the so-called animal reservoir; there is no known cycle in some lower animal. Epidemics, heretofore, have followed in the wake of war as certainly as death and taxes, simply because habitual sanitation and segregation, which prevent the spread of lice, could not be constantly maintained among the soldiers or civilians. At the beginning of the First World War as many as 2,500 new cases a day were hospitalized with typhus in the Serbian Army; among civilians the number was said to be three times greater. The outbreak temporarily checked the impending invasion of the Austrian Army at the Serbian borders more effectively than any

970134°—52——12

military strategy. Napoleon's retreat from Moscow is believed to have been due more to typhus than to cold weather.

Trench fever, another disease of soldiers, is also louse-borne. It occurred in the First World War and also in the Second World War on the Russian-German front. The causative agent is thought to be related to typhus fever. It does not kill, but it can be a debilitating epidemic disease among louse-infested troops.

Relapsing fever, also transmitted by the body louse, is caused by a spirochete, an organism entirely different from the one that causes typhus. The disease is most prevalent in parts of North Africa and Asia. Here again the louse-man-louse cycle is all that is needed to maintain the infection. How louse-borne relapsing fever and typhus are maintained between epidemics is a mystery, because transmission through the egg from one generation of lice to the next seldom occurs, if ever.

Lice can be controlled easily by 10 percent DDT powder. In 1944 a simple method was devised to apply DDT powder by blowing it into the openings of the clothing while on the person. Thousands of individuals living under refugee conditions in Naples were so treated and a threatened outbreak of typhus was averted. However, the finding of DDT-resistant lice during the Korean conflict has made it necessary to use pyrethrum or lindane instead of DDT.

TICKS AND MITES comprise the Acarina—a class of arthropods separate from the Insecta because they have four instead of three pairs of legs in the nymphal and adult stages and their bodies lack the separate thoracic region of true insects.

Mites generally are smaller than ticks and diverse in habits. Only a few attack man and animals. Ticks require blood for their development and reproduction, but probably fewer than half of the species feed upon man.

Scabies of man is a condition caused by the itch mite, which burrows in the skin, where it lays its eggs. The mite causes intense itching and irritation. In aggravated cases, an extensive crusting and scabbing results, particularly over the arms and hands. The offenders are never seen except by careful dissection under a good lens. Observations in England during the war demonstrated that the major source of new cases was provided by actual body contact rather than through towels, bed clothing, and wearing apparel used by infested people.

Grocer's itch and harvester's rash—transient but often annoying—are the result of exposure to mites that ordinarily infest grain and stored-food products.

The tropical rat mite and a less common but also widely spread house-mouse-infesting mite, *Allodermanyssus sanguineus*, occasionally cause complaints through infestation of houses invaded by their rat or mouse hosts. The first species has been accused of acting as a vector of murine typhus and of plague, but experimental evidence has been conflicting, and its importance in this regard remains doubtful. But it can transmit rickettsialpox, the most recently discovered of the typhuslike diseases, which has occurred in some mouse-infested premises in New York and Boston. *A. sanguineus* is the natural transmitter of rickettsialpox in New York suburban settlements. Some of these mites have also been reported as transmitting tularemia in Russia.

Chicken mites and related species occasionally annoy man by their bloodsucking habit but do not remain on him long.

Chiggers belong to another group of mites of the family Trombiculidae. Only the first or larval stage is parasitic on vertebrates and must have a blood meal for further development. Chiggers are so minute that they are seldom seen by man even though the numerous sites of attachment such as the belt line are evident. In eastern and southern areas of the United States where chiggers are most prevalent, they are not known to carry any disease, but their attack produces severe itching, which may result in secondary infections. This type of attack in the southwest Pacific area is known as scrub itch.

Scrub typhus, a serious malady in the Far East, is called tsutsugamushi disease in Japan, where it was first recognized. It is carried by certain species of the chiggers. The disease agent, related to the typhus group, is passed from one generation of mites to the next through the egg.

The chiggers usually parasitize rats and other rodents, but certain species will attack man. The mortality from scrub typhus can be extremely high—more than 60 percent of cases in some parts of Japan, or as low as 0.6 percent among Americans in an epidemic in the Schouten Islands, where 1,469 cases occurred in 6 months. Even with this low death rate, the situation is serious when incapacitation averages 2 months or more. Chloromycetin and aureomycin, however, are markedly reducing hospitalization and will aid in progress against this dread disease.

More people have an acquaintance with ticks than with mites. Yet many do not know that there is one family, the Argasidae, or soft ticks, which feed on man rather rapidly like bed bugs and do not remain attached.

The notorious relapsing-fever tick of tropical Africa has become almost completely domesticated, and natives sleeping on the floors of their huts pay little attention to it. A number of related species in various parts of the world, including the United States, have since been found to cause human cases of relapsing fever. These are mostly species that rodents bring into living quarters, mountain cabins, native huts, and the like. Several similar forms of relapsing fever are carried by different species of these soft ticks.

Another group of ticks, the hard ticks, of the family Ixodidae, customarily require several days to complete engorgement after attachment. In temperate climates where cold seasons intervene, some species may require 2 years to complete a generation. The Rocky Mountain wood tick is an example. The adults have been known to survive three winters when kept outside. Many ticks have simple eyes with which they can discern the passing shadow of a potential victim. Others have no eyes. Special sense organs enable them to detect animals 25 feet or more away, so that an unwitting camper may attract ticks from a considerable area. Many ticks are thus able to select favorable sites—game trails, for instance—for seeking their host.

Ticks have numerous progeny and few enemies, are not greatly affected by weather conditions, can feed upon various kinds of animals, and permit the passage of disease organisms from stage to stage as well as from one generation to another through the egg. Instances of secondary infection at the point of tick attack occur often.

"Spring-summer" encephalitis in Soviet Russia and Siberia is the most important of the filterable viruses carried by several Russian species. Another tick-borne virus is the rather mild, nonfatal Colorado tick fever of our Rocky Mountain region.

Tick-borne typhuslike diseases are assuming increasing importance in various parts of the world. These include American or Rocky Mountain spotted fever in various countries of the New World, and a group of usually less severe diseases in Europe, Africa, Asia, and probably Australia, related to boutonneuse fever, which was first recognized in the Mediterranean region. The latter group of diseases includes South African tick-bite fever, Kenya typhus, and Siberian, Indian, and probably Queensland tick typhuses. In the United States, the Rocky Mountain wood tick in the West, the American dog tick in the East and South, and probably the lone star tick in the South are the chief criminals in human infection with spotted fever.

Q fever is a peculiar, recently recognized disease due to a typhuslike agent which is being discovered in many parts of the world. Ticks have been found naturally infected in North America, Australia, Spain, and parts of North Africa, but only in Australia have they shown any importance in relation to human infection.

Tularemia, an important bacterial disease affecting man, occasionally is transmitted by ticks.

Tick paralysis of man and animals is due to a presumed toxin secreted in the saliva of ticks. Though more frequently observed in tick-infested animals, a number of human cases have been reported in the United States, Canada, and Australia. The ascending paralysis is caused by a rapidly engorging female tick attached to the base of the head, where the hair may hide its presence for longer periods. Complete recovery has followed within 24 to 48 hours of removal of the offending tick. Death occurs if the ascending paralysis reaches the respiratory centers of the human or animal victim before the tick has dropped off or has been removed.

The Acarina are more difficult than insects to control because they are more resistant to insecticides. Benzyl benzoate ointment is one of the best materials for the control of scabies. This acaricide in combination with dibutyl phthalate is an excellent clothing impregnant against chiggers and is more durable than many chemicals previously tried. Chiggers can be controlled in infested areas by applying 1 to 2 pounds of chlordane or toxaphene or one-fourth pound of lindane per acre, employing dusts or sprays. Such mixtures are being constantly improved.

Several substances effective against ticks have been discovered. The control of livestock and wild animals upon which ticks feed reduces the number of these pests. Many of the ticks in infested ground areas can be destroyed by spraying with a 5 percent DDT emulsion. Certain ticks congregate near roads and trails and an insecticide should be applied especially on those areas. Clearing of brush and close cutting of grass is a material aid in tick control.

The best way to remove ticks that are attached to persons is to pull them out. Some ticks have long beaks and their removal may require a needle or knife.

F. C. BISHOPP *has general direction of the research in the Bureau of Entomology and Plant Quarantine on injurious and beneficial insects. In 1909 he began investigating ticks and various insects as annoyers of man and carriers of disease. In 1926 he was put in charge of the Bureau's division of insects affecting man and animals and in 1941 became assistant chief of the Bureau.*

CORNELIUS B. PHILIP *is principal medical entomologist and assistant director of the Rocky Mountain Laboratory, United States Public Health Service, Hamilton, Mont., and a member of the National Defense Virus and Rickettsial Disease Commission. He has studied insect-borne diseases in many parts of the world, in part as a colonel in the Sanitary Corps of the Army during the Second World War, and is an authority on medical entomology.*

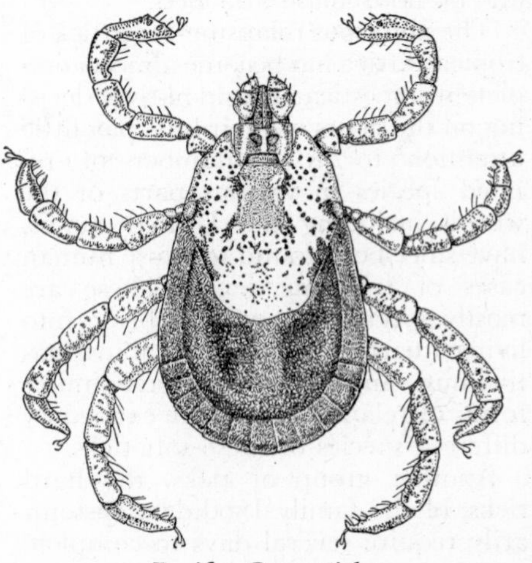

Pacific Coast tick.

Carriers of Animal Diseases

Gerard Dikmans, A. O. Foster
C. D. Stein, L. T. Giltner

Flies, ticks, and other arthropods spread and perpetuate many livestock diseases. Most are of comparatively minor concern as direct causes of injury or annoyance but, like the fever ticks of cattle, are important as reservoirs and vectors of disease-causing organisms. Some, like the tsetse flies in Africa, are of no consequence as pests, yet are a limiting factor in the production of livestock.

The remarkable ways of insects and their allies in transmitting diseases are as varied and spectacular as the diseases themselves and the vectors that transmit them. Common house flies, however benign and unspectacular they may seem, often carry on their feet and mouth parts or in their bodies the contaminating germs of everyday skin and generalized infections and sometimes even the dreaded bacilli of anthrax or the fatal toxin of botulism. Other insects, mites, and bugs of various kinds transmit the infective stages of numerous parasites, final infection usually resulting from accidental swallowing of the infected vector by a susceptible animal. Disease caused by tropical warble flies, which are next in importance to the cattle fever tick among the external parasites of livestock in Latin America and analogous to the better known warble flies of Temperate Zones, is essentially insect-borne—the flies attach their eggs to captured mosquitoes (*Psorophora*), which in turn transport the infection to cattle and other animals.

The afore-mentioned examples are illustrative only of the ways in which insects carry diseases. With the notable exceptions of tick-borne fever of cattle and tsetse fly disease, they are scarcely typical of the principal arthropod-borne diseases of livestock. As might be suspected, the chief vectors are predominantly bloodsucking species, and the diseases transmitted by them are essentially blood infections. Those vectors ordinarily spread and propagate disease in two ways. One, mechanical transmission, is the direct transfer (or its equivalent) of infective blood from diseased to healthy animals. The other, biological transmission, represents a specialized and complex relationship among vector, organism, and host, which is characterized by reproduction and structural change of the disease-causing organism within the body of the vector. Some biting flies function naturally in both ways. For a short period, probably not more than 2 hours, after feeding on the blood of a diseased animal, the dangerous organisms may be carried to healthy, susceptible animals on which the fly may chance to feed. For a longer period thereafter, from a few days to several weeks, the fly is incapable of transmitting the infection. Then it may again become infective in consequence of a biological reconstitution of the organism, culminating in the production of new infective stages in its salivary glands or other tissues.

The arthropod-borne diseases of domestic animals are of two main kinds: Those caused by plant micro-organisms and those caused by animal micro-organisms. The former comprise bacteria, spirochetes (*Borrelia*), Rickettsiae (*Coxiella*), and viruses. The latter, in part, are pathogenic protozoa, including piroplasms (*Babesia*), Theileriae, the trypanosomes, Leishmaniae, Leucocytozoa, and a species of *Haemoproteus*. Animals that recover from disease caused by some of these organisms may remain carriers, or apparently healthy animals that are dangerous seedbeds of infection, for long periods or for life.

The bacterial diseases that are sometimes carried by arthropods are anthrax, tularemia, swine erysipelas, and botulism (limber neck of birds). All are spread by other means, and the role of arthropods is accidental and mechanical.

Anthrax, an acute disease caused by *Bacillus anthracis,* affects all classes of mammals, including man. Infections in livestock are generally acquired during grazing. Incidence is especially high during the fly season, and outbreaks in cattle have been ascribed to fly transmission. The vectors are the black horse fly and other horse flies, the stable fly, mosquitoes (*Psorophora sayi* and *Aedes sylvestris*), and several nonbiting species, including the house fly and blow flies (*Calliphora*). The ear tick and even ants also have been suspected.

Tularemia, caused by *Bacterium tularense,* is primarily an infection of small wild animals, such as rabbits, squirrels, rats, mice, woodchucks, opossums, and grouse, but it can be transmitted to man, sheep, swine, dogs, and cats. The disease is transmitted commonly by contact, sometimes by the ingestion of contaminated food and water, and occasionally by the bites of ticks, flies, lice, and bed bugs.

Swine erysipelas is a prevalent infectious disease that biting flies may spread from pig to pig. We do not know the extent to which it is insect-borne, but such transmission has been demonstrated experimentally with the stable fly. The infectious organism, *Erysipelothrix rhusiopathiae,* is an invader of the blood, joint membranes, and other tissues. Death is uncommon, but condition and marketability are seriously affected.

Botulism, or limber neck of chickens, is a fatal condition induced by the potent toxin of *Clostridium botulinum.* Ordinarily it follows ingestion of canned vegetables that have become contaminated with the organism. At times chickens become ill and die from ingesting blow fly maggots that have developed in contaminated meat.

SPIROCHETES affect all animals and get from host to host in many ways. They are minute, spiral organisms, which show some affinities to the protozoa but are commonly regarded as bacteria. We mention two examples, both tick-borne.

Borrelia theileri is responsible in South Africa for a benign, febrile disease of cattle, sheep, and horses. It occurs in the blood stream and is transmitted biologically by one- and two-host ticks, *Boophilus decoloratus* and *Rhipicephalus evertsi,* and possibly by others.

Borrelia anserina causes relapsing fever, or spirochetosis, in chickens, turkeys, ducks, and geese. It occurs in Asia, Africa, South America, and elsewhere. It has been found in a few epizootics of turkeys in the United States. It causes a rapidly fatal blood infection. The fowl tick and probably the chicken mite are vectors. Mosquitoes also are suspected.

RICKETTSIAE, which are intermediate between bacteria and viruses, cause many serious diseases of man as well as animals. One of these, Q fever, caused by *Coxiella burnetii,* is a disease of man, but cattle probably are the source of most human infections. The disease is recognized now in many parts of the world, including the United States. Ticks carry the organisms, and natural infections have been found in numerous species (Rocky Mountain wood tick, Pacific Coast tick, lone star tick, brown dog tick, and others).

A few other rickettsial infections of livestock, such as heart water fever of ruminants, occur outside the United States. Ticks, as far as we know, are the only vectors.

VIRUS DISEASES are numerous, and many are mechanically transmitted, wholly or in part, by arthropods, particularly biting flies.

The ones transmitted mainly by these agents are equine infectious anemia, infectious equine encephalomyelitis, African horse sickness, Japanese B encephalitis, louping ill of sheep, Nairobi disease of sheep, blue tongue of sheep, and rift valley fever. At times arthropods are presumably instrumental also in the transmission of fowl pox, swine pox, myxomatosis of rabbits, and infectious enteritis of cats.

Equine infectious anemia, or swamp fever, occurs throughout the world. It destroys the working efficiency of thousands of horses, mules, and donkeys. Its natural spread is imperfectly understood, but the disease is readily produced experimentally in susceptible animals by injection of infectious material, such as blood or other tissue fluids from infected animals. Under experimental conditions, the virus has been transmitted by horse flies (*Tabanus septentrionalis* and *T. sulcifrons*), stable flies, mosquitoes (*Psorophora columbiae*), and biting lice (*Bovicola pilosa*?). The probability that direct mechanical transmission by biting flies commonly occurs is emphasized both by the summer intensity of the disease and the persistence of the virus in the blood of infected hosts.

Infectious equine encephalomyelitis is caused by so-called Eastern, Western, and Venezuelan types of virus in North and South America and neighboring islands. Man is susceptible to all types. Natural reservoirs, particularly birds, are a probable source of infection to mosquitoes, which are the common vectors of the virus. The virus types have been recovered from or experimentally transmitted by a large number of arthropod species, among them the yellow-fever mosquito, salt-marsh mosquitoes (*Aedes*), other mosquitoes (*Culex, Culiseta,* and *Mansonia*), the bloodsucking conenose, the Rocky Mountain wood tick, the chicken mite, and chicken lice (*Menopon pallidum* and *Eumenacanthus stramineus*). In the tick, the virus is present at all stages of development, but scientists do not know yet whether the virus passes through the egg.

African horse sickness, an acute and virulent infection of equine species in central and southern Africa, is presumed to be transmitted by arthropods, mainly because of apparently convincing evidence that the disease does not pass directly from animal to animal. Mosquitoes, horse flies, midges, and other insects have been suspected as vectors.

Japanese B encephalitis, a fatal virus infection of man, is not a disease of domestic animals, but domestic animals, especially the horse, are dangerous reservoirs of the virus. It occurs in the Far East, where it is transmitted biologically by hibernating culicine mosquitoes (the southern house mosquito and others).

Several virus infections of sheep, all of which affect other animals in some degree and most of which are transmissible to man, are biologically and exclusively spread by arthropods. They are serious diseases in several parts of the world. Louping ill, transmitted by the castor bean tick (*Ixodes ricinus*), is prevalent in the British Isles. Rift valley fever, transmitted by mosquitoes (*Eretmopodites*), and Nairobi disease, carried by ticks (*Rhipicephalus appendiculatus*), occur in Kenya, British East Africa. Blue tongue, a more widespread disease, is carried by midges (*Culicoides*).

Fowl pox, a widespread and serious disease of chickens, turkeys, and pheasants, is often transmitted by the northern house mosquito and the yellow-fever mosquito, possibly, in some instances, by a biological mechanism. Ordinarily, however, it is passed directly from bird to bird. Swine pox, another virus disease, does not appear to be directly infectious but is probably transmitted mainly by the sucking lice of hogs (*Haematopinus suis*). Feline infectious enteritis is a common, fatal disease of kittens. The cat flea is presumed to be an important vector, although the disease is more commonly spread by direct contact with diseased animals or contaminated quarters. Myxomatosis, which occurs in California, is a fast-spreading, fatal disease of rabbits, that is carried both by contact and by mosquitoes (*Culex annulirostris* and *Aedes theoboldi*?).

Tick paralysis of cattle is actually caused, rather than carried, by ticks, yet it is a specific clinical entity characterized by complete paralysis in severe cases. Outbreaks in the Rocky Mountain States and British Columbia have resulted from infestation with the Rocky Mountain wood tick. Tick removal usually affords prompt relief. Other ticks (the American dog tick in the East and species of *Ixodes* in Australia and elsewhere) cause the condition. The symptoms are apparently due to the injection of toxin by female ticks at a particular stage in their sexual development.

Arthropod-borne, protozoan diseases of livestock, in contrast to most of the diseases already discussed, are distinct from those affecting man. The only exceptions, known technically as leishmaniasis and Chagas' disease (*Trypanosoma cruzi* infection), are predominantly human afflictions, although they also occur naturally in dogs and some other animals. A disease of extreme importance in man and of even greater importance in livestock is sometimes referred to as African trypanosomiasis but the specific organisms that cause disease in animals are not infective to man. On the other hand, the species affecting man (*Trypanosoma gambiense* and *T. rhodesiense*), although experimentally transmissible, are diagnosable in animals only as *T. brucei,* which is a most serious disease-causing species.

Poultry (chickens, turkeys, pigeons, ducks, and geese) are subject to two insect-borne diseases caused by related protozoan parasites, namely, *Haemoproteus columbae* and *Leucocytozoan smithi.* Both occur in the United States. The former is a parasite of pigeons, although this or related species also occur in other birds. Commonly referred to as pigeon malaria, the disease is carried by pigeon flies (*Lynchia maura* and *Pseudolynchia canariensis*). The latter, possibly comprising more than one species, affects other classes of poultry and is transmitted by black flies (*Simulium occidentale, S. venustum, S. nigroparum, S. slossonae,* and *S. jenningsi*) and perhaps by mosquitoes.

Anaplasmosis, caused by *Anaplasma marginale,* an organism of indefinite classification, clinically resembles cattle fever and was not recognized as a widespread disease in the United States until fever ticks were eradicated from a large part of the cattle fever area. Because the disease is coextensive with cattle fever, vectors of the latter are presumed to be transmitters of anaplasmosis. This incriminates the principal species of fever ticks (*Boophilus annulatus, B. microplus,* and *B. decoloratus*). However, the persistence of the disease, which is not contagious, in areas without fever ticks indicated clearly that there were other vectors. Much experimental work has revealed that other ticks (American dog tick, Rocky Mountain wood tick, Pacific Coast tick, brown dog tick, and possibly others) can transmit the disease, although we do not know their natural capacity to do so. Several species of horse flies and some mosquitoes have also been demonstrated to be potential mechanical vectors.

Aegyptianellosis, caused by *Aegyptianella pullorum,* another organism of uncertain zoological classification, affects chickens, ducks, and geese. It is transmitted by the fowl tick and occurs in Africa and in parts of Europe and Asia.

Piroplasmosis, one of the most devastating groups of diseases of domestic animals, affects cattle, horses, sheep, swine, and dogs.

The causative organisms, all biologically transmitted by ticks, are: In cattle, *Babesia bigemina, B. argentina,* and *B. bovis;* in horses, *B. equi* and *B. caballi;* in sheep, *B. motasi* and *B. ovis;* in swine, *B. trautmanni* and *B. perroncitoi;* and in dogs, *B. canis* and *B. gibsoni.* These are microscopic, single-celled parasites that enter and destroy the red blood cells. When the disease is acute, or fulminating, the parasites multiply rapidly and cause death in most cases. The symptoms are those associated with destruction of red blood cells, namely, fever, anemia, jaundice, thick bile, enlargement of liver and spleen, and emaciation. Ticks ingest the organisms during their engorgement on infected animals. Carriers, rather than acutely ill animals, are commonly the chief source of tick infection. In ticks, the parasites multiply and invade all tissues, including the salivary glands. The cattle tick, all stages of which live on one animal, transmits the parasites through its eggs to the next generation of larvae, or seed ticks, which carry the disease to a new host.

CATTLE TICK FEVER, or bovine piroplasmosis, is prevalent throughout the world. It causes incalculable losses. The history of the disease in the United States is a remarkable chapter of medical science. First came the demonstration in 1893 of tick transmission by Theobald Smith and F. L. Kilborne, of the Department of Agriculture—a discovery of immense benefit because it pointed the way to the solution of other disease problems. Then came the remarkable campaign, begun in 1906, to eradicate the cattle tick, and with it, cattle fever. The painstaking studies that laid the groundwork for success included researches into the habits and distribution of cattle ticks, determinations of their capacity to transmit cattle fever, establishment of the northern limits of the disease, the promulgation and enforcement of quarantines governing the shipment of cattle, and the critical evaluation of arsenical dips against the cattle tick. When the program of tick eradication was finally devised, cattle fever was causing losses exceeding 40 million dollars annually in the South and Southwest. As of 1952, and for more than a decade, the disease and fever ticks have been all but eradicated from the country. The fight against this disease is the most extensive campaign ever waged against parasitic disease in livestock. The total cost amounted to scarcely more than the toll that was formerly taken by the disease in a single year.

In the areas of their respective distributions, many ticks transmit the three afore-mentioned species of *Babesia* among cattle. Chief among them are *Boophilus annulatus, B. microplus, B. decoloratus, Rhipicephalus appendiculatus, R. evertsi, R. bursa, Ixodes ricinus, I. persulcatus,* and *Haemaphysalis cinnabarina.*

Tick fever of horses does not occur in the United States but is a common and serious disease throughout tropical and temperate zones. The two species of *Babesia* utilize tick vectors belonging principally to the genera *Rhipicephalus, Hyalomma,* and *Dermacentor.*

The story of the piroplasmoses affecting other animals is similar, although *Babesia* infections of sheep, swine, and dogs are not of comparable economic importance to those affecting cattle and horses. Canine piroplasmosis occurs in the United States. It is the only *Babesia* infection of domestic animals that has been found in this country since 1939. The brown dog tick and probably other ticks (*Dermacentor reticulatus, D. andersoni, Haemaphysalis leachi,* and *H. bispinosa*) are vectors of the species of *Babesia* affecting dogs.

THEILERIASIS principally affects cattle in Africa, but it occurs in sheep, goats, and dogs and on other continents. It is similar to piroplasmosis but does not commonly cause jaundice, hemoglobinuria (hemoglobin in the urine), or anemia. Theileriae do not multiply in and destroy red cells but enter them only after multiplication in the so-called endothelial tissues. The causative organisms are: In cattle, *Theileria parva, T. annulata,* and *T. mutans;* in sheep and goats, *T. ovis* and *T. recondita;* and in dogs, *Rangelia vitali. T. mutans* is an essentially harmless species. The species of *Theileria* are transmitted by two- and three-host ticks in contrast to the usual transmission of *Babesia* of cattle fever by one-host ticks. Associated with this difference in vectors are differences in the biology of transmission. Theileriae develop in successive stages of ticks and are not transmitted hereditarily, or through the eggs, to successive generations as in the case of *Babesia.* Ticks usually acquire the organisms during their larval stages and carry them to new hosts during succeeding nymphal stages.

EAST COAST FEVER, caused by *Theileria parva,* is a fatal disease of cattle in South Africa. The chief vectors are species of *Rhipicephalus* (*R. appendiculatus, R. capensis, R. evertsi,* and *R. simus*). A milder form of bovine theileriasis, caused by *T. annulata,* is transmitted by *Hyalomma mauritanicum* in North Africa and by *H. dromedarii asiaticum* in Central Asia.

In sheep, goats, and dogs, theileriasis, although a serious infection, is not of comparable importance to the disease in cattle. Of interest is the fact that a soft, or argasid, tick (*Ornithodorus lahorensis*) is presumed on experimental grounds to be a vector of the disease among sheep and goats. All other ticks that transmit protozoan infections are hard, or ixodid, ticks.

TRYPANOSOMIASIS is a group name for several related diseases, each of which is caused by a specific trypanosome. It includes some of the worst illnesses of domestic animals and man. It is the only disease that by itself has denied vast areas of land to all domestic animals other than poultry. The areas of complete denial are all in Africa. One-fourth of Africa is controlled by tsetse flies (*Glossina*), which are principal vectors of trypanosomes. The disease is, however, a major livestock scourge in every continent except Australia. Moreover, the exclusive occurrence of tsetses in Africa makes it evident that other vectors and mechanisms are responsible for the spread of the disease outside of Africa and, indeed, that they are operative within the tsetse fly area.

Nine species of trypanosomes produce disease of livestock. Four (*Trypanosoma congolense, T. brucei, T. simiae,* and *T. uniforme*) are found only in the tsetse fly areas. Two others (*T. vivax* and *T. theileri*) exist therein but are also established in other areas, where they are mechanically transmitted by horse flies (*Tabanus*) and other biting flies, exclusive of tsetses. These are the half-dozen species responsible for nagana, the African animal trypanosomiasis. The three remaining species (*T. evansi, T. equinium,* and *T. equiperdum*) cause severe diseases in horses (surra, mal de caderas, and dourine). Mal de caderas occurs in South America. Surra and dourine occur worldwide. Both have occurred in the United States, but constant vigilance and prompt eradicative measures have kept them from becoming established. Surra and dourine also employ particularly interesting methods of transmission. The former is usually transmitted mechanically by horse flies and other biting insects. However, it is probably identical with murrina, an affliction of horses in Panama that has heretofore been ascribed to *Trypanosoma hippicum* rather than *T. evansi.* This infection (murrina) incriminates the vampire bat (*Desmodus rotundus murinus*), this being the only instance of mammalian transmission of a protozoan disease. Dourine, on the other hand, is ordinarily transmitted during coitus, and is therefore frequently referred to as horse syphilis. It is consequently confined to horses and donkeys, occurring chiefly among breeding stock.

Eight (all but *T. equinium*) of the nine disease-causing trypanosomes of livestock are encountered in Africa; namely, the four afore-mentioned, indigenous species, two of cosmopolitan distribution that affect horses, and two extra-African species that also cause nagana. The latter, *T. vivax* and *T. theileri,* have outgrown their dependence on tsetse flies. In Africa, however, *T. vivax* is associated closely with *Glossina* and is as dependent as *T. congolense. T. vivax* is a cause of cattle trypanosomiasis in South and Central America, where biting flies presumably transmit it. *T. theileri,* similarly spread, is of cosmopolitan distribution in cattle but only occasionally causes severe disease. It occurs in North America, where it is apparently noninjurious.

Nagana, or African trypanosomiasis of animals, caused by some six species, already named, affects all mammals. Economically it is the most important protozoan disease of livestock. In cattle the species responsible for the disease, in order of importance, are *T. congolense, T. vivax,* and *T. uniforme.* The first two account for most of the cases. *T. congolense* occurs throughout the tsetse fly areas and is the most virulent trypanosome affecting animals. The organisms are found only in the blood. In the case of *T. vivax,* organisms are not readily found in the blood stream but may generally be demonstrated in a gland smear.

A study of cattle losses in Nigeria revealed that 30 of every 100 deaths were due to nagana.

In horses, the principal species causing nagana are *T. brucei* and *T. congolense. T. vivax* sometimes infects horses but rarely causes symptoms. *T. brucei,* like *T. vivax,* is more readily found in glandular tissue than in blood. Horses infected with either *T. brucei* or *T. congolense* almost always die unless they are adequately treated.

In sheep and goats, nagana is caused by the same species that cause it in horses. *T. congolense* infections, in contrast to those associated with other trypanosomes, is characterized by a sameness of grave disease in cattle, horses, sheep, and goats.

In swine, the chief pathogen is *T. simiae,* which has been called the lightning destroyer of pigs. Swine are susceptible to infection with *T. brucei* and *T. congolense,* but these species rarely produce symptoms. *T. simiae* infection of pigs is extremely acute. Animals in apparently good health are taken ill overnight and die the next day.

Camels and dogs are notably susceptible to trypanosomiases; in them, *T. evansi,* the cause of surra in horses, produces the same disease. Some authorities regard surra as a predominantly camel disease. Camels and dogs are also victims of severe and fatal disease caused by *T. congolense* and *T. brucei.* Camels, but not dogs, are subject to the same hyperacute disease caused by *T. simiae* that occurs in pigs. This species, as suggested by its name, also causes fatal illness in monkeys.

The transmission of nagana is both biological and mechanical. Tsetse flies are the only biological vectors, but they and other biting flies transmit the infections mechanically. The cyclical development of trypanosomes in tsetse flies is exceedingly complicated, since it varies with different species of trypanosomes and even with the same species in different tsetse fly species. In general, *T. congolense,* for example, initiates its development in the alimentary tract of the fly. Then elongated organisms move to the hypopharynx, where attached intermediate forms and free trypanosomes successively develop. In the case of *T. vivax,* all development takes place in the mouth parts of the fly. Usually from 2 to 4 weeks are required for multiplication and metamorphosis in the fly.

All forms of nagana are also spread by the interrupted feeding of biting flies, including tsetses, and this may be the normal method of transmission when outbreaks occur. Throughout the tsetse fly region of equatorial Africa, there exist numerous horse flies and other biting flies, notably *Chrysops* and *Haematopota.* With reference to these genera, probably all species act as mechanical vectors. Small flies are poorer vectors than large ones.

Extensive studies of nagana seem to warrant the general deduction that mechanical vectors have a large part in the spread of African trypanosomiases but that cyclical development in tsetse flies is essential to the perpetuation of the diseases. Eradication of tsetse flies from any area has always eliminated nagana completely.

Tsetse flies, found only in Africa,

owe their importance entirely to the fact that they are vectors of trypanosomes. The principal species, about 20, vary considerably in size, abundance, distribution, habits, susceptibility to adverse environment, and economic importance. They are about the size of house flies. Low mean temperatures generally are unfavorable to them. They cannot endure dry heat or temperature above 106° F., even in areas of high humidity. Vegetation must be ample for the support of reservoir and other host animals, since blood is the sole food of tsetses, but treeless grassland, deciduous bushland, and woodlands with a thick underbrush are unfavorable. Rainfall or fresh-water streams must be abundant where the flies and their mammalian hosts reach maximum populations. Some tsetses in East Africa, however, are well adapted to comparatively arid districts. Because of this delicate environmental adjustment, tree clearance, burning of grass and brush, establishment of zones of vegetation-clearance, and like measures have been useful in controlling the flies. Seasonal changes and other natural factors cause expansion and contraction of fly belts.

Unlike mosquitoes, which are the only insects of greater medical importance than the tsetses, males as well as females are bloodsuckers. They feed mainly on large game and domestic animals. Native game, however, are comparatively resistant but serve as reservoirs of trypanosomes. Probably no trypanosome is pathogenic to its normal host. In any event, notwithstanding a complete dependence on large mammals, neither tsetse flies nor trypanosomes are especially host-specific. Some authorities also believe that any species of tsetse fly probably can transmit any species of pathogenic trypanosome with which it comes in common contact.

In addition to peculiar feeding habits and the comparative immunity of native game reservoirs, the method of reproduction of tsetse flies increases the difficulties of control. Females do not lay eggs like most insects. They give birth to live young and deposit the larvae in haunts that are peculiar to the individual species. Larvicides therefore are of no avail, and breeding places cannot be eradicated.

Adult tsetse flies probably do not live longer than 8 or 10 months. Their cycle of development is comparatively simple and direct. Females produce their first larvae about 3 or 4 weeks after mating. One large larva is produced at a time, but a new larva begins its development as soon as one is born. Successive larvae are produced every 9 to 14 days. The larvae pupate promptly in warm, loose soil of protected, shady areas. Pupation lasts 2 weeks to 4 months, and the adults rarely emerge unless the temperature is above 70° and below 87°.

The control of nagana—tsetse fly disease, or African animal trypanosomiasis—is much more than an entomological or veterinary problem. It is acutely beset with economic and sociological obstacles and with the basic agricultural problems of land usage and soil erosion. But such considerations do not lower the value of continued effort to achieve better control through therapy, prophylaxis, and immunization directed against the trypanosomes, through eradicative and limiting measures directed against tsetse flies, and through modifications of the environment to make it unfavorable for the continuance of trypanosomal diseases. Increased utilization of disease-resistant breeds of livestock, such as the West African Shorthorn cattle, for example, may also be a measure of great potential value.

THE OUTLOOK for better control of insect-borne diseases is bright. The discoveries of new insecticides and the devising of effective formulations and methods of application have in large measure provided the means for a concerted attack upon the insect vectors. New chemicals for treatment of these diseases and methods of immunization against them are also available. Finally, an ever-increasing knowledge of all aspects of insect-borne diseases has provided the foundations essential to the success of applied control measures. Seemingly the major limiting factor in the achievement of unprecedented, constructive victories is the modest economic burden that would be temporarily imposed.

GERARD DIKMANS, *a graduate veterinarian from Michigan State College and holder of a master's degree from Minnesota and a doctor's degree from Georgetown University, has been a parasitologist in the Bureau of Animal Industry since 1926. For several years he has been in charge of investigations of ruminant parasites.*

A. O. FOSTER, *a parasitologist in the Bureau of Animal Industry, is in charge of anthelmintic investigations. He was trained at the Johns Hopkins University School of Hygiene and Public Health and served for 5 years on the staff of the Gorgas Memorial Laboratory of Tropical and Preventive Medicine in Panama.*

C. D. STEIN *is a veterinarian in the Bureau of Animal Industry. For many years he has contributed important researches on anthrax, equine infectious anemia, and other diseases of large and small animals.*

L. T. GILTNER, *a veterinarian, is pathology consultant in the Bureau of Animal Industry. He was assistant chief of the pathological division for many years and has pursued or directed investigations on nearly all aspects of animal diseases.*

Camponotus castaneus, a common ant.

Insects and Helminths

Everett E. Wehr, John T. Lucker

Many species of the helminths, or parasitic worms, of livestock and poultry can pass through certain of their early stages only within the body of an insect. These species are transmitted, in the true sense, by insects. Beetle mites or grass mites similarly transmit others. One species is transmitted by a tick as well as by insects. These particular species of worms are obligatory parasites of insects, or their allies, just as truly as they are obligatory parasites of farm animals or birds. For their continued existence and propagation, for their survival as species, they depend equally upon insect and upon avian or mammalian hosts.

The life cycle of a helminth of one of these species, like the life cycle of all other parasitic helminths, is initiated by the eggs or microscopic larvae produced by the mature female or hermaphroditic individual. But depending on its specific identity, its eggs or larvae are infectious only to an insect or a mite or perhaps a tick. If ingested by a suitable insect, for example, each egg or larva gives rise to a more advanced developmental stage of the parasite, which takes up its abode in some part of the insect's body. There, however, the development of the worm stops at a stage far short of reproductive maturity. Unless this arrested-developmental stage gains access to the body of a suitable vertebrate animal, the life cycle of the parasite cannot be completed. Obviously, therefore, any step that can be taken to destroy infected insects will aid in preventing the infection of livestock and poultry with worms that have this type of life cycle. The world-wide extermination of the insect vectors, were this possible, would result automatically in the extermination of a goodly proportion of the species of worms that now afflict man and his domestic animals and many others that live in wild animals and birds.

Worms that are obliged to undergo development in two or more hosts are called heteroxenous parasites. The hosts in which they can reach reproductive maturity are called final or definitive hosts. Hosts in which their larval stages must develop before the parasites can take up life in a final host are called intermediate hosts.

Some instances of the transmission of parasitic worms by insects were discovered before it was learned that insects are also vectors of some of the most devastating protozoal and infectious diseases known to medical and veterinary science. Some years before the transmission of malaria or yellow fever by mosquitoes or of southern cattle fever by ticks was discovered, it had been demonstrated that the larvae of a nematode worm, *Wuchereria bancrofti,* which causes human filiariasis, could be sucked up by a feeding mosquito and would undergo developmental transformation in its body.

Very few kinds of parasitic worms can multiply—that is, reproduce through successive generations—entirely within the body of the animal in which they mature. The eggs or larvae of nearly all species must leave the host's body to perpetuate the parasite.

The eggs or larvae of worms that live in the digestive tract or in an organ or system (such as the liver or respiratory system) that communicates with the digestive tract or in the urinary system ordinarily pass from the host with its feces or urine. The presence of the progeny of the worms in those substances, which in natural circumstances are deposited by livestock and poultry on the ground, leads to their ingestion by various kinds of invertebrate and vertebrate animals. Although the insects and their close relatives are perhaps the most ubiquitous of the invertebrates and are of outstanding importance as vectors of parasitic worms, the eggs and larvae of some of the heteroxenous worms of farm animals and birds are not infectious to them. Other arthropods, snails, slugs, earthworms, or other animals serve as intermediate hosts in those instances.

Some of the insect vectors of worms that produce eggs, which leave the definitive host's body in the manner described, habitually feed upon the excrement of higher animals. In the process they ingest the worm eggs and thus become infected. Others are not susceptible as adults to infection or at least do not become infected. They habitually deposit their eggs in excrement or in materials contaminated by it. The larvae that hatch from their eggs ingest the worm eggs and are susceptible to infection by them. In other instances the insects involved cannot be classified as coprophagous—dung eating—nor do they customarily or preferentially breed in manure. But natural forces continually scatter worm eggs into their habitats. They ingest quite incidentally the worm eggs that contaminate their normal food supply.

Some of the vectors are themselves ectoparasites of farm animals. They normally feed upon the cellular debris or detritus on the skin of their hosts. They take in worm eggs when the skin is contaminated with fecal matter or crushed parts of worms.

Some of the heteroxenous worms live in situations, such as the circulatory system or subcutaneous tissues, that have no connection with the external body openings of the host. They include several species of viviparous roundworms, or Nematoda, which eject the larvae they produce into their host's blood, or lymph, or dermal skin layers. There the larvae remain, ultimately to perish unless they are ingested by a biting or bloodsucking insect.

Not only do the habits, habitats, and structural modifications of the various insects and certain of their close relatives lead these arthropods to ingest the microscopic progeny of parasitic worms of many kinds. The insects likewise afford an almost ideal means of transport of the infectious stages of the worms back to the definitive hosts, livestock or poultry. Many of them form part of the normal diet of birds. In grazing, swine, sheep, cattle, and horses cannot avoid taking in beetles, mites, and similar insects along with the herbage they consume. A dog or cat suffering from infestation by fleas or lice, bites and licks at the noxious creatures and swallows some of them. A female mosquito must have a blood meal before it can lay fertile eggs and a further blood meal between every two batches of eggs it lays. If, between meals, infectious worm larvae have developed in its body, it injects these into the blood of the next animal it bites.

Many adaptations exist among insects, parasitic worms, and the definitive hosts of the worms. Farmers can take advantage of some of these adaptations to protect livestock and poultry against the inroads of insect-borne worm infections.

INSECTS FREQUENT FECAL and related waste materials because those substances are essential for their growth and development or because they contain something that attracts insects—a bright or moving object, for example. Segments of tapeworms, because of their bright color or ability to move, readily attract insects and mites and often are eaten by them.

Insect-borne worms of livestock and poultry include representatives of all four of the major groups of helminths: Roundworms (Nematoda), tapeworms (Cestoda), thorny-headed worms (Acanthocephala), and flukes (Trematoda). Those that are transmitted by habitual or accidental dung feeders inhabit the digestive tract of the definitive host or organs that communicate with this tract; as has been noted, the eggs or larvae of worms living in these situations occur in the host's feces.

Various species of tumble bugs and dung beetles are intermediate hosts for worms occurring in swine, sheep, cattle, poultry, cats, and dogs. Two stomach worms, *Ascarops strongylina* and *Physocephalus sexalatus,* of swine, and the gullet worm, *Gongylonema pulchrum,* which occurs in swine, sheep and cattle, utilize such coprophagous beetles as *Copris, Aphodius, Passalurus, Onthophagus, Scarabaeus, Gymnopleurus, Ataenius, Canthon, Phanaeus,* and *Geotrupes* as intermediate hosts. The German cockroach also serves as an intermediate host of the gullet worm. The eggs ingested by the insects contain well-developed embryos at the time of oviposition. On hatching in the insect's gut, the larvae first enter the abdominal cavity of the intermediate host and finally come to rest in the walls of the Malpighian tubules or musculature, where they become encysted. Completely formed cysts are usually found free in the abdominal part of the body cavity. The larvae become infective in the intermediate host in a month or so.

The larvae of the esophageal worm, *Spirocerca lupi,* of the dog develop to the infective stage in the beetle, *Scarabaeus sacer,* and other beetles. The infective larvae become encysted in these insects, chiefly on the tracheal tubes. If such beetles are swallowed by an unsuitable host, such as a frog, snake, bird, or a small mammal, the larval worms become encysted again in the esophagus, mesentery, or other organs of these animals. This phenomenon is also known to occur in the case of the swine stomach worm, *Physocephalus sexalatus,* the larvae of which have been found naturally reencysted in the wall of the digestive tract of such birds as the loggerhead shrike, screech owl, and red-tailed hawk in southern Georgia and northern Florida. Reencystment of the larvae was found in experiments to occur in many different animals, including birds, mammals, and reptiles, to which beetles containing infective larvae were fed.

One of the commonest species of tapeworms, *Hymenolepis carioca,* found in the domestic fowl, is transmitted by beetles (*Aphodius, Choeridium, Hister,* and maybe *Anisotarsus*).

Another species of tapeworm, *Hymenolepis cantaniana,* found in chickens, turkeys, and quail of the Eastern States, develops in the beetles *Ataenius* and *Choeridium.* Its development in its intermediate host is unusual. The larva elongates to form a somewhat branched myceliumlike structure; buds along the branches develop into the cysticercoids, or small larval forms, which contain the tapeworm heads. Tapeworms belonging to the genera *Joyeuxiella* and *Diplopylidium,* which are closely related to *Dipylidium,* occur in cats and apparently develop in dung beetles and related insects. It takes about 3 weeks to 2 months, depending on temperature, for the cysticercoids to develop within the insect host. Completely developed cysts are found in its body cavity. The tapeworm *Metroliasthes lucida,* commonly found in the small intestine of the domestic and wild turkey, is reported to have the grasshoppers *Melanoplus* sp., *Chorthippus longicornis,* and *Paroxya clavuliger* as intermediate hosts. Guinea fowls are also susceptible to infection with this tapeworm.

Dermestid beetles, darkling beetles, fungus beetles, and other groups of beetles and several species of grasshoppers have been infected experimentally, or found to be infected naturally with the larvae of the gizzard worm of poultry, *Cheilospirura hamulosa.*

Small numbers of these worms in the gizzard do not produce any serious results. In heavy infections, the lining of the gizzard may show ulcerations, which may also involve the musculature. Soft nodules enclosing the parasites are often found in the muscular portions, especially in the thinner parts of the gizzard. In the intermediate host, the infective larva of the gizzard worm is found encysted in the musculature of the body wall, where it is found to be tightly coiled. The infective stage is reached in about 19 days.

Darkling beetles (*Alphitobius, Gonocephalum,* and *Ammophorus*), the ring-legged earwig, and the hide beetle have been reported as being infected with the third-stage larvae of *Subulura brumpti,* the cecal worm of poultry. The final host becomes infected through the ingestion of the infected intermediate host and the larvae pass to the cecum, the blind gut. Many species of darkling beetles and ground beetles have been incriminated as intermediate hosts of *Raillietina cesticillus,* the broad-headed tapeworm of poultry and of another poultry tapeworm, *Choanotaenia infundibulum.* The latter also develops in the red-legged grasshopper and in the house fly. The chief effect of this tapeworm, even in heavy infestations, is to retard the growth rate of its host.

The Surinam roach, and possibly other species of cockroaches, is an intermediate host for three nematodes of poultry, namely, the eyeworms, *Oxyspirura mansoni* and *O. parvovum,* and the proventricular worm, *Seurocyrnea colini,* of the turkey and bobwhite quail. Infections with the eyeworms result in a marked irritation, which interferes seriously with vision. It often is accompanied by continual winking as if to dislodge a foreign body. The nictitating membrane of the eye becomes inflamed and appears as a puffy elevation. Heavy infestations may cause blindness. The German cockroach has been shown in experiments to serve as an intermediate host for *Seurocyrnea colini.* This cockroach, the red-legged grasshopper, and the differential grasshopper have been reported to be suitable intermediate hosts for the globular stomach worm, *Tetrameres americana,* of chickens, bobwhite quail, and turkeys. After the eggs are ingested by the intermediate hosts, the larvae of this stomach worm pass into the body cavity and become quite active for the first 10 days after infection. They then penetrate the muscles and become loosely encysted. In about 42 days, or possibly sooner, the infective larvae have completed their development. The vitality of grasshoppers is greatly reduced by infections with this parasite. Some die and some become inactive and an easy prey to birds. The infection is transmitted to the bird through the ingestion of the infected intermediate host. Serious infections with these species of stomach worms have not been noted in domestic birds in the United States.

Several species of ants, of the genera *Tetramorium* and *Pheidole,* are naturally infected with cysticercoids of two closely related poultry tapeworms, *Raillietina tetragona* and *R. echinobothrida.* Experimental attempts to infect ants of these and other genera by feeding to them eggs of these tapeworms resulted in failure, but naturally infected ants were fed to chickens and infections resulted.

Quail are said to be seriously parasitized by *R. tetragona* and death losses have been attributed to this tapeworm, but its pathogenicity has not been experimentally verified.

However, *R. echinobothrida* is definitely known to be one of the most injurious tapeworm parasites of poultry. It causes the formation of tuberclelike nodules on the intestinal wall, which closely resemble the nodules of tuberculosis. The absence of the nodules in the liver, spleen, and other internal organs and the presence of tapeworms in the small intestine warrant the diagnosis of this infection and exclude tuberculosis.

Biting lice are minor vectors of worm parasites. The only known instance involves the dog biting louse, which is reported to be an intermediate host of the double-pored tapeworm, *Dipylidium caninum,* of the dog and cat. Because this louse normally feeds on particles of dried skin of its host, it can hardly be classified as a coprophagous insect. It is presumed that the skin of the dog and cat, especially in the perianal region, becomes contaminated with eggs of the tapeworm, which are more or less incidentally eaten by the louse.

Beetle mites, also known as oribatid or galumnid mites, serve as vectors of the broad tapeworm, *Moniezia expansa,* of cattle, sheep, and goats. After being expelled with the host's feces, the tapeworm eggs must become fairly dry and well anchored before the mites can ingest them. The mites usually do not eat the entire egg. They make a hole in its shell and ingest its contents. This tapeworm adversely affects the growth of infected lambs. Several investigators have reported that *M. expansa* produced scouring in range lambs. In experiments, however, infected lambs have not shown scouring.

The life history of *M. expansa,* which had defied investigators for many years, was solved in 1937. Since then it has been shown that oribatid mites also are the vectors of several other anoplocephalid tapeworms of domestic animals. They transmit *Cittotaenia ctenoides* and *C. denticulata* of rabbits; *Anoplocephala perfoliata, A. magna,* and *Paranoplocephala mamillana* of horses; and *Moniezia benedini* and *Thysaniezia giardi* of ruminants.

Beetle mites are most apt to be abundant in moist, shady places. They are found in pastures both winter and summer, but they increase markedly in numbers with the new growth in spring. The mites are generally distributed throughout the world.

THE NUMBER of groups of insects in which infection takes place in the larval or immature stage is small, compared to those that acquire the infection in the adult stage. In some instances the mouth parts of the adult insect are of the sucking type so that solid materials cannot be ingested, or its feeding habits are such that it does not come in contact with materials containing the worm eggs and larvae. The larval insects, however, hatch out in such material, and their mouth parts are adapted for its ingestion.

The house fly and the stable fly breed abundantly in horse manure. Their maggots migrate extensively throughout manure piles and feed promiscuously on the materials found therein. The maggots of the house fly are the

970134°—52——13

intermediate hosts for two nematodes (roundworms) commonly found in the stomachs of horses—*Habronema muscae* and *Drashia megastoma.* Those of the stable fly are suitable hosts for the development of a third horse-stomach worm, *Habronema majus.*

The nematode larvae undergo several molts within the body of the fly maggot and reach the infective stage about the time the fly hatches. The adult fly harbors the infective larvae free in the body cavity, but some of the larvae may migrate into the mouth parts of the fly. The horse presumably becomes infected when the flies in feeding deposit worm larvae on its lips or by ingesting flies which get into its food or water.

The thorny-headed worm is a rather common parasite of swine, particularly in the South. Characteristic nodules form at the sites of attachment of the worms to the wall of the small intestine. Sometimes they change their places of attachment, thus leaving the previous sites of attachment to become ulcerative. Perforation of the intestinal wall occasionally may occur. The parasite makes the intestines worthless for sausage casings. White grubs, the larvae of May and June beetles, serve as its intermediate hosts. White grubs are found abundantly just below the surface of the soil, particularly in grasslands, and are relished by hogs, which uncover them as they root up the ground.

The eggs of the thorny-headed worm, which are expelled in the feces of the swine, hatch when they are ingested by the white grubs. In the grubs, the larvae hatching from the eggs are released in the midgut; then they migrate to the body cavity and there develop into the infective stage within 2 to 3 months in summer. Since the infective larvae persist when the pupal and beetle stages of the insect develop, pigs become infected by ingesting infected grubs, pupae, or adults.

The larvae of the dog and cat fleas are vectors of the double-pored tapeworm, *Dipylidium caninum.* Because the adult flea has sucking mouth parts, infection in this stage is impossible. Flea larvae ingest the eggs of the tapeworm. In the larva, the tapeworm grows but slightly. It grows more in the pupal stage and transforms into the infective stage in the adult flea. The

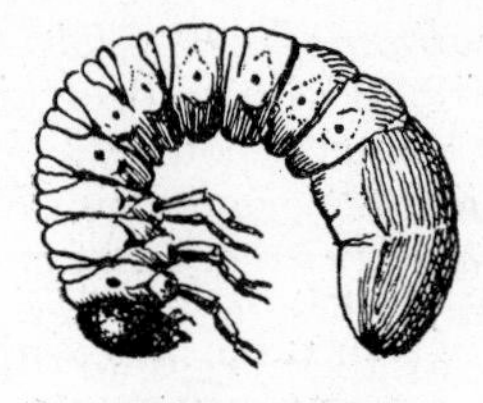

White grub.

cysticercoid lies free in the body cavity of the flea. The cat or dog becomes infected by ingesting fleas or lice.

More than one kind of intermediate host is required in the development of some of the heteroxenous worms. One of them may be an insect—as in the case of the oviduct fluke of poultry, *Prosthogonimus macrorchis,* which utilizes a snail, *Amnicola limosa porata,* as its first intermediate host and dragonflies as its second intermediate hosts. Species of several genera of dragonflies, *Leucorrhinia, Tetragoneuria, Epicordulia,* and *Mesothemis,* may serve in the capacity of secondary intermediate hosts for this trematode.

In the United States, the oviduct fluke is found naturally in ducks, Canada geese, and chickens, chiefly in the Great Lakes region. Here the snail that is the intermediate host is found in abundance on the under sides of boards and sticks and may be found traveling along the lake bottom in water 1 to 2 feet deep.

The snail becomes infected by ingesting the eggs of the fluke. After going through several stages of development in the snail, the young flukes (cercariae) escape from its body and swim freely about in the water. The free-swimming organisms are drawn into the anal openings of aquatic naiads, or immature dragonflies, with the water that is alternately taken in and forced out by the organs of respiration located at the posterior end of the alimentary canal. After entrance into the body of the naiad, the young flukes encyst in the muscles and in most instances are found in the ventral portions of the posterior part of the body. Infection of the secondary intermediate host usually takes place during the late spring and early summer, so that the young flukes sometimes remain in the insect host for 1 or 2 years before they are ingested by the definitive host.

Infection of the bird host occurs usually at the end of May or beginning of June, when the dragonfly naiads are transforming into adults. Infection may also occur by the ingestion of infected mature dragonflies, which can be easily captured by birds in the early morning. The immature worms pass posteriorly to the diverticulum of the cloaca or to the cloaca itself, where they develop to maturity. Some of the worms develop to maturity in the oviduct and have been found in eggs laid by infected hens. The presence of this fluke in laying hens may result in a sharp drop in egg production, the laying of soft-shelled eggs, and, in advanced cases, peritonitis.

Prosthogonimus macrorchis is probably the most important fluke parasite of poultry in the United States. However, it is localized around certain sections of the Great Lakes region. That is cause for not too great alarm, because the sections are not important poultry centers.

MANY ADULT INSECTS depend on blood for food. Among those that have been reported to be vectors for worms of livestock are mosquitoes, midges, fleas, sucking lice, and ticks. They ingest worm larvae as they feed on the blood or lymph of infested animals. All the worms they transmit are roundworms of the group Filarioidea.

Mosquitoes of the genera *Anopheles, Aedes,* and *Culex,* the dog flea, and the cat flea are suitable intermediate hosts of the dog and cat heartworm. This large worm, 5 to 12 inches long, occurs mainly in the right ventricle of the heart and the pulmonary artery of the dog, cat, fox, and wolf. Many studies indicate that it occurs principally in the Southern States. It may occur throughout most of the United States, although not endemically. Hunting dogs are more seriously affected than other breeds. The infected animal tires easily, gasps for breath, and may collapse. Severe complications, such as inflammation of the kidney and urinary bladder, may arise. In severe cases, the animal becomes poor, and the hair and skin are dry. Abnormal heart sounds are infrequently noted, but moist rales are occasionally present.

About 24 to 36 hours after the mosquito or flea has sucked blood of an infected animal, the larvae or microfilariae may be found within the tissue cells of the Malpighian tubules. There they develop to the infective stage within 5 to 10 days, when they migrate to the mouth parts of the intermediate hosts and are ready to be transferred to a final host during the act of biting.

Mosquitoes of the genera *Aedes* and *Anopheles* are vectors for *Dirofilaria repens,* a rather small worm occurring in the subcutaneous tissue of dogs in southern Europe, Asia, and South America. The worms may cause pruritis without skin lesions.

The dog sucking louse, the dog flea, and the brown dog tick have been reported as vectors of *Dipetalonema reconditum,* originally reported from the perirenal tissue of the dog in Europe. The worm also occurs in other organs and tissues, including the vascular system, lungs, and liver. The brown dog tick also transmits *D. grassi,* which occurs in the subcutaneous tissue and body cavity of the dog in Italy.

Twelve days after microfilariae of *Dirofilaria scapiceps,* which lives under the skin in the loins and in the subcutaneous tissues of the fore and hind legs of wild rabbits in the United States, had been ingested by *Aedes* mosquitoes, infective larvae were seen actively moving in the proboscis of the insects. Microfilariae also were observed in the gut contents of an unidentified engorged tick. Attempts to infect rabbits experimentally with this roundworm by allowing infected mosquitoes to feed on them have failed. The rabbit tick may also be a suitable intermediate host of this worm, although it has not been incriminated.

Species of biting midges, or sand flies, and black flies have been incriminated as intermediate hosts of species of the genus *Onchocerca*. *O. reticulata* occurs in various countries in the large tendon supporting the neck of the horse and mule and has been reported as a possible causative agent of poll evil and fistulous withers. This worm supposedly is transmitted by *Culicoides nubeculosus*. *Simulium ornatum* is the vector of *Onchocerca gutterosa,* which occurs in the neck tendon and other parts of the body of cattle. *Onchocerca gibsoni,* which lives in the subcutaneous connective tissue of cattle, often giving rise on the brisket and the external surfaces of the hind limbs to nodules, in which the worms lie coiled up, is reported to develop in *Culicoides pungens* and also in black flies. The microfilariae, infrequently found in the nodules or worm nests, are more often found in the walls of the blood vessels and along the lymph spaces. Infected animals show no symptoms except the nodular swellings under the skin, but their carcasses are condemned as unsuitable for sale on most markets.

The stable fly is a reported vector for *Setaria cervi,* which occurs free in the body cavity of cattle and various species of antelope and deer. This worm has been found in the eyes of horses and the udder of a cow.

Other reports indicate that in Asia this parasite is transmitted by three species of mosquitoes (*Anopheles hyrcans sinensis, Armigeres obturbans,* and *Aedes togoi*). The last is also a vector for *S. equina* of horses. Larvae of both species are said to invade the central nervous system of horses, causing lumbar paralysis.

Skin lesions due to the presence in the lesions of both adults and microfilariae of *Stephanofilaria stilesi, S. dedoesi, S. kaeli,* and *S. assamensis* have been reported from the abdomen and legs of cattle in North America, Java, Malay Peninsula, and India, respectively. Presumably insects transmit them.

The invasion of the skin of sheep by the microfilariae of *Elaeophora schneideri,* which lives in its host's carotid and iliac arteries, produces a dermatitis primarily in the back part of the head but tending to spread over the face to the nostrils. Similar lesions are sometimes noted on the hind foot used to scratch the head. The presence of the larvae in the tissues results in intense itching, which causes the animal to scratch itself. The scratching causes destruction of tissue. The condition has been confined to summer mountain ranges in New Mexico, Arizona, Colorado, and possibly Utah. The life history is unknown, but it is suspected that bloodsucking insects serve as intermediate hosts of the parasite.

In the solution of the problem of the control of insect-borne worm infections of livestock and poultry, six general avenues of approach are available: The use of drugs therapeutically; the use of drugs prophylactically; physical and chemical sterilization of stable and poultry manure and sanitary disposal of excrements; elimination of the breeding places of insects; destruction of insects and their larvae chemically and mechanically; and mechanical prevention of the access of insects to farm animals.

Although the primary purpose of therapeutic treatments directed against the worm infections is to improve the health and efficiency of the sick animal, they have some value in control. After treatment, which eliminates worms from the animal's body or kills them in the body, there is, until reinfection occurs, a reduction in the number of eggs or larvae voided by the animal or the number of larvae entering its tissues. Drugs may be used prophylactically to combat certain of the insect-borne worm infections. Hetrazan administered orally to persons having filariasis causes a rapid and marked reduction in the number of microfilariae in the blood even though the adult worms are not killed. Fouadin, one of the standard drugs in the treatment of heartworm infections in dogs, has a similar effect when injected into these animals. It also inhibits the reproductive capacity of the adult female worms. It is likely that other drugs may be found to operate similarly against the microfilariae of other worms of domesticated animals.

When the economic value of the animal to be protected warrants, stable manure or poultry manure may be promptly collected and stored so as to exclude flies and perhaps other insects from it. Horse manure may be stored in piles so that some of the worm eggs and larvae in it will be destroyed by the heat of its decomposition. This effect may be heightened by storing it and cow manure in covered insulated wooden manure boxes. Evidently it has not been determined specifically that the eggs and larvae of heteroxenous worms are killed by these procedures; however, in all cases investigated it has been found that the eggs and larvae of worm parasites generally are killed by approximately the same degree of heat (about 140° F.).

Several chemical agents will kill the eggs and larvae of monoxenous worm parasites in stable manure. None, to our knowledge, has been specifically demonstrated to be effective against the eggs and larvae of the heteroxenous worms. Some of the agents do kill ascarid eggs, which are thick-shelled, and the means for killing chemically all types of worm eggs and larvae in manure probably are at hand. Investigation to prove this is needed, however. Stable or poultry manure which has not been processed in some manner ought not be used on the farm for fertilizer.

The destruction of breeding places and direct attacks against insects and their larvae are weapons that can be applied generally to control these vectors. Usually both lines of attack should be employed, but the habits and life histories of insects are so diverse that the weapon of choice—habitat destruction or larvicide or destruction of the adult—may differ with the insect to be fought.

Attacks against the house fly can be directed most feasibly and easily against the larvae. DDT has been reported to be effective against the maggots of this fly when used in a water emulsion. Such an emulsion was found to be effective also against certain other species of flies breeding in poultry manure. DDT, methoxychlor, chlordane, lindane, and other insecticides are recommended as residual sprays directed toward the control of the adults. Important supplemental measures include disposal of manure, chemical treatment of manure, the use of properly baited fly traps, and the use of pyrethrum fly sprays.

The stable fly likewise is most vulnerable to attack in its larval stage. A principal measure for its control—applicable also in the case of the house fly—is the destruction of its breeding places. When it is impossible to locate and eliminate all of these, insecticides as recommended for controlling the housefly are distinctly useful against the adult stable flies.

Mosquitoes, biting midges, and black flies breed in water, and the elimination of their breeding places is not always feasible or desirable. Ponds, small pools, and useless swampy areas may often be filled in or drained. Since the maintenance of large ponds and streams is desirable, treating the water with oils to kill the larvae mechanically and with such larvicides as paris green long has been one of the approaches to the problem of mosquito control. DDT when incorporated into an oily vehicle for application to the water surface is effective for the destruction of the mosquito larvae. This insecticide also is of value in killing the adults of mosquitoes, biting midges, and black flies. Tests have indicated that the larvae of black flies are susceptible to DDT, TDE, and other new chlorinated insecticides.

Cat and dog fleas in and around buildings may be controlled effectively by the use of DDT sprays or dusts. One to two gallons of 5 percent DDT in oil sprayed lightly over areas of 1,000 to 2,000 square feet has been found effective in the complete eradication of adult fleas. Five percent DDT powder, applied with a dust can, is recommended for the destruction of fleas on dogs. The application of the dust to the building will destroy the larvae and adults as they emerge.

Methods are available for the control of grasshoppers, earwigs, and cockroaches. Beetles frequenting poultry manure likewise may be controlled chemically. The use of insecticides against these beetles probably would not be practical in seeking to control worms in poultry flocks having access to large areas, but the confinement of birds, as presently widely practiced, favors the feasibility of measures for beetle destruction in accumulated manure.

In theory, beetles frequenting manure on pastures no doubt also may be dealt with by means of insecticidal dusts or sprays, but we know of no work demonstrating that this is practical. Since it has been demonstrated that the feeding of small amounts of drugs, such as phenothiazine, to cattle prevents the development of horn flies in their dung, it would seem advisable to investigate the possibility that beetles might be controlled as worm vectors by the routine incorporation of suitable insecticidal materials into the diet of farm animals and birds. Manure deposits on pastures may be broken up and spread to reduce the attractiveness of the manure to insects. The maximum adverse effects of dryness and sunlight on worm eggs and larvae may also be had by this step. The chemical destruction of beetle mites on pastures and grazing land apparently has not been investigated, but even were it possible, its practicability seems doubtful. It seems probable that other means will have to be sought for the prevention of tapeworm infections transmitted by these mites.

EVERETT E. WEHR *is a parasitologist doing research in parasitology in the zoological division, Bureau of Animal Industry, at Beltsville, Md. He has been associated with the division since 1928 and has been in charge of its investigations on the parasitic diseases of poultry since 1936. He is the author of numerous papers on the worms and other parasites of livestock and poultry. He has particularly investigated the nematodes of birds. Dr. Wehr is a graduate of the University of Idaho, University of California, and George Washington University.*

JOHN T. LUCKER *is a parasitologist and has been associated with the zoological division since 1930. He also is stationed at Beltsville. The identification of nematodes has been one of his chief assignments since 1940. He is a graduate of the University of Washington and George Washington University.*

For further reference:

Joseph E. Alicata: Early Developmental Stages of Nematodes Occurring in Swine, *U. S. D. A. Technical Bulletin 489, 1935;* The Life History of the Gizzard Worm (Cheilospirura hamulosa) and Its Mode of Transmission to Chickens With Special Reference to Hawaiian Conditions, *in* Livro Jubilar do Professor Lauro Travassos, 1938.

Eloise B. Cram: Developmental Stages of Some Nematodes of the Spiruroidea Parasitic in Poultry and Game Birds, *U. S. D. A. Technical Bulletin 227. 1931.*

Ashton C. Cuckler and Joseph E. Alicata: The Life History of Subulura brumpti, a Cecal Nematode of Poultry in Hawaii, *Transactions of the American Microscopical Society, volume 63, pages 345–357. 1944.*

G. Dikmans: Skin Lesions of Domestic Animals in the United States Due to Nematode Infestation, *The Cornell Veterinarian, volume 38, pages 3–23. 1948.*

R. I. Hewitt, E. White, D. B. Hewitt, S. M. Hardy, W. S. Wallace, and R. Anduze: The First Year's Results of a Mass Treatment Program With Hetrazan for the Control of Bancroftian Filariasis on St. Croix, American Virgin Islands, *American Journal of Tropical Medicine, volume 30, pages 443–452. 1950.*

Paul R. Highby: Development of the Microfilaria of Dirofilaria scapiceps (Leidy, 1886) in Mosquitoes of Minnesota, *Journal of Parasitology (Supplement), volume 24, page 36. 1938.*

Myrna F. Jones: Life History of Metroliasthes lucida, a Tapeworm of the Turkey, *Journal of Parasitology, volume 17, page 53, 1930 (part of Proceedings of the Helminthological Society of Washington);* Metroliasthes lucida, a Cestode of Galliform Birds, in Arthropod and Avian Hosts, *Proceedings of the Helminthological Society of Washington, volume 3, pages 26–30, 1936;* Development and Morphology of the Cestode Hymenolepis cantaniana, in Coleopteran and Avian Hosts, *with J. E. Alicata, Journal of the Washington Academy of Sciences, volume 25, pages 237–247, 1935.*

Kenneth C. Kates: Development of the Swine Thorn-Headed Worm, Macracanthorhynchus hirundinaceus, in its Intermediate Host, *American Journal of Veterinary Research, volume 4, pages 173–181, 1943;* Observations on Oribatid Mite Vectors of Moniezia expansa on Pastures, with a Report of Several New Vectors from the United States, *with C. E. Runkel, Proceedings of the Helminthological Society of Washington, vol. 15, pp. 10, 19–33, 1948.*

H. E. Kemper: Filarial Dermatosis of Sheep, *North American Veterinarian, volume 19, No. 9, pages 36–41. 1938.*

Wendell H. Krull: Observations on the Distribution and Ecology of the Oribatid Mites, *Journal of the Washington Academy of Science, volume 29, pages 519–528. 1939.*

George W. Luttermoser: Meal Beetle Larvae as Intermediate Hosts of the Poultry Tapeworm Raillietina cesticillus, *Poultry Science, volume 19, pages 177–179. 1940.*

Ralph W. Macy: Studies on the Taxonomy, Morphology, and Biology of Prosthogonimus macrorchis Macy, A Common Oviduct Fluke of Domestic Fowls in North America, *Minnesota Agricultural Experiment Station Technical Bulletin 98. 1934.*

Horace W. Stunkard: The Life Cycle of Anoplocephaline Cestodes, *Journal of Parasitology, volume 23, page 569, 1937;* The Development of Moniezia expansa in the Intermediate Host, *Parasitology, volume 30, pages 491–501, 1939.*

William A. Summers: Fleas as Acceptable Intermediate Hosts of the Dog Heartworm, Dirofilaria immitis, *Proceedings of the Society of Experimental Biology and Medicine, volume 43, pages 448–450. 1940.*

Y. Tanada, F. G. Holdaway, and J. H. Quisenberry: DDT to Control Flies Breeding in Poultry Manure, *Journal of Economic Entomology, volume 43, pages 30–36. 1950.*

Willard H. Wright and Paul C. Underwood: Fouadin in the Treatment of Infestations With the Dog Heartworm, Dirofilaria immitis, *Veterinary Medicine, volume 29, pages 234–246. 1934.*

Insects and the Plant Viruses

L. D. Christenson, Floyd F. Smith

The Russian scientist D. Iwanowski demonstrated in 1892 that sap from tobacco plants with a mosaic disease is infectious after passing through a bacteria-proof filter. It was the first discovery of an amazing group of agents that cannot be seen with ordinary microscopes and that now are called viruses. Many of our most serious and difficult plant-disease problems have been shown to be the results of infections of plants by these minute entities, which are smaller than bacteria. A few of the many different kinds of viruses are even smaller than the largest molecules known to chemists.

Tulip mosaic, peach yellows, aster yellows, sugar-beet curly top, phloem necrosis of elm, tobacco mosaic, raspberry mosaic, blueberry stunt disease, potato leaf roll, pea mosaic, tomato spotted wilt, and sugarcane mosaic are examples of plant diseases caused by viruses. Virus agents also cause serious diseases of man and animals—smallpox, measles, mumps, the common cold, rabies, distemper, and foot-and-mouth disease. Others, like the sacbrood virus of honey bees, infect invertebrate animals.

For a long time we knew little about the nature of viruses. Now, as a result of the studies of W. M. Stanley, F. C. Bawden, N. W. Pirie, and others, they are believed to consist of complex nucleoproteins that have some of the attributes of living organisms. Like living organisms, the individual virus particles can reproduce or multiply. They also can change or mutate during the multiplication process. They do not seem able to grow or multiply, however, except within the living cells of their hosts, and, unlike living organisms, they cannot carry on the complicated processes of respiration, digestion, and other metabolic functions.

Most of the plant viruses have been discovered since 1900, but they are not of recent origin. Old Dutch masters recorded in their paintings the variegations in the petals of tulips caused by a virus now known as tulip mosaic. Dutch bulb growers knew as early as 1637 how to graft healthy bulbs with variegated bulbs to get the coveted many-colored flowers even though they did not know what caused them. Potato viruses had become so abundant in Europe by 1775 that the production of potatoes had to be abandoned in many areas because of what was then termed the "running-out" of potatoes. In the United States, the virus disease now known as peach yellows was described as early as 1791. We have evidence that it was doing damage in peach orchards as early as 1750.

Only a few viruses kill the plants they infect. Plants affected by most of them never recover, but they do not die as a result of the infection. Their growth and productivity may be seriously affected. Some species and varieties of plants apparently are not attacked by viruses. Others may be tolerant of them or only mildly affected when their tissues are invaded by the virus particles. Trees, shrubs, other plants in uncultivated areas, and weeds on farms may be infected by viruses that also attack cultivated plants. When that is so, the wild plants serve as important sources of danger to the cultivated plants. Otherwise the viruses in the uncultivated plants are not economically important. No viruses are yet known that attack coniferous trees, such as pine and spruce.

Our cultivated crops annually suffer heavy losses because of virus diseases. Phony peach has plagued peach growers in the Southeastern States for at least half a century, making it necessary for them to take out more than 2,600,000 peach trees. Years ago in the Northeastern States, peach yellows destroyed the productiveness of hundreds of thousands of trees. Sometimes it was necessary to destroy entire orchards. Tobacco mosaic has been estimated to cause an annual loss of millions of pounds of tobacco. Viruses have seriously affected the production of potatoes each year. To reduce their losses, the growers here and in England and other countries have to expend large sums to get healthy seed potatoes grown in areas where potato viruses are not serious. Production of head lettuce in the East has not been profitable because of infection by the virus known as aster yellows. Losses caused by the curly-top virus in sugar beets have been so severe in the Western States that some sugar factories have had to be abandoned. The same virus has caused crop failures in tomato fields. Similar heavy tolls may be levied by the viruses that attack many of our ornamental plants and flowers.

Plant diseases caused by viruses spread in several ways. Some are so infectious that contact between the leaves of normal and diseased plants is all that is necessary. Highly contagious diseases such as these may be spread by mechanical means. A few instances of spread through seeds are known. A serious method of spread is through the use of parts of infected plants to start new plantings. For example, viruses that persist from year to year in potato tubers, in bulbs, and in rhizomes infect plants growing from them. Viruses may also be spread through cuttings or suckers from infected plants and through budding and grafting procedures employed in nurseries.

Insects are the worst spreaders. A Japanese scientist in 1901 found that a leafhopper could transmit stunt disease of rice from diseased rice plants to healthy plants.

The first insect to gain prominence in North America as a carrier of a plant virus was the beet leafhopper. It was found to be spreading curly-top disease in sugar-beet fields in Utah and other Western States only a few years after the discovery of the insect carrier of stunt disease of rice. We now know that many of our plant virus disease outbreaks are the result of insect-carrier activity, and it is suspected that insects are involved in the spread of many other plant virus diseases.

Insect carriers of plant viruses are

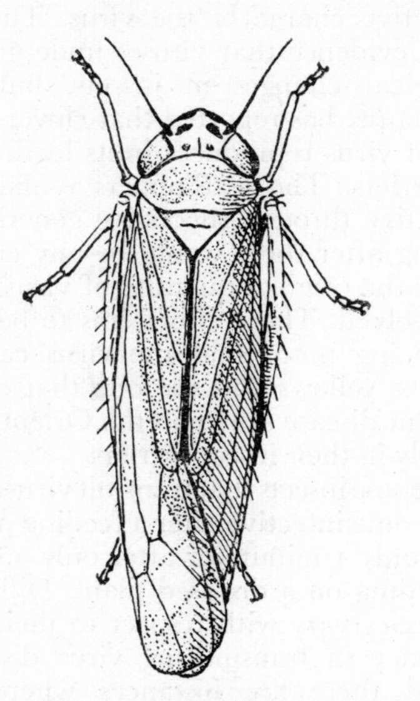

Six-spotted leafhopper.

known to occur in only six of the major orders of insects—the Homoptera (aphids, leafhoppers, whiteflies, mealybugs, scales), Thysanoptera (thrips), Heteroptera (plant bugs, lace bugs), Coleoptera (the beetles), Orthoptera (grasshoppers), and Dermaptera (earwigs). Most of the carriers have sucking mouth parts, and among them the aphids and leafhoppers seem to be the most proficient. A few insects with chewing mouth parts, such as grasshoppers and leaf-feeding beetles, also spread certain virus diseases.

To accomplish transmission, the vector has to get the virus from a diseased plant, which it does while feeding, and then move to a healthy plant, which it infects during the feeding process. With the sucking insects, the virus particles apparently are injected into plants with the saliva.

The relationships between plant viruses and their vectors have commanded the attention of many entomologists, plant pathologists, and other biologists. Striking advances have been made, and we now know a great deal about many insects that transmit viruses, something about what happens to the virus during its period in the insect body, and something about the factors involved in the transmission process. There is still much to be explained, however: We do not know why certain species can transmit viruses while other similar insects cannot, or why certain insects can transmit so many different kinds of plant viruses but not others. The many other vectors awaiting discovery also remain a challenge.

Plant viruses are considered as belonging to two general groups.

In the group called the nonpersistent viruses, the insect carrier can transmit the virus soon after feeding on a diseased plant. This ability to cause new infections is quickly lost, however, after the insects feed on healthy or immune plants. A starvation period before feeding on infected plants usually increases the transmission efficiency of the vectors of the viruses, which usually can be transmitted by mechanical means, as by wiping the sap of an infected plant over the leaves of a healthy plant. The insect carriers sometimes include many different kinds of insects. Many viruses transmitted by aphids and chewing insects belong to this group. Perhaps some of the nonpersistent viruses are transmitted through contamination of the mouth parts of the insect carriers with virus particles, but for many others the transmission process does not seem to be that simple.

The other group includes the persistent viruses. When they are taken in with the food of their vectors, an interval (the incubation, or latent, period) is necessary before the insects can infect healthy plants with them. Once having the ability, insect carriers of persistent viruses usually can transmit them to healthy plants for an extended period, often for life. In two instances involving leafhoppers, persistent viruses are transmitted to the succeeding generation through the eggs. Some of these viruses are transmitted by only one or a few closely related insects. Most of the viruses that leafhoppers transmit are persistent viruses. A few aphids or other insects also transmit persistent viruses.

The incubation period of the persistent viruses in insects sometimes lasts only a few hours or less. It may last as long as 5 days in some aphids or several weeks in some leafhoppers. The incubation period of the virus that causes western X-disease of peach is usually longer than 30 days in the geminate leafhopper. Incubation periods as long as 40 days have been reported for some leafhoppers that transmit aster yellows, although in most of them the period is about 2 weeks. One of the four leafhopper carriers of phony peach in the Southeastern States has transmitted the disease to healthy peach trees 14 days after first feeding on a phony tree, but in another leafhopper the shortest incubation period observed thus far has been 19 days. Temperature may influence the length of an incubation period of a virus in an insect.

The meaning of the incubation period of the viruses is moot. Some investigators believe it is a true incubation period, during which the virus goes through some kind of necessary developmental or reproductive stage. Others consider it merely the time necessary for the virus particles to make their way through the intestinal walls of the insect into the blood stream and thence into the salivary glands, where they can be introduced with saliva into healthy plants during feeding.

Both points of view can be justified, depending on the virus involved. Some leafhoppers transmit persistent viruses throughout their lives once they become infective. Others may lose the ability after a period. In some individuals the ability to transmit a virus may become much less pronounced as they near the end of their life span—perhaps the original supplies of virus taken in have become exhausted during the intervening feeding periods on healthy plants and there has been no multiplication of the virus particles within the insect, or at least not sufficient reproduction to maintain an infective charge of the virus. There is no evidence that viruses undergo biological changes in insects, but one scientist has reported that clover club-leaf virus reproduces in its leafhopper carriers. The leafhoppers remain infective through successive generations long after there would be any chance for the original quantity of virus to be involved. There also seems to be convincing proof that the virus causing aster yellows and the one that causes stunt disease of rice in the Orient multiply in their insect carriers.

Some insects that transmit viruses can become infective after a feeding period of only 1 minute or after only a single feeding on a diseased plant. Different species vary with respect to their efficiency in transmitting virus diseases, and there are instances where the nymphs or immature stages seem to be less efficient than the adult insects. Some vectors can pick up viruses while they are in immature stages but cannot transmit them until the adult stage is reached. The suggested explanation, in the case of a leafhopper carrier of aster yellows, is that the incubation period is not completed before the nymphs reach the adult stage. But that is not the explanation in the case of thrips, which transmit spotted wilt virus, because adults become infective only after picking up the virus while in the larval stage.

A plant virus may have a single species of insect serving as its vector, or there may be several kinds able to transmit the same virus. Sometimes the latter are entirely unrelated species. Single insects can infect plants with virus diseases, but even an infective individual cannot cause an infection every time it feeds on a healthy plant. In some instances this seems to be be-

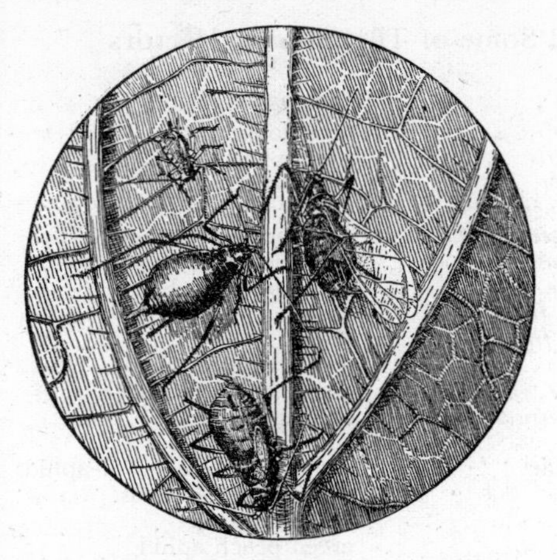

Macrosiphum ambrosiae, aphids.

cause the virus must be introduced into certain types of plant tissue which the vector does not always reach with its mouth parts; in other cases the reasons are not apparent. Viruses do not seem to affect their insect carriers in any way, even though they cause serious diseases of plants.

THE APHIDS, or plant-lice, have developed the ability to serve as carriers of plant viruses to the greatest degree. These minute, soft-bodied insects feed by sucking sap through their beaks, which they insert into plant tissues. They attack practically all kinds of plants. Most species produce both winged and wingless individuals. The former are chiefly responsible for the spread of virus diseases in fields.

The green peach aphid is outstanding among aphid carriers of plant virus diseases. It is known to transmit more than 50 kinds, mostly of the nonpersistent type.

The green peach aphid occurs almost everywhere and feeds on many kinds of plants. It is a serious pest of potatoes because it can transmit leaf roll and other viruses. In potato-growing areas where the winters are mild, the green peach aphid spends the winter on weeds and such vegetables as spinach and kale. Winged individuals produced on the winter host plants migrate into the potato fields when the plants are small. As they move from plant to plant, the winged migrants leave a few young aphids here and there and spread potato viruses from diseased plants to healthy plants. The young aphids left behind start new aphid colonies throughout the potato field. When the colonies become overcrowded, enormous numbers of winged aphids may be produced. They swarm over the field and cause another wave of infection. Individual potato farmers are helpless in their efforts to protect their crops when tremendous numbers of migrating aphids are present.

In northern Maine and other potato-growing areas where winters are cold, the green peach aphid overwinters in the egg stage. The eggs are laid on twigs of peach and plum trees by female aphids, which are produced in the late summer or early fall. Relatively few winged aphids are produced in colonies developing from these eggs, and consequently infestations in potato fields are extremely light early in the spring. Although large numbers of winged aphids may be present later in the summer, there is usually not so much spread of virus diseases in northern potato-growing areas as there is in areas with warmer winters. The amount of potato leaf roll in the following year's crop may be predicted rather accurately from the abundance of the winged forms of peach aphid during the summer.

The green peach aphid and other aphids that develop on potatoes and other plants may migrate across a gladiolus field and pick up yellow bean mosaic virus. The virus causes only mild symptoms in gladiolus, but when the aphids transmit it to beans, a destructive disease results. Celery in Florida is infected with cucumber mosaic by aphids which pick it up as they feed on commelina, a weed that grows along ditchbanks.

Lilies in fields containing a few plants infected with the nonpersistent coarse mottle and cucumber mosaic vi-

Examples of Plant Viruses and Some of Their Insect Vectors

Virus	*Vector*	*Common name*
Potato spindle tuber	*Melanoplus* spp	grasshoppers.
	Epitrix cucumeris	potato flea beetle.
	Systena taeniata	flea beetle.
	Disonycha triangularis	leaf beetle.
	Leptinotarsa decemlineata	Colorado potato beetle.
	Lygus oblineatus	tarnished plant bug.
	Myzus persicae	green peach aphid.
Strawberry yellow edge	*Pentatrichopus fragariae*	aphid.
Strawberry crinkle	*Pentatrichopus fragariae*	aphid.
Onion yellow dwarf	*Aphis gossypii*	melon aphid.
	Myzus persicae	green peach aphid.
	Brevicoryne brassicae	cabbage aphid.
	Aphis maidis	corn leaf aphid.
	Other Aphidae	At least 50 species of aphids transmit this virus.
Cucumber mosaic	*Aphis gossypii*	melon aphid.
	Myzus persicae	green peach aphid.
	Myzus circumflexus	crescent-marked lily aphid.
	Myzus solani	foxglove aphid.
Raspberry mosaics	*Amphorophora rubi*	aphid.
	Amphorophora sensoriata	aphid.
Pea mosaic	*Macrosiphum pisi*	pea aphid.
	Myzus persicae	green peach aphid.
Potato leaf roll	*Myzus persicae*	green peach aphid.
	Myzus circumflexus	crescent-marked lily aphid.
	Myzus solani	foxglove aphid.
	Macrosiphum solanifolii	potato aphid.
Sugarcane mosaic	*Aphis maidis*	corn leaf aphid.
	Hysteroneura setariae	rusty plum aphid.
Citrus quick decline	*Aphis gossypii*	melon aphid.
Potato yellow dwarf	*Aceratagallia sanguinolenta*	clover leafhopper.
	Aceratagallia curvata	leafhopper.
	Aceratagallia longula	leafhopper.
	Aceratagallia obscura	leafhopper.
Sugar-beet curly top	*Circulifer tenellus*	beet leafhopper.
Pierce's disease of grapevines	*Draeculacephala minerva*	leafhopper.
	Helochara delta	leafhopper.
	Carneocephala fulgida	leafhopper.
	Other Cicadellidae	At least 14 species can transmit this virus.
	Aphrophora annulata	spittlebug.
	Aphrophora permutata	spittlebug.
	Clastoptera brunnea	spittlebug.
	Philaenus leucophthalmus	meadow spittlebug.
Phloem necrosis of elm	*Scaphoideus luteolus*	leafhopper.
Peach yellows	*Macropsis trimaculata*	plum leafhopper.
Phony peach	*Homalodisca triquetra*	leafhopper.
	Oncometopia undata	leafhopper.
	Graphocephala versuta	leafhopper.
	Cuerna costalis	leafhopper.
Western X-disease of peach	*Colladonus geminatus*	geminate leafhopper.
Papaya bunchy-top	*Empoasca papayae*	leafhopper.
Cranberry false-blossom	*Scleroracus vaccinii*	blunt-nosed cranberry leafhopper.
Blueberry stunt disease	*Scaphytopius* sp	leafhopper.
Tomato spotted wilt	*Thysanoptera*	thrips.
Tobacco mosaic	Aphidae	A few aphids have been reported to transmit this virus.
	Melanoplus differentialis	differential grasshopper.
Latent potato virus (potato virus X).	*Melanoplus differentialis*	differential grasshopper.
Tobacco ringspot	*Melanoplus differentialis*	differential grasshopper.
Cotton leaf curl (in Africa)	*Bemisia gossypiperda*	whitefly.

ruses soon become almost completely diseased when the fields are planted near potatoes or other plants where the aphid carriers of these diseases develop. Lily rosette, a persistent virus, is transmitted by the melon aphid after an incubation period of the virus in the aphid lasting 3 or 4 days. This aphid develops on young lily plants; both the wingless aphids (which crawl to adjacent plants) or winged migrants (which fly to plants farther away) may spread lily rosette.

The melon aphid also transmits a virus that causes a condition known as lily symptomless disease. The disease has spread slowly throughout most commercial stocks of lilies. In itself it is not serious, but when the same plants get cucumber mosaic the double infection termed necrotic fleck makes them worthless. Necrotic fleck was chiefly responsible for the failure of Easter lily bulb production in the United States. To meet our needs, as many as 25 million Easter lily bulbs have been imported in a year.

The strawberry aphid in England transmits three viruses of strawberries, which cause the "running out" of desirable varieties. This aphid and two related species occur in the United States and live throughout the year on strawberry plants. Similar diseases and possibly others are devastating strawberries in the United States. These three strawberry aphids have been shown to be vectors of strawberry viruses in America and are believed to be chiefly responsible for their dispersal under field conditions. The Department of Agriculture has helped the strawberry industry by locating virus-free strawberry plants of the more valuable varieties and furnishing foundation stocks to cooperating nurseries for mass propagation and replacement of infected plants.

Winged aphids from overwintering pea aphid colonies on alfalfa transmit a serious virus disease of peas, which kills the tips and interferes with the productivity of the plants.

Aphids may also spread viruses that affect trees. An example is the citrus quick decline disease, which in a few years has caused the loss of many thousands of orange trees in California. The vector of quick decline is the melon aphid. Another aphid, which does not occur in the United States, is the vector of a similar virus disease of citrus in South America.

THE LEAFHOPPERS are our second most important carriers of plant viruses. They are small, slender, variously colored insects, which have sucking beaks similar to those of the aphids. They are active jumpers. The adults fly freely and some of them can cover long distances in migratory flights. A characteristic habit of young and adults is that of walking sideways. All leafhoppers are plant feeders. Certain kinds are called sharpshooters, and other names such as whitefly and greenfly have been used for some of them.

Leafhoppers transmit at least three serious virus diseases to peach trees. The oldest is peach yellows. Its vector was a mystery until the 1930's, when it was discovered that the plum leafhopper is the carrier.

The plum leafhopper feeds on the twigs and is seldom seen on the leaves. Plum is its favored host. Rarely is it found on peach. The leafhopper may obtain the virus, which it transmits to peach trees, from peach and plum trees. The latter are symptomless carriers of the yellows virus. In orchards adjacent to woodlands, correlations between the numbers of the leafhoppers, the abundance of wild plum, and the amount of yellows disease in peach have been noted. No other vectors of peach yellows have been discovered.

The plum leafhopper is present in all areas where peach yellows occurs. Although peach yellows is no longer a serious problem, new cases each year give warning that the vector is still active and that peach growers in the Northeastern States cannot afford to relax their vigilance with respect to the disease.

Phony peach disease poses a problem

for peach growers in Southeastern States, particularly in parts of Georgia and Alabama, where it is difficult to control with the usual method of inspecting orchards and removing all diseased trees. An intensive 12-year search for vectors ended in 1949, when it was

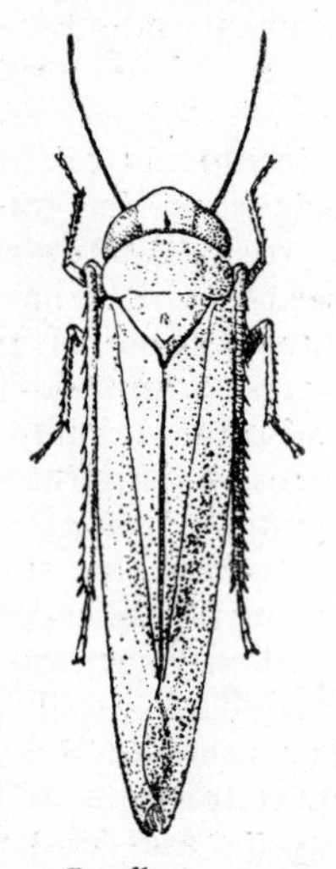

Leafhopper.

announced that four leafhoppers can spread the disease. They are all general feeders.

Two are believed to be main vectors in spreading the disease in orchards. They spend the winter as adults and occasionally as nymphs under trash and debris in woodlands and possibly along ditchbanks. In spring they become active, leave the woods, and move to a variety of plants, including peach trees, where they feed on the twigs. When preferred herbaceous plants later become available, they leave the peach trees and go to them. Very few are found on peach trees in summer but they reappear on this host early in the fall. They continue to feed on the twigs of peach trees even after the trees become fully dormant until they are forced into hibernation by cold weather.

Presumably phony peach spreads mostly during the periods in spring and fall when the leafhoppers are on peach trees. After sucking sap from infected trees, they cannot cause phony infections until after an incubation period of 14 to 40 days. Infective leafhoppers can transmit the phony peach virus for a long time, possibly for life, but we do not know whether the virus persists in them through the long periods of hibernation. When feeding, the hoppers insert their beaks into the woody tissue of peach twigs where the phony peach virus seems to be localized. They can obtain the virus from both diseased peach and wild plum trees, but not all peach trees seem to be equally good sources of the virus.

Fruit growers in the Pacific Northwest are plagued by several devastating peach and cherry virus diseases. One, the western X-disease of peach, is transmitted by the geminate leafhopper, which might also spread a little-cherry condition caused by the same virus. The incubation period of the virus in this leafhopper is usually longer than 30 days. Single leafhoppers have transmitted western X-disease; some have retained the ability to cause infections for at least 80 days. The leafhopper prefers legumes and grasses, but it feeds on many other plants. Nymphs seldom occur on peach trees but the adults frequently visit them and other stone fruits. The leafhopper also occurs on chokecherry, a wild host of the western X-disease.

At least 14 species of leafhoppers transmit the virus that causes Pierce's disease of grapevines. The same virus also infects alfalfa, causing a disease called alfalfa dwarf. A remarkable thing about the leafhopper carriers of Pierce's disease is that they are all closely related and belong to the same subfamily, which includes all known vectors of phony peach disease. The leafhoppers vary greatly in their efficiency and importance as vectors of Pierce's disease. Infective leafhoppers have been found far from vineyards or alfalfa fields—perhaps there are still other plant hosts of the virus.

Aster yellows virus affects many vegetables, flowers, and other herbaceous plants. In the Eastern States only one strain of the virus and only one vector, the six-spotted leafhopper, are known. A number of leafhoppers can transmit the western strains of the virus. The strain affecting celery, for example, is carried by at least 22 kinds of leafhoppers. The geminate and mountain leafhoppers transmit the celery strain of the virus, but they cannot transmit a related strain that causes yellows disease in asters. Both of these western virus strains, however, are transmitted by the six-spotted leafhopper. This curious relationship, and a similar situation found among the leafhoppers which transmit potato yellow dwarf virus, suggest that some virus strains may have developed in relation to their insect vectors rather than their plant hosts. The vector of aster yellows in the East cannot cause infections when exposed to high temperatures, but it regains the ability when the temperature goes down.

The wide variety of leafhoppers that transmit aster yellows, Pierce's disease of grapevines, and phony peach has brought up the point that the ability to transmit virus diseases may be determined somewhat by the ability and inclination of leafhoppers to feed on a definite part of the plant host. Of course that would be true only of the species that meet all biological requirements necessary for them to serve as vectors.

Curly-top virus causes serious diseases of sugar beets, tomatoes, and beans in Western States. The only vector known in this country is the beet leafhopper, apparently an introduced species with no close relatives in the New World. The curly-top problem and its leafhopper vector are the subjects of another article, on page 544.

Other kinds of sucking insects spread plant virus diseases. Besides many leafhoppers, four species of froghoppers, or spittlebugs, transmit Pierce's disease of grapevines. A lace bug is a vector of a virus disease of sugar beets. Mealybugs and whiteflies transmit serious diseases of cacao, cassava, or cotton in other countries. A scale insect may be involved in the spread of sudden death of clove trees.

THRIPS are tiny insects that feed by macerating the surface layers of plant cells and then sucking up the juices. Certain thrips are notorious as vectors of the spotted wilt virus of tomatoes and pineapples. The virus, or strains of it, occurs in many parts of the world and affects many kinds of plants. It causes one of the major diseases of pineapples in the Hawaiian Islands. Adult thrips cannot acquire the virus by feeding on infected plants. However, the adults that develop from nymphs that have fed on diseased plants become infective; the virus survives the pupal, or resting, stage which the insects undergo. In spotted wilt of tomatoes, the incubation period of the virus in the insects is 5 to 7 days and the ability to cause infections is retained for several weeks. Thrips develop on a wide variety of host plants and can cause severe damage even when not transmitting viruses.

Insects with biting and chewing mouth parts are involved in the transmission of a few plant viruses. Grasshoppers and leaf-feeding beetles are vectors of the highly infectious disease of potatoes called spindle tuber. Cucumber beetles transmit a mosaic disease of cucumber. The role of these insects—of spindle tuber at least—seems to be that of a mechanical carrier. The disease is also spread by many kinds of insects.

The differential grasshopper apparently can transmit tobacco mosaic, latent potato virus, and tobacco ringspot virus to healthy tobacco plants. Aphid vectors had been reported for tobacco mosaic, but repeated trials have failed to implicate insects in the transmission of latent potato virus or tobacco ringspot virus. The differential grasshopper apparently can infect tobacco plants immediately after feeding on diseased plants; infection results after only one or two feedings on a healthy plant. The transmission process is believed to be a simple mechanical transfer of virus particles on the mouth parts of the grasshopper. It is likely that virus particles on the feet of the grasshoppers may also start infections.

Some of the reports of insect transmission of plant viruses upon further investigation may be found to be a result of direct-feeding injuries that resemble symptoms of virus diseases. The foxglove aphid on lilies and several vegetable crops and an aphid on carnation cause spotting and distortion of leaves that look like viruses in the same hosts. Tarnished plant bugs cause stunting, distortion, and dead areas much like virus infection in some plants. Alfalfa yellows and a condition in potatoes known as hopperburn were suspected of being virus diseases until investigations showed that they resulted from direct feeding by the potato leafhopper. Feeding by the broad mite causes mottling, distortion, and stunting that have been mistaken for virus diseases. Infections by leaf-infesting nematodes result in yellowing, mottling, and dead areas like virus symptoms. Such direct injuries appear to be due to toxic principles in the saliva injected while feeding or to mutilation of cells in very young tissue that later develops abnormally or declines prematurely. Symptoms left by the potato leafhopper result from injury to vascular tissue in the plants, which interferes with translocation of food.

In a few diseases, the viruses move into new shoots less rapidly than growth occurs. When that happens (for example, when dahlia roots are infected with spotted wilt) healthy plants can be obtained from shoots that grow from the crowns if cuttings are removed before they are invaded by the virus. The use of healthy planting material is an obvious first precaution for reducing losses caused by many virus diseases.

Rotation of crops sometimes eliminates virus sources in volunteer plants that would infect the crop if it were grown in the same field the following year.

Rogueing, the removal of infected plants as soon as symptoms of diseases appear, maintains or even improves the health of potato, raspberry, strawberry, and other crops. The procedure, together with nursery practices to make sure that young trees used for new plantings are not infected, has been the principal method for controlling serious virus diseases of stone fruits such as peach yellows, phony peach, and peach mosaic. In isolated areas, where the vectors apparently are not very active, it has even been possible to achieve eradication of these diseases by this method.

When they are available, the use of resistant or immune varieties is an effective way to prevent losses caused by virus diseases. Losses can also be avoided by growing crops in areas where serious virus diseases are not present or where vector activity is at a low ebb.

Means have been sought for curing plants affected by virus diseases with heat treatments or chemicals administered internally. Often viruses may be killed by exposures to high temperatures that are tolerated by the infected plant tissue. Heat cures are of practical value for eliminating the viruses of sereh and chlorotic streak diseases in sugarcane seed pieces. For stone fruits a heat treatment has been suggested for yellows and X-diseases of peach but has not been used practically as yet. Its value is primarily in providing disease-free planting material.

A practical chemical treatment for inactivating viruses in plants, usable under field conditions, would be a boon to agriculturists everywhere.

The spread of plant viruses may also be prevented or retarded by methods that eliminate or reduce the insect carriers below critical transmission levels. The problem is not simple. Treatments must be exceptionally effective, even more than when the direct injury caused by the insects is the only concern. A light population of the insect carriers may be able to infect many additional plants when abundant sources of virus are available, or start a new outbreak of disease. The presence of numerous widely distributed carriers with different seasonal histories further complicates the problem. Because insects may move in constantly from untreated areas, some of them already infective, continuous protection throughout the growing season may be required when insecticides are used. Despite such difficulties, some progress can be reported.

Some benefits have been obtained with methods for reducing the numbers of insect carriers or for preventing or avoiding their activity without using insecticides. The elimination of host plants of insect carriers is often beneficial. Cloth of a special coarse weave, supported by posts and wire, effectively excludes the leafhoppers that transmit yellows infection to China asters.

Potato virus diseases are largely controlled by using seed potatoes grown in isolated areas or in places where the aphid vectors are scarce. Relatively few potatoes are infected under those conditions, and the seed pieces produce a high proportion of healthy plants. Northern locations or high altitudes with cool temperatures and almost constant winds are best for growing seed potatoes, because those conditions are unfavorable for aphid development or flight. Frequent rogueing and applications of insecticides help to maintain the healthy seed stock. Similar procedures are used for developing and maintaining healthy source stocks of strawberries in England, and they may be practical for lilies, gladiolus, and other economic plants in the United States.

Many experiments have been made to determine the usefulness of insecticides in controlling the carriers of plant virus diseases. The materials available before 1940 were seldom effective enough. The situation has improved with the development of new insecticides, such as DDT.

970134°—52——14

Applications of insecticides to cultivated crops can be expected to control virus diseases best if the diseases are spread solely within the crop by the insect carriers that develop on the crop. Residual insecticides may be of value in reducing the amount of disease caused by carriers coming in from outside sources. To be effective, the insecticide must kill rapidly enough to destroy the insects before they can do much feeding. They must also remain toxic to later invaders for several days or until the next application of insecticide is made. The application of insecticides to vector breeding areas to destroy the insects before they reach cultivated plantings may have merit in certain situations.

DDT has been the most useful of the new insecticides for controlling insect carriers of plant virus diseases. It is effective against nearly all leafhoppers and it destroys some of the important aphid vectors. It is now almost universally applied to potato fields to eliminate aphids. The applications greatly reduce the number of wingless aphids and winged summer migrants which develop, and the spread of potato leaf roll is now much less than in former years. Aster yellows has been reduced by about 90 percent in lettuce fields in New York and Maryland by DDT applications, which destroy the six-spotted leafhopper, the most important carrier of the disease. The DDT residues are also effective against additional leafhoppers that move into lettuce fields each day. Good results with DDT for controlling aster yellows in carrots have also been reported.

DDT has been studied in Western States to determine its usefulness in preventing curly-top virus infections in sugar beets, tomatoes, and beans. The DDT reduces the number of beet leafhoppers and has good residual toxicity, but it does not prevent the feeding of the leafhoppers that reinfest the fields. The incidence of the disease in tomatoes therefore may not be appreciably reduced by DDT if reinfestation occurs. In fields where reinfestation does not occur, single applications may give good results. Insecticidal control of leafhoppers on weed hosts growing on idle and waste land, which contribute large populations to cultivated areas, has been used in California to combat a serious curly-top problem. Experiments with the method have also been made in Idaho. When control of the leafhoppers in their breeding grounds is undertaken, it is desirable to eliminate the host plants of the insects as fast as possible, and replace them with plants, such as grasses, on which the beet leafhoppers do not breed.

First results of experiments suggest that DDT may have an appreciable effect on the insect carriers of phony peach disease and that it may be possible to retard its spread with DDT, but much remains to be done on the problem before practical suggestions for the use of DDT for the purpose can be made.

Systemic insecticides, which invade entire plants after being taken in through the roots or leaves, are toxic to aphids that feed on the treated plants. The spread of yellows in beets and other virus diseases in strawberries, all aphid-transmitted, is said to have been greatly reduced through the use of systemic insecticides on farms in England. Studies in the United States indicate that the method has possibilities for aphid-transmitted viruses, which attack ornamental plants, such as lilies, tulips, narcissus, and other plants propagated in nurseries. The method may also be feasible for treating food crops if it is found that the insecticide or its decomposition products in the plant are not harmful.

In greenhouses, the spread of viruses is easily prevented by maintaining strict control over all insects. Fumigation with various materials or the use of aerosols containing one of the new organic phosphate insecticides are effective.

The new advances in insecticidal control of plant virus diseases probably will lead to others. With such an array of new insecticides for evaluation and with the new equipment for applying them rapidly and effectively, the entomologists may make even greater contributions to the control of plant virus diseases than has been possible in the past.

But it is too much to expect that the problem will be solved entirely even then: Still needed will be cooperation among growers in control programs, constant emphasis on preventive measures, and the enforcement of quarantines to prevent the spread of viruses into new localities and to prevent the introduction of additional virus diseases into the United States.

L. D. Christenson *is entomologist in charge, oriental fruit fly investigations, Bureau of Entomology and Plant Quarantine, in Hawaii. He attended the Utah State Agricultural College, the University of Minnesota, and the University of California. From 1929 to 1942 his principal assignments were concerned with studies of the relationships of insects to sugarcane, cotton, and stone fruit diseases in Cuba and in Southern and Western States. From 1946 to 1951 he was assistant to the chief of fruit insect investigations, Bureau of Entomology and Plant Quarantine.*

Floyd F. Smith, *a senior entomologist in the Bureau of Entomology and Plant Quarantine, has devoted 28 years to the study of insects affecting greenhouse and ornamental plants. He has published many articles on the biology and control of those pests and on insects as vectors of plant diseases. In recognition of his research on the aerosol method of applying insecticides in greenhouses, the Society of American Florists gave him an award for the most important contribution to floriculture in 1947. He is a graduate of Ohio State University.*

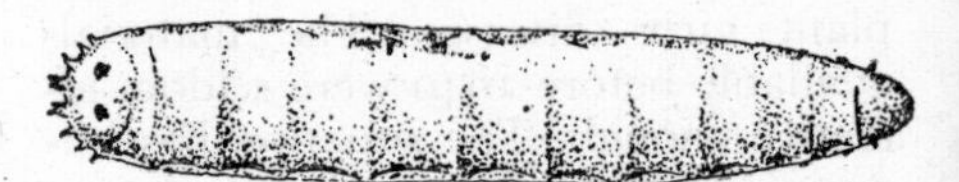

Seed-corn maggot.

Insects, Bacteria, and Fungi

J. G. Leach

Some insects do great damage by aiding in the spread and development of plant diseases.

The insect first proved by experiments to be a vector of a plant disease was the honey bee, which everyone considered completely beneficial; no one had thought of suspecting one of man's best friends.

The experiments that indicted the honey bee were a landmark in agricultural science. For many years the damage done to plants by insects had been measured only in terms of direct injury from their feeding and breeding.

M. B. Waite, an employee of the Department of Agriculture, discovered in 1891 and proved experimentally that the honey bee, while visiting apple and pear blossoms in search of nectar, became contaminated with the bacteria causing fire blight and transmitted the disease from blossom to blossom and from tree to tree.

That was a new idea, one that plant pathologists and entomologists were slow to accept. The recognized importance of the honey bee in pollinating flowering plants and producing honey made many reluctant to believe that it could be guilty of transmitting a disease.

All this was discouraging to Waite, but his work was confirmed by J. C. Arthur, working at the New York Agricultural Experiment Station at Geneva. Soon plant pathologists and entomologists began to suspect other insects of transmitting plant diseases.

A few years later Erwin S. Smith, another pioneer worker of the Department of Agriculture, and his associates reported that a destructive bacterial wilt of cucumber and muskmelons was transmitted by two species of cucumber beetles. Further work has demonstrated that the bacteria causing the disease survive the winter within the bodies of the insects and that, in nature, the disease depends completely on the insects both for survival over winter and for spread from plant to plant in summer. A similar relationship exists between the bacterial wilt of sweet corn and two species of flea beetles.

Ergot of rye and related cereals and grasses was perhaps the earliest fungus disease to be recognized as transmitted by insects. The fungus affects the young flowers and replaces the normal seed with a hard, black mass called a sclerotium. In early stages of blossom infection, the fungus secretes a sugary fluid in which masses of spores are produced. The fluid has a foul odor that attracts flies. When the flies feed on the sugary solution, they become contaminated internally and externally with the ergot spores. Some of the flies also feed on the pollen grains of the healthy flowers. On them they deposit the ergot spores and thus spread the disease from plant to plant. In this instance, a mutually beneficial relationship exists between the fungus and its insect vector. The flies derive nourishment from the sugary fluid. In return for the food, the flies transmit the spores of the fungus from flower to flower and enable the fungus to survive. An association of this type is called mutualistic symbiosis.

Similar mutualistic symbiosis occurs in other instances of insect transmission. The seed-corn maggot and other dipterous insects carry the soft rot bacteria which affect many vegetable crops. The flies lay their eggs in the soil near vegetable tissue or directly on it. When the eggs hatch, the young maggots bore into the plant tissues, taking the soft rot bacteria with them. The maggots will not grow and develop normally in sterile plant tissue but grow rapidly when the tissues are decayed by the bacteria. Thus the bacteria are essential for the normal development of the insect. The bacteria may also provide essential vitamins for the insect and aid in the digestion of plant tissues. The soft rot bacteria are wound parasites and cannot penetrate uninjured plant tissues. The insects make the necessary wounds. The bacteria in return provide the necessary vitamins and aid the insects in deriving nourishment from the plant. Both the insect and the bacteria thus benefit from the association.

Because the young maggot would be helpless without the bacteria, which it may or may not obtain from the soil, the insect insures their presence when needed by harboring the bacteria within its body. The bacteria survive within the intestinal tract of the insect in all stages of metamorphosis. Freshly deposited eggs are usually contaminated. The insect carries with it at all times a culture of the bacteria that are essential for the nourishment of the young maggots. It is evident that the transmission of plant diseases by insects often is not a simple matter of chance but is a complicated association that has evolved over a long period.

Fire blight is a bacterial disease of orchard fruits, principally pears and apples. It chiefly affects blossoms and young tender shoots. It may also form destructive cankers on the trunk and larger branches. It is caused by bacteria that overwinter in the bark surrounding the cankers. Sap oozes in spring from the edges of infected cankers. A microscopic examination of the sap shows it to be teeming with the fire blight bacteria. Insects, principally ants and flies, feed on the ooze and then visit blossoms in search of nectar. Thus the bacteria are introduced into the nectar, from which they spread into the blossoms, causing the blossom-blight stage of the disease. Bees, wasps, and other insects that visit the flowers in search of nectar or pollen spread the bacteria from blossom to blossom and from one tree to another.

Shortly after the blossoms have been blighted, the young and tender shoots become infected, turn black or brown, and wither. Heavily infected trees look as if they had been scorched by fire, hence the name fire blight. The young shoots are inoculated with the bacteria by sucking insects, including several species of aphids and leafhoppers. These insects become contaminated by feeding upon or crawling over infected tissue. Later, when the contaminated insects pierce healthy twigs with their needlelike mouth parts, the bacteria are carried deep into the tissues and the twig is inoculated.

The bacteria of fire blight may be disseminated also by wind-blown rain and by pruning tools. Whatever the relative importance of the various methods of spread, it is agreed that if all dissemination by insects could be eliminated the disease would be much less serious.

Bacterial wilt of cucurbits damages cucumbers, muskmelons, and squashes in the North and East. The bacteria causing the disease are found in the water-conducting vessels of the plants, in which they grow in white, sticky masses and interfere with normal movement of water from root to leaves. Affected plants wilt as if suffering from drought and usually die before any fruits mature.

The bacteria gain entrance into the plant only through the feeding wounds made by two species of cucumber beetles, the striped cucumber beetle and the spotted cucumber beetle. The bacteria survive the winter within the bodies of the beetles and are introduced into the wounds from their mouth parts. Not all beetles are contaminated with the bacteria, but any beetle that feeds upon a diseased plant is likely to become contaminated. The beetles hibernate in the adult stage and in some years a relatively high percentage of overwintering beetles harbor the bacteria. Such beetles may transmit the disease to any susceptible plant on which they feed in the spring.

No other method of infection or survival over winter is known to occur in nature. The only way to control the disease is to prevent the beetles from feeding on the plants. The only satisfactory way to protect the plants used to be to grow them under insectproof cages. Some organic insecticides, such as methoxychlor, have given promise

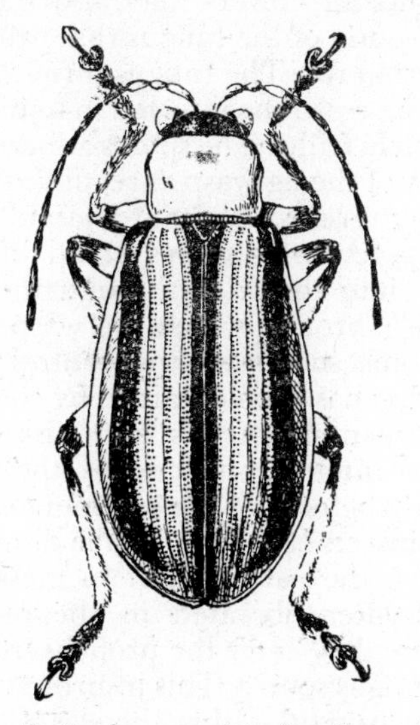

Striped cucumber beetle.

against the beetles and may be a more practical means of controlling bacterial wilt.

Bacterial soft rot of vegetables is caused by several related strains of bacteria. It affects a variety of plants, including most plants with succulent tissue that is not too acid in reaction. The bacteria are strictly wound parasites and generally do not penetrate uninjured tissues. A wounded plant normally attempts to heal the wound by laying down a layer of cork cells, which will prevent infection. If conditions do not favor cork formation, the bacteria may infect and cause a rot before the healing action is completed. The soft rot bacteria can be found in most agricultural soils. Any wound in susceptible tissue thus is a potential point of infection for soft rot. If the wound heals quickly enough, infection may not take place, but if something interferes with wound-cork formation, the disease is likely to occur. It is common practice in some potato-growing regions therefore to store cut seed pieces under conditions that permit rapid healing or suberization of the cut surfaces.

Wounds made by insects on the roots of plants or on stems or leaves near the ground are common points of infection. Among the most effective insects in making the wounds are the dipterous insects, such as the seed-corn maggot, the cabbage maggot, and the onion maggot, which live in mutualistic symbiosis with bacteria. They harbor the bacteria within their bodies. When the maggots burrow into the plant tissues, they usually introduce the bacteria into the plant. Moreover, the maggots, by continually burrowing into the tissues, prevent the wound from healing or puncture each new layer of cork as it is formed.

Because the insects live in decaying plant tissue, they used to be considered harmless scavengers, coming in only after the plant tissues had already decayed. Actually, however, the insects, by transmitting the soft rot bacteria and making the necessary wound, inoculate the plant, and thereby produce their own rotted tissue.

The bacterial wilt of sweet corn for a long time was a highly destructive disease, but new wilt-resistant hybrids have reduced its importance. It may kill susceptible varieties in any stage of their development. The bacteria are found chiefly in the vascular bundles, through which they may spread to all parts of the plant. Sometimes, when the plant is not killed until the ears have formed, the bacteria may reach the young kernels and penetrate beneath the seed coat. People therefore once believed that the disease was transmitted through the seeds. We now know that even though the bacteria may be present under the seed coat the disease will not develop unless wounds are made on the young plant. Such wounds, through which the bacteria may infect the plant, are made chiefly by the larvae of the spotted cucumber beetle, commonly called the southern corn rootworm when it is found on corn.

A more common means of transmission of the disease is provided by two species of small, black flea beetles, the toothed flea beetle and the corn flea beetle. They feed on the corn leaves and so cause wounds into which they introduce the bacteria. The beetles usually pick up the bacteria when they feed on leaves of diseased plants. The bacteria may live over winter within the bodies of adult beetles. Such beetles are responsible for the primary infection each year as well as for secondary spread throughout the summer.

AMONG THE FUNGUS diseases transmitted by insects are the Dutch elm disease and the blue stain of conifers, which are transmitted almost entirely by bark beetles. They are discussed on page 688.

Another group of insect-transmitted fungus diseases are the fruit-spoilage diseases of figs. Most common are endosepsis, smut, and souring.

Endosepsis, or internal rot, of the caprified fig is caused by a fungus and is transmitted by the fig wasp. The wasp develops only in figs. It is necessary for the pollination and normal development of the fig. It overwinters in the fruit of the mammae, or late summer, crop. In early spring the male wasps fertilize the females while they are still within the fruit. The females then leave the old mammae fruit and enter the young spring, or profichi, crop. There they lay eggs in the ovules of the young flowers that are within the young fig fruit. The eggs hatch into a new brood of wasps, whose females emerge and enter the fruits of the summer, or mammoni, crop to oviposit. When they leave the profichi fruit they rub against staminate flowers that surround the "eye" and become covered with pollen. The pollen is carried into the mammoni fruit and fertilizes the developing florets. The insects cannot oviposit in mammoni fruit because the styles of its flowers are too long. Thus, although the mammoni fruit is effectively pollinated and develops normally, the insects do not develop. The fruits of the mammoni crop constitute the edible fig of commerce.

The female insects that transport the pollen from the profichi flowers to the mammoni flowers may also transport the spores of the fungus that causes the internal rot. The fungus forms numerous spores in the infected mammae and profichi fruits. The spores adhere to the body of the fig wasp as readily as do the pollen grains. Without the aid of the wasp, few or no spores would find their way into the fruit through the small "eye" through which the wasp enters.

Some success in the control of the disease has been obtained by collecting the mammae fruits and disinfecting them internally to destroy the fungus spores before the insects emerge. When the insects emerge from the disinfected fruits, they are caught in glass tubes and later liberated in the orchards where they enter the profichi fruit free of fungus spores. This insures a healthy profichi crop so that the wasps leaving the profichi fruits and entering the mammoni fruits will not be contaminated with fungus spores.

Souring of figs begins as a fermentation of the sugary sap of the ripe fruit by several species of yeast. The fruit is further decomposed by secondary fungi and bacteria. Both the common fig (which does not require pollination by insects) and the caprified fig are affected, but the disease is more prevalent on the common fig. The yeasts are introduced into the fig fruit through the "eye" by two insects, the dried-fruit beetle and the pomace or vinegar flies, which enter in search of food. The yeasts seem constantly to be associated internally and externally with the insects. Because the yeasts grow also on many other kinds of spoiled fruits and the insects breed in them, the control of souring depends largely on destruction of the waste fruits in which the insects and the fungi breed.

Smut of figs is not a true smut but a mold. It is caused by a strain of the common black mold that grows on all kinds of spoiled fruits. The fungus produces spores in a black smutlike mass.

Some of the spores are introduced into the healthy fig fruits through the "eyes" by the same insects that transport the yeasts that cause souring. The control measures for smut, like those for souring, are based on sanitation and control of the insects by destroying the waste fruit in which they breed.

STIGMATOMYCOSIS applies to a type of injury to plants long known to be associated with the feeding punctures of several kinds of true bugs. For many years the injury was attributed to the supposed toxic effect of the salivary secretions of the insects. It is really caused by fungi introduced into the plant tissues by the insects while feeding.

The role of fungi in stigmatomycosis was discovered in a study of the bugs known as cotton stainers (Pyrrhocoridae), which feed on cotton bolls. The bugs pierce the cotton bolls with their needlelike mouth parts. The cotton fibers beneath each puncture become stained and matted in a hard clump of worthless fibers. The staining of the fibers is caused by several species of a yeastlike fungus that are introduced on the mouth parts of the bugs when they feed on the cotton bolls. The staining occurs only on bolls that have been punctured by the bugs, and all evidence indicates that the disease depends entirely on the bugs for its entrance into the bolls. The fungi are not constantly associated with the bugs but are picked up by them while they are feeding on infected material. When noncontaminated bugs feed on cotton bolls, the fiber is not stained and little injury is caused. Once a bug has been contaminated, however, it apparently remains contaminated for the rest of its life and introduces the fungus with each feeding puncture.

Like relationships exist between other bugs and similar fungi on other crops. For example, the green stink bug transmits the fungus that causes the destructive yeast spot on lima beans. The kernel spot of pecan, long considered to be caused by the mechanical injury and toxic substances associated with the feeding of a stink bug, is now known to be caused by a fungus transmitted by the bug.

IN MOST of my examples of insect transmission, the insects make the wounds through which the fungi or bacteria penetrate the plant and also transport the micro-organisms from plant to plant. In some instances the insect may not be so important in transporting the spores of a fungus but may provide wounds through which wind-blown spores may enter.

That appears to be the case in the association between the brown rot of peaches and plums and the plum curculio. A relationship between the curculio and brown rot of peaches and plums has been observed for a long time, but the importance of the relationship was not fully realized until organic insecticides like benzene hexachloride and parathion became available and effective control of the curculio became possible.

In orchards where the curculio is effectively controlled, much less brown rot occurs than where the curculio is not controlled. There is no evidence that the curculio is a major factor in disseminating the spores of brown rot, which are readily wind-blown. But the insects influence the development of brown rot by making wounds in immature plums and peaches through which wind-blown spores are able to infect. The fungus has difficulty in infecting immature fruits if the skin is uninjured, but the fungus grows readily in the punctures made by the curculio. Spores formed on the injured green fruits provide an abundant source of infection for the ripening fruit later in the season.

The logical method of control for insect-borne diseases is to control the insect vectors. But that has not always worked, because our best methods for controlling the insects were not good enough. Many insect-control measures have reduced losses from direct-feeding injuries but have permitted enough insects to survive to transmit the disease effectively. DDT, lindane, parathion, methoxychlor, and other new organic insecticides have given more complete control—good enough to give us the idea that the possible control of all insect-transmitted diseases should be reconsidered from the standpoint of better control of the insect vector.

Moreover, when it has not been possible to control an insect effectively, it has been difficult to determine accurately to what extent the insect is responsible for transmitting a disease. By using the more effective insecticides to get more nearly complete control of known or suspected insect vectors, a more accurate measure of the importance of insect transmission of many plant diseases can be had.

A relationship also exists between insects and the rust fungi. Many of the rust fungi, such as the destructive black stem rust of cereals, reproduce sexually and produce structures that have functions comparable to the male and female organs of the flowering plants. To complete the life cycle, a male cell must enter the female organ so fertilization can take place. The rust fungi depend largely on insects for this process of "pollination."

In the black stem rust of wheat the process occurs on the leaves of the barberry bush (*Berberis vulgaris, B. canadensis,* and *B. fendleri*), which is the alternate host of the fungus. The spores come from the grass host and infect the barberry leaf. They are of two sexes usually designated as + and −, because there are no morphological differences that would identify them as male and female. On the barberry leaf each spore produces a spot in which are formed numerous flask-shaped structures, the pycnia. Each pycnium produces thousands of small spores (pycniospores) and numerous short hyphae. If the pycnium originated from a + spore, the nuclei in the pycniospores and hyphae are of the + sex. Those arising from − spores have nuclei of the − sex.

The spores function as gametes comparable to the pollen of higher plants. The fungus hypha correspond in function to the stigmata and are called receptive hyphae. If a pycniospore comes in contact with a receptive hypha of the opposite sex, it germinates and fuses with a cell of the receptive hypha. The nucleus of the spore passes into the cell of the receptive hypha and becomes associated with the nucleus of the opposite sex and eventually fuses with it, thus effecting fertilization. The pycnia are self-sterile—the spores produced in a + pycnium will not fuse with the receptive hyphae of the same pycnium or of other pycnia of the same sex. They must be transported to a receptive hypha of the opposite sex if fertilization is to take place.

The pycnia are produced on the upper side of the barberry leaf in a bright yellow spot, and the spores and receptive hyphae are covered with a drop of sugary, fragrant solution. Flies and other insects are attracted to infected barberry leaves by the bright color of the spots and the solution, on which they feed. In feeding on the solution and moving from one spot to another, the insects transfer spores from + to − pycnia and vice versa, thus insuring "pollination" of the fungus.

Sexual reproduction often results in hybridization between different races of rust and results in the production of new races, some of which will attack the new varieties of wheat that have been bred for rust resistance. Thus the insects, with the aid of the barberry bushes, are breeding new varieties of rust almost as fast as the plant breeders can breed new varieties of wheat.

J. G. LEACH *has been head of the department of plant pathology and bacteriology in West Virginia University since 1938. Before that he was professor of plant pathology in the University of Minnesota. He has done extensive research with insects in relation to plant diseases. He is author of a book,* Insect Transmission of Plant Diseases. *He is a former president of the American Phytopathological Society.*

The Nature of Insecticides

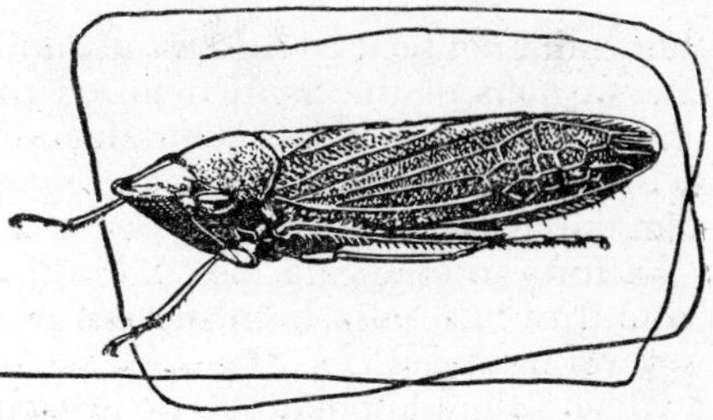

Can Insects Be Eradicated?

Clay Lyle

We know that insects have survived for 250 million years and that they are endowed with marvelous mechanisms by which they should be able to survive for many more years. We know also that no species of insect has disappeared from the earth because of man's activities, as have the dodo, the passenger pigeon, and some other animals. Yet I give an unqualified *yes* to the question, Can insects be eradicated?

It is possible to wipe out destructive insects and it is desirable to do so. When insects first migrate to a new locality they should be destroyed, while their numbers are still small, even at great expense, lest they continue to spread and cause losses to farmers that year and every succeeding year.

Several insects have been eradicated from such large areas that the complete extermination of their species throughout the world could probably be accomplished. It is true, though, that climate, natural enemies, food supply, and some other factors that affect any one species vary so greatly the world over that eradication might be practicable in one country and unimportant or impossible in another.

Three insects and one snail which had become well established in the United States have been eradicated and were not known to occur within our continental limits in the year 1952.

The Mediterranean fruit fly was exterminated from parts of 20 counties in Florida in about a year—an outstanding example of eradication.

The parlatoria date scale was destroyed in several places in Arizona, California, and Texas.

The citrus blackfly was expelled from Key West, Fla., although fears of a reinfestation of the United States from Mexico have been expressed.

The white garden snail has been eradicated from several counties in southern California.

Several other pests have been exterminated within definite areas, although they are still present in other sections of the United States or even in the same areas after reinfestation from outside sources. Among them are:

Pink bollworm, from northern Florida, Georgia, and large areas in Texas, New Mexico, Arizona, Oklahoma, and Louisiana, some of which have been reinfested from Mexico.

Sweetpotato weevil, from areas in several Southern States, which have since become reinfested.

Gypsy moth, entirely from Pennsylvania and New Jersey and greatly reduced in some other Eastern States.

Argentine ant, from several towns in Mississippi.

Citrus whitefly, from 16 counties in California; new infestations occurred after 1942 in 2 counties in California, but were eradicated by 1950.

Obscure scale, from Los Angeles and San Diego Counties, Calif.

Cattle tick, practically eradicated from the United States after a fight of more than 50 years. Effective methods of eradication were known before 1900 but could not be used successfully until the farmers of the South realized the importance of livestock production. The tick carries the protozoan organism that causes Texas fever.

Efforts to eradicate insects in other countries have also been successful in several instances.

The Colorado potato beetle first appeared in Europe in Germany in 1877. It was found again in 1887, 1914, and 1934. Each time it was promptly eradicated, but Germany, Belgium, the Netherlands, and Switzerland have since become infested through its spread from France, where it was first found in 1922. Infestations in England in 1901 and 1933 were quickly stopped. Reinfestations still occur in England as the beetle spreads over continental Europe.

The dangerous African mosquito (*Anopheles gambiae*), which caused 20,000 deaths in Brazil in 1938 and 130,000 in Egypt in 1943 by transmitting malaria, was apparently eradicated from Brazil by 1940 and from Egypt by the end of 1945. The Rockefeller Foundation assisted the governments of the two countries in the work. Large areas of Brazil have also been freed of the yellow-fever mosquito.

Sleeping sickness in sections of Africa is being reduced through the eradication of several species of tsetse flies (*Glossina* spp.) by chemical and cultural methods.

The brown-tail moth has been eradicated from Nova Scotia and New Brunswick; the gypsy moth from southern Quebec and New Brunswick; the codling moth from western Australia; and two species of cattle grubs (northern cattle grub and common cattle grub) from Clare Island, Ireland.

Most of the foregoing examples of eradication occurred before the development of the new insecticides and equipment. Several other pests could doubtless have been wiped out except that the necessary measures would have been considered as interference with an individual. For example, human lice could easily be eradicated in this country but a Nation-wide compulsory physical examination would be necessary to find the few infested persons. The boll weevil, which has caused millions of dollars of damage to cotton every year, could be eradicated quickly by establishing a series of zones across the Cotton States in which no cotton could be grown for a while. The farm adjustments and loss of income for even a year to ginners, oil millers, and others would keep any State from adopting the necessary legislation, however.

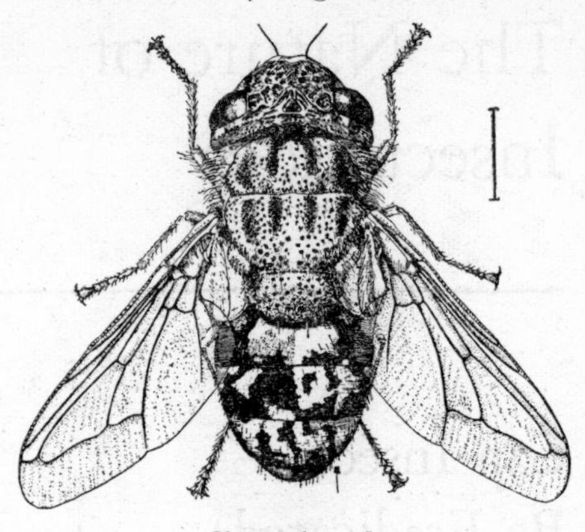

Sheep bot fly.

If we examine again the insect problems of the United States and take into consideration the value of the new chemicals and machines, very likely we would agree on the practicability of a full-scale onslaught against other pests, especially those that attack livestock.

One of the first would be the two species of cattle grubs, which cause an estimated annual loss in the United States of 100 million to 300 million dollars. The eradication of both from Clare Island by the slow painful method of squeezing the grubs out of the animals by hand shows that the present convenient and inexpensive chemical treatment could be effectively used for eradication if the public demanded it.

Any community that undertakes to eradicate cattle grubs might well in-

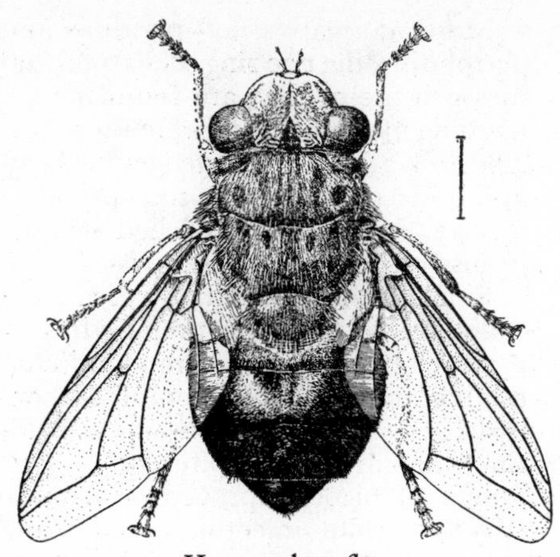

Human bot fly.

clude cattle lice in the program; the cost of eliminating the two groups of pests would be little more than the cost for one alone. Cattle lice were almost unknown in parts of the South during the compulsory tick-eradication program, and it seems certain that present methods of controlling lice would result in quick eradication in any areas that undertake to do so.

The screw-worm does not ordinarily overwinter north of Florida and the extreme southern part of Texas, but it occurs much farther north in mild winters. From those areas it spreads north each season. If it would be stamped out in Florida during a cold winter, all the Southeastern States would be freed from attacks. Eradication seems quite possible technically, especially with the improved treatments that kill the adult flies and the larvae, but the presence of wild hogs and other wild animals in remote areas would make eradication more difficult.

The effective control of the sheep bot fly with a Lysol nose drench makes it possible to get rid of the pest, because it overwinters only in the nasal passages of sheep. Associations of sheep raisers might well consider a combined program to eradicate the sheep-tick and the sheep bot fly at one time.

The reduction in the number of horses on farms in the United States has made the eradication of the horse bot fly, nose bot fly, and throat bot fly only a question of whether there is enough interest to justify such an undertaking. Controls are effective and areas could be cleaned up quickly in a vigorous campaign.

The eradication in any State of the several livestock pests I have mentioned probably would not be too difficult technically, but much of the value would be lost unless the programs were undertaken on a national or continental basis, for some of the pests would quickly spread back from other areas. Required, therefore, would be the concerted, simultaneous effort of the States to bring about the desired results. Pests more or less restricted to the bodies of their hosts, such as cattle lice, the sheep bot fly, and the sheep-tick, might be eradicated within limited areas and their reintroduction prevented by strict enforcement of quarantine measures, but I think it would be more desirable, even so, to have a Nation-wide program.

That is a challenge to entomologists and farmers. No eradication project can succeed, no matter how effective the controls devised by the entomologist, without the full cooperation of farmers in initiating and supporting the necessary enforcement laws and regulations and in carrying out the recommendations.

CLAY LYLE *is director of the Mississippi Agricultural Experiment Station and Agricultural Extension Service and dean of the School of Agriculture of Mississippi State College. Before he assumed those positions on July 1, 1951, he was entomologist for the Mississippi Agricultural Experiment Station, entomologist and executive officer of the State Plant Board of Mississippi, professor and head of the Department of Zoology and Entomology, and dean of the School of Science of Mississippi State College. He began his entomological work in Mississippi in 1920. He has degrees from Mississippi State College and Iowa State College.*

How Insecticides Are Developed

R. C. Roark

New insecticides are developed in two ways.

The first is by determining the structure of the active principles of plants recognized as toxic to insects. Then the principles or other compounds closely related to them are synthesized—put together again to make the whole.

The second is by testing compounds of known structure and unknown toxicity upon several species of insects and selecting the ones that are effective.

The first method starts with a material of known toxicity but unknown structure. The second starts with a compound of known structure but unknown toxic value.

The insecticidal principles—parts or elements—of plants have a complicated make-up. Even after their formulas are known it may be impossible to reconstruct them: The structural formulas of rotenone and deguelin have been known since 1932, but the chemist does not know how to attempt their synthesis.

An example of the first method is the synthesis of anabasine. For that, nicotine, a compound of known structure isolated from a plant, was used as a model.

The chief insecticidal principle of tobacco, the liquid alkaloid nicotine, 1-methyl-2-(3-pyridyl) pyrrolidine, kills many kinds of insects. When a systematic search for new synthetic insecticides was undertaken in the Depart of Agriculture in 1922 by C. R. Smith, he naturally turned to nicotine as the first model of compounds to be synthesized. Its structure was determined a half century ago, but no commercially feasible process of making it synthetically on a large scale is known.

Many derivatives of pyridine and pyrrolidine, the two rings of carbon and nitrogen atoms that are found in the nicotine molecule, then were prepared. The derivatives were tested on the bean aphid, a species highly susceptible to nicotine, but none approached nicotine in insecticidal effectiveness.

Finally in 1928 Smith, by the action of sodium on pyridine, prepared 2-(3-pyridyl) piperidine, a compound containing the same number of carbon, hydrogen, and nitrogen atoms as nicotine but arranged differently. This isomer of nicotine proved even more effective than nicotine for killing aphids. Because of its resemblance to nicotine, Smith named the new compound neonicotine. Shortly after its synthesis was announced, Russian chemists found the alkaloid in *Anabasis aphylla,* a weed belonging to the goosefoot family, and named it anabasine.

Another example is the synthesis of allethrin. For nearly 30 years chemists sought to learn the nature of the insecticidal constituents of the pyrethrum flowers. Two Swiss chemists, H. Staudinger and L. Ruzicka, in 1924 announced that two compounds containing carbon, hydrogen, and oxygen in pyrethrum flowers were responsible for the insecticidal value of the flowers. They explained the structure of the compounds, called pyrethrin I and pyrethrin II, and described their unsuccessful efforts to synthesize them. F. B. LaForge and associates in the Department of Agriculture reexamined pyrethrum in 1934 and discovered two additional insecticidal esters in the flowers. They named them cinerin I and cinerin II.

Of the four active principles in pyrethrum flowers, cinerin I has the simplest structure. It was taken as the pattern when synthetic work was undertaken. Compounds closely related to cinerin I were made. One of them, called the allyl homolog of cinerin I, was found to equal the natural compound in killing house flies. About a dozen steps are required in synthesizing it. The large-scale manufacture of the ester has been accomplished, and 10,000 pounds of it were used in 1951 in liquefied-gas aerosol bombs. To avoid the cumbersome "allyl homolog of cinerin I," the name allethrin was coined for the compound.

Allethrin is a light-yellow, viscous liquid. It has a slight but pleasant odor. It is insoluble in water but readily soluble in the solvents used in fly sprays and in Freons 11 and 12, used in aerosol bombs. It is more stable than pyrethrum extract and is free from the Freon-insoluble material present in the natural product. Allethrin has been tested by pharmacologists and pronounced to be as safe as pyrethrum to man; pyrethrum is regarded as the least objectional of all insecticides in toxicity to people. Its many desirable properties should mean a wide use of allethrin in aerosol bombs, fly sprays, and agricultural insecticides. The development of allethrin is a vindication of the thesis that it is possible to develop synthetic insecticides that rival the constituents of insecticidal plants, but this achievement is possible only when the structure of the plant insecticide is known.

Another insecticide of plant origin is scabrin, a constituent of the root of *Heliopsis scabra*. An account of the work leading to the discovery of this toxicant illustrates the method of developing new insecticidal chemicals through research on insecticidal plants.

In 1943 the division of insecticide investigations of the Bureau of Entomology and Plant Quarantine received from Mexico City the roots of a plant reported to be used by Mexicans as an insecticide. The plant was incorrectly labeled *Erigeron affinis,* but Department botanists later identified it as *Heliopsis longipes*. The active principle was isolated and was identified as *n*-isobutyl-2,6,8-decatrienamide. Three other species of the genus *Heliopsis* were collected in several parts of the United States and tested for insecticidal value. Laboratory tests disclosed that all the species, particularly their roots, were toxic to house flies. From the most toxic of the species, *Heliopsis scabra,* there was isolated an amide $C_{22}H_{35}NO$, called scabrin, which proved to be nearly three times as toxic as the pyrethrins to house flies.

THE FIRST SYNTHETIC organic compounds used to kill insects were employed as fumigants. Carbon disulfide, made by the direct combination of carbon and sulfur, may be regarded as one of the simplest organic compounds. It was first used as an insecticide nearly 100 years ago in France. Paradichlorobenzene, originally a byproduct in the manufacture of chlorobenzene, was used as a substitute for naphthalene in combatting clothes moths in Germany in 1911. Chloropicrin emulsified in water was proposed as an insecticide in Austria in 1907 and was tested as a fumigant in the United States about 1917.

In 1922 a systematic search for new fumigants was undertaken by Department chemists and entomologists with the object of finding substitutes for the dangerously inflammable carbon disulfide widely used for fumigating weevily grain. The search resulted in the discovery of several new fumigants, all synthetic organic compounds. Among those that have come into commercial use are ethylene dichloride; propylene dichloride; dichloroethyl ether; ethylene dibromide; the methyl, ethyl, and isopropyl esters of formic acid; and ethylene oxide. About 10 years later methyl bromide was first used as an insecticidal fumigant in France. D-D mixture (containing 1,3-dichloropropene, 1,2-dichloropropane, and other chlorides) has come into use in California and the Hawaiian Islands as a soil fumigant.

As I mentioned, the early synthetic work in the Department of Agriculture to develop new contact and stomach poisons for insects was based on nicotine as a model. Later the empirical method of approach was used—synthetic organic compounds were tested irrespective of their structure. The work led to the development of phenothiazine as a pesticide. First it was tested against mosquito larvae and found to be highly toxic to them. It was then tested against a variety of agricultural pests and found to be amazingly effective in controlling codling moth on apple. More than 3 million pounds were used as an intestinal worm remedy in 1951.

The modern synthetic chlorinated organic insecticides DDT and benzene hexachloride were discovered in the same way that phenothiazine was discovered—that is, by screening thousands of compounds of known structure but unknown toxic value. As yet too little is known of the relationship between the chemical structure of compounds and their insecticidal value to serve as a guide to the synthesis of new insecticides. Every candidate insecticide must be tested against the insect it is designed to control.

Often compounds closely related chemically differ widely in insecticidal value. As more compounds are tested, the chemist should be able to find a relationship between the chemical structure and insecticidal value of organic compounds. Eventually he will be able to synthesize a compound for the control of a specific insect pest. Meanwhile the study of the constituents of insecticidal plants will help enlarge our knowledge of how chemical structure affects toxicity.

R. C. Roark *is in charge of the division of insecticide investigations, Bureau of Entomology and Plant Quarantine. He has been engaged in research on insecticides since 1910. He is a native of Kentucky and holds degrees from the University of Cincinnati, University of Illinois, and George Washington University. In 1948 his division received an award for Distinguished Service from the Secretary of Agriculture for chemical research that discovered new insecticidal chemicals, new means of increasing the usefulness of insecticides, new methods of chemical analysis, and new ways of applying insecticides.*

How Insecticides Are Mixed

H. L. Haller

Insecticidal chemicals have to be mixed properly before they can be used as insecticides. To use them in pure or undiluted form would often be too costly, and their physical properties—usually they are coarse or sticky solids or viscous liquids—make them unsuited for direct application. Dust diluents, solvents, and wetting, emulsifying, spreading, penetrating, sticking, and stabilizing agents are added to them.

Proper mixing of the accessory components has to take into account several factors: Whether the preparation will be applied to plants, animals, or humans; whether it will come into contact with foods or feeds; the insect to be controlled; the cost of the treatment; the ease of application; and the effect of the accessory materials on the toxicity.

For example: An oil solution would be chosen to protect a wooden post against termites because oil helps the insecticide to penetrate the post and give more than surface protection. But oils harm plants and on them water emulsions or dusts are used.

Five types of insecticide formulations are employed to control insect pests: Dusts, wettable powders, emulsions, solutions, and aerosols. Dusts are applied in hand dusters or power-driven devices; wettable powders, emulsions, and solutions are applied as sprays. Aerosols are of the liquefied gas type or smokes or mechanically generated oil clouds.

Before proceeding to consider them, let me define some terms that apply here and to other chapters in this book.

A pesticide is a substance or mixture of substances that may be used to destroy or otherwise control any unwanted form of plant or animal life. (The ending *-cide* means *killer.*)

Among the many types of pesticides are:

An *insecticide* is used against insects and their near relatives. Insecticides of more specific use are often designated by such terms as *larvicide, aphicide,* or *miticide,* which kill larvae, aphids, and mites, respectively.

A *fungicide* is used against fungi, particularly those causing diseases of plants. Some fungicides also act as insecticides.

A *herbicide* is used against plants growing as weeds. It often is called a weed killer.

A *rodenticide* is used against rodents, especially rats and mice.

Some of the terms pertaining to insecticides are:

Wettable powders are insecticidal materials manufactured into powders that can be readily mixed with water. They often contain wetting and conditioning agents.

Suspension sprays are mixtures in which the finely divided particles of powdered insecticide are dispersed in a liquid.

Emulsion concentrates are insecticidal materials manufactured into liquid concentrates so formulated that they will form an emulsion when mixed with water or another liquid.

Emulsion sprays are mixtures made with emulsion concentrates and a liquid, usually water.

Conventional or dilute sprays contain a relatively small amount of insecticide in a relatively large amount of water, such as 4 pounds per 100 gallons.

Concentrated sprays contain large amounts of insecticides in small amounts of liquid, such as 1 pound in 1 to 5 gallons.

Terms like *stomach insecticide* and *contact insecticide* indicate the way the insecticide enters the body of the insect. A stomach insecticide is eaten and swallowed. A contact insecticide enters through the skin. The terms have no significance as to how or where the materials exert their effect. Some substances can enter in only one way. Others reach the vital organs in both ways.

INSECTICIDAL DUSTS usually are made with talcs, clays, and diatomaceous earth. Sometimes finely ground plant material, such as walnut-shell flour, is used.

Diluents of dusts are classed according to whether they have low or high bulk density. By this is meant the weight of the dust occupying a definite volume. The low bulk density, or light, type is illustrated by silica gel, hydrated alumina, calcium silicate, and diatomaceous earth. Examples of the high bulk density, or heavy, type are pyrophyllite, talc, calcite, and clays. Mixtures of both types often are used to prepare products that have practical bulk-density values and will also resist caking on storage at high temperatures. The use of the heavy diluents alone may yield products that become packed or lumpy on storage.

Dusts also may be prepared by mixing a solution of the insecticidal chemical in a volatile organic solvent, such as acetone or benzene, with the dust diluent; the solvent is then allowed to evaporate, and the mixture is ground. Or a solution of the insecticide may be sprayed into the dust diluent during the mixing and grinding process. Sometimes the chemical is dissolved in a nonvolatile solvent and mixed with the diluent. When this is done, care must be taken so that the amount of the solvent used is not so great as to impair the dusting qualities of the finished dust. The concentration of the active ingredient of dusts ranges from 1 to 20 percent, depending on the insecticide and its use.

Wettable powders, which can be dispersed or suspended in water for use as sprays or dips, are made by adding wetting agents to dusts. With some kaolin types of clay as the diluent the addition of a wetting agent is unnecessary. The wetting agent may be adversely affected by the type of diluent or kind of water, such as extremely hard or highly alkaline. The amount of wetting agent must be carefully adjusted to avoid excessive run-off when the spray is applied to plants.

EMULSIONS are obtained by adding water to an emulsifiable—or emulsion—concentrate. Such concentrates are made by dissolving the insecticidal chemical and an emulsifying agent in an organic solvent. Usually the solvent is substantially insoluble in water as water-miscible solvents have not in general proved satisfactory.

Two general types of solvents have been used: (1) Solvents, such as toluene or xylene, which evaporate after spraying or dipping to leave a deposit of the toxicant; and (2) nonvolatile solvents, such as alkylated naphthalenes or a petroleum oil, which leave the treated surface coated with a solution of the toxicant in oil after the water has evaporated. Solvents such as toluene and xylene under certain conditions may constitute a fire hazard. The use of high-boiling aromatic solvents, such as the alkylated naphthalenes, may be dangerous when the emulsion is applied to animals.

Three classes of emulsifiers are generally recognized—anion-active, cation-active, and nonionic. Soap is typical of an anion-active agent. Lauryl pyridinium chloride is an example of a cation-active emulsifier. Nonionic emulsifiers, as the name implies, do not ionize. An example of a nonionic emulsifier is the reaction product obtained from 10 to 12 moles of ethylene oxide to 1 mole of dodecyl alcohol. Several hundred emulsifiers are commercially available under various trade names. No one class of emulsifiers may be said to be superior to another. The type best suited will depend on the insecticide and can only be determined by experimentation. When extremely small particle size or permanence of the emulsion is not essential, or if agitation can be maintained after the concentrate has been diluted with water, the proportion of emulsifying agent in the concentrate may be reduced considerably.

Oil solutions of insecticidal chemicals are usually made with crude or refined kerosene and other petroleum oils. The selection of a solvent depends on its ability to hold the chemical in solution at ordinary temperatures, whether it is toxic to plants, and whether it constitutes a fire hazard. Sometimes more than one solvent is used, particularly when a preferred solvent does not dissolve sufficient of the insecticidal chemical to provide a solution of the desired concentration. An example is DDT in refined kerosene. This solvent does not dissolve enough DDT to permit the preparation of a 5-percent solution. One has to add an auxiliary solvent. Auxiliary solvents dissolve larger quantities of the chemical. Cost, toxicity, and fire hazard keep them from being used as the only solvent. When a solution is made up of two solvents, one of which is a poor one and the other a good one for a particular chemical, the solubility in the mixed solvent may not equal the sum of the solubilities in the individual components. The quantity of a chemical that a solvent will dissolve varies widely with the temperature.

All in all, so many factors are involved in the formulation of insecticides that it usually behooves a person to buy the ready-to-use insecticides rather than to try to mix the chemicals himself.

H. L. HALLER *is assistant chief of the Bureau of Entomology and Plant Quarantine. His duties cover the various chemical aspects of the Bureau's problems and involve the development and use of products for the control of insect pests. He has been engaged since 1929 in studies on insecticides in the Department, which he joined in 1919 following service in the First World War. From 1923 to 1929 he was on the staff of the Rockefeller Institute for Medical Research as an associate in chemistry.*

How Insecticides Poison Insects

John J. Pratt, Jr., Frank H. Babers

Somebody has said that because insects are small an insecticide kills them all over. Our knowledge of the subject is incomplete, but it is enough to belie the statement.

Poisons affect the normal functions of specific cells and tissues of insects just as they are known to do in humans and other higher animals. Basically some chemical process in the animal is affected so as to bring about changes in its functions. Those changes are secondary to the original process that was affected and are frequently mistaken for the initial action of the poison.

A complete knowledge of the way a chemical poisons an insect would have great value in the formulation of insecticides. While preparing an insecticidal mixture, for example, we could add a substance that would help the poison reach the target—the organ or tissue it acts upon. Chemicals could be added to weaken or destroy the mechanisms that protect the insect against the poison in question. If we know how one poison acts, we could select or synthesize other chemicals of similar action. Research is giving us that knowledge so that before too long such ideals should become realities.

Insecticides have been classified according to the way they get into the insect's body cavity: Stomach poisons are eaten, contact poisons enter through the skin, and fumigants enter through the breathing tubes or the skin as gases. Some insecticides may enter by all three routes. But often such a classification is used wrongly to refer to the *mode of action* of an insecticide—an entirely different term, which means the way in which a chemical acts on an animal's system.

970134°—52——15

In studying the mode of action of an insecticide, we often rely for clues on what we know of the action of the poison on man or other higher animals. Sometimes the mode of action may be similar in vertebrates and in insects, but without experimental evidence it is unwise to assume that such a similarity exists.

The poisonous properties of the inorganic arsenic compounds (paris green, calcium and lead arsenate, sodium arsenite) are due to the formation of the water-soluble compounds, arsenious or arsenic acid, in the digestive tract.

Arsenic is considered a general protoplasmic poison; that is, it poisons the contents of all types of cells. Most tissues and organs therefore are affected in arsenic poisoning. One well-known effect of arsenic on vertebrate animals is the abrasion and destruction of the lining of the intestine. A similar destruction occurs in the mid-intestine of insects. Often it is said that such destruction is the primary reason that arsenic insecticides kill insects. If that were true, it still would not explain what biochemical process is disturbed in order to bring about destruction of the intestinal cells. Investigations with vertebrate animals have shown that arsenic poisons unidentified enzymes, which function in the metabolism of carbohydrates by cells. Probably arsenic acts on the insect system in the same manner.

Nicotine first stimulates and then depresses the nervous system of animals. Paralysis follows rapidly and results in the failure of organs to function. In insects, as in higher animals, the poisoning action of nicotine occurs in the nerve ganglia, which are clumps of nerve tissue at various places in the nervous system. Nicotine seems to have practically no effect on nerve fibers or on the junctions of nerves with muscles. The chemical process of nicotine poisoning in insects is not known.

Pyrethrum powder, the ground flowers of certain species of the chrysanthemum, contains the chemicals, pyrethrin I and II and cinerin I and II, which are the main toxic principles. The rapid paralyzing action of pyrethrum is evident to anybody who has sprayed a room with a household fly spray and watched the flies drop almost immediately to the floor. The insects recover from the paralysis, however, unless a lethal amount of the poison gets on them. Pyrethrin acts directly on the central nervous system of insects. The paralysis is a result of the blocking of transmission of nerve impulses. We know that destructive changes occur in the nervous tissue of insects poisoned with pyrethrin, but the reason for the changes is obscure.

Rotenone causes paralysis of the breathing mechanism in mammals, possibly by acting on bronchial tissues. All we know now about the method by which rotenone kills insects is that it slows the rate of heart action and breathing. The symptoms may indicate disturbances in the functions of practically any tissues so they really tell us little of the fundamental basis for rotenone poisoning.

Several theories have been advanced to explain how oils kill insects: Oils penetrate the insect's breathing tubes, thus causing suffocation; or they penetrate the tissues and poison them; or certain poisonous, volatile substances in the oils kill by penetrating the tissues as gases. None of the theories has been proved. Maybe each may have some merit, depending on the oil in question.

Nonvolatile oils (such as mineral oil) that contain no poisonous compounds might kill an insect through suffocation. For oils (such as kerosene) that contain volatile, poisonous constituents, the second and third theories might account for the killing action.

In vertebrates, such volatile petroleums as gasoline act first as stimulants then as depressants of the central nervous system. Death is due to respiratory failure if the animal is exposed to the oil for a long time. Work done by George D. Shafer many years ago at the Michigan Agricultural Experiment Station indicates that a similar action occurs in insects. E. H. Smith and G. W. Pearce of the New York State Agricultural Experiment Station demonstrated that oil does not kill eggs of the oriental fruit moth by depriving them of oxygen (suffocation). They obtained some evidence that the oil prevented unknown poisonous substances formed by the egg from passing outward through the eggshell.

The dinitrophenols are used in several phases of insect control—most commonly the sodium, calcium, and dicyclohexylamine salts of 2,4,dinitro-6-cyclohexylphenol and the sodium and calcium salts of 4,6,dinitro-*o*-cresol.

Dinitrophenol increases the metabolic rate of warm-blooded animals. Perhaps the poison acts directly on cells, causing them to increase the rate at which they use oxygen. Fat metabolism is involved because the excess oxygen is used only for burning this body food. Dinitrophenol and dinitrocresol act in the same manner on insects and raise the oxygen requirements by as much as three times the normal amount. The mechanism by which the dinitrophenols cause cells to use abnormally high amounts of oxygen has not been determined.

The characteristic tremors of DDT poisoning are symptoms of a disturbance of the nervous system.

The sensory nerves—which carry impulses to the central nervous system—are the most sensitive to DDT poisoning, the nerve ganglia the least sensitive. When DDT gets on an insect's body, it affects hundreds of sensory nerve endings. The nerves then produce impulses faster and stronger than normal. These cause the nerves responsible for moving muscles to produce the tremors typical of DDT poisoning. The capacity of the central nervous system to coordinate sensory impulses is also disrupted—as seen in the stumbling gait and general instability of the insect.

We do not know why DDT poisons nervous tissue. It has been suspected that DDT poisons the enzymes cholinesterase, which is important in the proper functioning of nerves, but considerable research has failed to show that DDT affects the enzyme. Perhaps another enzyme system in nervous tissue is involved. One theory is that DDT causes a depletion of calcium in nervous tissue, which in turn causes spontaneous activity of the nerve.

Promising leads are emerging from research on house flies that are resistant to DDT. Flies can change DDT in their bodies to a nonpoisonous substance and DDT-resistant flies can do this faster than susceptible flies can. The chemical processes involved in this breakdown of DDT are being elucidated and should tell us much about the mode of action of DDT.

Other effects of DDT on the physiology of insects include an increase in the consumption of oxygen and a decrease in the amount of stored food substances in the body. Those are probably secondary effects of DDT poisoning.

Benzene hexachloride occurs in several forms, or isomers, each of which has a slightly different molecular shape. Of the 16 possible isomers, 5 are known—the alpha, beta, gamma, delta, and epsilon. The gamma isomer, commonly called lindane, is several hundred times more toxic to insects than the others are.

In vertebrate animals, gamma benzene hexachloride causes stimulation of the central nervous system, but the beta and delta isomers cause depression. The external symptoms of poisoning in insects resemble those of DDT, except that they usually appear more rapidly. As in DDT poisoning, the tremors suggest an effect upon the nervous system, but whether the mechanism of poisoning is the same as that of DDT remains for future research to explain.

Shortly after the insecticidal properties of benzene hexachloride were discovered, it was suggested that (because of possible similarity in molecular shape) the poison might act as an antimetabolite to *meso*-inositol, one of the B vitamins—that is, it might compete with and replace *meso*-inositol in some vital physiological process. *Meso*-inositol will alleviate somewhat the poisoning of certain yeasts by gamma benzene hexachloride, but several attempts to demonstrate a similar process in insects have failed. Chemical investigations, which now indicate that *meso*-inositol and gamma benzene hexachloride do not have similar molecular shapes, may explain the failure to prove the hypothesis.

The organic phosphates—hexaethyl tetraphosphate (HETP), tetraethyl pyrophosphate (TEPP), and diethyl *p*-nitrophenyl thiophosphate (parathion)—are highly toxic to animals. In insects and in warm-blooded animals, they poison the cholinesterase.

A chemical called acetylcholine is formed in certain nerves and aids in the transmission of nerve impulses. If it is not destroyed immediately after it has served its purpose, it will continue to cause impulses to move along the nerve. The enzyme cholinesterase is always at hand to destroy the acetylcholine. The organic phosphate insecticides poison the enzyme, thus allowing the acetylcholine to accumulate, and cause uncoordinated nervous activity through the whole animal. The results are tremors, convulsions, muscle paralysis, and finally death. It is possible that the organic phosphates poison insects in other ways, but the action we described is the major one now known.

Another organic phosphorus compound that shows much promise for control of some insects and mites is schradan (octamethyl pyrophosphoramide). Many plants absorb it from the soil. Insects and mites that feed on the plant sap are poisoned. Schradan seems to have little effect on the cholinesterase system of insects; it is not particularly toxic when it is sprayed on them. But the fact that the sap of plants that have taken it up is highly poisonous to cholinesterase indicates that the mode of action is the same as that of the other phosphates—only, however, after it has been changed in some manner by plant tissue. Animal liver cells also increase the anticholinesterase activity of schradan.

Of the cyanides used in controlling insects, hydrocyanic acid, or prussic acid, is a liquid that evaporates rapidly; calcium cyanide is a solid that gives off hydrogen cyanide gas more slowly. Both are classed as fumigants because the killing action is due to gaseous hydrogen cyanide.

Hydrogen cyanide is extremely toxic and acts quickly on all animals. In warm-blooded animals it poisons the enzymes that enable cells to use the oxygen supplied to them. As all living cells require a constant supply of oxygen, the failure of the supply results in the rapid and widespread poisoning of tissues that is characteristic of cyanide. The poisoning action of cyanide on insects is probably the same, for the enzymes involved are common to practically all living cells.

Methyl bromide, also used as a fumigant, is less toxic than hydrogen cyanide, and its poisoning action is much slower.

The mode of action of methyl bromide on insects has not been studied. Research with vertebrates has yielded two opposing theories. One states that methyl bromide is changed in the animal to methyl alcohol and a harmless bromine salt. The methyl alcohol then poisons the animal. Another theory proposes that the methyl bromide is not changed in the animal but poisons as methyl bromide. Whatever the mode of action may be in vertebrates, it will probably be similar in insects, for the effects of methyl bromide seem to be common to all animals.

Ten years ago we had a dozen or so insecticides and knew little about their modes of action. Today we have several dozen new ones and know nothing of how they act. Entomologists are gradually turning from trial-and-error ways of discovering new insecticides, however. These are being replaced by research on the fundamental aspects of poisoning action. Eventually we will be able to predict whether a chemical will be poisonous and to what insects. Then we can make insecticides to suit our needs.

JOHN J. PRATT, JR., *is an entomologist in the Bureau of Entomology and Plant Quarantine. He has degrees from the University of Massachusetts, North Carolina State College, and Cornell University. During the war he served with the Army and the United States Public Health Service, and joined the Bureau of Entomology and Plant Quarantine in 1948. Dr. Pratt conducts research on the physiology of insects.*

FRANK H. BABERS, *a biochemist in the Bureau of Entomology and Plant Quarantine, has charge of research on insect physiology and the mode of action of insecticides.*

For further reading:

Dietrich Bodenstein: Investigation on the Locus of Action of DDT in Flies (Drosophila), *Biological Bulletin, volume 90, pages 148–157. 1946.*

G. J. Goble and R. L. Patton: The Mode of Toxic Action of Dinitro Compounds on the Honeybee, *Journal of Economic Entomology, volume 39, pages 177–180. 1946.*

Louis Goodman and Alfred Gilman: The Pharmacological Basis of Therapeutics, *The Macmillan Co., New York. 1941.*

Harold T. Gordon and John H. Welsh: The Role of Ions in Axon Surface Reactions to Toxic Organic Compounds, *Journal of Cellular and Comparative Physiology, volume 31, pages 395–420. 1948.*

W. M. Hoskins: Recent Contributions of Insect Physiology to Insect Toxicology and Control, *Hilgardia, volume 13, pages 307–386. 1940.*

D. D. Irish, E. M. Adams, H. C. Spencer, and V. K. Rowe: Chemical Changes of Methyl Bromide in the Animal Body in Relation to Its Physiological Effects, *Journal of Industrial Hygiene and Toxicology, volume 22, pages 408–411. 1941.*

S. Kirkwood and Paul H. Phillips: The Antiinositol Effect of γ-Hexachlorocyclohexane, *Journal of Biological Chemistry, volume 163, pages 251–254. 1946.*

Bernard P. McNamara and Stephen Krop: Observations on the Pharmacology of the Isomers of Hexachlorocyclohexane, *Journal of Pharmacology and Experimental Therapeutics, volume 92, pages 140–146. 1948.*

Robert L. Metcalf: The Mode of Action of Organic Insecticides, *National Research Council, Washington, 1948;* Studies of the Mode of Action of Parathion and Its Derivatives and Their Toxicity to Insects, *with Ralph B. March, Journal of Economic Entomology, volume 42, pages 721–728, 1949.*

W. E. Ripper, R. M. Greenslade, and L. A. Lickerish: Combined Chemical and Biological Control of Insects by Means of a Systemic Insecticide, *Nature (London), volume 163, pages 787–789. 1949.*

Kenneth D. Roeder and Elizabeth A. Weiant: The Site of Action of DDT in the Cockroach, *Science, volume 103, pages 304–307, 1946;* The Effect of DDT on Sensory and Motor Structures in the Cockroach Leg, *Journal of Cellular and Comparative Physiology, volume 32, pages 175–186, 1948.*

George D. Shafer: How Contact Insecticides Kill. I and II, *Michigan Agricultural College Technical Bulletin 11, 1911;* How Contact Insecticides Kill. III, *Technical Bulletin 21, 1915.*

E. H. Smith and G. W. Pearce: The Mode of Action of Petroleum Oils as Ovicides, *Journal of Economic Entomology, volume 41, pages 173–180. 1948.*

J. M. Tobias and J. J. Kollros: Loci of Action of DDT in the Cockroach (Periplaneta americana), *Biological Bulletin, volume 91, pages 247–255. 1946.*

G. W. van Vloten, Ch. A. Kruissink, B. Strijk, and J. M. Bijvoet: Crystal Structure of "Gammexane," *Nature (London), volume 162, page 771. 1948.*

J. Franklin Yeager and Sam C. Munson: Physiological Evidence of a Site of Action of DDT in an Insect, *Science, volume 102, pages 305–307. 1945.*

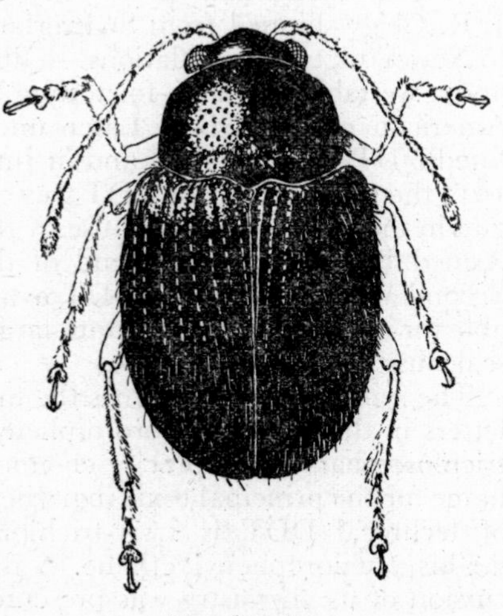

Flea beetle.

The Organic Insecticides

C. V. Bowen, S. A. Hall

The best known of the synthetic organic insecticides is DDT, but it was not the first. Some of them have been in use for decades. Carbon disulfide, *p*-dichlorobenzene, and naphthalene stand out as old-timers. Ethylene dichloride, ethylene dibromide, methyl bromide, and thiocyanates have been used for the past quarter century. Thousands of similar compounds—man-made materials whose basis is carbon—have been investigated as to insecticidal value. The Department of Agriculture in 1922 or so began a study of their use as repellents and fumigants and began later the synthesis of materials for testing as poisons for insects.

Phenothiazine, thiodiphenylamine, introduced as an insecticide in 1935, may be considered one of the early members of the newer synthetic age. It is used now to only a limited extent as a codling moth insecticide, but it is used extensively for the internal medication of livestock for the control and removal of injurious nematodes that infest cattle, horses, sheep, and goats.

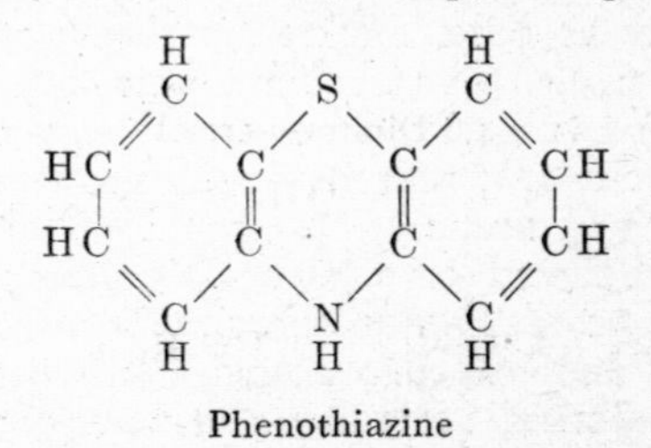

Phenothiazine

Azobenzene, an orange crystalline material, was found in 1943 to be effective as a fumigant for the control of mites in greenhouses. Because azobenzene sublimes readily, a solution containing it may be applied to steam pipes and allowed to vaporize. The development of the organic phosphorus compounds, however, has greatly lessened its use.

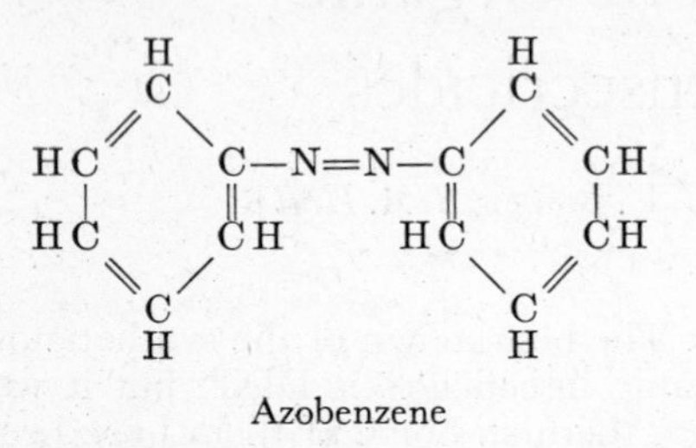

Azobenzene

A group of dinitro derivatives of phenol and cresol came into use before the Second World War as dormant sprays in apple orchards. The simplest of these, 4,6-dinitro-*o*-cresol, DNOC, formerly known as 3,5-dinitro-*o*-cresol, is a solid melting at 85.8° C. and not very soluble in water. The sodium derivative (called a salt) often is used in the dormant sprays because of its greater solubility in water. Analogs—similar substances—in which the methyl group of the cresol has been replaced by cyclohexyl or by some other group are also used. Salts other than sodium, such as the dicyclohexylamine or triethanolamine salt, are also in use.

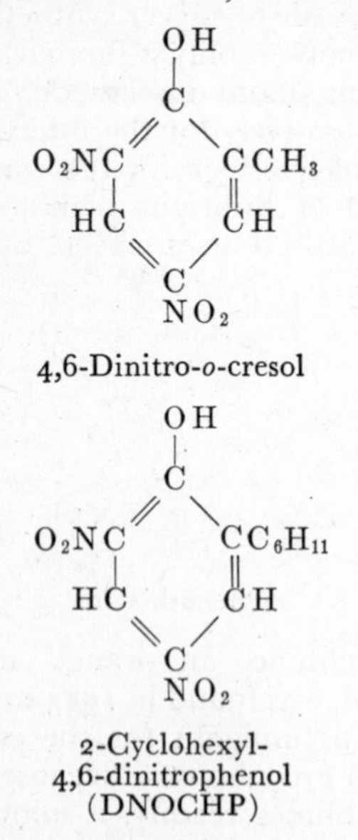

4,6-Dinitro-*o*-cresol

2-Cyclohexyl-4,6-dinitrophenol (DNOCHP)

Aliphatic, alicyclic, and aromatic esters of thiocyanic acid were used before the Second World War in household and horticultural sprays. The so-called lauryl thiocyanate is a mixture of compounds containing alkyl groups derived from the natural fatty acids of coconut oil in which the lauryl, or 12-carbon, chain predominates. Other thiocyanates used as insecticides are the 2-(2-butoxyethoxy)ethyl ester of thiocyanic acid, diethylene glycol diester of thiocyanic acid, β-thiocyanoethyl esters of aliphatic fatty acids averaging from 10 to 18 carbon atoms, and isobornyl thiocyanoacetate. Because some of them may injure growing plants, care should be exercised in using them.

In recent years a great deal has been said about chlorinated hydrocarbons as insecticides. The use of this type of compound is not new, for carbon tetrachloride and *p*-dichlorobenzene, which have been used for years, are chlorinated hydrocarbons.

DDT is a chlorinated hydrocarbon insecticide. The raw materials for its manufacture are chlorine, benzene, and alcohol. DDT was first described in 1874 by a German chemist, Othmar Zeidler, but its insecticidal value was not discovered until about 1939 by Paul Müller, in Switzerland. It was first introduced into the United States in August 1942 when the dye firm of J. R. Geigy shipped from Switzerland to New York two formulations—a dust and a wettable powder—for testing by American entomologists. Later undiluted DDT was imported, and in June 1943 the manufacture of DDT was begun in the United States for use by the Armed Forces. When the end of the Second World War made DDT available for civilian use, it came into large-scale use as an insecticide.

The symbol DDT combines the first letters in the name dichloro-diphenyl-trichloroethane. The precise chemical name for the principal toxic ingredient of technical DDT is 1,1,1-trichloro-2,2-bis(*p*-chlorophenyl)ethane. A discussion of its chemistry was presented in *Science in Farming,* the Yearbook of Agriculture for 1943–1947. DDT is unstable in the presence of alkalies and consequently is not compatible with alkaline agricultural chemicals. It is also decomposed by iron and some iron salts.

Benzene hexachloride, or 1,2,3,4,5,6-hexachlorocyclohexane (i. e., BHC, HCH, or HCCH), is a chlorinated hydrocarbon made by reacting chlorine with benzene in the presence of ultraviolet light to produce a compound with the molecular formula which the English designated as 666. The material was first made by Michael Faraday in 1825, but its insecticidal action was not known until many years later. Harry Bender, an American chemist, in a United States patent application for a method of chlorinating hydrocarbons, mentioned in 1933 that the benzene hexachlorides appeared to be good insecticides, but apparently no use was made of the idea. A. P. W. Dupire in France in 1941 applied for a French patent on the use of benzene hexachloride as an insecticide based on entomological tests conducted in 1940. In 1942 a sample of benzene hexachloride made by F. D. Leicester in England was found to be insecticidal, and the compound came into use in that country in place of derris in flea beetle powder.

Technical benzene hexachloride is made up of a mixture of isomers, compounds that are identical in chemical structure except for a difference in the orientation in space of some of the constituent atoms. F. J. D. Thomas in England in 1943 found that the insecticidal principle of technical benzene hexachloride was the gamma isomer. The isomers had been named alpha, beta, gamma, and delta in the order in which they had been isolated, alpha and beta by F. E. Matthews in 1891 and gamma and delta by T. von der Linden, a German chemist, in 1912. In 1949, the common name lindane was selected for the gamma isomer of benzene hexachloride of not less than 99 percent purity after von der Linden. The gamma isomer comprises about 12.5 percent of crude benzene hexachloride. Because of its odor and the off-flavor it imparts to certain food products, technical benzene hexachloride is limited in use. Lindane, however, is practically odorless. Investigations were started in 1947 to check its effect on the flavor of fruits, vegetables, and meats. It is a white crystalline solid, soluble in most of the common organic solvents but insoluble in water. It has some fumigant properties and is a contact and stomach poison.

In the early study of DDT, analyses of the technical material revealed 4 percent of an impurity that has insecticidal properties. The impurity was identified as 1,1-dichloro-2,2-bis(*p*-chlorophenyl)ethane, a byproduct of the reaction used in making DDT. The compound has been referred to as DDD and as TDE, from its generic names dichloro-diphenyl-dichloroethane and tetrachloro-diphenylethane. It is closely related to DDT in chemical structure and properties. It will react with alkalies and consequently should not be formulated with alkaline materials.

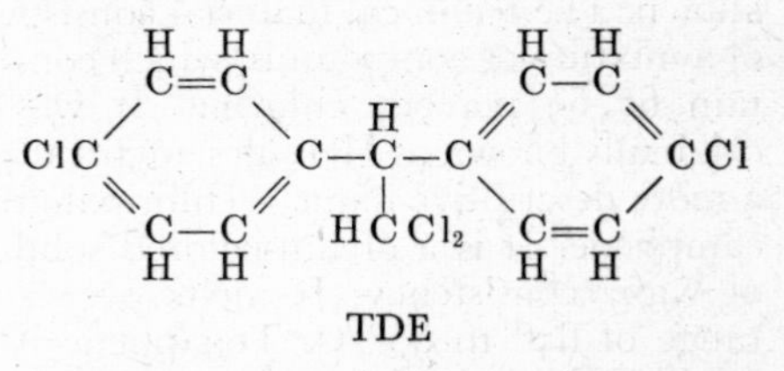

TDE

Another of the analogs of DDT has been given the common name methoxychlor because it has a formula in which two of the chlorine atoms of DDT have been replaced by the methoxy group (CH_3O–). Like DDT, technical methoxychlor (which contains about 80 percent of 1,1,1-trichloro-2-2-bis(*p*-methoxyphenyl)ethane) also is a white solid, soluble in the common organic solvents and insoluble in water. It is less effective than DDT against most insects but is less toxic to warm-blooded animals. Alkaline materials promote decomposition of methoxychlor and consequently must not be used in its formulations.

Analogs of DDT containing bromine and fluorine have been tested for insecticidal action. 2,2-Bis(*p*-bromophenyl)-1,1,1-trichloroethane sometimes has been referred to as Colorado 9. 1,1,1 - Trichloro - 2,2-bis(*p*-fluorophenyl) ethane is a constituent of an insecticide which the Germans called Gix. Although insecticidal in action, neither material has come into commercial use in the United States, probably because their cost is greater than that of DDT.

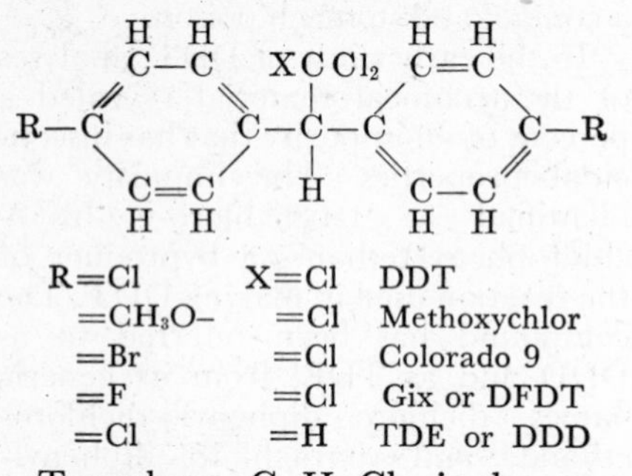

Toxaphene, $C_{10}H_{10}Cl_8$, is the common name for a product obtained by reacting chlorine with camphene. It is more complex than benzene hexachloride. Its structure is not completely known. The technical material consists of a mixture of compounds, which contain 67–69 percent chlorine. It was originally known as Hercules 3956, but a more descriptive name is chlorinated camphene. It is a cream-colored solid of waxy consistency. It melts over a range of 65° to 90° C. Toxaphene is readily soluble in the common organic solvents. Toxaphene will dehydrochlorinate in the presence of alkalies. Like DDT, it slowly splits off hydrochloric acid on heating and in the presence of materials, such as iron compounds, that may act as catalysts.

Chlordane, 1,2,4,5,6,7,8,8-octachloro-2,3,3a,4,7,7a-hexahydro-4,7 - methanoindene, formerly known as Velsicol 1068, is a chlorinated hydrocarbon obtained by subjecting two compounds called hexachlorocyclopentadiene and cyclopentadiene to a reaction of a type developed by two German chemists, Otto Diels and Kurt Alder, and treating the resulting product with chlorine. Diels and Alder received the Nobel prize in chemistry in 1950 for their work on this type of diene synthesis. Chlordane is a nearly odorless, viscous, amber-colored liquid that can be distilled only under high vacuum and is soluble in the common organic solvents. Chlordane is also a good solvent for DDT. It decomposes in the presence of alkalies with a resulting loss of insecticidal toxicity; consequently it cannot be formulated with alkaline materials.

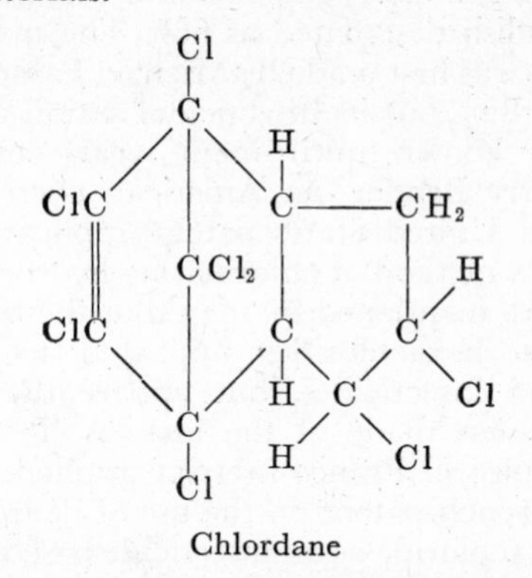

Chlordane

Two of the newer synthetic chlorinated hydrocarbons, which were known during their experimental testing period as Julius Hyman and Company Compounds 118 and 497, have been given the common names, aldrin and dieldrin, honoring Alder and Diels. Aldrin has been defined as containing not less than 95 percent of 1,2,3,4,10,10-hexachloro-1,4,4a,5,8,8a-hexahydro-1,4,5,8-dimethanonaphthalene. Dieldrin (pronounced *deel*-drin) has been defined as containing not less than 85 percent of 1,2,3,4,10,10-hexachloro-6,7-epoxy-1,4,4a,5,6,7,8,8a - octahydro - 1,4,5,8 - dimethanonaphthalene. Aldrin is a white solid with a melting point of 104°–104.5° C. It is practically odorless at room temperature, but it has a pinelike odor when warm. Dieldrin melts at 175°–176° C. and is odorless. Aldrin is soluble in the common organic solvents. Dieldrin is moderately soluble in the same solvents. Neither is soluble in water. Aldrin is stable in the presence of organic and inorganic alkalies and hydrated metallic chlorides and therefore is compatible with most agricultural chemicals.

Unlike DDT, the DDT analogs, toxaphene, and chlordane, dieldrin is unaffected by alkalies. Insecticidal effectiveness is not lost in the presence of alkaline and acid materials that would occur in formulation; thus it is compatible with most agricultural chemicals. It does react chemically with strong acids. Aldrin, with a vapor pressure approximating that of lindane, is about 20 times more volatile than dieldrin.

Because aldrin and dieldrin are highly toxic, technical products and insecticidal formulations containing them must be handled with extreme care.

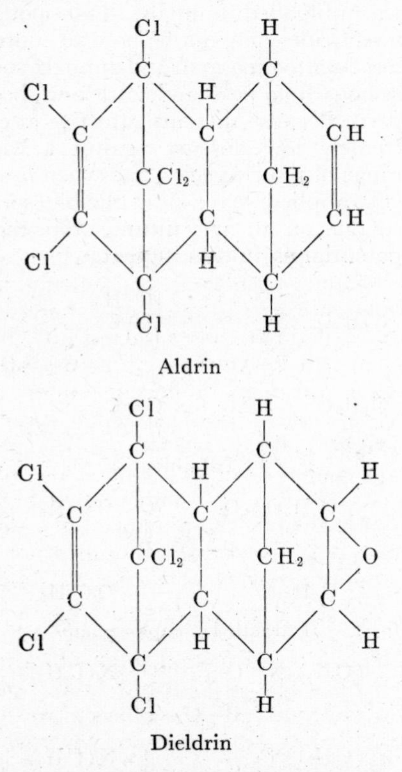

Aldrin

Dieldrin

Bis(*p*-chlorophenoxy) methane, formerly called K–1875, is a solid that melts at 68°–68.5° C. It is rather soluble in acetone, benzene, and ethyl ether. It is not appreciably soluble in ethanol and the aliphatic hydrocarbons. It is insoluble in water. It belongs to the class of compounds known as acetals and is stable to alkalies, but on boiling with dilute aqueous acids it is hydrolyzed. It is used to control mites in fruit orchards.

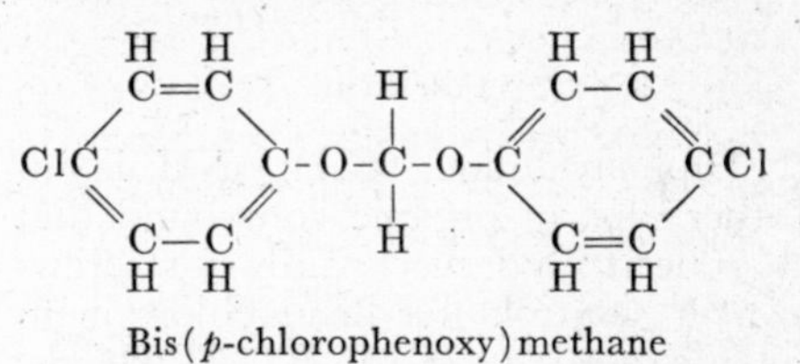

Bis(*p*-chlorophenoxy) methane

One of the new insecticides that came out of the Second World War the Germans called "Lauseto neu." It is chloromethyl *p*-chlorophenyl sulfone and is not a chlorinated hydrocarbon. It is a good insecticide but is less effective than DDT against certain strains of lice, flies, and mosquitoes.

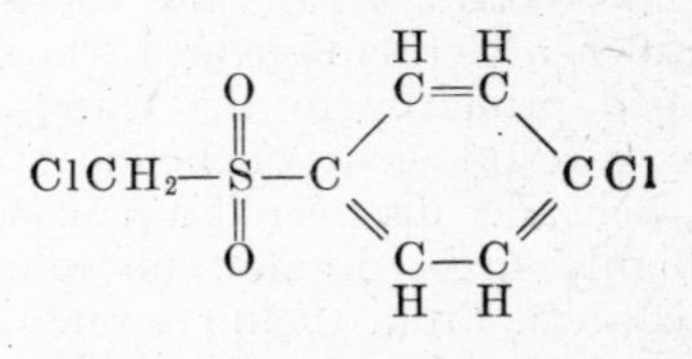

Lauseto neu

An interesting accomplishment in the preparation of synthetic organic insecticides was the synthesis of compounds that resemble the pyrethrins and cinerins, the toxic materials in pyrethrum flowers. In 1948, after 15 years of investigation of the structure of these naturally occurring insecticides, chemists of the Bureau of Entomology and Plant Quarantine prepared pyrethrin-type esters similar to cinerin I. One of these synthetic esters, the *dl*-2-allyl-4-hydroxy-3-methyl-2-cyclopenten-1-one ester of a mixture of cis and trans *dl*-chrysanthemum carboxylic acid, has been produced commercially and has been given the common name of allethrin by the Interdepartmental Committee on Pest Control. Allethrin is a light, yellow-colored oil and possesses solubilities similiar to those of the natural products so that it may be used in the same manner in fly sprays and aerosols.

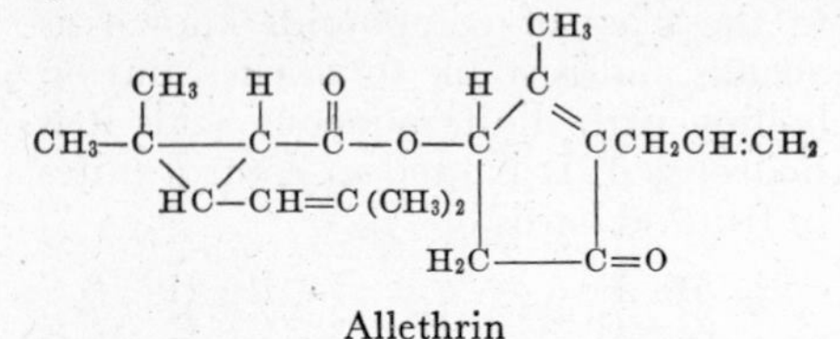

Allethrin

Diphenylamine, $(C_6H_5)_2NH$, is another type of organic compound that has been used successfully for screw-worm control. 1,1-Bis(*p*-chlorophenyl)ethanol, $(Cl_2C_6H_4)_2COHCH_3$, (also called DMC from the generic name dichlorophenyl methylcarbinol) is used against mites. Pentachlorophenol, C_6Cl_5OH, is used to control termites.

A NEW FIELD of organic phosphorus insecticides was opened up during the Second World War by Gerhard Schrader, a German chemist who was engaged primarily in the search for more powerful agents of chemical warfare. Schrader discovered a new series of highly toxic organic phosphorus compounds. From them, through extensive tests, came several effective insecticides. The list includes parathion, tetraethyl pyrophosphate (including the so-called hexaethyl tetraphosphate), and octamethyl pyrophosphoramide.

Parathion, a remarkably effective insecticide, has been put to use in many countries to control many kinds of insects infesting various crops.

Tetraethyl pyrophosphate and octamethyl pyrophosphoramide are used chiefly against aphids and some mites.

Tetraethyl pyrophosphate kills insects rapidly, almost as soon as the material is applied, and then, having performed its task, the toxic insecticide soon decomposes by hydrolysis into nontoxic and water-soluble products. Thus, there is no spray-residue problem connected with its use.

Octamethyl pyrophosphoramide has been manufactured in the United States only on a relatively small scale. British investigators have called it a systemic insecticide because, when it is applied either to the leaf or root system of a living plant, it is absorbed into the sap stream and translocated, rendering the plant insecticidal to certain insect species for several weeks. Its general use on food or fodder crops is not recommended. Experiments have indicated that it may prove useful on ornamental plants and cotton plants. Cottonseed has been soaked in a very dilute water solution of octamethyl pyrophosphoramide and then planted. The cotton seedlings that emerged were found to be insecticidal to aphids and mites for about a month. It may also be useful on sugar beets to kill aphids that carry virus yellows disease.

Because of their extreme toxicity to warm-blooded animals, these potent insecticides may not be used to control insects affecting man and animals, such as household pests and cattle and sheep pests. Because they are effective at extremely low dosages against a wide range of insect species, and when properly applied leave a negligible spray residue on an agricultural crop, their potential usefulness is great.

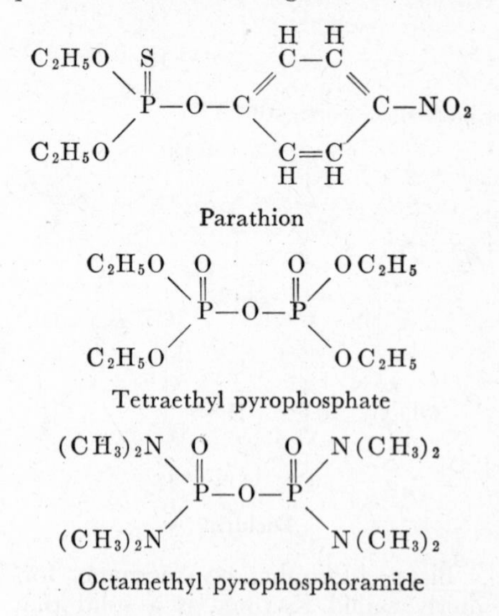

SYNTHETIC ORGANIC CHEMICALS have been used as fumigants for nearly a century. They are low-boiling compounds of rather simple structure. They include hydrocarbon derivatives that contain sulfur, oxygen, chlorine, bromine, and nitrogen. Carbon disulfide (CS_2), prepared now from sulfur and coke by heating in an electric furnace, was the pioneer. Ethylene oxide, $(CH_2)_2O$, is a gas at ordinary temperature and was proposed as a fumigant in 1928. One part is used with 10 parts of carbon dioxide to reduce the fire hazards.

Among the chlorinated hydrocarbons we find carbon tetrachloride, CCl_4, used with ethylene dichloride, $C_2H_4Cl_2$, (1:3) since 1927; propylene dichloride, $C_3H_6Cl_2$; ethylene dichloride alone; and a mixture of 1,2-dichloropropane, $C_3H_6Cl_2$, and 1,3-dichloropropylene, $C_3H_4Cl_2$, known as D-D. These materials and certain bromine compounds—methyl bromide, CH_3Br, and ethylene dibromide, $C_2H_4Br_2$—are of value against wireworms and nematodes.

Hydrocyanic acid, or hydrogen cyanide (HCN), is a highly poisonous gas used in fumigation of citrus trees as well as a space fumigant for warehouses and other enclosed places.

Some compounds of higher boiling point and more complex structure are also used as fumigants because of their high vapor pressure. Chloropicrin, Cl_3CNO_2, boils at 112.4° C. and is used as a fumigant for grain and soil. It is most effective in a mixture of 1 pound to 1 gallon of carbon tetrachloride.

Dichloroethyl ether—$(C_2H_4Cl)_2O$, bis(2-chloroethyl) ether—with a boiling point of 178.5° C. produces vapors much heavier than air and is of value as a soil fumigant.

Naphthalene, $C_{10}H_8$, is one of the older organic insecticides not obtained from plants or oil. It is a hydrocarbon obtained by the destructive distillation of coal. This flaky white solid has been used for a half century to protect woolen cloth against clothes moths. It has a fumigating action, but its objectionable odor is not easily removed from the fabric. The newer mothproofing materials do not have that disadvantage.

p-Dichlorobenzene, $C_6H_4Cl_2$, a white, odorous solid, which melts at about 53° C., has wide use for control of peach tree borers and clothes moths. It is synthesized by reacting chlorine with benzene in the presence of the proper catalysts. It is one of the best known fumigants because of its long and wide usage.

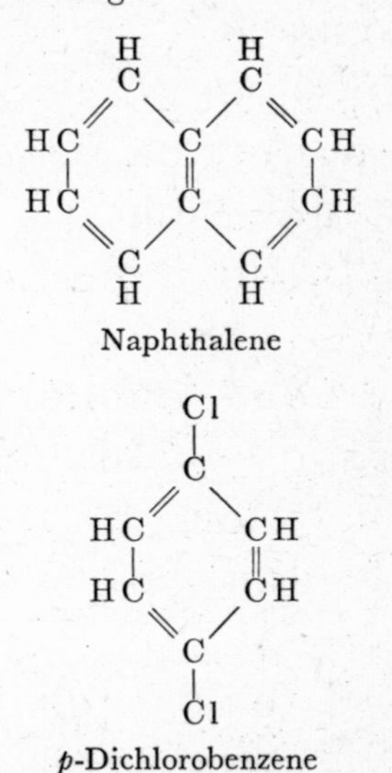

Naphthalene

p-Dichlorobenzene

A desire to find materials that would increase the toxicity and thus extend the supply of scarce insecticides, such as pyrethrum, has encouraged investigation in this field. Such materials are known as synergists. N-isobutylundecylenamide, N-isobutylhendecenamide, the first synergist developed for pyrethrum, was introduced in 1938. It may be considered a synthetic material, although castor oil is the basic material for its preparation. The value of sesame oil as a synergist for pyrethrum was discovered about the same time. Its effectiveness was shown to be due to the presence of sesamin. Knowledge of the structure of sesamin led to the synthesis of related compounds, including piperonyl cyclonene and piperonyl butoxide.

Piperonyl butoxide, also known as (butyl carbitol) (6-propylpiperonyl)

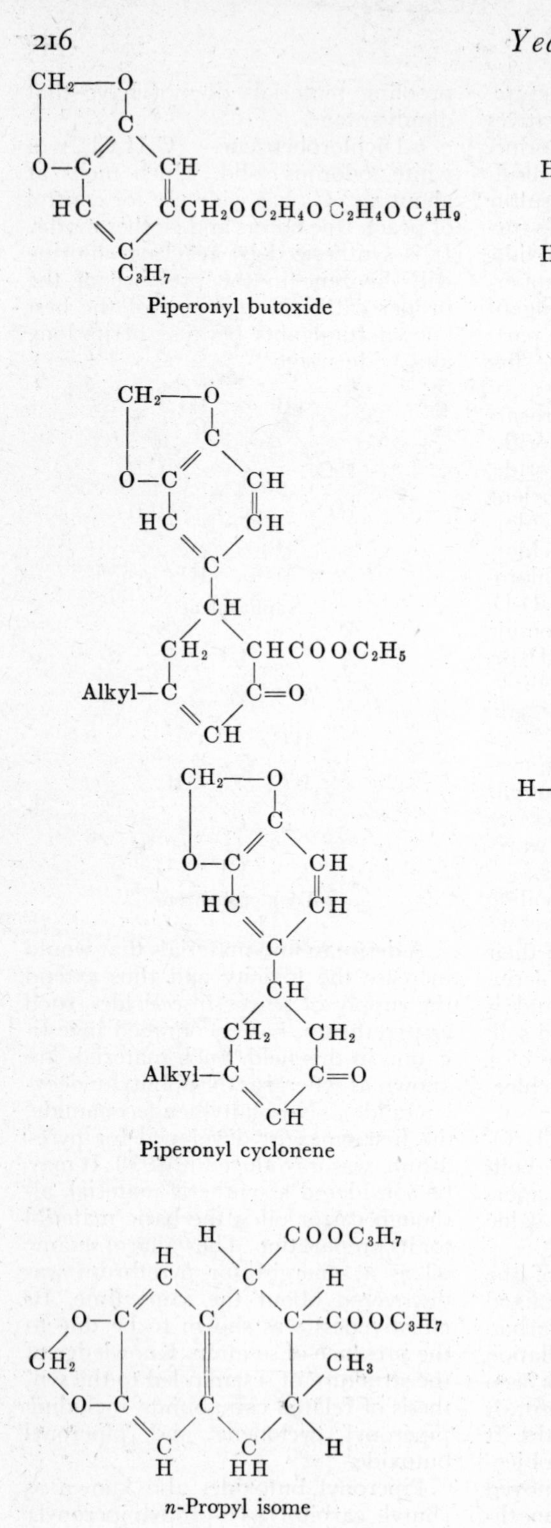

Piperonyl butoxide

Piperonyl cyclonene

n-Propyl isome

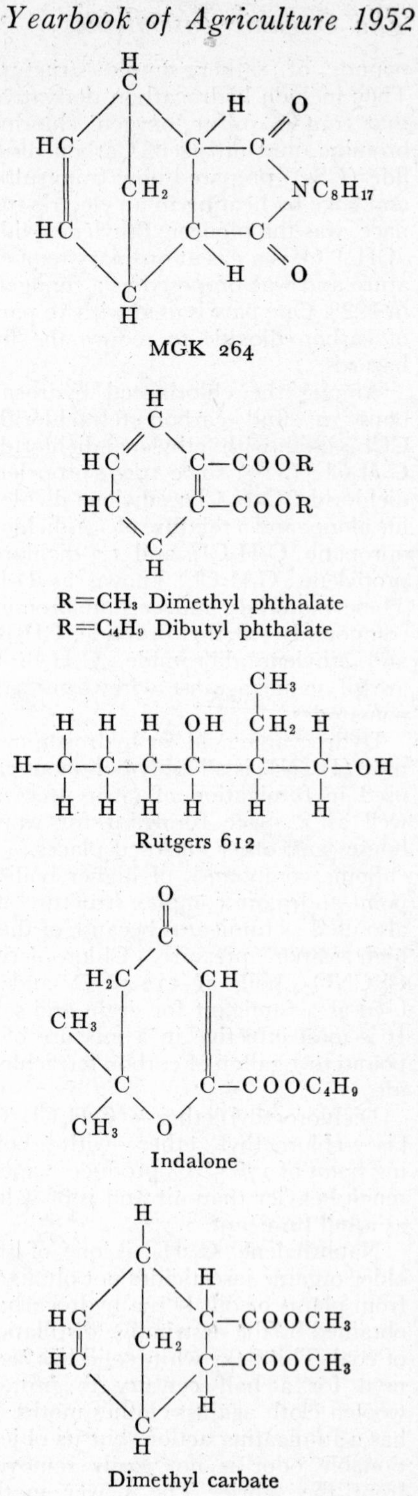

MGK 264

R=CH_3 Dimethyl phthalate
R=C_4H_9 Dibutyl phthalate

Rutgers 612

Indalone

Dimethyl carbate

ether, is a thick, viscous liquid that contains as its principal active constituent α-[2-(2-butoxyethoxy) ethoxy]-4,5-methylenedioxy-2-propyltoluene. Piperonyl cyclonene, formerly known as piperonyl cyclohexenone, is the common name for a mixture comprised of 3-alkyl-6-carbethoxy-5-(3,4-methylenedioxyphenyl)-2-cyclohexen-1-one and 3-alkyl-5-(3,4-methylenedioxyphenyl)-2-cyclohexen-1-one, in which the "alkyl" refers to aliphatic radicals that may be varied. It is a thick, viscous liquid. Another synergist for pyrethrum is *n*-propyl isome, the dipropyl ester of 1,2,3,4-tetrahydro-3-methyl-6,7-methylenedioxy-1,2-naphthalenedicarboxylic acid. Like sesamin, the three materials all contain the methylenedioxyphenyl group.

One of the later organic insecticides, N-octylbicyclo[2.2.1]-5-heptene-2,3-dicarboximide, MGK 264, was introduced as a synergist for pyrethrins but has also been found to be effective as an ovicide. It is an amber-colored and rather viscous liquid. It is slightly heavier than water. It is readily soluble in the usual organic solvents and is itself a good solvent for quite a few of the other newly discovered insecticides.

Oil of citronella, a plant product, was the standard repellent for mosquitoes before the Second World War. During the war, however, the need for repellents for chiggers, mosquitoes, and fleas instigated the testing of many synthetic organic compounds, Benzil, $C_6H_5COCOC_6H_5$, and benzyl benzoate, $C_6H_5COOCH_2C_6H_5$, were found to be repellent to chiggers; dimethyl phthalate to mosquitoes and mites; Rutgers 612 (2-ethyl-1,3-hexanediol), Indalone (often called *n*-butyl mesityl oxide oxalate but more properly the butyl ester of 3,4-dihydro-2,2-dimethyl-4-oxo-2H-pyran-6-carboxylic acid) and dimethyl carbate (the dimethyl ester of *cis*-bicyclo [2.2.1]-5-heptene-2,3-dicarboxylic acid) to mosquitoes, chiggers, and fleas. A mixture of Indalone, dimethyl phthalate, and Rutgers 612 is used as an all-purpose insect repellent.

Only a few synthetic organic compounds have been used to attract insects. Metaldehyde, $(C_2H_4O)_4$, a polymer (condensation product) of acetaldehyde, is used in baits for the control of garden snails and slugs. Isoamyl salicylate, $HOC_6H_4COOC_5H_{11}$, an ester, is used to attract tobacco hornworm moths into traps. Methyl eugenol has proved attractive to the male oriental fruit fly in tests in Hawaii. The paucity of synthetic materials used as attractants would indicate that this might be a good subject for more intensive investigation.

Besides the synthetic organic insecticides we have discussed, others of less importance are in use. Still others are in the experimental and developmental stages. The wide variety of compounds that we have considered here gives evidence that the chemistry of synthetic organic insecticides covers the entire field of organic chemistry.

C. V. Bowen, *head chemist at the Orlando, Fla., laboratory of the division of insects affecting man and animals, Bureau of Entomology and Plant Quarantine, entered Government employ in 1923 in the Insecticide and Fungicide Board. He taught chemistry at Washington and Jefferson College from 1925 until 1937, when he returned to the division of insecticide investigations. His principal interest has been in research on the preparation, analysis, and formulation of synthetic organic insecticides.*

S. A. Hall, *a chemist, began analytical work with the Treasury Department in 1934 and in 1939 transferred to the Bureau of Agricultural and Industrial Chemistry to do research on naval stores. In 1943 he joined the division of insecticide investigations, Bureau of Entomology and Plant Quarantine, at Beltsville, Md., where he first worked on DDT and the development of insect repellents.*

For further reading on organic insecticides the authors recommend:

Bureau of Entomology and Plant Quarantine publications: E–733, Results of

Screening Tests with Materials Evaluated as Insecticides, Miticides, and Repellents at the Orlando, Fla., Laboratory, April 1942 to April 1947, *1947; E–802,* A Digest of Information on Toxaphene, *by R. C. Roark. 1950.*

In Advances in Chemistry, volume 1: Organic Phosphorus Insecticides, *by S. A. Hall, pages 150–159;* Alkali-Stable Polychloro Organic Insect Toxicants, Aldrin and Dieldrin, *by R. E. Lidov, H. Bluestone, S. B. Soloway, and C. W. Kearns, pages 175–183. 1950.*

In Chemistry and Industry: The Gamma-Isomer of Hexachlorocyclohexane (Gammexane), *by R. E. Slade, volume 40, pages 314–319. 1950.*

In Science in Farming, *Yearbook of Agriculture 1943–1947:* The Chemistry of DDT, *by H. L. Haller and Ruth L. Busbey, pages 616–622;* Pests That Attack Man, *by E. F. Knipling, pages 632–642. 1947.*

N. Y. State Flower Growers Bulletin 7, Revised Recommendations for Azobenzene, *by W. E. Blauvelt, pages 15–16. 1946.*

United States Patents: 2,291,193, Insecticide, *patented by Lloyd E. Smith, July 28, 1942 (U. S. Patent Office Official Gazette, volume 540, page 827); 2,010,841,* Chlorination, *patented by Harry Bender, August 13, 1935 (volume 457, page 302).*

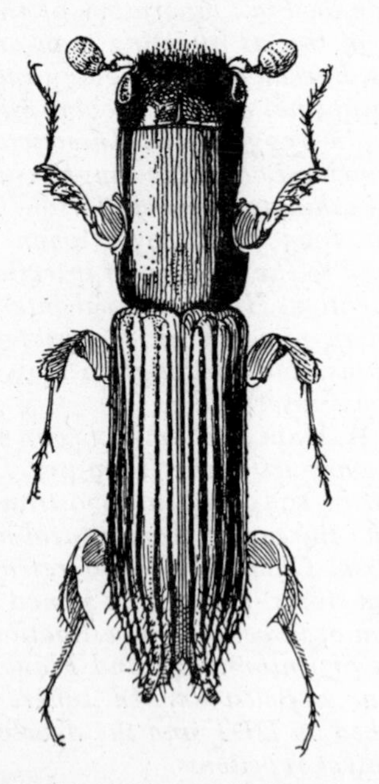

This cylindrical fungus-feeding beetle is admirably suited for living in round tunnels which it bores into forest trees for the propagation of its food.

The Inorganic Insecticides

R. H. Carter

Inorganic insecticides are of mineral origin, mainly compounds of antimony, arsenic, barium, boron, copper, fluorine, mercury, selenium, sulfur, thallium, and zinc, and elemental phosphorus and sulfur.

Antimonyl potassium tartrate, tartar emetic, $K(SbO)C_4H_4O_6.1/2H_2O$, is a white powder soluble in water. It is sometimes used as the toxic agent in ant poisons and for the control of thrips.

Arsenical compounds are the most widely used inorganic insecticides. Recommendations for their use date from 1681. They were probably used before that. The poisonous properties of arsenic trioxide were well known during the Middle Ages and it was a favorite instrument of murder as practiced by the Borgias. This knowledge of the poisonous properties of arsenic compounds probably led to their use as insecticides.

Arsenic trioxide, As_2O_3, also called arsenious oxide, is a white crystalline material sometimes referred to as white or gray arsenic. It is the starting material in the manufacture of arsenical compounds used as plant insecticides and it is sometimes used in weed killers. It is obtained from the flue dust from copper smelters. Our supply comes from domestic and foreign sources. It is sometimes used as the toxic agent in baits to control grasshoppers, cutworms, and other insects.

The calcium arsenate that is sold commercially as an insecticide is not a single chemical compound but a complex mixture of several calcium arsenates and an excess of calcium hydroxide. The material is made from arsenic trioxide by first oxidizing it to arsenic pentoxide with nitric acid and then reacting the solution of arsenic pentoxide or arsenic acid with a slurry of calcium hydroxide. The conditions of temperature, concentration, and duration of reaction are important because of their influence on the physical nature of the product. Commercial calcium arsenate generally is colored pink and is alkaline in reaction. It is a finely divided powder. It has been used extensively against certain insects affecting field crops, especially cotton. It cannot be used safely on apples, peaches, beans, and some other crops because of its burning effect on the foliage and fruit.

Calcium arsenate-calcium arsenite mixture is sold under the name london purple. It has some use for poisoning insects on cotton.

Among the insecticidal materials containing copper and arsenic, copper-aceto-arsenite (or paris green), 3 $Cu(AsO_2)_2.Cu(C_2H_3O_2)_2$, is by far the most important. It has been used as an insecticide since about 1870. For many years it was the most widely used insecticide in the United States for control of Colorado potato beetles. It has largely been supplanted by some of the newer materials, but approximately 4 million pounds are used annually by farmers and gardeners.

Copper arsenite, $Cu_3(AsO_3)_2.xH_2O$; copper meta arsenite, $Cu(AsO_3)_2$-H_2O; and basic copper arsenate, $Cu_3(AsO_4)_2.Cu(OH)_2$, have all been proposed as insecticides but have not been used to any extent. Compounds similar to paris green made from organic acids other than acetic have also been tested but have not developed into commercial use.

Several chemically different compounds are known as lead arsenate. Two of them are commonly used as insecticides. Acid lead arsenate (dilead-ortho arsenate), $PbHAsO_4$, is formed by the action of arsenic acid on litharge salt. It is a white powder, insoluble in water. Basic lead arsenate (lead hydroxy arsenate), $Pb_4(PbOH)(AsO_4)_3$, also is a white insoluble powder.

Both forms should contain very little water-soluble arsenic pentoxide in order to minimize plant damage. Generally they are much less apt to burn plant foliage than is calcium arsenate or paris green. The basic compound is safer to use on growing plants in some localities (for example, the foggy regions of California) than is the acid compound, but in general it is not so toxic to insects.

Acid lead arsenate is used extensively to control chewing insects on fruits, such as apple and pear, on flowers, trees, and shrubs, and on vegetables, such as potato and tomato. It also has extensive use in treating soil to control Japanese beetle and Asiatic garden beetle larvae and related soil-infesting forms.

A number of United States patents cover processes for the manufacture of magnesium arsenates for use as insecticides. The magnesium arsenates tested as insecticides consisted generally of the dimagnesium arsenate, $MgHAsO_4$, the trimagnesium arsenate, $Mg_3(AsO_4)_2$, or the pyroarsenate, $Mg_2As_2O_7$, with varying amounts of water of crystallization and excess magnesium oxide or hydroxide.

Magnesium arsenate has been tested against a large number of insects affecting fruits and vegetables and at one time was recommended for the control of the Mexican bean beetle, but its use has declined.

A crude manganese arsenate once was proposed as an insecticide for combatting caterpillars on tobacco because its brown color made it less conspicuous on cured tobacco leaves than the white lead arsenate.

Sodium arsenite is formed by dissolving arsenic trioxide in sodium hydroxide solution. Depending on the ratios of the reacting materials, the products range from the monosodium compound, $NaAsO_2$, to the trisodium arsenite, Na_3AsO_3. A standard formula for making so-called liquid sodium arsenite requires 4 pounds of white arsenic and 1 pound of sodium hydroxide per gallon of solution.

Sodium arsenite is not used as an insecticide on field crops because of its corrosive action. It is used as an ingredient in poison baits for grasshoppers, crickets, roaches, ants, and other insects, and in stock dips. It has been used extensively as a weed killer.

Zinc meta arsenite, $Zn(AsO_2)_2$, is formed when a soluble zinc salt is reacted with arsenious acid or white arsenic under carefully controlled conditions, as it is soluble in either acid or alkaline solutions.

Zinc arsenite is used in wood preservation but is not used in household insecticides or as a constituent of formulations to be used on field crops.

Zinc arsenate, $Zn_3(AsO_4)_2$, has been proposed in place of lead arsenate in codling moth control, principally because it avoids lead residues.

Arsenates and arsenites of many of the other elements have been investigated for insecticidal use but none has been developed into satisfactory materials. Organic arsenicals have likewise failed to find a place as insecticides.

Barium carbonate, $BaCO_3$, is a white, finely divided powder which is sometimes used as the toxic agent in rat poisons.

Borax, $Na_2B_4O_7$, and boric acid, H_3BO_3, have been used in roach powders, but more effective compounds, such as sodium fluoride, DDT, and chlordane, are available now.

Bordeaux, or bordeaux mixture, is the name applied to the compounds formed by reacting dilute solutions of copper sulfate with calcium hydroxide suspensions. If equivalent amounts of the two materials are used, an intimate mixture of the copper hydroxide, $Cu(OH)_2$, and calcium sulfate, $CaSO_4$, is formed. This suspension has a blue color and leaves a bluish-white deposit on sprayed surfaces.

Bordeaux mixture is primarily a fungicide but is often used in connection with insecticides such as nicotine, lead arsenate, and calcium arsenate. It is sometimes used to control the potato leafhopper and as a repellent for flea beetles on various vegetables and flowering plants. It is sometimes used also as an emulsifier for lubricating-oil sprays applied to fruit trees, such as apple, pear, quince, and peach, when they are dormant.

Several other copper compounds, including the oxide, oxychloride, phosphate, quinolinolate, silicate, basic sulfate, and cyanide are used as spray materials. They have little insecticidal value but are potent fungicides.

Hydrated lime, or calcium hydroxide $Ca(OH)_2$, is used in the manufacture of lime-sulfur, calcium arsenate, and bordeaux mixture. When limestone, $CaCO_3$, is heated, the carbon dioxide is driven off, leaving the product known as quicklime, CaO. When quicklime reacts with water, heat is evolved and the resulting product is hydrated lime, $Ca(OH)_2$. Hydrated lime is not primarily an insecticide but is used as a safener with some of the arsenical sprays.

Calcium cynanide, $Ca(CN)_2$, reacts slowly with moisture in the air to liberate hydrocyanic acid gas, a highly toxic organic compound used as an insecticidal fumigant.

Compounds that contain fluorine have been in use as insecticides since about 1890. Barium fluosilicate, $BaSiF_6$, a white, finely divided powder, has been tested extensively as a substitute for arsenicals in the control of fruit and vegetable crop insects. It has some value in the control of flea beetles, blister beetles, Mexican bean beetle, and others.

Cryolite, or sodium fluoaluminate, Na_3AlF_6, is a white crystalline material. Natural cryolite (ice-stone) is mined in Greenland and imported into this country. Synthetic cryolite, of similar composition, has been manufactured and sold for insecticidal use. For most uses there is little difference in their effectiveness. Large quantities have been used on codling moth in the Pacific Northwest and on the tomato pinworm, tomato fruitworm, lima-bean pod borer, corn earworm, Mexican bean beetle, walnut husk fly, pepper weevil, cabbage caterpillars, blister beetles, and flea beetles. It is generally used as a spray but may be diluted with talc, pyrophyllite, or other diluents to form a dust.

Sodium fluoride, NaF, is a white powder. Sometimes it is colored green or blue so it will not be mistaken for baking soda. It is used extensively as a roach powder and is effective against chicken and animal lice of various kinds. It causes serious damage on plants.

Sodium fluosilicate, Na_2SiF_6, is a white crystalline powder much less soluble than sodium fluoride in water. It has been used as a dust and spray in the control of some insects on field crops, as a poison in cutworm, mole cricket, and grasshopper baits and is effective as a mothproofing agent for woolen fabrics. A large number of fluorine compounds, both inorganic and organic, have been patented for use as mothproofing agents.

Some compounds of mercury are used as insecticides. Mercuric chloride (corrosive sublimate), $HgCl_2$, and mercurous chloride (calomel), HgCl, are used against fungus gnats, earthworms, cabbage maggots, and onion maggots. Mercuric chloride is also used for the treatment of dormant gladiolus corms and as a fungicide and germicide. Formulations containing mercury compounds are sometimes used to control insects affecting man and animals.

Pastes containing elemental phosphorus are made by grinding yellow phosphorus in the presence of water and then mixing with flour. Glycerin is sometimes used as an ingredient. Such pastes are effective against the American cockroach.

Selenium compounds have been tested as insecticides, but because of their toxicity to man their use is not recommended on crops intended for human or animal consumption.

Sodium selenate, Na_2SeO_4, is a water-soluble salt. Plants can take it up from the soil in sufficient amounts to kill aphids feeding on the plants. A product containing selenium and sulfur of the formula $(KNH_4S)_5Se$ has been used in the Pacific Northwest to combat mites on apples and grapes.

The use of elemental sulfur and alkaline sulfides as insecticides and fungicides on field crops and in greenhouses dates back many years. The materials are elemental sulfur, sulfides, polysulfides or salts of some of the oxygen acids of sulfur. Elemental sulfur is used alone as a dust or in combination with other insecticides with many of which it is compatible. The sulfur is reduced to a very fine state of subdivision by grinding, precipitation, or sublimation.

Dusting sulfur, or conditioned sulfur, is finely divided elemental sulfur made into a free-flowing powder by the admixture of 1 to 5 percent of clay, talc, gypsum, tri-calcium phosphate, or similar materials. Flotation sulfur, colloidal sulfur, and precipitated sulfur refer to finely divided sulfur formed as a result of chemical reactions of sulfur-containing compounds with other compounds. Wettable sulfur is finely divided sulfur that has been treated with wetting agents of various kinds to render it wettable by water and thus susceptible to suspension in spray formulations. The alkaline sulfides and polysulfides, sometimes referred to as soluble sulfurs, are prepared by the reduction of the salts of some of the oxygen acids of sulfur or by the action of alkaline solutions on elemental sulfur. The most important compounds of this class are the polysulfides of calcium, ammonium, barium, and sodium.

Calcium monosulfide, CaS, has been used to a limited extent. It is formed by the reduction of calcium sulfate. Liquid lime-sulfur or calcium polysulfide, CaS_x, is formed by the reactions between calcium hydroxide and elemental sulfur when they are boiled together in water. It is assumed to contain a mixture of the sulfides up to and including the pentasulfide, CaS_5. The theoretical reaction between 3 moles of hydrated lime, $Ca(OH)_2$, and 12 moles of sulfur results in the formation of 2 moles of calcium pentasulfide, CaS_5, 1 mole of calcium thiosulfate, CaS_2O_3, and 3 moles of water, H_2O.

970134°—52——16

Dry lime-sulfur is made by adding a stabilizer such as cane sugar to liquid lime-sulfur and evaporating to dryness. Self-boiled lime-sulfur is made by utilizing the heat of hydration or slaking of quicklime, CaO, to carry on the reactions with sulfur.

Ammonium polysulfide and sodium polysulfide are made by passing hydrogen sulfide gas, H_2S, into ammonium or sodium hydroxide containing excess sulfur. It is supposed that the chemical reactions are similar to those taking place in the preparation of lime-sulfur.

Sulfur is used under some conditions for the control of potato leafhopper, the cotton fleahopper, tomato psyllid, mites, and plant bugs.

Organic sulfur compounds, including thiocyanates, xanthates, and thiuram disulfides, have some insecticidal properties although they are used largely as fungicides.

Sulfur dioxide, SO_2, made by burning sulfur, is sometimes used to kill insects in closed spaces.

Thallium sulfate, Tl_2SO_4, sometimes is used as the toxic agent in ant poisons.

Several zinc compounds are in limited use as insecticides. Zinc sulfate, $ZnSO_4$, is sometimes used in place of copper sulfate in reactions with hydrated lime to form a zinc bordeaux mixture that has special uses. Zinc chloride, $ZnCl_2$, is used to protect against termites.

R. H. Carter *is a chemist in the Bureau of Entomology and Plant Quarantine, assigned to the division of insecticide investigations at the Agricultural Research Center at Beltsville, Md. After graduation from Morningside College and the State University of Iowa, he was employed in chemical research in the Chemical Warfare Service for 10 years. Since joining the Department of Agriculture in 1927, he has been engaged in research in the development of insecticides, investigations of spray residue problems, and toxicological investigations of the effects of insecticide materials on farm animals.*

Insecticides From Plants

Louis Feinstein

More than 2,000 species of plants are said to have some value as insect killers. They belong to 170-odd families. Commercial insecticides of plant origin are found in five families: Nicotine in the Solanaceae family; pyrethrum in Compositae; derris, cube, and timbo in Leguminosae; hellebore in Liliaceae; and anabasine in Chenopodiaceae. Anabasine is also found in Solanaceae.

Who first discovered the insecticidal value of plants is not known. The Romans divided poisons into three groups, animal, plant, and mineral. They used two species of false hellebore in medicines and in rat and mice powders and insecticides. The Chinese discovered the insecticidal value of derris.

Chemists in the Bureau of Entomology and Plant Quarantine since 1927 have conducted research on the principal insecticides of plant origin, such as nicotine, nornicotine, anabasine, rotenone, deguelin and related rotenoids, quassin, and the pyrethrins. They also have worked on more than 450 plants in an effort to discover new sources of these and other insecticides, as well as attractants, repellents, and adjuvants. They have learned that many of the species in the 170 families do not warrant further investigation and that botanical classification is not a dependable guide in the search for insecticidal plants.

Plant insecticides are only a small fraction of the insecticidal material used each year. Yet in the development of new insecticides they deserve careful consideration: Often they are highly effective against many insect enemies that are not successfully controlled by inorganic insecticides. The plant insecticides often are relatively nontoxic to man and other plants. Poisonous spray residues on fruits and vegetables may menace public health. The relative safety of plant insecticides to man helps to maintain their continued use.

In this article I discuss the commercial plant insecticides and other plants that appear promising as insecticides. Included here are plants only of the higher orders (phanerogams). They are listed alphabetically according to plant family and genus. The plants are sufficiently promising to warrant intensive chemical and toxicological studies.

The lower orders of plants (cryptogams) include the algae, fungi, mosses, ferns, and horsetails. A more complete study of them may also prove to be worth while.

Aesculaceae (*Horsechestnut Family*). *Aesculus californica* is called the California buckeye. The horsechestnut is a highly prized street and lawn shrub and tree. The common horsechestnut casts the densest shade of almost any cultivated tree. George H. Vansell and his coworkers in California found that bees feeding on buckeye blossoms became paralyzed and died. Reports of other investigators, however, show that the insecticidal value of species of the horsechestnut family varies.

Annonaceae (*Custard-Apple Family*). The genus *Annona* includes some 90 species of trees and shrubs, mainly in tropical America. S. H. Harper, C. Potter, and E. M. Gillham in England extracted *Annona reticulata* and *A. squamosa* seeds and roots with ether. The petroleum ether solution of this extract at 0° C. precipitated out an insecticidal material that was 50 to 100 times more potent than the original ether extract. Against some insects the concentrate had about the same toxicity as rotenone. More work should be done with the custard-apple.

Apocynaceae (*Dogbane Family*). *Haplophyton cimicidum*, the cockroach plant, has been used to combat cockroaches, flies, mosquitoes, fleas, lice, and other insects in Mexico. The dried leaves are toxic to the Mexican fruit fly. The water extract of the stems of plants grown in Arizona is toxic to adult house flies. The crude alkaloid from this plant is effective against most insects. It is as toxic as pyrethrum to the squash bug.

Boraginaceae (*Borage Family*). *Heliotropium peruvianum*. The borage family contains many well-known garden plants and often is called the heliotrope family. The compound heliotropine was one of the best chemicals tested against the body louse, being apparently nontoxic to the skin and lasting more than 168 hours when used in cocoa butter.

Tournefortia hirsutissima is used as a general insecticide in Haiti.

Cannaceae (*Canna Family*). Members of this family mostly have tuberous rootstocks, stately, broad leaves, and showy flowers. The leaves and stems of canna plants contain an insecticide that gives results similar to tobacco in greenhouse fumigation.

Celastraceae (*Staff-Tree Family*). *Tripterygium wilfordii*, the thunder-god vine, is a common insecticidal plant in southern China. The poison in it has been found in the root bark. Its chemistry has been investigated by M. Beroza, who reported that wilfordine is a mixture composed mainly of two similar alkaloids, α- and β-wilfordine. Both are insecticidally active ester alkaloids. Powdered fresh small roots are toxic to first-stage larvae of the codling moth, the diamondback moth, and the imported cabbageworm. Alcoholic extracts of the roots are more toxic. Small roots, powdered, are about half as toxic as pyrethrum to the American cockroach. The large and medium roots are nontoxic.

Chenopodiaceae (*Goosefoot Family*). *Anabasis aphylla* contains the alkaloid anabasine, closely related to nicotine. It is the only commercial source for the alkaloid. It grows mainly in Russia and is not available in the United States. *Anabasis aphylla* is related to the American tumbleweed. In this country my coworkers and I extracted anabasine from *Nicotiana glauca*.

Clusiaceae (*Balsam Tree Family*). *Mammea americana* is known as mamey, "mamey de Santo Domingo." Harold K. Plank of the Federal Experiment Station at Mayaguez, P. R., believes that this indigenous West Indian tree has greater insecticidal potentialities than any other plant he examined. The active principle in the mature seeds, the most toxic part, is a type of substance somewhat similar in composition and effect to pyrethrins. Plank found that six of the nine parts of the plant were appreciably or highly toxic to one or more insects. The bark has little toxic material.

Cochlospermaceae. Cochlospermum gossypium. Kutira gum increases the effectiveness of nicotine sulfate sprays. The kutira appears to be a synergist to nicotine sulfate in its action against the bean aphid.

Compositae (*Thistle or Aster Family*). This large family of plants includes thousands of herbs, vines, trees, and shrubs. The dahlia, chrysanthemum, coreopsis, marigold, aster, cosmos, and many other garden flowers are composites. To the dried flowers of *Chrysanthemum cinerariaefolium* the name pyrethrum is applied. Pyrethrum, a safe and effective insecticide, is widely used in household sprays. Four compounds exist in pyrethrum—pyrethrins I and II and cinerins I and II. Pyrethrins are practically nontoxic to warm-blooded animals and can be safely used in the home.

Heliopsis scabra is called oxeye. M. Jacobson, at the Agricultural Research Center, discovered that these plants contain compounds toxic to the house fly. Nearly all the toxic material is extracted by petroleum ether. Jacobson purified the petroleum ether extract and named one of the toxic materials scabrin. W. A. Gersdorff and N. Mitlin, entomologists in the Department of Agriculture, reported that scabrin compares well with pyrethrum in killing value.

Cucurbitaceae (*Gourd Family*). The cucumber family is often called the gourd, melon, or squash family. *Cucurbita pepo* commonly is called pumpkin. Freshly cut pumpkin leaves rubbed on cattle and horses reputedly repel flies. Acetone extracts of pumpkin seeds killed mosquito larvae in experiments conducted by A. Hartzell and F. Wilcoxon of Boyce Thompson Institute.

Euphorbiaceae (*Spurge Family*). *Croton tiglium* contains croton oil. The plant is cultivated in China, where the seeds are the source of a homemade insecticide. The plant has insecticidal value against aphids. J. R. Spies, a chemist in the Department of Agriculture, reported that an acetone extract of the seeds was more toxic to goldfish than derris extract and that croton resin was more toxic than rotenone.

Ricinus communis, the castor-bean plant, is said to have some insecticidal value. If that is true, the insecticidal principle is present only under certain conditions with respect to variety, cultural practice, and environment. A valuable synergist is prepared from isobutylamine and undecylenic acid, which results from the chemical decomposition by heat of castor oil. By the action of sulfuric acid on castor oil, we get a useful emulsifier for insecticidal oils.

Flacourtiaceae. Ryania speciosa. The active principles of the plant are alkaloids and are effective in the control of the European corn borer. The roots and stems contain the insecticide, which is commercially prepared for use as dusts and sprays.

Fagaceae (*Beech Family*). *Castanea dentata* is called the American chestnut. F. W. Metzger and D. H. Grant found that a commercial dyeing and tanning extract of the American chestnut was a good repellent against the Japanese beetle.

Labiatae (*Mint Family*). *Ocimum basilicum* is known as common basil or sweet basil. Its oil killed 95 percent of the mosquito larvae tested at a concentration of 50 parts per million, but an extract made from the whole plant killed none. H. D. Hively obtained a patent in 1940 for the use of the plant as an insecticide. It is successful as a contact poison against flies, Colorado potato beetles, and many other insects.

Salvia officinalis, or garden sage. Salvias are grown for their flowers and for their leaves. The leaves of some species are used for seasoning. Hartzell and Wilcoxon found that acetone extracts of the leaves killed 80 percent and extracts of the roots killed 95 percent of the mosquito larvae they tested.

Leguminosae (*Pea Family*). The pea family is one of the most important group of garden plants in the world. *Haematoxylon campechianum* is called logwood. Hematoxylon is from the Greek for blood and wood, in allusion to the red wood. Metzger and Grant reported that two commercial extracts were good repellents against the Japanese beetle.

Millettia pachycarpa, fish-poison climber, is worth further investigation. The ground seeds kill several species of insects. Alcoholic extracts of the roots from China paralyze the bean aphid. The plant contains a large amount of saponin and rotenone. The plant acts as a contact and stomach poison when it is mixed with soap.

Mundulea sericea, or *M. suberosa,* is a promising insecticidal plant. It was discovered in the 1930's. It is a rotenone-yielding species. The plants from India are toxic, but those from various locations in Tanganyika and Zanzibar fall into two main divisions, those with smooth barks, which are toxic, and those with rough, corky barks, which are nontoxic.

Pachyrhizus erosus, or the yam bean. In some tropical countries the seeds of the yam bean plant are used as an insecticide and fish poison. Tests in the United States by R. Hansberry and C. Lee gave promising results against the bean aphid and the Mexican bean beetle.

Tephrosia virginiana is known as devils-shoestring. It is a pretty little native plant, which prefers dry, open, somewhat sandy places. It has long been known to possess insecticidal properties. The most toxic samples of devils-shoestring were slightly more poisonous than pyrethrum, but less poisonous than derris. Against five species of insects the plants showed promise as a contact spray. Technical Bulletin No. 595 of the Department of Agriculture outlines studies of the possibilities of devils-shoestring as a commercial source of insecticides.

Liliaceae (*Lily Family*). The foliage and rootstock of most species contain a poisonous juice. *Amianthium muscaetoxicum,* crowpoison, shows promise as an insecticide against the house fly, cockroaches, grasshoppers, and bees. It is inefficient against tent caterpillars and aphids. The powdered bulbs and leaves are used as dusts. Water extracts show a slow but considerable insecticidal effect against Colorado potato beetle larvae and cockroaches.

Melanthium virginicum, bunchflower. L. H. Pammel in 1911 stated that the bunchflower had long been used to poison flies.

Schoenocaulon officinale is commonly known as sabadilla. R. J. Dicke in a thesis submitted to the University of Wisconsin in 1943 reviewed 76 references on this plant, which has been used as an insecticide since the sixteenth century. The University of Wisconsin has patented a method for increasing the toxicity of sabadilla: Heating the powdered seed in kerosene or other solvent to 150° C. for 1 hour. Sabadilla is effective against squash bugs, chinch bugs, harlequin bugs, and lygus bugs. Scientists in the Department of Agriculture in 1949 began a chemical study of the constituents of sabadilla seed.

Veratrum. Three plants are popularly called hellebore—*Veratrum album, V. viride,* and *Helleborus niger.* The term hellebore is incorrect when it is applied to the first two plants. The last, which is the true hellebore, grows in Europe and is not a commercial product in the United States. *V. viride* is the American plant. Powdered roots of the first two plants prevent the emergence of house flies from horse manure.

Veratrum viride is often called

American false-hellebore, swamp hellebore, Indian poke, and itchweed in the United States. Its active principles are alkaloids, which are toxic to man. Its value as an insecticide for the control of chewing insects on ripening fruit is due to its rapid loss of toxicity on exposure to light and air.

Meliaceae (*Mahogany Family*). *Melia azedarach* is called chinaberry. Water extracts of the berries affect cockroaches slightly but are more toxic against honey bees. Leaves applied to the soil greatly reduce attacks of termites. An alkaline extract of the fruits is effective against aphids. Cultivated plants sprayed with extracts of the chinaberry leaves are not touched by locusts. The active principle is soluble in hot water, alcohol, chloroform, or benzene but not in petroleum ether.

Myrtaceae (*Myrtle Family*). *Pimenta racemosa* is the bay-rum tree. The oil of the leaves is toxic to mosquito larvae. Bay rum has been used in Venezuela to kill insects. A foreign patent covers its use in a mixture of several substances. Applied to summer garments, it protects the wearer against gnats. Effective as baits to attract Japanese beetles are 90 parts of geraniol and 10 parts of the leaf oil of a *Pimenta* species, or 90 parts of anethole and 10 parts of the oil.

Pedaliaceae. Sesamum inducum, sesame. The seeds yield sesame oil, which contains sesamin, a powerful synergist for pyrethrum. In the Second World War the Armed Forces used more than 40 million aerosol bombs containing pyrethrum, liquefied gas, and sesame oil. The later bombs used 8 percent of the oil in the formula. Sesame oil also acts as a synergist for rotenone.

Ranunculaceae (*Crowfoot Family*). *Delphinium consolida* is called field larkspur. The oil from larkspur seed tested as a contact spray (2-percent emulsion) was effective against spider mites and aphids but had little value against some other insects. The alkaloids of this plant were also effective against insects in various degrees.

Rutaceae (*Rue Family*). *Phellodendron amurense,* the Amur corktree, is native to several Asiatic countries and was introduced into the United States in 1856. The unsaponifiable portion of the oil of the fruit is toxic to house flies in acetone solution but not in high-boiling kerosene. The residue of the fruit, the oil having been removed, is toxic to mosquito larvae, house flies, and larvae of codling moth. The material is a fast-acting poison like pyrethrum and nicotine.

Zanthoxylum clavaherculis, the southern prickly-ash, contains asarinin, a compound structurally related to sesamin and, like it, a good synergist for pyrethrum against house flies. The southern prickly-ash also contains herculin, a pungent substance highly toxic to house flies. It is closely related to several other isobutylamides previously isolated from plant materials. A trace of the active material, when placed on the tongue, produces an intense burning, paralytic effect on the tongue and on the mucous membranes of the lips and mouth. Herculin has approximately the same order of paralyzing action and toxicity to house flies as the pyrethrins.

Sapindaceae (*Soapberry Family*). *Sapindus marginatus.* This tree, up to 30 feet high, is native in Florida. It is planted occasionally for interest or ornament. The word sapindus comes from the Latin for soap, combined with Indian, in allusion to the Indians' use of the berries for soap; the pulp lathers easily like soap. S. L. Hoover obtained a patent for the use of the berries of the tree as an insecticide or insectifuge. Three berries protected a bushel of wheat against infestation. In powdered or liquid form and mixed with dried foodstuffs, it repelled weevils and other insects.

Simarubaceae (*Ailanthus or Quassia Family*). This tree stands smoke and city conditions well, but the male flowers have a strong odor, which is offensive to some persons. The bark and wood contain insecticidal principles, which are used on only a few crops.

Solanaceae (*Nightshade or Potato Family*). The potato family, often called the tobacco or tomato family, includes vegetables of world-wide cultivation, narcotics, drugs, tobacco, and a large number of garden flowers. *Duboisia hopwoodii,* called pituri, is an Australian species and often is mentioned in discussions of nicotine. C. V. Bowen, a chemist in the Department of Agriculture, analyzed the dried leaves and larger stems and found the leaves to contain 3.3 percent and the larger stems 0.5 percent of nornicotine. H. H. Smith and C. R. Smith of the Department studied 29 wild species of *Nicotiana.* They found that 5 species contained the alkaloid nornicotine only and 18 a mixture of nornicotine and nicotine. Against some insects, nornicotine is superior to nicotine. Nornicotine is more toxic to a nasturtium aphid and the pea aphid; about equally toxic to the cabbage aphid, the citrus red mite, and other spider mites; but less toxic to the celery leaf tier, the large milkweed bug, and larvae of codling moth.

Nicandra physalodes is also known as the Peruvian groundcherry or shoo-fly plant. It repels insects. In India it is used as an insecticide. Stories told about it are many: The plant distributed around a room repels flies; in a greenhouse it causes the whitefly to disappear; a few hundred planted near a barn apparently keep the animals from being bothered by flies.

Physalis mollis is commonly known as smooth groundcherry. Thomas A. Nuttall described it in 1834. It grows throughout Oklahoma. Before the development of prepared fly sprays, the fresh plant was used to control house flies. The bruised leaves and stems, mixed with a little water and sugar, killed flies. L. E. Harris of Ohio State University isolated a glycoside in an impure form; it was toxic to flies. He also isolated an alkaloid, but it was not toxic to flies in the small dosage used.

Nicotiana glauca, tree tobacco, is a wild, fast-growing plant in Texas, Arizona, and California. Patrick J. Hannan and I were granted patents covering two methods useful in extracting the alkaloids from *Nicotiana* species, including the alkaloid anabasine from *Nicotiana glauca.* Anabasine is a liquid alkaloid that closely resembles nicotine in its physical, chemical, toxicological, and insecticidal properties. It has been reported to be four or five times as toxic as nicotine to certain aphids of economic importance.

Nicotiana spp. Tobacco and its chief alkaloid, nicotine, have been used since 1690 as insecticides. Nicotine forms salts with acids and most of the nicotine used for insecticidal purposes in the United States is in the form of the sulfate. More than 29 species of *Nicotiana* have been analyzed for their alkaloid content. Some American tobaccos used in making cigars of low nicotine content contain as much as 0.7 percent of nornicotine. One-eighth of the total alkaloids in certain samples of commercial nicotine sulfate solutions was nornicotine. Most species of aphids may be controlled with concentrations of 1 part nicotine to 1,000 parts of water. Nicotine is recommended against only those insects that have soft bodies and those that are minute in size, such as aphids, whiteflies, leafhoppers, psyllids, thrips, spider mites, and some external parasites on animals.

Stemonaceae. Stemona tuberosa, or paipu, has long been known and used in China as an insecticide. Decoctions of the dried roots are said to be toxic to crickets, weevils, and the caterpillars of moths and butterflies. A 50-percent alcoholic extract of the plant is effective against lice and fleas.

Umbelliferae (*Carrot Family*). *Carum carvi* is called caraway and contains oil of caraway, which will help cure scaly-leg of poultry. Hartzell and Wilcoxon found that acetone extracts of the seed killed 90 percent of the mosquito larvae they tested.

Conium maculatum, poison hemlock, contains an alkaloid, coniine, which is related to nicotine.

Coriandum sativum, or coriander, contains an oil that repels screwworms. Applied in a 2-percent oil emulsion spray, it kills spider mites and cotton aphids. Coriander oil repels house flies, green bottle flies (*Lucilia sericata*), and black blow flies.

Pimpinella anisum is anise. Clothing treated with a soapy emulsion of anise oil protects wearers from the sting of gnats. Anise oil repels black blow flies, house flies, and green bottle flies.

Vitaceae (*Grape Family*). *Parthenocissus quinquefolia,* or Virginia creeper. An old reference to it states that a bunch of leaves rubbed on an infested area of an apple tree and crushing all the woolly apple aphids, made the tree entirely free of aphids a week later. Formerly the tree could not be kept free of aphids for any length of time.

THE PLANT WORLD contains many interesting and useful insecticides that have not been investigated yet. Only a few have been mentioned here. The entomologists and chemists have passed by many thousands of plants in their search for an insecticide that kills insects but is safe to people and animals.

Once a scientist discovers a plant useful as an insecticide, he must take the plant apart and discover the active principles in it. The discovery is only the first step toward the commercial usefulness of the plant. The next steps take time and effort.

That a plant is poisonous to other animals or is a common weed rarely attacked by insects is not a positive indication of insecticidal properties. The insecticidal principles may be present in one or more of the following parts: Leaves and leaflets, flowers, petioles, seeds and seed hulls, fruits, twigs and stems, roots, bark, and wood.

Often the plant will be insecticidal when it is ground up, but the extract of the material will not be poisonous.

The farmer and the general public share in the discovery and development of new insecticides from plants. Growing new plants for insecticides means new income to the farmer; the public gets farm products that are clean and free from insects and poisonous residues. Since 1947 Department research on plant insecticides covering only six plants—tree tobacco, oxeye, sabadilla, devils-shoestring, thunder-god vine, and sesame—has led to the publication of more than 17 papers and the granting of three public service patents.

LOUIS FEINSTEIN, *a research chemist, joined the Department of Agriculture in 1939. He holds degrees from Georgetown University and the University of Pennsylvania. Dr. Feinstein has published papers on vitamins and nicotine alkaloids and holds patents on the extraction of alkaloids and other materials from plants.*

For further reference:

G. T. Bottger and C. V. Bowen: Comparative Toxicity Tests of Anabasine, Nornicotine, and Nicotine, *Bureau of Entomology and Plant Quarantine publication E-710. 1946.*

R. N. Chopra and R. L. Badhwar: Poisonous Plants in India, *The Indian Journal of Agricultural Science, volume 10, pages 1–44. 1940.*

E. O. Eddy and C. M. Meadows: Karaya Gum in Nicotine Sprays, *Journal of Economic Entomology, volume 30, pages 430–432. 1937.*

W. A. Gersdorff and Norman Mitlin: Insecticidal Action of American Species of Heliopsis, *Journal of Economic Entomology, volume 43, pages 554–555. 1950.*

H. L. Haller, E. R. McGovran, L. D. Goodhue, and W. N. Sullivan: The Synergistic Action of Sesamin With Pyrethrum Insecticides, *The Journal of Organic Chemistry, volume 7, pages 183–184. 1942.*

Roy Hansberry and Cecil Lee: The Yam Bean, Pachyrrhizus erosus Urban, As a Possible Insecticide, *Journal of Economic Entomology (scientific note), volume 36, pages 351–352. 1943.*

S. H. Harper, C. Potter, and E. M. Gillham: Annona Species as Insecticides, *Annals of Applied Biology, volume 34, pages 104–112. 1947.*

L. E. Harris: Chemical Studies in Oklahoma Plants. VI. Physallis mollis Nuttall—A Plant Insecticide, *Journal of the American Pharmaceutical Association, scientific edition, volume 37, pages 145–146. 1948.*

Albert Hartzell and Fredericka Wilcoxon: A Survey of Plant Products for Insecticidal Properties, *Contributions from Boyce Thompson Institute, volume 12, 1941.*

Ralph E. Heal, Edward F. Rogers, Robert T. Wallace, and Ordway Starnes: A Survey of Plants for Insecticidal Activity, *Lloydia, volume 13, pages 89–162. 1950.*

Martin Jacobson: Herculin, A Pungent Insecticidal Constituent of Southern Prickly Ash Bark, *The Journal of the American Chemical Society, volume 70, pages 4234–4237. 1948.*

F. B. LaForge: Constituents of Pyrethrum Flowers. XX. The Partial Synthesis of Pyrethrins and Cinerins and Their Relative Toxicities, *with W. F. Barthel, The Journal of Organic Chemistry, volume 12, pages 199–202, 1947;* The Presence of an Insecticidal Principle in the Bark of Southern Prickly Ash, *with H. L. Haller and W. H. Sullivan, The Journal of the American Chemical Society, volume 64, page 187. 1942.*

N. E. McIndoo: The Castor-Bean Plant as a Source of Insecticides; A Review of the Literature, *Bureau of Entomology and Plant Quarantine publication E–666, 1945;* Plants of Possible Insecticidal Value; A Review of the Literature up to 1941, *E–661, 1945;* A Bibliography of Nicotine. Part II. The Insecticidal Uses of Nicotine and Tobacco, *with R. C. Roark and R. L. Busbey, E–392, 1936;* Plants Tested for or Reported to Possess Insecticidal Properties, *with A. F. Sievers, U. S. D. A. Publication 1201. 1924.*

H. K. Plank: Insecticidal Properties of Some Plants Growing in Puerto Rico, *Puerto Rico Federal Experiment Station (Mayaguez) Bulletin 49. 1950.*

R. C. Roark: Excerpts from Consular Correspondence Relating to Insecticidal and Fish-Poison Plants, *United States Bureau of Chemistry and Soils, 1931;* A Third Index of Patented Mothproofing Materials, *with R. L. Busbey, Bureau of Entomology and Plant Quarantine. 1936.*

M. S. Schechter and H. L. Haller: The Insecticidal Principle in the Fruit of the Amur Corktree, *The Journal of Organic Chemistry, volume 8, pages 194–197. 1943.*

E. H. Siegler and C. V. Bowen: Toxicity of Nicotine, Nornicotine, and Anabasine to Codling Moth Larvae, *Journal of Economic Entomology, volume 39, pages 673–674. 1946.*

United States Patents: 1,619,258, Insecticide, *patented by Sidney L. Hoover, March 1, 1927 (U. S. Patent Office Official Gazette, volume 356, page 132); 2,223,367,* Insecticide, *patented by Howard D. Hively, December 3, 1940 (volume 521, page 58); 2,525,784,* Process for Extracting Alkaloidals from Plants with Aqueous Aluminum Sulfate, *and 2,525,785,* Process for Extracting Alkaloidals from Plants with Aqueous Ammonia-Ethylene Dichloride Mixture, *patented by Louis Feinstein and Patrick J. Hannan, October 17, 1950 (volume 639, pages 719–720).*

Oil Sprays for Fruit Trees

P. J. Chapman, L. A. Riehl
G. W. Pearce

Petroleum oils are used in several ways to control pests. Some kill insects and mites directly through their own action. Some supplement the action of other insecticides as co-toxicants, solvents and carriers, stickers, or stabilizers.

In the water-borne oil sprays commonly applied to fruit trees, the oil usually is the sole or primary insecticidal agent. That is also true of oils used to rid bodies of water of mosquitoes.

Light petroleum fractions are widely used as solvents and carriers for many insecticides. The original fly sprays are a good example. The introduction of DDT and other organic insecticides has meant a great increase in the use of oil as the carrier for applying insecticides, especially the chemicals used to control household and building pests. These oil-insecticide mixtures usually are applied in the form of fine mists. With heat and a suitable generator they can be applied also as thermal fogs, which remind one of military smoke screens.

Often oils are added to insecticidal and fungicidal spray, dust, and poison-bait formulations as stickers, stabilizers, and conditioning agents.

In this chapter we discuss the water-borne oil sprays as they are used to control pests of citrus and deciduous fruit trees.

Kerosene was apparently the first petroleum product used for the control of plant pests in the United States. A. J. Cook of Michigan State College introduced in 1877 a kerosene-soap emulsion which was widely employed to combat aphids and scale insects.

Entomologists sought something more effective and turned to crude petroleum. It proved to be too injurious to most plants. A search was then started for some fraction or series of fractions of petroleum that would be highly effective as insecticides, but relatively noninjurious to plants. Progress has been made in the search.

Oil sprays are used most commonly in horticulture to control scale insects and mites, among which are many of our major fruit pests. Oil sprays are also used to control psyllids (pear psylla), plant bugs (apple red bugs), mealybugs, aleyrodids (whiteflies, citrus blackfly), thrips, aphids (newly hatched), membracids (buffalo treehopper), and others. Oil sprays readily destroy eggs of many lepidopterous pests, like the codling moth, oriental fruit moth, various leaf rollers, and cankerworms. Those insects are now more commonly controlled in the larval stage with the newer insecticides.

More than 15 million gallons of oil are used annually in this country for horticultural sprays. Emulsified and diluted to a 2-percent strength, that amount makes 750 million gallons of spray—enough to provide for the single coverage of 40 million to 50 million orange or apple trees.

Tree spray oils are of two classes. Those intended for use on the hardy tree fruits during the dormant period are called dormant oils. Those applied to trees in foliage are the summer oils. The oils used on citrus in California may be classed as summer oils. The two groups differ chiefly in the degree of refinement of the oil and in its heaviness, or viscosity. Summer oils have been more highly refined and are of lighter weight than dormant oils. The classification is rather arbitrary, and because the trend has been toward using the so-called dormant oils after growth starts and using more highly refined products, the distinction between dormant and summer oils has had less and less meaning.

The first major step in refining petroleum is its division into fractions by distillation. First to distill over are the low-boiling naphthas, then come increasingly higher-boiling lots, through gasoline, kerosene, fuel oils, and, finally, the lubricant fractions. Horticultural spray oils are derived from the fuel-oil and light-lubricant portions of petroleum; those from the lubricant portion predominate.

Crude petroleums vary greatly in composition. Differences exist among crudes from the major production fields and even among wells in one field. We recognize three general types—paraffinic base, asphaltic or naphthenic base, and mixed base or midcontinent crudes. Spray oils have been prepared from all crude classes. Asphaltic-base crudes are utilized in California primarily because the local petroleum supply is generally of that class. East of the Rockies the midcontinent crudes are more commonly used.

Before we consider specifications for horticultural spray oils, it is well to have an understanding of their nature.

The spray oils are composed essentially of hydrocarbons—compounds containing hydrogen and carbon. The arrangement of the atoms of the two elements in individual molecules is varied and complex. Only three basic classes of carbon structures occur, however—paraffin chains, aromatic rings, and naphthene rings. It is possible by analysis to determine the approximate percentage of each structure-class in any oil. As will be brought out later, oil composition has an important bearing on both insecticidal efficiency and plant safety. The composition one might find for spray oils, manufactured from paraffinic and naphthenic crudes, is:

		Percentage of each structure		
Type of oil	*Refinement*	*Paraffin chains*	*Naphthene rings*	*Aromatic rings*
Paraffinic	Conventional	75	15	10
Naphthenic	Moderate acid	50	40	10
Naphthenic	Conventional	45	38	17

Research workers learned long ago that the safeness of spray oils to plants in leaf is related to the aromatics and other unsaturates present. It is now generally agreed that oils can be made increasingly safer for use on evergreen plants and on deciduous plants in their growth period by lowering the aromatic-ring content. That may be accomplished in part in refining operations by treating the oil with strong sulfuric acid or its equivalent. The aromatics and other unsaturated structures react to form sulfonates, which can be separated from the remainder of the oil. The process has given rise to the term unsulfonated residue, or U. R. The term is widely used to indicate the degree of refinement of the oil or its degree of freedom from aromatic structures. Oils intended for foliage sprays have U. R. values ranging from about 90 to 96 percent. Products used on deciduous trees in the dormant period may range from about 50 to 90 U. R.

Until 1940 or so, oil composition was thought to have little practical relation to the insecticidal efficiency of horticultural spray oils. Since then, however, studies made at the New York State Agricultural Experiment Station and elsewhere have established that efficiency is related to the paraffinicity of an oil. Thus efficiency increases as the paraffinic character in oils increases. The relationship has been demonstrated in the case of the major oil-susceptible pests of both deciduous and citrus fruit trees. It should not be inferred that the so-called naphthenic oils make unsatisfactory spray oils. They are in a sense simply low paraffin oils and consequently are used at greater strengths in the spray mixture to achieve results equal to those had with highly paraffinic items.

Another factor affecting the insecticidal value of an oil is the size of its molecules. More familiar but less accurate terms for this property are viscosity and relative heaviness: Oils of small molecular size, such as kerosene, for example, have little separate value in killing horticultural pests, but there seems to be no advantage in going above a certain molecular size.

VISCOSITY AND BOILING-RANGE data are the criteria most commonly used in commerce to indicate the molecular-size property of an oil. Viscosity is measured at certain temperatures by recording the time required in seconds for a sample to flow through a standard opening. It depends on the principle that molecular size controls flow speed, with the rate decreasing as size increases. In addition to size, however, flow rate is also affected by the shape of the molecules. That means that one cannot depend on viscosity measurements alone to classify products as to their suitability for horticultural sprays among oils of different origin. For example, a highly paraffinic oil having a viscosity of only 50 seconds Saybolt at 100° F. may be more effective insecticidally than extremely naphthenic products of 125–130 seconds. Viscosity measurements are useful in indicating heaviness ranges among oils of common origin and manufacture.

A more accurate indication of molecular size in an oil can be obtained from distillation- or boiling-range data. Moreover, that measure has two advantages over viscosity data for spray-oil purposes: It indicates molecular-size range, and it permits a fairly close practical comparison, insecticidally, even among oils of different composition.

The California Department of Agriculture in 1932 established distillation-range standards to regulate the sale of spray oils in that State. Five grades of summer or foliage-spray oils and three grades of dormant oils were set up, based on a minimum U. R., and the percentage of the product that distilled over at 636° F. The system has not been adopted generally, but it has worked out well on the west coast, partly because spray oils in the area are made from the same general class of crude petroleum.

Oil sprays kill insects and mites by what appears to be essentially a smothering action. By enveloping the pest with a continuous film of oil, the oil interferes with its respiration and ultimately causes death. That is the conclusion to be drawn from studies made by E. H. Smith and G. W. Pearce, who used eggs of the oriental fruit moth as test subjects. That the action is largely physical was shown by the ability of some eggs to survive 24-hour exposure to a lethal dosage of oil. In the experiment the oil was removed 24 hours after application through the use of an oil solvent.

Similar results were obtained earlier by this technique on the winter eggs of the fruit tree leaf roller. In that instance, some eggs hatched after having been exposed a week to a deposit that would have killed all eggs had it not been removed.

Oil sprays may kill hatched forms of insects in essentially the same manner as just described for eggs. Instead of a direct exchange of gases through the wall or shell, as in the case of an egg, however, respiration in hatched forms usually takes place through openings—spiracles—in the body wall connected with branching tubes extending inwards (the tracheal system). Killing seems to be effected by oil flowing into the tracheae and plugging them, with death resulting from suffocation. In his studies on California red scale, Walter Ebeling found that the usual route of oil to the insect proper is under the scale covering from its edge. Some oil may penetrate directly through the armor. Besides killing the individuals that it touches, an oil film on the plant interferes with the successful establishment of the young that may hatch for some days following treatment. Such a residual effect is an important part of the total action achieved in the control of citrus mites and scale insects.

Oil and water, despite the old saying, can be made to mix in the form of emulsions wherein the oil is dispersed as minute droplets throughout the water. Oil is usually applied to fruit trees in the form of emulsions containing about 1 percent to 4 percent oil. Emulsification is brought about by agitation and the addition of a substance, known as an emulsifying agent, that reduces interfacial tension.

Oils are applied as emulsions primarily to regulate the amount of oil deposited on the plant. That is important: A rather direct relationship exists between oil deposit and both insecticidal efficiency and plant injury. The object is to lay down a deposit sufficient tc kill the pests present and yet below that which will cause plant injury. Often the operational margin is quite narrow. Oil-deposition rate is determined chiefly by four factors: The oil strength in the spray mixture, the kind and amount of emulsifying agent used, the nature of the plant surface sprayed, and the amount of spray applied.

The first requirement of an emulsifying agent, of course, is that it produce a satisfactory emulsion. It also should maintain a uniform concentration of oil throughout the batch of dilute emulsion in the spray tank. These conditions can be met by forming highly stable emulsions. Unfortunately stable emulsions generally lay down low oil deposits in spraying. To obtain at least moderate-deposition properties in the mixture, one must sacrifice some stability. Actually, agitation can largely offset this disadvantage. Most modern spraying machines are equipped with agitation systems that permit the use of relatively unstable emulsions.

The influence of the emulsifier on oil-deposition rate in spraying may be great. An emulsion prepared with one emulsifier may lay down as much oil on the plant at a 1-percent strength as others used at 2-, 3-, or even 4-percent strengths. Further wide variations in deposition can be expected as the amount of any given emulsifier is varied. The deposition rate for a given emulsifier generally decreases as the amount used is increased.

Another factor is the nature of the plant surface—whether bark, leaves, or fruit, or, indeed, old and new bark, young and mature fruit, old and new leaves, and often the upper and lower surfaces of leaves. The surface factor is of less importance in treating deciduous fruit trees during the semidormant period, when relatively small variations in bark surface are involved. The treatment of trees in leaf is something else again. The surface factor is of special importance in treating citrus trees for the control of pests like the California red scale, which occurs on all parts of the tree. If a pest must be controlled on two or more types of surfaces, the amount of emulsifier should be so adjusted that at least a minimum effective dosage will be laid down on all surfaces.

Thus, any recommendations for oil sprays should consider the concentration of oil in the spray mixture and its oil-deposition rate as well. There has been a trend towards adjusting deposition rates to common standards.

Probably no single oil-deposition standard will prove satisfactory for all purposes. When the oil deposit must be rigidly controlled, as in spraying oil-sensitive shade trees during dormancy and deciduous fruit trees in leaf, a relatively stable light-depositing emulsion is indicated. But deciduous fruit trees are relatively tolerant of oil in the dormant period. Some overdosing of all or part of the tree then would be of little importance. Consequently less stable emulsions may then be used on fruit trees.

Growers can buy a stock oil product in which the emulsifying agent is incorporated or buy the straight oil and emulsifier separately and prepare the emulsion themselves in the spraying machine immediately before use. The latter is called tank mixing. Satisfactory spray-strength emulsions can be prepared by tank mixing as well as through the use of commercial stocks. Tank mixing costs less, but factory-made formulations offer convenience in handling and uniform performance.

Commercial spray-oil stocks are of two classes, concentrated emulsions and emulsible oils. Such terms as emulsive oils, miscible oils, and soluble oils are also applied to the second type. Concentrated emulsions—preformed emulsions in a concentrated state—resemble a thin, whitish paste and usually contain about 83 percent oil by volume. The concentrated emulsions will flow readily through the standard 2-inch bung for metal drums.

The emulsible oils consist of oil in which one or more emulsifying agents have been dissolved. They usually contain 95 to 99 percent oil and often resemble straight oil in appearance. They are not emulsions in the state in which they are sold but produce emulsions when added to water in the spray tank. They vary in the readiness with which an emulsion is formed in the tank. Some formulations produce an emulsion instantly; others first require some preliminary agitation in the presence of only a small amount of water. Some authorities prefer to designate the former type of product as miscible oils, reserving the term emulsible oil for the latter. Although the so-called miscible oils emulsify readily, they lay down low oil deposits in spraying.

The tank-mixing procedure is quite simple in principle. A 2-percent oil spray mixture can be prepared thus, in a high-pressure orchard-spraying machine equipped with a 400-gallon tank: With the engine running, just enough water is drawn into the tank to operate the pump—15 to 25 gallons. The emulsifying agent is added, then the oil (which would be 8 gallons in this example). A spray gun directed into the tank is next opened and held open for 1 to 2 minutes. The circulation of water, oil, and emulsifier through the pump and its discharge or injection under high pressure into the tank effects emulsification. At this point the mixture should have a uniform, creamy appearance. The final step is to fill the tank with water, and the mixture is ready for use.

The foregoing procedure will produce the most satisfactory type of tank-mixed emulsion, but it is not absolutely necessary to pass the mixture through a spray gun. In the citrus area of California a general practice is to wait a minute or two before filling the tank for the agitators to create the emulsion. An improvement on the practice is to operate the pumps under full pressure during the prefill mixing.

Many emulsifying agents may be used in tank mixing. Blood albumin has been widely used. In California a 25-percent product is used at the rate of 4 ounces for each 100 gallons of spray-strength emulsion. An 8-ounce rate is advised in New York.

Application of more of the oil-spray mixture than may be needed to cover all or part of the tree usually causes no harmful effects. There is a limit to how much oil can be deposited in continuous spraying when most dilute emulsions are used. It simply runs off beyond this point. An important exception is when part of a tree may be sprayed twice with a drying period between. The situation may occur when growers follow the practice of spraying one side of the row when the wind, say, is in the west, and covering the east side several days later when the wind shifts. Almost twice as much oil will be deposited where the two coverages overlap as elsewhere on the tree. One should try to cover the whole tree in one operation. If each side of the row is sprayed separately, the opposite side should be treated 15 or 20 minutes later, or before the spray applied in the first half of the operation has dried.

PETROLEUM-OIL SPRAYS have been used on citrus trees since about 1900. Commercial control of the major pests in most California citrus districts can be had with a single annual application of an oil spray. Such a program, the most economical of those available, has been widely followed in California. The dominant position of oil sprays on citrus is being challenged as the search continues for more efficient insecticides and for ones without the objectionable effect on trees and fruit that is attributed to oil.

Different practices are followed with oil sprays on citrus in Florida because of differences in climate, cultural practices, varieties, and in marketing. Florida citrus trees are apparently more tolerant of oil sprays than are those of California—at least there seems to be greater latitude in the kinds of oil that can be used with relative safety on citrus in Florida. Growers in Florida in 1945 were using oils that ranged in viscosity from 69 to 108 seconds Saybolt at 100° F. and from 75 to 92 percent in U. R. Both naphthenic- and paraffinic-type products were employed. Practices in California were more standardized; the spray oils were prepared from much the same class of crude (California naphthenic-base) stock, refined to a U. R. of 90 percent or higher, and were available in a series of relatively narrow boiling fractions.

The California Department of Agriculture in 1932 established specifications for spray oils that were based on certain U. R. and distillation standards. The latter property was measured as the percentage of the product that distilled up to 636° F.

Five grades of oils were established for use on citrus fruit trees—light, light-medium, medium, heavy-medium, and heavy. The minimum required standards for each grade are given in the accompanying table. Kerosene and mineral-seal oil are also included because they have sometimes been applied on citrus.

Citrus oil sprays are usually used in California at an actual oil concentration of 1.66 to 1.75 percent—the rate used in tank mixing or in employing commercial emulsible oil stocks. Concentrated emulsion stocks—containing 80 to 85 percent of oil—are commonly used at a 2-percent strength. The general plan has been to keep the oil dosage in the spray mixture more or less constant and to vary the oil heaviness to achieve the desired results in pest control or as tree tolerance may dictate. In general, pest-control efficiency as well as plant-injury hazards increase as oils of increasing heaviness are used.

Spray Oils Used on Citrus in California

Grade	*Minimum U. R. (percent)*	*Distilled at 636° F. percent)*	*Viscosity in seconds Saybolt at 100° F.*
STANDARD GRADES OF FOLIAGE SPRAY OILS			
Light	90	64–79	55–65
Light-medium	92	52–61	60–75
Medium	92	40–49	70–85
Heavy-medium	92	28–37	80–95
Heavy	94	10–25	90–105
LIGHT OILS SOMETIMES USED ON CITRUS			
Kerosene	95	100	[1]
Odorless kerosene	98	100	[1]
Mineral seal oil	91	95	40–50

[1] Viscosity values of oils lighter than mineral seal oil are much lower; comparable determinations are difficult to obtain and relatively unimportant.

The main consideration is selection of the proper grade, tree tolerance being a limiting factor. One has to consider the kind of citrus fruit to be treated, the insect or mite present, the general district, previous experience with oil in the particular orchard or locality, and the season. The factors are interrelated.

The tolerance of the California citrus fruits to oil sprays may be listed in the following decreasing order: Lemon, grapefruit, Valencia orange, navel orange, tangerine, and lime. A heavier grade oil is generally applied to lemons than to oranges.

Mites and scale insects comprise the two major groups of oil-susceptible citrus pests. Unarmored scale insects, such as the black scale and the citricola scale, may be controlled with a lighter grade oil than armored species like the California red scale, yellow scale, and purple scale. A light-medium oil is considered enough for unarmored ones.

Growers who depend on a single annual treatment to control the armored scales usually apply a medium-grade oil on oranges and a heavy-medium on lemons. Satisfactory control of the California red scale and citrus red mite on lemons is obtained in some localities with two applications—one in the spring and the other in the fall—of a light-medium oil.

The oil sprays applied against scale insects will also control the citrus red mite and citrus bud mite. In fact, in certain localities oil sprays may be applied primarily for the control of mites. Oil heaviness is apparently not a factor in controlling the citrus bud mite, but against the red mite there is a correlation between the length of the protective period afforded by treatment and oil heaviness.

Citrus is grown under three somewhat distinct climatic zones, coastal, intermediate, and interior, in southern California. Citrus trees generally are more tolerant of oil spray in the cooler coastal zone than in the warmer, more arid interior zone. Experience has shown that oils heavier than light-medium should not be used on oranges in the interior, although lemons there will generally tolerate a medium-grade oil. By contrast, a heavy-medium oil (or, on occasion, a heavy oil) can be used on lemons in the coastal zone. Medium oil may be used on oranges in the intermediate zone and a heavy-medium grade on lemons.

Oil sprays are most commonly applied in California from late July through September. A time is selected when the younger, more susceptible stages of the scale insects predominate. Growers of lemons are inclined to delay treatment until October and November to avoid high temperatures, which could result in fruit drop should they occur immediately after the application is made.

Most of the serious effects encountered in the early use of spray oils, such as leaf burn and heavy leaf and fruit drop, largely have been overcome by the use of better oils, minimum effective dosages, and better timing of sprays. Certain more subtle effects remain, however. It has been fairly well established, for example, that the juice of oranges from oil-sprayed trees will usually have a somewhat lower total content of soluble solids than that from untreated trees or trees fumigated with hydrogen cyanide. Flavor of the fruit is linked to the soluble solids; any appreciable lowering of these constituents is undesirable.

Other difficulties charged to the use of oil sprays include: Retarded fruit rind-color development; inhibition of "degreening"—development of color with ethylene gas—of the fruit after harvest; accentuation of the "waterspot" condition of navel oranges grown in certain districts in California; and in Florida a possible predisposition of trees to winter injury. Difficulties with rind-color development can be minimized by spraying at the recommended season and by avoiding applications immediately prior to harvest.

Oil sprays have been suspected—wrongly—of lowering crop yields, of reducing the size of the fruit, of increasing the tendency of stems and small branches to die out, and of lowering the over-all vigor of the trees.

Dinitro compounds, such as dinitro-*o*-cyclohexylphenol, and sulfur may be applied to citrus trees. Neither is compatible with oil sprays and should not be used in combination with them. Besides, injury may result if an oil spray is applied within 2 weeks of a dinitro treatment or up to 2 months following the use of sulfur.

Spraying should be done as closely after an irrigation as practicable. Spraying should be discontinued when it is evident that temperatures will rise above the safe maximum for the district. It may be possible to escape injury by working during the cooler parts of the day, but it is better to cease work when hot weather is forecast for several days in succession. The safe maximum is 80° F. for the California coastal region and 95° for the interior district. Spraying should also be avoided during periods of very low humidity and possible frosts.

The leaf- and fruit-drop difficulties can be greatly reduced by putting a minute amount of some growth-regulating substance, like 2,4–D, in the oil spray. The recommendation stems from research done by W. S. Stewart, L. A. Riehl, and others at the California Citrus Experiment Station. Dosages suggested, in acid equivalent, are 4 parts per million of ester preparations or 8 p. p. m. of metallic or alkanoamine salts. The amounts refer to the concentration of 2,4–D that will occur in the dilute spray mixture.

The compound cryolite also may be added to oil sprays to save the cost of making a separate treatment. Cryolite is applied to control orange tortrix and similar species. Rotenone is said to improve the efficiency of oil spray against scale insects; rotenized oil sprays may be helpful against the black scale, but against California red scale it has not proved effective enough to warrant a general recommendation.

Oil sprays are usually applied in California with high-pressure spraying equipment mounted on trucks. Spraying is done from the ground with 60- to 75-foot leads of hose and single-nozzle spray guns. The most satisfactory equipment also has an hydraulically operated telescoping tower topped with a platform. It permits a man to work 30 feet from the ground so he can cover the tops of trees. A spray crew normally has two ground sprayers, a tower man, and the truck driver.

To control red scale, particularly, the interior of the tree has to be sprayed as thoroughly as the outside. The growth of citrus trees often is dense, and the necessary coverage cannot be attained by spraying from the outside alone. For inside coverage, most spray men insert their spray gun through the foliage at four points around the circumference.

To cut labor costs, growers have been interested in the development of more mechanized means of spraying. Several new kinds of vertical spray booms have proved satisfactory, especially when the aim is to get fast outside coverage. Other equipment works on the principle of carrying the spray into the tree by means of an air-blast. The booms and air-blast-type machines, however, had not been adopted for general use on citrus in California in 1952.

Florida citrus, as we indicated, apparently is not so sensitive to the oil sprays as are citrus trees in California. Consequently growers can use a variety of oils. The usual concentration of oil in Florida is about 1.2 to 1.33 percent of actual oil. July is considered the best time to apply oil sprays. Treatments made then give good control of scale insects and avoid unfavorable effects that may result from the misuse of oil sprays. High-pressure equipment and air-blast machines are widely used by citrus growers in Florida.

DECIDUOUS FRUIT TREES are commonly treated with oil sprays in spring, when the trees are semidormant. Highly refined oils used to be included in many summer sprays, but the practice has been greatly curtailed since the introduction of DDT, parathion, and other new toxicants, which have largely replaced summer oils.

Considerable differences exist in Eastern and Western States in the kind of oils and the ways they are used. Custom accounts for some of the differences. Other factors involve differences in petroleum supply, climate, and pest problems.

In the Pacific Northwest oil sprays are applied in the spring before any green tissue appears in the buds. Later applications of dormant oils are not advised because of the danger of injuring the buds. If oil is used alone in dormant sprays, it is at strengths of 3 to 4 percent. Such treatment is advised for San Jose scale, pear psylla, and the European red mite and clover mite, which overwinter as eggs.

Another practice in the Northwest is to combine oil with liquid lime-sulfur for a dormant treatment; the oil is used at a 1- or 2-percent strength and the lime-sulfur at 3 percent. This combination spray is effective against scale insects, pear leaf blister mite, and apple rust mite; if 2 percent oil is used, it will also destroy winter eggs of European red mite and clover mite.

The dormant spray oils used west of the Rockies are made from California petroleum crudes. Specifications call for an oil of 100–120-second Saybolt viscosity at 100° F. and allow an unsulfonated residue value of 50 to 70 percent.

Some Canadians have favored heavier viscosity oils than those generally advised in the United States. Products of 200–220 seconds viscosity are preferred. The oils used in British Columbia are naphthenic, being produced from California crudes. Heavier viscosity oils are favored in British Columbia because they are thought safer and apparently more efficient than the 100–120-second naphthenic oils.

FRUIT GROWERS in Northeastern States commonly apply early-season oil sprays after some new growth has appeared in the buds rather than in the full dormant stage. On apples that avoids combining oil with dinitro insecticides, which must be applied when the buds are dormant. Oil-dinitro mixtures may cause serious bud injury. Another reason for later spraying is that a higher kill of winter eggs of the European red mite is had. The eggs become increasingly more susceptible to oil as their hatching period approaches. A higher kill of mite eggs may be expected with a 2 percent oil spray applied in the delayed-dormant stage than the same oil applied in the dormant period at a 4-percent strength. Apple trees are considered to be in the delayed-dormant stage when about a half inch of leaf tissue is exposed in blossom buds.

TO INSURE reasonable safety in dormant oils after new growth has appeared, oils, different from the ones formerly used in the Northeast (and still favored in the Northwest) were needed. Such oils, called superior dormant tree-spray oils, were perfected largely as the result of research by chemists and entomologists at the New York State Agricultural Experiment Station. The oils are widely used by orchardists in New York and are rapidly gaining acceptance elsewhere in

970134°—52——17

the Northeast. They have these specifications:

Viscosity (Saybolt, at 100° F.).	90–120 seconds
Viscosity index (Kinematic).	90 (minimum)
Gravity (A. P. I. degrees).	31 (minimum)
Unsulfonated residue (A. S. T. M.).	90 (minimum)
Pour point	Not greater than 30° F.
Homogeneity	A relatively narrow boiling distillate portion of petroleum.

The following methods of testing spray oils are to be used: *Kinematic Viscosity,* A. S. T. M. designation: D445–39T. *Conversion to Saybolt Universal Viscosity,* A. S. T. M. designation: D446–39. *Kinematic Viscosity Index,* A. S. T. M. designation: D567–40T. A. P. I. *Gravity,* A. S. T. M. designation: D287–39. *Pour point,* A. S. T. M. designation: D97–39. *Unsulfonated Residue,* A. S. T. M. designation: D483–40.

Those specifications define an oil of high paraffinic character and fairly low aromatic content. The paraffinicity relates primarily to insecticidal efficiency and the aromatics to plant safety considerations. Oils having a 90 percent unsulfonated residue rating or higher—roughly 10 percent or less aromatics—generally have proved safe to use on New York apple trees in the delayed-dormant bud stage.

As we pointed out, all spray oils contain some paraffinic structures, but differ in degree of paraffinicity. The oil content of a spray, to achieve control, may be decreased as products of increasing paraffinic content are used. This relationship has been shown for the following: San Jose scale, European fruit lecanium, cottony peach scale, scurfy scale, apple red bug (eggs), eggs of the European red mite and probably the clover mite, fruit tree leaf roller and related species, and the eggs of codling moth, oriental fruit moth, grape berry moth, and eye-spotted bud moth.

Superior dormant tree-spray oils are sold as straight oil for tank mixing or as commercial concentrated emulsions or emulsible oils. Many New York growers tank-mix and use blood albumin as the emulsifying agent.

A fungicide is usually included in delayed-dormant applications of oil on apple trees in the Northeast to provide protection against apple scab. Bordeaux mixture, 2–4–100, or its equivalent in a proprietary copper fungicide are commonly used.

For the most resistant pests, such as scurfy scale, cottony peach scale, apple red bug, and fruit tree leaf roller, superior oils are employed at a 3-percent strength. A 2-percent concentration is considered adequate under New York conditions for the control of San Jose scale, pear psylla, European fruit lecanium, and the European red mite. In areas south of New York, a 2-percent concentration is considered insufficient for the control of the San Jose scale. Strengths of 2.5 and 3 percent are advised there to combat the pest. The suggested spray concentrations are based on the oil-deposition properties imparted to an emulsion by blood albumin. Higher or lower dosages may be needed if the emulsions used differ greatly from blood albumin emulsions in oil-deposition rate.

Dormant or semidormant treatments often are used to control the various species of aphids that are troublesome to the hardy fruits. They may be applied with the object of killing either the overwintering eggs or the newly hatched aphids on the opening buds. Conventional spray oils are not particularly effective aphicides in either case. In the Pacific Northwest green-tip or delayed-dormant applications of oil are suggested for the control of fruit aphids.

Growers in the East rely on dormant applications of dinitro insecticides to destroy the eggs or on the inclusion of nicotine sulfate or parathion in the delayed-dormant spray. Apparently there is little relationship between paraffinicity and the response of aphid eggs to oil sprays. If anything, the correlation lies between response and the aromatic content of oils. It is well known, for example, that aphid eggs are highly susceptible to such aromatic products as cresylic acid and the tar oils. From this one might conclude that there would be an advantage in using oils of high aromatic content, that is, having low U. R. values. Unfortunately, such oils apparently cannot be depended upon alone to control aphids; furthermore, their use must be restricted to dormant applications.

The older types of summer oils have declined in popularity. Much of this situation can be attributed to their incompatibility with fungicides and other insecticides. Sulfur has long been the stumbling block to the more extensive use of summer oils in the Eastern States. Serious direct foliage burn or delayed leaf drop may result from the use of oil and sulfur on the hardy tree fruits. Similar harmful effects have been noted with DDT and oil combinations.

No very definite specifications have been established for summer spray oils. A product meeting the following specifications should prove satisfactory for use in the East: A narrow-boiling-range product having a Saybolt viscosity at 100° F. of 65–70 seconds, a minimum U. R. of 92 percent, and an A. P. I. gravity of 33. Such an oil would be used at a 1-percent concentration to combat summer infestations of mites, the cottony peach scale, and, combined with nicotine sulfate or rotenone, the pear psylla.

The use of oil sprays in the future depends on several considerations.

Most of the objections to them revolve around unfavorable plant responses. If safer oils could be produced, particularly for use on the more sensitive plants, the use of oil should increase. It should be possible to produce safer and more efficient oils—synthetic oils and special fractions of petroleum, for example.

Oils are less toxic than many other insecticidal materials to man. Their relative safety in that respect recommends them for wider use.

Insects have shown a disturbing ability to develop resistance to some insecticides, but so far not to oils. The way oils kill insects and mites, apparently through physical means, merits attention; it may prove to be a valuable quality in the future use of chemical treatments for the control of pests.

P. J. Chapman *is professor of entomology and head of the division of entomology at the New York State Agricultural Experiment Station at Geneva, a unit of Cornell University. A native of California, he was trained at Stanford University, Oregon State College, and Cornell University. He was granted a doctor's degree from Cornell in 1928. From 1923 to 1928 he engaged in extension activities at Cornell and from 1928 to 1930 served as entomologist of the Virginia Truck Experiment Station at Norfolk.*

L. A. Riehl *is an assistant entomologist of the division of entomology at the University of California Citrus Experiment Station at Riverside. He was trained at the University of California at Berkeley and at Iowa State College, which granted him a doctor's degree in 1942. From 1942 to 1945 he was employed by the Rockefeller Foundation and served as a consultant on insect-borne diseases to the Surgeon General, United States Army. For those services he was awarded the bronze star and the medal of the United States of America Typhus Commission. From the Egyptian Government he received the Order of the Nile (Chevalier) and the Gambia Eradication Medal.*

G. W. Pearce *in 1951 was appointed chief of the chemistry section of the technical development services in the Communicable Disease Center of the United States Public Health Service in Savannah, Ga. From 1930 to 1951 he was a member of the staff of the New York State Agricultural Experiment Station at Geneva. He holds three degrees from Pennsylvania State College. Dr. Pearce has worked on investigations of insecticides and fungicides, especially their analysis and chemistry in relation to their use on fruits.*

Aerosols and Insects

W. N. Sullivan, R. A. Fulton
Alfred H. Yeomans

An aerosol, like fog or mist, is an assemblage of particles suspended in air. An insecticidal aerosol has particles whose diameters range from 1 to 50 microns—from 1/25,400 to 50/25,400 inch.

Insecticidal aerosols are dispersed in air by burning organic material, atomizing mechanically, vaporizing with heat, or liberating through a small opening an insecticide that has been dissolved in a liquefied gas. In the last the liquefied gas evaporates and leaves small particles suspended in air.

Many householders have become acquainted with aerosols in small containers—so-called bombs, although of course they are not explosive. A more general application has been in use a long time. The Mono Indians of California knew the value of smoke in stupefying insects so that they could be easily collected for food. They prepared a smooth floor under trees containing the full-grown larvae of the pandora moth and built a smudge fire. The smoke caused the caterpillars to drop to the ground in countless numbers. They were then raked into the fire, partly cooked, dried, and later eaten as a stew.

Another example of an aerosol was seen in the Northeastern States one day in September 1950, when the sun turned an eerie purple and darkness came at 2 p. m. A mass of cold air had drifted down from northwestern Canada and brought along the smoke from forest fires in the Alberta and Mackenzie district—an illustration of how aerosols can be dispersed in air currents from one point through large areas.

Aerosol bombs were developed in 1941, when L. D. Goodhue and W. N. Sullivan of the Bureau of Entomology and Plant Quarantine discovered that aerosols produced by spraying a solution of liquefied gas and insecticide through a small hole into the air were highly toxic to mosquitos and flies. The aerosol solution was made by dissolving pyrethrum and sesame oil insecticides in a liquefied gas commonly used in household refrigerators and called dichlorodifluoromethane. The liquid has a vapor pressure of approximately 75 pounds per square inch at room temperature.

The aerosol solution is held in a strong steel container with an outlet tube to the bottom. In operation, the vapor pressure of the liquefied gas is sufficient to force the solution out of the tube and into the air through an orifice that may vary from 0.013 to 0.024 inch in diameter. The gas immediately evaporates and the tiny particles of insecticide are dispersed as a fine mist.

The scientists knew the gas was nontoxic and noninflammable, and they found it to be nontoxic to man and animals when they mixed it with insecticide. The ease of application, the high concentration of insecticide, and the ability of the small aerosol particles to disperse and to stay suspended in the air for a long time fulfilled requirements for a good household insecticide. A public service patent was issued on the invention and assigned to the Secretary of Agriculture for the free use of the people of the United States. Licenses are issued, royalty free, for the manufacture, use, and sale of products produced under the patent.

So urgent was the need for a better way to kill mosquitoes and flies in war zones and so good was cooperation of the Department of Agriculture, the military, and industry that our troops used aerosol bombs within a year after they were discovered. Throughout the war the bombs were highly efficient against disease-carrying insects in barracks, mess halls, tents, and foxholes. They became standard equipment in long-distance airplanes, in which they were used to prevent the spread of hitchhiking insects. Occasionally one was used to cool the beer of a jungle fighter. In all, more than 40 million aerosol bombs were made for the Armed Forces.

At the end of the war aerosol bombs were made for civilian use. Strong, inexpensive containers and suitable push-button valves were developed. New low-pressure propellants and solvents were perfected. The earlier formulations were modified to include combinations of pyrethrum, a pyrethrum synergist, and DDT or methoxychlor.

Making low-pressure aerosol containers is a growing business. It has expanded to include deodorants, disinfectants, and other products, besides insecticides. It amounted to 33 million dollars in 1949, with prospects of going above 100 million dollars in later years.

THE AEROSOL BOMB is a good servant in kitchen, pantry, living room, bedroom, and cellar. Before it is used, the windows and doors of a room should be closed. Pets, birds, fish bowls, and food should be removed or covered. The container should be held upright with the opening away from the face, so the aerosol will go toward the ceiling. The operator walks around the room to give a good initial distribution. The bomb should not be held closer than 3 feet to any object, or the aerosol may stain furniture, wallpaper, curtains, or draperies. It can be held 6 to 12 inches from baseboards and cracks where insects like roaches and ants crawl or hide.

In treating the average room (1,000 cubic feet) to control such fliers as the mosquitoes, house flies, sand flies, black flies, gnats, and moths, the bomb valve should be opened to release the aerosol for about 6 seconds. This dosage will also kill some types of ants, but is not effective against the larvae of clothes moths. A 15-second release will kill fleas, wasps, and hornets. Roaches can be decimated but it takes at least 2 minutes of spraying per room and a whole bomb (12 ounces) for good results in the cellar. Spiders are hard to kill with aerosols.

The room should be kept closed for 10 or 15 minutes after treatment for flying insects and ants, 30 minutes for fleas, and 1 hour or more for roaches. Then the room may be aired out, but that is not necessary.

Gas-propelled aerosols are widely used to control insects in greenhouses. They cut the usual time for treating greenhouses from 48 man-hours to 10 minutes, eliminate black spot on roses, and can increase production 25 to 50 percent, depending on the degree of infestation.

The formula originally developed for greenhouses contained 10 percent of hexaethyl tetraphosphate and 90 percent of methyl chloride. Parathion partly has replaced hexaethyl tetraphosphate because it has lasting effect. Because parathion gives unsatisfactory control of resistant spider mites and aphids, new materials and formulas had to be found. Tetraethyl dithiopyrophosphate came into use in localities where resistant insects have been found. A newer material, octamethyl pyrophosphoramide, applied as an aerosol, has appeared promising against resistant greenhouse insects.

Liquefied gas aerosols have been used also against such insects as pea aphids on peas in the field. The liquefied gas is released close to the peas through nozzles on a boom that has a shield above it. The aerosol thus is distributed so that much of it is held near the plants for a long enough time.

The work that led to the development of the aerosol bomb started with a study of insecticidal smokes. Insects were subjected to a burning mixture of derris or pyrethrum, cornstalks, and sodium nitrate. The mixture burned like Fourth-of-July fireworks, and the smoke did kill insects, but such dispersal of nonvolatile or slightly volatile insecticides was wasteful.

The next step was to spray oil solutions of rotenone and pyrethrum on a hot plate. On contact with the heated surface (about 375° C.), the droplets were partly vaporized and formed particles of aerosol size. Aerosols so produced are called heat-generated. It is an efficient way to produce insecticidal aerosols.

Aerosols were then produced in the same way by spraying them onto the inner walls of a tube heated with electricity. After that, the hot exhaust of a small gasoline engine was used as the source of heat energy. From that came the suggestion that an Army smoke-screen generator be used to produce insecticidal aerosols to treat large areas for mosquitoes and flies.

Smoke was formed in the generators by running a mixture containing a little water in oil through coils passing through a combustion chamber, which was heated by an oil or gasoline burner. The oil-water mixture was completely volatilized by the heat and condensed into a smoke on contact with the outer air. The aerosol particle thus created was ideal for an Army screening smoke because it gave a good scattering of transmitted light and remained suspended in the air for a long time. It turned out, however, that the particle size was too small for efficient insect kill. A larger particle size and better insect kill was obtained by using a 50–50 mixture of water and oil and operating the machine at a lower temperature.

Another Army smoke generator used incomplete combustion to produce smoke. It was later modified to an insecticide aerosol generator by using a gasoline motor to drive a rotary air pump. The pumped air passes through and is heated in a gasoline-burning combustion chamber regulated at 482° C. The hot air then passes through special nozzles into which the insecticide is injected. The particle size is regulated by the flow of insecticidal solution through the nozzle.

Several methods have been used since the war to generate aerosols on a large scale. One machine uses a number of spinning disks to break up the solution. One uses the exhaust gases from a small pulse-jet engine. Another employs steam to atomize the solution as it issues from a nozzle.

Many small indoor types of aerosol generators have been placed on the market. They use electrically driven spinning disks, rotors, and pressure pumps, electrically generated vaporizers, and steam atomizers. One of the machines uses extremely high pressure generated by hand-pumping the liquid solution against a fixed charge of nitrogen. There are also convenient packages of mixtures for partly burning and releasing the insecticide as a fine aerosol smoke.

FOR BEST RESULTS, the farmer or health official must study his problem in detail before applying an insecticide with an aerosol generator. The machines can be set to produce different particle sizes. The choice of machine depends on the use to which it is to be put, whether for insects in confined spaces, flying insects, or those that attack his field crops. These principles may guide the prospective purchaser:

Aerosols are used indoors effectively as a way to control flying insects and to apply a light deposit on the top of exposed horizontal surfaces.

The particle size has a bearing on the effectiveness of the aerosol. The particle size is critical for the amount that collects on an insect as it flies through the aerosol. Particles that are too small are deflected from the flying insect as smoke is from a moving automobile. Particles that are too large settle rapidly, and their dispersion is poor; therefore their chance of touching the insect is also poor. When an insect does collide with an oversized droplet, the excess insecticide is wasted. Our research has shown that the best particle size to use for flying insects is between 10 and 20 microns mass median diameter.

Aerosols are dispersed by air currents. The particles will not be conveyed into dead-end cracks or into material through which air does not circulate. The distance to which particles will be carried depends generally on their settling rate.

An oil particle 1 micron in diameter will settle 10 feet in 26.5 hours. A particle of 15 microns will settle 10 feet in 15 minutes. In unheated buildings air currents are at a minimum, but heating sets up air convection currents that are a great aid to dispersion. Sometimes large-volume air blowers are used to aid dispersion. In an unheated room with a ceiling height of 8 feet, aerosols with a mass median diameter of 5 microns disperse fairly uniformly over an area 30 feet from the source, those of 15 microns over an area of 15 feet, and those of 25 microns less than 10 feet.

The deposit as a result of an aerosol settling is about 95 percent on the top of horizontal surfaces and the rest on walls and ceiling. The amount of deposit on a horizontal surface depends on the concentration of the aerosol above the surface so that if the aerosol is evenly dispersed throughout a room the resulting deposit will be proportional to the height above the surface.

In large closed warehouses that contain packaged food, the problem of flying and exposed crawling insects can be controlled by aerosol treatments. Aerosols of various particle sizes were tested; a size of about 5 microns mass median diameter was selected as most effective and easiest to apply. These small particles are produced by thermal aerosol generators that can be operated outside the warehouse; the fine particles are introduced through an open door. The aerosol is carried first to the ceiling. By the time the treatment is complete, the aerosol is well distributed throughout the interior by convection currents. The door is then closed. Overnight the particles penetrate into most of the cracks and crevices and settle on the top of exposed horizontal surfaces.

It is sometimes necessary to limit the time of application in some closed interiors. The particle size then must be large enough to settle out in the time available. A 10- to 15-minute exposure time is the minimum for satisfactory results. An aerosol having a mass median diameter of 15 to 20 microns is sufficient for the short-exposure application.

Equipment sometimes limits the particle size. When heat from thermal generators causes excess breakdown of the insecticide, equipment that produces larger particle sizes must be used. They then must be released from more than one point to cover adequately areas whose dimensions are larger than the distances of uniform deposit. Heated rooms will about double the dispersion area; rooms with high ceilings will add slightly to the dispersion.

When treating greenhouses, it should be remembered that foliage injury can be caused by a particle size larger than the foliage can tolerate with the type of formulations used.

Some formulas that we have used indoors are: (1) 1 pound of technical DDT dissolved in 7.5 pints of Sovacide 544C (Socony Vacuum) to make 1 gallon. (2) 1 pound of technical DDT dissolved in 2 quarts carbon tetrachloride; to it are added 3.5 pints of No. 3 fuel oil to make 1 gallon. This formula is relatively safe from explosion. (3) 1 quart of 10 percent pyrethrum in deobase; 1 pint of piperonyl butoxide and 1 pint No. 3 fuel oil are added.

Because of the explosion hazard when oil solutions are used indoors, not more than 1 gallon of the solutions should be used per 100,000 cubic feet. They should not be released near an open flame. Workers should wear proper respirators. The third formula, which contains pyrethrum, is recommended for use around foodstuffs.

The formulations should contain a proportion of relatively nonvolatile oil to maintain the desired particle size while it is suspended in the air. In closed warehouses, 1 pound of DDT in 1 gallon of solution per 100,000 cubic feet of space, applied about every 2 weeks in summer, will provide protection against insect infestation.

The main problem in applying the aerosols outside, other than for temporary control of flying insects, is to put down a uniform deposit. To do that the aerosols are applied as wind-borne clouds. For best results the wind should be light, steady in direction, and moving at ½ to 8 miles an hour. The air temperature at ground level should be a little cooler than at 6 feet or more. This surface inversion keeps the aerosol cloud close to the ground; it is most important when low-growing crops are treated and least important for trees having a canopy of foliage. Good inversion usually occurs from 1 hour after sunset until sunrise but may exist all day if rain has cooled the ground.

The dosage depends on how much has to be deposited on an acre to kill the insect. The deposit is heaviest nearest the point of release and decreases as the distance from the release point increases, because the larger particles settle first. Under the best conditions, only 25 to 50 percent of an aerosol containing particles less than 50 microns in average diameter is deposited over an open area in swaths up to 2,000 feet; most of it drifts beyond the area under treatment. In wooded places the deposit would be greater. When more than one swath is used, however, the dosage can be cut about 10 percent for each successive swath because of overlapping up to a total of 50 percent.

The swath width should be selected according to the location of accessible roads, to places where the wheels of the machine will do the least damage to the crop, and places where oil deposits will not injure the foliage.

Some recommended particle sizes in microns mass median diameter for various swath widths and wind velocities are as follows:

Swath width in feet	*Wind velocity in miles per hour*			
	1	*3*	*5*	*7*
100	40	70	90	100
200	30	50	65	75
300	25	40	55	65
500	20	35	40	50
1,000	15	20	30	35
1,500	10	20	25	30

At least one-fourth of the aerosol solution should be nonvolatile. Results are best with a concentrated solution. A popular formula is 5 to 7.5 pounds of DDT dissolved in 2 gallons of benzene or xylene plus 3 gallons of SAE 10 W motor oil or agricultural oil. Oil-soluble technical BHC may be used in the formula in place of DDT. The operators should wear protective masks and clothing.

AEROSOL GENERATORS are useful in military and civilian situations in which mosquitoes and flies create problems of public health. They make it easy to clean up infestations in towns or camps and are particularly effective along the seashore. They are less well suited for the control of agricultural pests outdoors. Some problems require the use of fungicides and insecticides together, and the fungicides may be too bulky for efficient handling in aerosol generators. Field-model aerosol machines using concentrated DDT solutions have been employed successfully against gypsy moths, lygus bugs, tarnished plant bugs, pentatomids, potato flea beetles, and leafhoppers.

The aerosol machines are not suitable for treating individual trees or areas of less than an acre because the aerosol fog is placed entirely by wind drift and the initial thrust of about 10 feet given by the generator is sufficient only to place the aerosol in the wind.

W. N. SULLIVAN *is an entomologist in the Bureau of Entomology and Plant Quarantine. He is a native of Massachusetts and a graduate of the University of Massachusetts.*

R. A. FULTON, *a chemist in the same Bureau, is a native of Oregon. He holds degrees from Oregon State College, the University of Wisconsin, and Stanford University.*

ALFRED H. YEOMANS, *a technologist in the Bureau, has been engaged in investigating and developing equipment used in insect control. He is a native of California and a graduate of Ohio State University.*

Applying Insecticides

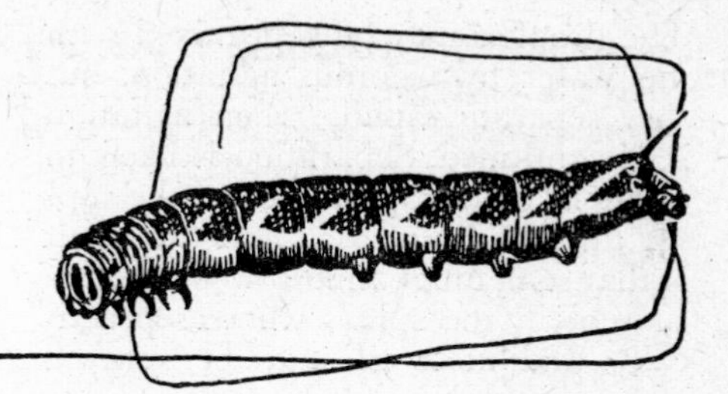

Using Insecticides Effectively

E. J. Newcomer, W. E. Westlake
B. J. Landis

Merely to secure effective insecticides and apply them is not enough. The best material may fail if it is used at the wrong time or in the wrong way. The user will do well to learn something about the habits of the pests he wants to get rid of, the physical properties of insecticides, and the influence of weather and type of plant growth on their effectiveness.

The contact insecticides—those that kill only the insects they touch—must be applied thoroughly. Because many materials retain their effectiveness for only a short time, the chance that the insects in moving about will later come into contact with them is not great. Also, many kinds of pests, such as some aphids and scale insects, cannot move about, although if the insecticide has some fumigating action it may suffice to place it within a short distance of the insect. Nicotine, for example, in hot weather will kill aphids not actually wet by it.

Thorough application of the stomach poisons, those that kill the insects that eat them, is less necessary. Many leaf-feeding insects move about. Larvae or caterpillars may travel from leaf to leaf on a plant; flying insects travel from plant to plant. Killing them at the earliest possible time may be unimportant. An application that reaches only one surface of the foliage or perhaps reaches only a part of the foliage may be enough. For a boring insect, such as the larva of the codling moth, however, thoroughness is essential in order to destroy it before it gets out of reach of the poison.

Consideration should be given to possible residual action of insecticides. Some are effective only for 24 hours or less. They evaporate or decompose rapidly, and often are particularly useful if a pest has to be dispatched shortly before harvest, as they do not leave harmful residues.

Other insecticides disappear more slowly and are effective for a week or more. They are of value in arid farming areas, for example, where row crops and orchards must be irrigated at intervals, during which time it may not be possible to apply insecticides. Still other insecticides, particularly the stomach poisons, may retain their effectiveness indefinitely.

Thus, if the period during which control is needed is long, frequent applications of an insecticide like tetraethyl pyrophosphate (TEPP), which decomposes rapidly, may be necessary. On the other hand, a single application of DDT in the soil has been known to control some soil-inhabiting pests for 5 years or more.

THE PHYSICAL CONDITION of insecticides affects their efficiency.

Emulsions—droplets of oil suspended in water—are an example. The size of the droplets largely is governed by the kind and amount of emulsifier used in the mixture. If the size is large, the emulsion will not be stable; the oil tends to rise and float on the surface.

The droplets may be kept mixed with the water by vigorous agitation, but they separate rapidly when agitation is discontinued. Separation is likely to occur in the spray tank or in the supply lines to the nozzles, and the result is that sometimes almost no oil will be present in the spray, whereas practically undiluted oil may be sprayed when the tank is nearly empty.

But if the oil droplets are very small, the emulsion may be so stable that virtually no separation will occur, even after standing for hours. For insecticidal use we require something in between. It is desirable to have an emulsion that is sufficiently stable to remain in suspension in the spray tank and supply lines but unstable enough to break immediately after leaving the nozzle, or upon contact with the surface being treated. Such an emulsion gives a much higher deposit of the oil than the more stable type.

Wettable powders are widely used as insecticides. The insecticide and diluent are combined into a dry powder, which is mixed with water before use to form a suspension. The particles must be less than 10 microns in size in order to give maximum efficiency. Larger particles do not adhere well to plant foliage and give less complete coverage, as there are fewer of them in a given quantity of material. Some commercial preparations even have an average particle size of 1 micron or less.

The physical properties of insecticidal dusts, such as particle size, bulk density, and flowability, are important. A dust, carried to the plants by a blast of air, is easily diverted by natural air currents. Also, the adherence of the particles to the surface being treated depends partly on the velocity at which they strike the surfaces. Very small particles are not desirable in dusts since they tend to drift with the air currents and lose their velocity quickly after leaving the outlet of the machine. As a rule, dusts should pass through a 325-mesh screen, by washing with a suitable medium. Such a screen will pass particles as large as 44 microns in diameter. The usual dust mixture will contain particles much smaller than this, of course, but the average size may be far above that desirable for use in sprays. Particles in excess of about 40 microns in diameter are not desirable because they will not adhere well to the foliage.

Bulk density, the weight of the uncompacted powder per unit volume, may be expressed in pounds per cubic foot. The greater the weight the less tendency there will be for the dust to float or drift. Bulk density is particularly important in aircraft application because then the dust settles quickly to the ground to avoid excessive drift. Dusts so used should have a bulk density of not less than 40 pounds per cubic foot. For application by ground equipment, 30 pounds per cubic foot may be enough.

Mineral oil at the rate of 1 to 2 percent by weight aids in reducing the drift of dusts and probably increases adherence to plants. The addition of mineral oil to dusts for aircraft application is required in some areas.

Dusts must resist packing in the hopper well enough to permit them to flow freely and uniformly into the feed mechanism. A dust that packs will not give a uniform rate of flow from the machine and the coverage will be uneven. Flowability is determined by the diluent used. Some of the better diluents from the standpoint of bulk density do not flow well while some free-flowing materials are too light. Often a mixture of a small amount of a free-flowing material added to one of high bulk density is used to give the desired properties.

Proper timing is important. If put on too early insecticides may be dissipated before the pest is present or in a susceptible condition. If they are applied too late, the pest may already have caused injury. Timing is sometime determined by the stage of growth of the crop. For example, it is not desirable to treat crops when they are in bloom. Bees visiting the blossoms may be killed and the yield of fruit or seed crops seriously reduced because of lack of pollination. The blossoms themselves may be injured. Sometimes a compromise must be made. For example, eggs of the European red mite often hatch just as apple trees are coming into bloom. An application of lime-sulfur just before blossoming is apt to be too early; one made afterwards is too late for the early-hatching mites. If thorough control is desired at this time both applications must be made.

Some pests, such as the green peach aphid or the two-spotted spider mite, which attack numerous crops, are present during most of the growing season. Effective and economical control of such pests depends on proper spacing of applications so that the crops are protected from injury with not too many sprayings or dustings. Control may be needed over a longer period in an early season than in a late one because the active period of the pests is lengthened.

The location of the pests on the plants also must be considered. If they feed chiefly on the lower surfaces of the leaves, those surfaces may have to be reached, especially if a contact material is being used. If they are on the roots, a soil insecticide is needed. If they climb the trees to feed on the foliage, a treatment of the trunk may be indicated, or perhaps merely a mechanical barrier will suffice.

As TO WEATHER: The United States Weather Bureau has numerous stations and cooperative observers and can supply weather information for practically any farming area in the country. Information on temperature, rainfall, and wind is especially useful. Much of this information is given in the Yearbook of Agriculture for 1941, *Climate and Man*. By studying his local conditions over a period of years, a grower can learn to avoid bad weather or take advantage of good weather to a great extent when controlling insect pests.

Wind often limits the application of insecticides. If it is blowing more than 5 or 6 miles an hour, spraying is interfered with, although at times spraying may be necessary in windy weather in order to provide some protection from immediate insect attack. A study of the occurrence of wind may help to determine when to spray or dust. In the Yakima Valley of Washington, for example, the average percentages of good spraying weather during daylight hours in the spring when dormant sprays need to be applied to fruit trees are: March 1–15, 35 percent; March 16–31, 22 percent; April 1–15, 15 percent; and April 16–30, 14 percent. Thus it is advantageous to get this spraying done early in this valley, because good spraying weather is less frequent as the season advances.

Application of dusts by aircraft should be made in the early morning or evening. Usually, after the sun has warmed the air, rising currents tend to carry the dust away from the crop. The same limitation often holds when dusting with machines on the ground. Perfectly calm weather is not necessary, and a slight drift may be advantageous. An air movement of 1 to 8 miles an hour is preferred when aerosols are used.

Temperature inversion, which occurs most often early in the morning or after sunset, should be taken advantage of when using aerosols. The temperature near the ground is then slightly cooler than at a height of several feet; the cloud of insecticide is kept from rising and therefore coats the plants more thoroughly.

Air currents tend to carry away volatile insecticides, such as oils, and therefore somewhat heavier dosages must be used outdoors than inside. Strong winds blow considerable quantities of dust from the plants, and they cause a loss of spray deposit by rubbing the leaves together or by rubbing leaves against the fruit.

Temperature becomes important in the application of insecticides only when it is extreme. Most materials are effective at ordinary temperatures.

Nicotine sulfate is an exception, as it kills insects much better at temperatures above 75° F., partly because of increased fumigating action. There is danger of injury to fruit or foliage if some materials are used in hot weather, although their effectiveness is not lessened. There is also danger of injury from oil sprays if followed by extremely cold weather.

Rains may wash off insecticides that are soluble in water, and their effectiveness is lost. Most of our modern insecticides are not especially soluble in water. Most of them are available in a form that adheres well to fruit and foliage. Their effectiveness is not reduced so much by ordinary rainfall as is sometimes supposed if the application has become thoroughly dry before it rains. Hard, driving rains, however, will remove much of the insecticide from exposed surfaces. This may be the reason why it is necessary, for example, to spray more often with DDT to control the codling moth in the Midwest, where rainstorms occur in summer, than in the drier parts of the Northwest, where such storms are infrequent. Dusts are removed more extensively than sprays by rains.

Trees or other plants may be sprayed when they are damp, but it is best not to spray them if they are dripping wet. The presence of dew or other moisture on plants is sometimes a help when dusting; it causes the dust to adhere better than if the surface is dry. A light spray of water has been used experimentally with a dust to increase its adherence.

The condition of the plant itself may often influence the effectiveness of an insecticide. Some plants or fruits grow faster than others, and fast-growing plants, such as potatoes, require more frequent applications than those that are growing slowly. Some grow more rapidly at one season than at another. The surface area of apples, for instance, may double within 2 weeks early in the season, although later on it may not double in less than 3 months. The surface, if it is to be kept covered with an insecticide, must be sprayed or dusted more often in the early part of the season than later.

Any very smooth or waxy leaf or fruit surface is not easily coated with insecticides. Cabbage leaves are especially difficult to cover thoroughly with liquids. Dusts often adhere better to such surfaces. Rough or hairy surfaces are more easily covered with either dusts or liquids. The shape and density of the foliage is a factor, too. Very heavy foliage interferes seriously at times with getting an insecticide to the pests.

A PERSON who is not familiar with insects and insecticides will do well to consult his county agricultural agent about the pest that is bothering him and the best insecticide for it.

The home gardener also can get a great deal of practical information from the label of the insecticide he buys. Such directions usually suggest mixing certain amounts of the concentrated insecticide material in a given amount of water. That may require mixing the insecticide on a weight or volume basis. Scales that weigh small amounts in ounces or a few pounds are useful. For measuring a given volume of dust or liquid, users should have on hand measuring equipment for teaspoonfuls, tablespoonfuls, and cupfuls, pints, and quarts. For safety and convenience, it is recommended that such measuring equipment be provided and used only for mixing insecticide materials.

Mixing large quantities of spray is usually just a matter of using one or more packages, the net weight being given on the label. For small amounts of spray there is no rule-of-thumb that may be followed because materials differ greatly in specific gravity. Some packages have a dilution table on the label. If there is none, perhaps the easiest way is to have the insecticide dealer determine the weight of a tablespoonful, cupful, or pint and record those details on the label for future reference. Tables of equivalents for various quantities of spray will be found in the appendix to this volume.

The old saying, "If a little is good, more is better" does not hold true in the use of insecticides. The use of excessive amounts is wasteful, expensive, and often injurious to the plants, animals, or soil.

Sometimes one can combine various insecticides, insecticides and fungicides, or insecticides and fertilizers and save time and money in so doing. Again, though, it is well to read the labels of the preparations or consult official publications or competent authorities before making those mixtures at home. Many compounds are not compatible, and harmful combinations may be formed when they are mixed.

The same equipment can be used for applying insecticides, fungicides, and herbicides, but one should be aware of the danger of using spray equipment for insecticides and fungicides that has been used to apply weed killers. Ordinary rinsing of the sprayer is not enough to remove the weed killer completely. The sprayer, hose, and nozzle should be washed carefully with a suspension of activated charcoal, 1.3 ounces per gallon of water, or the sprayer should be filled with a solution of household ammonia, 2 tablespoonfuls per quart of water, and allowed to soak for 24 hours. If that cannot be done, a separate sprayer should be used for herbicides.

In summary, some points to be followed in using insecticides:

If the insect is not known to you, find out what it is from the county agricultural agent, extension entomologist, or similar authority.

Recommendations for the proper insecticide to be used on a given pest may be obtained from those authorities, from State or Federal publications, from entomologists representing insecticide manufacturers, or from pest-control operators.

Prepare and use the insecticide in accordance with recommendations. Read the label. Follow precautions and other directions carefully.

Do a thorough, careful, but not wasteful job of application. The proper insecticide, proper application, and proper timing are of equal importance.

Store insecticides in a safe place.

Clean up and care for dusting and spraying equipment as you would with any good piece of machinery.

E. J. NEWCOMER *is an entomologist in the Bureau of Entomology and Plant Quarantine. He has been associated with research on the control of the insect pests of deciduous fruit trees since his graduation from Stanford University in 1911, most of the time in the State of Washington.*

W. E. WESTLAKE, *a chemist in the Bureau of Entomology and Plant Quarantine, works chiefly on problems concerning insecticides for fruit insect control in the State of Washington. He has degrees from Montana State College and the University of Minnesota.*

B. J. LANDIS *is an entomologist in the Bureau of Entomology and Plant Quarantine. Since 1941 he has been in charge of the Union Gap, Wash., field laboratory of the division of truck crop and garden insect investigations, and has carried on investigations of potato insects.*

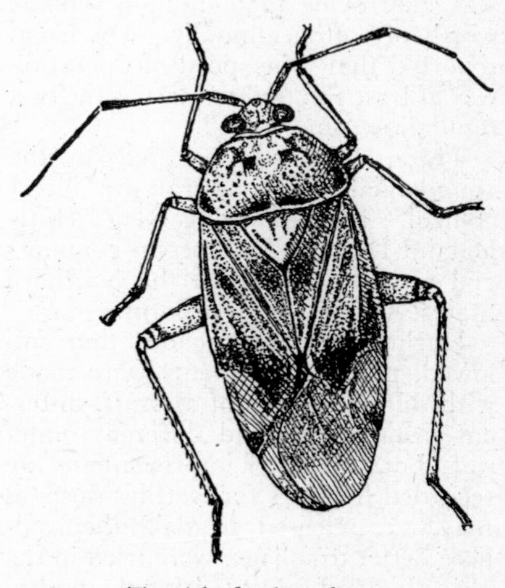

Tarnished plant bug.

From 0 to 5,000 in 34 Years

Kenneth Messenger, W. L. Popham

The airplane has become such a useful tool in the fight against insects that in 1952 more than 5,000 of them were equipped for that purpose in the United States.

Attempts were made as early as 1918 to control insects in this country by dumping poison dust from airplanes while flying over crops. But by 1921 a specially equipped airplane demonstrated its effectiveness in controlling an infestation of the catalpa sphinx near Dayton, Ohio. The lead arsenate dust that was released from a Curtiss biplane under the supervision of C. R. Neillie and J. S. Houser was unusually effective.

The following year B. R. Coad, of the Bureau of Entomology and Plant Quarantine, borrowed two airplanes of the same type from the United States Air Service and applied dust to fields of cotton near Tallulah, La., for the control of the boll weevil, which then was destroying 250 million dollars worth of cotton annually. Dr. Coad reported that "the speed of operation was at least 100 times as fast as the best mule-drawn machine."

Those demonstrations led to the commercial use of aircraft for insect control. The following year Huff-Daland Dusters, Inc., began commercial aircraft dusting in the Southern States. An industry was born.

During the two decades that followed, many experiments were made with different types of aircraft, different installations, and different materials, but few major improvements are recorded. Devices for wetting dusts as they were released, to make them adhere better to foliage, were tried in the New England forests with only moderate success. Autogiros and a blimp were tested in the belief that their slower forward speed might improve forest coverage. But it was not until the early part of the Second World War that the airplane's real potential as a pest-control vehicle became obvious. At that time the exposure of troops to insect-borne diseases challenged the initiative of entomologists, chemists, and military leaders. The answer to that challenge — broad sheets of DDT spray streaming from fast transport aircraft, blanketing otherwise inaccessible insect-breeding areas—saved countless lives and countless dollars.

As early as 1911 a German forest warden applied for a patent covering the use of aircraft in combatting forest pests. His effort apparently aroused no great interest in Germany until 1925 when several investigations, similar to those previously carried on in the United States, were undertaken. In that year a stand of mixed timber was treated to suppress an outbreak of the nun moth. Officials called the results "excellent, with no apparent harmful effects on birds or game."

Airplane dusting to control locusts was tried about the same time by the Russians. In 1925, near Haguenau, France, a forest plantation was dusted by aircraft. In 1927, on Cape Breton Island, Nova Scotia, the airplane was used to dust spruce and balsam in an attempt to control a spruce budworm outbreak.

Mosquito-breeding areas in South Africa, the United States, and other parts of the world were treated before 1930 with paris green. So encouraging were the results that it was forecast that the day would come when the airplane could be used to eradicate from entire continents the tsetse fly, carrier of sleeping sickness, and the malaria-carrying mosquitoes.

At the Orlando, Fla., laboratory of the Bureau of Entomology and Plant Quarantine, E. F. Knipling and two of his associates, C. N. Husman and O. M. Longcoy, demonstrated that DDT in a concentrated solution applied from aircraft at the rate of 1 gallon or less per acre gave good control of both mosquitoes and flies. Husman developed several devices for military trainer biplanes that made it possible to appraise accurately the effectiveness of this method of pest control. He continued this work during an assignment by the Navy in the South Pacific and developed improved equipment quite similar to that in use today. David G. Hall, also an employee of the Bureau, further developed and supervised methods of spraying mosquito-infested areas while in the service of the Army Transport Command in the South Pacific. In this work, he equipped and directed C–47 transports with great effectiveness.

Another type of equipment installed in aircraft for mosquito control was tested extensively by the Tennessee Valley Authority during 1945 and 1946. This consisted of an exhaust generator which produced DDT aerosols. It gave a rather uniform coverage over wide swaths at exceedingly low rates of discharge. The installation was simple and inexpensive, but its use was limited to specific problems. Although it effectively penetrated heavy vegetation, the drop size of the spray was so small that it had very little residual value.

Although the cost of aircraft applications was fairly high in the postwar period, it has been progressively reduced as a result of continued research in the development of concentrated materials and application equipment. The improvements and the growing realization of the versatility and effectiveness of the airplane resulted in a marked increase in the number used each year since the war.

Despite shortcomings—the difficulty of controlling the distribution of an insecticide from the air, the drift of fine sprays into nearby areas, the sometimes higher costs—nearly 500,000 hours are flown by pest-control aircraft annually.

Illustrative of the importance of the airplane in suppressing large emergency outbreaks of insect pests are the following projects, conducted cooperatively by the Bureau of Entomology and Plant Quarantine, the Forest Service, States, and other organizations.

During the few years before 1952, hundreds of thousands of acres were sprayed by aircraft for the control of the gypsy moth in New England. In this work it is estimated that just one load of insecticide released by a C–47 airplane treats as large an area as could be covered by one truck-borne spray rig in 4 years—and more effectively.

Also during recent years, several million acres in the Northwest have been sprayed with aircraft for the control of the spruce budworm. In 1948 an outbreak of the tussock moth in the Northwest infested 450,000 acres. Within a period of a few weeks the entire area was sprayed so effectively that the treatment did not have to be repeated. Each year between 1949 and 1952, several hundred thousand acres were treated with baits and sprays to control grasshoppers on forage lands of Wyoming and Montana.

KENNETH MESSENGER, *a graduate of the University of California, has worked on agricultural pest-control programs since 1933. He is in charge of the Aircraft and Special Equipment Center at Oklahoma City of the Bureau of Entomology and Plant Quarantine.*

W. L. POPHAM *has taken part in large-scale plant disease and insect control programs since his graduation from Montana State College in 1924. He has been assistant chief of the Bureau of Entomology and Plant Quarantine since 1941. He received the degree of doctor of science from Montana State College in 1948.*

More information about the use of aircraft for applying insecticides will be found in the following chapter and in many of the chapters in the second half of this book, which give details about types of aircraft and spray formulations used to control specific insects.

Research on Aerial Spraying

J. S. Yuill, D. A. Isler
George D. Childress

Some day it may be said that the air age in insect control arrived with the discovery of the unusual values of DDT during the Second World War.

In the two preceding decades, the application of insecticides by airplane had been tried against various pests, but the method was not used extensively except over cotton fields. Its advantages were recognized—large acreages could be covered quickly with no mechanical damage to the soil or to plants, and forest and swamps and other inaccessible places could be reached by air. There was one great limitation, though: The large quantity of insecticides that had to be applied for satisfactory control made the cost too high, even when the poisons were applied as undiluted dry powders. Liquid sprays, being less concentrated, required even greater quantities.

DDT changed that situation. In their search for better insecticides for combatting malaria-carrying mosquitoes in the Pacific and other war theaters, entomologists found that DDT in an oil-solution spray gave good results when as little as one-fifth to one-fourth pound per acre was used. Engineers developed spraying apparatus for several types of military planes, and before long entire islands were being sprayed as a routine protective measure against mosquitoes and flies.

The end of the war brought a great demand for adapting aerial spraying to a variety of civil needs. Stimulating influences were the publicity given wartime developments, the availability of war-surplus airplanes at low prices and former military pilots who wanted peacetime occupation in aviation, the discovery of other insecticides, and increasing labor costs. Farmers, owners of timberlands, public health authorities, and we all became air-minded about insect control. Hopes were so high, in fact, that some people got the idea that airplanes and the new insecticides would quickly end all insect problems.

But we soon learned that man's war with insects was not yet over. More was needed than a mere abundance of planes, pilots, and DDT. Much of the wartime development had been made in haste to meet specific military requirements, to get a job done, regardless of cost; in peacetime the idea is to do a job but to do it effectively and economically. After the war, therefore, it was necessary to do a great deal of research to reconvert wartime developments to peacetime uses.

Several Federal and State agencies and many commercial operators conducted the research or assisted by furnishing equipment for making experimental control tests. The investigations have centered on the development of more efficient distributing apparatus and more effective insecticide formulations and the improvement of aircraft for insect-control operations.

Their methods have included generalized observations or appraisals in the field, trial-and-error experiments of limited scope, and broader studies of the principles governing the dispersal and deposition of insecticides from aircraft. Their objective has been to develop wider uses for aerial application of insecticides and to apply them better, faster, and cheaper. Because sprays are less affected by wind and adhere better to foliage, the greater emphasis has been placed on spraying equipment. In the first year or two after the war a great variety of spray equipment was being used. Experimentation and experience, however, have gradually narrowed the field to three main types, boom and nozzles, rotary devices, and exhaust sprayers.

The boom and nozzle sprayer was most commonly in use in 1952. Originally developed for light planes, it has been adapted to large transports. The sprayer usually consists of a spray tank carried inside the plane from which the spray liquid flows to a wind-driven pump. The pump forces the liquids into a tubular boom mounted beneath the wing (beneath the lower wing of biplanes), from which it is discharged as a spray through atomizing nozzles. The spray is turned on or off by a quick-opening gate valve, and a constant pressure in the spray lines is maintained by the use of an adjustable pressure regulator installed in the line between the pump and gate valve.

The chief advantages of this sprayer over others are the simplicity of its installation and maintenance; the ease with which the degree of atomization of the spray or its rate of application can be changed (it is necessary only to changes the size or the number of the nozzles); the use of a pressure regulator, thereby insuring a constant pressure in the system and a uniform discharge rate; and the fact that any excess flow of liquid from the pump is returned to the tank through the bypass from the pressure regulator, thus providing agitation or stirring action in the tank.

VARIATIONS in design have been made for specialized jobs. For example, the boom has been placed inside the wing, and nozzles have been attached to it by short pipe connections that extend vertically beneath the lower surface of the wing. In areas where uniformity of spray coverage has not been a prime requirement, other modifications have been to place the nozzles in clusters near the wing tips, on the rear edge of the wing, and on the tail assembly. Those installations improve the flight performance of the plane by reducing the air resistance, but they do not allow rapid adjustments of flow rate and atomization, which may be necessary for controlling different pests.

Considerable work has been done on adapting standard pumps and developing special pumps for the sprayers. Both centrifugal and positive-displacement types have given satisfactory performance. The latter develop higher pressures but often are subject to excessive wear when they are used with certain wettable powders that contain abrasive materials.

Other developments include devices for driving pumps directly from the airplane engine, by hydraulic systems, or by electric motors; the substitution of aluminum for brass or iron to reduce weight; special pump bearings; and pump packing and rubber parts resistant to the solvent action of sprays. Some attempts have been made to eliminate the pump entirely and to depend on gravity flow of the spray liquid from the tank to the boom. It has been found, however, that gravity systems do not deliver at a uniform rate unless some means is provided to compensate for the decreasing hydrostatic pressure as the tank empties.

Many atomizing devices, such as nozzles, jets, slotted orifices, and small venturi tubes, have been tested with varying success. None has been developed which will break up the liquid into drops of a uniform size. In general, though, nozzles that discharge the spray either in a hollow-cone pattern (similar to that of the common sprinkling nozzle) or in a flat fanlike sheet have been the most satisfactory and are the ones most commonly used.

Rotary sprayers were originally developed for applying oils and concentrated slurries of the older type of insecticides, which were too thick to go through pumps. Later they were used for other materials. Some mechanical improvements have been made in postwar models for distributing the newer insecticides, but those sprayers have been less popular than the boom and nozzle type.

The distinctive part of a rotary sprayer is the atomizing unit. It has a shaft with suitable housing and bearings; in front is a small, wind-driven propeller, and on the other end is a series of concave disks or circular wire brushes. The units may be placed on

970134°—52——18

the wings or on outriggers on the sides of the fuselage. Either way, the shaft is parallel to the fuselage. In flight the liquid flows by gravity from the tank to the center of the disks or brushes. It is then thrown outward by centrifugal force to the periphery of the rotating units, where the passing air shears the liquid into drops. One can change the output by regulating the rate of flow of the material to the units. The speed of rotation, the number and spacing of disks or brushes, and, in the latter, the size of the individual bristles govern the atomization.

Exhaust sprayers, first made for mosquito control, were designed to produce a cloud of spray like the mist sometimes applied inside buildings. The spray liquid is atomized by injecting it into the exhaust of the airplane engine. Usually the exhaust pipe is extended somewhat beyond the engine, and the liquid is introduced into the throat of a venturi or into a special atomizing head on the end of the pipe. The apparatus must be carefully designed for each engine because any restriction in the flow of the exhaust gases may create a dangerous back pressure against the engine. Since the war a few exhaust sprayers have been used in combatting some species of mosquitoes and other biting pests, but they have not come into general use for two reasons: The application rate is too low to kill many kinds of insects, and the spray is so fine that much of it may be carried away by wind or may evaporate before reaching the ground.

Work with dusting equipment has been directed mainly toward getting a wider and more uniform distribution of the materials beneath the plane. The materials usually are discharged from a spreader, like a venturi, on the under side of the fuselage. Consequently a heavy deposit frequently forms along the flight lines and the lateral spread is limited. Efforts have been made to correct the condition, chiefly by changing the design of the spreaders. Some redesigned spreaders have wide openings at the discharge ends or longitudinal deflecting vanes so arranged that the dust is thrown outward on a diagonal. Other spreaders are bifurcated, each branch being curved outward for the same effect. In the project for development of an agricultural airplane, described later, plans have been made to try building streamlined dusting units into the wings.

One advance in a special field is the development of equipment to distribute grasshopper bait from a multi-engine plane. Such poisoned baits have been applied by small aircraft, but the planes cover only limited areas. In order to combat extensive outbreaks, therefore, a bait spreader was designed for a C–47 transport plane. A large hopper holding 8,000 pounds of dry bait was built into the cargo space. A large air duct on each side of the fuselage extends from an opening near the leading edge of the wing, along the floor of the cargo space, and opens to the outside again near the rear of the fuselage. In operation, vaned rollers feed the bait from the hopper into the ducts. The flow of air carries it to the outside. Such a plane can treat 10,000 acres in a day, compared to 1,000 acres for the biplanes commonly used in crop work. The equipment has been modified to permit its use for applying sprays as well as baits by installing removable tanks inside the bait hopper.

The new distributing apparatus has given reasonably good performance in the control of a number of insect pests, but there is need for improvement. Some progress can be made by refinements in existing equipment, but in the long run the maximum efficiency can be had only by developing equipment on the basis of the fundamental factors that govern distribution of insecticides from the air.

Research projects have been started to study those factors, particularly the effect of the aerodynamic forces created by the plane, the size of the spray drops or dust particles, and weather conditions.

We have evidence that, aside from the effect of wind, the aerodynamic forces created by the airplane, particularly in the wake behind the plane, are largely responsible for the way the insecticide is finally distributed on the ground. This conclusion is based on results from several investigations, which we summarize here:

1. When a plane with a full-span spray boom is flown 3 to 10 feet from the ground, the spray swath laid down has about the same width as the wing span. When the altitude approximately equals the wing span, however, the swath width is increased four or five times. A further increase in altitude does not further increase the swath.

2. At the low altitude, the spray is driven downward, as evidenced by its reaching the less exposed parts of the plants, but in the higher-altitude flights the spray has very little downward force when it reaches the ground and does not penetrate a dense ground cover. The same effect has been observed in the application of dusts.

3. Increasing the discharge rate of the spray does not increase the swath width but merely deposits a greater amount within the swath.

4. In either the low- or high-altitude flight, the swath width is greater when the outlets are spaced over half or more of the wing span. Releasing the spray from a short boom or single outlet directly beneath the fuselage gives a very narrow swath, but extending the boom beyond the wing tips has not given any greater swath than the full-span boom.

5. When repeated tests are made under carefully selected weather conditions, certain random variations always occur in the amount of spray deposited that cannot be accounted for by weather conditions alone.

Aeronautical engineers have long known that the flow of air created by an airplane in flight is turbulent and spreads backward, outward, and downward. The paths of this airflow are complex and have not been completely worked out, but it seems certain that their general direction governs the differences in swath width we described and that the turbulence of the air flow causes the random irregularities in deposit.

Some research has been done to find out how the size of spray drops or dust particles affects the deposition of the insecticides. The aim is to determine the most effective size. None of the practical atomizing devices known today, whether used on the ground or in the air, will produce uniform spray drops. The average size of the drops can be made large or small, of course, but there is always a range of sizes above and below the average; the larger the average size the greater is the range. Therefore the terms coarse, medium, or fine, when applied to sprays, are only relative expressions.

Flight tests have shown that the degree of spray atomization markedly affects the width of the spray swath and the distribution of the deposit within the swath, especially when the plane is flown at an altitude equal to or greater than the wing span. A very fine spray of an average drop size of about 50 microns (1 micron equals about 0.00004 inch) gives a wider swath and a more uniform deposit than a coarse spray in which the drops average about 200 microns. Because the larger, heavier drops in the latter are less affected by the outward forces in the wake of the plane, they fall more nearly vertically and hence tend to concentrate the spray in the center of the swath. On the other hand, very fine sprays have much greater loss of drops by wind and evaporation.

There may also be a difference in the insecticidal efficiency in the deposits of coarse and fine sprays. The loss of the fine sprays is much greater, but field observations indicate that they penetrate crop or forest foliage better than do coarse sprays. Therefore it would seem that they should be more effective in reaching insects at the base of crop plants or those living beneath a forest canopy. As a matter of fact, in laboratory tests on certain species of insects, deposits of fine sprays have given somewhat higher mortality than equal deposits of coarse sprays. On the other hand, the coarse sprays have had a longer residual effect. Similar tests of residual effectiveness with aerial applications in the field have not given conclusive results on this point.

Some studies on the effect of particle size on distribution have been made with dusts, but the extent of the work has been limited because the particles, being irregular in shape and considerably smaller than spray drops, are much harder to collect and measure. As with spray drops, fine dust particles give a wider swath and cover foliage better than coarse ones. They are more subject to the effects of wind, however. In the case of diluted dusts, if the carrier or diluent (usually a clay, lime, or talc) is made up of particles different in size from those in the active ingredient, the two components may separate in the air and give a very irregular deposit of poison on the plants.

The least controllable factors that limit the effectiveness of aerial applications are air movement (wind and convection), temperature, and humidity—factors that may change greatly within seconds and over only a few hundred feet.

Wind is surely the most important. It may cause irregular coverage of the treated plants and may cause the spray or dust to drift beyond the treated area. The amount of loss by drift will not depend on the wind velocity alone, however. Size of the drops and altitude of flight also affect the loss. For example, in a wind of 1 mile an hour, a 200-micron drop released 10 feet above the ground will drift about 6 feet. But if the drop is released in a 10-mile-an-hour wind from an altitude of 50 feet it will be carried about 300 feet. Under the same conditions, a 20-micron drop will travel some 3.5 miles. Aside from reducing the amount of insecticide reaching the insects, drift may cause most of the material to strike the plant horizontally. That may result in an uneven distribution on the foliage of plants or trees.

The effect of the wind on spray distribution from planes is especially important when the more potent new insecticides are used. It may cause the spray or dust to drift from the area being treated, thereby contaminating nearby crops sufficiently to be a hazard to people and livestock. The maximum permissible wind velocity when treating crops or spraying for mosquito control generally should not exceed 10 to 15 miles an hour, and when treating forest it should not be greater than 8 miles an hour. Local conditions, of course, may be such that even those velocities are too high.

Convection is another factor. It is an upward flow of air that takes place when the ground temperature is higher than the air temperature. Convection currents usually become noticeable as the sun warms the ground during the morning. They may develop considerable force by afternoon. They affect sprays and dusts much as wind does. They are more variable than wind but, unlike wind, they carry the drops of particles upward instead of horizontally. We have no simple way to determine the amount of convection in an area during spraying or dusting operations. A fairly workable rule of thumb is that the operations should be stopped when the pilot finds the air is becoming bumpy, or when the lighter parts of the spray or dust cloud show a tendency to rise.

Temperature and humidity affect spray distribution indirectly. Increasing temperature promotes convection and increases evaporation rate. The latter may be particularly important when finely atomized, highly volatile materials are being applied. Humidity is chiefly important for its effect on the evaporation of water spray. We know of at least one instance in which a finely atomized water spray, applied on a hot, dry morning, evaporated before it reached the ground.

The best time to apply insecticides from the air is usually from daylight to 9 or 10 o'clock in the morning. Air movement and temperature then are at their lowest and humidity at the highest. In some localities the short time just before sunset also is satisfactory.

The fundamental factors interact closely. No one can be isolated and studied by itself. Furthermore, when the control of an insect is being studied the effects of all factors must be considered in respect to its habits and environment, and the insecticide to be used.

Many of the new organic insecticides, primarily the chlorinated hydrocarbons and hydrocarbons containing phosphorus, are highly effective in small amounts. Their development has advanced all methods, air and ground, that employ low volumes of concentrated insecticides. The discovery of each has made it necessary to work out spray or dust formulas for each pest by testing the new compound in combination with other compounds, with different solvents or dust carriers, and at different concentrations.

Some research has been directed toward finding how the physical properties of spray liquids affect dispersal and the efficiency in killing insects. An example is the finding that liquids of high viscosity are more coarsely atomized than less viscous ones and therefore give a narrower spray swath. The more volatile the spray, however, the more rapidly it evaporates; therefore a smaller amount reaches the insects.

Compared to the amount of research on distributing apparatus and insecticides for use in aircraft, the research on developing aircraft especially for spraying and dusting has been very limited. Most of the need for planes immediately after the war was met by adapting war-surplus biplane trainers because they were cheap and sturdy and could carry up to 1,200 pounds of insecticide. Many an operator, however, has preferred small, two-place, high-wing monoplanes, particularly for treating small acreages. Their performance has been improved. Some spray and dust equipment has been designed so it can be removed easily and the plane can be used for other purposes.

One builder of aircraft dispensing equipment has designed a spray tank in the shape of a seat, the back and bottom having a capacity of about 30 gallons. Such tanks need not be removed.

THE HELICOPTER was designed for general-purpose uses, but its ability to fly low and slow has been of particular advantage in spraying and dusting. It is well suited for treating small, inaccessible areas. It can be landed near or in the field being treated, and considerable ferry time is saved. The helicopter is said to be more effective than fixed-wing aircraft in giving thorough coverage to plants, but its first cost and operating costs are quite high.

In order to fill the need for a fixed-wing aircraft which would be more suitable for agricultural purposes than war-surplus trainers, the National Flying Farmers Association, Texas Agricultural and Mechanical College, the Civil Aeronautics Administration, and the United States Department of Agriculture sponsored the development of such a plane. The prototype model was constructed at the Personal Aircraft Research Center of the Texas Agricultural and Mechanical College. The design was based on findings in a survey among commercial operators and research organizations to determine the essential characteristics that it should have.

SAFETY was given special consideration. The cockpit is located so as to give the pilot excellent visibility. For protection in a forced landing, all loads and heavy masses are located in the wings or forward of the cockpit, and the pilot has a special seat, safety belt, and shoulder harness. The leading edge of the landing gear is sharp so it can cut wires it might accidentally touch in flight. Two structural members and a crash tripod over the cockpit give additional protection. The all-metal, low-wing monoplane can carry 1,200 pounds of insecticide. It operates at speeds up to 100 miles an hour. Specially designed flaps and ailerons give excellent slow-flight characteristics and slow landing speeds, less than 40 miles an hour.

Special types of distributing apparatus were developed. Space for the equipment is in the fuselage and the wing, which was made extra thick for the purpose. The sprayer has tanks and a boom in the wing and an engine-driven pump in the fuselage. The fuselage has a dust hopper with a conventional spreader underneath. On the drawing boards were plans for other types of distributing apparatus, particularly duster units mounted in the wing to give a wider and more uniform swath and equipment for distributing seeds and fertilizers. The plane was flown successfully in 1950.

J. S. Yuill *has been an entomologist in the division of forest insect investigations, Bureau of Entomology and Plant Quarantine, since 1935. Since 1946 he has been engaged in the development of aerial spraying for forest-insect control. He attended the University of Arizona and the University of California.*

D. A. Isler *is a senior agricultural engineer in the division of farm machinery, Bureau of Plant Industry, Soils, and Agricultural Engineering. A graduate of Ohio State University, he joined the Department of Agriculture in 1927 and has worked on the development of equipment for control of various insect pests. Since 1945 he has worked at the Agricultural Research Center at Beltsville, Md., on the development of aerial spraying equipment for control of forest pests.*

George D. Childress *is chief of the aviation extension division in the Office of Aviation Development, Civil Aeronautics Administration. A native of Virginia, he engaged in commercial airport and flying school operations in and around Roanoke from 1927 to 1939, when he joined CAA as an assistant aeronautical inspector.*

Machines for Applying Insecticides

Howard Ingerson, Frank Irons

Machines for applying insecticides are available in many makes, models, types, and sizes. They offer a wide range of selection for different conditions and uses. They save labor and provide more efficient ways to combat pests.

Power equipment is of six types—high-pressure sprayers, low-pressure sprayers, air-type sprayers, mist sprayers, dusters, and fog applicators.

The power source usually has been gasoline engines, either by separate engine or through power take-off from a tractor. The trend during the past few years has been toward air-cooled engines for the engine-powered units because they weigh less and are more compact than the water-cooled types. Water-cooled engines are used particularly for the higher horsepower requirements, however, because suitable air-cooled engines have not been available for the larger machines. The engines in use range from one-horsepower, air-cooled types to the large industrial water-cooled engines of 75 horsepower or more.

Tractors, besides hauling the equipment, furnish power to operate the machine. A standard power take-off attachment extends from the rear of the tractor through a power shaft and is connected with the drive shaft of the sprayer or duster.

The vehicles and mountings for carrying the application equipment are: Trailer type, tractor-mounted, motor-truck-mounted, self - propelled, and wheelbarrow and pushcart types.

Trailer-type and tractor-drawn machines commonly are used in orchards and on row crops, especially when heavy machines are required.

Tractor-mounted dusters and low-gallonage sprayers are widely used for field and row-crop applications. This type of mounting is limited to the weight-carrying capacity of the tractor and tires. Motor trucks are sometimes used for carrying orchard and row-crop equipment and they are regularly employed for carrying mist sprayers for shade-tree spraying. Wheelbarrow- and pushcart-type power sprayers and dusters have come into common use around greenhouses, farm buildings, small truck farms, and estates.

Special self-propelled, high-clearance sprayers and dusters have been developed for treating corn for European corn borer and corn earworm. Some of the machines are adaptations of the detasseling vehicles used in the production of hybrid seed corn and have a clearance of 4 feet to 7 feet.

The high-pressure sprayers, commonly spoken of as hydraulic, are designed for working at pressures of 100 to 600 pounds per square inch and are rated in terms of the number of gallons per minute that the pump discharges at a given pressure. The hydraulic pumps have one to four cylinders and are vertical or horizontal. Some are of open-type design. Others are completely enclosed with oil-bath lubrication comparable to tractor and automotive engine design. The tanks are of wood or steel and usually are from 10 to 20 times the capacity of the pump—for example, a pump of 7 gallons per minute capacity might be used with a tank of 150 gallons capacity; a 20-gallon pump is used with a 300- or 400-gallon tank.

Uniform and complete agitation of unstable mixtures is essential for satisfactory results. Most sprayers have a mechanical agitator, a power-driven shaft, which extends through the tank and has several paddles on it.

The pumps and other parts that come in contact with the chemicals must resist their corrosive and abrasive properties. Hence, they usually are made of brass, bronze, rubber, stainless steel, and porcelain.

Large, stationary, and high-pressure spraying systems have been installed in some orchards that are too hilly for portable machines. Pipe lines, underground or elevated, carry the spray under controlled pressure to all parts of the orchard. Outlets are provided at intervals along the pipe system for connecting hand-operated spray guns with long-lead hose.

Improvements are being made all the time in the distributing attachments.

To replace the one or two nozzles on the end of a 10- to 14-foot spray rod, the adjustable spray gun was invented and is in general commercial use. The multinozzle spray gun, commonly called a broom or spray head, later came into general use. Now we have attachments to make the spraying of large orchards automatic. They are best suited to sprayers with a pump capacity of at least 20 gallons a minute.

High-pressure sprayers equipped with special booms have been perfected for row crops, including potatoes and tomatoes. The booms are arranged to cover 2 to 30 rows or swaths of 6 to 40 feet. The number of nozzles per row and their arrangement on the boom depend on the crop, plant growth, and coverage needed.

Livestock spraying requires high pressure to drive the spray material through the hair or wool and to cover the animals evenly and completely. Adjustable-type spray guns are used. Clusters of nozzles that direct the spray from underneath the animals complete the operation.

High-pressure sprayers are used also for spraying shade trees and sanitation spraying to control flies and mosquitoes.

The pumps used in low-pressure spraying are mostly of the gear type. They generally have either bronze or brass parts, resist corrosion, and are suitable for spraying solutions and emulsions. They are not suited for use with suspensions that carry abrasive chemicals. Such sprayers have been introduced into the cotton areas. They are mounted directly on a tractor and operated by power take-off.

AIR SPRAYERS use air as the carrier for the spray chemicals. The air blast replaces the water-carrying power of high-pressure and high-gallonage machines. The fans or blowers in air sprayers are of three types—axial, radial, and centrifugal.

The requirements of air spraying are: Proper balance between the volume and velocity of air; nozzles adapted to the particular air velocity and volume; the proper placement of the nozzles in relation to the air stream; and the arrangement of the air-discharge outlet so as to direct the air that carries the spray chemicals so that it will cover the plants.

Air sprayers are rated in terms of air capacity in cubic feet per minute and velocity in miles per hour. They range from 250 cubic feet a minute at 150 miles an hour to 45,000 cubic feet a minute at 100 miles an hour. Some air sprayers are designed for use with dilute spray materials and for applying semiconcentrated and concentrated materials. Other types are designed solely for applying concentrated materials and often are designated as mist sprayers. Mist sprayers are used more and more to control flies and mosquitoes indoors and outdoors and have made sanitation spraying practical and economical. Mist sprayers have been adapted for use on shade trees to save labor and materials.

The air-blast machines blow finely divided spray into the trees, and their air-moving capacity should be sufficient to agitate all the air within the tree and displace much of it.

Ralph V. Newcomb and Arthur D. Borden, working in California, determined the discharge volume of spray in cubic feet per minute needed to spray trees of various sizes when the machine is traveling at various specified rates of speed and is spraying trees on both sides of the line of travel. The volumes are given in the table below.

These investigators tell us that a relatively low air velocity works better than a high velocity and causes less injury to the fruit and foliage. With the rates of travel and the discharge volumes shown in the table, an air velocity of 90 to 110 miles per hour at the nozzles is enough. Nozzles should be used which will break the spray up into droplets 30 to 50 microns in size. Such droplets will produce uniform coating of spray on fruit and foliage with very little runoff.

James Marshall, in British Columbia, and others have developed smaller machines, spraying to one side only, which can be operated partially underneath the overhanging branches of the trees. The discharge volume of these machines needs to be only half that of the two-way machines and are there-

Discharge Volumes of Sprays

Travel		*Discharge volume of spray needed to spray trees measuring—*		
		10'x10'x10' (1,000 cubic feet)	*20'x20'x20' (8,000 cubic feet)*	*30'x30'x25' (22,500 cubic feet)*
Miles per hour	*Feet per minute*	*Cubic feet per minute*		
½	44	4, 400	17, 600	32, 850
1	88	8, 800	35, 200	65, 700
1½	132	13, 200	52, 800	98, 550
2	176	17, 600	70, 400	....
2½	220	22, 000	....	....
3	264	26, 400	....	....
3½	308	30, 800	....	....
4	352	35, 200	....	....

Power Equipment for Applying Insecticides

Uses		*Power sprayer recommendations*			
Type	*Units protected*	*Type*	*Pump capacity*	*Tank capacity*	*Price*
	Acres of mature trees		*GPM*	*Gallons*	*Dollars*
Orchards (apples, pears, peaches, cherries, citrus and other tree fruits, and nuts).	1–3	High pressure.....	3–4	50–100	400–475
	4–10	.....do.........	5–7	50–150	500–750
	10–20	.....do.........	10–20	200–400	800–1, 400
	20–40	High pressure or small air type.	20–35	300–500	1, 500–2, 500
	40–75	High pressure or medium air type.	35–60	400–600	2, 500–3, 500
	75–200	Large air type....	50–65	400–600	4, 000–6, 000
	Acres				
Row crops (potatoes, melons, tomatoes, celery, beans, onions).	1–10	High pressure.....	6–7	100–150	650–800
	10–20	.....do.........	7–20	150–200	750–1, 650
	20–50	.....do.........	20–35	200–400	1, 700–2, 000
	50–100	.....do.........	35–60	400–600	2, 000–2, 500
	100–200	.....do.........	60	400–600	2, 200–2, 800
	Number of trees				
Shade trees.........	1, 000–3, 000	High pressure.....	35	400–500	2, 000–2, 500
	3, 000–5, 000	.....do.........	60	500–600	3, 000–3, 500
	1, 000–3, 000	Mist sprayer......	3–5	50–100	1, 500–2, 000
	3, 000–5, 000	.....do.........	5–6	100–150	2, 000–2, 500
	Number of mature cattle				
Livestock...........	10–30	High pressure.....	3–4	10–15	200–250
	30–100	.....do.........	3–4	15–50	200–450
	100–500	.....do.........	6–7	100–150	600–750
	500–5, 000	.....do.........	15–20	200–300	1, 200–1, 800
General farm livestock and weed control.	10–50	Low pressure.....	3–5	50	175–250
	50–150	High pressure.....	4–7	50–150	450–750
	150–500	.....do.........	7–20	150–300	600–1, 650

fore smaller and less expensive. Fruit growers in the Pacific Northwest have had satisfactory results with machines having a somewhat lower discharge volume than indicated in the table.

Many insecticides may be used in the air-blast machines at 2 to 5 times the concentration normally employed with spray guns. Much less water is needed. For example, in mature apple orchards in the Pacific Northwest it is sometimes necessary to use 20 pounds of 50 percent DDT per acre per application to control the codling moth. Applied with spray guns and using the DDT at 1 pound per 100 gallons, 2,000 gallons would be needed. With an air-blast machine, the same acre could be sprayed by applying the 20 pounds of DDT in 500 gallons of water. Some saving of insecticide can even be made with the latter method because when such a machine is properly used much less of the spray drips to the ground than when spray guns are used.

The cost is also much less. One orchardist in Washington reduced his per acre cost from $164 in 1947, when he applied lead arsenate and oil with guns, to $42 in 1949, when he applied DDT and parathion with an air-blast machine. He had only 5 percent of cull apples in 1949 as compared with 10 percent in 1947.

Dusters use air to distribute dry materials. They are used in nearly all fields of insect control as the sole means of treatment or to supplement sprayers.

They are of two general types. Single-outlet dusters are used primarily for dusting in orchards. Multiple-outlet dusters with flexible conductor tubes and spreader nozzles at the ends of the tubes are designed for direct application of dust to field and row crops.

Dusters can be used only when there is little air movement. The dusts adhere less well than liquids. Dusters have the advantages of being lighter in weight and they can carry enough insecticide for long periods of operation. Dusting is popular in places where water supplies are limited.

Fog applicators were developed during the Second World War primarily for spraying enclosed space. Some have been used to control flies and mosquitoes in buildings and outdoor areas. Few are used by farmers; they are generally considered unsatisfactory for providing adequate residual deposits and coverage because they rely on air drift to carry the insecticide.

Sprayers and dusters have to be cleaned and oiled systematically. The corrosive and abrasive properties of spray and dust materials make it essential that tanks and dust hoppers be emptied and cleaned at the end of each day of use. Pumps and all accessories should be washed out to reduce corrosion and nozzle-clogging troubles. Pumps and engines must be drained during freezing weather. Lubrication of all wearing parts according to the manufacturer's instructions will allow the equipment to operate smoothly and increase its useful life. Replacement or repair of wearing parts as needed is good economy.

HOWARD INGERSON *joined the Bureau of Entomology and Plant Quarantine upon graduation from Pennsylvania State College. Later he managed commercial orchards in Ohio. Since 1935 he has been agricultural sales manager and research representative of a firm in Lansing, Mich.*

FRANK IRONS *is an agricultural engineer in the Bureau of Plant Industry, Soils, and Agricultural Engineering. He is leader of a research project that studies machinery used to control pests and plant diseases. He is stationed in Toledo, Ohio.*

Choosing and Using Hand Equipment

T. E. Bronson, Earl D. Anderson

Hand-operated sprayers and dusters are suitable for applying insecticides around the home and garden; in stores, restaurants, hospitals, and other commercial and public buildings; and on farms for protecting livestock, poultry, and buildings. Small fields of 5 or 10 acres or less, depending on the type of crop, may be treated with hand or traction equipment, although power machines are generally desirable in larger fields, especially if time is a factor and if labor costs are high. Hand equipment is used also to supplement power equipment in large fields—for spot treatment of localized infestations, for instance.

It was to combat the ravages of one species of insect, known only as a museum specimen from 1819 to about 1850, that the modern sprayer had its beginning. As the pioneers of this country moved westward, attracted by free land and the discoveries of gold, some of the pioneers stopped in the foothills of the Rockies and planted crops, including potatoes.

Between 1850 and 1860 many of the early settlers were threatened by starvation as hordes of the insects, with a pleasing new source of food, rapidly increased in population as they devoured one field of potatoes after another. By the time the migration of the insects reached the older settled Atlantic coast area, experimentation had proved that the insect was vulnerable to the poison later known as paris green. Impatient with such makeshift methods of application as whisk brooms and hand dusting for protecting their own potato crops, early inventors, such as John Bean of California, D. B. Smith of New York, and

Brandt Brothers of Minnesota, developed and improved the first hand sprayers. Thus it was that a small insect, the Colorado potato beetle, was largely responsible for the early development of suitable equipment for applying insecticides.

Hand-operated equipment includes household sprayers, electric sprayers, general utility sprayers (compressed-air sprayers, knapsack sprayers, wheelbarrow sprayers, and hand spray pumps and accessories), and dusters (plunger dusters, crank dusters, knapsack dusters, and wheelbarrow dusters). Of each there may be many sizes, models, and types. Some are best suited for one particular type of job. Others have features of design that adapt them for several different uses. In any event, the insecticide has to be applied properly if it is to be most effective.

The main function of a sprayer is to break the liquid into droplets of effective size and distribute them uniformly over the surface or space to be protected. Another function is to regulate the amount of insecticide to avoid excessive application that might prove harmful or wasteful.

Dusters have similar functions. Dusting is not a suitable method of knocking down insects in flight, but it is used to control crawling insects in the home, garden, and field. Properly applied dusts and sprays usually are equally effective. Dusts cost more but they need no mixing by the user. For home use, a small plunger-type duster ready to take to the garden on the daily inspection trip is desirable. If more than one insecticide is often used, it is well to have two of these small dusters.

The sprayer or duster best suited for a specific job can be determined more readily when the basic requirements for chemical control of insects are considered. The bothersome insects that we wish to control in and around buildings are either crawling insects or flying insects.

Crawling insects are generally controlled by applying a residual coating of an insecticide to the surface upon which the insects may crawl or rest, such as the floor, wall, or ceiling of a structure, the bodies of animals, or the foliage of a plant. The insects are killed by coming in contact with the chemical deposit or by ingesting it.

Chemical dusts and sprays are used for the purpose, although, of course, only sprays are used for treating walls and ceilings of structures. In choosing a duster, size to fit the job is the primary consideration, but for some applications there is a choice between units that provide intermittent or continuous discharge of the dust.

A sprayer that delivers droplets large enough to wet the surface readily should be used for proper application of surface or residual sprays. Extremely fine droplets tend to be diverted by air currents and be wasted.

To control flying insects, one can use residual sprays on surfaces where the insects may rest or discharge a knockdown type of insecticide into the air in which the insects are flying, killing them upon contact. A sprayer is needed that will produce a fine mist or a fog, which will stay suspended in the air for a time.

One chart shows some of the equipment for the control of insects pests of lawn, garden, or field, which feed on vegetation or live in it. Such insects also may be classified as sucking insects or chewing insects. Sucking insects generally are controlled by applying a contact insecticide, which kills the insect by absorption through the respiratory system or through the body wall. In the liquid form, the contact insecticide should be applied by a sprayer that will produce a fine-droplet mist or fog. The size of duster to be used to apply the dry form of the insecticide should be chosen to fit the size of the job. The chewing insects may be controlled by the use of either a contact insecticide, such as used for controlling sucking insects, or a residual or surface type of insecticide, of the kind used to control crawling insects in and around buildings.

Household sprayers of the hand-

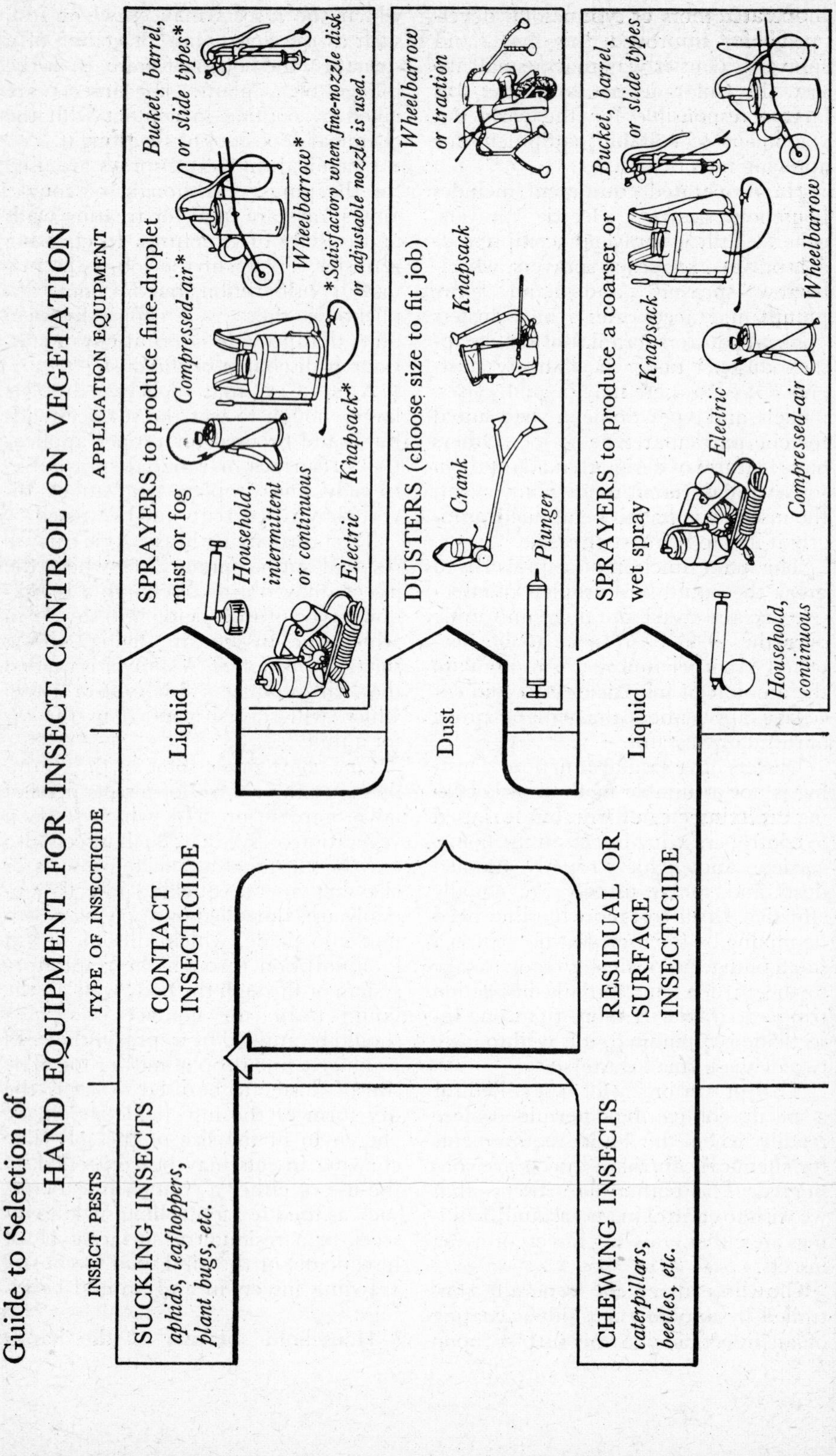

Guide to Selection of

HAND EQUIPMENT FOR INSECT CONTROL ON VEGETATION

INSECT PESTS | TYPE OF INSECTICIDE | APPLICATION EQUIPMENT

SUCKING INSECTS
aphids, leafhoppers, plant bugs, etc.

CONTACT INSECTICIDE

Liquid

SPRAYERS to produce fine-droplet mist or fog

Household, intermittent or continuous
Electric
*Compressed-air**
*Knapsack**
*Bucket, barrel, or slide types**
*Wheelbarrow**

** Satisfactory when fine-nozzle disk or adjustable nozzle is used.*

Dust

DUSTERS (choose size to fit job)

Plunger
Crank
Knapsack
Wheelbarrow or traction

CHEWING INSECTS
caterpillars, beetles, etc.

RESIDUAL OR SURFACE INSECTICIDE

Liquid

SPRAYERS to produce a coarser or wet spray

Household, continuous
Electric
Compressed-air
Knapsack
Bucket, barrel, or slide types
Wheelbarrow

operated plunger type are used principally for applying sediment-free liquid insecticides in the home to control flies, moths, mosquitoes, and other pests. They are also used for applying insecticide or disinfectant sprays in stores, restaurants, and dairy barns. They are the simplest and least expensive sprayers.

The typical sprayer consists of a tank holding several ounces to about 3 quarts of liquid. Air pressure from the built-in plunger pump breaks up the liquid into droplets. The sprayers usually are made of tin and may cost as little as 25 cents.

Plunger sprayers are of two types—the intermittent, or single, action, and the continuous action.

The intermittent sprayer discharges the spray material only with each forward stroke of the pump. It delivers a finely atomized spray and is designed for applying space or knock-down insecticides to kill flying insects in closed rooms.

The continuous-type sprayers produce a constant discharge while the pump is being operated. Some have twin nozzles, one of which is used to produce the fine-droplet space sprays and the other to produce the coarser-droplet surface or residual sprays. Another type has a single nozzle, which may be quickly adjusted from one type of spray to the other.

Compression-sprayer performance is obtained with some of the larger sprayers—usually the 3-quart size—which are equipped with a lever-operated cut-off valve. This feature permits pumping up a head of air pressure while the tank is placed on the floor or ground. The spray is released by depressing the valve lever. These sprayers are used extensively for spraying small dairy herds and for the larger spraying jobs around the home, such as control of clothes moths and flies.

Electrically operated household sprayers are used extensively in restaurants, factories, and public buildings by professional pest-control operators. They are used also in the home and in farm buildings. The most common type has a metal or glass supply tank holding about a pint or a quart of insecticide. The force for expelling the liquid is supplied by an electrically driven rotary-type air compressor or by a piston-type liquid pump operated by an electric vibrator. The sprayers have adjustable nozzles for the application of either space- or residual-type sprays. With proper attachments they can be used for spraying paint and applying insecticidal dusts. The cost varies from about 5 to 10 dollars for a home type unit and up to 50 dollars or more for the industrial type, which is equipped with a time switch.

General utility sprayers fill a variety of needs for which the household sprayer, because of its small size and capacity, is inadequate. They are designed particularly for applying sprays in the yard, garden, and dairy barns. They may be used for spraying small trees and for applying residual insecticides around the home, in farm buildings, on livestock, or on public health projects involving insect control. Their nozzle design permits the use of a wide range of insecticide formulations, including emulsions and wettable powders.

The compressed-air sprayer is a common tool in gardens and farmyards. The newer insecticides, which are applied in highly concentrated form, extend the area of usefulness of this unit to the treatment of small acreages of field crops, such as cotton. It is also the mainstay of most public health projects involving insect control the world over because of its simple design and operation and relatively low cost.

Compressed-air sprayers consist essentially of a 2- to 5-gallon tank, airtight filler cap, air pump for compressing the air in the tank above the liquid, and outlet connection. The discharge hose is fitted with control valve, strainer, and nozzle; usually it has an extension tube to permit easier coverage. Several different nozzle disks, hav-

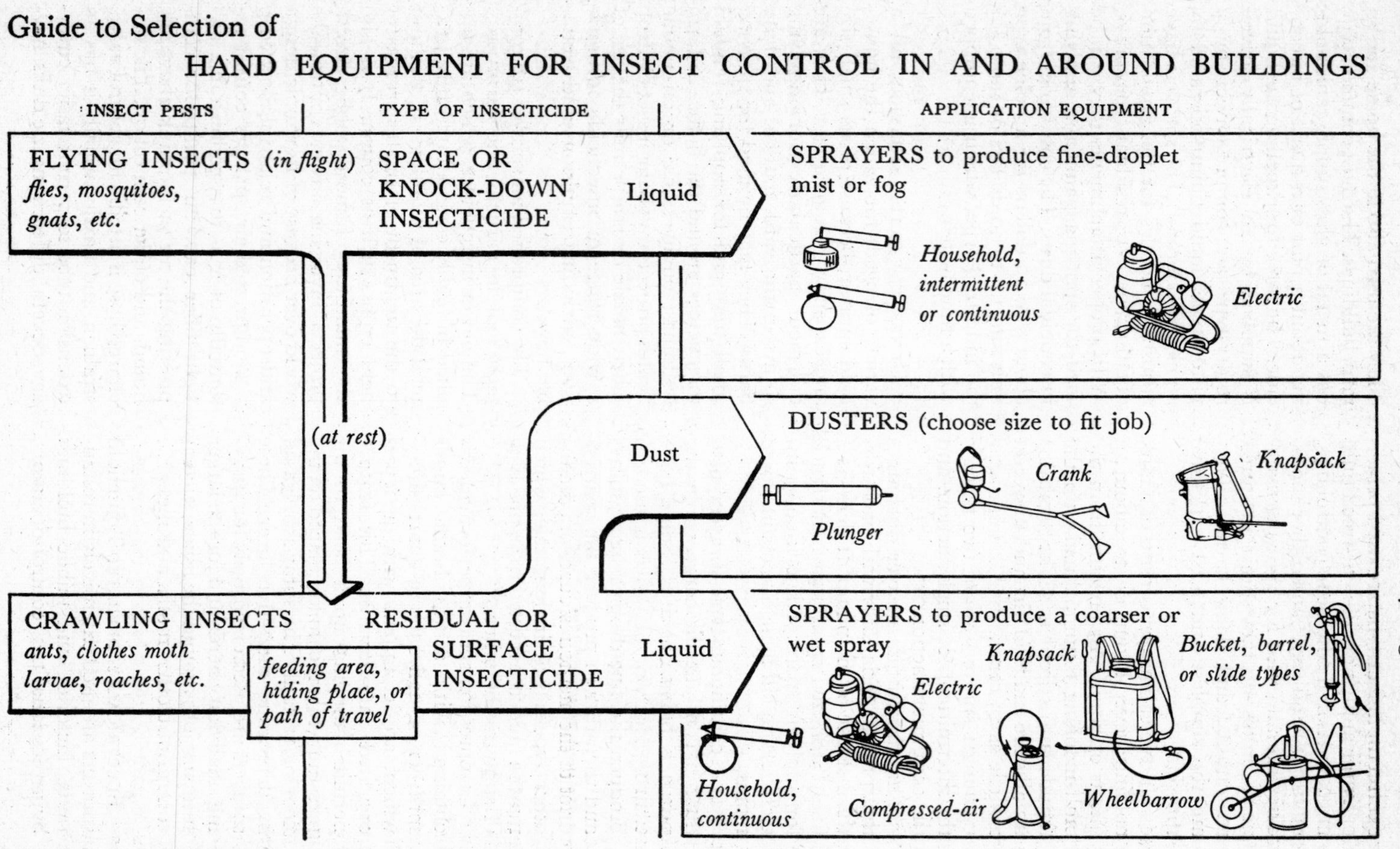
Guide to Selection of
HAND EQUIPMENT FOR INSECT CONTROL IN AND AROUND BUILDINGS
INSECT PESTS
TYPE OF INSECTICIDE
APPLICATION EQUIPMENT
FLYING INSECTS (in flight)
flies, mosquitoes, gnats, etc.
SPACE OR KNOCK-DOWN INSECTICIDE
Liquid
SPRAYERS to produce fine-droplet mist or fog
Household, intermittent or continuous
Electric
(at rest)
Dust
DUSTERS (choose size to fit job)
Plunger
Crank
Knapsack
CRAWLING INSECTS
ants, clothes moth larvae, roaches, etc.
feeding area, hiding place, or path of travel
RESIDUAL OR SURFACE INSECTICIDE
Liquid
SPRAYERS to produce a coarser or wet spray
Household, continuous
Electric
Compressed-air
Knapsack
Wheelbarrow
Bucket, barrel, or slide types

ing different size and shape of aperture, are supplied to provide a selection of spray patterns. These usually include solid cone and hollow cone (both coarse and fine) and flat fan and solid stream. Most of these sprayers are made of galvanized steel, although some are made of copper, brass, or stainless steel for industrial uses or for use by professional pest-control operators. They cost about 5 to 25 dollars.

These sprayers should be filled not more than three-fourths full of liquid, so that space is left for building up a head of air pressure. Occasional pumpings maintain the normal operating pressure of 30 to 50 pounds. The sprayer should be shaken occasionally to prevent the material from settling. When equipped with the usual cone or flat-fan nozzle disk, the nozzle is normally held about 6 to 18 inches from the surface to be sprayed. Some models of compressed-air sprayers are equipped with refillable CO_2 cylinders, which eliminate hand pumping of the sprayer. The cylinder or cartridge holds enough gas to expell three or four tankfuls of spray material at a constant pressure.

Knapsack sprayers differ from the compressed-air sprayers primarily with respect to the method of carrying, type of pump used, and the provision for agitation. These sprayers are carried on the back like a knapsack and are held in place by two shoulder straps. They are equipped with liquid-type pumps, which can develop maximum pressures of 80 to 180 pounds per square inch, a feature that broadens their field of use and permits the spraying of higher trees, for example. An internal pump of the piston or diaphragm type is commonly used and with it an air chamber to develop a steady spraying pressure. Spray agitation is also provided either by means of a bypass stream from the pump or by a paddle connected to the pump handle. On some makes the pump handle may be attached to either side to permit right- or left-hand operation.

Some models are equipped with a double-acting external slide-type pump. The pump of the knapsack sprayer, regardless of type, is operated continuously while spraying. The tanks of these sprayers are usually made of galvanized steel and have a capacity of 4 to 6 gallons. Special models are available with tanks of copper or stainless steel.

Several different nozzle disks are usually furnished with the conventional nozzle, or the sprayer may be equipped with an adjustable nozzle to provide a wide range of spray patterns such as a fine mist for tender flowers or a coarser spray to wet the surface of a building for residual fly control.

Because these sprayers develop higher pressures and have greater capacity than most compressed-air sprayers, they are better adapted for use on larger spraying jobs such as for large gardens or truck farms. The cost varies from about 15 to 50 dollars for the different models.

Wheelbarrow sprayers are the largest of the hand-operated spray units. They are particularly useful where the amount of spraying is too great to be handled adequately by a knapsack or compressed-air sprayer. Large gardens, greenhouses, small acreages of truck crops, and farm buildings where the cost of power equipment may not be warranted are some of the places where wheelbarrow sprayers are particularly suitable. This equipment is also satisfactory for spraying small numbers of fruit trees, because of its adequate capacity and pressure. The tanks have capacities of 12 to 18 gallons. A barrel-type piston pump mounted in the tank develops pressures up to 250 pounds. The tank unit is mounted on a wheelbarrow frame fitted with one or two wheels with either steel or rubber tires for convenience in moving from place to place. This sprayer is equipped with a mechanical agitator and the usual discharge hose, extension tube, shut-off valve, and nozzle with an assortment of disks.

Special equipment available with some models includes an air-pressure tank and pressure gage supplied with the necessary fittings and extra length of hose to permit one-man operation. After pumping up pressure in the air tank the operator can spray some distance from the machine returning occasionally to rebuild the pressure and move the machine as the work progresses. Wheelbarrow sprayers sell for 30 to 80 dollars or so.

HAND SPRAY PUMPS are inexpensive and efficient for occasional sprayings where more expensive equipment may not be justified. Sufficient pressure may be developed with these pumps to spray average-size fruit trees. No spray container is furnished with them.

They are of three types—bucket, barrel, and slide.

Bucket pumps are of the positive-acting plunger type equipped with an air chamber for constant pressure and with a discharge hose, nozzle, and strainer. A foot rest or bracket is provided for supporting the pump. As they develop pressures up to 250 pounds, they can be used for a number of spray jobs. Because of their simplicity in design and operation, the entire malaria-control program in some countries is planned largely around this piece of equipment for insecticidal application.

Barrel pumps are similar to bucket pumps but are larger and of heavier construction. They have clamps for attachment to a barrel and a mechanical agitator.

A slide pump consists of a telescoping-type pump which serves as part of the discharge system, a fixed or adjustable nozzle, a supply hose, and an intake strainer. These pumps develop pressures up to 180 pounds. The range in price of these sprayers is about as follows: Bucket pumps, 5 to 10 dollars; barrel pumps, 10 to 25 dollars; and slide pumps, 5 to 15 dollars.

Accessories and fittings of many kinds for special spraying needs are provided by manufacturers—special nozzles, discharge extension tubes, and multiple-nozzle booms, to mention a few. There is a wide variety of nozzles adapted to special uses, i, e., angle nozzles for under-leaf spraying, swivel-head nozzles, fan-type nozzles, and adjustable nozzles that provide a spray ranging from a fine mist to a solid stream. Special disk inserts are available for use in standard nozzles to give different droplet sizes or patterns such as flat fan, solid cone, or hollow cone. The multiple-nozzle boom is an accessory which greatly speeds up the usual spraying operation. It is especially useful for fly and mosquito control in buildings and around the home grounds and as special equipment on knapsack sprayers to be used in areas inaccessible to power sprayers. Another useful accessory is the sprayer cart which provides mobility to compressed-air sprayers and is handy for transporting the larger size sprayers, especially if the source of water is some distance from the area to be sprayed.

PLUNGER DUSTERS are the most practical for use around the average home. The smaller household dusters are especially convenient for placing insecticidal dusts in kitchens, pantries, and basements for control of ants and other crawling insects. The larger garden-size duster is ideal for applying dusts for the control of insects and plant diseases in the home garden.

The principal parts of the duster consist of the chamber for holding the dust, the air pump for supplying the air blast, and the delivery tube and nozzle. The dust chamber may be of glass or metal construction. The nozzles on some dusters may be adjusted at various angles to obtain better under-leaf coverage. These dusters sell for 50 cents to 2 or 3 dollars.

Crank and knapsack dusters are designed for use on estates, in large gardens or small acreages of truck crops, and on field crops such as cotton or tobacco. They are also useful for controlling spot infestations in larger fields before making a general treatment with large equipment.

The crank and knapsack dusters are provided with dust hoppers holding from 5 to 25 pounds of dust, an agitator to prevent the dust from packing, and a mechanism to feed the dust uniformly into the outlet. An extension tube may be fitted to this outlet for dusting small fruit trees.

The crank duster is suspended in front of the operator by means of shoulder straps. An air blast is generated by a manually operated rotary fan or blower, which provides a continuous discharge of dust. To treat row crops, the dust may be put out through one or more tubes arranged to cover either one or two rows in front of or behind the operator.

The knapsack duster develops an air blast by means of a bellows rather than by a fan or blower. The dust is therefore discharged intermittently and for this reason the knapsack duster is particularly adapted for treating crops planted in hills or for spot dusting of crops in which the plants are widely spaced in the row. By continuous operation, however, this duster may be used for applying dust to other crops.

Wheelbarrow or traction dusters are intermediate between hand and power equipment. They are used for continuous dusting of small acreages of row crops. Because of their light weight and mobility, they may often supplement power dusters when fields are soft or rough.

These dusters are like the crank dusters but are of heavier construction and are mounted on wheelbarrow frames. Power is derived from the traction wheel of the unit; the fan is driven by a chain or belt. Wheelbarrow dusters are usually designed for two-row coverage and use two discharge nozzles per row. The nozzles are adjustable for crops of different height or for applying dust to the under sides of the leaves. The hoppers hold 15 to 50 pounds of dust and the discharge rate may be varied from about 5 to 45 pounds per acre. A clutch is provided for intermittent use in the field. Some larger models have a front hitch for use in attaching to horse, mule, or garden tractor when larger fields are to be dusted. Crank and knapsack dusters range in price from 20 to 50 dollars and wheelbarrow dusters from about 75 to 125 dollars.

Household sprayers require little maintenance because of their simple design. They should be stored in a dry place. If the pump should lose its compression, a little lubricant should be applied in the air hole at the end of the cylinder to soften the pump leather and keep the seal with the cylinder wall.

Before the beginning of the spraying season, the general utility sprayer should be disassembled and inspected to make sure that it is in good shape. Worn parts, which may interfere with the operation of the unit, should be replaced. Repair or replacement parts can be bought from the local retail dealer or from the manufacturer. The sprayers should be cleaned after each use. After safe disposal of any insecticides remaining in the sprayer, the tank should be rinsed with clean water. Then the nozzle should be disassembled and cleaned and some clean water should be forced from the tank through the discharge line to remove any foreign deposits. The tank should then be dried or inverted for drainage and the whole unit stored in a dry place.

Before dusters are placed in seasonal storage, the dust reservoir should be emptied and thoroughly cleaned. Extension tubes should also be disassembled and all the joints cleaned of any dust deposits. Working parts on the larger dusters should be cared for in the manner prescribed by the manufacturer.

T. E. Bronson, *an entomologist, was associated with the Bureau of Entomology and Plant Quarantine from 1924 until 1951, when he resigned to join a chemical company. He is a graduate of the University of Wisconsin.*

Earl D. Anderson *is secretary of the National Sprayer and Duster Association. He has degrees in agricultural engineering from Iowa State College.*

970134°—52——19

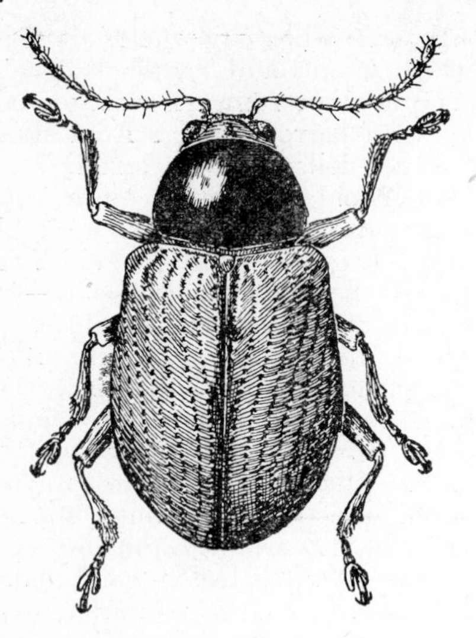

Strawberry leaf beetle.

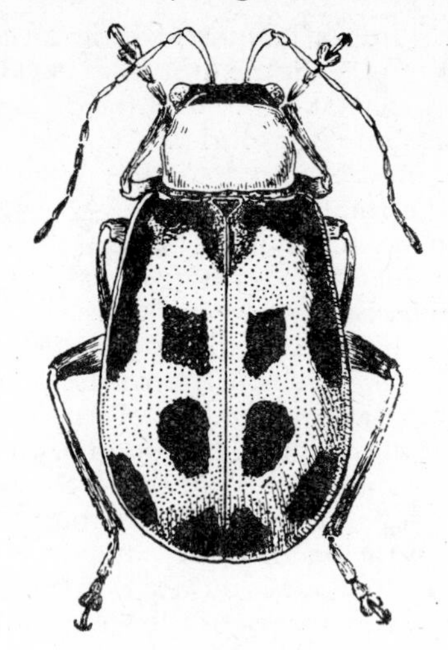

Bean leaf beetle.

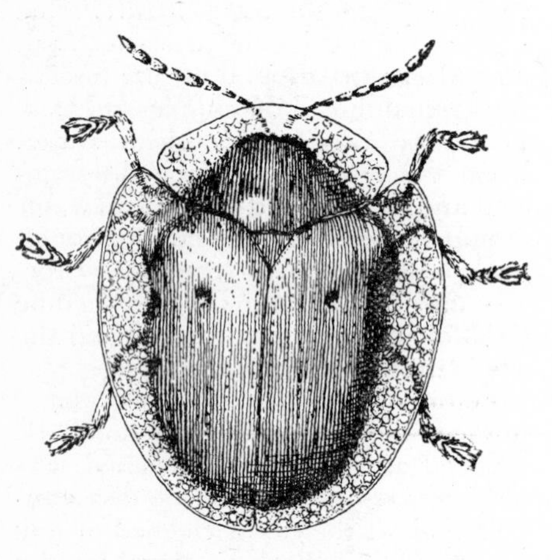

Tortoise beetle.

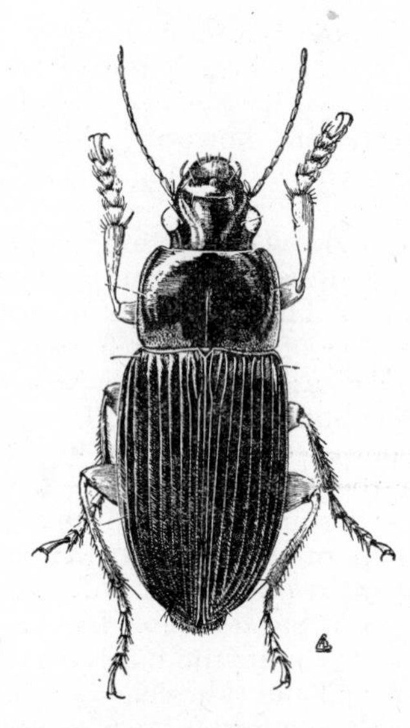

Harpalus pennsylvanicus, a ground beetle.

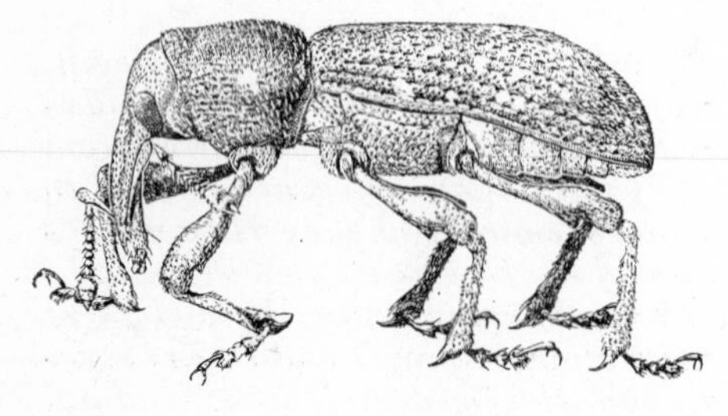

Pales weevil.

Striped blister beetle.

Warnings as to Insecticides

The Safe Use of Insecticides

F. C. Bishopp, John L. Horsfall

Insecticides kill insects because they affect a life process like respiration, digestion, circulation, and nerve reactions. A person also might experience some effect on his life processes if enough of the chemicals should get into the body by mouth, with or without food; through the nose, by breathing vapors or particles of dusts or liquids; or through the skin, by absorption.

Any person who plans to use an insecticide should inform himself therefore of its characteristics. What man, in his right mind, would attempt to fly an airplane without first learning how to do so?

Many sources give the characteristics of the various insecticides and directions for using them safely. The Department of Agriculture, county agricultural agents, most of the State agricultural colleges, agricultural experiment stations, and extension services can furnish, on request, printed matter that describes the characteristics of insecticides and the precautions to be observed in using them.

Another important source of information is the label on the container. Every user, before he opens the package, should read all the statements, directions, and warnings on it because it relates specifically to the material in the package. The instructions are there for good reason—the user's safety.

The Insecticide, Fungicide, and Rodenticide Act requires that insecticides entering interstate commerce be registered and that labels on them carry information to safeguard the user and the public. The Food and Drug Administration, a unit of the Federal Security Agency, establishes tolerances; that is, levels of insecticidal residues that are safe on foods. Many States have laws requiring appropriate labels and controlling the application of pesticides by custom applicators.

Insecticides differ in degree of toxicity—the amount that would harm livestock or man: Man could tolerate pyrethrum and sulfur in rather large quantities, but small amounts of calcium arsenate or sodium fluoride would be dangerous.

Insecticides differ also in the way they act. Some (like nicotine sulfate) may be very poisonous, but show little cumulative effect. Others (like lead arsenate) are less acutely poisonous but build up in the system and produce ill effects if they are taken repeatedly into the body.

Some insecticides (like hexaethyl tetraphosphate) may be poisonous to insects and higher animals when first applied but lose their strength quickly. Others (like DDT) are less poisonous but persist for considerable periods.

Thus very poisonous materials must be handled and applied carefully. In the use of the less toxic but more persistent materials the hazards from residues must receive the major attention.

The danger always exists that a person may exercise great care when first using an insecticide and, experiencing no ill effects, may become more and more careless.

The home gardener who needs to control pests in his back yard would select insecticides from the group which need only a minimum of care in their use—pyrethrum and rotenone, for example. The main precautions for him are to avoid getting the insecticides into the eyes or mouth or on the skin. Like all other insecticides, they should be stored in a place where children cannot touch them and where they cannot contaminate food.

A NONHAZARDOUS COMPOUND usually does not carry a poison label. If it includes a compound in solution with a propellant and is to be applied as a fine mist or if it is dissolved in deodorized kerosene and is to be applied as a spray to control household pests, a precaution on the label would state that contamination of foods should be avoided. If the spray contains a kerosene solvent, it should not be applied near an open flame. It is harmful if swallowed.

Insecticides with limited hazards are used commercially and many are recommended for the home gardener. A person who uses them should avoid breathing dust or spray mist, avoid contamination of feed and foodstuffs, keep the insecticides away from children and domestic animals, and wash himself thoroughly after using the materials.

The home gardener who uses a hand duster or sprayer, by observing the wind direction, can avoid breathing the dust or mist. If he happens to be particularly susceptible to inhalation of dusts of any kind he can obtain protection by using an inexpensive respirator of the type having a cloth filter pad. A handkerchief tied over the nose and mouth will give some protection.

Commercial operators who are exposed to inhalation of spray mists or dusts day after day should use a simple pad respirator. The warning not to contaminate feed and foodstuffs should make it obvious that this group of insecticides may leave residues on fruit and vegetables if they are used too near harvest.

Other insecticide formulations in this group may have vapors that should not be inhaled. They may have a slight hazard because of possible skin absorption or irritation. They may be harmful if swallowed.

If the label indicates a hazard from breathing the vapors, a respirator having a cartridge filter through which the air passes will furnish protection.

If danger of skin absorption is indicated on the label, contact with it should be avoided. Rubber gloves will be useful when handling it. Some solvents affect synthetic rubber quickly, and it is best to use gloves of natural rubber.

If the insecticide might harm the eyes, goggles should be worn. After spraying or dusting, clothing should be changed and the body carefully bathed. Clothing considerably contaminated should be laundered before being worn again.

Some of the insecticides of this class are used to control household pests. Even though the risk is not unduly great, the instructions on the labels should be followed.

HAZARDOUS COMPOUNDS may or may not bear the word "poison" on the label, depending on their concentration, but all are labeled to show that they are dangerous and may cause death if swallowed. Empty containers should be promptly destroyed or buried. They should never be left where children or domestic animals can get at them. Such insecticides should not be stored where contamination of food or feed can take place. The user should familiarize himself with the antidote mentioned on the label for accidental poisoning. Nearly all these insecticides, at the concentrations indicated, are used chiefly by commercial growers or those who apply insecticides on a contract basis.

Certain concentrated volatile insecticides are intended for mite control in chicken houses. Anyone using them should take special care to avoid breathing the vapors and letting them touch the skin.

Users of hazardous sprays should wash thoroughly and change clothing after working with the material for any length of time. A person who uses dusts day after day should use a good respirator and change the pads frequently.

Particular hazards are associated with the commercial use of organic phosphorus compounds. They are hazardous if swallowed, inhaled, or absorbed through the skin or eyes. Protective gloves, clothing, goggles, and a respirator with a special canister capable of absorbing the vapors should be worn. Users should wash thoroughly with soap and water after each day's operation.

Aerosol bombs may contain pyrethrum, allethrin, or DDT as the insect-killing agent. The use of amounts indicated on the label creates no hazard, but it is best to close a treated room and remain outside for 15 minutes or more.

DDT solutions used in the form of thermal aerosols or fogs to control flies and mosquitoes over large areas cause practically no hazard to the operator or to persons in the fogged area who might breathe the mists for a short time. The air dilution and short exposure are protective factors. To remain in such aerosol clouds for long periods is inadvisable, however.

Aerosols are sometimes used to destroy insects on vegetation. The insecticide is dissolved in an organic solvent in the aerosol formulation. This may present some hazard from skin absorption, and care should be taken when handling such solutions. Gloves of natural rubber should be worn. Hands and skin should be washed if there is contact with the solution. Goggles and a respirator should be worn to avoid breathing the fumes.

Organic phosphorus insecticides are not recommended for use in these fogs for outdoor-area treatment. Aerosols in which they are combined with a propellant are released from cylinders for controlling greenhouse pests. The operator should wear protective clothing, gloves, and a face mask equipped with a universal-type N-canister. Treated greenhouses should be posted and locked, and no one should enter them until they are thoroughly aired.

With the increased use of insecticides since 1945, however, more precautions have become necessary to protect pilots and flagmen as well as other people, livestock, and wildlife in the treated and adjacent areas.

Special care must be observed when pilots or helpers apply sprays or dusts containing organic phosphorus compounds. It is necessary to avoid breathing the dust, vapor, or spray mist and to avoid skin contact. Loaders must wear a full-face mask provided with a universal-type N-canister, because of their severe exposure to the insecticide concentrates. Pilots and helpers should wear respirators with a fume-type filter and chemical-absorbing cartridge. Freshly laundered, waterproof, or protective clothing that covers all exposed skin surfaces should be worn. The clothing should be changed daily. The equipment should be checked before loading to make sure all connections are tight and the system is functioning properly. The pilot should lay out his course so as to avoid flying back through an insecticide cloud.

Clean, natural-rubber or rubber-dipped gloves should be worn. They should be replaced frequently. The pilot and helpers should bathe thoroughly and change clothing after flying operations.

Fumigants, which kill insects in more or less enclosed spaces, have different degrees of hazards. Fumigants that present minimum hazards, such as ethylene dichloride-carbon tetrachloride mixture, may be used safely by farmers to treat stored grain. Others, which require greater precautions, like carbon disulfide, should be used only by commercial pest-control operators. The most hazardous fumigants, such as hydrocyanic acid gas, should never be used by the novice. The pest-control operator is trained to handle them and knows the proper precautions. Any fumigant that is toxic to insects is also toxic to human beings.

Before any fumigant is used, the various sources of information should be consulted and labels should be carefully read. Antidotes and first-aid treatments should be noted.

Two principal precautions that should be taken when a fumigant is used, regardless of its degree of toxicity, are to avoid exposure to a heavy concentration or inhalation of vapors for a long time and to avoid spilling the fumigant on the skin or clothing.

A farmer who may be using a limited amount to treat one or two grain bins and who is using a fumigant recommended for farm use is exposed to it only for a short time. Protection from breathing the fumes is usually not necessary, as he can avoid prolonged inhalation. When the fumigant is used repeatedly over a long period and in enclosed spaces, protection against inhalation is necessary. If there is exposure to high concentrations, a full-face mask should be worn. The mask should have a canister suitable for the fumigant used; not every canister will afford protection against all gases. Because the life of a canister is limited, new ones must be supplied whenever those in use show signs of weakness. Gas masks are not designed for protection against prolonged exposure to heavy gas concentrations, and exposure should be limited to the short period necessary to release the fumigant and to open the building for airing.

Many fumigants readily penetrate the skin and may be taken up by the blood stream. Gloves resistant to the fumigant should be worn, particularly if large quantities are involved. If material is spilled on the skin or work clothes, a bath with soap and water should be taken and the clothing changed. This precaution should be followed immediately with the most dangerous fumigants.

Persons not actually engaged in applying the fumigant should be protected from drift or leakage or from gaining entrance to the enclosed space during the fumigation. The buildings should be locked and posted. Keeping watchmen on duty during the exposure period is desirable.

Some fumigants, such as carbon disulfide, have a fire or explosion hazard, and care should be taken to avoid any spark or flame near the vapors.

Contamination of food products being fumigated directly or when stored in warehouses receiving a general fumigation must be avoided. Certain fumigants, such as hydrocyanic acid gas and methyl bromide, are absorbed, especially in moist materials, and therefore such products should not be used as food until thoroughly aired and found to contain no appreciable residue. Damp mattresses and clothing may absorb the gas and thorough airing before they are used is important.

DRIFT OF INSECTICIDES outside of the area being treated may create a danger, especially if extremely poisonous materials are being applied. People living or working in the line of drift may be made seriously ill in extreme cases. A few insecticides, such as hexaethyl pyrophosphate and parathion, present hazards because of their vapors or dusts. They might cause serious consequences if large quantities drifted over areas where human beings, domestic animals, or fowl might be subjected to concentrations of the vapor or dusts for considerable time. Areas to be treated should be vacated until after the vapors or dusts have dissipated, unless one is certain that no hazard would exist.

Sprays are less likely to drift than dusts. Certain insecticides are stomach poisons of low solubility in water. If they should drift to gardens of leafy vegetables or small fruits the residue might be dangerous. Some insecticides might remain on the plants for some time and be difficult to wash off. It would not be safe to eat products from such gardens soon afterwards. Drift of such insecticides over pastures might create a hazard to grazing stock—more because of the amount they take in with their food than because of actual contact of the material with their bodies. Similar drift to fields of hay crops may leave deposits sufficient to make the resulting hay injurious to livestock or indirectly to the public through the contamination of milk or meat.

Obviously one has to consider the general situation before starting to apply the insecticides. If possible, the application should be made at a time when hazards from drift will not be created, regardless of the kind of insecticide used. Applications from the air are more likely to contaminate adjacent fields, gardens, and pastures than ground applications. Therefore only competent and reliable pilots should be employed to do such work, fields should be posted, and the owner should be on hand to supervise the operation. Canopies or hoods on ground equipment help to keep the materials from drifting and so add to the effectiveness of the application.

INSECTICIDES OR REPELLENTS often are applied to livestock and household pets.

Pyrethrum and rotenone, for example, present no hazards if kept out of the animal's eyes, but solutions and emulsions containing toxaphene, benzene hexachloride, and chlordane may be harmful if the concentration is too high. Formulations containing parathion and hexaethyl pyrophosphate should never be used on animals, regardless of the formulation. Solvents such as oils and xylene in themselves are irritating and may cause loss of hair and scaling of the skin. They may also facilitate the penetration of the insecticide into the animal's body. For those reasons only insecticides and formulations recommended by proper authorities and labeled with specific instructions should be used on livestock or pets. Precautions on the label should be observed.

Because some crops may be injured by insecticides, labels should indicate susceptible crops and the insecticide concentration that should be employed against pests. Solvents or other ingredients may be safe on one crop but injure another. For example, it has been shown that cucumbers and squash are likely to be injured by DDT insecticides, although the same strength and dosage would be perfectly safe on most crops. Even certain varieties of a given vegetable may be easily injured by an insecticide that would not affect others.

SOME INSECTICIDES are poisonous to fish, toads, lizards, and snakes. For example, DDT and most of the new chlorinated materials, particularly toxaphene, kill fish at a very low concentration. Care must be taken to avoid insecticidal treatments or drift over open water, such as wide rivers and lakes, since wind may concentrate the material along a margin in sufficient quantity to kill fish. Remnants of spray from tanks and spray equipment should be drained and washed into a hole in the earth where they will not gain access to streams and ponds. Insecticides should never be mixed on or near wells.

Awareness of hazards and adoption of safeguards in using and storing pesticides are urgently needed. The object of instructions to that end is not to frighten people so that they will not use pesticides but to get them to observe proper precautions. The intelligent use of pesticides will enable users to derive the greatest good with the least chance of adverse effect.

F. C. BISHOPP *is an assistant chief of the Bureau of Entomology and Plant Quarantine.*

JOHN L. HORSFALL, *a graduate of the State University of Iowa, is chief entomologist of the American Cyanamid Company. He has been engaged in research and development of chemicals for pest control since 1920.*

Toxicity to Livestock

R. D. Radeleff, R. C. Bushland
H. V. Claborn

An insecticide for use against parasites of livestock must meet several specifications. It should be effective against the parasites, but it must not immediately harm the host when used as recommended, nor should it cause injury if the treatment is repeated frequently over a long period. It should be safe even when somewhat carelessly used. The ideal insecticide should not be stored in the body of the treated animal nor appear in the milk of lactating animals. Materials that are safe at first even in large quantities are often the worst problem from the standpoint of storage in meat and secretion in milk; because such residues are so important to public health they are a significant part of the study of the toxicology of insecticides.

So far, we do not have an insecticide that meets all the requirements. Some very safe materials destroy some parasites. Some destroy many parasites but are not entirely safe when they are applied to animals.

Petroleum oils have been extensively used as insecticides or as components of insecticide formulations. Applied to the skin, they are harmless in small amounts, but in large amounts (4 ounces or more per animal) they cause severe reactions—blistering, excessive salivation, difficult breathing, loss of appetite, depression, and death in cattle, horses, sheep, and goats.

The effect of the oils usually is observed in the first few days following application and may continue for some time. Many cases of poisoning of livestock have been attributed to the insecticide dissolved in the oil because of the failure to recognize the dangers associated with the oil itself.

Straight oil solutions of insecticides therefore are never recommended for use on livestock other than as mist sprays applied at rates not exceeding 2 ounces per cow. In producing emulsion concentrates intended for use on livestock, manufacturers must devise their formulas so the use of recommended amounts of the product will not lead to excessive doses of the oils. The stockman should use only the recommended dosages lest he increase the dosage of oil to a toxic level, although he may be using safe limits of the dissolved insecticide.

Solvents are used in nearly all liquid preparations of insecticides. They may be oils, in which case we know their reaction, or they may be higher alcohols or special synthetic products, whose reaction is not known. The solvent may or may not be actively toxic but it should be considered when losses of animals occur following treatment. Although solvents will influence the speed of absorption of insecticides into the body, it is significant that the total absorption is essentially the same, regardless of the solvent.

Some solvents, notably xylene and toluene, cause itching and burning for a short time after application in the hot sunshine, even though used in small amounts. If the concentration is high enough (6 percent), the animal may become dizzy or even be anesthetized. If still higher (25 percent), death may result.

Each manufacturer is responsible for making certain that the solvents he uses are not toxic in the amounts recommended. Labeling laws governing the interstate shipment of insecticides as well as most State labeling laws do not require a statement on the package of the solvent content. The livestock man therefore often has no way of choosing his materials on the basis of the solvent used.

Insecticides produced from plants generally are safe for use upon livestock. They are neither acutely toxic nor capable of being stored within the animals sufficiently to create a hazard to humans. Pyrethrum and rotenone are notable examples of safety.

An exception is nicotine, which, in the form of nicotine sulfate, is used principally to control mange or scab. As nicotine sulfate is most commonly used by regulatory officials, who are skilled in its use and have a reliable test for the strength of the dip, poisoning from it as a result of dipping is uncommon. Animals poisoned by nicotine sulfate show tremors, nausea, and disturbed respiration and finally enter a comatose condition, in which they may die.

Some plant products are irritants and cause discomfort when they are applied to animals, but rarely is an animal killed by an insecticide derived from plants.

SULFUR, LIME-SULFUR, AND ARSENIC have been used to treat livestock. Sulfur, used externally, is almost completely nontoxic to mammals. Lime-sulfur, which is actually a complex of sulfides, may cause irritation, general discomfort, and even severe burning. Rarely does it kill an animal.

Arsenic, as used in cattle dips, is extremely poisonous. It has given remarkable control of the cattle tick. The many losses of livestock, in deaths and in injuries as a result of burning and blistering after dipping, amply illustrate the toxic nature of arsenical dips.

Arsenic is absorbed through the unbroken skin and stored in tissues but is not excreted or secreted in the milk of lactating animals in detectable amounts.

Acute arsenical poisoning causes death in 1 or 2 days from the time of treatment. At autopsy, the intestinal tract shows marked inflammation, the liver and other organs may be swollen, and the lungs may be severely congested. Less acute poisoning may cause blistering; cracking and peeling of the skin; profuse diarrhea, possibly with free blood; rapid emaciation; poor appetite; and obvious pain.

Poisoning by arsenical dips is not always the result of excessive dosage. Even a normally safe dosage may produce burning or death if the animals are treated in wet weather or they are overheated.

Because arsenical dips are primarily solutions of arsenic in water and an accurate test is available, losses have been less than if the dipping solutions could not be easily checked.

The many arsenical compounds used in treating field crops may be poisonous to livestock that eat them. Poisoning frequently has resulted from dusts that drift across fields into pastures and dusts remaining in containers carelessly left on premises occupied by livestock. Sometimes a dipping vat is emptied on an unprotected pasture. Some animals seem to crave arsenic and will seek out spots contaminated with it.

The synthetic organic materials have simplified parasite control on livestock, but they also have hazards. The most important are the cumulative effects of repeated exposure and the problems of residues in meat and milk. As each of the new insecticides is a study in itself, it is best to discuss each one individually.

DDT IS A relatively safe insecticide. All livestock can tolerate single applications of 8 percent DDT. As many as 10 applications of 2 percent DDT at 2-week intervals have failed to produce clinical changes. Cattle have also tolerated 36 applications of 0.5 percent DDT at the same intervals. Cattle, horses, sheep, goats, and hogs all tolerated 8 treatments with 1.5 percent DDT at 4-day intervals.

DDT also is safe for dogs, but it must be used sparingly on cats, as they may be poisoned by relatively small amounts. Chickens should not be sprayed with DDT or dipped in it.

Mice and rats are very susceptible to DDT, as is seen in the number of dead rodents found in barns that were treated with DDT.

DDT occurs in the milk of cattle soon after spraying. Scientists at the

Oklahoma Agricultural and Mechanical College discovered that in 1947. Immediately the Department of Agriculture began a study of samples of milk taken weekly from dairy herds that were sprayed once a month with 0.5 percent DDT. All the samples contained 0.1 to 2.0 p. p. m. (parts per million) of DDT. The average was between 0.6 to 0.7 p. p. m. Similar studies were made in 1948 on milk from dairy cattle sprayed with 0.5 percent DDT only as needed to control horn flies. The average DDT content of that milk was 0.25 p. p. m. Additional tests made under controlled conditions with individual cows thoroughly sprayed with 0.5 percent DDT indicated that a maximum of 2.6 p. p. m. was reached the second day after spraying and that the figure gradually dropped to 0.3 after 21 days.

In some tests an increase of DDT was found in milk after barns were sprayed. The contamination varied in intensity. Even when the spraying was done most carefully some DDT was found in the milk of cows later fed in the barn, except when the feed troughs were completely protected during spraying or washed after spraying.

DDT may be stored in the fat of sprayed cattle or of cattle fed contaminated feed. In a series of experiments at the Department's laboratory at Kerrville, Tex., Hereford cows with sucking calves were sprayed five times with 0.5 percent DDT at 4-week intervals. One-half the calves were sprayed each time and the others received no treatment. Two weeks after the fifth treatment, the fat of the cows contained an average of 15 p. p. m. of DDT. The unsprayed calves that sucked the sprayed cows averaged 25 p. p. m. Sprayed calves that sucked the sprayed cows averaged 52 p. p. m. of DDT.

Yearling Hereford steers were sprayed at 3-week intervals with 0.5 percent DDT emulsion. Three weeks after one application their fat contained 18 p. p. m. Three weeks after the second treatment the average was 31 p. p. m. After the fourth it was 32.8, and after the sixth, 35.2. The steers gradually lost the DDT, having 4.7 p. p. m. in the fat 24 weeks after the last spraying. Yearling steers sprayed once with 0.5 percent DDT showed 11.2 p. p. m. 2 weeks later, but after 22 weeks they showed 2.9 p. p. m.

Yearling Herefords fed 10 p. p. m. of DDT in all items of their feed for 30 days showed 6.8 p. p. m. in the fat on the last day of the feeding. Sheep fed the same diet showed 3.1 p. p. m. in the fat at the end of the feeding period and 1.2 p. p. m. 90 days after the feeding of the insecticide was discontinued.

ONLY THE GAMMA ISOMER of technical benzene hexachloride is useful against pests of livestock.

The gamma isomer may be separated from the other isomers of technical benzene hexachloride and a purified product obtained, which is composed of 99 percent or more of the gamma isomer. This purified product is known as lindane. Most farm animals are resistant to poisoning by gamma benzene hexachloride. In single treatments, adult cattle and horses can withstand sprays or dips containing 0.25 percent gamma isomer. Sheep, goats, and hogs can withstand 0.5 percent. Young calves are quite susceptible, however, and the gamma isomer must be used with caution on them. Experiments so far have not established a fixed point of danger, but enough young Jersey calves have been poisoned by 0.05-percent sprays to cause such a dose to be set as slightly above the maximum that is safe. No deaths or poisonings resulted from the use of 0.03-percent sprays or dips on thousands of calves.

The gamma isomer of benzene hexachloride has little danger as a chronic toxicant. The use of 0.2-percent wettable powders on range cattle resulted in no clinical disturbances, although the dose was repeated 10 times at 2-week intervals.

Benzene hexachloride is stored in

the body of animals as a mixture of isomers. Yearling Hereford cattle were sprayed 12 times at 2-week intervals with a 0.25-percent emulsion of benzene hexachloride (0.03 gamma isomer); 2 weeks after the final spraying there appeared to be 31 parts per million of benzene hexachloride present in their fat. Ten weeks after the final spraying no residue was present in the fat. This storage, in the light of later studies, was due mostly to isomers other than the gamma.

The pure gamma isomer (lindane is 99+ percent gamma isomer) is readily stored but is eliminated just as readily. Steers sprayed once with 0.03 percent lindane showed no residue 2 weeks after spraying. Steers sprayed six times at 3-week intervals with 0.03 percent lindane sprays showed no detectable residues 3 weeks after each treatment.

Lindane is also secreted in milk following spraying. Dairy cows sprayed with 0.05 percent lindane showed 1.0 p. p. m. of lindane in the milk on the day after they were sprayed. The milk was negative for lindane after 7 days. Cows sprayed with 0.1 percent sprays showed 1.5 p. p. m. lindane in the milk on the day after spraying. The milk was negative for lindane by the fourteenth day.

Hereford cattle fed 10 p. p. m. of lindane in every item of feed stored 8 p. p. m. in their fat after 70 days of feeding. Cattle fed 100 p. p. m. stored 98 p. p. m. in their fat. This stored material disappeared rapidly, the fat being negative for the 10 p. p. m. in 6 to 10 weeks and 10 to 14 weeks for those fed 100 p. p. m.

Benzene hexachloride is safe for dogs and cats at 0.5 percent gamma isomer in dry dusts. It should not be used excessively on cats, because they are susceptible to poisoning. If benzene hexachloride is used as a poultry-house treatment, care should be taken to avoid wetting the birds, as they are easily poisoned.

CHLORDANE is relatively safe as to acute toxicity. Most farm animals, except young calves, can withstand 2.0-percent sprays and dips. Young Jersey calves are killed occasionally by 1.0-percent sprays.

Chlordane is not so safe as to its chronic effects. Cattle can withstand one or two treatments of 2.0 percent chlordane at 2-week intervals but are killed by three such applications. That seems to be true of other farm animals.

We are not sure whether chlordane appears in the milk of treated cattle. Studies of milk from dairy cattle sprayed with 0.5 percent chlordane indicate a possible contamination of less than 1 p. p. m. of chlordane. Conclusive statements can only be made when more specific analytical techniques become available.

Chlordane does appear to be stored readily in the fat of treated animals. Steers sprayed 12 times with 0.5 percent chlordane showed the equivalent of 20 p. p. m. chlordane in their fat 2 weeks after the twelfth application. No detectable residue was found 10 weeks after the twelfth spraying. A single spraying with 0.5 percent chlordane left a possible 2.5 p. p. m. of chlordane in the fat 2 weeks after spraying.

Yearling Hereford cattle fed 25 p. p. m. of chlordane in every item of feed for 56 days showed only 12 p. p. m. in the fat on the twenty-eighth day and 19 p. p. m. on the fifty-sixth day of feeding. Only 5 p. p. m. of the insecticide remained in the fat 12 weeks after the feeding was discontinued and it had disappeared completely after 20 weeks. Delaine sheep fed the same diet showed only 7 p. p. m. at the twenty-eighth day and 12 p. p. m. on the fifty-sixth day. No insecticide residue was found in the fat 4 weeks after the feeding was discontinued. Yearling Herefords fed 10 p. p. m. of chlordane in every item of the diet for 112 days had 11 p. p. m. in the fat at the end of the feeding period. Fat of Delaine sheep fed on the same diet contained 9 p. p. m. in the fat after the same feeding period.

Chlordane is a safe insecticide for dogs and cats if it is used in recommended amounts according to the manufacturer's directions.

As with DDT, many dead mice and rats will be found after treatment of premises.

Toxaphene is reasonably safe when it is used as a spray for farm animals. Dip formulations have caused trouble, however, and the cause of the difficulties has been hard to determine.

As an acute toxicant, toxaphene is most dangerous for the young calf. Concentrations of 1.0 percent toxaphene have killed very young calves. Adult cattle, sheep, goats, horses, and hogs withstand 2.0-percent concentrations.

We have no indication that toxaphene is chronically toxic to farm animals when it is used at recommended strengths. Cattle treated 10 times with 2.0-percent sprays displayed no clinical disturbances. Nor have we a specific method for determining the presence or absence of toxaphene in milk. The evidence in 1952 indicated that less than 1 p. p. m. would appear in milk following the spraying of a cow with 0.5 percent toxaphene.

Toxaphene has little tendency to be stored in the fat of animals. Hereford steers under feed-lot conditions were sprayed with 0.5 percent toxaphene every 2 weeks for 24 weeks. One week after the twelfth spraying no detectable residue existed in the fat. During the sprayings, the level may have gone as high as 5 p. p. m. In a repetition of this experiment, except with the cattle kept under range conditions, approximately 8 p. p. m. of toxaphene was present in the fat 2 weeks after the twelfth spraying.

Steers and sheep fed 10 p. p. m. of toxaphene in all items of their feed showed no toxaphene in the fat on the thirtieth day of feeding, as indicated by organic chloride analysis.

Toxaphene is highly toxic to dogs. Its toxicity to cats has not been studied. Pets should not be treated with it. Toxaphene should not be used directly on chickens.

Methoxychlor is safe from all standpoints. Even calves 1 week old have tolerated 8.0-percent sprays, and young chickens were not affected by 4.0-percent dips.

Methoxychlor is secreted in the milk of cows, reaching 0.4 p. p. m. 1 day after treatment with 0.5-percent sprays. Because of the low toxicity of methoxychlor, the presence of small amounts of it in milk is not considered cause for alarm.

Methoxychlor does not tend to be stored in the fat of cattle or sheep in large quantities. Two weeks after a single spraying of 0.5 percent methoxychlor, steers showed only 2.8 p. p. m. in the fat. When cattle were sprayed six times at 3-week intervals with 0.5-percent sprays and the fat sampled 3 weeks after the sprayings, the fat content was as follows: One spray, 1.5 p. p. m.; two sprays, 1.5 p. p. m.; six sprays, 2.4 p. p. m. All residue had disappeared 12 weeks after the sixth spraying.

Yearling Hereford cattle fed 10 p. p. m. of methoxychlor in every item of the diet showed no methoxychlor on the thirtieth day of feeding. Delaine sheep fed the same diet also showed no methoxychlor in the fat after the same feeding period.

TDE is practically like DDT in toxicity to animals, storage in fat, and secretion in milk.

Dieldrin is toxic to week-old calves at 0.25 percent concentration, to cattle at 2.0 percent, and to sheep and goats at 3.0 percent. Hogs appear able to stand about 4.0 percent. It is not so safe when it is used repeatedly. Cattle sprayed three times at 2-week intervals with 0.5-percent material showed clinical symptoms of poisoning.

Dieldrin may be stored in the fat of cattle. Two sprayings at 0.25 percent at 3-week intervals produced 17 p. p. m. in the fat 3 weeks after the second application; eight applications produced 14 p. p. m. in the fat 3 weeks after final treatment. It took 13 weeks for a residue of 14 p. p. m. to disappear.

Yearling Hereford cattle fed 25 p. p. m. of dieldrin in every item of feed showed 75 p. p. m. in the fat on the twenty-eighth day of feeding, and 74 p. p. m. on the fifty-sixth day. Delaine sheep fed the same diet showed 43 p. p. m. in the fat after 28 days of feeding, and 69 p. p. m. after 56 days of feeding. Detectable amounts of dieldrin were still present in the fat of both sheep and calves 32 weeks after the feeding was discontinued.

Dieldrin is secreted in the milk of treated cattle. Dairy cows treated with 0.5-percent sprays showed a maximum of 7 p. p. m. in the milk on the third day after spraying. The milk was practically free of dieldrin 21 days after treatment.

Aldrin appears to be slightly less toxic than dieldrin. Week-old calves seem to be able to stand nearly 0.25-percent concentrations. Very little is known of the toxicity of aldrin for other animals.

Hereford cattle fed 25 p. p. m. of aldrin in every item of feed showed 49 p. p. m. in the fat after 28 days of feeding and 78 p. p. m. after 56 days. Delaine sheep fed on the same diet showed 60 p. p. m. on the twenty-eighth day of feeding and 78 p. p. m. on the fifty-sixth day. Detectable amounts of aldrin were still present in the fat of sheep and calves 32 weeks after feeding was discontinued. Hereford cattle fed 10 p. p. m. of aldrin in every item of the diet for 112 days had 49 p. p. m. in the fat at the end of the feeding period. Delaine sheep fed on the same diet showed 55 p. p. m. in the fat at the end of the feeding period.

Some explanation of how experiments are conducted to determine the foregoing facts is in order.

To determine the amount of insecticide which may kill, several animals of each particular species are treated with sprays or dips, beginning at a high concentration and working up or down as may seem desirable. A sufficient number of animals and of different concentrations are used to produce poisoning and to find a maximum safe dose and a minimum toxic dose.

In every instance, the animals are completely saturated with the spray or dip. They are allowed to be under normal conditions and free to roll or lie down and to lick themselves or one another.

All animals are observed at close intervals for 48 hours or longer for symptoms of poisoning. If symptoms are seen they are recorded in detail to establish a means of recognizing the particular poisoning in other animals. Records are kept of the many possible variables, time of application, type of equipment, details of formulation, time of onset of symptoms, time of death, and any other indicated data that might be needed.

If an animal dies from poisoning, an autopsy is performed promptly. Records are made of any lesions and samples of tissue are preserved for study under the microscope.

We have mentioned toxic doses. Those doses, however, did not necessarily kill the animal in question. Toxic doses are those that cause some abnormal activities or otherwise affect the normal health of the most susceptible of the animals treated. When minimum toxic doses are mentioned, it is understood that at that dosage only one, or at most a few, out of the treated group became affected.

Studies of chronic effects are made in the same way; the applications and observations are simply repeated.

Contamination of milk is studied by thoroughly spraying or dipping lactating animals and collecting milk samples at intervals. Generally samples of milk are taken for several days before the treatment and at frequent intervals after treatment. The samples may be taken as a portion of the total milk drawn by a mechanical milker into individual buckets or may be drawn by inserting a canula into the teat and drawing the milk into closed containers through flexible tubing.

In all cases, every piece of equipment is specially cleaned, scoured, and dried. The animal's udder is cleaned and dried. From inside the udder until the chemist completes his analysis there is no chance given for outside insecticides to contaminate the milk to be studied.

To determine the amounts of insecticides in animal tissue, two methods are used. Appropriate amounts may be taken of various tissues during autopsies after death from poisoning or following slaughter. Samples taken after slaughter may be expensive, because if the residues be large the meat is not sold for human consumption and must be destroyed. The method also involves the use of many animals.

In studies of autopsy samples from cattle and sheep, it was found that even when the insecticide residues reached several hundred parts per million in the fat there were less than 2 p. p. m. in muscle tissue. It was then decided that fat would be the tissue of choice for later analytical work. The values given in this paper are all for fat—the amount of insecticide in a given cut of meat will be in proportion to the percentage of fat contained in that meat. The values we give, therefore, are actually the extremes that would be found under the conditions of treatment stated.

A biopsy technique was devised to eliminate waste of animals and to provide better data. Treated animals are cast, suitably anesthetized, and a 2-ounce sample of fat is then taken from the caul through an abdominal incision. The process is much like an appendectomy. The method allows samples to be taken before treatment as well as several times after, or during, treatment. It also allows us to make sure that there are no measurable deposits of insecticide within an animal at the end of an experiment. The method allows one animal to provide the data that six or seven did by the autopsy method. It also produces more valuable data.

Observations on the behavior of treated animals also are of value.

The chlorinated hydrocarbons outwardly show their effect on an animal by various nervous disturbances. No two animals poisoned by a given insecticide will show exactly the same chain of symptoms, yet the symptoms are enough alike to enable one to identify them.

An affected animal will generally first become excitable and a little more alert to its surroundings. Twitches of various muscles soon follow, beginning usually at the head and going backward along the body. The twitches may increase in intensity until there are spasms and, finally, convulsions. In addition, the animal might assume abnormal attitudes, such as standing with the head between the forelegs and under the body, a sternal position with the hind legs in standing position, and persistent chewing movements. Occasionally the animal attacks any moving object. There is usually profuse salivation, rolling of the eyes, dribbling of urine, and bawling. The body temperature may climb to 114° F.

Some animals show none of these active symptoms; instead they are depressed and unaware of their surroundings. Some animals are alternately depressed and excited. Severity of symptoms is no index of the likelihood of death or survival. Death may occur an hour or several weeks after exposure. Most cases run their course within 72 hours.

Findings at autopsy are somewhat variable. Alone, they never are diagnostic of poisoning by these insecticides. There will usually be cyanosis (blue-colored skin and membranes), congestion, and small hemorrhages of various organs, most frequently on the heart. The lungs usually are congested, heavy, and dark in color, suggesting primary stages of pneumonia. Often an excess of fluid occurs in and around the brain and spinal cord.

If the animal was affected over a long period, the carcass may be thin and lacking in moisture. The liver and kidneys may show abnormal consistencies.

Microscopic lesions in animals dying quickly are few, other than those mentioned, as observable at autopsy. In prolonged cases, there are fatty changes in the liver and kidney, some degeneration in those organs, and degeneration in the brain. Otherwise, few if any significant changes can be seen.

We prevent untold numbers of deaths of livestock and costly economic losses by making these experiments before new materials are widely used. Some animals have to be sacrificed in carefully controlled experiments in order that safe methods may be worked out enabling the livestock grower to use the new chemicals for improved pest control.

R. D. RADELEFF, *a veterinarian in the Bureau of Animal Industry, is stationed at Kerrville, Tex. He is a graduate of Schreiner Institute and the Agricultural and Mechanical College of Texas. Since 1947 he has engaged in work on the problems of insecticide toxicology.*

R. C. BUSHLAND *is in charge of the Kerrville laboratory of the Bureau of Entomology and Plant Quarantine. After studying at South Dakota State College and Kansas State College, he joined the Bureau in 1935. Most of his research has been on insecticides. At the Bureau's Orlando laboratory during the Second World War, he was one of the group who first investigated the chlorinated hydrocarbon insecticides to establish their value in the field of medical entomology.*

H. V. CLABORN, *a chemist of the Bureau of Entomology and Plant Quarantine, is also stationed at Kerrville. Since 1929 he has worked for the division of insecticide investigations, the research laboratories of the Bureau of Dairy Industry, and the Food and Drug Administration. He is a native of Arkansas and a graduate of George Washington University.*

For further reference:

R. C. Bushland, H. V. Claborn, H. F. Beckman, R. D. Radeleff, and R. W. Wells: Contamination of Meat and Milk by Chlorinated Hydrocarbon Insecticides Used for Livestock Pest Control, *Journal of Economic Entomology, volume 43, pages 649–652. 1950.*

R. C. Bushland, R. W. Wells, and R. D. Radeleff: Effect on Livestock of Sprays and Dips Containing New Chlorinated Insecticides, *Journal of Economic Entomology, volume 41, pages 642–645. 1948.*

R. H. Carter: Estimation of DDT in Milk by Determination of Organic Chlorine, *Analytical Chemistry, volume 19, page 54, 1947;* The Chlorinated Hydrocarbon Content of Milk from Cattle Sprayed for Control of Horn Flies, *with R. W. Wells, R. D. Radeleff, C. L. Smith, P. E. Hubanks, and H. D. Mann, Journal of Economic Entomology, volume 42, pages 116–118, 1949.*

H. V. Claborn, H. F. Beckman, and R. W. Wells: Excretion of DDT and TDE in Milk from Cows Treated With These Insecticides, *Journal of Economic Entomology, volume 43, pages 850–852, 1950;* Contamination of Milk from DDT Sprays Applied to Dairy Barns, *Journal of Economic Entomology, volume 43, pages 723–724, 1950.*

D. E. Howell, H. W. Cave, V. G. Heller, and W. G. Gross: The Amount of DDT Found in Milk of Cows Following Spraying, *Journal of Dairy Science, volume 30, pages 717–721. 1947.*

R. D. Radeleff: Chlordane Poisoning: Symptomatology and Pathology, *Veterinary Medicine, volume 43, pages 342–347, 1948;* Toxaphene Poisoning; Symptomology and Pathology, *Veterinary Medicine, volume 44, pages 436–442, 1949;* Omentectomy of Cattle for Studying Insecticide Residue in the Body, *Veterinary Medicine, volume 45, pages 125–128, 1950;* Acute Toxicity of Chlorinated Insecticides Applied to Livestock, *with R. C. Bushland, Journal of Economic Entomology, volume 43, pages 358–364, 1950.*

Milton S. Schechter, Milton A. Pogorelskin, and H. L. Haller: Colorimetric Determination of DDT in Milk and Fatty Materials, *Analytical Chemistry, volume 19, pages 51–53. 1947.*

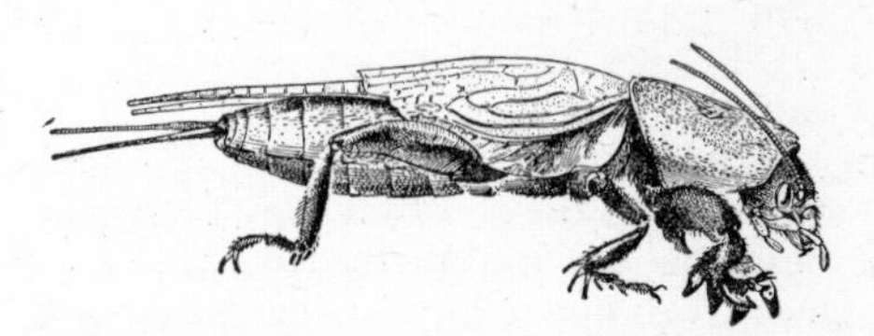

The mole cricket, like the mole, has developed strong forelegs for tunneling in the ground, where it feeds upon the roots of plants.

Residues, Soils, and Plants

Victor R. Boswell

Since the mid-1940's there has been a renewed and heightened interest in questions involving residues of agricultural chemicals in soil. This has occurred because agriculture has been recently supplied with a number of entirely new synthetic compounds for pest control, of largely unknown stability and toxicity to plants when present in the soil.

During the Second World War, when DDT first came into use in this country, one of its properties that especially intrigued us was its unusual persistence. It seemed almost too good to be true that a single application of a small amount of DDT solution upon window or door screens, walls, or trim would remain effective as a fly killer for many weeks. There were hopes that it would prove highly persistent in the soil for the killing of harmful insects there. It appeared highly desirable that we should have an insecticide of such persistence that a single treatment of the soil for insect control would remain effective for years. DDT has proved to be just that kind of remarkable substance. Entomologists in the eastern United States have found that DDT applied to the soil at 25 pounds per acre in 1945 was still effective against Japanese beetle grubs in 1950. In certain tropical and other soils, however, DDT loses its effectiveness relatively rapidly.

This stability or persistence of an insecticide in the soil that may be highly desirable for insect control can, however, turn out to be a serious disadvantage under some conditions. Is it harmful to plants, to soil bacteria, or fungi? How long will this or that insecticide remain in the soil without leaching out, without gradually vaporizing, or without being rendered inactive to plants or insects by chemical change or by the action of soil micro-organisms? If any amount is harmful to plants or to the soil bacteria and fungi, is it also so persistent that residues reaching the soil after dusting or spraying crops will accumulate to an extent that will harm plant growth? If residues can accumulate, how fast? How often and how heavily can a particular substance be used without danger of lowering the productivity of the soil after some years? Can a harmful amount of such residue be removed or corrected by special treatment of the soil? These are questions that must be answered not only for insecticides but for any agricultural chemical that is purposely applied to or that incidentally reaches the soil.

One of the first reports of crop injury believed to be due to an accumulation of an insecticide in the soil appeared in 1908. Symptoms of injury were evident in apple trees in an orchard in Colorado that had been sprayed repeatedly with lead arsenate. Soil analysis showed 61 p. p. m. (parts per million) of arsenic in the soil of the orchard, much more than the amount naturally present. Later work suggests that the injury in question was not due directly to the arsenic in the surface soil of the orchard. The old work, however, did demonstrate that ordinary use of an arsenical insecticide in an orchard results in an arsenic accumulation in the surface soil.

During the years 1930 to 1933, in South Carolina, several investigators reported a series of observations and studies of toxicity of arsenic in the soil to crop plants. They found that on heavy soils—Cecil clay and Davidson clay in those instances—cereals and cotton were uninjured by thousands of pounds of calcium arsenate per acre. Vetch and cowpeas were injured by 1,000 to 1,500 pounds per acre or more. On the clay soil soybeans were uninjured by large amounts, but on

Norfolk sandy loam 200 to 300 pounds per acre caused serious injury. They found that the crops on soils low in iron content were injured by much smaller amounts of arsenic in the soil than when they were grown on soils high in iron. Soybeans were seriously injured on Norfolk sandy loam following only 3 years of cotton dusted with calcium arsenate to control boll weevil. In Louisiana, about the same time others also found that a given amount of calcium arsenate caused much more injury on a light soil than on a heavy one. On Crowley silty clay neither 50 nor 150 pounds per acre had any effect on rice. On Crowley very fine sandy loam, however, 50 pounds reduced the rice yield 45 percent and 150 pounds reduced it 65 percent.

In the 1940's, work in central New Jersey showed that most vegetables are sensitive to arsenic. Lima bean, snap bean, and turnip were especially sensitive; they were killed by 1,000 or 2,000 pounds per acre in the surface 3 inches of soil. Early growth of all crops was retarded, and some crops very seriously, but if the plants survived long enough for the roots to penetrate below the treated zone, they made considerable recovery.

The greatest accumulations of arsenic residues from the spraying of crops have been noted in the orchard soils of the Pacific Northwest, especially Washington, where heavy lead arsenate sprays have been applied annually for many years. Most of the arsenic residue is confined to the surface 6 to 8 inches of soil, the amounts found below 8 inches rarely exceeding those occurring naturally in the soil. The old orchard trees have been apparently uninjured by the great accumulations sometimes found because the arsenic accumulated only in the surface 6 to 8 inches after most of the tree roots were well established in the deeper levels of the soil. In some orchards amounts up to approximately 1,400 pounds per acre of accumulated arsenic trioxide have been determined in the surface 8 inches. Arsenic up to 30 times and lead 40 times the amount occurring naturally have been found. Although a large amount of arsenic in the surface soil may not harm the trees, it is definitely harmful to many kinds of cover crops, and cover crops are essential to profitable tree yields over a long period of time. As lead arsenate has accumulated, legume cover crops have become progressively poorer in many orchards.

During the depression years of the 1930's many of the less productive orchards in Washington were pulled out, and efforts made to grow alfalfa or annual crops on the old orchard sites. Alfalfa and beans often died on those high-arsenic tracts although they thrived on immediately adjacent sites that received no spray residues. Of the vegetable gardens observed on numerous old orchard sites, none was entirely successful and many were failures. Several years after heavily sprayed trees had been removed, rye and potatoes grew fairly well but beans and peas still showed marked sensitivity. After several years tomatoes, asparagus, and grapes showed intermediate sensitivity, but they grew poorly on land from which the trees had been recently removed.

If the roots of orchard trees encounter the high accumulations of arsenic found in the upper layers of some old orchard soils, the trees may be definitely injured. Specific arsenic toxicity symptoms have appeared in peach and apricot trees planted on land from which old sprayed apple orchards had been removed.

As the years pass, the arsenic toxicity of the former orchard soils is gradually decreasing. With the cessation of applications of arsenicals, with the gradual leaching effects of rainfall and irrigation, and with continued culture of the less sensitive crops, the productivity of those soils in the Pacific Northwest should be ultimately restored after many years. In South Carolina also it was noted that after the arsenic applications (to cotton) were stopped, productivity gradually returned to those soils that had been damaged.

970134°—52——20

SINCE 1945 large quantities of new synthetic organic insecticides have been used. The most important of these can be classified in one or another of two general groups of substances: (1) chlorinated hydrocarbons, such as DDT and BHC; and (2) phosphorus compounds such as parathion and HETP. With no background of earlier experience with these or related substances for use as insecticides, there was no basis for knowing whether any one of them would prove to be more persistent or toxic in the soil to plants, than lead arsenate, for example, or less so. The almost unbelievable insect-killing power of some of them, the apparent stability of DDT, and even the "newness" of these materials all combined to give a genuine urgency to the questions that arose about them. The instances of damage to orchard and cotton soil by arsenic accumulations stood as warnings of what *might* result from long-continued use. If one of these new substances should, when mixed in the soil, happen to be many times as toxic as lead arsenate is to common crop plants (some are many times as toxic as lead arsenate to insects in the soil) and as persistent as lead arsenate or more so, there would surely be trouble ahead. From the first, some feared that under certain conditions of use farmers might encounter damaging effects to crops by soil residues in a shorter time and of a more troublesome character than had resulted from using lead arsenate. Soon there were not just one or two compounds to consider, but a dozen of them; and it was important to find out as soon as possible what their potential long-time effects might be.

Perhaps one of the most striking observations on plant response is that various insecticides, when present in the soil in appreciable amounts, may definitely reduce rate of growth, total growth, and yield (as of seed or fruit) without producing above ground any symptoms of injury whatever. This inability to detect any harmful effect by inspection of the above-ground parts of the plant may very well result in overlooking many instances of unsuspected insecticide residue injury. The crop may appear entirely normal, but if there are no exactly comparable plants nearby on residue-free soil, the retarded growth cannot be detected unless it is rather severe. Definite symptoms of injury show up, usually, only when growth has been retarded so severely that it would be noticed whether other symptoms were present or not. Leaf and stem discolorations and malformations are among the last symptoms to appear. Much harm may be done before they become evident.

Below ground, the situation is not quite so difficult to detect. In general, plants that are retarded in growth by DDT or BHC will show root abnormalities although the tops appear normal. The moderately affected plants may show only somewhat stunted and shortened root systems. In more severe cases the roots are sometimes discolored and abnormally short, numerous, and virtually without root hairs. Extreme injury is characterized by very numerous short, thickened, stubby roots. The roots appear to have been stopped in growth soon after starting, with successive flushes of roots emerging only to suffer the same fate.

Strangely, DDT in the soil seems to have little effect on germination and emergence although many plants are rather highly sensitive to it after emergence. Technical BHC, on the other hand, has shown a consistent and very harmful effect on germination and emergence as well as later growth. Many investigators have described the abnormal seedlings of various seeds germinated in media containing BHC. The thickening and distortion of tissue in extreme cases is suggestive of that induced by some of the so-called growth-regulating substances such as 2,4-D which are effective in extremely small amounts. Seeds of many crops sown soon after mixing chlordane (25 pounds per acre or more) with the soil also give poor stands of plants. The amounts of various substances required to produce such marked effects are discussed later.

DETERMINATIONS OF RATES of accumulation and of persistence of insecticides in the soil obviously involve many years of work. On the other hand, the relative sensitivity of different kinds of plants to various insecticides can be found in a much shorter time. If very large quantities of certain insecticides in the soil are harmless to a wide range of plants, there is little concern over any potential dangers from their accumulation—assuming that they do accumulate and that their decomposition products are not harmful to crop growth or quality. If mixtures representing relatively small accumulations in the soil produce undesired effects on any plants, it immediately becomes important to know what plants differ in sensitivity, and what amounts of the substance can be tolerated without harm.

In studying the tolerance of plants to various insecticides in the soil the investigator usually treats a series of plots with successively heavier applications, most of the treatments purposely much larger than would ever be applied at once, or even in a year, in practice. He not only wants to know that plants may be uninjured at ordinary rates of use, but also wants to know how much of a given substance is required to produce injury. It is important to know not only what amounts are safe, but also what amounts are unsafe for normal plant growth. It is for these reasons that many experiments mentioned in these pages involve some truly massive dosages.

Growth habit of a particular plant and the cultural conditions under which it grows may determine whether or not its roots come into contact with an insecticide to which it is known to be—or may be—sensitive. As in the instance of arsenic, DDT accumulates in the surface soil. It is highly insoluble, stable, and does not move down into the zone where most of the tree roots are. DDT has been applied to the surface of undisturbed soil beneath large apple trees at rates as high as 3,000 pounds per acre without affecting the tree. Up to 50 pounds of DDT per acre for the destruction of Japanese beetle grubs has been applied to the surface of the soil in which a very wide range of woody nursery plants were established without injuring them. Established peach trees are apparently unharmed by years of accumulation of DDT in the surface soil, but roots of peach seedlings are definitely sensitive to amounts of 100 pounds per acre or more of DDT in the soil in which they are planted. In general, trees and bushes are probably no more resistant to one or another of these potent compounds than are the annual crops that have been tested, but they apparently escape injury because the toxic material does not reach their roots.

We have seen a few instances of partial recovery of annual plants from mild injury that appear to be due to the fact that deep roots finally penetrated below the toxic surface soil into noncontaminated soil. Shallow-rooting species or seriously injured plants in highly toxic soils are usually unable to establish sufficient roots below the toxic zone to make any recovery.

NOT ONLY DO species of plants differ widely in their sensitivity to this or that insecticide in the soil, but varieties within species sometimes show big differences. The conventional botanical relationships are not always a safe basis for predicting how a given species or variety will react.

The effects of DDT and BHC have been studied more extensively than those of other new insecticides and thus afford more examples that can be cited. By no means have all important crops been tested extensively enough with most of the new compounds to permit a classification according to sensitivity to each one.

CORN AND OTHER CEREAL plants that have been tested are generally tolerant to relatively large doses of DDT in the soil, although there are some striking exceptions. In fact, frequent exceptions occur in the general behavior of many plant groups in response to various insecticides mixed with soil. Few generalizations appear safe at this stage of our knowledge.

Instances of reduced germination and stand of corn have been reported as due to dosages of 100 to 400 pounds per acre of DDT in the soil but most observations show no effect of such amounts upon either germination and stand or upon later growth. Two investigators have reported that DDT appears to stimulate growth of corn slightly, quite aside from any insecticidal effect. Dosages as high as 1,000 pounds per acre have been without effect in some tests. Wheat is generally tolerant, as are most of the few varieties of barley and oats tested. Some varieties of rye, especially Abruzzi and Rosen, are highly sensitive to DDT. Dosages of 50 to 100 pounds per acre markedly reduce growth of Abruzzi rye, and under some conditions as little as 25 pounds is sometimes harmful. Residue accumulation in a peach orchard after only 4 years of normal use (about 100 pounds total per acre) seriously interfered with the growth of Abruzzi rye as a winter cover.

The potato is another important crop that, so far, appears to be tolerant to rather large amounts of DDT in the soil—up to 400 pounds per acre, possibly more on some soils. Members of the cabbage family are also much more tolerant than some other crops. The few varieties of cabbage, broccoli, collards, and turnips tested have shown no effects on young growth from dosages up to 400 pounds per acre. Tobacco has tolerated 100 pounds. Cotton, soybeans, peanuts, and many other major crops have been tested so little that their classification is uncertain. In the few tests reported, however, they appear somewhat sensitive but not highly so.

Some members of the pea family are highly sensitive to DDT while others are not. In general, snap beans and lima beans are sensitive, some varieties extremely so; Stringless Black Valentine snap bean is probably as sensitive as any variety of a common crop plant observed to date. As little as 25 to 50 pounds per acre may affect its growth. Under some field conditions, 100 pounds has markedly reduced growth and 200 pounds has reduced yields by one-half. Other common varieties appear somewhat less sensitive. Spinach, beet, and tomato also are highly sensitive to DDT in the soil, as little as 25 pounds per acre producing noticeable depression in growth under some conditions.

In general, the members of the pumpkin family are sensitive to very sensitive, but here again there are exceptions. Summer squash and pumpkins of the same species (*Cucurbita pepo*) are extremely sensitive and cucumbers are moderately so while muskmelon appears rather tolerant.

Among the fruits, only peach and strawberry have been tested in such a way that the feeding roots were exposed to soil containing DDT. Peach is sensitive. Strawberry is highly sensitive. Strawberry is so very sensitive that merely dusting the rows of young mother plants as for insect control leaves enough DDT in the surface soil to interfere seriously with the formation of daughter plants. Apparently rooting at the nodes of the runners is markedly reduced by the DDT in the surface soil through which the young roots must pass if they are to become established and support a daughter plant.

How various plants react to DDT in the soil is no indication whatever as to how they will react to BHC. In fact, many of the relative differences among crops in response to DDT are reversed with BHC. For example, corn is either unaffected or slightly stimulated by DDT while snap beans are highly sensitive; but corn is sometimes nearly killed by concentrations of BHC that snap beans tolerate with no measurable harm. Despite the high sensitivity of some plants to DDT, many important ones appear highly tolerant. None, however, will tolerate anywhere near as much BHC as DDT is tolerated by some, and most of those tested are either highly susceptible or susceptible to BHC. Honey Dew muskmelon is one of the most sensitive plants tested in soil containing BHC. Strawberries, on the other hand, highly sensitive to DDT, appear unusually tolerant to BHC.

A large number of observations on effects of BHC has been reported both from Europe and here in America. One of the most striking features of these diverse reports is the consistently harmful effects of getting BHC concentrated in close proximity to, or contact with, seeds upon planting. Because of its remarkable control of many soil-inhabiting insects that attack seeds or seedlings before emergence, a number of experiments have been conducted in which BHC was dusted on the seed in the open row or drill in the soil before covering the seed with the soil. Marked injury usually resulted although only a pound or two up to 5 or 6 pounds of technical BHC per acre was applied. Coating bean and corn seed with 4 ounces of technical BHC per bushel, with a "sticker," resulted in serious injury.

As little as 3 parts per million (about 6 pounds per acre of soil 6⅔ inches deep) of technical BHC was somewhat harmful to red clover, soybean, and vetch, while 30 parts per million caused serious injury. Up to 15 pounds per acre thoroughly mixed with the soil has been reported harmless to grain crops while reports on other trials under other conditions showed 20 to 50 pounds harmful to wheat, oats, and barley. Dosages of 50 pounds per acre or more have been generally harmful to most crops grown the same year the technical BHC was applied. Fifty to 80 pounds, however, was not harmful to cotton or tobacco the following year.

Experimental applications of 100 to 200 pounds of technical BHC per acre—in efforts to find upper limits of tolerance of "resistant" crops—have consistently ruined the plantings.

Some potato varieties have made normal-appearing growth and yield on soil treated with as much as 80 pounds, while others under different conditions have been injured supposedly by only 20 pounds. Regardless of the effect on growth, it is now well known that BHC must never be used in growing potatoes, sweetpotatoes, carrots, beets, other root crops, or peanuts—any crop of which the edible part develops in contact with the soil—because the insecticide spoils the flavor or imparts a bad odor to the product.

When a single application of BHC is no greater than recommended for the control of a specific pest in the soil and when it is thoroughly mixed in the soil so that it will not be too concentrated near the seed and young plant, it is by no means always harmful. It is highly toxic to the germinating seeds and roots of most plants, however, and must be used with discretion.

Investigators in India and in Europe, after studying the abnormalities of plant tissues and plant cells that were caused by contact with BHC, have gone so far as to suggest the possibility that repeated growing and seed saving of a single stock of a sensitive crop on soil containing appreciable amounts of BHC may cause the stock to deteriorate genetically. While this appears to be an extreme view, only time can tell whether or not it is well founded.

Lindane, a relatively pure preparation of the gamma isomer of BHC, contains very little of the several odorous impurities present in technical BHC that have little or no insecticidal value but that are nevertheless highly toxic to plants. Lindane is of particular interest because only about one-eighth as much is required for insect control as is required of the technical BHC, and because it is less odorous. Several workers have shown that although it has little if any harmful effect on germination and stand it tends to be about as toxic to later growth, *pound for pound,* as technical BHC. In practice, of course, the probabilities of adding large amounts of lindane in a short time are remote—especially since the cost per unit of gamma isomer is higher in the form of lindane than in technical BHC.

Chlordane and toxaphene have been used less extensively than DDT and BHC and their possible toxic effects on plants have been studied less.

In the field, at applications up to 20 pounds per acre chlordane has been harmless to tobacco, cotton, soybean, cowpeas, corn, and rye. In other fields 28 pounds stunted beans slightly when they were planted soon after applying the chlordane to the soil. Twenty to 25 pounds per acre had no effect on a wide range of species of grasses but as much as 40 to 80 pounds of chlordane applied to lawns or sods caused some temporary injury. In greenhouse tests at 200 pounds per acre chlordane was more toxic to four varieties of sorghum than to most varieties of cereals tested. Strawberries appeared highly tolerant.

The effects of chlordane on the germination and stand of vegetable crops have been rather variable. Some investigators have found 20 pounds per acre to have no effect on germination of a wide range of vegetables while others have found beans, beets, tomatoes, and members of the pumpkin family to be injured by 20 to 25 pounds or more per acre. A hundred pounds or more hurt germination of those crops seriously. On the other hand, germination of lima bean, corn, and members of the cabbage family was affected but little by 100 pounds.

Effects of chlordane on later growth of vegetables have also been variable. As little as 5 pounds per acre has been reported to affect the growth of sensitive varieties of squash in some tests but 25 pounds or more has not been harmful in others. Sometimes other vegetables apparently are harmed after emergence by no more than 20 pounds per acre, and in other instances unharmed by 100 pounds per acre. Muskmelon, especially Honey Dew, some varieties of squash, and cucumber, however, have appeared rather highly sensitive.

Four pounds of chlordane per acre applied in the furrow before covering sugarcane seed pieces slightly stimulated the emergence of the shoots and caused no injury.

Of the few reports on the effects of toxaphene none show any harmful effect on germination and stand or upon growth after plant emergence, where no more than 25 pounds per acre have been used. One investigator found tomato germination and the post-emergence growth of pumpkin, squash, and watermelon to be depressed about a third by 100 pounds per acre of toxaphene. Two hundred pounds depressed the growth of sorghum nearly 50 percent, and of beans and tomatoes about 30 percent. Most cereals and lima beans tested were little affected at this rate.

Two other insecticides, aldrin and dieldrin, are so new that they have been used and studied even less than those discussed in the preceding pages. The limited data available indicate that to most crop plants they are more toxic than DDT, chlordane, and toxaphene, *pound for pound,* but less toxic than BHC and lindane. Dieldrin appears generally more toxic than aldrin. Because of their great potency the recommended dosages are very small. Therefore their accumulation as soil residues harmful to plants does not now seem likely to occur in a short time, if ever.

Parathion in the soil, up to 50 to 100 pounds per acre, has produced no harmful effect on growth of vegetables with the possible exception of snap beans and muskmelons, planted soon after treating the soil. Plantings made later than 3 to 4 months after treating the soil were not harmed. There was some depression of germination soon after heavy treatments were applied, but later plantings were unaffected.

Parathion stimulated the growth of strawberries.

Extensive tests of DDT with many crops show that certain acid muck soils render large amounts of DDT nontoxic to plants that are seriously injured by equal amounts that are applied to certain mineral soils. Mineral soils show some differences in the degree of injury that is produced by a given amount of DDT mixed in them. From the little now known, it appears that on light, sandy soils low in clay, silt, or organic matter, plants sensitive to DDT will be harmed the most. On loamy and claylike soils they will be injured a little less, and on certain muck soils little or no injury is expected to most crops when treated with less than 400 pounds per acre. Many factors besides texture doubtless are involved in these differences among soils.

Bush squash, a highly sensitive crop, was harmed little on muck at 400 pounds, but on mineral soils was injured at 100 pounds. Beans, also highly sensitive on mineral soil were unharmed by 400 pounds on muck.

As yet there is no adequate evidence regarding the effect of soil conditions on the plant toxicity of residues of organic insecticides other than DDT. It is logical to suppose, however, that mineral colloids and organic matter may well affect plant response to residues of some other compounds somewhat as they have to DDT and arsenic.

As yet there has been no good evidence that a plant will absorb DDT from the soil and translocate it into its edible parts. Numerous analyses of various parts of plants from DDT-treated soil have always failed to show DDT within the plant.

There is ample evidence, however, that BHC in the soil does contaminate those edible parts of plants that develop below the soil surface. Some potato growers have suffered heavy loss—and some consumers and merchants have also suffered loss—because the BHC that was added to potato fields to control insects imparted a disagreeable flavor and odor to the potatoes. This bad odor and flavor of BHC persists in the soil for a considerable time, certainly for more than a year, but for how long is not known. Some fields erroneously treated with BHC may be unfit for the growing of potatoes or edible root crops for several years. There have been a few instances of spoiling the flavor and odor of peanuts either by treating the soil or dusting the young plants in such a way that the BHC directly reached the soil in which the pods developed. Chemical analysis has revealed that when BHC is put in the fertilizer for peanuts it may enter the seeds in measurable amounts.

Chlordane also has been found as a contaminant of root crops harvested from soil treated with chlordane to control soil-inhabiting insects. Amounts of some insecticides in the soil too small to harm plant growth may make some products grown therein unfit for food or feed.

This whole question of absorption of insecticides from the soil by plants is of major practical importance to consumers, to the food industry, to the manufacturers of insecticides, and to research and regulatory agencies alike.

Although a persistent insecticidal residue in the soil may show no immediately harmful direct effect on crop plants, it might possibly affect some of the soil bacteria, fungi, or other micro-organisms either for good or ill.

The few microbiological studies that have been made with such insecticides as DDT, BHC, chlordane, and toxaphene show that the soil micro-organisms tolerate these chemicals better than crop plants do. DDT up to about 250 pounds per acre had no significant effect on numbers of organisms, or the power of organisms to produce nitrates or ammonia in the soil.

BHC, on the other hand, kills off certain soil fungi and nitrifying bacteria for some months at 100 to 500 pounds per acre. Twenty pounds of BHC had no marked effect on nitrifying or ammonifying bacteria.

Chlordane is somewhat fungicidal in large doses in the soil and depressed nitrate formation at 100 to 500 pounds, but at 20 pounds had no clearly significant effect. Chlordane produced as great effects after the treated soil had been stored in the laboratory for a year as it did soon after treatment.

Toxaphene is unusual, among the chlorinated hydrocarbon insecticides studied so far, in that it appears to be attacked by soil micro-organisms and used as a source of food by them.

From all that is now known, DDT is an unusually stable organic compound when in the soil. Of large amounts added to certain soils only about 5 percent per year is decomposed. Reference has been made to its phenomenal persistence in the control of Japanese beetle grubs. In the soil its toxicity to plants appears to be just as persistent as its insecticidal qualities, or more so. And, unhappily, it also appears that some of its probable decomposition products are also persistent and toxic to plants. How long those decomposition products might persist in the soil, no one knows. Some small plots treated with different amounts of DDT in 1945 appeared in 1951 to be practically as toxic as at first. It is hardly conceivable that the soil will show no decrease in toxicity in the foreseeable future, but there is not now any basis for estimating how long it will take for the toxicity of 100, 200, or 400 pounds per acre to disappear.

Soil analyses in orchards sprayed with DDT, using organic chlorine content as an index, have shown that the amounts of DDT accumulated in the surface soil beneath the trees roughly approximate the total number of pounds per acre used during the years it has been applied to those trees. Experience has shown that this accumulation will interfere with the growth of rye cover crops in as little as 4 to 5 years under a heavy spray schedule.

Pound for pound, BHC is more toxic to more crops than is DDT. Fortunately, however, evidence is developing that it is definitely less persistent than DDT. Large dosages in the soil decomposed at the rate of about 10 percent or more per year. Mild injury from BHC in the field in the season it was added to the soil has sometimes failed to recur. This may be due, in part, to further dilution of the BHC by mixing it with a larger volume of soil as the field is plowed and fitted for another year's crops.

Chemical analysis of soils years after a large amount of BHC has been applied, or after it has been applied annually for years, has detected substantially lower proportions of the total amount supplied than has been found with DDT. Furthermore, some small carefully controlled plots that received massive doses, 100 and 200 pounds per acre in 1946, were showing marked loss of toxicity by 1950. After 3 years both the 100- and 200-pound plots were still toxic to beans, a moderately sensitive crop. By 1950 beans grew equally well on both the treatments and on the controls, indicating a substantial disappearance of the BHC. When planted to very sensitive corn, however, immediately after the less sensitive beans were removed, it became clear that a relatively large proportion of the 200-pound treatment still persisted. The corn in the 100-pound plots was nearly equal to the control, but in the 200-pound plots, growth stopped at about 8 inches in height, and the plants were badly yellowed. BHC, therefore, does disappear slowly from the soil but much work will need to be done to determine how much can be dissipated or destroyed per year in different kinds of soil in different climates. Under the conditions of the experiment cited, it appears that as much as 15 to 20 pounds of the material toxic to plant growth might become dissipated under some conditions but that is only a rough indication.

INFORMATION ON THE persistence of chlordane is still meager. Its insecticidal persistence is much less than that of DDT. Of heavy dosages in soil about 15 to 20 percent per year disappears, while large percentages of small dosages appear to be lost. While its toxicity to plants is almost certainly less persistent than DDT, it should perhaps be considered as having potentialities for developing accumulations in the soil where it is used heavily and repeatedly.

Toxaphene also is much less stable than DDT. The meager data available suggest that large dosages disappear at about the same rate as chlordane. Residues reaching the soil following foliage applications, however, appear to accumulate faster than chlordane and BHC and slower than DDT.

Aldrin and dieldrin appear intermediate in their persistence and tendency to accumulate, but because of the small dosages used will accumulate only slowly. Following foliage applications, aldrin accumulates about like chlordane, and dieldrin more rapidly.

The new phosphorus compounds such as parathion are known to be highly unstable and thus are no cause for concern as potential harmful residues in the soil.

The insecticides manufactured from plants, such as derris and pyrethrum, are natural plant products that are presumed to decompose readily in the soil. There is no evidence that they either do or do not contribute any harmful residue to the soil, but it is hardly conceivable that they should, considering their origin and make-up.

Fumigants such as D-D mixture, methyl bromide, chloropicrin, and others are all highly toxic to plants. It is necessary to delay planting for several days after treatment to allow time for the toxic vapors to diffuse out of the soil. Since, however, these substances are rapidly and completely vaporized there is no fear of a residue problem with them. Some fumigants temporarily kill off certain beneficial bacteria, fungi, and other soil life, or at least upset micro-life temporarily. There is no evidence, as yet, that their repeated use leads to any accumulative persistent undesirable effects.

BEARING IN MIND the relative toxicity to plants and the apparent persistence of various insecticides in the soil, rate of use must be considered in order to estimate the probability that any one substance will lead to trouble under a given set of conditions. Attempting to predict, with our present small knowledge, is admittedly hazardous. We believe, however, that failure to be guided by the best estimates we can make may be even more hazardous.

MOST OF THE so-called field crops that are sprayed or dusted with DDT receive relatively small amounts in any one year, only 1 or 2 up to 4 or 5 pounds per acre per year. Ordinarily the field crops grown on a given tract over a period of years do not all require treatment so that DDT is not applied to such fields every year. Supposing that in a 20-year interval half the crops required treatment and that amounts near the maximum customary rate of use were applied, the maximum total application would probably be about 50 pounds. Even if all this reached the soil and no loss occurred in 20 years—hardly probable—that amount would represent no important hazard to any field crop we have tested.

On some field crops, larger amounts of DDT are used: Up to 8 or 9 pounds per acre for European corn borer on corn, aphids on peas, and leafhoppers on beets, and 10 to 12 pounds on cotton. It is probable that in one of the more intensive general farming systems involving several such crops over a 20-year period the total DDT used would be closer to 100 pounds than to 50 pounds. This 100 pounds may well represent a borderline level for injury of moderately sensitive crops but not for tolerant ones. Before DDT has been so used for 20 years we will know much more about its limitations than we know now and will be able to guard against excessive use on our principal farm crops.

Our cause for immediate concern about accumulations of harmful residues of DDT in the soil is not its use at 1 to 5 pounds per acre on staple farm crops in some years, but its heavy use every year on the same tracts of land planted to orchards or to truck or other special crops. As with arsenicals, DDT goes into the soils of orchards much more heavily than into soils growing other crops. As much as 50 to 60 or more pounds per acre per year is used in some orchards. All evidence points to early trouble in the growing of susceptible cover crops such as Abruzzi rye and some legumes in such orchards. Although most grasses are tolerant, and there have been few, if any, instances of suspected injury to sod covers, accumulations that will harm orchard sods should not be considered impossible. Furthermore, a given tract does not remain in orchard indefinitely. What use can be made of it after an orchard is removed following 10 or 20 years' treatment? Heavy repeated dosages are used on sweet corn and some other truck crops in some districts with the probability of developing enough residue in the soil to harm sensitive crops.

The potato crop receives up to about 20 pounds of DDT per acre per year in some districts, more often about 6 to 10 pounds. The potato is highly tolerant to DDT, but many of the crops grown in rotation with it are not. In intensive potato districts, especially in which DDT is used on crops in rotation with potatoes, there is the possibility of adverse effects on some crops within 10 years.

For most truck crops commonly treated with DDT only 2 to 5 pounds per acre per crop is recommended. In the milder parts of the country two and even three truck crops requiring insect control with DDT may be grown annually, raising the not improbable use of DDT to 6 to 15 pounds per acre or more annually. We must remember, too, that many farmers tend to use insecticides, fungicides, fertilizers, and seed, at rates much higher than necessary, "just for good measure." Misuse must be avoided.

Despite its great value and its firm place for many purposes, some current uses of DDT seem to have real potentialities for impairing the usefulness of the soils on which it is being used heavily. Furthermore, there is no assurance as to how rapidly a toxic level of DDT in the soil will decrease to a harmless level. Indications are that it will be very slow.

Because the disagreeable flavor and odor of BHC are readily imparted to food products it is unsafe to apply it to the tops of food plants after the above-ground edible parts have developed appreciably; and it should never be put in the soil before planting any crop, the edible part of which develops below the soil surface. This characteristic of BHC has sharply limited its use in the growing of food crops.

BHC is used rather heavily, early in the season, for controlling certain fruit insects such as plum curculio—3 to 6 pounds of the gamma isomer or equivalent per acre in a mature orchard. In the form of lindane this represents but 3 to 6 pounds; but in the form of the less expensive technical BHC it represents 25 to 50 pounds. About 40 to 50 pounds per acre of technical BHC are used very extensively to control cotton insects and 5 to 10 pounds per acre are extensively used in the soil to control soil-borne pests of various grain and other farm crops.

From the rates of disappearance of BHC from the soils that we have observed it seems probable that soil applications of 5 to 10 pounds of technical grade (or 1 to 2 pounds of lindane) at intervals of 1 or 2 years will rarely if ever develop residues that impair the growth or yield of crops. These small amounts, however, will probably contaminate foods that develop below the soil surface.

As much as 50 pounds of BHC per acre added directly to the soil year after year will almost certainly build up an amount in 5 years or less that will be definitely harmful to several important crops. BHC is somewhat volatile, however, loses its plant and insect toxicity in the soil much less slowly than DDT, and is believed to "weather away" and decompose appreciably after it is applied to the foliage of plants. It has, therefore, appeared unlikely that as large a proportion of the amount applied will actually reach the soil as occurs with DDT. Experiments only 2 years in progress (1951) tend to confirm this view. While BHC actually accumulates in the soil following heavy applications to the foliage of crops, such accumulation appears to be substantially less than with DDT with which it is being compared.

At heavy rates, however, it accumulates, and it is toxic to plants.

CHLORDANE IS RARELY used at rates in excess of 10 pounds per acre per crop, generally at 6 pounds or less. Ten- and 20-pound applications directly to the soil have shown considerable loss of insecticidal value after 1 year. Chemical analysis of plots so treated indicated that only 4 to 5 pounds of chlordane remained a year after application. Thus, although chlordane does seem to be only moderately persistent, some of a normal application persists more than a year, indicating that if used repeatedly at intervals of about a year a slow accumulation of a residue may be expected. These statements on persistence are admittedly based on meagre evidence and may have to be modified later. Nevertheless, chlordane seems to present a definitely less immediate and potentially serious problem than does DDT.

As indicated on preceding pages, toxaphene, and parathion and other phosphorus compounds appear to involve no hazard through the accumulating of residues in the soil.

Methoxychlor, TDE, aldrin, dieldrin, heptachlor, and other new synthetic insecticides have appeared so recently that too little has been learned about their plant toxicity and persistence in the soil to permit specific statements about them as this is written (1952). Early results, however, indicate that methoxyclor, TDE, and DDT are rather similar in persistence and that DDT is more toxic than the first two. Chlordane, aldrin, and dieldrin appear persistent but somewhat less so than DDT.

Since it has been shown that some of these remarkably efficient and economical insecticides may and do accumulate to an undesirable degree in the soil under certain conditions, we may confidently look to the research chemist and to the chemical manufacturer for still newer compounds that will have the advantages of those now in use but without the disadvantages of too great stability and toxicity to plants in the soil. Since a few good insecticides are already known that appear now to present no soil-residue problem, others doubtless will be produced. It is true that those now known to be relatively unstable and less toxic to plants may not be as effective or economical for controlling certain farm pests as some of the more persistent ones are. There is no reason, however, to suppose that it will always be so. Highly effective nonaccumulative insecticides will surely be developed for use where desirable. Their further development, production, and use to replace the too persistent ones should be urged.

VICTOR R. BOSWELL *is head of the division of vegetable crops and diseases at the Plant Industry Station at Beltsville, Md. He grew up on a small farm in southwest Missouri and studied horticulture at the University of Missouri and the University of Maryland. After 6 years of teaching and research experience in Maryland he entered the Bureau of Plant Industry of the Department of Agriculture in 1928, with responsibility for the vegetable crop investigations in that Bureau, which responsibility he still holds. He became assistant head of the division of fruit and vegetable crops and diseases in 1941. Dr. Boswell has written many publications on a wide range of problems relating to the production, growth, development, yield, and quality of vegetable crops. He was assigned to the War Department in 1945–46 as a member of the National Resources Section of SCAP in Tokyo where he was responsible for the production branch in the agriculture division. He was president of the American Society for Horticultural Science in 1939.*

For further reference:

J. d'Aguilar and P. Grison: Premières études sur le problème des taupins en Bretagne, *Comptes Rendus Hebdomadaires des Seances dé l'Académie d'Agriculture de France, volume 34, pages 261–267. 1948.*

W. B. Albert: Arsenic Toxicity in Soils, *Forty-sixth Annual Report of the South Carolina Agricultural Experiment Station, pages 44–45. 1933.*

Earle C. Blodgett: A Systemic Arsenic Toxicity of Peach and Apricot on Old Apple Land, *Plant Disease Reporter, volume 25, pages 549–551. 1941.*

M. L. Bonnemaison: Essais préliminaires de traitements contre les taupins, *Comptes Rendus Hebdomadaires des Seance de l'Académie d'Agriculture de France, volume 33, pages 556–559. 1947.*

B. A. Bourne: Effects of Benzene Hexachloride and Chlordane on the Germination of Sugarcane Cuttings, *Sugar Journal, volume 10, number 8, pages 3–4, 20. 1948.*

T. A. Brindley, R. Schopp, and F. G. Hinman: Effect of Initial High Dosages of DDT on Yields of Peas and Wheat, *Journal of Economic Entomology, volume 43, pages 565–567. 1950.*

J. W. Brooks and L. D. Anderson: Toxicity Tests of Some New Insecticides, *Journal of Economic Entomology, volume 40, pages 220–228. 1947.*

R. K. Chapman and T. C. Allen: Stimulation and Suppression of Some Vegetable Plants by DDT, *Journal of Economic Entomology, volume 41, pages 616–623. 1948.*

Karl Chulski: The Effect of Benzene-Hexachloride on Some Crops Grown on Various Soil Types, *Michigan Agricultural Experiment Station Quarterly Bulletin, volume 31, pages 170–177. 1948.*

H. P. Cooper, W. R. Paden, E. E. Hall, and others: Effect of Calcium Arsenate on the Productivity of Certain Soil Types, *Forty-fourth Annual Report of the South Carolina Agricultural Experiment Station, pages 28–36, 1931;* Soils Differ Markedly in Their Response to Additions of Calcium Arsenate, *Forty-fifth Annual Report of the South Carolina Agricultural Experiment Station, pages 23–28, 1932.*

W. E. Fleming: Chlordan for Control of Japanese Beetle Larvae, *Journal of Economic Entomology, volume 41, pages 905–912, 1948;* Effect on Plants of DDT Applied to Soil for the Destruction of Japanese Beetle Larvae, *Bureau of Entomology and Plant Quarantine publication E–737, 1948;* Persistence of Effect of DDT on Japanese Beetle Larvae in New Jersey Soils, *Journal of Economic Entomology, volume 43, pages 87–89, 1950;* Effect of Lead Arsenate in Soil on Vegetables, *with F. E. Baker and L. Koblitsky, Journal of Economic Entomology, volume 36, pages 231–233, 1943.*

Arthur C. Foster: Some Plant Responses to Certain Insecticides in the Soil, *U. S. D. A. Circular 862. 1951.*

M. C. Goldsworthy, in Plant Disease Reporter, volume 32: Effect of Soil Applications of Various Chlorinated Hydrocarbons on the Top Growth of Blakemore Strawberry Plants, *pages 186–188;* Effect of Technical DDT, Incorporated in Quartz Sand and Soils, on the Growth of Pear Trees, *pages 437–441;* The Effect of Incorporating Technical DDT in Soil on the Growth of Blakemore Strawberry Plants, *with J. C. Dunegan, pages 139–143;* Effect of Soil Applications of "Parathion" on the Top Growth of Blakemore Strawberry Plants, *with R. A. Wilson, pages 388–390.*

J. M. Grayson and F. W. Poos: Southern Corn Rootworm as a Pest of Peanuts, *Journal of Economic Entomology, volume 40, pages 251–256. 1947.*

Wm. P. Headden: Arsenical Poisoning of Fruit Trees, *Colorado Agricultural Experiment Station Bulletin 131. 1908.*

B. Hocking: On the Effect of Crude Benzene Hexachloride on Cereal Seedlings, *Scientific Agriculture, volume 30, pages 183–193. 1950.*

H. R. Jameson, F. J. D. Thomas, and R. C. Woodward: The Practical Control of Wireworm by γ-Benzene Hexachloride ('Gammexane'): Comparisons with Dichlorodiphenyltrichlorethane (D. D. T.), *Annals of Applied Biology, volume 34, pages 346–356. 1947.*

J. S. Jones and M. B. Hatch, in Soil Science: The Significance of Inorganic Spray Residue Accumulations in Orchard Soils, *volume 44, pages 37–62, 1937;* Spray Residues and Assimilation of Arsenic and Lead, *volume 60, pages 277–288. 1945.*

L. W. Jones: Are Insecticides Toxic to Soil Microorganisms? *Farm and Home Science (Utah Agricultural Experiment Station), volume 11, pages 58–59. 1950.*

W. M. Kulash, in Journal of Economic Entomology: Soil Treatment for Wireworms and Cutworms, *volume 40, pages 851–854, 1947;* Further Tests With Soil Insecticides to Control Southern Corn Rootworm, *volume 42, pages 558–559, 1949.*

M. C. Lane, M. W. Stone, H. P. Lanchester, E. W. Jones, and K. E. Gibson: Studies with DDT as a Control for Wireworms in Irrigated Lands—Progress Report, *Bureau of Entomology and Plant Quarantine publication E–765. 1948.*

W. S. McLeod: Effect of Hexachlorocyclohexane on Onion Seedlings, *Journal of Economic Entomology (scientific note), volume 39, page 815. 1946.*

H. E. Morrison, H. H. Crowell, S. E. Crumb, Jr., and R. W. Lauderdale: The Effects of Certain New Soil Insecticides on Plants, *Journal of Economic Entomology, volume 41, pages 374–378. 1948.*

B. B. Pepper, C. A. Wilson, and J. C. Campbell: Benzene Hexachloride and Other Compounds for Control of Wireworms Infecting Potatoes, *Journal of Economic Entomology, volume 40, pages 727–730. 1947.*

P. T. Riherd: DDT and Benzene Hexachloride to Control Southern Corn Rootworm, *Journal of Economic Entomology, volume 42, pages 992–993. 1949.*

K. Sakimura: Residual Toxicity of Hexachlorocyclohexane Incorporated in Soil, *Journal of Economic Entomology, volume 41, pages 665–666. 1948.*

M. S. Smith: Persistence of D. D. T. and Benzene Hexachloride in Soils, *Annals of Applied Biology, volume 35, pages 494–504.*

Nathan R. Smith and Marie E. Wenzel: Soil Microorganisms Are Affected by Some of the New Insecticides, *Soil Science Society of America Proceedings, volume 12, pages 227–233. 1947.*

L. L. Stitt and James Evanson: Phytotoxicity and Off-quality of Vegetables Grown in Soil Treated With Insecticides, *Journal of Economic Entomology, volume 42, pages 614–617. 1949.*

Rosemary I. Stoker: The Phytotoxicity of D. D. T. and Benzene Hexachloride, *Annals of Applied Biology, volume 35, pages 110–122. 1948.*

C. L. Vincent: Problems in Vegetable and Small Fruit Production on Toxic Orchard Soils of Central Washington, *American Society for Horticultural Science, Proceedings, volume 37, pages 680–684. 1939.*

J. K. Wilson and R. S. Choudri: Effects of DDT on Certain Microbiological Processes in the Soil, *Journal of Economic Entomology, volume 39, pages 537–538, 1946;* The Effect of Benzene Hexachloride on Soil Organisms, *Journal of Agricultural Research, volume 77, pages 25–32. 1948.*

H. C. Young and J. B. Gill: Soil Treatments with DDT to Control the White-Fringed Beetle, *Bureau of Entomology and Plant Quarantine publication E–750. 1948.*

Residues on Fruits and Vegetables

B. A. Porter, J. E. Fahey

How to use a chemical to control insects on fruits and vegetables without harming the person who eats them remains a serious problem.

It concerns the chemists who develop insecticides, the growers who use them, food officials of State and Federal agencies, and home gardeners, who might not always treat the poisons with the respect due them. Many scientists, who realize that worms and insect debris in fruits and vegetables would lower their value to grower and consumer, have done a tremendous amount of research on ways to keep the foods free of dangerous contamination with insecticides.

It seemed that the problem was settled in 1880, when in reporting the first official tests of arsenicals, the investigator, A. J. Cook, of Michigan, took into account the possible effect of the insecticide on the consumer. Materials then available were paris green and london purple. The results of the analyses were taken to mean that there was no danger that injurious quantities of poison could reach the consumer when those insecticides were used. Further reassurance was given 11 years later by another official worker, C. P. Gillette, of the Iowa Agricultural Experiment Station. He also studied the matter carefully and announced that a person would have to eat at one sitting 30 cabbages that had been dusted with paris green to get enough poison to hurt him. Evidently he assumed that the insecticide would be evenly distributed and the loose leaves trimmed off. In those early days, spraying and dusting were light compared with later practice, and the insecticides in use had poor sticking qualities. The conclusions of the early investigators were probably correct at the time.

But the problem since has become intensified. Our cropping areas have become more concentrated. Insect pests have become more abundant and hard to control. Spray and dust programs have included more and heavier applications. Fears increased that with the growing use of insecticides the fruits and vegetables on the consumer's table might have excessive residues on them. Men in the Department of Agriculture therefore, in surveys in 1915 to 1919, analyzed hundreds of samples of peaches, cherries, plums, apples, pears, grapes, cranberries, tomatoes, celery, and cucumbers for lead, arsenic and copper. The investigators concluded that only little spray residue remained on fruit or vegetables that had been sprayed according to standard recommendations. They reported, however, that excessive residues remained on fruits or vegetables that had been oversprayed or sprayed too close to harvesttime.

Another complication has arisen since then. At first the possible immediate effect of spray residues on consumers was chiefly considered. Less thought was given to the possible cumulative effect of taking in extremely small quantities of poison day after day. Such effects are hard to detect and easy to confuse with other conditions. Cases of sickness developing immediately after the poisons were taken in have been rare, if they have occurred at all. But since the 1920's the belief has grown that the gradual accumulation of poisons in the system might have unfavorable effects.

The problems of spray residue on vegetable crops have been met in several ways. Many insects that attack vegetable crops, such as the Mexican bean beetle and several kinds of cabbage caterpillars, can be controlled by the use of pyrethrum or materials that contain rotenone. Residues of both are considered unobjectionable. Both are also effective against most of the insects that attack small fruits like currants, raspberries, and cranberries. Commercial practices often eliminate residues of insecticides on vegetable crops. For instance, the part of the cabbage plant that has been exposed to the insecticide is often trimmed off in preparing the cabbages for the market. The use of insecticides can be limited to the early stages of the growth of the plant when the part to be eaten has not yet formed.

Many of the insects that affect tree fruits can be controlled without causing excessive spray residue. The plum curculio, which also feeds extensively on peach and apple, lays most of its eggs and causes the most damage in most localities in late spring or early summer. Insecticides can be used freely then, because only the smallest traces will remain on the fruit at picking time. Many insects attack tree fruits throughout the growing season, however. The most important of these has been the codling moth on apples and pears. Since this problem received major attention from the early 1920's until the early 1940's, we review its history during that period in some detail.

The codling moth is often called the appleworm. Many have had the experience of biting into an apple containing a worm or into an apple in which a worm had lived. Wormy apples rot quickly in storage or during shipment. Uncontrolled, the worms can ruin 50 to 90 percent of the crop. A crop that is even 50-percent wormy has little commercial value, since the cost of handling and sorting it is often more than the value of the part that can be salvaged. Such apples are fit only for immediate local use, or for low-grade byproducts.

Lead arsenate was the standard insecticide against the codling moth from early in the present century until 1945. As the worms became more and more abundant and hard to control, the number of spray applications, the strength of the spray mixture, and the number of gallons applied per tree steadily increased. The amount of lead and arsenic on the fruit at harvesttime also increased steadily. Western pears in 1919 were condemned by the Boston Board of Health because of excessive residues of arsenic. A few years later British health authorities objected to shipments of American apples for the same reason. By 1925 it had become evident that the use of lead arsenate sprays had increased to the point where American apples and pears were carrying quantities of residues that were at least potentially dangerous to public health.

As soon as the serious nature of the problem became clear, the Department of Agriculture moved to carry out its responsibility for the enforcement of the Food and Drug Act. An administrative tolerance for arsenic (as of As_2O_3) of 0.025 grain per pound of fruit (about 3.5 parts per million) was established, following a conference of health authorities. Efforts were made to reduce the residues below this figure, and by 1932 the amount of arsenic permitted on apples and pears under the administrative tolerances had been progressively reduced to 0.01 grain per pound of fruit (about 1.4 parts per million).

During the 1920's attention was focused entirely on the arsenic portion of lead arsenate, on the assumption that if the arsenic were reduced to safe quantities, the lead would also be eliminated as a hazard. It was found later that the lead did not always weather off as rapidly as the arsenic and that it was not always so completely removed by washing. Since the early 1930's residues of lead arsenate have therefore been judged largely by their lead content.

Although both lead and arsenic have long been known to be serious poisons, precise information was lacking on the quantities of those materials that could be taken into the human body in the form of spray residues without harm. To shed light on this problem, the United States Public Health Service carried on an investigation from 1937 to 1940 around Wenatchee, Wash., a leading apple-growing section, where during the 1930's as much as 7 million pounds of lead arsenate was used annually. A careful study was made of 1,231 persons, many of whom worked or lived in or close to apple orchards and were thus extensively exposed to lead arsenate, both in their diet and their surroundings. The following is quoted from the report of the studies:

"Only six men and one woman had a *combination* of clinical and laboratory findings directly referable to the absorption of lead arsenate. Some physicians may interpret these cases as minimal lead arsenate intoxication. However, as regards lead, these cases do not come up to the criteria of the Committee on Lead Poisoning of the American Public Health Association for lead intoxication, incipient plumbism or lead poisoning. These subjects were all orchardists and ranged in age from 23 to 68 years."

Although such a study is less exact than experimentation on guinea pigs, mice, or other laboratory animals, it gives an approximate indication of what actually happens to human beings exposed regularly to lead arsenate. Many of the persons examined had undoubtedly taken much greater quantities of lead arsenate than the general consuming public. On the basis of the results of the study, the administrative tolerances for apples and pears were increased to 0.025 grain of arsenic (as arsenic trioxide) per pound and 0.05 grain of lead per pound of fruit (about 3.5 and 7 parts per million, respectively). That eased the situation greatly from the standpoint of the growers. It was then possible for most growers in the East and Midwest to market apples without washing them and for the growers in the Northwest to clean their fruit satisfactorily with mild washing programs.

During the 1920's and ever since, vigorous efforts have been made to solve the problem of spray residues on apples and pears. These efforts have taken two directions: The development of methods and equipment for removing the excessive residue after the fruit was harvested, and the development of effective insecticides or other methods of control less objectionable from the standpoint of residues.

Effective washing methods and machinery were promptly developed for removing most of the residues before the fruit is marketed. In the washing process the apples are passed through dilute hydrochloric acid and then through a spray of clean water to rinse off the acid and the poison. In extreme cases a double wash is used; the apples are passed through a dilute alkaline solution, rinsed, passed through a dilute acid, and then rinsed again. To aid in removal, the wash solutions are sometimes heated. The development of such equipment permitted the safe marketing of the apples, but the cost of installing, maintaining, and operating the machinery came at a bad time. Prices during the 1930's were abnormally low, and many growers were having difficulty in meeting their obligations. Washing the fruit added one more item of production cost. It was a real hardship to many growers, and some of them even lost their orchards.

The ultimate solution of the problem evidently should be sought in another direction. The old-time practice of trapping the worms in bands placed around the trunks of the trees was revived and improved by a chemical treatment of the bands. Traps baited with fermenting sugar solutions with the addition of attractive chemicals were developed. The possibilities in light traps, orchard clean-up, and parasites were explored. Many of those practices had control value, but they did not reduce infestations to a point where the spray program could be materially shortened.

The first efforts to develop new insecticides produced few practical results. With all its shortcomings, lead arsenate was a good insecticide, and finding a better one proved to be a hard job. During the 1930's several new materials nearly met the needs, but not quite. Nicotine bentonite and other nicotine mixtures were used effectively in a number of midwestern orchards. Cryolite, a compound containing fluorine, proved to be about equal to lead arsenate in the Northwest, but ineffective or undependable elsewhere and objectionable from the standpoint of residues.

DDT, the first of the new, complex organic compounds, since 1945 has largely replaced lead arsenate in the control of codling moth. Less DDT is needed and in many areas fewer applications are necessary. As a result, residues from DDT programs are much less than the former residues from lead arsenate. But residues of DDT are hard to remove. If they are found to be too great, the problem will have to be met by adjustments in the spray program or by the substitution of less objectionable spray materials during the latter part of the growing season.

The codling moth is only one of many insect pests that the grower must control. Now that the codling moth has been reduced to a comparatively minor status, other pests have assumed greater importance. Some, such as the orchard mites or spider mites, have become more abundant and destructive following the use of DDT. To meet this situation the development of additional new pesticides is being pushed by Department of Agriculture and State workers and insecticide companies, who have had to conduct extensive research in several fields. The work of the chemists and entomologists in developing, testing, and evaluating insecticides is only the beginning. A chemical that shows promise must be evaluated as to residues, particularly whether the residues are likely to be a potential hazard if the material is used commercially. The pharmacologist must carry on experiments with the new product on laboratory animals. The determination of the dosages that are fatal or that cause obvious distress is the simplest part of the job. The potential danger of taking in tiny quantities of an insecticide day after day must also be determined. Any effect on consumers of spray residues would come about by repeated consumption of small quantities. As indicated earlier, the quantities found on marketed fruits and vegetables are rarely, if ever, great enough to have any immediate effect. To secure information on cumulative effects, experiments must extend over many months, as much as 2 years.

The investigations have created some problems for the chemists. The amounts to be measured are so small that they are expressed as parts per million. During the interval between the last insecticide application and harvest the residue may be reduced in three ways—by crop growth, by physical weathering, and by chemical breakdown of the insecticide—so that the residues at harvest, expressed in parts per million, are lower than they were immediately after application of the spray or dust.

To determine such tiny quantities of insecticides, the chemist must develop highly sensitive methods of analysis. Such metods are rarely available for use with the new insecticides, and the development of the required highly accurate methods is often difficult.

Many of the new insecticides are chlorinated hydrocarbons. If it is definitely known what compound is present, all that has to be done is to determine the amount of organic chlorine in it and then compute from that figure the amount of the original compound that is present. For example, DDT contains 50 percent of chlorine. If DDT is known to be the only insecticide that has been used, the amount of chlorine present is determined. The resulting figure is then multiplied by 2, which gives the amount of DDT present. The problem is rarely that simple, however. Sometimes the analysis of untreated fruits or vegetables shows considerable amounts of natural organic chlorine that must be allowed for.

Sometimes two chlorinated hydrocarbon insecticides are used on the same fruit or vegetable. It is then impossible to compute the amounts of each from the organic chlorine determination, and special methods have to be worked out to measure the different compounds separately. Some of the chemical determinations are made by comparing the color of a solution containing poison dissolved from the sprayed fruit with the color of a solution containing a known quantity of the chemical. Some fruits or vegetables contain substances that produce colors similar to those being measured. These natural color changes interfere with the accuracy of the analysis, and must be eliminated or allowed for. The solution of these difficulties requires great ingenuity on the part of the chemist.

Although the establishment of tolerances as a result of hearings conducted by the Federal Security Agency in 1950 may have a stabilizing influence, the situation will never be a static one. Insect-control problems are changing continually. New insecticides will continue to appear and create new problems. The residue factor will always be an important consideration. We are confident that steady progress will be made, and the public will be insured of a safe, adequate, and continuous supply of fruits and vegetables of high quality.

B. A. Porter *is in charge of the division of fruit insect investigations in the Bureau of Entomology and Plant Quarantine. He joined the Department in 1917, and for many years conducted field investigations of various orchard-insect problems in Connecticut and Indiana. He is a graduate of Massachusetts Agricultural College.*

J. E. Fahey *is a chemist in the Bureau of Entomology and Plant Quarantine. Since 1934 he has been in charge of the chemical work at the Department's fruit insect laboratory at Vincennes, Ind. He has made special studies of spray residues on fruits and other agricultural products. He was graduated from Oregon State College in 1928.*

970134°—52——21

State Pesticide Laws

Allen B. Lemmon

Ordinarily the user of a pest-control material cannot himself investigate or test the effectiveness of the product. He must rely on the manufacturer's warranties. Various State laws give him—as well as the manufacturers and the public—a measure of protection.

The first pesticide law was adopted by New York State in 1898 to regulate the sale of paris green, then the most important insecticide. Similar laws were adopted the following year by Oregon and Texas, and in 1901 by California, Louisiana, and Washington. In 1910, the Federal Insecticide Act was enacted. It was supplanted in 1947 by the Federal Insecticide, Fungicide, and Rodenticide Act, which provides coverage of additional types of pest-control materials.

The scope of the State pesticide laws was similarly increased as the importance of new materials has been realized. Before the Second World War, many of the State pesticide laws followed the general pattern set by the Federal Insecticide Act of 1910. Some of them pertained only to certain types of pest-control chemicals. With the development and widespread use of DDT and other synthetic organic pesticides, the need for control of the labeling and sale of these economically important and potentially injurious materials has been reflected by the enactment and amendment of State laws. The scope of many laws has now been extended to include any substance intended to be used for preventing, destroying, repelling, or controlling any insects, fungi, bacteria, weeds, rodents, predatory animals, or any other form of plant or animal life which is a pest.

It would serve no useful purpose to tabulate the details of individual State laws now in effect because this type of legislation is particularly active, and amendments anticipated in many States would soon render the information obsolete. The table gives a summary of the general characteristics of State pesticide laws and the names and addresses of the agencies enforcing them at the end of 1951.

A uniform State act has been adopted by 19 States. One of these dropped the registration procedure and several have omitted the provision with regard to registration under protest. Eight States have no economic poisons law. Two others have such limited coverage as to be in the class with those that have none. This leaves 19 States with various laws, some of which are more inclusive than the uniform act, and others that will probably be brought up to date as legislators have time. Requirements of the individual laws and information with regard to their administration may be had by writing to the agency concerned.

At the time the Federal law was modernized it was realized that corresponding action should be taken to modernize the different State pest-control laws. At the request of the National Association of Commissioners, Secretaries, and Directors of Agriculture, the Council of State Governments developed a proposed State insecticide, fungicide, and rodenticide act. This was drafted for the convenience of States that might wish to consider legislation to protect the public against misbranded or adulterated pesticides and to establish uniform State and Federal requirements for the marketing of these materials.

When State laws and regulations covering insecticides and other economic poisons vary greatly from State to State, it is difficult for a manufacturer to prepare a label that will meet both Federal and State requirements. If he has national distribution, several different labels may be required for the same product, and the possibility always exists that improperly labeled material will be sent into a State that requires a different type of label. This places a heavy burden on the manufacturers who operate in more than one State. The result is an increase in the costs of doing business and ultimately in higher prices paid by farmers and other users.

The uniform State insecticide, fungicide, and rodenticide act provides a basis for uniform action by the States. As used in the act the term "economic poison" means any substance or mixture of substances intended for preventing, destroying, repelling, or mitigating any insects, rodents, fungi, weeds, or other forms of plant or animal life or viruses (except viruses on or in living man or other animals) that the commissioner declares to be a pest. To avoid the implication that all economic poisons are highly toxic to human beings, or that the scope of the law is restricted to poisons, as that term is commonly used, it is becoming customary to refer to pest-control chemicals as *pesticides*.

An important provision of the law is with regard to registration of pesticides before they are offered for sale in a State. Registration serves as a screen to prevent ineffective, fraudulent, or dangerous economic poisons from being marketed in the State. It helps enforcement and permits correction of unsatisfactory or illegal labeling before a product enters trade.

Some State laws provide that registration of any pesticide may be refused or canceled after a hearing, if the product is of little or no value for the purpose for which it is intended or is detrimental to vegetation (except weeds), domestic animals, or public health and safety when properly used. Similar action may be taken if false or misleading statements concerning the product are made or implied by the firm or its agent, orally or in writing or in advertising.

In the States where laws do not provide for refusal of registration and there is disagreement between the applicant and the enforcement agency with regard to the acceptability of a product, the applicant may demand "registration under protest." This is a controversial provision in the uniform State insecticide, fungicide, and rodenticide act and many, believing that an official should not be required to register a questionable product under protest, prefer a hearing procedure whereby the facts can be determined and registration absolutely refused for a product that is worthless or too hazardous to use. The registrant is protected against misjudgment or arbitrary action of the administration in that he can bring court action if he believes the official's actions are in violation of law.

REGISTRATION of new pesticides is a difficult administrative problem. New products are constantly being developed, involving new chemicals, new combinations of chemicals, or new uses for chemicals. (In California, for example, the number of pesticides registered for sale has doubled every 10 years, and approximately 10,000 products are registered now.) Before an economic poison can be accepted for registration, adequate data must be available to demonstrate its effectiveness for the purpose intended, and that the proposed handling and use do not present any intolerable hazard. The necessary data depend somewhat upon the particular type of product involved. Although not all the items are pertinent to a specific product, the type of information that may be needed to establish the eligibility of the product for general sale is suggested by the following outline:

Chemical and physical:

1. Chemical name.
2. Chemical formula.
3. Chemical structure.
4. Melting point.
5. Boiling point.
6. Vapor pressures at various temperatures.
7. Solubilities in various solvents.
8. Odor.
9. Density. (This is important for

some liquid products to compare dosages by volume and by weight.)

10. Corrosive action on metals.

11. Flammability.

12. Stability (hydrolysis, oxidation, sunlight, explosion hazard).

13. Compatibility with other economic poisons.

14. Suitable diluents.

15. Purities, grades, or mixtures to be available commercially.

Proposed usage:

1. Name or names of the pest, pests, or type of pest for which the product affords control.

2. Name or names of the plants, crops, animals, or places to which product is to be applied.

3. Dilution recommended. (For example, "Use without dilution." "Use 1 gallon with 99 gallons water to make 100 gallons of spray.")

4. Preparation for use. (For example, "Fill the tank one-quarter full of water. Start agitator running. Slowly add the emulsion and then fill the tank." "Maintain agitation while using.")

5. Method of application. (For example, "Apply as a spray, using particular care to wet thoroughly the lower side of the leaves." "Dust plants thoroughly to touch as many of the insects as possible.")

6. Rate of application. (For example, "Apply 15 gallons per tree." "Use 5 pounds per thousand square feet of lawn." "Apply 25 pounds per acre." "Apply 200 pounds per acre and disk into the soil.")

7. Time of application. (For example, "Apply when buds begin to swell in spring." "Apply when jackets are falling from the fruits." "Apply when insects first appear." "Apply before plants start to head." "Do not apply during blooming period."

8. Frequency of application. (For example, "Dust plants thoroughly at 3-week intervals during growing season." "Do not spray oftener than twice a year.")

Effectiveness:

Experimental data available to demonstrate the effectiveness and suitability of the product for the intended usage. This must include pests treated on specific crops under climatic and soil conditions similar to that of State where registration is requested.

Hazards and cautions:

1. The primary hazards to human beings who handle the compound, the particular parts of the body affected, the symptoms of poisoning, and their duration.

2. The acute toxicity to the particular species of animals on which it has been determined by inhalation, ingestion, skin absorption.

3. The chronic toxicity to the particular species of animals on which it has been determined by inhalation, ingestion, skin absorption.

4. Information on first aid or medical treatment of injured persons or animals.

5. Toxicity or harmfulness to valuable plants or animals on which it might be used.

(a) Are certain plants sensitive? (For example, cantaloups and apricots are sensitive to dusting sulfur. White clover in lawns may be injured by 2,4-D. Beans may be injured by arsenicals.)

(b) Are certain animals sensitive? (For example, cats may be injured by coal-tar dips or some of the chlorinated hydrocarbons. Calves may be injured by oil sprays. Caged birds may be injured by dusts.)

(c) Is it injurious to plants under certain conditions? (For example, petroleum-oil sprays may injure plants if applied when plants are abnormally dry or when temperatures are above 90° F. Coal-tar products may be suitable for application to dormant deciduous trees but they are injurious to foliage.)

6. Other possible hazards.

(a) Does it leave a stain or unsightly residue where these might be objectionable? (For example, aerosols may stain walls or furnishings if the applicator is held too close to the surface. Bordeaux mixture, lime-sulfur, ferric dimethyl dithiocarbamate, and some other products may leave objectionable residues on ornamental plants, flowers, or fruits. Oil sprays may blemish table grapes or plums.)

(b) Does it impart an obnoxious taste to prepared foods, food crops, or to meat animals, as benzene hexachloride insecticides or coal-tar disinfectants do?

(c) Does it injure asphalt-tile floors as kerosene-base household sprays do?

(d) Does it present a hazard to honey bees?

(e) Is it particularly injurious to cats, fish, or caged birds?

(f) Does it persist in the soil and injure crops subsequently planted?

(g) Is it absorbed by dairy cattle and excreted in the milk?

(h) Does it corrode or otherwise injure spray equipment?

(i) Is it absorbed in treated foodstuffs, as parathion is absorbed in citrus peel and in mature olives?

(j) Are precautions necessary in disposal of empty containers to avoid possible injury?

(k) Are any special precautions necessary in cleaning spraying or dusting equipment?

Analytical methods:

1. Analytical methods available for:

(a) The technical material.

(b) Commercial products containing it with other ingredients.

(c) Spray and dust residues or other minute amounts on foodstuffs or other contaminated material.

2. If analytical methods are not available, how is the quality of the manufactured product controlled?

Spray residue:

If it is to be applied to foodstuffs, how may residues be removed?

A TROUBLESOME problem to all concerned has been that of fees charged for registration. In many States it is the general policy of the Government to charge fees against the industries regulated in sufficient amount to carry the cost of enforcement work. In other States the costs of operation are charged against the general taxes and no special fees are collected. In 1951, 32 States had economic-poisons registration fees of one type or another. Sixteen States had no fee of any type. The fees vary from a nominal amount of $2 an item in New Mexico to those in Florida which has a license fee of $125 with an additional registration fee of $2.50 an item. If a manufacturer were to register 12 different economic poisons in all States requiring fees (including Hawaii), his total cost for registration fees would be approximately $2,000.

Manufacturers have pointed out that in many cases the fee is excessive in relation to the amount of business done and acts as a handicap to a manufacturer doing a small business in several States. On the other hand, the amounts collected in some States are so small that adequate enforcement work is not possible. It is generally agreed that the money collected should be expended for enforcement work, and if fees are collected with no enforcement work, proper protection is not afforded.

Another step toward simplification would be more uniformity as to the registration period. If all renewals were required at one time, for example January 1 or July 1, instead of different months throughout the year for different States, the manufacturer could take care of all his registration applications at one time, with considerable savings in his handling of registration.

Most laws are in agreement that pesticides should be sold only in the unbroken original package of a registrant. In some cases sales out of open packages have been permitted under State laws, but to prevent adulteration and to fix responsibility, the uniform act requires products to be sold only in the original package of a registrant. It is hazardous to permit highly toxic materials to be sold in broken packages, and possibilities of misuse or accidents are greatly increased when a material is handled in bulk without proper labeling.

Summary of General Characteristics of State Pesticide Laws

State	*Scope*	*Annual registration period expires—*	*Fee*	*Enforcing agency*
Alabama	Uniform State act except devices not included.	Sept. 30	$15 an item	Division of Agricultural Chemistry, Montgomery 1.
Arizona	Same as Federal act except devices and household pesticides not included.	Dec. 31	$25 first item; $10 for each additional.	State Chemist, Feed, Fertilizer Laboratories, Tucson.
Arkansas	Same as Federal act	June 30	Set by Plant Board	Arkansas State Plant Board, Little Rock.
California	Same as Federal act except devices not included.	do	$50 for 10 items; $2 for each additional.	Bureau of Chemistry, State Department of Agriculture, Sacramento.
Colorado	Uniform State act	do	$5 an item with $50 maximum.	State Entomologist, Denver.
Connecticut	Insecticides and fungicides.	No registration		State Chemist, Department of Analytical Chemistry, New Haven.
Delaware	No law			
Florida	Agricultural insecticides and fungicides only.	Dec. 31	$125 plus $2.50 an item	State Chemist, Agricultural Department, Chemical Division, Tallahassee.
Georgia	Uniform State act	do	$5 an item with $200 maximum.	State Chemist, Department of Agriculture, Atlanta.
Idaho	No law			
Illinois	Paris green insecticides only.	No registration		Superintendent of Registration, Department of Registration and Education, Springfield
Indiana	No law			
Iowa	Insecticides and fungicides.	No registration		Dairy and Food Division, Department of Agriculture, Des Moines.
Kansas	Uniform State act except devices not included.	Dec. 31	$15 an item for first 10; $5 for each additional.	Control Division, State Board of Agriculture, Topeka.
Kentucky	No law except some insecticides and fungicides under food and drug act.			Director, Division of Food, Drugs, and Hotels, Louisville.
Louisiana	Agricultural insecticides, fungicides, and herbicides.	Permanent registration.	Inspection fee of 10¢ per 100 lbs. due Feb. 1 of each year; penalty of 10% if not paid by Feb. 20.	Commissioner, Department of Agriculture and Immigration, Baton Rouge.

Maine	Same as Federal act except devices not included.	Dec. 31	$5 an item; no maximum	Division of Inspection, Department of Agriculture, Augusta.
Maryland	Agricultural pesticides	....do	$5 an item with $75 maximum.	State Chemist, Inspection and Regulatory Service, College Park.
Massachusetts	No law, except for DDT			
Michigan	Uniform State act	Oct. 31	$5 an item for first 10; $2 for each additional.	Chief Chemist, Bureau of Chemical Laboratories, Department of Agriculture, Lansing.
Minnesota	Same as Federal act	June 30	$5 an item with $25 maximum.	Chief Chemist, Department of Agriculture, Dairy, and Food, St. Paul.
Mississippi	Uniform State act except devices not included.	Dec. 31	$5 an item with $25 maximum.	Chief Chemist, Department of Agriculture, State College.
Missouri	No law			
Montana	Uniform State act except devices not included.	Dec. 31	No fee	Food and Drug Division, Board of Health, Helena.
Nebraska	No law			
Nevada	....do			
New Hampshire	Uniform State act except devices not included.	Dec. 31	$10 an item with $100 maximum.	Control Supervisor, Department of Agriculture, State House, Concord.
New Jersey	....do	....do	$5 an item for first 10; $2 for each additional.	State Chemist, Agricultural Experiment Station, New Brunswick.
New Mexico	Uniform State act	Annually	$2 an item	Board of Regents, State College.
New York	Same as Federal act except devices not included.	No registration	No fee	Plant Industry Bureau, Department of Agriculture, Albany.
North Carolina	Uniform State act	Dec. 31	$10 an item	State Chemist, Department of Agriculture, Raleigh.
North Dakota	....do	....do	$5 an item for first 5; $1 for each additional.	State Food Commissioner, State Laboratories Department, Bismarck.
Ohio	No law except some products included under livestock remedy law.			Insect and Plant Disease Control, Department of Agriculture, Columbus.
Oklahoma	Uniform State act	Dec. 31	$5 an item	Entomology and Plant Control Division, Department of Agriculture, Oklahoma City.
Oregon	Same as Federal act	....do	$20 an item for first 3; $75 for 4 to 25 items, plus $2 for each item in excess of 25.	Chief Chemist, Division of Foods and Dairies, Department of Agriculture, Salem.

Summary of General Characteristics of State Pesticide Laws—*Continued*

State	*Scope*	*Annual registration period expires—*	*Fee*	*Enforcing agency*
Pennsylvania	Insecticides and fungicides.	Dec. 31	$5 an item for first 5; $1 for each additional.	Bureau of Foods and Chemistry, Department of Agriculture, Harrisburg.
Rhode Island	Uniform State act; certain exemptions if federally registered.	Annually	$10 an item with $50 maximum.	Director of Agriculture and Conservation, Providence.
South Carolina	Agricultural insecticides and fungicides.	Dec. 31	No fee	Associate State Entomologist, Crop Pest Commission, Clemson.
South Dakota	Uniform State act	June 30	$5 an item for first 5; $1 for each additional.	State Chemist, Department of Agriculture, Vermillion.
Tennessee	....do	....do	$5 an item	Superintendent and State Chemist, Division of Dairies, Foods and Drugs, Nashville.
Texas	Agricultural pesticides	Aug. 31	$25 an item with $100 maximum.	State Chemist, Agricultural Experiment Station, College Station; Commissioner of Agriculture, Austin.
Utah	Uniform State act	June 30	$5 an item with $50 maximum.	State Chemist, Department of Agriculture, Salt Lake City.
Vermont	Uniform State act except devices not included; certain exemptions if imported and registered by Federal office.	Annually	$5 a brand with $50 maximum.	Division of Plant Pest Control, Department of Agriculture, Montpelier.
Virginia	Uniform State act	Dec. 31	$10 an item for first 20; $5 for each additional.	Division of Chemistry, Department of Agriculture and Immigration, Richmond.
Washington	Same as Federal act except devices not included.	....do	$10 for first item; $5 for each additional.	Division of Chemistry, Agricultural Experiment Station, Pullman.
West Virginia	No law			
Wisconsin	Same as Federal act except devices not included.	Dec. 31	$10 an item with $100 maximum.	State Entomologist, Department of Agriculture, Madison.
Wyoming	....do	June 30	$2 an item with $25 maximum.	State Entomologist, Department of Agriculture, Powell.
Hawaii	....do	July 1	$10 an item	Division of Marketing, Board of Commissioners of Agriculture and Forestry, Honolulu.

Careful attention has been given to the definition of the term "ingredient statement." There are two options for an ingredient statement on the label of pesticides as set forth in the uniform act. Option 1, which is preferred, consists of a statement of the name and percentage of each active ingredient, together with the total percentage of inert ingredients in the economic poison. Option 2 is a statement of the name of each active ingredient together with the name of each inert ingredient and the total percentage of inert ingredients, if there are any in the economic poison. The act provides that Option 1 shall apply if the preparation is highly toxic to man and, furthermore, in case an economic poison contains arsenic in any form, there must be shown a statement of the percentage of total arsenic expressed as metallic and water-soluble arsenic expressed as metallic. This requirement is the same as that in the Federal act.

Because many pesticides can cause serious injury if improperly handled, precautions or appropriate information concerning the particular hazards is a necessary part of adequate labeling. Sometimes the existence or the severity of a hazard is not discovered until accidents occur after a product has been marketed. The complete toxicological properties of all pesticides are not available, and not infrequently labeling of products requires revision in light of newly developed information. As individual States attempt to get adequate precautionary labeling of hazardous materials, there is need for uniform action to avoid conflicting requirements and multiplication of the manufacturer's problems. Several manufacturers' organizations have realized that development of proper labeling of hazardous chemicals is a part of good business procedure. They have found that attacking the problem themselves does much to forestall the need for corrective action by State administrations, therefore avoiding troublesome conflicts that arise when each State attempts to solve the problem separately. The Manufacturing Chemists' Association has studied the problem and issued a guide for the preparation of warning labels.

The problem of precautionary labeling of pesticides is further complicated by the fact that, in many States, some poisonous or caustic pesticides come under the jurisdiction of a pharmacy act as well as a pesticide act. In other States the labeling of hazardous pesticides is left solely to one administration.

Some laws require protective coloring of certain poisonous materials. In general, the requirements pertain only to calcium arsenate, lead arsenate, and sodium fluoride, but additional chemicals may be included. The need for such legislation, and the consequent problem of uniform action by different States, is avoided when manufacturers on their own initiative color the chemicals that might be confused with foodstuffs.

One of the purposes of pesticide laws is to assure delivery of materials that conform to the guaranteed analysis shown on the label. This requires sampling products offered for sale in the State and performing the necessary examinations and chemical and physical analyses. The sampling should be on a scale large enough to provide an adequate analysis of the materials used and to make certain that they comply with the law. Publication of the official findings is a benefit of a well-functioning law.

In the administration of laws covering such a highly technical and rapidly expanding field as economic poisons, there should be free exchange of information among regulatory officials, Federal and State. An Association of Economic Poisons Control Officials has been formed. Its executive committee meets regularly with representatives of the Federal office to consider matters of policy, particularly with regard to proper labeling requirements. Such cooperation, recognized by provisions in both the uniform State act and the Federal Insecticide, Fungicide, and

Rodenticide Act of 1947, has been beneficial to users of pest-control materials as well as to manufacturers. Many things, such as information with regard to the toxicity of a particular chemical, can best be developed by a Federal agency and then distributed to the State officials.

California has a law with regard to prohibiting the sale of fresh or dried fruits or vegetables carrying deleterious spray residue. Although other States did not have such a specific law, the same control may be exercised through the different State food and drug acts.

ALL IN ALL, economic poisons probably are as closely regulated as any other class of materials generally sold. Besides Federal registration before a product can be shipped in interstate commerce, State laws require registration in the individual States.

In the enforcement of these laws, official samples are drawn from materials offered for sale, and analyses are made to determine if the products correspond to guarantee. Sale of a deficient material is a violation which is usually considered a misdemeanor. Also, publishing the analyses of official samples serves as a strong deterrent to sale of adulterated materials.

Effective enforcement by regulatory offices assures purchasers of properly labeled pest-control materials that conform to the guarantee stated on the label by the manufacturer.

ALLEN B. LEMMON *is chief of the Bureau of Chemistry, California Department of Agriculture. The Bureau administers laws relating to the labeling and sale in California of agricultural chemicals, including economic poisons. Mr. Lemmon received a bachelor's degree in engineering from Stanford University in 1930 and a degree of engineer in 1932. He joined the California Department of Agriculture in 1933, as an inspector of economic poisons and fertilizers, and advanced to chief of the Bureau of Chemistry in 1946.*

The Federal Act of 1947

W. G. Reed

The Federal Insecticide, Fungicide, and Rodenticide Act regulates the marketing in interstate commerce of economic poisons—insecticides, fungicides, rodenticides, and herbicides. Products intended for trapping, destroying, repelling, or mitigating insects or rodents, or destroying, repelling, or mitigating fungi, are also subject to the act.

The law was enacted June 25, 1947, and became fully effective June 25, 1948. It replaced and expanded the protection afforded by the Insecticide Act of 1910. The old act regulated only insecticides and fungicides and became effective at a time when such products were comparatively simple, consisting mainly of paris green, pyrethrum, bordeaux mixtures, and like goods.

The purpose of the 1947 Act is to protect the public in the use of economic poisons, many of which are dangerous and all of which are subject to limitations in application. Products subject to the Act must be registered with the United States Department of Agriculture prior to introduction in interstate commerce. Provision is made for testing products as they are encountered in the regular channels of trade to determine whether they are in compliance with the law. Those that are found to be in violation may be seized by the Government to remove them from the channels of trade. The manufacturer may be prosecuted if such action is warranted.

To furnish necessary information to the users of economic poisons and guide them in using such materials safely and effectively, the Act provides that every product must have attached to it a label showing:

1. The name and address of the manufacturer or person for whom manufactured.

2. The name, brand, or trade-mark under which the article is sold.

3. The net contents.

4. An ingredient declaration.

5. An appropriate warning or caution statement, when necessary, to prevent injury to man, animals, vegetation, and useful invertebrate animals.

In addition, labels on highly toxic products must contain the word *POISON* in red, the skull and crossbones, and a statement of an antidote. Adequate directions for use must accompany each product.

It is unlawful to market in interstate commerce any economic poison that has not been registered with the Department or one that is misbranded or adulterated. A product is adulterated if its strength or purity falls below the professed standard or quality as expressed on its labeling or under which it is sold, or if any substance has been substituted wholly or in part for the article, or if any valuable constituent of the article has been wholly or in part abstracted. An economic poison or device is misbranded if its labeling bears any statement, design, or graphic representation relative thereto or to its ingredients which is false or misleading in any particular. An economic poison is misbranded:

1. If it is an imitation of or is offered for sale under the name of another economic poison.

2. If its labeling bears any reference to registration under the Act.

3. If the labeling accompanying it does not contain directions for use that are necessary and, if complied with, adequate for the protection of the public.

4. If the label does not contain a warning or caution statement which may be necessary and, if complied with, adequate to prevent injury to living man and other vertebrate animals, vegetation, and useful invertebrate animals.

5. If the label does not bear an ingredient statement on that part of the immediate container and on the outside container or wrapper, if there is one, through which the ingredient statement on the immediate container cannot be clearly read, of the retail package which is presented or displayed under customary conditions of purchase. (The Secretary of Agriculture may permit the ingredient statement to appear prominently on some other part of the container, if the size or form of the container makes it impracticable to place it on the part of the retail package which is presented or displayed under customary conditions of purchase.)

6. If any word, statement, or other information required by or under authority of this Act to appear on the label or labeling is not prominently placed thereon with such conspicuousness (as compared with other words, statements, designs, or graphic matter in the labeling) and in such terms as to render it likely to be read and understood by the ordinary individual under customary conditions of purchase and use.

7. If in the case of an insecticide, fungicide, or herbicide when used as directed or in accordance with commonly recognized practice it shall be injurious to living man or other vertebrate animals, or vegetation, except weeds, to which it is applied, or to the person applying such economic poison.

One of the most important provisions of the law is the one that requires insecticides and other economic poisons to be registered with the United States Department of Agriculture prior to introduction into interstate commerce. This gives the public additional protection and assists manufacturers and distributors in complying with other provisions of the law. To obtain registration, an application, together with information concerning the composition and proposed labeling, must be submitted to the Department. The material is carefully scrutinized by specially trained scientific personnel in the various fields involved, and if the product, its labeling, and other material appear to be in compliance with the law, a registration notice is issued.

Occasionally proposed labeling contains recommendations for uses about which there is little or no published information. In such instances the applicant is requested, if he has not already done so, to furnish a full description of the tests that have been made with the product and the results thereof upon which the claims are based. That information is reviewed; if it appears to warrant the claims and the product and its labeling are otherwise in compliance with the law, the product is registered. If it does not appear that the article is such as to warrant the proposed claims, or if it and the labeling or other material required to be submitted do not comply with the law, the applicant is notified of the deficiencies and given an opportunity to make necessary corrections. If he then insists, in writing, that such corrections are not necessary and requests that the article be registered, the law requires that it be registered under protest. In general, manufacturers and distributors have cooperated in making whatever changes in formulations or labeling the Department has considered necessary. Also, because of the higher penalties that are imposed under the law if a person or firm is found guilty in court of marketing a misbranded or adulterated product that has been registered under protest, few requests for this type of registration have been received.

Before a new economic poison is offered for registration and general distribution, usually experiments by qualified people have been carried on to determine how it can be used safely and effectively. Frequently laboratory and field tests are conducted over a period of several years before enough information can be obtained to prepare adequate directions for use and appropriate precautionary labeling. During this period of research and investigation, materials may be transported in interstate commerce without legal restrictions if they are intended solely for experimental use by or under the supervision of a Federal or State agency authorized by law to conduct research in the field of economic poisons or by others if a permit from the Department has been obtained before shipment.

To obtain an experimental permit, the shipper or person making the delivery is required to submit a signed application showing: The name and address of the shipper and place or places from which the shipment or shipments will be made; the proposed date of shipment or proposed shipping period, not to exceed 1 year; the identification of material to be covered by the permit; the approximate quantity to be shipped and types of tests that will be made; whether the product is to be sold or delivered without cost; that the economic poison is intended for experimental use only; and the proposed labeling, which, besides other statements, must state that the product is for experimental use only.

The Department of Agriculture carries on investigations continually throughout the country to determine whether economic poisons that are being marketed in interstate commerce are properly registered and otherwise in compliance with the law. Investigators visit retail stores, warehouses, and other places to investigate shipments and collect samples. The samples are selected from unopened packages and proof of interstate shipment is obtained. Each sample is sealed by the investigator and sent to one of the Department's laboratories. Usually it is first analyzed chemically to learn if the composition and net contents are as declared on the label. In addition, other types of laboratory tests and field trials are frequently necessary to see whether the product will perform satisfactorily when the label directions are followed. For instance, an agricultural insecticide or fungicide may be tested in an orchard or on growing crops to see if it is effective for the purposes intended and not injurious to the vegetation to which it is applied. A weed killer may be tested in the greenhouse or in a field to find out whether it will give satisfactory control under actual conditions of use. Products recommended for use in controlling livestock pests are tested on the species of animals they are intended to protect, and rodenticides are tested on rodents. Sometimes an insecticide is an effective bug killer but it will burn or shrivel the vegetation to which it is applied or give it an off-flavor. Effects such as these cannot be detected by chemical analysis and are apparent only after field trials have been conducted.

If, as a result of its investigations, the Department finds a sample to be in violation of the law, action may be taken leading to prosecution of the manufacturer or shipper. Federal court action can be taken to seize the material in question to remove it from the market. If prosecution is contemplated, the law provides that before such action is taken notice must be given to the person against whom legal action is contemplated and such person given an opportunity to present his views regarding the alleged violation. If the facts appear to warrant prosecution, they are certified to the proper United States Attorney.

The law also provides that an economic poison subject to it may be seized if it is adulterated or misbranded; if it has not been registered in accordance with the provisions of the Act; if it fails to bear on its label the information required by the Act; or if it is a white powder that is not colored or discolored as required by the Act.

The owner may, of course, contest the seizure in Federal court before a judge and jury. The Government must prove that the goods are in violation to sustain the seizure and maintain the control of the goods. If the Government fails to do that, the goods are returned to the owner. If an article is condemned under the seizure provision, it must be disposed of by destruction or sale as the court may direct, but it cannot be sold contrary to the provisions of the law. However, upon payment of the costs of the libel proceedings and the execution and delivery of a good and sufficient bond conditioned that the article shall not be sold or otherwise disposed of contrary to the provisions of any laws having jurisdiction over it, the court may direct that such article be delivered to the owner. The owner may then relabel or otherwise treat the article to bring it into compliance with the law, after which it may be released by the court and the bond cancelled.

Persons or firms found guilty of marketing an economic poison without registration, or of making claims different in substance from those made at time of registration, upon conviction may be fined not more than $1,000. That penalty applies if the composition of the product differs from that represented in connection with registration. With respect to products registered under protest, in each instance, upon conviction for an offense concerning which a registrant had been warned, the person may be fined not to exceed $1,000 or imprisoned for not more than 1 year, or both such fine and imprisonment.

Persons guilty of violating other provisions of the law may be fined up to $500 for the first offense, and on conviction for each subsequent offense, may be fined up to $1,000 or imprisoned for not more than 1 year, or both such fine and imprisonment.

Economic poisons imported into the United States are subject to the same requirements, including registration, as those produced in this country. Samples of imports are examined. If they appear to be in violation of the law or are otherwise dangerous to public health or are of a kind forbidden entry into or forbidden to be sold or restricted in sale in the country in which they are made or from which exported, they may be refused admission into the United States.

Manufacturers and distributors of economic poisons in the past have found it difficult to prepare labeling that would comply with the various State and Federal laws under which they must operate. The present Federal law recognizes the difficulty and authorizes administrative officials to cooperate with State regulatory agencies in carrying out the provisions of the law and in securing uniformity of regulations. Full advantage is taken of this authorization both through cooperative arrangements for enforcement work and by conferences with representative groups of State officials.

The Federal Insecticide, Fungicide, and Rodenticide Act is a relatively new law and the benefits that have resulted from it cannot yet be fully evaluated. However, it can be stated that farmers and other users of economic poisons and the general public are now being given better protection than ever before against worthless, dangerous, and inadequately labeled economic poisons.

W. G. Reed *has been engaged in regulatory work on insecticides and other economic poisons since 1945, when he was made chief of the insecticide division, which is now in the livestock branch of the Production and Marketing Administration of the Department. This division administers the Federal Insecticide, Fungicide, and Rodenticide Act. Dr. Reed, a native of Iowa, first joined the Department in the Meat Inspection Service in 1929. He holds a degree of Doctor of Veterinary Medicine from the Chicago Veterinary College.*

Readers may be interested in the chapter "The Insecticide Industry," page 450, in which the author discusses the work undertaken by manufacturers of insecticides to insure the safe use of their products and the interest of the industry in supporting State and Federal legislation to regulate the distribution and use of insecticides, fungicides, and related products.

Insecticides and the Pure Food Law

P. B. Dunbar

In this paper I discuss the provisions of the Federal Food, Drug, and Cosmetic Act of June 25, 1938, as they concern insecticidal residues, and recent activities under these provisions.

First, a few fundamentals: (1) Congress, in passing the law, recognized that the use of insecticides is necessary, both to bring many agricultural food crops to maturity in a condition suitable for human consumption and to protect many foods against insect depredations during manufacturing operations and storage. (2) By and large, insecticides are poisons, their toxicity varying only in degree. (3) The terms of the law do not preclude the use of insecticides, but they make provisions which guarantee that when they are used the health of consumers eating foods so treated shall be protected.

The House Committee on Interstate and Foreign Commerce of the 75th Congress, in a report on the bill which became the law in 1938, made the following comment on section 406, which relates specifically to insecticidal residues:

"This subsection first prohibits the unnecessary addition of poisons. Where such additions are necessary, the establishment of tolerances is authorized, based upon the practical necessities for the use of poisonous substances. It is well recognized that an adequate fruit and vegetable supply could not be brought to maturity without the use of toxic insecticides and fungicides. But the situation is made extremely complex by the number of poisonous substances used for different crops in different localities, and by contaminations which unavoidably occur in many manufacturing processes. The purpose of the subsection is to insure that the total amount of poisons the consumer receives will not be sufficient to jeopardize health. The needs of each branch of the food-producing industry can be met and the public health can be adequately protected."

The law attacks the problem of protecting the public against poisons in foods by defining any food as adulterated if it contains a poisonous or deleterious substance that may render it injurious to health, or if it contains any such substance that is not required in the production of the food or that can be avoided by good manufacturing practice, or (where it is so required or cannot be so avoided) if it exceeds tolerances prescribed by the Federal Security Administrator after public hearing. In prescribing a tolerance, the law directs the Administrator to take into account the extent to which the poisonous or deleterious substance is required or cannot be avoided in the production of each food and the other ways in which the consumer may be affected by the same or other deleterious substances. In any event, the Administrator is enjoined by the statute to prescribe the tolerances at such levels that the public health will be protected.

This law has been on the statute books for more than a decade. Undoubtedly numerous tolerances would have been established long before this had it not been for the intervention of the Second World War and the resultant preoccupation of all concerned with other urgent matters. During the war period and immediately afterwards, many new and potent insecticides were developed. Scientists knew little about their toxicity, either to the person who applied the sprays or to the consumer who ate the finished food product. In some instances accurate methods for the estimation of the residual spray left on or absorbed by the food product were lacking. It was not known whether the residues remained intact, whether they were altered by weathering to nontoxic or more toxic residues, whether they could be removed by washing, or whether they were absorbed into the plant structures and therefore could not be removed.

It is a commentary on the changing attitude of the times that with the multiplication of new spray substances manufacturing groups, growers' organizations, entomologists, plant pathologists, and physicians, as well as consumer groups, began to recognize that it was high time to attack the residue problem and the question of safe tolerances in a fundamental fashion. The Bureau of Entomology and Plant Quarantine and other bureaus of the Department of Agriculture, the Interdepartmental Committee on Pest Control, organized groups in the insecticide-manufacturing industry, scientific workers in entomology and plant industry, food manufacturers using the raw materials of agriculture, and the growers themselves have shown a constructive interest in reaching some kind of a sound conclusion on the subject of spray-residue tolerances.

And so, in January 1950, it seemed that everyone was ready to begin the hearings on statutory tolerances. The hearings, called by the Federal Security Administrator, were in session, with occasional recesses, from January 17 to September 15, 1950. Those who attended them were impressed with the spirit of cooperation and good will manifested throughout the sessions.

The hearings were limited to the tolerances on fresh fruits and vegetables. Testimony on the necessity for using any particular insecticide or fungicide on any particular fruit or vegetable came first. Next, the question of which pesticides are poisonous or deleterious in themselves was thoroughly explored. Subsequent sessions dealt with "the amounts of these substances which are poisonous or deleterious, which are received from all sources by consumers," and with "the toxicity of the substances for which limits are to be established." The final session was devoted to relevant evidence not previously covered. Evidence was also taken at that time on amending the fluorine tolerance which had been duly promulgated in 1944 and soon after nullified on a legal technicality.

The record consisted of 9,000 pages of testimony (by 255 witnesses) and nearly 1,300 exhibits. It encompassed the investigations of scientific workers in many fields, the considered opinions of medical and toxicological minds, and factual information bearing on the aggregate intake by the consuming public of agricultural and other poisons. Many have repeated the opinion that the value and completeness of the record is unequaled anywhere.

An editorial in "Agricultural Chemicals" for April 1950 said:

"Assimilation of this material may take a long time, but we have a feeling that eventually it will be the means of correcting much of the confusion which has existed in the field for several years. The establishment of tolerances for pesticides old and new will set universally-recognized standards to guide future planning.

"It is doubtful that without the hearing, such a collection of data would ever have been assembled. It was a job too big for the industry itself to have undertaken; both from the standpoint of prohibitive cost and because of a lack of proper coordination. Also, the findings of an investigation conducted entirely by manufacturers could be regarded as biased."

TOLERANCES are sure to exert an enormous stabilizing effect. But it would be the worst sort of Pollyanna philosophy to relax into an attitude of complacency. Insects do not stand still; in fact, some of them seem to meet the situation by breeding poison-resistant strains. Teams of entomologists and chemists, in and out of Government, are constantly tailoring new insecticides to measure. Among the other scientists, who are by no means idle, we must give credit to the toxicologists, food technologists, analytical chemists, and others who are all fighting the insect menace, without losing sight of their primary obligation to safeguard the public health.

What of the future? In our fight against an implacable enemy, perhaps we will learn how to kill with a rapier instead of a bludgeon. Perhaps, too, we can develop rapiers that will do their job on insects but will not affect man and his domestic animals. The synthesis of additional naturally occurring organic agricultural poisons is one of the hopeful approaches. After all, most of these natural products seem to be relatively benign in their potential threat to consumers, as well as to soils and crops.

It is the men of vision who will win this battle. Too often in the past scientific thinking has had but a single objective among the many aspects of the insect war. Such slogans as: "Kill all the insects," "Produce fruit without spot or blemish," "An enormous yield is everything," "We must do something quick; never mind the future," and the like, have all borne bitter fruit. There is no one answer to the "insect menace" any more than to the other problems of modern civilization. "Of nothing too much" was the Greek motto, and it's worth remembering now.

P. B. DUNBAR *was Commissioner of Food and Drugs in the Food and Drug Administration of the Federal Security Agency until his retirement in May 1951, after 44 years of Federal service.*

Firefly.

Resistance to Insecticides

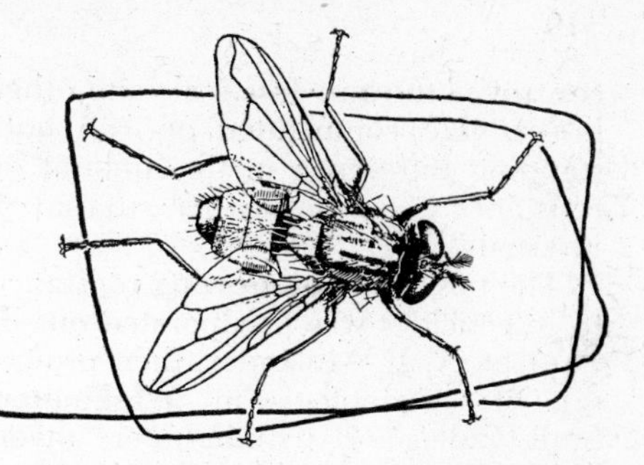

Insects Are Harder To Kill

B. A. Porter

Some people have discovered that "insects are getting harder and harder to kill." They are partly right. A few of the hundreds of pests that farmers must control have developed resistance to insecticides.

That means that an insect can survive and thrive in the presence of a chemical that is supposed to kill it. It does not mean that every insect of the kind involved will survive the application of the insecticide. If a sizable proportion can survive the insecticide at a practical strength, the pest is said to be resistant. Sometimes insects from one source are harder to kill than those of the same kind from another source. The group harder to kill usually is referred to as a resistant strain.

The development of resistance by an insect can be explained simply in a general way, but the actual details of the process in a given kind of insect, with respect to a given insecticide, are complex and not understood fully.

A few principles are basic. No two living creatures are exactly alike. Among people there are differences in color of hair and eyes, height, weight, health, and many other details. People vary also in the effect that diseases have on them. An epidemic of disease in a community may attack some persons seriously but not touch others.

So it is with insects. A speck of an insecticide may kill one insect but leave another of the same kind unaffected. If the amount of the insecticide to which the insects are exposed is great enough, all will be killed, of course, but often the amount applied is insufficient to kill all the insects present. The least resistant are killed at once. The resistant ones survive.

Apparently what has happened when insects have developed increased resistance is that the offspring of the resistant survivors have a similar degree of resistance. After that selective process has gone on for several generations, most of the insects that are easily killed have been eliminated and only the resistant ones are left. More applications or greater quantities of the insecticides are needed then for adequate control. The point finally is reached where the particular insecticide becomes so ineffective that some other material or method of control must be developed.

The men who have made a special study of the development of resistance do not agree entirely on the technical details of just what happens. Exact information on the subject is essential from a scientific standpoint but is not needed for our understanding of the general subject as discussed in this article.

The possibility of differences in the susceptibility of insects of the same kind to insecticides has been recognized for more than a half century. As early as 1897, John B. Smith, entomologist of the New Jersey Agricultural Experiment Station, mentioned variations in results in the

970134°—52——22

control of the San Jose scale and other insects. He commented on "an outstanding difference in the amount of resistance to poisons, either external or internal."

The possibility of growing resistance to insecticides was first pointed out in 1914 by A. L. Melander, then professor of entomology in Washington State College. His studies were made on the San Jose scale, which for some years apparently had been well controlled by spraying with a strong solution of lime-sulfur. At the time, the San Jose scale was much harder to kill with lime-sulfur in the Clarkston area of Washington than it was in the Wenatchee and Yakima valleys or elsewhere.

A similar situation developed in the early 1920's in southern Illinois, southern Indiana, northwestern Arkansas, and elsewhere in the Midwest. Lime-sulfur suddenly seemed to have little effect on the San Jose scale in many orchards although previously it had given good control. The insect killed the trees in several thousand acres of fine orchards despite careful and liberal applications of lime-sulfur.

The work of Melander and others suggested that the San Jose scale might have developed resistance in some localities, but their studies did not entirely rule out the possibility that differences in resistance were caused by seasonal or local conditions. The development of resistance among other insects was demonstrated within a few years, however.

Perhaps the first clear-cut demonstration of strains of insects differing in resistance and the possibility that their average resistance could increase was reported by H. J. Quayle, of the California Citrus Experiment Station at Riverside. In 1916 he published an article, "Are Scales Becoming Resistant to Fumigation?"

A standard method of controlling scale insects on citrus in California for many years was to place canvas tents over the trees and fumigate them with hydrocyanic acid. Quayle brought to Riverside scale insects from Corona, Riverside County, Calif., where there had been serious difficulty in getting control by fumigation, and other scale insects from Orange County, where control was easy. Both lots of insects were fumigated under the same tent over an artificial tree. The results paralleled those obtained at the places where the stocks of scale originated. Five percent of the scale insects from Corona survived, but fewer than 1 percent of those from Orange County survived. Quayle and his associates studied the problem at least 25 years.

Since 1930 the Department's citrus insect laboratory at Whittier, Calif., has also carried on studies of the resistance of the California red scale to hydrocyanic acid. Several strains of the scale insect have been reared in the laboratory through many generations and have been fumigated in various ways. Their resistance has been determined from time to time.

The results of the research can thus be summarized: Some strains of the California red scale differ greatly in their resistance to fumigation with hydrocyanic acid. The differences persist through many generations when the scales are reared under laboratory conditions. If the California red scale is subjected to repeated fumigation in the laboratory, the strain developed from the survivors is much more resistant than the original stock and requires many times the original dose of cyanide to give control equal to that obtained on the nonresistant strain.

Parallel studies, but much less extensive, have been made with the black scale and the citricola scale, species that seem also to have developed resistance to fumigation with hydrocyanic acid.

One practical result in California citrus orchards has been a marked reduction in use of fumigation against the California red scale and other scale insects. Growers have found it necessary to resort to spraying with oil, sometimes supplemented with ground derris or cube root, or with extracts from them.

THE NEXT MAJOR INSECT pest known to have developed resistance was the codling moth, or appleworm, against which lead arsenate was the chief insecticide for more than 40 years. It has always been hard to control in many of the drier western regions and in some eastern localities where the growing season is long and hot. In other places in the East, control was not especially difficult in the early decades of the century, although even there the number of applications of lead arsenate needed for adequate worm control had steadily increased. The differences in the efforts required to control the worms generally were attributed to differences in climate and other conditions.

W. S. Hough, of the Virginia Agricultural Experiment Station, was the first to attack the problem. He started in the late 1920's. He carried on his studies in an insectary—a screened shelter—where conditions were like those in the shade of an apple tree. He brought together strains of codling moth from areas that needed different degrees of spraying. Apples from unsprayed trees were thoroughly sprayed with lead arsenate. Then he allowed newly hatched worms to try to chew their way in, as they do in the orchard. In the experiments Hough eliminated any differences due to locality, spray practices, or abundance of codling moth. Differences in the proportion of the worms that could get through the spray covering without being killed would indicate differences in resistance to the insecticide.

Hough compared worms from Virginia orchards, in which three or four sprays gave almost complete control, with worms from near Grand Junction, Colo., where the insect was notoriously hard to control. In the first season's tests, 31 to 39 percent of the Colorado worms got through the poison successfully, but only 5 to 7 percent of the Virginia worms survived. Hough raised both strains of worms in the insectary through 14 or more generations and continued to find the same differences.

He later found that appleworms from Virginia orchards that had been regularly well sprayed with lead arsenate entered sprayed fruit in much greater numbers than those from unsprayed or poorly sprayed orchards. Strains from various Virginia orchards fed through successive generations in the insectary on sprayed fruit became more and more resistant to lead arsenate and were able to enter sprayed fruit in increasing numbers.

L. F. Steiner and associates at the Department's fruit insect laboratory at Vincennes, Ind., later made a similar study and reached similar general conclusions. They found that codling moth stocks from different orchards in the Ohio Valley differed greatly in ability to enter sprayed fruit. The greatest resistance was in codling moth worms from an orchard that had been heavily sprayed with lead arsenate the preceding 5 years. Worms from a similar orchard that had been unsprayed for 5 years were much more readily killed.

It is not always easy to prove that an insect has developed resistance. Two or more strains of the insects have to be kept under the same conditions, although separated from each other in such a way that the strains cannot become mixed, before differences in the results with an insecticide can be said to be caused by differences in the insect itself. The control results in one year may be quite different from those obtained in another. Such differences do not necessarily mean resistance. They could as well be caused by seasonal or local factors.

On the other hand, the development of resistance has sometimes gone unrecognized or has been minimized by skeptics who have felt that some other factor was responsible: Even after Hough's first results were published, some workers in other areas averred that the trouble was that Colorado growers did not know how to spray.

Resistance is most likely to develop when all insects in a given situation are exposed to the insecticide and there is little reinfestation by insects not exposed. For instance, when a citrus grove is fumigated for the California red scale, the cyanide gas reaches all parts of the trees, and there is little movement of scales from untreated to the treated area. When an orchard is sprayed for the codling moth, an effort is made to spray every tree thoroughly. Repeated applications are made the same season. That means that almost all of the California red scales or codling moth worms in an orchard are exposed to the action of the insecticides. But with many of our common insects, only a small part of the total number present in an area may be exposed to insecticides. For example, only a small portion of the food plants attacked by the Japanese beetle in a given area are usually covered with an insecticide. Many home gardeners in cities do little spraying; shade trees on private property and many on public land rarely are well sprayed. Often they are not sprayed at all. The area surrounding the city usually has many beetles in wasteland or in other situations where spraying is impractical or unprofitable. Up to 1952 there had been little or no indication that the Japanese beetle had built up resistance to DDT, the insecticide most commonly used in its control.

The development of resistance to standard insecticides has practical significance. Such would be the testimony of growers in Colorado and elsewhere who gave up trying to raise apples because they could not get rid of the worms with lead arsenate. Such developments have made it necessary for entomologists to develop new insecticides and alternate methods of control.

B. A. Porter *is in charge of the division of fruit insect investigations in the Bureau of Entomology and Plant Quarantine. He joined the Department in 1917 and for many years conducted field investigations of various orchard insect problems in Connecticut and Indiana. He was graduated from Massachusetts Agricultural College in 1914.*

Insecticides and Flies

W. N. Bruce

Today spray applications that almost eradicated house flies on treated premises a few years ago are not noticeably reducing the fly populations found in the field. Heavy and frequent treatments with DDT, methoxyclor, chlordane, dieldrin, and lindane have failed to give satisfactory control of certain field strains of flies.

Resistance to insecticides was probably first noticed by the farmer or the field observer as a failure in the control of house flies, but it was not proved until several laboratory methods of determining the degrees of resistance were perfected.

The methods are of two kinds—those that treat individual flies and those that treat large numbers of flies in one operation. The first is represented by the long-used microsyringe method of testing, which is used by the California Citrus Experiment Station and the Illinois Natural History Survey, and by the micro-loop method, which is used by the Department of Agriculture and the Public Health Service. The second is represented by the spray-chamber method, used by Department of Agriculture workers, and by the residual panel test method, which is used quite extensively by the Public Health Service.

The topical, or local, application with a microsyringe is a good laboratory method of obtaining quantitative data on the amounts of insecticides needed to kill adult house flies. Individual females are selected from flies anesthetized with carbon dioxide and treated with acetone solutions of the insecticide. The actual treatment is accomplished within a carbon dioxide anesthetizing chamber, in which a

0.25-milliliter syringe is actuated by a micrometer caliper. A minute, measured amount of insecticidal solution is applied to the prothorax of the fly. Treated flies are placed in clean paper containers and fed. The numbers of dead and live flies are recorded 24 hours later and the percentage of mortality is calculated.

The micro-loop method also is valuable in computing the amounts of insecticides needed to kill adult house flies. A micro-loop is a very small loop made on the end of a piece of fine, noncorrosive wire. The loop is dipped into the insecticidal solution. The liquid retained in the loop is transferred to an anesthetized fly. Treated flies are fed and retained for a 24-hour mortality count.

We also can get the relative degrees of resistance of groups of house flies by using a spray chamber. The usual procedure is to place caged flies in the chamber, which we then fill with mist of the insecticidal solution by means of a small atomizer. We then transfer the flies to clean cages to be fed and retained for the 24-hour mortality count. A comparison between mortality produced in cages containing flies of standard laboratory strains and mortality in cages containing flies of questionable resistance reveals the relative degrees of resistance. By adjusting spray concentrations, we can measure very high or low degrees of fly resistance.

From a practical standpoint, the relative resistance can best be determined by exposing the groups to panels treated with the insecticide. Panel tests cannot be used to determine quantitatively the amount of insecticide needed to kill flies but rather gives the practical answer to the question of effective kill by surface treatments. Degrees of relative resistance are determined by varying the length of fly exposure to the treated panels and sometimes by varying the amount of insecticide on the panel. After flies are exposed to a treated panel, they are fed and held for the 24-hour mortality counts.

Often in comparing the effectiveness of insecticides we use the term "median lethal dosage (LD–50)" to express relative toxicity values. In studies on resistant flies, a median lethal dosage is the amount of insecticide in micrograms per fly required to kill one-half of the sample of flies treated.

LD–50 values of insecticides on flies are influenced significantly by the room temperature during and after treatment. In cool holding temperatures, flies are more easily killed by DDT-like compounds and less easily by chlordane or dieldrin. Flies used in computing the LD–50 values in tables 1 and 2 were retained at 80°. Flies used for test results shown in tables 3 and 4 were held at 60°. The temperatures explain differences in the LD–50 values of the various insecticides in relation to standard laboratory strains of flies.

THE FIRST RECOGNIZED OCCURRENCE of DDT-resistant flies was reported in 1947 by Giuseppe Saccà and A. Missiroli of Italy. The first widespread use of DDT was made by American occupation forces in Italy. Dr. R. Weismann, also in 1947, reported a strain of flies in Sweden that exhibited a significant amount of resistance to DDT.

In 1948 an alarming amount of DDT resistance was discovered among flies infesting southern California and scattered places in the Southern, Eastern, and Central States. By the end of the 1949 growing season, resistance to DDT had become prevalent among flies in most parts of the United States. A survey conducted in 1949 by the Illinois Natural History Survey showed that 87 percent of the farms in Illinois were infested with DDT-resistant flies. A survey in 1950 revealed the presence of DDT resistance in all populations of wild flies that were tested. The surveys gave evidence that the wild susceptible strains were becoming resistant to DDT over a period of 2 or 3 years.

The actual trends in development of DDT-resistant strains on two Illinois farms from 1945 to 1950 are shown in table 1. The 1950 levels of DDT resistance for the farms are significantly higher than the 1948 or 1949 levels, even in the absence of applications of DDT. Investigators in California observed the same phenomenon after the use of DDT for fly control had been discontinued for 2 years.

Several investigators have attempted since 1947 to produce DDT-resistant flies by exposing successive generations of susceptible flies to DDT in the laboratory. Richard Fay and his associates of the Public Health Service exposed adult flies in partially treated stock cages to produce a strain of a rather low order of resistance in 45 generations of adults. Starting in 1946, W. V. King and the staff of the laboratory in Orlando, Fla., produced a strain of flies highly resistant to DDT by exposing 55 generations of adults to sprays of DDT solutions. At the Illinois Natural History Survey laboratory, George C. Decker and I got spectacular results by exposing both larvae and adults to DDT. We contaminated the larval media and treated the adult stock cages with near-lethal dosages of DDT solutions. In that way we could select strains highly resistant to DDT in 9 to 18 generations from the standard laboratory strain. We attempted to simulate field conditions in which barn surfaces and manure piles are treated with insecticides.

As to the nature of the trend in the acquisition of DDT resistance by the standard laboratory strain when both larvae and adults were selected by DDT treatment, it appears that the process of segregation or the initial establishment of resistance to DDT is slow, but, when resistance is once established, its intensification is rapid and proceeds to a maximum level, which is reached when the DDT found in the environment no longer acts as a selective agent.

Research results that I reported in December 1949 revealed the development of strains of flies resistant to dieldrin, chlordane, lindane, toxaphene, methoxychlor, pyrethrins, para-oxon, and a mixture of all the effective chlorinated hydrocarbons. Since that report, all of the resistant laboratory strains except the para-oxon and pyrethrins strains have reached a maximum resistance point or have risen as high as is selectively possible by the method I used. A strain that showed a threefold increase in tolerance for dieldrin in November 1949 had risen to a 2,000-fold tolerance by July 1950. The dosages needed to kill individuals of these strains far exceed those which could be applied in the control of field populations of house flies.

Three kinds of trends characterized increased tolerance or resistance in experiments in 1948 and 1949.

The DDT type of acquisition trend, in which a susceptible fly strain slowly developed characters that permitted a more rapid selection in succeeding generations, was characteristic of dieldrin, methoxychlor, and chlordane, as well as DDT.

1. LD–50 Value of DDT on Two Field Strains

	Farm A		*Farm B*	
	Treatment on farm	*LD–50*	*Treatment on farm*	*LD–50*
1945	DDT	0.2	DDT	0.18
1946	DDT	.3	DDT	.4
1947	DDT	.8	DDT	.7
1948	DDT	8.1	DDT	9.0
1949	Dieldrin [1]	4.0	Lindane [2]	8.5
1950	Dieldrin [3]	18.0	Lindane [4]	42.0

[1] Barns completely insulated and old DDT covered.
[2] Much DDT still adhering to the walls, etc.
[3] Dieldrin-resistant flies began to develop.
[4] Lindane-resistant flies began to develop.

2. Topical Applications Showing Comparative 24-hour LD–50's of Insecticides in Micrograms per Fly of the Several Strains of House Flies Developed in the Laboratory

Strains	*Generations exposure of adults and larvae to the insecticide to reach a maximum level of resistance*		*Origin of strain*	*Insecticide*							
	Generations	*Insecticide*		*DDT*	*Methoxychlor*	*Lindane*	*Chlordane*	*Dieldrin*	*10:1 mixture of piperonyl-butoxide and pyrethrins*	*Para-oxon*	*Dilan*
Laboratory susceptible			N.A.I.D.M.	0.33	0.99	0.03	0.12	0.019	1.13	0.045	2.40
DDT I	18	DDT	lab	>100.00	14.40	.11	.24	.048	1.77	.07	2.50
Methoxychlor	12	Methoxychlor	lab	.30	>100.00	.07	.25	.010	1.60	.05	2.30
Lindane	46	Lindane	lab	1.20	1.10	>10.00	1.86	.40	1.40	.05	2.91
Dieldrin	36	Dieldrin	lab	2.50	3.90	.60	>100.00	>100.00	1.90	.07	2.60
Multi VII	17	Lindane	DDT I	>100.00	16.70	>10.00	.96	.60	1.50	.09	2.95
Multi VI	19	Lindane	Methoxychlor.	.80	>100.00	>10.00	2.70	.70	1.40	.06	2.75
Multi I	4	Methoxychlor	DDT I	>100.00	>100.00	.12	.23	.08	1.80	.07	2.54
Multi IX	19	Chlordane, lindane, dieldrin, toxaphene, DDT, methoxychlor.	Multi I	>100.00	>100.00	>100.00	>100.00	>100.00	2.00	.07	2.25
Dilan	5	Dilan	Multi IX	>100.00	>100.00	>100.00	>100.00	>100.00	2.10	.08	>100.00
Pyro I	30	Pyrenone	lab	.68	1.10	.16	.32	.026	>23.20	.07	4.20
Para-oxon	....	Para-oxon	lab	.45	1.00	.05	.15	.02	1.22	>.51	2.46

A second type, a lindane type, in which a susceptible fly strain gradually attained a higher and higher degree of tolerance, but in which there was no noticeable abrupt change in the rate of acquisition, was characteristic of paraoxon and toxaphene, as well as lindane.

The third type was the one exhibited by strains of flies already resistant to one or more compounds. In this case the DDT- or methoxychlor-resistant strains rapidly took on resistance to other related or nonrelated chlorinated compounds. Thus, DDT-resistant house flies developed a high degree of resistance to lindane in one-half to one-third the number of generations that were required to develop the same degree of resistance from a susceptible strain of house flies.

OUR LABORATORY studies forecast rather accurately events in the field. That a fly strain resistant to one insecticide has a small but significant amount of resistance to other insecticides may explain the rapid build-up of resistance to other insecticides by the DDT-resistant flies. In all probability such DDT-resistant strains possess selected genetical characters associated with the development of resistance to other chlorinated insecticides not found in susceptible strains.

Field strains of DDT-resistant flies are found to have acquired resistance to the newer chemicals (chlordane, dieldrin, and lindane) used for fly control in place of DDT. These strains acquired resistance to the new insecticides much faster than they had initially acquired resistance to DDT. Field observations agreed with laboratory findings. Increased resistance to dieldrin, toxaphene, and lindane was reported by Ralph March and Robert Metcalf, of the California Citrus Experiment Station, to have occurred in the DDT-resistant Pollard strains following just three applications of lindane. Similar findings were reported by Kenneth D. Quarterman of the Savannah, Ga., laboratories of the Public Health Service, and by E. F. Knipling, of the Bureau of Entomology and Plant Quarantine.

In Illinois such an added resistance or tolerance occurred after two seasons of application of lindane or dieldrin. In studying this added dieldrin and lindane resistance acquired by field strains, investigators in California and Illinois noted that the levels of DDT resistance also had increased, apparently by the selective action of lindane or dieldrin.

MARCH AND METCALF discovered that DDT-resistant field strains of house flies usually are quite resistant to DDT-like compounds or analogs. They also reported that DDT-resistant flies subjected to lindane treatment developed tolerances for dieldrin, heptachlor, aldrin, chlordane, and toxaphene, as well as the expected lindane resistance. The Pollard DDT-resistant strain became resistant to all of the chlorinated hydrocarbons that might be used for fly control after only three applications of lindane. Apparently these multiple-resistant field strains were not resistant to the nitro-paraffin derivatives of DDT.

Decker and I were able to develop, from standard laboratory stock, flies that were highly resistant to lindane and only slightly resistant to the other toxicants. We also produced methoxychlor-resistant flies that were susceptible to DDT. These are two known exceptions to the classification proposed by March and Metcalf that there are in the field two types of resistant house flies—those resistant to DDT and its analogs (Bellflower strain, table 3) and those resistant to all the chlorinated hydrocarbons (Pollard strain, table 3) which are used as residual applications.

Although flies can be developed that resist a specific insecticide, changes are associated with their development that make the strains moderately resistant to other insecticides related chemically or by mode of action. A small amount of tolerance also seems to be acquired for unrelated compounds. An examination of tables 2, 3, and 4 will show

3. Measured Drop Tests Showing Comparative 24-Hour Topical LD–50's in Micrograms per Female Fly for Laboratory, Bellflower, and Pollard Strains

	24-hour LD–50's		
Compound	*Laboratory*	*Bellflower*	*Pollard*
DDT	0.033	11	>100
DFDT	.10	4.0	1.2
DTDT [1]	.16	.70	2.7
DEtDT [2]	.11	1.3	2.7
Methoxychlor	.068	.96	1.4
DDD	.13	60	>100
Lindane	.010	.080	.25
Heptachlor [3]	.032	.060	1.5
Aldrin	.044	.076	.78
Dieldrin	.031	.050	.86
Toxaphene	.22	.62	3.4
Parathion	.015	.020	.023
Pyrethrins	1.0	.94	1.6
Allethrin [4]	.43	.97	.50

[1] 2,2-bis(*p*-tolyl)-1,1,1-trichloroethane.

[2] 2,2-bis(*p*-ethylphenyl)-1,1,1-trichloroethane.

[3] The most toxic ingredient of technical chlordane.

[4] Allyl analog of Cinerin I

4. Measured Drop Tests Showing Comparative 24-Hour Topical LD–50's in Micrograms per Female Fly for Laboratory, Bellflower, and Pollard Strains

	24-hour LD–50's		
Compound	*Laboratory*	*Bellflower*	*Pollard*
1,1-bis(*p*-chlorophenyl)-2-nitropropane [1]	0.095	0.15	0.11
1,1-bis(*p*-chlorophenyl)-2-nitrobutane [1]	.15	.18	.11
DDT	.033	11	100

[1] A mixture of 2 parts of the first compound and 1 part of the second compound is marketed as Dilan.

Data from Ralph B. March and Robert Metcalf of the California Citrus Experiment Station.

the magnitudes of these conferred tolerances.

THE MAGNITUDE of the degrees of tolerance for toxicants acquired by house fly populations precludes the possibility of any important individual adaptation, but rather indicates a real change in the genetic make-up of the insecticide-resistant populations. Such a genetical change probably is brought about by a gradual selection of adaptive mutations which alter the physiological processes in such a way that the insecticides are more quickly inactivated or detoxified.

Attempts to learn the genetics of resistance show that both males and females carry DDT-resistant characters and that crosses produce what would be called physiological blends. In other words, the first hybrid generation possesses an intermediate degree of resistance.

From the standpoint of genetics, we have little hope of eliminating resistance by crossing resistant flies with susceptible flies, because resistance probably results from several gene changes, which cannot easily be defined as dominant or recessive. The resistant flies, although well adapted to a DDT environment, however, may not be so well adapted as susceptible flies to a DDT-free environment. Along with the advantageous mutation occurring during the development of resistant stock, there are probably many disadvantageous mutations that may be reflected in a decreased rate of reproduction.

SEVERAL POSSIBLE CHANGES might make field strains of house flies more and more difficult to control: The permeability of the cuticula might change, the rate of detoxification might increase, the toxicant might repel the insect, selection might produce flies with protective habits of resting in places not ordinarily treated, and morphological changes in the dimensions of the fly might occur.

We easily can demonstrate some of these changes. Workers in Illinois found that their Multi I strain of DDT-resistant flies decomposed DDT as quickly as it entered the body to produce a nontoxic DDE [2,2-bis (*p*-chlorophenyl) - 1,1 - dichloroethylene], whereas susceptible strains did not. Other DDT-resistant strains of flies were found to break down only part of the DDT that enters the body of the fly. Because not all the DDT can be recovered as DDT or DDE, an unidentified fraction remains. Flies of the DDT-resistant laboratory strain from the Orlando laboratories are apparently larger than susceptible flies. There also seems be a close correlation between the rate of larval development and resistance to insecticides. Insecticide-resistant house flies grow more slowly than the susceptible flies.

Field observers have noticed changes in resting-site habits of some resistant flies. Those insects rested on floors and lower parts of buildings but not on treated ceilings and walls. Some field strains of house flies are paralyzed by DDT more rapidly than are susceptible laboratory strains, but they completely recover from the initial paralysis of DDT poisoning. The quick paralysis and complete recovery serves as a protective mechanism in the field by preventing flies from resting on walls or ceilings long enough to absorb a lethal dose of poison.

Resistance to insecticides seems to be closely correlated with the ability of the fly to degrade chemically the toxicant to a nontoxic chemical. The site of the degradation appears to be in the hypodermal layer of the body wall of the insect. We do not know the actual mechanics of the process.

WHAT IS THE SOLUTION to our problem? If we had an easy solution we would have no serious problem. A solution is needed, and to that end I offer four items for investigation and thought.

1. The usefulness of DDT and other chlorinated compounds is coming to an end in the control of house flies unless some promising chemicals can be found that will prevent the flies from chemically degrading or evading the toxic effects of them. The Public Health Service has tested a large number of DDT activators and found that 1,1-bis(*p*-chlorophenyl) ethanol greatly increased the effectiveness of DDT on DDT-resistant house flies. It remains to be seen whether flies will become resistant to the combination.

2. New insecticides will have to be developed that are not chemically related to the chlorinated hydrocarbons. Some of the new phosphate compounds may become useful in controlling resistant house flies now found in the field. Dilan, a nitro-paraffin derivative of 1,1-bis(*p*-chlorophenyl), has shown some promise in field and laboratory tests, according to Ralph March. But the usefulness of Dilan may be short-lived because Dilan-resistant flies have been developed from a multiresistant strain in five generations.

3. Some investigators believe that field strains will revert to susceptibility in the absence of treatment. Field strains tested by workers in California and Illinois and investigators of the Public Health Service showed no loss of DDT resistance 2 years after DDT was discontinued as a residual treatment for fly control. DDT-resistant strains retained in the laboratory in the absence of DDT retained their high levels of tolerance for 30 to 50 generations. On the other hand, some investigators have reported instances of reversion of DDT-resistant flies to more susceptible strains of flies. We of the Illinois Natural History Survey have laboratory data that indicate that resistant flies may produce fewer progeny and in some cases have a longer life cycle than susceptible flies. Gordon Bender, of the University of Illinois, working with fly-muscle preparations, found that respiration rates were higher in resistant than in the susceptible flies. These two facts suggest that resistant flies may not be so well adapted physiologically to their environment and are not so efficient as susceptible flies. If so, then one can expect a gradual loss of resistance to insecticides among field strains of houseflies, as the susceptible strains literally outproduce the resistant strains. If the flies in the field lose their resistance to

the insecticides, when treatments have been discontinued and residues on walls and in the soil disappear, then the chlorinated hydrocarbons will again become useful as chemicals to reduce fly populations.

4. Still greater emphasis should be placed on sanitation. Insecticides should be used only to augment the fly control obtained by strict sanitation. There is no substitute for sanitation.

W. N. Bruce, *a native of Nebraska and a graduate of the University of Nebraska, is associate entomologist for the Illinois Natural History Survey. He worked at Iowa State College for 2 years as instructor and research associate and has conducted research on insects affecting man and animals for the Illinois Natural History Survey since 1945.*

For further reading on resistant flies, Mr. Bruce suggests his articles, Latest Report on Fly Control, *Pests, volume 17, number 6, pages 7, 28 (1949), and* House Fly Tolerance for Insecticides, *with G. C. Decker, Soap and Sanitary Chemicals, volume 26, number 3, pages 122–125, 145–147 (1950), and articles by—*

W. V. King and J. B. Gahan: Failure of DDT to Control House Flies, *Journal of Economic Entomology, volume 42, pages 405–409. 1949.*

Arthur W. Lindquist and H. G. Wilson: Development of a Strain of Houseflies Resistant to DDT, *Science, volume 107, page 276. 1948.*

Ralph B. March and Robert L. Metcalf: Insecticide-Resistant Flies, *Soap and Sanitary Chemicals, number 7, pages 121, 123, 125, 139. 1950.*

A. Missiroli: Riduzione o eradicazione degli anofeli? *Rivista di Parassitologia, volume 8, number 2/3, pages 141–169. 1947.*

K. D. Quarterman: The Status of Fly Resistance to Insecticides in the Savannah Area and Its Implications in the General Problems of Fly Control, *C. D. C. Bulletin, volume 9, number 11, pages 3–7. 1950.*

Giuseppe Saccà: Sull'esistenza di mosche domestiche resistenti al DDT, *Rivista di Parassitologia, volume 8, number 2/3, pages 127–128. 1947.*

James Sternburg, C. W. Kearns, and W. N. Bruce: Absorption and Metabolism of DDT by Resistant and Susceptible House Flies, *Journal of Economic Entomology, volume 43, pages 214–219. 1950.*

Mosquitoes and DDT

W. V. King

Increased resistance to DDT has been recorded for several species of mosquitoes in widely separated parts of the world. Included are the house mosquitoes, *Culex pipiens* in Italy and *C. quinquefasciatus* in India; two saltmarsh species, *Aedes taeniorhynchus* and *A. sollicitans,* in Florida; and two floodwater species, *Aedes nigromaculis* and *A. dorsalis,* as well as *Culex tarsalis* in California. An encouraging fact is that two species of *Anopheles* failed to show increased resistance in areas where they had been exposed for several years to DDT residual treatment in buildings.

E. Mosna was apparently the first to report increased resistance in a species of mosquito, *Culex pipiens autogenicus* (*molestus*) from the Pontine marshes in Italy. He found many live specimens of the species in bedrooms of houses in May 1947, where for the second year 5 percent DDT in kerosene had been applied as a residue for the control of *Anopheles.* Specimens he collected from the interiors were exposed to the treated walls and were alive after 48 to 72 hours, but specimens from a laboratory strain died within 3 to 5 hours. He thought it possible that two races of this variety of mosquito might exist, distinguished basically by the different grade of resistance to DDT. Laboratory tests with the eighth generation reared from resistant material showed that the resistance was transmitted through eight generations without marked diminution. From preliminary laboratory and field tests with chlordane and benzene hexachloride, Mosna learned that the insecticides had residual action lasting more than 4 months and were therefore suited to practical control of *Culex* that are resistant to DDT.

In India, from experiments conducted for 10 months, J. F. Newman and others learned that successive generations of the southern house mosquito exposed in the laboratory to DDT residues showed a marked increase in resistance to DDT. A 20-minute exposure caused 100 percent mortality of females originally, but no mortality resulted from 30-minute exposures a few months later. A similar resistance to benzene hexachloride also was shown.

The failure of DDT sprays to give satisfactory control of the common salt-marsh mosquito and another salt-marsh species, *Aedes taeniorhynchus,* in Broward County in Florida, was first noticed in 1947 in Hollywood, where much DDT had been applied in previous years to control heavy infestations.

The failure was observed again in 1948 and 1949, when similar difficulty was experienced in Brevard County near Cocoa Beach and the Banana River Airbase, where an extensive salt marsh had been treated repeatedly with DDT sprays the previous 4 years. In June 1949 the results of aerial spraying operations in the area were checked by members of the Orlando laboratory of the Bureau of Entomology and Plant Quarantine. It became evident that satisfactory reduction of adults of the two salt-marsh species *A. taeniorhynchus* and *A. sollicitans* was not obtained with the standard dosage of 0.2 pound of DDT per acre. Even twice that dosage failed to give as good control as had been obtained with the standard dosage. This indication of increased resistance was confirmed by laboratory tests in which larvae and reared adults of *A. taeniorhynchus* and *A. sollicitans* were compared for susceptibility to DDT with similar specimen material of *A. taeniorhynchus* from other areas in the same county that were not known to have received DDT applications previously or only an occasional treatment for adult control. *A. sollicitans* were not present in the untreated areas at the time the collections were made for the tests.

The evidence from the laboratory tests demonstrated the increased tolerance of the specimens from the treated areas. In the larvicide tests, the mortality of fourth-stage larvae averaged about 16 percent, compared with an average of nearly 90 percent for the control larvae. Similarly, in space-spray tests with 1 percent DDT solutions against reared females, the comparable figures were 18 percent and 83 percent. The results indicated a fourfold increase in tolerance or more. Larvae of *Aedes taeniorhynchus* collected in 1949 from a treated area in Sarasota County on the Gulf Coast also showed increased resistance.

In tests on mosquito specimens from Brevard County, chlordane and benzene hexachloride, both technical and refined (lindane), produced about the same mortalities of larvae and adults from the treated areas as from untreated areas at similar dosages. That was true also of parathion in larvicide tests. Parathion was not included against the adults. TDE, like DDT, was much less toxic to the specimens from the treated area. Toxaphene was somewhat less toxic. Lindane was by far the most toxic compound to adults, and parathion to the larvae from all areas.

Aerial spray tests with several insecticides were also carried out against the DDT-resistant mosquitoes. Lindane, the most effective of the insecticides tested, gave good control of adults at dosages of 0.05 and 0.1 pound per acre. Technical benzene hexachloride (12 percent gamma) at 0.2 and 0.4 pound and dieldrin and parathion at 0.05 and 0.1 pound gave results nearly equal to lindane. Chlordane and DDT at 0.2 and 0.3 pound per acre and toxaphene at 0.2 pound were not highly effective in most tests.

Larvicidal tests on small plots were conducted with several insecticides applied as emulsions. In the Cocoa Beach area DDT was much less effective than in untreated areas, but the other materials—dieldrin, parathion, lindane, technical benzene hexachloride, and toxaphene—all gave good and approximately similar results in both the treated and untreated marshes. Dieldrin and parathion were the most effective at dosages of 0.025 and 0.05 pound per acre, closely followed by lindane and toxaphene.

Indications of increased resistance to the effects of DDT in larvae of *Aedes nigromaculis* and *A. dorsalis* in Kern County, Calif., were noticed in the fall of 1947 and early in 1948 on a large ranch that had been regularly treated by truck and plane and had also been used for experiments on the applications of DDT emulsion siphoned into the irrigation water. The dosage was increased from 0.15 to 0.25 parts per million with continued failure. Later a part of the fields was treated with DDT by plane at the rate of 0.4 pound per acre and part with toxaphene at 0.3 pound. The toxaphene killed all stages of larvae, but the DDT failed to kill even the first stages. Complaints that DDT was not giving good control of the larvae of *Culex tarsalis* were also received in the district at about the same time.

R. M. Bohart and W. D. Murray reported that unsatisfactory results in the control of *Aedes nigromaculis* was experienced in Tulare and Merced Counties in 1949. To confirm the field observations, laboratory tests were made with larvae of the species collected in three pastures, which had previously received repeated DDT larvicide applications, in the mosquito-abatement district in Tulare County. They compared the larvae with larvae from three pastures in Kings County not known to have been previously treated with DDT. Based on the dosages required to cause 50 percent mortality, the average for the larvae from Tulare County was more than 10 times that for the control larvae. The least resistant of the larval lots from the treated fields required about three times as much DDT as the most resistant lot from the control area. In comparative tests between DDT and toxaphene, the latter was considerably the more toxic to the DDT-resistant larvae but less toxic to the control lots.

DDT residues applied to walls of living quarters and other buildings have been widely used in different countries to control carriers of malaria. Tests to determine whether an increase in tolerance had occurred were carried out in two areas where this method of control had been in operation for several years. The results were negative.

In the Mexican village of Temixco, DDT sprays were applied to the interior wall surfaces of all houses and other buildings once in early spring each year from 1945 to 1948. The sprays reduced markedly the numbers of *Anopheles pseudopunctipennis* in the village and in the surrounding rice fields. Laboratory tests were run in 1948 under the direction of J. B. Gahan and Wilbur G. Downs to determine the relative susceptibility of adults that had been collected in the village and the untreated village of San Jose, about 10 miles away. In June and July 96 tests were conducted with about 2,000 adult mosquitoes from each village. The insects were reared from gravid females collected in the two places and were tested by exposure to cloth panels impregnated with DDT. The average mortality was somewhat higher for the mosquitoes from the treated village than it was for those from the untreated village (56 percent versus 43 percent for the two sexes combined). The finding seemed to demonstrate that no loss of susceptibility had occurred.

G. F. Ludvik and others reported in 1950 on the first year of a study of DDT resistance in *Anopheles quadrimaculatus* in the Tennessee River Valley after 5 years of routine treatment, in which were used DDT residues against larvae and adults. They subjected specimen material to a variety of tests in comparison with similar material from untreated areas. The comparisons consisted of laboratory larvicidal tests in suspensions of

DDT, exposures of larvae in pans to aerial DDT sprays, exposures of adults to DDT-treated panels, and release of adults in residue-treated rooms. The mosquitoes from treated areas showed slightly greater tolerance to DDT in some of the tests, but the workers concluded from their preliminary studies that they had not developed an outstanding resistance.

R. W. Fay and others have reported the results of preliminary experiments to determine the possible development of a resistant strain of *Anopheles quadrimaculatus*. Adults of an insectary-reared colony of the species were exposed for four successive generations to DDT-treated panels for enough time to give mortalities of about 66 percent. Eggs from the surviving females then were obtained for rearing. In tests of susceptibility to DDT of the exposed strains, the mean mortality showed a slight but statistically significant drop in the first generation. No change occurred during the next three generations but was followed by an increase to the original level in the first generation after discontinuance of exposure to DDT. In tests against other insecticides, a similar loss of susceptibility was shown to methoxychlor but not to chlordane, benzene hexachloride, aldrin, or TDE (DDD). Because the pattern of increase and decrease in resistance was basically different in these tests from that reported for house flies (in which the changes in each direction were much more gradual) further confirmation of these results seems necessary before conclusions can be drawn.

W. V. King *is a technical consultant in the Orlando laboratory of the division of insects affecting man and animals, Bureau of Entomology and Plant Quarantine. The work at the laboratory is supported by funds allotted by the Secretary for Defense for investigations of entomological problems of medical importance to the military forces and the development of methods of control of the insects involved. Dr. King has been with the Bureau most of the time since 1912 and his work has been chiefly on insects affecting man. As a special agent of the Rockefeller Foundation, he spent 3 years in the Philippines on investigations of malaria mosquitoes. On active duty in the Sanitary Corps of the Army during the Second World War, he spent nearly 3 years in New Guinea and other parts of the western Pacific on malaria control and mosquito investigations. He was in charge of the Orlando laboratory until 1951, when he relinquished his administrative duties.*

Dr. King cites the following articles for some of the information in his article and suggests them for further reading:

J. H. Bertholf: DDT Resistant Mosquitoes in Broward County, Fla., *Florida Anti-Mosquito Association Proceedings, pages 80–83. 1950.*

R. M. Bohart and W. D. Murray: DDT Resistance in Aedes nigromaculis Larvae, *Proceedings of the 18th Annual Conference of the California Mosquito Control Association, pages 20–21. 1950.*

Thomas L. Cain, Jr.: Observations on DDT-resistant Species of Mosquitoes Found in Brevard County, *Florida Anti-Mosquito Association Proceedings, pages 84–85. 1950.*

C. C. Deonier: Aerial Spray Tests on Adult Salt-Marsh Mosquitoes Resistant to DDT, *with T. L. Cain, Jr., and W. C. McDuffie, Journal of Economic Entomology, volume 43, pages 506–510, 1950;* Resistance of Salt-Marsh Mosquitoes to DDT and Other Insecticides, *with I. H. Gilbert, Mosquito News, volume 10, pages 138–143. 1950.*

R. W. Fay, W. C. Baker, and M. M. Grainger: Laboratory Studies of the Resistance of Anopheles quadrimaculatus to DDT and Other Insecticides, *National Malaria Society Journal, volume 8, pages 137–146. 1949.*

James B. Gahan, Wilbur G. Downs, and Heliodoro Celis S.: Control of Anopheles pseudopunctipennis in Mexico with DDT Residual Sprays Applied in Buildings. Part II, *American Journal of Hygiene, volume 49, pages 285–289. 1949.*

W. V. King: DDT–Resistant House Flies and Mosquitoes, *Journal of Economic Entomology, volume 43, pages 527–532. 1950.*

G. F. Ludvik, W. E. Snow, and W. B. Hawkins: The Susceptibility of Anopheles quadrimaculatus to DDT after Five Years of Routine Treatment in the Tennessee River Valley, *National Malaria Society Journal, volume 10, pages 23–34. 1951.*

Fumigants

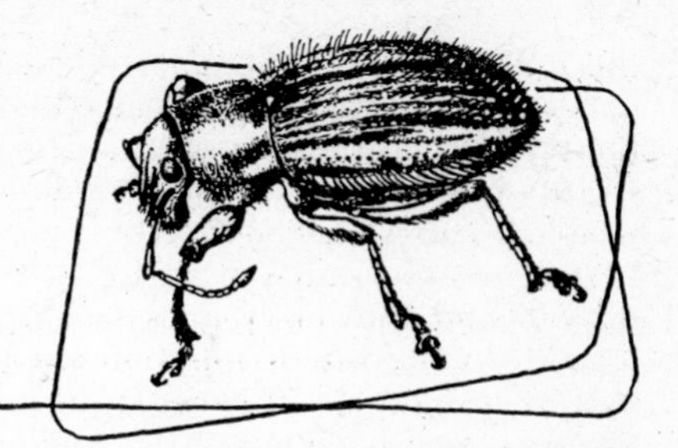

Nature and Uses of Fumigants

Robert D. Chisholm

Fumigants are chemicals that give off poisonous vapors. Their value for killing insects was known to the Greeks and Romans, Homer referred to the use of sulfur for the purpose. About 200 B. C. Cato mentioned that the fumes from a mixture of sulfur and asphalt would kill tree-infesting insects. Since then many compounds have been found to be valuable as fumigants for a large number of species—for some, in fact, fumigation offers the only practical means of control. For others it provides an alternate means to supplement spraying or dusting.

The selection of the right fumigant depends on several factors besides its ability to kill. It must not injure the commodity or thing attacked by the insects or nearby objects. It must not leave a residue that is toxic to humans or that imparts an unpleasant odor or taste if it is used on foodstuffs. Its cost must be less than the value of the materials saved from the insects. It must have certain properties—adequate vapor pressure or rate of vaporization, ability to penetrate the commodities fumigated, little sorption by the commodities, and chemical stability.

Because of the large number of insect species and the variety of their environments, the ideal fumigant has not been discovered. Fumigants are not equally effective against all insect species. A fumigant, furthermore, that can be used to kill insects in one environment perhaps cannot be used in another environment.

Fumigants usually are applied in enclosed spaces—vaults, houses, warehouses, mills, ships, bins, tanks, tents, or vacuum chambers, all of sufficiently tight construction to prevent undue loss of the vapors. Air presure is used sometimes to test for tightness. Losses from enclosed spaces that are protected from wind are much less than the losses from exposed places. Within practical limits, cracks or other openings should be sealed before a fumigant is applied. Sometimes fumigants are applied to soils.

Some fumigants are gases at ordinary room temperatures (about 70° F.). Others are liquids or solids that vaporize slowly at ordinary temperatures or require heating for effective use. The gases are usually compressed in cylinders, from which they are released as gases or liquids. (An exception is sulfur dioxide, which is generated by the burning of sulfur.) Fumigants that are liquids can be sprayed or sprinkled onto the commodity or throughout the enclosed space. Some are vaporized from pans, often with the aid of heat. Liquids used for soil fumigation are injected into the soil or applied as solutions or water emulsions. Solid fumigants can be vaporized by heating or scattered on and throughout the commodity or within the space, where they vaporize slowly.

Successful and economical fumigation depends on uniform distribution of the vapors. Some vapors are lighter than air and tend to concentrate in the upper level in an enclosed space, particularly if they are released near the top. Others, heavier than air, may stratify in the lower levels. Such undesirable features may be overcome partly if light vapors are released near the bottom and the heavy ones near the top. More uniform distribution can be had by using a circulating fan to mix the vapors with the air. After mixing, stratification at different levels is often of little importance.

Distribution in soils depends on the structure, moisture content, and temperature of the soils and the uniformity and depth of application.

The vapors of many compounds will kill insects, but relatively few are used for the purpose.

Carbon disulfide (CS_2) is a liquid at ordinary room temperatures. The chemically pure form is colorless, but commercial grades are slightly yellow. It has a disagreeable odor. Other properties: Boiling point 46.3° C., melting point −111.6° C., specific gravity 1.261 22°/20° C., and a vapor pressure of 297.5 millimeters at 20° C. It evaporates rapidly at ordinary temperatures and its vapors are 2.6 times as heavy as air (calculated from molecular weights).

The vapors of carbon disulfide are explosive when mixed with 1 to 99 volume of air. At 147° C. it ignites spontaneously. The mixtures may be exploded on contact with flames, live coals, sparks from electrical fixtures, or hot steam pipes. Great caution in its use is essential.

People should avoid lengthy exposure to the vapors. Short exposures may cause only headache or nausea. If exposure is continued, the symptoms become severe as a result of pathological changes due to the solubility of lipoids in carbon disulfide. Such changes may cause death.

Carbon disulfide has been employed as a fumigant since 1854. Its use has increased steadily until recent years. Other fumigants or a mixture of 1 part of carbon disulfide with 4 parts of carbon tetrachloride have largely replaced it. It has been used extensively for the fumigation of houses, warehouses, and stored products such as grains. Because it is toxic to all forms of life, it cannot be used for the fumigation of plants in greenhouses. Grains fumigated with carbon disulfide when they are moist are apt to germinate poorly.

Carbon disulfide is used also as a soil fumigant, originally having been found useful for the treatment of soil about the roots of grapes infested with root aphids. Later it was used in emulsions for the control of larvae of the Japanese beetle and other soil-inhabiting insects.

Carbon tetrachloride, or tetrachloromethane (CCl_4), is a liquid at ordinary room temperatures. It smells like chloroform. Other properties: Boiling point 76.8° C., melting point −23.0° C., specific gravity 1.595 20°/4° C., vapor pressure 159.6 millimeters 20° C., and vapor weight about 5.3 times that of air.

Its vapors are noninflammable—it is safe for use where a fire hazard is present.

In liquid or vapor form, carbon tetrachloride is toxic to humans. Symptoms of poisoning may be produced by absorption through the skin. Some of the characteristic symptoms are fatigue, backache, burning of the eyes, stomach disturbances, and liver injury. A constant exposure to more than 100 parts per million of air is considered dangerous. Exposure to 10,000 parts per million or less for an hour may produce symptoms that last only a short time. In the presence of an open flame, carbon tetrachloride is converted to phosgene and its toxicity is increased greatly.

Carbon tetrachloride has rather low insecticidal value. Consequently its cost is too high for many purposes. Its use is largely limited to operations where a fire hazard is present or in small-scale fumigations where cost is unimportant. Its principal use is in mixture with other fumigants, such as carbon disulfide or ethylene dichloride, to reduce fire hazard. It is used also as a diluent for more toxic fumigants, such as methyl bromide or ethylene dibromide, to assist in the distribution of the vapors of the more toxic compounds. Large quantities are used in such mixtures, particularly in grain fumigation.

CHLOROPICRIN, or trichloronitromethane (CCl_3NO_2), is a colorless liquid at room temperatures. It causes vomiting and intense irritation of the eyes and throat at relatively low concentrations. Other properties: Boiling point 112.4° C., melting point −64° C., specific gravity 1.651 20°/4° C., and a vapor pressure of 18.3 millimeters at 20° C. Its vapors are about 5.7 times as heavy as air.

It is noninflammable and is substantially free of fire or explosion hazards. In that respect it excels certain other fumigants, such as carbon disulfide or ethylene oxide.

It is toxic to humans. It was used in mixture with other more toxic gases during the First World War and was known as vomiting gas—soldiers who removed their masks were thus exposed to higher concentrations of the other gas in the mixture. It is sometimes added to hydrocyanic acid and methyl bromide as a warning agent.

To fumigate stored products, it may be poured or sprayed on the infested material. Because it has a low rate of volatility, it is often mixed with carbon tetrachloride or ethylene dichloride to promote vaporization and distribution of the vapors. It has the disadvantage of being retained by the fumigated product and can only be removed by prolonged airing. It is apt to injure living plants and seeds.

To control soil-inhabiting insects, it is usually injected into the soil in mixture with the diluents previously named or with xylene. Sometimes it is emulsified in water, and the emulsion is sprinkled on the surface or poured into holes. Such treatments will control certain species of fungi, nematodes, and weeds, but it must not be used where plants are growing.

970134°—52——23

D-D MIXTURE is essentially a mixture of 1,3-dichloropropylene and 1,2-dichloropropane obtained as a byproduct in the manufacture of allyl alcohol from petroleum.

Its composition is somewhat variable. A typical lot contained 30 to 33 percent of low-boiling and 30 to 33 percent of high-boiling 1,3-dichloropropylene, 30 to 35 percent 1,2-dichloropropane, and about 5 percent of heavy trichlorides of propane. It is a dark-colored liquid at ordinary temperatures and has a sharp, disagreeable odor. A typical lot had a boiling point of 93° C. On distillation 95 percent was recovered at 142° C. and dryness resulted at 163°. It had a specific gravity of 1.198 20°/4° C., a vapor pressure of about 31.3 millimeters at 20° C., and a flash point (Tag. open cup) of 80° F.

D-D mixture is inflammable and is dangerous to use in enclosed spaces in the presence of sparks or open flames.

It is dangerous to humans. Prolonged breathing of its vapors may cause the symptoms associated with the inhalation of the vapors of chlorinated hydrocarbons. The seriousness of such symptoms depends on the concentration of the vapors and the length of the exposure. It is very dangerous if spilled on the skin, shoes, or clothing and is likely to cause irritation, a burning sensation, and blistering. If it is spilled on clothes, the garment should be removed immediately and the skin in contact with it washed thoroughly. The garment should be washed and aired until the odor of D-D mixture can no longer be detected.

The chief use of D-D mixture is to fumigate soil against wireworms, garden centipedes, and such. It is highly effective against nematodes and reduces the populations of fungi and bacteria. For small-scale use it is poured into holes or furrows. For large-scale use it is applied in a continuous stream in the bottom of the furrow while plowing or by a mechanical trailer applicator, which injects the material under pressure at the desired depth and fills the furrows.

D-D mixture is apt to cause injury to plants and is therefore used almost entirely before planting. The soil should be thoroughly aerated 10 to 14 days after treatment. If that is done properly, most crops can be planted 3 to 4 weeks after treatment.

DICHLOROETHYL ETHER or 1-chloro-2- (β-chloroethoxy) ethane ($C_4H_8Cl_2O$) is used as an insect fumigant. It is a colorless liquid at ordinary temperatures. It has a mild, distinct, but not particularly objectionable odor. Other properties: Boiling point 178° C., melting point −50° C., specific gravity 1.222 20°/4° C., vapor pressure 0.7 millimeter at 20° C., vapor weight about 4.9 times that of air.

Dichloroethyl ether is a safe fumigant as to danger from explosion. It should not be used near open flames as its decomposition products are dangerous if people breathe them. At high concentrations the vapors are irritating to the eyes, nose, and throat. If such exposure is continued for a long period, anesthesia followed by death may result. At low concentrations there is little irritation.

It is valuable as a fumigant for many soil-inhabiting insects in lawns and gardens and is useful for the treatment of soils in greenhouses. Its high boiling point and low vapor pressure allow such fumigations to proceed over a long period and provide for the retention of toxic concentrations of the vapors in the soil for extended periods. The compound will kill a number of insect species, but it may also injure growing plants. It is best used where no plants are growing. The soil should be aerated before planting. Some plants, roses and carnations among them, are more susceptible to injury than grasses are.

ORTHODICHLOROBENZENE, or 1,2-dichlorobenzene ($C_6H_4Cl_2$), is a colorless liquid at ordinary temperatures. It has a strong, characteristic odor. Other properties: Boiling point 180–3° C., melting point −17.5° C., specific gravity 1.3048 20°/4° C., and vapor weight about 5 times that of air.

Orthodichlorobenzene can support combustion with difficulty and burns with a sooty flame. Under many conditions it is free from fire or explosion hazards.

It is poisonous to people. Prolonged breathing of its vapors should be avoided. It may be absorbed through the skin. If spilled on the person, the wet clothing should be removed at once and the affected part should be washed thoroughly with soap and water.

It injures growing plants. Its principal use is to treat logs or trees infested with bark beetles, such as the Black Hills beetle and the Engelmann spruce beetle. Such trees are usually in a dead or dying condition. The insecticide is applied to prevent the spread of the beetles to healthy trees. During the Second World War it was used as a fly larvicide, usually diluted with fuel oil, for the treatment of pit latrines and cadavers.

PARADICHLOROBENZENE, or 1,4-dichlorobenzene ($C_6H_4Cl_2$), is a white crystalline compound at room temperatures. It has a characteristic odor that at low concentrations is not unpleasant. Other properties: Boiling point 173.4° C., melting point 53° C., specific gravity 1.4581 20°/4° C., vapor pressure 0.64 millimeter at 20° C., vapor weight about 5 times that of air.

Paradichlorobenzene is safe from fire and explosion hazards under most conditions of use.

It is harmful to humans. Prolonged breathing of its vapors should be avoided. At high concentrations the vapors cause smarting of the eyes and some throat irritation.

It is used in large amounts against many species, notably the peach tree borer. It is placed in a shallow trench around the tree trunk at a distance of about 2 inches and then covered with soil. As a household fumigant, particularly for clothes moths, it can be scattered on the shelves or suspended in small cloth bags from the hangers in closets. That way allows the heavy vapors to be more uniformly distributed through the closet when the door is closed—better than spreading the crystals on the floor. It may be scattered on and under carpets, under furniture cushions, and in closed containers used to store blankets and other woolens. No air should circulate in the space being fumigated for at least 24 hours. Living quarters should be thoroughly aired out before they are used. Open flames should be kept away.

ETHYLENE DIBROMIDE, or 1,2-dibromoethane (CH_2BrCH_2Br), is a colorless liquid at room temperatures. It has a sharp, chloroformlike odor. Other properties: Boiling point 131.6° C., melting point 10° C., specific gravity 2.1701 25°/4° C., and vapor weight about 6.5 times that of air.

Ethylene dibromide has neither a flash point nor a fire point. There is no danger of fire or explosion. It is highly toxic to humans. Prolonged breathing of its vapors even at low concentrations should be avoided. It may be absorbed through the skin. Any clothing that it touches should be removed immediately. Parts of the body wet with it should be washed thoroughly with soap and water. Symptoms of poisoning include headache and nausea. Unconsciousness or death may occur several hours after prolonged exposure. Reddening or blistering may result from contact of the liquid with the skin.

It is used for the control of many insects. It is effective against nematodes, Japanese beetle larvae, wireworms, and other soil-inhabiting species. It may be diluted with a light petroleum fraction or xylene and drilled into the soil, using the same methods described earlier for D-D mixture. For other purposes, such as the control of the Japanese beetle where those methods are not practical, it is emulsified with water and applied to the surface of the soil, or infested plant balls may be dipped in a dilute water solution.

Ethylene dibromide is toxic to many plants, and soils treated with it should be aired thoroughly before planting.

It is effective against more than 50 insect species that infest grain in storage or grain mills. For that purpose it is generally mixed with other liquids, such as ethylene dichloride, carbon tetrachloride, carbon disulfide, or methylene chloride. The solutions are sprayed on top of the grain in bins, which should have tight-fitting covers. In grain mills the solutions are sprayed or poured into various parts of the machinery and splashed around the inside of empty bins.

ETHYLENE DICHLORIDE, or 1,2-dichloroethane (CH_2ClCH_2Cl), is a colorless liquid at ordinary temperatures. It has an odor like that of chloroform. Other properties: Boiling point 83.7° C., melting point −35.3° C., specific gravity 1.257 20°/4° C., vapor pressure 62.9 millimeters at 20° C. Its vapors are about 3.5 times as heavy as air.

Ethylene dichloride supports combustion with difficulty and burns with a smoky flame. Under many conditions it is not dangerously explosive. Mixtures of 6 to 16 percent with air are inflammable. To eliminate such hazards, it is often mixed with 3 volumes of carbon tetrachloride.

It is toxic to humans. Prolonged breathing of its vapors should be avoided. Some of the symptoms of poisoning are dizziness, headache, or nausea. Exposure to high concentrations may produce unconsciousness and death.

It is widely used to control many insect species, usually mixed with other fumigants, as mentioned previously. It is an effective general-purpose fumigant in buildings and in vaults, where it may be evaporated from shallow pans, placed preferably in elevated locations in the enclosed space. Evaporation may be hastened by heating electrically and by blowing a stream of air over the liquid. Often it is sprayed on the surface of grain bins. Grains and seeds may be so fumigated with little danger to germination. Foodstuffs, especially those having a high fat content, may retain a disagreeable taste and odor after fumigation.

Emulsions of ethylene dichloride are used as soil fumigants. For the peach tree borer, an emulsion is poured on the ground close to (but not touching) the tree and covered with soil. Dosage and concentration are regulated according to the age of the tree. Water solutions are used against Japanese beetle larvae; infested plant balls are dipped in the solution, or it is poured on the soil of potted plants.

Ethylene dichloride is toxic to certain plants. The degree of toxicity appears to be related to plant species and to the type and moisture content of the soil.

ETHYLENE OXIDE, or 1,2-epoxy ethane ($(CH_2)_2O$), is a gas at ordinary room temperatures. It has a mild odor at low concentrations and a more distinct one when the concentration is increased. Other properties: Boiling point 10.7° C., melting point −111.3° C., specific gravity 0.887 7°/4° C., vapor pressure 760 millimeters at 10.7° C., and vapor weight about 1.5 times that of air.

The vapors of ethylene oxide are inflammable and at concentrations of 3 to 80 percent can form explosive mixtures with air. To reduce such hazards it is usually mixed with carbon dioxide before application or with dry ice at the time of application. A commercial mixture, containing ethylene oxide at the rate of 1 pound to 9 pounds of carbon dioxide, is available in metal cylinders.

Ethylene oxide can harm people. Prolonged breathing of its vapors should be avoided. At low concentrations its effect may be hardly detectable. High concentrations cause severe irritation of the eyes, nose, and throat, and serious injury may result from such exposure.

It is highly effective for destroying insect life in many kinds of stored products, especially packaged cereals, bagged rice, tobacco, clothing, and furs in vaults. For such purposes it is ideal because it is highly effective and leaves no odor, flavor, or deleterious residue in the fumigated product. It may, however, injure foods like nuts, dried fruits, and such fresh fruits as raspberries, blackberries, and bananas. It may lower the germination of grains and of other seeds. It does not affect the milling qualities of grains.

Another important use is to fumigate historical documents in the Federal Archives Building in Washington. It is often best employed in vacuum fumigation chambers or it may be released from cylinders or mixed with dry ice to form slush that is added to grain as the bin or elevator is being filled.

Another use is to destroy molds, fungi, and other plant life in spices.

HYDROCYANIC ACID, or hydrogen cyanide (HCN), is a colorless gas at room temperatures. For most people it has a strong, characteristic odor like that of bitter almonds, but some people cannot detect it. Other properties: Boiling point 26° C., melting point −14° C., specific gravity 0.697 18°/4° C., vapor pressure 610 millimeters at 20° C. Its vapors are slightly lighter than air.

Hydrocyanic acid is inflammable. At concentrations between 5.6 and 40 percent it forms explosive mixtures with air, but in fumigations the concentrations are so low that little danger of explosion in the presence of sparks exists.

It is extremely toxic to humans and is very dangerous to use.

It may be breathed into the system or absorbed through the skin. Consequently fumigators must wear efficient gas masks and proper protective clothing. Inexperienced persons should not attempt to use it. Its action is so fast that one may have no warning symptoms before unconsciousness or death occurs. It unites with the hemoglobin of the blood and prevents the tissues from absorbing the oxygen transported to them.

Despite the dangers, hydrocyanic acid is widely used. For some purposes it is measured from cylinders with the aid of air pressure. For others it is generated by addition of its sodium or potassium salts to a mixture of sulfuric acid and water. For special uses it is packaged with an absorbent such as felt or diatomaceous earth. The gas is released on distribution of the absorbent in the space to be fumigated. It also is released on distributing granular calcium cyanide in the presence of moist air.

Its first important use as a fumigant was developed in California in the 1880's for the control of scale insects on citrus trees. At first the gas was generated under a tent covering the tree. Liquid hydrocyanic acid, made available since, has become the most important source of the fumigant. The method can be used without serious injury to the trees in the drier parts of California, but it has not been successful in more humid areas, such as Florida and Louisiana.

It long has been used as a fumigant for plants in greenhouses. Such fumigations, and those of citrus trees, are made at night to reduce the hazard of plant injury; during daylight hours, plants absorb the gas more readily. The plants must be dry when fumigated, or the gas will dissolve in the moisture on the plant and may cause injury.

Houses, warehouses, flour mills, storage vaults, and ships are often fumigated with hydrocyanic acid to destroy insects. It is very important that all be thoroughly aired out before anyone enters them. Things like mattresses and pillows require long airing. It is absorbed so rapidly that it may not penetrate throughout large bulks of milled cereals. Fresh fruits and vegetables, dried fruits, grain, flour, and other foodstuffs have been fumigated with hydrocyanic acid. Most of those that have hard rinds or skins do not absorb dangerous amounts of the fumigant. Others, such as green vegetables, immature potatoes, or bananas, may be injured severely. After airing, the amounts absorbed from ordinary fumigation concentrations and exposures are not considered to be unduly hazardous to humans.

METHYL BROMIDE, or bromomethane (CH_3Br), is a colorless gas at room temperatures. It is almost odorless. Its boiling point is 4.6° C., melting point $-93°$ C., specific gravity 1.732 0°/0° C., and vapor pressure 760 millimeters at 4.6° C. Its vapors are about 3.3 times as heavy as air.

It is noninflammable. Its vapors mixed with air cannot be ignited by a flame. It is therefore useful as a fire extinguisher. Specific conditions can be established to provide for ignition by means of an intense electric spark, but they are not encountered during ordinary fumigations.

Methyl bromide is toxic to humans. Prolonged breathing of its vapors should be avoided. The lack of a warning odor makes it especially dangerous. Poisoning, which may not be apparent until hours or a day after exposure, may result from breathing its vapors. A gas mask should always be worn when exposure is possible. In mild cases the symptoms are disturbance of the equilibrium, double vision, headache, and vertigo. In acute cases delirium, loss of consciousness, convulsions, and sometimes death occur.

Its use as a fumigant has increased rapidly since 1932, when its usefulness was first reported. Its many advantages make it one of the most widely used of all fumigants.

It is highly toxic to many kinds of insects in all stages of development. It is chemically stable, is only slightly soluble in water, and (at the concentrations required) has no deleterious effect on most plant tissues. It imparts no objectionable taste or odor to foodstuffs, and usually leaves no dangerous residue. It is convenient to handle, for it is readily liquefied, and yet it vaporizes at temperatures encountered in fumigating.

The action of methyl bromide on insects may be slow. Certain species, such as larvae of the Japanese beetle, may show little evidence of being affected after fumigation; death may occur a week or more later. With other fumigants, such as hydrocyanic acid, death generally occurs during fumigation or shortly thereafter or the apparently dead insect may recover.

Some of the important uses of methyl bromide are for the fumigation of warehouses, flour mills, ships, and residences, and flour, grains, seeds, fruits, vegetables, tobacco, and bulbs in vaults, bins, tanks, or railroad cars. It is also highly effective as a soil fumigant; often it is used to treat nursery stock infested with certain insects against which quarantines have been established. Besides, it is used to rid many varieties of potted greenhouse plants of various insect species.

All plants and vegetables will not tolerate methyl bromide fumigation. A few varieties of azaleas and evergreens are apt to be injured. The ripening of tomatoes may be delayed and sweetpotatoes may spoil.

NAPHTHALENE ($C_{10}H_8$) is a white crystalline compound at room temperatures. It has a strong, characteristic odor. Other properties: Melting point 80.22° C., boiling point 217.9° C., density 1.145, vapor pressure 0.08 millimeter at 20° C. Its vapors are about 4.4 times as heavy as air.

Its vapors burn with a luminous but smoky flame. It is one of the safer fumigants with reference to explosion hazard. Because specific mixtures of its vapors and air can be ignited, it should not be used near open flames.

Under ordinary fumigating conditions, naphthalene is not dangerous to humans. Its strong odor at high concentrations and the irritating effect of its vapors on the eyes and nose offer ample warning to prevent the breathing of injurious amounts. Prolonged breathing of its vapors may cause a delirious condition. If the crystals are ingested, the symptoms include excessive vomiting, purging, and great abdominal pain, followed by nephritis.

The main use of naphthalene as a fumigant is for the protection of woolen goods and furs, and it is commonly known as moth balls or moth flakes. Paradichlorobenzene in cake or crystal form is often used in place of it.

It has been used to a limited extent as a soil fumigant for the control of wireworms or the larvae of certain insect species, such as the Japanese beetle. Newer and more effective fumigants include ethylene dibromide and methyl bromide.

NICOTINE, or 1-methyl-2-(3-pyridyl) pyrolidine ($C_{10}H_{14}N_2$), is the chief alkaloid of tobacco. It is an oily, colorless liquid. It is almost odorless when it is pure but develops a tobaccolike smell on standing and rapidly turns brown when it is exposed to air. Other properties: Boiling point 247.3° C., melting point below −80° C., specific gravity 1.00093 20°/4° C., vapor pressures 0.08 millimeter at 20° C. and 7.00 millimeters at 100° C. Its vapors are about 5.6 times as heavy as air.

As far as fire and explosion dangers are concerned, nicotine is one of the safer fumigants. Only 0.04 pound of it is required to saturate 1,000 cubic feet of air at 68° F. Much lower concentrations are required to kill certain insects. It is inflammable, so it is best to avoid using it near open flames.

Nicotine is one of the most virulent poisons known to man. Serious or fatal poisoning may result from ingestion of very small amounts of it, from absorption through the skin or from breathing its vapors. Its strong odor, very irritating to the nose, provides warning of its presence during fumigations. If it is spilled on the skin, it should be washed off immediately. It causes contraction of the blood vessels with marked increase in the blood pressure, followed, after larger doses, with vascular dilation and fall of pressure. The pulse rate is lowered at first and later becomes rapid.

The principal use of nicotine as a fumigant is for the control of insects in greenhouses. It was first used for the purpose about 1825, tobacco being burned in an enclosed space. Later it was volatilized from water solutions, or the alkaloid was heated and the vapors distributed by means of a fan. Nicotine aerosols have been highly effective. Very likely the effectiveness of nicotine in sprays and dusts applied to trees and other plants is due partly to fumigation and partly to absorption or ingestion.

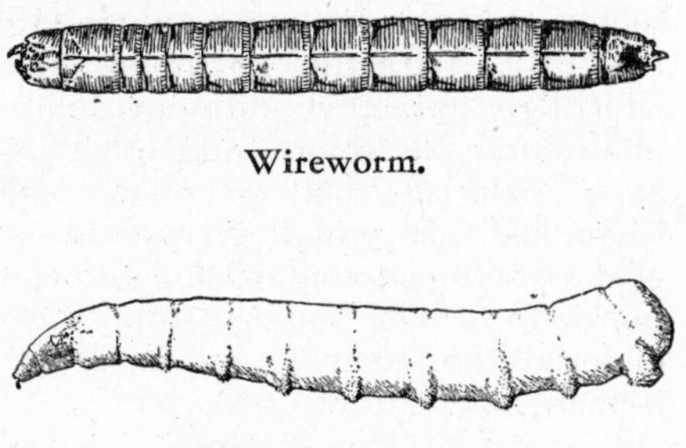

Wireworm.

House fly larva.

SULFUR DIOXIDE (SO_2) is a colorless gas at room temperatures. It has a strong, characteristic odor. Its boiling point is $-10°$ C., melting point $-72.7°$ C., and liquid density 1.434. It is about 2.2 times as heavy as air.

It is noninflammable and can be used without danger from fire or explosion.

It is highly toxic to humans, but its vapors at low concentrations are so irritating to the eyes, nose, and throat that acute poisoning is rare. At high concentrations it is absorbed by the moist surfaces of the respiratory tract and results in inflammation and swelling. A person is usually unable to remain long enough in a space being fumigated with sulfur dioxide to receive a toxic dose.

It is one of the first known of the fumigants, but other fumigants have largely taken its place. It is soluble in water, forming sulfurous acid, which is corrosive, and is a powerful bleaching agent. Under moist conditions, it is apt to tarnish metals and cause injury to colored wallpaper and fabrics. In moist or dry climate it is toxic to many insects. It has long been used as a home fumigant or in other locations where the hazards mentioned are not important or are preferable to the presence of the insects. It is a practical fumigant for refrigerator cars in which fresh fruit is shipped. It may be distributed in enclosed spaces by burning sulfur or by releasing it from commercial cylinders.

Sulfur dioxide is injurious to growing plants, many kinds of fruits and vegetables, and wheat and flour for bread making. It adversely affects seed germination.

OTHER FUMIGANTS used in limited amounts to meet specific insect-control problems include acrylonitrile, 1,1-dichloro-1-nitroethane, 1,1-dichloro-1-nitropropane, ethyl formate, methallyl chloride, methylene chloride, methyl formate, propylene dichloride, and tetrachloroethane.

ROBERT D. CHISHOLM *is a chemist in charge of the Moorestown, N. J., laboratory of the division of insecticide investigations, Bureau of Entomology and Plant Quarantine. After graduation from the University of Massachusetts, he was engaged for about 15 years as a chemist in the commercial manufacture of insecticides and fungicides. He joined the Department in 1935. Much of his work has been on the development of insecticides, attractants, and equipment for the control of the Japanese beetle and of bark beetles.*

The references given for insecticides in the bibliography in the appendix are recommended for further reading on fumigants.

Fumigating Soils and Plants

Randall Latta, M. C. Lane

Fumigants differ from other types of insecticides in that the fumes must be confined so that the insect is exposed to a considerable concentration for some time. The length of exposure and the strength of the concentration are interrelated—the higher the concentration, the shorter the lethal exposure; the lower the concentration, the longer the exposure.

Fumigants therefore are not well adapted for controlling insects on growing crops. They are often the only efficient method for treating plant commodities, however, when the insect is protected within seeds, pulp, or stems or is in the soil around the roots and when the treatment must be effective within hours so that the commodity can be moved into commerce.

Fumigants serve three general purposes: To treat growing crops, to destroy insects in soil, and to treat plant commodities.

An example of the use of a fumigant on a growing crop is the treatment of citrus trees for controlling scale insects and other citrus pests. Hydrocyanic acid gas, HCN, has long been utilized for that purpose. Rows of trees are covered with tents. The dosage, in proportion to the tree size, is injected or blown under the edge of each tent in the row, and the trees are exposed to the fumes for an hour. The tents are moved to the next line of trees, and the process is repeated. The fumigation is carried on when there is little or no air movement, usually in the late evening. The method has been adopted for the control of Hall scale, an insect on stone-fruit trees.

Fumigation of growing plants in greenhouses and mushroom houses is an old practice. HCN evolved from granular calcium cyanide and gas evolved from nicotine compounds heated, burned, or painted on hot-water pipes are often used. Many other fumigants have been tried, but none has been so widely accepted as those two.

Organic phosphate insecticides—such as hexaethyl tetraphosphate (HETP), tetraethyl pyrophosphate (TEPP), tetraethyl dithiopyrophosphate, and parathion—and other organic materials, such as lindane, can be applied as aerosols in greenhouses to give a combined contact and fumigation effect. The vapors from these materials are toxic to insects in extremely low concentrations.

FUMIGANT VAPORS may be retained for a long time in the soil, and they might be quite toxic to insects and other organisms living there. Probably the first such fumigant to have widespread use was carbon disulfide. It was employed to kill the grape phylloxera, a root-louse that was threatening the grape and wine industry in France. The chemical was tested against wireworms in the United States as early as 1891 and was recommended for use against various soil insects until recently. Paradichlorobenzene (applied in crystalline form in soil around tree trunks to control the peach borer) and napthalene flakes (worked into surface soil for wireworms) were other early soil fumigants. Chloropicrin, calcium cyanide, and many other fumigants have been used in attempting to control soil insects and nematodes. Most have been too costly or too difficult to apply to be practical on any large scale on the farm. All have limited use in greenhouses or seedbeds.

Because the damage caused by wireworms, symphilids, and nematodes is so great, many fumigants have been tested for use in soil. In some years, wireworm damage to the potato crop of the Pacific Northwest alone has caused losses of 4 million dollars to farmers. Soil pests have caused losses to the lima bean crop of several million dollars annually for many years in California. The damage to other crops probably has been proportionally as great.

During the late 1930's and early 1940's research for better fumigants was intensified. Many new organic chemicals came on the market. One, a mixture of the two chemicals dichloropropane and dichloropropylene and known as D-D, was used in 1943 against the pineapple mealybug in Hawaii and was found to be a potent agent against mealybugs and nematodes. Later tests in California demonstrated its effectiveness against wireworms. Another material, dichloronitroethane, proved to be more effective and suitable when soil temperatures were low.

Ethylene dibromide was found to be an efficient and economical fumigant for wireworms.

An increased interest in soil fumigation has led to an improvement in testing procedures. Until recently only the fumigants that had proved successful for fumigating grain or households were tested, and much the same testing methods were followed. Research workers later began testing fumigants in the presence of soil instead of exposing the insect alone. The newer tests disclosed that more fumigant was required when it was applied in soil, that it must be active enough to move around freely in the soil, and that it must not be too strongly absorbed by the soil.

Soil physicists have investigated the movement of gases in the soil. Some of their work can be applied to soil fumigation. The scientists agree that gases enter and leave and move around in the soil mass by diffusion. Diffusion is slow, especially in compact soil.

Experiments revealed that dichloronitroethane moved in compact soil about 24 inches in 16 days, or at an average rate of 1.5 inches a day. The rate is increased when the soil is loosened; the movement depends on the amount of free air space. Harrowing, rolling, or anything that reduces the free air space slows down the rate of diffusion. Plowing and disking, which loosen the soil, increase the rate of diffusion. The amount of water in the soil also influences diffusion, as water fills the air spaces and slows down the movement of gases. Experiments in 1949 showed that 10 to 30 times the amount of fumigant actually needed to kill wireworms must be applied to field soil for successful control. This large excess of fumigant is absorbed by the soil or escapes into the air.

The best and most widely used soil fumigants are ethylene dibromide and a mixture of dichloropropane and dichloropropylene. Both have been used successfully against wireworms and nematodes.

Ethylene dibromide, a heavy liquid with a rather low rate of evaporation, moves slowly through the soil. Its rate of escape from the surface also is slow. It should be used in loose soil to speed diffusion. Some sort of surface seal (such as provided by a light rolling or harrowing with a spike harrow) is desirable. It is about as efficient in cold soils, down to nearly freezing, as in warm soils. It is not greatly affected by soil moisture if the soil is not saturated with water. The wireworms common in the Pacific Northwest can be controlled by a dosage of about 2 gallons of ethylene dibromide to the acre. That amount is actually diluted with a highly refined light oil, such as paint thinner, because the available equipment does not readily measure or apply less than 6 to 8 gallons an acre. Larger doses are needed to control nematodes.

The dichloropropane-dichloropropylene mixture, also a liquid, is much lighter than ethylene dibromide and not nearly so toxic to insects. About 25 gallons to the acre are required to control wireworms in the Pacific Northwest. It is much more volatile than ethylene dibromide, and the soil surface must be sealed by harrowing or rolling after the fumigant is applied. Neither fumigant should be used in saturated soil. They should be given a week to 10 days to permeate the soil and kill the insects. Thereafter, if the odor of the fumigant is still strong in the soil, heavy disking or spring toothing will open it up and allow the fumigant to escape.

With these new and more practical fumigants has come the development of machines for applying them. The old hand-operated, single-row injection machines of earlier days were impractical on the large acreages that needed treatment in the Western States and Hawaii.

The many different machines that have been used are mostly of the power-injection or gravity-feed types. For the larger acreages the trailer- or tractor-mounted types are satisfactory. They can cover 10 to 40 acres a day. The liquid fumigant is released into the soil under pressure through tubes fastened to the rear of soil-chisel shanks mounted on draw bars so that the fumigant is injected at the best depths for maximum penetration. The chisel shanks are usually set 12 inches apart, and there may be 5 to 14 on a machine according to the power available to pull them through the soil. Some drawbacks of injection machines are their high cost, their inability to work well except on a prepared soil bed, and the rapid escape of the gas through the apertures left by the chisel shanks. Thousands of acres have been treated since 1945 with the machines, using D-D and ethylene dibromide.

The gravity-feed applicators are more suitable for the average farmer on a small acreage. Also known as plow applicators, they can be made on the farm from a second-hand gasoline tank, some quarter-inch copper tubing, and a valve or two attached to a standard tractor or plow. The fumigant is discharged by gravity just ahead of the plow or plows onto the exposed plow sole, where it is covered immediately by the soil of the next furrow. Needle valves regulate the flow according to the speed of the tractor and width of the furrow. The equipment is low in cost. The soil does not have to be prepared beforehand. If the surface is harrowed lightly after plowing, the toxic vapors are held in the soil long enough to give the most efficient diffusion of the fumigant.

Lindane and parathion are effective for treating soil to destroy insects in greenhouses and plant nurseries where plants are growing. Small amounts of the materials added to soil in the greenhouse bench will control symphilids. The effect is a combination of contact and fumigation.

OFFICIALS who enforce plant quarantines are interested in soil fumigation that will free restricted areas from a particular insect so that plants can be grown or stored there without hazard of infestation and subsequent dissemination of the pest.

Under the Japanese beetle quarantine, several methods were perfected. One is fumigating under tar paper or tarpaulin covers with carbon disulfide injected in holes 1 foot apart each way. Another is sprinkling a water solution of methyl bromide or a mixture of ethylene dibromide and ethylene dichloride over the soil surface.

A third is treating the soil that would make the ball of a balled and burlapped nursery plant. Before the plant is dug, a quantity of emulsions or solutions containing carbon disulfide, methyl bromide, or a mixture of ethylene dibromide and ethylene dichloride is applied to the area around the plant in the nursery row. A modification of the method is to dip the soil or root balls of nursery plants after digging in emulsions or solutions of carbon disulfide, ethylene dichloride, a mixture of ethylene dibromide and ethylene dichloride, or a mixture of a fumigant and a contact insecticide—ethylene dibromide and chlordane.

The white-fringed beetle, the object of another quarantine, is more resistant than the Japanese beetle in the young or larval stage. Fumigation under tar paper of plant-free soil areas with methyl bromide is effective in destroying larvae. It is used by itself or dissolved in an organic solvent such as ethylene dichloride and injected into the soil at spaced intervals. However, the various emulsions or solutions that are used around plants or as dips for the Japanese beetle treatments are not tolerated by nursery plants at the stronger concentrations needed to kill white-fringed beetles.

The incorporation of such stable insecticides as DDT and chlordane in the nursery soil has proved successful and has obviated much of the necessity for soil fumigation in relation to plant quarantine measures.

Fumigation of potting soil is likewise important in enforcing quarantines. Carbon disulfide, chloropicrin, and methyl bromide are used frequently to fumigate potting soil that is to be used under certified conditions.

Under the regulations that apply to plant products imported into the United States, fumigation is widely utilized—on shrubs, trees, corms, bulbs, roots, tubers, cut flowers, seeds, restricted fruit and vegetable products, cotton byproducts, and broomcorn.

The summary we give below of imported material treated in 1949 and 1950, mostly by fumigation, indicates the scope of such fumigation.

Because of infestations with living giant African snails, even shiploads of steel scrap from islands in the South Pacific have been fumigated.

In 1918 quarantine inspectors began to fumigate American railway cars on their return from Mexico. Many of the cars were used to haul cottonseed or another cotton product in Mexico and became contaminated with Mexican cottonseed, which might contain live larvae of the pink bollworm. Large fumigation houses, ranging in capacity from 2 to 20 freight cars, were maintained at six border points to treat all returning cars. The largest house had a capacity of more than 200,000 cubic feet and required 80 to 120 pounds of liquid hydrocyanic acid for one fumigation. In 1949 the practice was discontinued except for special reasons, because the precautions taken in Mexico reduced to a negligible point the probability of contamination of cars with infested cottonseed.

Fumigation is also used under various domestic plant quarantines. Under Japanese beetle quarantine regulations, methyl bromide fumigation of fruits and vegetables to eliminate any live adults was the preferred practice for many years. As many as 5,000 freight-car loads a year were so treated in the 1940's. Since then the use of DDT dust has replaced some of this fumigation. One to two million nursery plants were also fumigated. Under white-fringed beetle quarantines, fumigation of balled and burlapped nursery plants has been practiced since 1939. Fumigation is used also to treat white potatoes, peanut hay, and lupine seed. To combat the sweetpotato weevil, fumigation has been required for tablestock sweetpotatoes that move from quarantined areas to other growing areas in the South.

Fumigation with methyl bromide has been adapted to the treatment of Christmas trees and greens cut in localities infested with gypsy moth. It destroys dormant egg clusters on the

Imported Materials Fumigated in 2 Years

		1949	*1950*
Cotton lint, linters, and bagging	bales	500, 000	850, 000
Cottonseed cake and meal	pounds	40, 000	9, 324, 000
Cotton samples	number	17, 200	25, 500
Fruits and vegetables	cases	8, 400	60, 000
Chestnuts, cipollini bulbs, and pigeon peas	containers	47, 500	53, 500
Broomcorn	bales	36, 200	350
Plants, cuttings, bulbs, roots	units	2, 585, 500	4, 510, 000
	containers	5, 000	7, 264
Seeds	containers	1, 500	67, 300
	pounds	48, 700	52, 200
Miscellaneous plant products	lots	21, 500	19, 000

branches. Formerly the greens and trees had to be inspected one piece at a time.

Methyl bromide fumigation is used for treating cottonseed as an alternative to the long-standard heat treatment. Sacked cottonseed for planting can be fumigated in the manner usually practiced for most commodities, but cottonseed in bulk has to be fumigated under conditions of forced circulation in order to distribute the fumigant. To do that, special apparatus was devised to fit in with the normal handling practices of cottonseed. Large steel tanks, holding up to 600 tons of cottonseed, have blowers and a duct system that draw the fumigant down through seed more than 40 feet deep. The tanks are loaded and unloaded by mechanical conveyors commonly used in handling cottonseed. Fumigation is also done in freight cars by connecting a portable forced-circulation system, which operates outside the car, to flexible ducts attached to the floor and ceiling levels. More than 73,000 tons of cottonseed were fumigated in 1950 in storage tanks and more than 300 carloads were fumigated on a railroad siding. That is only a small part of the total amount of cottonseed treated for pink bollworm, but fumigation is a valuable alternative to heat treatment in newly discovered areas of infestation where heat-treating equipment is not available.

Fumigation likewise is used for treating commodities regulated by various State plant quarantines. Several States require the fumigation of white potatoes originating in California because of the potato tuberworm. Thousands of carloads of potatoes are fumigated with methyl bromide in compliance with those quarantines. California and Arizona require the fumigation of many plant-propagating materials as a condition of entry. When California removed restrictions on Texas citrus fruit because citrus canker was no longer found in Texas, many carloads of grapefruit were fumigated to destroy such surface insects as scales, to meet other California requirements. In 1940 or so, before the oriental fruit moth was found in Pacific Coast States, nursery-plant hosts that might carry overwintering larvae were allowed entry into Western States if they were fumigated before shipping; a large trade developed between midwestern nurseries and western fruit growers. When the insect was discovered on the west coast, fruit and fruit boxes were fumigated before moving from local quarantined areas to noninfested areas.

When Hawaii was quarantined because of the presence of the oriental fruit fly, two products were fumigated to permit movement to mainland markets. Millions of *Vanda* orchid flowers were fumigated in 1949 and 1950; later research established that the fruit fly could not finish its life cycle on the flowers even though eggs and young larvae were found on them. Then the restrictions were removed. Pineapples are shipped to mainland markets following fumigation to destroy eggs or larvae of the fruit fly attached to or embedded in the skin of the fruit.

RANDALL LATTA *was leader from 1942 to 1951 of a project to develop treatments for plants and plant products regulated by plant quarantines. His staff works with plant quarantine units in the Bureau of Entomology and Plant Quarantine to develop proper dosage schedules and procedures for fumigating quarantined materials. In 1951 he became leader of the division of stored product insect investigations.*

M. C. LANE *is in charge of the truck crop and garden insect investigations laboratory at Walla Walla, Wash. He has been with the Bureau of Entomology and Plant Quarantine since 1917 and has been studying the life history and control of wireworms of the Pacific Northwest since 1920. Besides evolving several cultural control methods for wireworms on irrigated lands, he and his coworkers have evolved methods of ridding soil of wireworms through the use of fumigants and soil insecticides.*

Fumigating Stored Foodstuffs

R. T. Cotton

Fumigants can penetrate large bulks of stored foodstuffs and get at insects working far beneath the surface. They work fast and effectively against all stages of insects, even those concealed within kernels of grain. Their volatile nature insures the eventual disappearance of poisonous residues from fumigated foodstuffs. The cost of fumigation usually is low. The materials are inexpensive. Small dosages suffice. Little equipment is required to apply them. Fumigation is usually considered a curative measure, but it is essential in most programs for the prevention of insect damage to foodstuffs in storage. Fumigants are available to treat any type of foodstuff under almost any circumstance and for a long enough time to kill insects in the places where they are.

For those reasons, fumigants are more important in preserving stored foods from insect damage than any other agent or combination of agents. They have some drawbacks, however.

Some foodstuffs, notably those rich in oil, may retain obnoxious odors from certain fumigants and others may be adversely affected by repeated fumigations or excessive concentrations. The viability of seed may be reduced by some fumigants under certain conditions. If the commodities are in good condition, however, some fumigant or other can be relied on to do an efficient job without materially affecting them.

Grains, milled cereals, feeds, dried fruits, nut meats, dried meats, cheeses, powdered milk and egg, beans, peas, chickpeas, spices, coffee, and practically all dried foodstuffs can be safely and effectively fumigated.

For proper fumigation, one should know the fumigant or fumigants best adapted for treating each type of commodity under the varied conditions of storage he might encounter and the capabilities and limitations of the more important fumigants.

For successful fumigation the insect must be surrounded by the fumigant in a concentration heavy enough and for a sufficient time to produce death. Special techniques may be needed to tighten enclosures and insure the uniform distribution of the vapors. If enclosures cannot be made tight enough to hold fumigants, foodstuffs can be treated in bins, atmospheric vaults, barges, vacuum chambers, railway cars, under tarpaulins, or in individual packages. With products such as grain in bulk it is possible to fumigate successfully large piles stored in loosely constructed buildings because of the ability of the grain to absorb and hold the vapors for considerable periods.

The infestation of grain by insects may start in the field or soon after it is placed in storage on the farm. As a preventive measure, it is wise to fumigate grain immediately after it is placed in storage in areas where field infestation occurs and within 6 weeks in all other areas.

The tendency of bulk grain to absorb fumigants makes it possible to treat grain successfully even though the bin in which it is stored is not airtight. The dosage of fumigant required will vary with the tightness of the bin and with the type of grain. Generally speaking, small grains require smaller dosages than corn since they retain the vapors for longer periods by their greater sorptive properties. On the other hand, the smaller size and still greater sorptive properties of grain sorghum obstruct the uniform diffusion of fumigants through the bin when they are applied to the surface, so that larger dosages are required for treating grain sorghum than for any other grain.

Low temperatures, layers of moist grain, and the presence of pockets of dockage in bins of grain are factors that adversely affect the performance of grain fumigants. All these factors usually are considered in calculating the required dosages.

Many proprietary fumigants on the market differ slightly in composition from the compounds I have listed in the table. They may be used at the dosages recommended for the mixtures that they most closely approximate.

For best results in fumigating grain in farm bins, the surface of the grain should be level and at least 6 inches below the top of the side walls of the bin. Because strong winds and high temperatures accelerate the evaporation and loss of fumigant, applications should be made in the cool part of the day and when the air is quiet. In applying fumigants, the operator should cover the surface of the grain as uniformly as possible with a coarse spray. He should treat the grain from the outside of the bin to avoid exposure to the fumes. For small operations, a bucket pump or a knapsack sprayer can be used, but for larger operations a power sprayer is desirable. A pump with bronze fittings, which will not be affected by carbon tetrachloride or similar chemicals, and one that will pump the chemical directly from the drum is useful. In all operations a plastic-lined hose or one that will resist the action of carbon tetrachloride should be used. Washers should also be resistant to this and similar chemicals.

FUMIGATION OF GRAIN in elevator storage is much simpler than in farm bins, because elevator bins are usually much tighter and the uniform distribution of the fumigant is facilitated by its introduction into the grain stream as the grain is transferred from one bin to another.

Dosages of fumigants listed in the table, as modified for use in steel bins, can be used for treating grain in steel or concrete elevators. Besides these fumigants, calcium cyanide at 10 pounds and chloropicrin at 2 pounds per 1,000 bushels of grain can be used. In wooden-crib elevator bins, the dosage should be doubled. These dosages will give an excellent kill of adult insects but will seldom kill all the immature stages of weevils that breed within the kernels. Somewhat heavier dosages therefore should be used if the kill is to be complete.

Because many factors affect the efficiency of grain fumigants, the results are not always predictable. Grain that is high in moisture content, is cold, contains a lot of dockage, or has stood for a long time without turning is difficult to fumigate and may require much heavier dosages than normally are used.

Under average conditions the fumigant can best be applied to the grain

Fumigants and Dosages for the Treatment of Grain Stored in Wooden Farm Bins [1]

Fumigant	*Dosage per 1,000 bushels*		
	Small grains except sorghums	*Sorghums*	*Corn*
	Gallons	*Gallons*	*Gallons*
Carbon tetrachloride	5	8	6
Carbon tetrachloride:			
4 parts + carbon disulfide 1 part [2]	3	8	6
1 part + ethylene dichloride 3 parts [2]	6	10	6
19 parts + ethylene dibromide 1 part	3	8	6

[1] In steel bins the dosages may be reduced 50 percent for small grains and about 20 percent for corn and grain sorghum.

[2] The addition of 5 percent by volume of ethylene dibromide improves the kill of immature stages of insects in grain.

stream while the bin is being filled. Special applicators designed to feed the fumigant into the grain stream at the desired rate are used for chloropicrin or calcium cyanide. Other fumigants are poured into the grain stream at regular intervals by hand or may be applied with an automatic applicator adjusted to operate continuously when the grain is running. When grain cannot be turned, the fumigants other than chloropicrin or calcium cyanide can be applied by spraying the entire dosage uniformly over the top layer. If grain temperatures are above 80° F., the vapors will penetrate the mass of grain to the bottom of the bin.

For control of surface infestation by the Indian-meal moth or the almond moth, the various bin openings (ventilators, manhole covers, loading chutes) should be closed and sealed and a fumigant applied as a fine spray or vapor. The aim is to retain the fumigant at the top of the bin rather than have it sink down through the mass of the grain. Chloropicrin alone can be applied by means of a garden sprayer to the space above the grain in closed-top bins at the rate of 1.5 to 2 pounds per 1,000 cubic feet of space above the grain. Mixtures of 80 percent methyl bromide and 20 percent chloropicrin, or 80 percent methyl bromide and 20 percent ethylene dibromide likewise can be applied at the rate of 1.5 pounds per 1,000 cubic feet of space above the grain.

Some grain-elevator bins in Europe and North Africa are equipped for circulating a gas within the bins during and immediately after its introduction. Although the method has not been adopted for elevator bins in the United States, it has been successfully used in the fumigation of grain in steel tanks of 350,000-bushel capacity in Texas.

Blowers introduce the fumigant into the top of the bin and pull it down through the grain and out through ducts to the blower again so that it can be recirculated. This method gives a uniform distribution of the fumigant within 30 minutes, and the fumigant can be removed and replaced with fresh air after the fumigation. Methyl bromide can be used successfully by this method at dosages so low that fumigation costs are extremely reasonable. For grain sorghum a dosage of 3 pounds of methyl bromide per 1,000 bushels of grain gives excellent results.

For the temporary storage of large stocks of surplus grain, Quonset huts, airplane hangars, barracks, and warehouses of all kinds are used. The grain is usually stored in a pile on the floor and seldom completely fills the structure. The buildings usually are not tight, and the problems of storage are complicated.

Piles of grain in such storages can be successfully treated with fumigants sprayed over the surface of the pile, even though the buildings are not tight. The grain mass holds the fumigant so well that excellent kills can be obtained. During cool weather, insect colonies tend to bunch together near the center of such piles. Such infestations are eliminated by spot applications of fumigants. The area of infestation can be determined by taking probe samples. The fumigant should be applied directly over the infested area, so that it covers a few feet beyond the limits of the infestation.

In both corn and wheat, dosages of 4 to 5 gallons of 4 parts of carbon tetrachloride and 1 of carbon disulfide per 1,000 bushels have given excellent results in spot treatments or in the fumigation of the entire pile.

The fumigant can be applied with a power sprayer that delivers the liquid rapidly as a coarse spray. Many Quonsets have roof hatches, through which the fumigant can be applied; if not, the operators can enter the building and spray the fumigant uniformly over the pile, starting from the rear and working towards the exit.

Adequate hose and a pump capable of throwing a stream about 75 feet at the rate of 100 gallons a minute should be used.

During manufacture and processing and subsequent storage in warehouses, dried foods are exposed to infestation by insects that become established in the machinery or in various parts of the mill, manufacturing plant, or warehouse. A planned program of fumigation can do much to prevent such infestation.

In former years a general fumigation once or twice a year with hydrocyanic acid, methyl bromide, or chloropicrin was relied on to keep premises free from insects. Modern demands for food entirely free from insect infestation have caused the adoption in many plants of a biweekly program of local fumigation, whereby individual milling units or food-handling machines are fumigated and the fumigated stock removed by heavy-duty vacuum cleaners. In some mills the biweekly application of local fumigants takes the place of a general fumigation. Local fumigants, if regularly used, will maintain a low insect population in milling machinery but cannot be expected to destroy infestations in all parts of the plant, so that an occasional general fumigation is helpful.

General fumigants are usually introduced into the open space of the building, but sometimes are also introduced through piping systems directly into the machinery.

Local fumigants may be applied by hand by pouring them into the individual milling units or machines. Liquid fumigants may also be applied with permanently installed dispensers. Portable fumigant dispensing tanks are used to force the fumigant into fabric tubes installed permanently inside conveyors or other units. A fully automatic system dispenses the fumigant in vapor form from a central supply connected by tubing to individual milling units.

Chloropicrin, hydrocyanic acid, and mixtures of carbon tetrachloride with ethylene dibromide, ethylene dichloride or other chemicals are used extensively as local fumigants.

For the fumigation of warehouses filled with grain, feed, flour, or other dried foodstuffs, methyl bromide or mixtures of methyl bromide with chloropicrin or ethylene dibromide have been found most effective. Perfect penetration of large stacks of bagged materials can be obtained with dosages of 1.5 pounds per 1,000 cubic feet of space. To obtain uniform distribution of the fumigant and to prevent stratification of the vapors near the floor, electric fans should be operated for 1 hour after release of the gas.

THE USE OF TARPAULINS or gas-proofed fabrics in the fumigation of stored foodstuffs sometimes may be more convenient than fumigating in large, partly filled warehouses or in atmospheric vaults. The tarpaulin, which takes the place of the fumigation chamber, is portable and occupies little space when not in use. The free air space is reduced to a minimum and aeration is facilitated by the complete removal of the tarpaulin from the stack of commodities after fumigation. The products to be fumigated are generally stacked on a concrete floor and covered completely by the tarpaulin, the edges of which are weighted down carefully to prevent leakage of gas around the base. Provision is made for an air dome at the top by using two sacks placed edgewise about 4 feet apart. The air dome will provide free air space to permit diffusion of the gas.

A rubberized fabric or a light duck material coated with ethyl cellulose usually is used. Any fumigant suitable for the treatment of bulk commodities in atmospheric vaults or warehouses can be used to treat foodstuffs under tarpaulins.

Atmospheric vaults are useful for the fumigation of foodstuffs when warehouses are not tight enough for efficient fumigation or when small lots—incoming raw materials, returned goods, used bags, and out-going products of all kinds—need treatment.

Many different materials can be used to construct atmospheric vaults, but a metal vault or one with a metal lining is most efficient. Tubing and spray nozzles for introducing volatile fumigants and fans for circulating the fumigant or exhausting the vapors are necessary.

The actual process of fumigation is simple. The commodity is loaded into the vault by hand or run in on trucks or skids. The door is closed and the fumigant introduced. At the end of the fumigation, the exhaust fan is turned on and allowed to run until the vapors, not absorbed by the fumigated commodity, have been removed. While the vault is being unloaded, the exhaust fan should be kept running. Sometimes auxiliary fans may be needed to supply fresh air for the workmen unless they wear gas masks.

Methyl bromide and mixtures of methyl bromide with chloropicrin or ethylene dibromide are most efficient for use in treating dried foodstuffs in atmospheric vaults, although hydrocyanic acid, chloropicrin, and many other fumigants can be used. Dosages depend on the commodity to be fumigated, the quantity involved, and the fumigant.

Fumigation by vacuum consists of placing the commodity in a gas-tight steel chamber, removing the air, and replacing it with a gas lethal to insects. By this method a more rapid penetration of commodities by the gas is obtained than in atmospheric fumigation, and insects are reached and killed faster than in an atmospheric vault. The removal of a large part of the oxygen from the chamber makes the insects more susceptible to fumigants. The length of exposure ranges from 1 to 3 hours, compared to 10 to 24 hours under atmospheric conditions—an important factor in industries where speed is essential in handling foodstuffs.

Vacuum fumigation has several other advantages. At the end of a fumigation, the removal of the fumigant from the treated commodities can be speeded up by a process known as air washing. It consists of drawing a vacuum of 27 inches or more and breaking it with air. There is little danger that workmen will enter a vault undergoing fumigation, and the danger from breathing the vapors during the unloading of a vault is lessened.

970134°—52——24

It is advantageous to draw as high a vacuum as possible and to hold the vacuum throughout the exposure. By circulating the gas in the tank for 15 minutes after it is introduced, the distribution of the fumigant will be aided greatly, and much less fumigant will be needed to effect a kill than if the gas is not circulated.

The fumigants usually employed in vacuum vaults are methyl bromide, hydrocyanic acid, and a 1–9 mixture of ethylene oxide and carbon dioxide.

Dosages vary with the fumigant, the commodity, and the length of the exposure. The shorter the exposure, the larger the amount of the fumigant required.

The fumigation of individual packages of foodstuffs is practiced in some food industries, but is expensive because comparatively large quantities of fumigant must be used. In this method, the individual packages traveling along a belt pass under an applicator, which automatically injects a certain amount of fumigant into each one. The packages are then sealed. Each package is its own fumigation chamber. The method was first used extensively in the United States to treat packages of dried fruit, for which ethyl formate, methyl formate, and isopropyl formate have been used. Other products so fumigated are dried soupstocks, rice, dog biscuits, popcorn, and such. Besides the formates, acrylonitrile in admixture with carbon tetrachloride has been used for individual packages.

R. T. Cotton *has been an entomologist in the Bureau of Entomology and Plant Quarantine since 1919 and has been in charge of field research on the control of the insect pests and stored-grain and milled-cereal products since 1934. He has specialized on fumigation and other methods of controlling the insect pests of stored foodstuffs. Dr. Cotton holds degrees from Cornell University and George Washington University.*

Quarantines

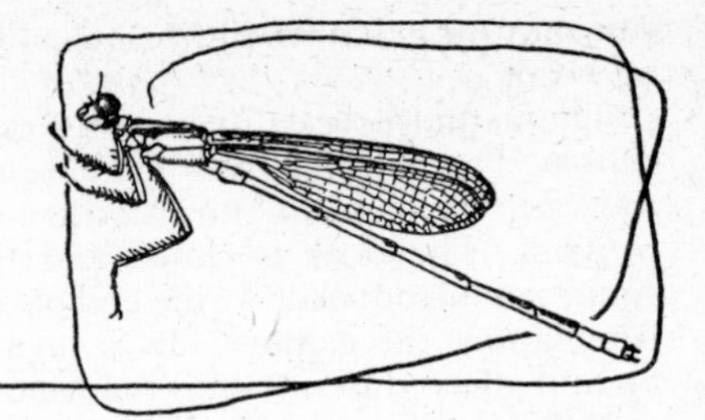

How Insects Gain Entry

Ralph B. Swain

Most of our major insect pests of foreign origin have been brought into the United States by man and chiefly aboard ship. From Mexico and Canada some have come by natural means. An understanding of the ways in which they enter is the basis for sound quarantines.

Insects, like other organisms, occupy well-defined niches in nature. Environmental factors and innate characteristics tend to restrict them to certain areas of the earth. But the variability in animals in time permits individuals of a species to adapt themselves to slight changes in their surroundings and acquire new food habits and immunities to diseases, extremes of climate, and insecticides. We therefore can expect that certain species with centers of distribution in Mexico or farther south, by normal dispersal of the adult insects, eventually will spread north of the Rio Grande, and that certain Canadian species (or European or Asiatic forms that become established in Canada) will descend from the north.

That has happened. The boll weevil and the harlequin bug are two of many injurious insects that have worked northward from Mexico as agriculture reclaimed parts of the southwestern desert, once an effective natural barrier to them. The elimination of the desert barriers has been accelerated with the building of great new irrigation projects.

The satin moth, a European species, spread from British Columbia into Washington and Oregon. It was discovered in eastern Canada and in New England at about the same time, and in that regard has had a parallel history with other forest pests that had no respect for the Canadian border. The gradual dissemination of a pest through adjacent or nearby fields of host plants is much more difficult to combat than are incipient infestations well separated from population centers.

Air currents and storms bring insects to us from Caribbean islands, Mexico, Central and South America, and Canada. We have evidence that the pink bollworm moth is brought into the border districts of Texas and New Mexico each year by winds from Mexico. The Mexican fruit fly enters citrus groves in the lower Rio Grande Valley every year, either flying or being windborne from south of the border.

Studies of the insect fauna of the upper air have shown that such weak-flying insects as aphids, psyllids, and leafhoppers are found at altitudes up to 14,000 feet. It is conceivable, therefore, that both native and introduced insects from the West Indies, Mexico, and places farther south may be borne to our shores by winds.

Other insects migrate annually, flying on strong wings from tropical areas and no doubt assisted by prevailing winds. One such is the cotton leafworm moth, a widespread pest in South America, which moves northward into the United States and in a few generations may even reach Canada. As with the Mexican fruit fly, a winter destroys our populations of cotton leafworms, but next season a new invasion may be expected. No way exists to keep such migrants out of the country short of controlling them in the lands whence they come.

People who have tramped Florida beaches in the wake of great storms know that in the driftrows are bits of vegetation, seeds, even large branches and logs, which obviously traveled from West Indian islands. Many additions to the Florida insect fauna, especially wood- and seed-boring species, must have arrived in such sea drift. Possibly living insects can travel even greater distances in floating plant debris, but by and large the seas are excellent barriers to natural spread, and insects, especially the immature stages, have small chance of survival when deposited on a wind-swept and wave-washed beach, far from food plants and other requisites for their existence.

Man also might introduce insects from contiguous land areas in personal baggage carried by pedestrians or in cargo or personal effects aboard automobiles, trucks, trains, and airplanes. An automobile or truck can transport insects in various ways—as adult stowaways or hitchhikers inside the vehicle; as adults, immature stages, or eggs in and on plants, fruits, seeds, and plant products; and as eggs or larvae in mud or dirt caked under the body and fenders, on wheels, or in tire treads.

SOME INSECTS TRAVEL from country to country on or in the bodies of man and his domesticated animals, or on animals brought in for food, processing, or exhibition. Various kinds of lice and mites may be on the bodies of travelers. The important species probably are already of world-wide distribution. It is possible that fly larvae of the sorts that may live in the flesh of man or invade the digestive and respiratory tracts could be brought into the country from abroad, although it is likely that such a sufferer would be detected by Public Health officers.

Most of the insects and mites likely to be introduced with domesticated or wild animals are already cosmopolitan, but some serious pests of domestic fowl have been discovered in this country in recent years. Migrating wild birds carry insect parasites on their bodies from one continent to another, but here again the species involved are not new to our fauna.

Insects certainly were among the first stowaways on sailing ships. Our various roaches of African origin arrived aboard slave ships. A large percentage of our household and storage pests, such as insects affecting fabrics, wood and wood products, and stored foods, came from other lands aboard ships in which they were able to maintain themselves and even breed in litter or filth. On the faster ships of today it is easier for insects, even rather delicate ones, to survive an ocean passage. The monarch butterfly and others have traveled from the continental United States to Hawaii and Europe as stowaways, and European forms have come to us in the same way.

Many factors work against the successful establishment in this country of an insect arriving as an adult stowaway aboard ship. Its chance for survival, particularly in the larger port areas, may be relatively slight even if it succeeds in gaining the shore. Much depends on the sex of the insect, its distance from food plants and good egg-laying sites, and on prevailing weather. From the standpoint of quarantine enforcement, it is fortunate that the commoner stowaways are already of nearly world-wide distribution and hence of significance from the standpoint of control rather than exclusion. The problem of ridding a ship of stowaway insects is one that has not been solved satisfactorily. No easy solution is in sight.

THE AIRPLANE potentially is a major distributor of insect stowaways because of its speed. Almost 3,000 species belonging to 293 families and most of the orders of insects, many of them alive, have been intercepted inside aircraft. Partly because of the precautions now taken to disinsectize airplanes from areas of greater pest risk, it is not possible to make a long list of economically important airborne insects. But at that the list is long enough to be distressing. The oriental fruit fly, one of the most destructive pests ever to strike the Hawaiian Islands, gained entrance during the Second World War at a time when proper precautions regarding military aircraft from the Marianas could not be taken. At Brownsville, Tex., a living Japanese beetle was found in a military plane that had arrived from New York City by way of Panama; evidently it had hitchhiked from an airport in the metropolitan area. We have two records of tropical, malaria-carrying mosquitoes taken near military airports in Florida. In one instance, a living larva was taken from the canal in which the stowaway parent evidently had laid its eggs.

Adult insects travel almost exclusively within the fuselage. The exterior surfaces and wheel housings are of no importance as carriers. It is thus relatively easy to eliminate insects aboard aircraft by properly applied combinations of space and surface insecticidal sprays. An interesting though minor problem has been posed by the egg masses of several species of moths found on outside surfaces. Possibly the moths, night fliers, were attracted to the bright exteriors of the craft as they rested on illuminated aprons or simply flew toward lights aboard. Frequently such eggs are alive. Even freshly hatched caterpillars have been found crawling about. Lights inside parked aircraft attract insects just as they do elsewhere and often are responsible for hundreds of insects finding their way in through open doors, hatches, and windows.

Military movements, especially during war, can undo in minutes what quarantines and control programs have accomplished in years. Then expediency rules, the usual civilian control may be impossible, and invading armies usually have little regard for the regulations of an enemy country. The Hessian troops that landed at New York during the Revolutionary War are believed to have brought the hessian fly in their straw bedding. It is well that we have never since suffered a large-scale invasion of foreign troops. Americans today are fortunate that the hazards to health and agriculture resulting from the bringing of foreign insects to this country are appreciated by the military branch, which cooperates with our quarantine agencies.

SHIP'S BALLAST has brought many insects from other lands, sometimes with the seeds or roots of their host plants. Ballast is of little consequence as a hazard if dumped far out at sea, but it can be dangerous when used for fills in a port area. Most modern ships no longer use earth ballast—instead they use water, which can be disposed of more inexpensively by pumping into the harbor at the end of the voyage. Earth as ballast is still in use, however, and at one time was used almost exclusively. It may consist of beach sand, gravel, rock, or topsoil. The soil would be most apt to contain insects, since it may hold any of thousands of soil-inhabitating species in all stages of development and the eggs and larval stages of innumerable others, which as adults live above ground. Quarantine inspectors, working directly with shipping companies, make recommendations and arrangements for the proper disposal of dangerous ballast.

Potentially destructive foreign insects are much more likely to arrive in cargo than in holds, compartments, and other interior spaces of ships and airplanes. We distinguish here the insects that rove freely about airplanes and vessels or are imprisoned in a hold or compartment without host plant or other food from the insects that are on or in fruits, vegetables, living plants, and plant products. The former are the stowaways. The latter constitute active infestations, perhaps of many individuals of the same species, which, in the absence of quarantines, might proceed directly to a nursery, farm, or backyard garden where the risk of establishment would be infinitely greater than in the immediate environs of a port or airport. There is, to be sure, the problem of stowaways inside the containers of plants and plant products, but that is solved by the same methods employed against the species infesting the merchandise. Against stowaways with manufactured articles and with raw materials not subject to plant quarantines we have no defense.

Importations of foreign nursery stock and other plants have long been considered the most dangerous means of introducing foreign insect pests. Commercial importations of nursery stock made before our present regulations as to freedom from soil and mandatory treatment are known to have been the carriers of specific foreign pests. The Japanese beetle, for example, certainly entered on nursery stock as grubs in the root balls. Adult insects, which could not possibly survive the journey as stowaways aboard ship with any other type of cargo, may be found feeding on the leaves and bark of plants in transit to this country. Today the most prolific source of insect interceptions is the occasional shipment of nursery stock that escapes the scrutiny of certifying officials abroad and arrives at one of our inspection houses with the roots in soil and packed in woods moss and forest litter, both of which are prohibited as packing materials.

Fruits, vegetables, cut flowers, seed-contaminated samples of cotton, cotton waste and cotton meal, broomcorn, soil samples imported for biological, sentimental, or commercial purposes, the wood of shipping containers, and various packing materials (including those used for such items as dishes and bottled goods) may harbor insect pests. Lumber and barked and unbarked logs can be a source of forest-insect pests and the diseases some of them spread. For example, the Dutch elm disease and one of the European beetles that transmits it to healthy trees came into the United States in elm logs. Even the narrow staves used in baling cork from Spain and northern Africa have been found infested with wood-boring insects not known to be established in this country and potentially quite destructive. It is regrettable that we do not have legislation insuring adequate protection against the introduction of insects in logs and lumber.

Cut flowers and certain fruits and vegetables formerly could not be brought to our country from overseas because of unfavorable factors of time and temperature. Fast refrigerator ships now bring us cut flowers from South Africa in quantity, and insects, if present, are not ordinarily injured by the brief cold-storage periods. They simply become quiescent and resume normal activity when the temperature rises. Airplanes speed cut flowers from Europe and from the Tropics. A great number of insect pests, including the various fruit flies, might be introduced with fruits and vegetables were it not for Federal quarantines and inspection procedures. Here again ship refrigeration helps to get the insects to us alive but can be and is used to kill fruit fly larvae in certain types of fruits during transit. Dried broomcorn stalks from Italy and some other Mediterranean countries are often badly infested with the European corn borer and another moth borer, which almost certainly would become a major pest of corn and sorghum in the South if it should become established here.

The fruits and vegetables taken aboard ships and airplanes as food for passengers and crew also are suspect. Were it not for the vigilance of plant quarantine and customs inspectors, infested foodstuffs might be taken from the ship by crew members or perhaps be placed in trade channels. As it is, prohibited items in stores may be seized and destroyed or officially sealed and kept thus until the ship or plane has departed.

The risk of pests in garbage from

ships or airplanes is about the same as that attending the introduction of the various fruits and vegetables that might be infested with injurious insects. The difficult thing is to enforce rules for proper disposal. Garbage dumped into salt water a safe distance from shore presents little risk, but the same material discharged into a river or bay may quickly wash ashore close to agricultural areas and food plants, upon which the insects present could subsist. Garbage brought ashore from ships or removed from aircraft must be kept in tightly closed containers until incinerated.

PLANTS BROUGHT into the country as passengers' baggage are apt to be from the gardens of relatives or friends and usually are uncertified by plant quarantine officials of the country of origin. Such plants are often prepared for shipment by persons quite ignorant of our quarantine requirements and so may be in soil and badly infested with insects; consequently they present great risk. Fruits that a passenger has forgotten or wishes to conceal frequently are discovered by alert inspectors in trunks, suitcases, and hand bundles. Often such contraband is infested with fruit flies and other injurious insects.

Insect pests are more likely to be found with plants in baggage shipments than in commercial ones even though the latter arrive in vastly greater quantity. The reason is that commercial shipments are usually from establishments with long experience in shipping to the United States; the plants have been grown under as sanitary field or greenhouse conditions as possible, are reasonably free of insects and diseases, and are packed with approved packing materials.

The mail could bring most of the insects that come to us in ballast, cargo, stores, and baggage. But for postal conventions that recognize the dangers of unrestricted international traffic in plants by mail and a permit system designed to bring mail shipments of plants and seeds to foreign plant quarantine inspection houses at certain ports of entry, it would be extremely difficult to control this broad avenue of ingress for pests.

Insect stowaways are less likely to occur in mail than in cargo shipments, and the average number of insects per container is smaller because of space considerations. It is extremely unlikely, moreover, that insects on the outside of mail parcels would be able to penetrate the packaging; in cargo, by contrast, this is relatively easy for the smaller species.

In former years, the mails did not lend themselves well to plant shipments, except dormant material and seeds, because of the time consumed and the difficulty in providing sufficient moisture to keep the plants alive. With the inauguration of international air parcel post, however, it has become possible to send parcels weighing up to 70 pounds by air to the United States.

Such comparatively delicate creatures as young leafhoppers, still actively feeding on the juices of the host plants, have been intercepted in the mails from tropical countries. Leafhoppers and their relatives, the aphids, have piercing-sucking mouth parts, which make them effective spreaders of plant virus diseases. It is not illogical to assume that plants afflicted with virus disease, quite undetectable by ordinary inspection methods at ports of entry, have come into the country and would today be economically significant if the appropriate insect vectors were available.

The mails are the most productive sources of what might be termed accidental introductions—when a well-intentioned individual, in pursuit of a hobby, has requested living specimens of the caterpillars or pupae of a butterfly or moth. In 1869, before we had legislation to hinder such things, the gypsy moth was purposely brought into Massachusetts by an amateur entomologist engaged in research on silkworms. Through his carelessness, the insects escaped and became established as a bad pest of trees in the Northeast.

Even now, living insects occasionally are intercepted in the mails, having been dispatched to someone unacquainted with our laws concerning such shipments. Useful parasitic and predacious insects and other species for scientific experiment are allowed in the mails only if accompanied by a permit issued by the Chief of the Bureau of Entomology and Plant Quarantine. Such permits are issued cautiously.

Because in total war the introduction of new insect pests into the enemy economy might be a spectacular weapon in the hands of a belligerent, a survey for new insect pests near ports of entry of the continental United States was conducted under the supervision of the Bureau of Entomology and Plant Quarantine during the later years of the Second World War.

No evidence of the malicious introductions of foreign insect pests was discovered. Charges of the deliberate introduction of insect pests made by one country against another have appeared from time to time in the world press. Such charges appear to have been mere propaganda. It would be a short-sighted gesture in the present stage of world unification for one country to set free in another country a destructive pest, whose ravages the malefactor would in the end have to pay for in some measure.

Ralph B. Swain *began part-time work for the division of cereal and forage insect investigations when he was a high school sophomore. He took his degrees at Iowa State College, Colorado Agricultural and Mechanical College, and the University of Colorado, between stretches of employment in the Bureau, and has since worked for the division of domestic plant quarantines on Mormon cricket and white-fringed beetle control projects. He was chief inspector at the Foreign Plant Quarantine Inspection House for the Port of New York in Hoboken, N. J., until July 1951, when he went to Nicaragua as entomologist with our Government's Point IV program.*

An Agricultural "Ellis Island"

George G. Becker

Within the Port of New York, at 209 River Street on the Hoboken, N. J., waterfront, is a four-story brick building where the Department of Agriculture fulfills a function of protecting the plant life of this country.

In this agricultural "Ellis Island" the Government, so to speak, examines the passports of incoming plant material and inspects and treats it before it is turned loose for planting.

The mere arrival and handling of some prohibited categories of plant material may involve a risk of pest introduction. The shipper must be informed of these prohibited categories. He must also know of the restrictions dealing with size and age, packing, certification, and other details. To be provided with the necessary information to send his shipper, the prospective importer must therefore get his passport, or import permit, in advance of shipment.

When plant propagating material arrives at Hoboken it is under customs bond and remains so until all customs, plant quarantine, and other Government requirements have been met. Before the material is imported the importer will have, or should have, procured a permit for its entry and with it appropriate instructions to send the shipper and to provide for its orderly entry. All plants, cuttings, and seeds and certain bulbs are required to move under customs bond to the designated inspection station, where they remain under customs custody until the customs have determined that all requirements are satisfied.

The inspection station at Hoboken is kept locked at all times. Importers are not allowed to see or know what their competitors import or where they get what they import. All windows are screened. Walls, floors, and ceilings where plant material is stored, inspected, or handled are of tile construction and can be disinfected readily. Ceilings, screens, and walls are sprayed often so that insects that escape from imported material will be knocked down when they alight upon treated surfaces.

Incoming material, arriving on the first floor, is stored apart from material that has cleared quarantine. On the second floor, material is inspected in one of two rooms, a large inspection room where large cargo shipments are handled, and a smaller room where mail and other small shipments are inspected. Besides the quarantine station at Hoboken, where most of the propagating material is handled, there are stations at San Francisco, Seattle, Miami, Laredo, Tex., San Juan, P. R., and Honolulu. The material that enters from Europe must clear Hoboken. The plants that arrive at the stations in San Francisco, Seattle, Laredo, and Miami are cleared there before being forwarded. The material may not move overland untreated.

These stations are operated by the Bureau of Entomology and Plant Quarantine. The Bureau of Plant Industry, Soils, and Agricultural Engineering maintains plant introduction stations at Glenn Dale, Md., Savannah, Ga., Coconut Grove, Fla., and Chico, Calif., and regional stations in cooperation with the States at Ames, Iowa, Experiment, Ga., and Pullman, Wash. At them, valuable importations of otherwise prohibited material are grown under quarantine until they are released by plant quarantine inspectors.

The inspection staff at Hoboken consists of entomologists, plant pathologists, and botanists. Besides their specialized knowledge, the inspectors must be well informed on the proper care of the valuable plant material in their custody as well as on methods of packing and forwarding. Inspectors take pride in the fact that material goes forward in as good or better condition than when it was received. Many shipments are reconditioned which, had they gone forward without passing through quarantine, would have been a total loss.

The inspectors must have the proper training to recognize plant pests. They must be able to identify plants and understand that some plants which may not be botanically related may nevertheless be tied together in a biological relationship to perpetuate an insect pest or plant disease. A native plant louse known as the woolly apple aphid uses our American elm as an alternate host. Therefore the American elm could be a means of introducing the pest into a new region. To protect the Nation's wheat industry the inspector must recognize species of barberry and closely related plants on which a stage of the destructive black stem rust of wheat develops. He must recognize species of currants, including our black currant, red currant, and many ornamental species. The black currant is an alternate host of a destructive disease, the white-pine blister rust, which attacks five-leaved pines. Many plants related to citrus must be recognized, as their entry is prohibited because of the possibility of introducing citrus canker.

To minimize the risk of introducing plant pests, the Department's Quarantine No. 37 imposes restrictions on the size and age of woody plants. The younger a plant the less chance it has had to become infested or infected with pests. The inspectors therefore must be able to determine whether plants offered for entry are within age limits. Another requirement is that woody material that can be grown from seed and will come true from seed may be imported only as seed. The eucalyptus trees of the west coast owe their picturesque shape to the fact that before the passage of the Federal Plant Quarantine Act of 1912, California horticultural authorities, profiting from previous experience, limited the introduction of eucalyptus species to seeds; thus they kept out a destructive beetle that eats the terminal buds and causes the development of trees of a bunchy growth. To enforce the no-woody-seedling requirement, inspectors must be able to distinguish between seedlings and plants produced by cuttings, budding, grafting, or layering.

INSPECTION FOR PLANT PESTS, like any other profession, has its own techniques. Inspectors learn what to expect in material coming from different parts of the world and how to look for pests. The most important function of inspection is not so much to find the expected as to find the unexpected. Interceptions have repeatedly revealed the occurrence of pests in countries in which they were not previously known to be present, and species of pests new to science are frequently encountered.

The inspector may be looking for specific pests, but he visualizes constantly what is normal for plant material of the kind he is handling. If his first inspection discloses something unusual, he makes a thorough investigation. With the normal in mind, he opens a bundle of perhaps 50 plants and spreads them out. Instead of examining each plant minutely, his eye may catch at a glance three or four plants on which he focuses his attention. He thus concentrates on material most likely to yield insect clues: He notices a tiny, clean-cut hole, such as might be made by a small needle. Lifting the bark with a knife blade, he may observe the work of a mining insect. A tiny grain, which the layman is likely to pass over as a grain of soil, he readily recognizes from its shape as the boring of an insect. The epidermis over a yellow spot on a leaf may cover the work of one of the many destructive species of leaf miner.

Going through a crate of bulbs, he develops a feel for them as he squeezes one bulb after another. He presses his thumb around a bulb at different places and may notice a slight give at one spot. On cutting into the bulb, which outwardly looks normal, he may find an insect larva.

A strand of silk on a plant may be the calling card of a leaf-feeding or other insect. A small knot on the root of a plant, which superficially looks like a little lump of soil, may be the home of an insect that has spun a cocoon camouflaged on the outside with tiny grains of soil.

An off-color plant is unfailingly investigated. On examining the under sides of pale-green leaves with a lens, the inspector may observe numerous tiny plant mites, but his interest does not cease with noting general color. A pinpoint of difference in color attracts him. Training his hand lens or the microscope on such a point, he may find it to be the egg of a plant mite. A tiny gray speck, the size of a flyspeck, may prove to be one of numerous species of sap-sucking scale insects.

Roughened bark at the base of buds and leaf scars is a place where some types of insects are likely to deposit their eggs. A scar on an otherwise smooth twig is likely to be evidence of the eggs of a leafhopper that were inserted under the bark. These, and others, are the clues an inspector uses for recognizing the presence of pests.

Character of growth may reflect the presence of insects as well as disease. A bunchy growth not normal to a plant may indicate the presence of insects that ate the terminal buds, with the result that lateral buds were forced into growth. A spindly, twiggy growth may be the symptom of a virus.

The temperature of the plant material is another factor. Living plants, even dormant woody material, have a feeling of coolness compared to dead material.

The inspector sometimes intercepts snails, lizards, and even tropical snakes with the plant material. While being photographed at the Hoboken inspection house, objects resembling beans, intercepted with orchid plants from South American jungles, were observed to move. Heat from the light used to photograph them completed the hatching of what proved to be snake eggs.

Among the plant pests that concern the inspector are wormlike animals—eelworms or nematodes—that are barely visible to the unaided eye. Some produce swellings on the roots of the plants they attack. The work of the common bulb nematode, *Ditylenchus dipsaci,* is recognized by cutting a cross section of the bulb. An infested bulb has concentric dark rings. The nematode commonly found in iris bulbs causes lengthwise yellow, brown, or nearly black streaks (according to age of the infestation and the species of iris) or brownish specks or splotches at the tips of the bulb. The symptoms can be seen only when the dry, brittle outer skin, or tunic, of the bulb is removed by a blast of compressed air.

A nematode for which the inspector is especially alert is the golden nematode, a serious pest of potatoes and tomatoes. The female dries up and forms a cyst in which her eggs are contained. The eggs may remain alive in the soil for 10 years or more. That is a reason why quarantine regulations prohibit the entry of plants in soil—the risk of introducing nematodes is great. Many species of nematodes can be identified by their cysts, which resemble round grains of soil or very small seeds. Occasionally plants or bulbs or plant litter in the bottom of a crate yield a bit of soil. If so, the inspector samples it for nematode cysts. He washes it and runs it through fine sieves. He puts what remains on a piece of absorbent paper to blot off the water and examines it under a microscope.

As important as keeping out plant pests is the work of excluding plant diseases. For instance, a number of plants may carry a virus disease of tobacco. Among them are primulas, of which only a small number are permitted entry. Arrangements must be made in advance of the importation so that provisions can be made at the inspection house for indexing. Indexing requires the sprouting of beans for use in tests. Juice of the primula to be tested is rubbed on a young bean leaf on which carborundum powder has been dusted. If virus is present, the bean sprouts develop visible spots or lesions in a few days.

The character of growth and the color of plants and plant parts are the symptoms that most often indicate the presence of disease. Virus diseases especially may affect character of growth. Streaking in leaves and even shapes of leaves may likewise indicate virus. Close examination of discolored areas on leaves or twigs may disclose the presence of invading organisms. Frequently the inspector may cut a twig or root and note from brown rings or other discoloration the presence of disease. Malformed parts of plants, such as galls or cankers, may be caused by insects or diseases or may be the result of mechanical injury.

The smell of plant material may be the guide to detecting diseased plants or to determining the species of a plant. Temperature may be the clue to the presence of diseased plants. Plunging his hands into the peat moss in which plant material may be packed, the inspector may encounter a warm spot—an almost certain sign of rotting plants, often caused by lack of ventilation.

The plant pathologists of the inspection station must also be concerned with the determination of fungi and bacteria. That often involves culturing. Agar, a gelatinous substance from seaweed, is made sterile, combined with a sterile nutrient, and used as a transplanting "garden," in which material infected with the organism is placed. The growth pattern of the organism in the culture medium enables the pathologist to determine the identity of the organism or at least to assign it to a group whose general habits are known in relation to plant growth.

It is not unusual to find insects among plants quite unrelated to the plants with which they arrive. Orchids from South American jungles are taken from the tops of trees and transported to the United States for growing in greenhouses. Some of them may be many years old. Among the roots accompanying the plants one finds an accumulation of trash and bits of tree bark in which many species of insects are likely to be found. Forest litter also contains many hibernating insects. As many as 40 species have been intercepted in such material that accompanied one case of plants.

Insects at the windows of the Hoboken inspection house, killed by the spray that is applied periodically, show that pests repeatedly enter with plants they are not known to attack. Insects are also collected that were known to have come with certain shipments although inspection of the shipments failed to show their presence. For example, serious pests of cabbage and related plants, a pest of strawberries, and other insects have been collected at the windows when they were not found in shipments with which they must have arrived. A pest of cabbage was found on the stem of a vine related to grape. Even insect vectors of human diseases have been intercepted in orchid plants from the South American jungles. We must therefore regard every insect that attacks plant life as a potential plant pest. We also must regard all plant material as potential carriers of such pests.

NEGATIVE INSPECTION FINDINGS are no guarantee that the material is free of pests; treatment also is needed.

The small size of some insects, the smaller size of their eggs, the fact that insects may be under leaf sheaths or buds or be imbedded in plant tissues are some of the reasons why we cannot depend entirely on inspection. While foreign certification as to freedom of plant material from plant pests is a requirement, the purpose of the requirement is to see that obviously infested material is not sent, thereby at least eliminating a known pest risk.

Treatment is required as a condition of entry for practically all plant material, most of which is fumigated with methyl bromide as a condition of release. To do that, the inspection house has six fumigation tanks. The dosages vary with the temperature, the pests, the material, and the fumigation process—under atmospheric pressure or vacuum. Material packed in peat moss requires fumigation under vacuum so the gas can penetrate to the plant material. All dosages have been determined by research to kill effectively the various types of pests and yet be within the range of tolerances the plants will stand.

Plants that will not stand fumigation are treated by some other method. Hot water, at 110° to 120° F. for various periods, is an alternative method. The inspection house has a room equipped for various types of heat treatment. There are tanks for hot-water treatments, an electric oven for dry-heat treatments, and chambers for vapor-heat treatments. The latter may also be used as driers by circulating heated dry air instead of vapor. Occasionally material other than living plant material is given a dry-heat treatment in an electric oven.

Liquid insecticides, in the form of dips or sprays, may also be used. Seeds of certain kinds, especially of corn and related plants, may be treated with a special device for coating them with a mercurial dust as a protection against the invasion of germinating disease spores that might be present.

Packing material arriving with diseased or contaminated plants is destroyed, fumigated, or sterilized under steam pressure. There are two autoclaves in the heat-treatment room for steam sterilization. Some of the vacuum fumigation tanks also are so arranged that steam may be injected for giving steam-sterilization treatment under pressure. The tanks are occasionally used to sterilize soil imported for religious or sentimental purposes.

COMPLAINTS OF FUMIGATION INJURY, usually unfounded, occasionally come in. When a permit holder receives an importation of plant material in poor condition, he is inclined to lay the blame on fumigation, not knowing what else to attribute it to. In years past, when fumigation was resorted to only when plants were actually found infested, we got complaints of such injury even when the material had not been fumigated.

Plant material shipped by air has repeatedly reached the inspection house, even in summer, with severe injury caused apparently by low temperatures. Presumably the plane flew at high altitudes and the material was stowed without adequate protection.

To get the best results from imported material the importer should:

(1) Be sure to get a permit in advance of importation by applying to the Import and Permit Section, Bureau of Entomology and Plant Quarantine, 209 River Street, Hoboken, N. J.

(2) Send complete instructions to the shipper as to certification, freedom from soil, and other requirements. (Information on these matters will be given when the permit is applied for.)

(3) Ask the Import and Permit Section for suggestions as to methods of packing perishable plant material if the shipper is not familiar with them.

(4) Make arrangements in advance for using the proper medium of transportation. That will vary with the perishable nature of the material, and if the material is not to be brought in by mail, advance arrangements should be made for a customs broker to attend to getting it promptly to the inspection house, to getting plant quarantine and customs clearance, and to forwarding the material to the destination. Many heavy losses of material have resulted because of failure to provide for customs clearance.

George G. Becker, *a graduate of the University of Maryland and Cornell University, is in charge of the import and permit section of the division of plant quarantines, bureau of Entomology and Plant Quarantine. Before he joined the Department in 1926, he was professor of entomology in the University of Arkansas, state entomologist of Arkansas, and chief inspector of the Plant Board of Arkansas.*

Our Domestic Quarantines

Herbert J. Conkle

An important function delegated by the Congress to the Secretary of Agriculture is the responsibility for preventing or retarding the spread of insects and plant diseases that are new to the United States or that have not become widely distributed here.

In 1905 the Congress passed the Insect Pest Act ,which provided authority to regulate the entry and interstate movement of injurious insects. It came none too soon—the foreign insects already here had had years in which to establish themselves so thoroughly that one group of them eats up nearly one-tenth of our grain crop and all of them cause losses of millions of dollars every year. About 90 percent of the introduced pests had come in with shipments of plants and seeds and most of the others with plant products—the most effective methods of inspection will not always reveal all injurious insects or plant diseases they may carry. There was need for regulating the importation and interstate movement of pest carriers, and recognition of that need resulted in the passage by the Congress in 1912 of the Plant Quarantine Act. The Act authorized the Secretary of Agriculture to promulgate and enforce quarantines and regulations needed to regulate the entry and interstate movement of known carriers of insect pests and plant diseases.

Soon a domestic plant quarantine was established to prevent further spread from New England of the gypsy moth and the brown-tail moth, destructive defoliators of trees, which had spread in New England and caused fears that the expanding commerce in materials that carried them would spread infestations unless quarantine action was taken promptly. Quarantine and control efforts by Federal and State Governments and local organizations greatly reduced the numbers of the moths in most infested areas and helped to keep them from becoming distributed over large areas of the United States.

At about the same time a quarantine was promulgated to prevent the further spread of two imported date palm scale insects from infested areas in Arizona, California, and Texas. One of these, the red date scale, was removed from consideration in 1932 as it was found to be commercially unimportant. The quarantine and control measures were so effective that the other one, the parlatoria date scale, was apparently eradicated and the quarantine was revoked in 1936.

Several other major agricultural insect pests of foreign origin later became established here. The existence of enabling legislation, however, permitted prompt and decisive action through quarantines to attempt to prevent their further spread while control and eradication measures were carried out.

Some of the insects spread rapidly despite quarantine and control efforts and eventually reached a status of distribution that made continuance of the Federal quarantines impracticable. For that and other reasons the Federal quarantines on account of the European corn borer, the satin moth, the Asiatic garden beetle, the oriental beetle, the thurberia weevil, and narcissus bulb pests were eventually revoked.

A quarantine on account of the Mediterranean fruit fly was put into effect in April 1929, soon after it was discovered in Florida. Quarantine action prevented its spread to other States. Control work was so effective that it was eradicated. The quarantine was revoked in November 1930.

Federal domestic plant quarantines were in effect in 1952 to assist in preventing further spread of six introduced insects, the gypsy and browntail moths, Japanese beetle, pink bollworm, Mexican fruit fly, and white-fringed beetles. Some spread of these insects has occurred beyond the areas of introduction, but their more extensive dissemination has been prevented through the quarantine and control measures.

Domestic plant quarantines are also in effect to prevent or retard further spread of two seriously destructive introduced plant diseases, the black stem rust of grains and the white-pine blister rust.

WHEN PLANT PESTS new to this country are found here, the Department of Agriculture determines the extent of infestation and the potential hazard to the agricultural and related interests of the Nation. When it seems apparent that a newly introduced pest would become a hazard to agriculture if it should spread, and that quarantine measures could be expected to prevent or retard the spread, the Secretary of Agriculture calls a public hearing. Interested persons present their views and arguments for or against quarantine action. If it is determined from evidence presented at the hearing that quarantine action is necessary in the public interest, the Secretary promulgates a quarantine. In general, such a quarantine regulates the interstate movement of articles that might serve to spread the pest. Intensive measures to attempt eradication or control of the infestation usually are put into effect immediately. They may include application of insecticides, eradication of host plants, or cultural practices known to be effective in reducing infestations. Such measures usually reduce the hazard of spread materially even though they may not eradicate the pest.

QUARANTINE REGULATIONS normally include four items: A description of areas from which the interstate movement of carriers of the pest will be regulated; a list of the articles the movement of which will be prohibited or regulated, including the live insect in any of its stages and things upon or in which the pest may be carried normally; the conditions under which regulated articles may be moved; and the provisions under which certificates or permits may be issued for movement of regulated articles.

The regulated area is primarily determined by the extent of infestation. Entire States in which infestations occur are placed under quarantine, but the regulated area is usually restricted to the infested area and a surrounding safety border. If the infestation is general throughout the State, the entire State may be included within the regulated area. Annual surveys are usually made to determine the limits of the infested areas or to discover incipient infestations that may occur at a distance from the known infested areas through natural spread of the pests or because of accidental artificial spread. Quarantine regulations are amended or revised as often as necessary to include additional areas in which the pests may be found.

It is possible sometimes to reduce the regulated areas when infestations apparently have been eradicated from an area and intensive inspection over a period of several years discloses no further infestation.

The regulated areas are kept as small as possible consistent with conditions that will permit effective prevention of spread of the pests and reasonable quarantine enforcement procedures. One requirement is regulation by the State concerned of the intrastate movement of regulated articles to prevent further spread within the State. Federal quarantine action with regard to infestations in some States or parts thereof sometimes is withheld because of the effectiveness of State quarantine and control measures in preventing spread.

Most Federal quarantines prohibit the interstate movement, except for scientific purposes, of any stage of the live insect subject to quarantine. Such action, authorized by the Insect Pest Act of 1905, is taken primarily to bring the restrictions of that Act pertaining to the specific insect involved to the attention of shippers within the regulated area who may become familiar with the quarantines applicable to them but who are not so generally aware of the Insect Pest Act.

The movement of articles is regulated when they are known to be general carriers of the pest in any of its live stages. It would be impracticable to regulate movement of every article that might be a carrier of such pests, because under some conditions almost anything could serve as a carrier. The list of regulated articles is therefore restricted to include only the ones that ordinarily may be considered hazardous in spreading the pests. Because other articles might be carriers at times, the newer quarantines usually include an additional feature to permit regulatory action by quarantine enforcement officers in regard to any other articles, products, or things, the movement of which may involve a hazard.

WHEN QUARANTINES involve insects that feed on a wide variety of plants or that are soil inhabiting, the movement of a wide variety of items may be regulated. Quarantines involving insects that are restrictive in their feeding or life-cycle habits and plant diseases that are restricted in their host relationships may regulate the movement of specific plants, fruits, or products. The gypsy moth and brown-tail moth quarantine regulates movement of woody nursery stock and forest products because the insects are pests primarily of forest and shade trees. Stone and quarry products also are regulated because the gypsy moth frequently lays its eggs on such materials. The Japanese beetle and the white-fringed beetle are soil inhabiting in their larval stages and in the adult stages feed on a wide variety of plants. With both insects it is necessary therefore to regulate movement of soil and related materials as well as plants and other things upon which the adults may be carried, and, in regard to the white-fringed beetle, several articles on which it may deposit eggs.

The pink bollworm harms cotton and okra. Therefore the quarantine on it regulates the movement of cotton plants or parts thereof and unmanufactured cotton products and things or machinery associated with the handling or processing of cotton. The pink bollworm quarantine also regulates the movement of okra.

As the Mexican fruit fly is a pest primarily of certain citrus and other fruits, the quarantine regulates the movement of the citrus fruits in which its larvae normally live and prohibits the movement from the infested area of other host fruits.

Sometimes articles that may carry plant pests cannot be freed from infestation satisfactorily by known methods of treatment, or freedom from infestation cannot be determined satisfactorily by inspection. Quarantines therefore have to prohibit movement of such materials from infested or regulated areas. Such prohibitions often impose serious hardships on shippers, but research organizations constantly are seeking ways to treat such materials effectively; when they are found and have proved satisfactory, they are put into use immediately. Prohibitions on movement can then be relaxed to permit movement after specified treatment.

The conditions under which regulated articles may move depend on the degree of hazard of pest spread represented. In general, no regulated articles may be moved from the regulated areas unless they are free from infestation.

Certificates authorizing the movement of such articles may be issued when they are known to have originated in a pest-free part of the regulated area; when they have been treated by approved methods known to be effective in killing any stage of the pest that may be present; when they have been processed or grown under conditions that preclude infestation; or when the shipment is made during a season of the year when no infestation would be present.

Examples of seasonal restrictions are those applied under the quarantines on account of the Japanese beetle and Mexican fruit fly. Under the Japanese beetle quarantine, certification of fruits and vegetables is required only during the summer or the period of heavy flight of the beetles.

The Mexican fruit fly quarantine provides for waiving certification during periods when no hazard of spread of the insect exists.

Certificates or permits are often issued to permit movement on the basis of annual or more frequent inspections, which determine apparent freedom from infestation of establishments growing nursery stock or shipping other regulated articles, or upon adherence by such establishments to specified practices that prevent the materials they wish to ship from becoming infested.

When inspectors cannot determine pest freedom in any other way, they must actually inspect the materials offered for shipment. It is usually a laborious and costly procedure, and other methods for assuring freedom from pests are used whenever possible. An example is the use of DDT in the soil used for growing nursery stock and other plants. DDT, worked into the soil at the rate of 25 to 50 pounds per acre, eliminates hazard of spread of white-fringed beetles and Japanese beetles in shipments of plants grown therein. Large amounts of nursery stock grown under specified conditions as to soil treatment with DDT thus may be certified for movement from regulated areas without further treatment as long as the DDT in the soil remains effective in killing the insects.

Sometimes it is necessary to move regulated products that may be infested to points within or outside the regulated areas for processing or other handling that will free them from infestation. When that is necessary, the movement may be allowed under a limited permit, which accompanies the shipment and is receipted for by an inspector at the point of destination.

Materials so moved are handled under specified conditions in transit to prevent any loss of the load en route that might spread infestation. At the processing plant necessary precautions are taken to keep the materials apart from those that originated in nonregulated areas and to handle them under conditions of sanitation that will prevent escape of infestation or contamination of other materials. Examples of regulated materials so handled are peanuts, stumpwood, and cottonseed in the white-fringed beetle regulated area and cotton products in the pink bollworm regulated area.

WHEN QUARANTINES are promulgated, amended, or revised, common carriers that operate within the regulated areas and postmasters at towns within such areas are notified of the quarantine and supplemental regulations. Information concerning them is also given as wide circulation as possible within the areas through newspapers. Known or potential commercial shippers of regulated materials are interviewed by Federal inspectors who explain the regulations to them and outline the conditions under which they may move their products. Most shippers and transportation agents thus become aware of the regulations and are willing to cooperate in preventing spread of insects or other plant pests. Occasionally through laxity, forgetfulness, or misunderstanding, shipments of regulated materials, which have not been certified as free of infestation, are accepted for transportation to distant points. It is seldom necessary, however, to institute legal proceedings against shippers or transportation agencies except in cases of flagrant violation of the quarantines.

There are always some individuals within regulated areas who are unaware of the regulations and of the hazard involved in making shipments of potential pest-carrying materials to other parts of the country. To ascertain compliance with quarantine measures, the Department of Agriculture maintains a transit-inspection service; inspectors are stationed at strategic transportation centers to inspect shipments that pass through such centers in moving from regulated to nonregulated areas. State quarantine enforcement officers assist in the work by reporting violations of Federal domestic plant quarantines that they find during their inspections of shipments to determine compliance with State plant quarantine regulations or that have been sent to them by the Post Office Department for inspection under provisions of the Terminal Inspection Act of 1915, as amended.

We believe that the few million dollars spent annually to suppress or prevent the introduction or spread of additional destructive plant pests are insurance for the future protection of the country's food supply and natural resources.

Public awareness of the importance to general welfare of quarantines and coordinated control and suppression programs has increased immeasurably since the first plant quarantines were put into effect.

HERBERT J. CONKLE *is a graduate of Ohio State University. In 1930 he began work with the Plant Quarantine and Control Administration of the Department of Agriculture in connection with enforcement of the Mediterranean fruit fly quarantine and since that time has had wide experience in transit inspection and other plant quarantine activities. In 1951 he became a member of the Washington headquarters staff of the division of plant quarantines.*

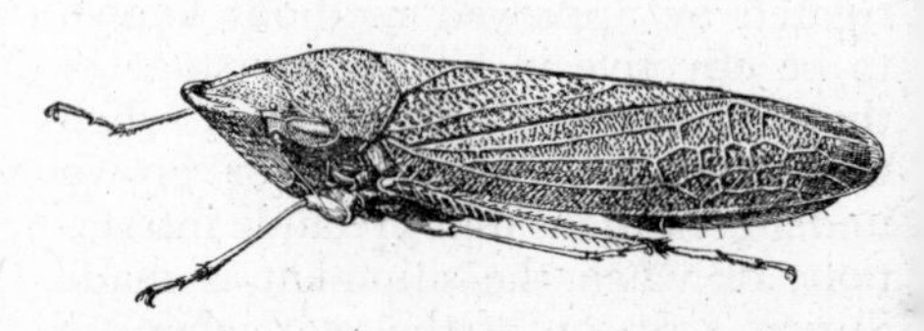

Draeculacephala minerva, a leafhopper.

Inspection in Transit

E. A. Burns

Transit inspection is the inspection of shipments of plants, plant products, and other quarantined articles moving in interstate commerce by mail, express, and freight to determine their compliance with the Federal domestic plant quarantines.

Enforcement of quarantines depends upon two types of knowledge—knowledge as to the articles with which the insects or plant diseases are likely to be associated and with which they might be carried, and, secondly, the means of transportation that may be employed in moving the articles from one area to another. Transit inspection is concerned with both.

Transit inspection was inaugurated at a few strategic midwestern railway terminals in 1920 to enforce the white-pine blister rust quarantine. Its importance in enforcing quarantines and preventing the artificial spread of insects and plant diseases was soon recognized, and the work was established by the Congress as an independent project on July 1, 1930.

The activity since has been expanded to include the enforcement of all Federal domestic plant quarantines that regulate the movement of dangerous host material within or from the continental United States.

Authority to conduct inspection is contained in the Plant Quarantine Act of 1912. Under Section 10, Paragraph 2, of that Act, transit inspectors have authority to stop and, without warrant, to search and examine any person, vehicle, receptacle, or vessel moving between States that they believe or have cause to believe possesses or contains nursery stock, plants, plant products, or other articles whose movement is prohibited or restricted by the Plant Quarantine Act or any quarantine or order promulgated thereunder. The inspectors also can seize, destroy, or otherwise dispose of material found moving contrary to regulations.

Domestic quarantines in force in 1952 relating to insects were those on account of the gypsy and brown-tail moths, Japanese beetle, pink bollworm, Mexican fruit fly, and white-fringed beetle.

Although they prohibit the movement of several commodities, these quarantines are predominantly restrictive, permitting movement from the regulated areas of restricted articles after certification based on visual inspection, treatment, or the meeting of specified conditions.

Inspectors also enforce the regulations governing the movement of plants and plant products into and out of the District of Columbia and the Insect Pest Act of 1905 as it pertains to interstate shipments. This latter Act prohibits, except under special conditions, the importation and interstate movement of living stages of insects notoriously injurious to cultivated crops.

The Postal Laws and Regulations recognize the hazards involved in the movement of insects and dangerous host material by restricting the movement of both. Nursery stock and other plant material may not be admitted to the mails unless accompanied by a certificate of inspection. The use of the mails is prohibited for the shipment of living stages of all insects except mealworms, hellgrammites, honey bees, and the true silkworm. Thus the Postal Laws and Regulations supplement the Plant Quarantine Act and the Insect Pest Act in an important way. Common carriers have likewise included plant quarantines, nursery stock inspection requirements, and related laws in their tariffs.

State quarantines and regulatory orders are important in preventing the spread of injurious pests through the country, and the Government cooperates in their enforcement. In line with

970134°—52——25

this policy, transit inspectors report to the proper State officials shipments seen moving contrary to State regulations. State quarantines cover a wide range of plant pests that are not the subject of Federal regulations. Transit inspectors give special attention to the so-called standardized State quarantines concerning insects or diseases in the control of which the Department participates. The one relating to the sweetpotato weevil is an example.

Transit inspectors in the States that have adopted the Terminal Inspection Act usually cooperate in the enforcement of that Act. Terminal inspection under the Terminal Inspection Act and transit inspection are two distinctly different activities. The Terminal Inspection Act is a Federal statute that provides the States with a means of inspecting mail shipments of plants and plant products destined to their particular State, and the work conducted thereunder is supported entirely by State funds. Transit inspection is conducted under the Plant Quarantine Act and is supported chiefly by Federal appropriations.

Quarantines cannot accomplish their full purpose—preventing the spread of dangerous pests into new localities—unless infested articles are prevented from being transported into those localities. Transit inspection has a significant part in controlling the movement of restricted articles and in stopping the movement of prohibited and dangerous material. All shipments, irrespective of their nature, are moved throughout this country by railroads, motor vehicles, airplanes, or merchant vessels or by a combination of these methods. Regardless of the means employed, well-established routing schemes are used, and the shipments moved for distances of 150 miles or more pass through strategically located transfer terminals or distribution centers. Potential pest-carrying shipments from any quarantined area are thus concentrated at these key points.

At such transportation gateways transit inspection work is conducted. By carefully timed and coordinated tours of inspection, a limited number of inspectors can examine a large volume of shipments from the quarantined areas. Control units, with suppression, control, or even eradication as their aim, are in operation within each quarantined area, with regulatory work as an important and necessary phase of their program. Stopping pests completely at their source is unattainable, for complete control from within can be had only with an army of inspectors and at a prohibitive cost. It is impossible to reach all shippers and carriers within a quarantined area or to overcome the indifference of some to regulations. The work of such control units must be supplemented by an activity that can keep the units informed of how well or how poorly the shippers are adhering to the safeguards required. Transit inspection serves that purpose.

Since its inception transit inspection has been carried on at some 40 major gateways through which parcel post, express, and freight are routed. Adjustments in operations have been made as a result of quarantine changes and the resulting effects upon the importance of a station. In 1952 work was conducted on a permanent basis at the quarantine-important stations of Atlanta, Boston, Buffalo, Chicago, Dallas, Detroit, Houston, Jacksonville, Memphis, New York, Omaha, Pittsburgh, St. Louis, St. Paul, Washington, D. C., and several points in California. Seasonal stations of importance included Albany, Columbus, Denver, Fort Worth, Indianapolis, Kansas City, New Orleans, and Springfield, Mass.

The nature of the work varies with the season of the year. Attention is focused in spring and fall on the movement of nursery stock; in summer, on fruit and vegetable consignments; in December, on the transportation of Christmas trees, greens, and other decorative material; and during the rest of the winter, on the movement of citrus and other crops from the South.

Actual inspections are made according to prearranged schedules at parcel-post terminals; at local post offices; at express terminals; in mail and express sorting rooms at railroad stations; in baggage, express, and mail-storage cars while standing in the stations or at loading platforms; at freight break-bulk points and classification yards; at motor freight terminals; at piers; at produce terminals; at flower markets; and at air terminals. Efforts are concentrated on the examination of material from the various quarantined areas and on the movement that is not or cannot be seen at other inspection stations. Tours of duty are scheduled so as to obtain the most effective coverage regardless of the day or hour, since parcel post and express are worked and transported every hour of the day and every day of the week. Inspections are timed so that eligible shipments are dispatched without delay. Waybill examinations are made of both carlot and less-than-carlot freight to supplement the examinations of the shipments themselves. Road patrol stations are not normally a function of transit inspection. Such activity is usually conducted by the control units on important highways leading out of a quarantined area.

Inspection involves not only the examination of shipments that are set aside for transit inspectors by cooperating carriers, but also the actual searching for parcels that contain or are suspected of containing restricted or prohibited material. Packages are not examined at random but are carefully selected. In screening shipments for an illegal one, the inspector is guided by a sort of sixth sense—a knack of detecting material of a contraband nature. From the size, shape, weight, markings, odor, degree of dampness, and the handling and shaking of parcels, the inspector can determine his interest in the shipment. Not all parcels selected are actually opened, for after checking the origin and destination, considering the infractions likely to be involved, and judging the contents, the inspector may determine that there is no need for further examination. An experienced inspector's appraisal of the contents of unopened parcels is almost unbelievably accurate.

I could give many examples. A package consigned to a tool company had the appearance and weight of metal but lacked a metallic sound when shaken; it was opened and found to contain strawberry plants in soil. A crate labeled and waybilled as "wire frames" aroused suspicion, and examination disclosed the contents to be restricted plant material. Subsequent investigation disclosed this misrepresentation to be a deliberate attempt to evade the regulations. A carton marked "Hats—Don't Crush" attracted the watchful eye of an inspector and was found to contain only uncertified holly branches. A securely wrapped and neatly disguised box of cuttings, shipped without the name or address of the sender, had a note inside that the parcel had once been refused by the carrier because of the "bug ban"—an instance of attempted smuggling. Six wooden boxes well covered with labels reading "orchids," an item exempt from certification, were thoroughly examined because of their weight and found to include restricted plants in soil. Evergreen cuttings, detected by their odor, were discovered in a completely closed crate of furniture. Uncertified evergreen boughs from the gypsy moth area have been found on several occasions in cartons labeled "laundry" and "clothing." Live plants labeled and declared as "cut flowers" have been intercepted many times.

Since 1935 transit inspectors have examined an average of 1,400,000 shipments a year for quarantine compliance. Out of these, an annual average of 2,260 have been found moving interstate in violation of Federal domestic plant quarantines. Year after year, the infractions have been destined to nearly all 48 States and the District of Columbia, with others consigned to Alaska, Canada, Cuba,

Hawaii, Mexico, Panama, the Canal Zone, and Puerto Rico.

Besides these interstate Federal violations, transit inspectors over the same period have reported to the enforcing organizations an annual average of more than 900 infractions of State requirements and District of Columbia regulations. Many of them were reported also to the Post Office Department as violations of the postal laws. Several others involved intrastate shipments relating to pests covered by Federal quarantines. Violations of the Insect Pest Act have not been numerous, but as many as 50 were reported in a year. A few infractions of foreign plant quarantines have also been uncovered.

Determining the presence or absence of insects or diseases in material found moving contrary to regulations is not the primary purpose of transit inspection. Since 1941, however, close examinations have been made of many uncertified shipments likely to harbor dangerous insects and diseases so that the work could be better evaluated. The results emphasize the importance of the work.

We have found the Japanese beetle in transit most frequently and in the greatest numbers. Hundreds of live adult Japanese beetles have been taken at Chicago, Cincinnati, and St. Louis from refrigerator carloads of fruits and vegetables originating in eastern Maryland and Virginia. As many as 61 were recovered from one car. Other adult Japanese beetles have been found in shipments of cut flowers destined to various points outside the quarantined area. Live larvae of the insect have had their journeys to agricultural areas throughout the country suddenly halted by transit inspectors. Such larvae have been found on strawberry plants expressed by a commercial grower to a rural area in Minnesota; in the soil ball of an azalea plant sent by an individual to a friend in southern Illinois; in the soil adhering to the roots of nut trees sent by freight from a nursery to a point in Ohio; on bedding plants mailed by a private person to a Montana destination; on chrysanthemum plants traveling as baggage to Florida; in grass sod sent by an individual to a Colorado address; and on a noncommercial shipment of iris rhizomes to California.

Egg masses of the gypsy moth were removed from a private shipment of decorative greens mailed to a Long Island address—one of the egg masses was found securely attached to plant material not normally restricted by the quarantine. Checking the New York City flower markets at Christmas time for uncertified truckloads of trees and boughs from the gypsy moth area, inspectors found egg masses on trees in two loads after examinations of only a few bundles in each load. Birch fireplace logs chemically treated so as to burn with colored flames were intercepted and found infested with viable egg masses.

The problem of migratory labor as an instrument in disseminating insects and diseases of economic importance is illustrated and emphasized by finding larvae of the pink bollworm in cotton-picking sacks shipped by an itinerant picker to a major uninfested cotton-producing area in Texas.

Turning now to the finding in transit of destructive insects against which there are no Federal regulations, we see that a wide variety of pests have been stopped. The sweetpotato weevil has been taken on several occasions from sweetpotato tubers destined to noninfested commercial producing areas in Texas. Okra pods infested with the cotton square borer were intercepted in a parcel-post shipment from Mississippi. The boll weevil was found on cotton plants from Georgia. Material infested with the Asiatic garden beetle has been uncovered several times, once in a disguised noncommercial parcel consigned to Georgia, where that insect had not been recorded. Corn on the cob infested with larvae of the European corn borer and the corn earworm has been intercepted frequently. Private shipments of plant material infested with the strawberry root weevil destined from New York to points in Georgia, Minnesota, and Oregon have been halted. Iris rhizomes heavily infested with the iris borer have been found en route to points in California, Florida, and North Carolina.

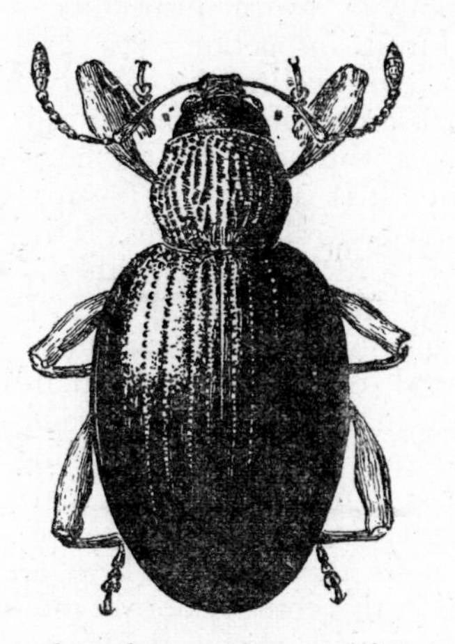

Strawberry root weevil.

A beetle of the genus *Carpophilus,* not previously recorded on oranges but known to attack corn and pineapples, was recovered from an orange in a noncommercial mail shipment.

Other interceptions included the almond moth, azalea leaf miner, azalea whitefly, boxwood leaf miner, chinch bug, citrus whitefly, codling moth, coffee bean weevil, Colorado potato beetle, eastern tent caterpillar, European pine shoot moth, hemispherical scale, holly leaf miner, imported cabbageworm, juniper scale, lesser bulb fly, Mexican bean beetle, mulberry whitefly, naval orangeworm, oak skeletonizer, oleander scale, oystershell scale, pine needle scale, plum web-spinning sawfly, pyriform scale, and San Jose scale. Even subterranean termites were found in a shipment of nursery stock. Violations of the Insect Pest Act included live larvae of the European corn borer shipped to a pet shop in Missouri and species of live grasshoppers, crickets, and ants consigned to various destinations.

Most of those insects were recovered from shipments that were moving contrary to one or more Federal quarantine orders. Others were found in consignments violating State regulations. A few were taken from shipments that involved no restrictions but were examined because of the possibility of an infraction. The size of uncertified and potentially dangerous shipments has ranged from a small parcel-post package to full freight carlots. Many of the shipments were destined to the most remote parts of the country. Many, infested with destructive insects, were en route to agricultural regions where the insects would have found conditions suitable for their establishment.

What disposition is made of shipments found moving in violation of Federal domestic plant quarantines? They are inspected in transit when practicable. If they are free from pests, they are certified and allowed to proceed. They are returned to the shipper when pest risk is involved. In serious cases, they are confiscated and destroyed.

The first procedure in no way weakens the enforcement structure, for in each instance the shipper and carrier, as in all other cases, are notified of the violation committed. Additional infractions from the same shipper are handled differently. If the restricted material is of such nature that a thorough examination cannot be made to establish its freedom from insects or diseases, the shipment is usually returned to the point of origin. Prohibited material in most instances is returned to the sender. When articles are found infested or infected with insects or diseases of importance, more drastic action is taken—treatment to render the articles innocuous, a closely supervised return to infested territory, or confiscation.

As a rule, prosecutions are limited to willful violations or to cases of gross negligence. A better policy is to inform the shippers and carriers about the regulations and the need for them.

In the absence of statutory authority,

transit inspectors do not return the shipments that are reported as violations of State regulations. When inspectors have been deputized to act for a State, other action may be taken.

The effectiveness of transit inspection depends largely on the cooperation received from postal clerks and employees of common carriers. Upon request, those workers set aside or direct to the inspector's attention the shipments that may be affected by quarantine regulations. Many of the violations reported by transit inspectors have actually been stopped by the able force of cooperating postal, express, and freight employees. Transit inspection is law enforcement, and enlisting the aid of such employees increases our surveillance a hundredfold. It is the inspector's job to keep the transportation employees aware of quarantine regulations and the type of material desired for examination.

Several States in which transfer points are located participate in transit inspection work by assigning State inspectors to the activity. They are appointed Federal collaborators, and at some stations the work is conducted entirely by them.

Each infraction of a Federal regulation is investigated in order to apprise the shipper and carrier of the quarantine requirements and of the hazards involved. Consequently commercial shippers take greater precautions in order to avoid the interception and return of future shipments. Postal clerks and carriers' agents become more cautious in accepting shipments, usually making thorough inquiry as to the contents of packages. Thus are forestalled untold numbers of potentially dangerous shipments which never appear on the record.

Considerably fewer violations of the older quarantines are now being intercepted—evidence, to me, of the effectiveness of the work. When new areas are quarantined and new articles restricted, interceptions are numerous, but a gradual decrease follows. Transit inspection has made many shippers and transportation employees aware of quarantine regulations and the hazards of pest distribution. Many potential infestations and the consequent probable spread of such insects and diseases have been prevented through timely interceptions by transit inspectors.

Transit inspection is a protective service, protecting the country against the dissemination of insects and plant diseases through the ordinary trade channels. It is a necessary supplement to pest-control programs. It is necessary in order to cope with the uninformed and the unscrupulous. It is the best means of assuring compliance with Federal domestic plant quarantines where mail, express, and freight shipments are concerned. Stopping shipments of uncertified host material is tantamount in many cases to stopping the pests themselves. There are vast areas in this country not yet infested or infected with destructive insects and diseases which have only a limited foothold, and such areas are entitled to the best possible protection we can give them. Transit inspection at gateways which control most of the traffic from infested areas or the movement to pest-free zones is an economical and effective way of protecting the billions of dollars already invested in pest control.

E. A. BURNS *is principal assistant at the Hoboken, N. J., inspection house, Bureau of Entomology and Plant Quarantine. He was formerly in charge of transit inspection in the Northern States Region. He was graduated from Tufts College in 1933 and joined the Bureau of Entomology and Plant Quarantine in 1935. After several details on control projects, he was assigned to the transit inspection unit and has performed transit inspection at many of the country's major transportation gateways.*

Readers may be interested in a summary of the Federal plant regulatory legislation, which appears in the appendix to this volume.

Inspection at Terminals

A. P. Messenger

Since 1881 the States have sought to protect themselves by legislation against the introduction of pest-infested plants and plant products that are shipped from one locality or State to another. Although the Federal Plant Quarantine Act recognized the authority of any State to place quarantines against products of other States that might be a means of introducing injurious agricultural pests, State laws did not apply to shipments of such articles by mail until the Postal Terminal Inspection Act was passed in 1915.

Before the parcel-post system was established in 1913, the weight limitations on fourth-class mail matter, including plants and seeds, was 4 pounds. That limit prevented the extensive use of the mails for shipping such articles. The original limit of 11 pounds for parcel post was increased to 20 pounds, then to 50 pounds, and finally to 70 pounds. The changes and the increase of the limit of size from 72 to 84 inches, then to 100 inches for length and girth combined, made parcel post available and more desirable for transporting nursery stock and plant products.

Long before the adoption of the Plant Quarantine Act, the Post Office Department adopted a regulation under which nursery stock is acceptable for mailing only when accompanied by a certificate from the State or Government inspector showing that the nursery or premises from which such matter is shipped has been inspected within a year and found free from injurious insects and plant diseases. The regulation has been a factor in retarding the spread of many serious pests established in nurseries.

With the increasing use of parcel-post facilities for transporting plants and plant products, officials of many States felt that the restrictions on nursery stock were inadequate, and through their efforts the Terminal Inspection Act was drafted and passed by the Congress on March 4, 1915. It requires that all such matter be held for inspection by the State officials before delivery to the consignee.

Any State that wants to take advantage of the provisions of the Terminal Inspection Act must establish and maintain a terminal inspection service of plants and plant products at its own expense at one or more places. The responsible State officials must submit to the Secretary of Agriculture a list of plants and plant products and the plant pests transmitted thereby that they believe should be subject to terminal inspection. Upon approval of the list, the Secretary of Agriculture transmits it to the Postmaster General. Thereafter, upon payment of postage therefor, all packages containing such plants or products are forwarded by the postmaster at the destination of the package to the proper State officer for inspection. The State inspector returns the plants or plant products to the place of inspection to be forwarded to the consignee if he finds that they do not violate a plant quarantine law and if they are free from injurious pests. He disinfests them if they are infested. If infested plants cannot be disinfested satisfactorily, the State official notifies the postmaster at the place of inspection, who in turn notifies the sender that they will be returned to him upon his request and at his expense or, in default of such request, the packages will be turned over to the State authority for destruction. The Act also requires that all such packages be plainly marked so their contents may be ascertained by an inspection of the outside. Whoever fails to mark such packages may be punished by a fine of not more than 100 dollars.

The handling of parcels subject to

the Act was later simplified with a saving of postage to the sender whereby shipments can be addressed in care of the State inspector at a designated terminal inspection point, from which they may be forwarded to their ultimate destination, postage collect. Another modification of the Act permits the release of any uninfested material in a package; the sender is asked whether the infested material in it should be returned to him at his expense.

Another change in the Act, made effective in October of 1936, provided further cooperation by the Post Office Department in the enforcement of State plant quarantine laws and regulations. Previously, mailed parcels could be rejected under State authority only if they were found to be infested with injurious pests and could not be disinfected satisfactorily. Under the Act as amended, delivery of the parcels is to be withheld if the plants or plant products were mailed in violation of a plant quarantine law or plant quarantine regulation of the State. This, however, can be done only after the State concerned has submitted a list of plants and plant products, and plant pests transmitted thereby, together with a description of the area from which such articles are prohibited by State plant quarantine laws or plant quarantine regulations. Upon receipt of notices from the Secretary of Agriculture of the approval of such lists, the Post Office Department issues instructions to the postmaster to prevent the acceptance of such material when presented for mailing in violation of State plant quarantine laws or regulations.

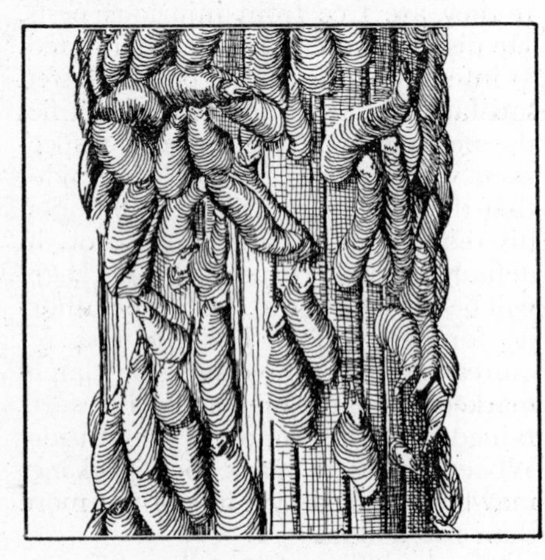

Oystershell scale.

The amendment has been of particular benefit to States in guarding against the entry of pests that are not detectable by inspection at time of entry. Also, through an official publication of the Post Office Department, every postmaster in the United States is informed of the articles prohibited by any such law or regulation and the pests transmitted thereby, and can properly advise the sender concerning such articles as are prohibited by the destination State, thus saving mailing costs and in many cases the article itself which could not be delivered.

Terminal inspection was required in 1952 in Arizona, Arkansas, California, the District of Columbia, Florida, Hawaii, Idaho, Minnesota, Mississippi, Montana, Oregon, Puerto Rico, Utah, and Washington.

Parcel post has become an important carrier of plants and many plant products. In California, one of the first States to enforce terminal inspection and a leader in efforts to obtain legislation amending the Act, the Terminal Inspection Act is now one of the most important laws in the effective enforcement of State plant quarantines.

A. P. MESSENGER *attended the University of California and spent 7 years in ranching before he joined the Department of Agriculture in 1921. He was in charge of the enforcement of plant quarantines at the ports of San Pedro and San Francisco for 24 years. He was assistant chief of the Bureau of Entomology and Plant Quarantine of the California Department of Agriculture from 1945 to 1948, when he became head of the Bureau of Plant Quarantine.*

Other Controls

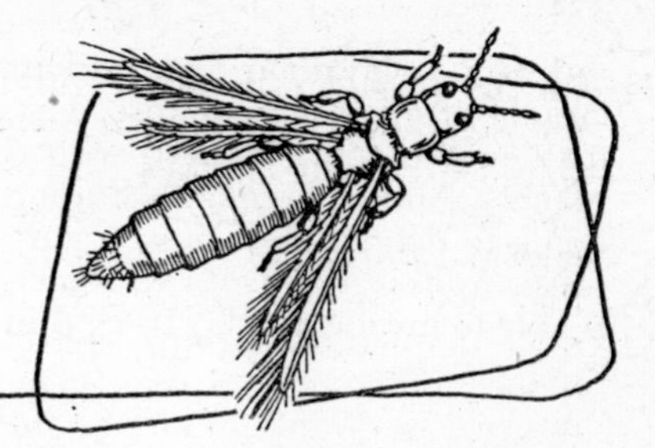

Insects, Enemies of Insects

Barnard D. Burks

A common sight in the country is the large gray paper nest built by the bald-faced hornet. Generally it hangs from the stout limb of a tree at the edge of a forest.

Within the nest the hornets live a social life much like that of the honey bee. Each nest has a single queen, the mother of the other members of the colony. The workers, the sterile females, care for the developing brood and perform other housekeeping duties in the nest or serve as foragers, ranging the countryside to gather food and materials for building and maintaining the nest.

The adult hornets ordinarily feed on the nectar of flowers, but they will take almost any available fluid foodstuffs. They take only liquids because their mouth openings are so small they cannot swallow solids. The food of the adults is mainly carbohydrate, but the growing brood back in the nest require proteins. To get that the hornets capture caterpillars.

The hornet recognizes her prey by sight. When she is out hunting caterpillars, she flies along near the ground or threads her way among leaves, intently looking for a suitable victim. When she sees one, she pounces on it.

She does not sting her victim to death but butchers it alive. She quickly dismembers the struggling caterpillar. Sometimes she carries it into the nest to cut it up, but usually she does so outside. If the caterpillar is small, the hornet suspends herself head down, hanging by one foot from a convenient twig, and proceeds to chew up the victim. If the caterpillar is large, she drops to the ground and cuts it up there.

Her treatment of the victim is cold-blooded and methodical. First she kneads it all over with her mandibles to soften the muscles and other tissues. Then she cuts it up with her teeth. As she proceeds with her carving, she swallows the liquids and forms the solid parts into pellets, which she carries back to the nest for the growing brood. If the caterpillar is too large to be disposed of at once, the hornet cuts up part of it, takes that to the nest, and then returns for the rest. When she must leave a part of her victim behind, she carefully reconnoiters the surrounding territory and notes the landmarks, for which she has a remarkable memory, so that she will be able to find again the spot where she left her prey. When she has finished slaughtering the caterpillar she discards the inedible parts.

Back in the nest, the nurse hornets take over the pellets of solid caterpillar flesh. They break them up into morsels and feed them to the brood. The inedible bits are carried out of the nest and thrown away.

THE HORNETS are not always the best of housekeepers, especially toward the end of the season, when the vigor of the colony declines. Some remnants of food may accumulate in the bottom of the nest. Various scavenger flies then move in to lay their eggs and rear a crop of maggots in the refuse. The nest may even become infested with cockroaches. And, although the hornets are quick to defend their nest, a parasitic wasp, *Sphecophaga burra,* sometimes is able to invade and lay its eggs in the bodies of some of the developing hornet larvae. The grubs that hatch from the eggs feed at first internally and later externally on the bodies of the immature hornets, eventually killing them. This parasite is itself sometimes parasitized and killed by a minute chalcid wasp, *Dimmockia incongrua.*

Nest of bald-faced hornet.

The bald-faced hornet is one of thousands of insects that live at the expense of other insects. Its life and activities exemplify a mechanism whereby nature keeps a species in check. We have all heard about the enormous reproductive capacity of insects—how, for example, flies would cover the entire earth to a depth of 47 feet within 5 months if all the progeny of only one pair of house flies lived to maturity and reproduced. Many insects often do become disastrously plentiful, but no species has yet even remotely approached the number of individuals it theoretically could, simply because no insect ever gets the chance to continue multiplying as fast as it can. Like most living things, insects are susceptible to bacterial and fungus diseases. Another ever-present control is their enemies.

Often their worst enemies are their own relatives.

Throughout their lives from egg to death, most insects are surrounded by others that are trying to eat them or to lay their eggs in them or on them or to seize and carry them off to become food for their own developing brood. Many insects pillage the food their more industrious relatives have accumulated. While the interlopers grow fat, the helpless young that should have had the food are killed or die of starvation.

No insects are completely safe from these depredations—no matter if they live in apparent safety inside trees, in nests of clay, beneath the surface of ponds or streams, or deep within the soil.

Consider also the horse guard, which is well known in rural districts of the South. It is a large, aggressive, loud-buzzing, black-and-yellow wasp. Farm animals, which are distressed by the relatively modest humming of the horse flies and bot flies, will stand quietly while the horse guards drone loudly all around them—they learn quickly that the wasps are catching the flies that are tormenting them. It is a mutually beneficial relationship. The animals attract the flies, so that hunting for flies is easy around them, and the wasps, in catching the flies, help rid the livestock of the pests.

The horse guard, which is equally watchful for the comfort of cattle and mules, does not catch the flies for food for herself. Like most of the adult wasps, she feeds on the nectar of flowers or the sweet honeydew that is given off by aphids and scale insects. The horse guard catches flies to feed to her young.

She rears her progeny in nests she digs in sandy, loose soil. Ordinarily she spends 2 days in excavating and finishing a nest. She tunnels into the earth for about 18 inches and at the end of the passageway she makes a small chamber where she lays one egg. When she has finished excavating the nest, she has heaped up a large pile of sand outside the entrance. This she is careful not to leave as a tell-tale marker to the portal of the nest. The horse guard carefully closes the entrance with sand and then scatters the heap of diggings, thoroughly smoothing the surface of the soil around the nest. When she has finished, there is no sign of any kind to show where the entrance to the nest lies, although she does not herself have any trouble finding it again.

The egg, deep within the nest, hatches within 2 days. Then the horse guard begins bringing in flies, one at a time, to feed the grub. She cruises over the surrounding territory, looking for flies of a suitable size. As the flies are most easily found around livestock, that is where she hunts. She catches the flies in the air, on the wing, and stings them to death. (Many other wasps that stock their nests with flies do not kill them, but only paralyze them by deftly stinging a vital nerve.)

The horse guard grasps the fly between her legs and carries it to the entrance of her nest. She scrapes aside the sand before the entrance and carries the fly in to the young larva, which begins eating the freshly killed fly at once. Then, having settled her offspring to its meal, the horse guard leaves the nest and again closes the entrance. She will return with another fly when her offspring has consumed the first one. She will continue bringing in one fly at a time to feed her larva until it is fully grown and refuses to eat more.

The growing larva eats all the soft parts of the flies, but rejects the legs, heads, and the wings. These it casts aside. But because the larva is essentially motionless, the refused parts of the flies do not get broken up. Consequently we can open one of the nests, remove the wings, and count them. Dividing the total by two gives a close reckoning of the number of flies the grub has consumed. In midsummer a grub will complete its growth in about 2 weeks. Counts of wings taken from nests of the horse guard show that the average number of flies one grub consumes during this growing period is 50. As most of the heads of the flies also are preserved intact, the flies often can be identified accurately. Nests which have been studied contained predominantly or exclusively female horse flies.

As the larva of the horse guard nears maturity, it consumes flies at a greater and greater rate. Since each horse guard rears several young simultaneously, she is kept extremely busy, catching flies to feed to her ravenous progeny.

In April and May we are almost certain to find the asparagus beetle coming out of hibernation in our asparagus beds. The pretty, checkered beetle appears almost as soon as the first asparagus spears thrust their way above ground. It begins at once to gnaw the tender buds at the tips of the spears and a few days later commences egg laying. It crawls over the spears, carefully studding them with bright orange eggs. Within 10 days the eggs should hatch and produce a horde of fat grubs, which will feed on the asparagus stems and the feathery leaves as they branch and unfold.

If we look closely, however, we will see that many of the eggs—sometimes nearly all—will not hatch. For scarcely has the asparagus beetle finished her laying when her chief enemy appears. It is a minute wasp, *Tetrastichus asparagi*, which is smaller than the asparagus beetle's egg itself. The wasp sets to work at once to destroy the eggs.

The Tetrastichus is methodical and deliberate in her work of destruction. She flies among the asparagus spears and then alights on one studded with the glistening eggs. She crawls over the spear, flicking her wings in a way characteristic of wasps, and explores the surface of the plant with her antennae. When she finds an egg of the asparagus beetle, she examines it carefully, using her antennae to test it from several angles. When she finally is satisfied

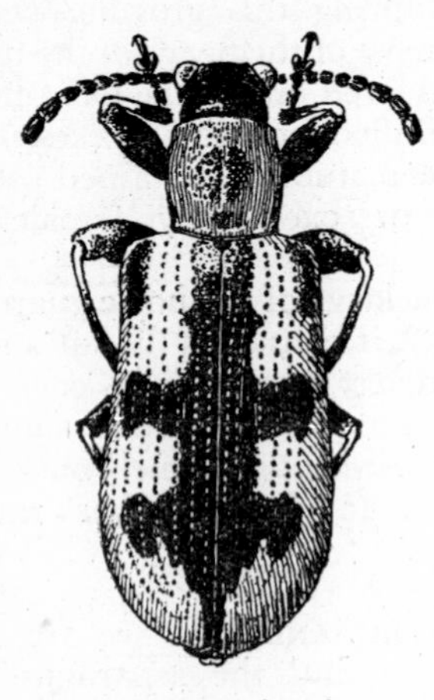

Asparagus beetle.

that the egg is just right for her uses, she climbs upon it. She unsheaths her ovipositor and plunges it into the egg. She withdraws it part way and then plunges it in again, at a slightly different angle. She continues thrusting her lance into the egg until its inner substance is thoroughly loosened. Then she climbs off the egg, applies her mouth to the hole she has broken in it, and sucks out the liquid contents until nothing remains but the shell. The Tetrastichus is smaller than the egg, but she manages to eat about five a day. As there are usually a great many of these wasps around every asparagus bed, often half to three-fourths of all the eggs laid by the asparagus beetles will be sucked clean and will never hatch.

But the Tetrastichus does not eat all the asparagus beetle eggs she encounters. Some must serve to receive her own eggs. She carefully inserts her ovipositor just beneath the surface of these eggs, taking care now not to break up the contents, and deposits one, two, or three of her eggs in each. She leaves the asparagus beetle eggs apparently intact. Only a minute wound shows where each has been punctured.

The eggs of the asparagus beetle containing the Tetrastichus eggs hatch normally and produce fat grubs in no way different, at least externally, from those that hatch from unmolested eggs. The grubs feed in the usual way and grow to maturity in 3 to 5 weeks. Then they leave the asparagus plants and drop to the ground, where they form cells in which to pupate, just as do normal beetle larvae. Once the cells have been formed, however, the larvae of the Tetrastichus, which have remained within the bodies of the beetle grubs all these weeks, begin to grow. They feed voraciously within the bodies of the grubs and reduce them to tattered, lifeless remnants in a week or so. The larvae now occupy the cells that should have contained developing asparagus beetles. They mature rapidly—only a week later they finish their pupal development and are ready to emerge as adults. The adults then come out of the soil and are ready to carry on their work of destroying asparagus beetles.

If the Tetrastichus should reach maturity within the beetle cells in the late fall, they will remain there, as fully grown larvae or pupae, through the winter. The following spring the adults will emerge only a few days after the asparagus beetles have come out of hibernation.

These destroyers of the asparagus beetle are a race of Amazons. So efficient have they become that even the uncertainties of courtship have been eliminated. Their tribe goes on generation after generation laying unfertilized eggs, which produce only females.

When the Japanese beetle became established in the United States, it multiplied rapidly because it was living here without the enemies that keep it in check in the Orient. An intensive search was made in Japan, Korea, and eastern China for native parasites of the beetles. One of the most promising was *Tiphia popilliavora,* which has been established from Connecticut to Virginia.

The adults of Tiphia are shining black wasps, each about three-fourths of an inch long. They emerge in August to mate and feed on the nectar and pollen of flowers. Then when a female is ready to begin laying her eggs, she flies to an area infested with Japanese beetle grubs and burrows under the sod to find them. When she locates a suitable one, she approaches it from the rear, grasps it firmly, and crawls over its back until her head is level with its head. The grub does a good bit of squirming, but seldom succeeds in escaping from this determined wasp. Thrusting the end of her abdomen around the side of the grub's body and between its legs, the Tiphia stings it several times on the ventral side of its thorax. As soon as she strikes the vital thoracic nerve center, the grub ceases its struggling and becomes inert.

The Tiphia kneads the entire ventral surface of the grub's abdomen with her mandibles. She then rasps the skin between the fifth and sixth abdominal segments with the end of her abdomen, to make a smooth, soft spot for the egg she will presently lay there. Finally, after about 15 minutes of this preparation, she glues an egg to the grub's abdomen. When she has finished, she gnaws a leg of the grub and laps up the body fluid that oozes from the wound. Then she goes away, leaving the grub to its fate.

The grub revives in about 30 minutes and begins again to feed on the grass roots. The Tiphia egg hatches in 5 to 8 days, depending on the temperature. The egg splits open at the end, and the young larva thrusts out its head. It immediately sinks its mandibles in the skin of the grub and sucks out the body fluids. The grub continues to live and feed, but its strength gradually ebbs as the parasite draws more and more of the fluids from its body.

As this first-stage larva grows, its increase in size splits the egg shell longitudinally, almost to the tip. When the larva is ready to molt, it does not come completely out of its old skin but leaves the posterior end of its body anchored in it. The shed skin remains fastened to the eggshell, which in turn is glued to the body wall of the grub. Thus does the Tiphia larva retain its hold on the grub.

Each time the Tiphia larva molts, the old mandibles are left imbedded in the skin of the grub, and a new feeding puncture is made with the fresh set of mandibles. The skins of the successive larval stages remain beneath the larva like a pad. During the fifth stage, the Japanese beetle grub finally succumbs. Then the larva quickly devours the grub's entire body, leaving only the head and legs. It even eats its own old, shed skins, as their usefulness has passed.

The Tiphia larva spends 2 to 4 weeks in completing its growth. Then it spins its cocoon. That takes 2 days, but at the end the Tiphia has made for itself a thick and serviceable shelter, rough on the outside and satiny smooth within. Here it slumbers through the winter, the following spring, and the early summer. It pupates in late July or early August and emerges as an adult in the middle or latter part of August.

On the warm, humid evenings of late spring, crowds of May beetles, or June beetles, come flying to outside lights. They circle erratically about the globes. Or they find a resting place nearby, settle down, and remain quietly staring into the hypnotizing glare. If they are disturbed they fall awkwardly to the ground and lie there thrashing and kicking their legs, but they soon recover and fly up to rejoin the throng about the lights.

Often they are not alone. Among them we may see their enemy, the Pyrgota fly. The flight of the May beetles is bumbling, but the Pyrgotas move swiftly and surely. One will fly into the swarm of beetles and, singling out a fat female, will make a lightning-swift jab with her stilettolike ovipositor and thrust an egg inside the body of the beetle. The Pyrgota strikes through the tender skin on the back, which is exposed only at the times the May beetle spreads her wings in flight. The stricken beetle drops to the ground instantly, but soon seems to recover. She rejoins the others in their flight about the light or flies away to engage in the normal nocturnal activities of such beetles—feeding on succulent foliage or mating.

When daylight returns, the beetle burrows beneath the soil to pass the day. The following evening she again emerges from her underground shelter. But already her time is growing short, for the egg within her body will hatch in 4 or 5 days.

When the egg hatches, the young Pyrgota larva feeds on the fluids and fat reserve within the body of the beetle, growing rapidly and sapping its strength. Each evening the beetle flies with less and less vigor. Within a week her vitality is so low that she cannot leave her burrow. Now, although she is still alive, she is overcome with feebleness. Meanwhile the Pyrgota larva, having consumed nearly all the body fluids and fat, boldly attacks the muscles and vital organs. In 10 to 14 days after the first attack, the May beetle is dead.

The larva now turns scavenger and completely hollows out the body of the dead beetle. Soon only the hard outer parts remain, and within this shell now lies the fat, fully grown Pyrgota larva. It soon transforms to a pupa and then settles down to a long quiescence.

The pupa remains inside the defunct beetle, in the underground burrow, throughout the summer and the following winter. The following spring it emerges as an adult fly, to begin attacking the new crop of beetles.

The Pyrgota flies and the May beetles are not very well synchronized. A new generation of Pyrgotas appears each year, but the beetles require 3 years to complete a generation. Some

May beetles flying around light, and Pyrgota fly ovipositing in a May beetle.

May beetles emerge each spring, of course, as the various broods overlap, but some broods are much more numerous than others. The Pyrgota flies that develop in a year when the beetles are abundant may emerge the following year to find them quite scarce. When that occurs, some Pyrgota flies perish without being able to find any beetles in which to lay their eggs.

The Pyrgota flies are not the only enemies of May beetles. Several larvaevorid, or tachinid, flies also harass them. But while the Pyrgota flies attack boldly and thrust their eggs into the bodies of the beetles, the larvaevorids attack stealthily. Surreptitiously they fasten their eggs to the bodies of the beetles while their backs are turned.

ANYONE WHO RAISES cabbages or other cruciferous vegetables is sure to become acquainted with the cabbage maggot. We set out young plants in the spring and expect them to grow vigorously, but they wilt and collapse instead. When we pull one up we find the roots and lower stem a flabby bundle of macerated and rotting tissue. Cabbage maggots are tunneling through this nauseous mess.

If we dig in the soil around the infested roots, we are apt to find tiny rove beetles, *Aleochara bimaculata*. Rove beetles, the main enemy of the cabbage maggot, are less than one-quarter inch long and have slender, shining black bodies and brown legs. When the little beetles run (they never seem to walk but are always in a hurry), they twist their flexible abdomens from side to side or up over their backs. They shun the light, and when we uncover them in the soil they quickly bury themselves again.

In the soil these interesting little creatures construct a series of interconnecting tunnels between tiny subterranean chambers. In this cozy labyrinth the beetles carry on their affairs. Usually several live together in a way that suggests a social life.

The adult beetles feed on cabbage maggots or on other fly maggots in the soil. They are ruthless predators and will attack and eat maggots much larger than themselves. They hunt singly or in small groups through the soil, and when they find a maggot they attack it, tear open its sides, and feed upon it.

The female Aleochara beetle, after mating, lays her eggs in places where the cabbage maggots occur. With that she evidently considers that her duty toward her offspring has been done; she leaves the young larvae to shift for themselves.

The larvae hatch about 10 days after the eggs are laid. They have brown and horny bodies, well-developed heads and mouth parts, and sense receptors and legs much like those of most rove beetle larvae. The minute larvae begin hunting through the soil for the pupae of the cabbage maggot. The pupae are enclosed in puparia formed from the tough and hardened skin of the last larval stage. Even that almost impervious covering is not strong enough to keep the Aleochara larvae out.

Aleochara attacking a cabbage maggot.

When it locates a cabbage maggot puparium, the Aleochara larva sets to work to gnaw a hole in it. It is slow work, but the larva can pierce the barrier after several hours of effort. It then crawls inside and seals the entrance hole behind it. Inside, the larva crawls over the slumbering cabbage maggot pupa until it reaches a spot on the back just at the base of the head. There it settles down to feed, piercing the skin of the pupa and lapping up the semiliquid contents.

Within 3 or 4 days the Aleochara is ready to molt. Its skin splits, and the second-stage larva emerges. That larva is different in structure from the active first-stage larva. Its body covering is soft and white, and the sense receptors, legs, and mouth parts have become rudimentary. The larva continues to feed by piercing the skin of the still-living pupa of the cabbage maggot and it grows rapidly. Within another week it has outgrown its second-stage skin and has molted again. It is now full-grown and nearly as large as the cabbage maggot pupa was at the start, while the latter has been reduced to an empty, shrivelled skin. The Aleochara rests for a few days and then pupates. Two weeks later the mature adult is ready to emerge.

The adult beetle chews a hole in the wall of the still-tough puparium and comes out. Now it will find a mate, take up the work of enlarging and maintaining the ancestral galleries and chambers, and continue the decimation of the cabbage maggots. In a season as many as 80 percent of the cabbage maggots in a field may fall victim to the aggressive beetles.

BARNARD D. BURKS *is an entomologist in the division of insect identification, Bureau of Entomology and Plant Quarantine. Born in New Mexico, he received his doctor's degree in entomology from the University of Illinois. He was a staff member of the Faunistic Survey Section of the Illinois Natural History Survey from 1937 to 1949, although 4 of those years he spent in military service.*

Alfalfa caterpillar and butterfly.

Parasites and Predators

C. P. Clausen

The cottony-cushion scale, a small, inactive insect that feeds on the sap of the leaves and twigs of citrus trees, was first found in California in 1872. Within 15 years it had spread over the entire citrus-producing area of the State and threatened to destroy the industry. In many orchards the fruit crop was a complete loss, and in some the trees themselves were killed. The situation was desperate, as no method of control was known, and many growers gave up hope of relief and pulled out their trees.

It was known that the scale occurred in Australia. It probably originated there and had reached California by unknown means, possibly on nursery stock. That knowledge yielded one ray of hope—a parasite was known to attack it and appeared to hold it in check in its native home.

C. V. Riley, entomologist of the United States Department of Agriculture, became keenly interested in the problem and laid plans to send a qualified entomologist to Australia to obtain the parasite. He selected Albert Koebele, at that time engaged in studying other insect problems in California. Koebele had studied the cottony-cushion scale, attempting to control it by various means, and it was he who first concluded that the pest must have come from Australia. Difficulties arose, however. At that time it was almost impossible to obtain funds for foreign travel. Finally Koebele went to Australia, but as a representative of the State Department to the Melbourne Exposition.

Koebele arrived in Sydney late in September 1888 and immediately with the aid of an Australian entomologist was able to find the parasite, a tiny fly,

Cryptochaetum iceryae. Many thousands were dispatched to California. Fortune favored him still more, however, when, a few weeks later, he discovered the previously unknown but now famous vedalia. Both the beetles themselves and their larvae were found to feed greedily upon the eggs and the larvae of the scale, and on them only.

The first shipment of vedalia by Koebele reached California November 30, 1888. It comprised 28 beetles. Additional shipments followed. By the end of the following March a total of 514 had been received.

The beetles thrived. In less than 2 years after the arrival of the first shipment, the scale was under complete control throughout the citrus-growing sections of the State. It has remained so ever since. This highly successful outcome was due to the beetle rather than to the parasitic fly, the original object of the search, though it likewise became established and abundant. Koebele's trip cost less than $5,000; it has saved the citrus industry millions.

Koebele's later investigations in New Zealand and Australia in 1891–92 and to other Pacific regions were financed by the Department of Agriculture and the California State Board of Horticulture. He found and forwarded several valuable mealybug and scale insect predators, four of which adapted themselves to California. Among them was the well-known Australian lady beetle which during the 1920's was reared and distributed to the number of 40 million or more each year for the control of the citrophilus mealybug, another citrus pest in California closely related to the cottony-cushion scale.

Koebele was the pioneer among entomological explorers who search the far places of the world for parasites and predators to be used in controlling insect pests in this country. This method is now termed "biological control" to distinguish it from chemical control, which involves the use of insecticides. All available natural enemies, including parasitic and predaceous insects and disease-producing organisms as well, whether native or of foreign origin, are used in this program. In biological control the first cost is usually the only cost; the application of chemicals, on the contrary, must be repeated year after year and often several times each season.

Most of our destructive insect pests are not native to this country. They have gained entry in various ways, some as long ago as Colonial days. Nearly every injurious insect is attacked in its native environment by one or more parasites and predators which hold it in check. When a pest gains entry into a new country, its natural enemies are usually left behind. The pest therefore can increase unhampered by their attack. That is why many insects of foreign origin are more destructive in the United States (or any new habitat) than in their home country.

One precedent for Koebele's work was not entirely successful. In 1883–84 and following years, C. V. Riley imported a small wasp, *Apanteles glomeratus,* from England to combat the imported cabbageworm, a European pest that appeared first in Canada about 100 years ago. The parasite became established and abundant in all sections, but failed to control it.

So spectacular was Koebele's success with the cottony-cushion scale that the Bureau of Entomology began a large-scale search in 1905 in Europe for natural enemies of the gypsy moth and brown-tail moth. Those two destroyed or damaged forest and ornamental trees over a wide area in New England. The explorations from 1905 to 1914 covered all Europe and Japan, and were renewed and completed in 1922–27. Thirteen species of parasites and predators were successfully established in New England as a result of this work. The frequency and destructiveness of the gypsy moth outbreaks have been appreciably reduced as a result of these importations. The brown-tail moth has subsided to a position of little importance.

970134°—52——26

Other forest- and shade-tree pests that have been dealt with in the same way are the satin moth, oriental moth, birch leaf miner, and larch casebearer. The satin moth was a serious pest of poplar and willow in New England and the Pacific Northwest before 1930. *Compsilura concinnata, Eupteromalus nidulans,* and *Apanteles solitarius* (which had been imported for use against the gypsy moth and the browntail moth) reduced greatly the infestations in New England. *Apanteles* and *Meteorus versicolor* gave satisfactory control in the Pacific Northwest.

The oriental moth occurs in a few places in Massachusetts. Its parasite, *Chaetexorista javana,* obtained from Japan in 1929–30, in most years has effectively controlled the pest, but it apparently cannot withstand the occasional severe winters in Massachusetts; consequently the pest increases during the seasons following such winters.

AMONG THE PESTS of cereal and forage crops, the alfalfa weevil, which had become established in Utah, was the first on which investigations were undertaken. Importations from Italy in 1911–13 resulted in the establishment of a parasite, *Bathyplectes curculionis,* which destroys a high proportion of the larvae. The real value of this parasite in controlling the pest is difficult to determine, but parasite attack, in conjunction with a change in cutting practices, has given fairly satisfactory control.

The project for biological control of the European corn borer is the largest yet undertaken. It covered the years from 1920 to 1935, with activities centered mainly in the European countries but extending also to Japan, Korea, and Manchuria. Six species of parasites are known to be well established as a result of shipments during the period. Unfortunately four of them are severely restricted by climatic conditions and are established only in limited areas. The two most valuable are *Lydella stabulans grisescens* and *Macrocentrus gifuensis. Lydella* is widely distributed in the Eastern, Middle Atlantic, and North Central States. In some localities it may parasitize 50 percent or more of the borers. *Macrocentrus* is common only in southern New England.

Several attempts have been made to find effective natural enemies of the sugarcane borer. A considerable number of parasites were found in Cuba and several South American countries and introductions have been made intermittently since 1915. Two large importations were from Argentina and Peru in 1929–32. Not a single species of the many that have been released in Louisiana has become established, because of climatic conditions, mainly winter temperatures too low for the parasites to survive, and because of the practice of cutting the cane annually, which eliminates most of the parasite population and provides unfavorable conditions for increase in the spring.

Two parasites, *Lixophaga diatraeae* from Cuba and *Bassus stigmaterus* from Peru, have become established in Florida. These, especially *Lixophaga,* have been responsible for a considerable degree of control in the Felsmere area.

The oriental fruit moth, which came to this country from Japan, is a destructive pest of peaches in the eastern half of the United States. A large-scale program was undertaken in the 1930's to import its natural enemies from Japan and Korea. More than 20 species of parasites were imported and colonized throughout the infested area. Several showed promise during the season of release, but winter conditions were unfavorable to them and they declined and disappeared in a few years. Only one species has been able to maintain itself, and that in small numbers in one locality in New Jersey.

Before undertaking the importations from the Far East, entomologists knew that a native parasite, *Macrocentrus ancylivorus,* frequently attacked the pest in New Jersey and Delaware. Its normal host is the strawberry leaf roller, but the new pest was just as suitable. Investigations revealed that the parasite, although limited in its distribution, was adaptable to most of the area infested by the fruit moth. Colonization in the infested orchards

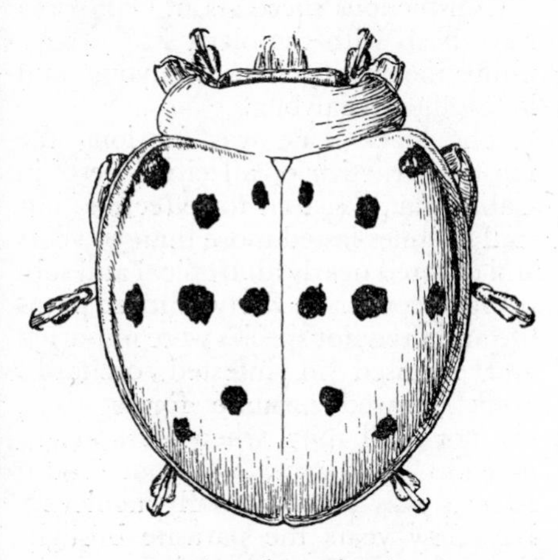

Mexican bean beetle.

in the spring reduced the later fruit injury as much as 80 percent. That benefit continued year after year. Large numbers were reared and distributed widely. It was the most dependable means of control before the development of the new insecticides. It is one of the few instances in which a native parasite has proved to be effective in combatting an introduced pest.

The Comstock mealybug, of Asiatic origin, has become a serious pest of apple in the Northeastern States since 1930. After a search for its parasites in Japan, two species, *Allotropa burrelli* and *Pseudaphycus malinus,* were imported and established. They and another parasite, *Clausenia purpurea,* which already had found its way to the United States, have been highly effective in bringing the pest under control throughout the infested area.

Disappointments can arise in a biological control project. Efforts with the Mexican bean beetle furnish an example. A promising parasite, *Paradexodes epilachnae,* was found in central Mexico and was imported, reared, and released in large numbers in the 1920's. The field colonies increased rapidly. Some destroyed 80 percent or more of the beetle larvae the first season. The problem appeared to be solved. But the following season revealed a discouraging situation. Not a single individual of the hundreds of colonies released in 19 States had survived the winter. The parasite is evidently adapted only to tropical or subtropical places, where it can breed throughout the year. In the United States the bean beetle hibernates as an adult, and consequently no larvae are available to the parasite for more than 6 months. Its survival under such conditions is obviously impossible.

A serious threat to our citrus industry is the citrus blackfly, which occurs in the West Indies, Central America, and Mexico. It is native to tropical Asia and was first found in the Western Hemisphere in Jamaica in 1913. Its occurrence near our borders caused apprehension and a realization of the need to adopt all possible measures to prevent its entry. One practical measure, of benefit both to us and to the nearby infested countries, was the reduction of the heavy existing infestations. Accordingly the United States Department of Agriculture and the Cuban Department of Agriculture, Labor, and Commerce undertook to import its natural enemies from Asia. A parasite, *Eretmocerus serius,* and a predaceous beetle, *Catana clauseni,* were established in Cuba between 1928 and 1931. The parasite increased rapidly. Within 2 years the pest was brought under full commercial control. No other measures have since been required against it. Equally effective control followed the establishment of the parasite in Jamaica, the Bahamas, Haiti, Panama, and Costa Rica.

The citrus blackfly, discovered in destructive numbers on the west coast of Mexico in 1935, has spread rapidly. It is now approaching our borders on both the east and west coasts. Here again a cooperative effort was required. The parasite was introduced and colonized at many points on the west coast in 1943 and was widely distributed thereafter. It was a surprise and a disappointment to find later that the expected degree of control, such as was attained in Cuba and elsewhere, did not materialize. Semiarid conditions in Mexico, with rainfall only in summer, prevented the parasite from attaining maximum effectiveness. Other natural enemies better adapted to those conditions therefore had to be brought in.

A search during 1949 and 1950 through western India and Pakistan, where the climate resembles that of Mexico, brought to light several effective parasites, two of which appeared to be responsible for holding the pest in control in nearly all areas. All have been shipped to Mexico and widely colonized. Three species have become established, but the outcome in terms of control was not known in 1952.

Another activity involving international cooperation is the sending of shipments of effective parasites and predators to foreign countries. It began in the early 1890's, shortly after the results of the work on cottony-cushion scale in California became generally known. Most of the shipments have comprised species that have been notably successful in biological control, such as the vedalia for cottony-cushion scale, the Australian lady beetle and a number of parasite species that control mealybugs, *Alphelinus mali,* an effective parasite of the woolly apple aphid, and others. More than 350 shipments have been made to 56 countries since 1890. Among them were 138 species of parasites and predators for use against 55 insects.

Work in California in biological control has been conducted by the University of California since 1923 and previously by the State Department of Agriculture and the State Commission of Horticulture. The first importations exclusively under State auspices were in 1904. In 1911 the work was placed on a permanent basis under the direction of Harry S. Smith. He has been responsible for the development and expansion of the State work from that date to 1951. Most of the work has been with pests of citrus, although it has been extended recently to include pests of other crops.

Conspicuous successes in California have been with the black scale, citrophilus mealybug, citrus mealybug, and long-tailed mealybug.

The black scale was for long the most destructive of all citrus pests in California. A search for effective natural enemies lasted more than 50 years and covered nearly all tropical and subtropical countries. Forty or more parasite and predator species were imported and released in infested orchards. Some showed promise for a time, but not until 1937, when *Metaphycus helvolus* was received from South Africa, was success finally achieved. In a few years the parasite brought the black scale under satisfactory commercial control in all sections except a part of the orchards in the even-hatch, or single-generation, area, although outbreaks sometimes follow unusually cold winters. The successful outcome of the long search has saved citrus growers several million dollars annually. The parasite also has been strikingly effective in eliminating a related scale insect, *Saissetia nigra,* which was destructive to ornamental plants in southern California.

The Australian lady beetle, which was introduced in 1891, has already been mentioned. For many years it persisted in the citrus orchards of California but was not conspicuously successful against mealybug pests. It was discovered that its ineffectiveness was due mainly to its inability to withstand winter conditions. Methods were then developed for the large-scale rearing of the beetles in the insectary, and releases were made in the orchard each spring at intervals as the infestations made necessary. The citrus mealybug and the citrophilus mealybug were satisfactorily controlled by this means for many years. State, county, and private organizations were engaged in producing the beetle, and hundreds of millions were reared and released at a cost of approximately $2.50 a thousand. The need for this program became less acute in the 1930's because of the introduction of highly effective internal parasites of several of the mealybug species.

THE CITROPHILUS MEALYBUG was first observed in southern California in 1913. It spread rapidly and quickly became a major pest in a number of sections. Two parasites, *Coccophagus gurneyi* and *Tetracnemus pretiosus,* were introduced from Australia in 1928, and the pest was brought quickly under control.

The long-tailed mealybug only occasionally becomes a serious pest of citrus but is better known for its attack on avocado. The internal parasites, *Anarhopus sydneyensis* (obtained from Australia in 1933) and *Tetracnemus peregrinus* (brought from Brazil in 1934), have brought about satisfactory field control.

The citrus mealybug, a serious pest for many years, was the species against which the Australian lady beetle was originally introduced. In 1914 an internal parasite, *Leptomastidea abnormis,* was imported from Sicily. It brought about field control in most sections, although releases of *Cryptolaemus* are still necessary in some orchards.

The California red scale is the most destructive of all the citrus insects in some sections of southern California and the search for effective natural enemies has been as long as that on the black scale. An effective parasite or predator has not yet been found, although nine species have been introduced. The yellow scale, a close relative of the red, has been controlled in some parts of the citrus-producing area by *Comperiella bifasciata,* introduced from China and Japan.

An attempt to utilize a virus disease of the alfalfa caterpillar in California is interesting. Scientists learned in 1948 that extensive outbreaks of the disease could be brought about by artificial dissemination of the virus. Field tests in the use of a virus for control of the alfalfa caterpillar, begun in 1947, demonstrated that the spray application of a suspension of virus material resulted in commercial control of the pest within 8 to 10 days. Also, the application of a water suspension of spores of a parasitic bacterium brought about similar control in only 2 days. The effect of the virus is more persistent than the bacterium, however, as the diseased caterpillars die and disintegrate on the foliage when killed by the virus, insuring infection of following broods of caterpillars, whereas those killed by the bacterium fall to the ground.

An outstanding contribution to biological control in California by Harry S. Smith and his coworkers has been in the development of methods for mass production of the imported parasites and predators. The procedure has permitted the widespread colonization of species within a short time after their importation and hence the advancing of the date on which control is accomplished.

The key to mass production is usually the rearing of adequate numbers of the pest insects themselves in the insectary, rather than the parasites and predators. The pest insects must, of course, be reared on plants, but use of citrus or other trees for the purpose was obviously impractical. The first big step was the discovery that the mealybugs could readily be reared on potato sprouts. The production of enormous numbers of *Cryptolaemus* beetles thus was made possible. Enough mealybugs can be reared on the sprouts from a ton of potatoes to produce more than 125,000 *Cryptolaemus.* The output of internal parasites is vastly greater than that.

It was later discovered that potato sprouts would serve equally well for the rearing of the black scale—the production of *Metaphycus helvolus* and other parasite species was thereby facilitated.

Equally successful results have been

obtained with the armored scale insects (California red scale, yellow scale, San Jose scale, and others). Potato tubers, squash, and several kinds of melons are used for insectary production rather than citrus or other plants.

A more recent use of potatoes to produce a host insect was in connection with the oriental fruit moth. The parasite, *Macrocentrus ancylivorus,* will develop as readily upon the potato tuberworm as upon the fruit moth. An elaborate production technique was developed that yielded approximately 235,000 parasites for each ton of potatoes used; 29 million parasites were produced in 1946.

THE MOST CONSISTENT RESULTS in the biological control of insect pests have been obtained in Hawaii—the mild climate there interposes no obstacles to the development of parasites at any season. The absence of a cold winter eliminates the long hibernation period, and there is no need for an alternate host to bridge this season. Those factors have been responsible for the ineffectiveness of many promising species in the continental United States. Also, Hawaii has no prolonged dry periods of high temperatures, which handicap the natural enemies by requiring a period of inactivity in summer.

As a result, the sugar industry of Hawaii is now free from serious attack by any insect pest. Several major pests and a number of lesser importance have been adequately controlled by imported parasites and predators.

The importation of parasites and predators of insect pests into Hawaii began in 1893, stimulated by the outcome of the work with the cottony-cushion scale. Albert Koebele, who had found the vedalia in Australia, was appointed to the staff of the Territorial Board of Agriculture and Forestry in that year. In the following decade he was responsible for the introduction and establishment of 18 or more beneficial insects from Australia and Asia. Most of these were general predators on scale insects and mealybugs. The Territorial Board has continued its activities and has introduced many natural enemies of miscellaneous agricultural pests other than those of sugarcane. Among them are the melon fly, Mediterranean fruit fly, taro leafhopper, and Asiatic rice borer.

The Experiment Station of the Hawaiian Sugar Planters' Association was organized in 1904. On its staff were four entomologists, R. C. L. Perkins, O. H. Swezey, G. W. Kirkaldy, and F. W. Terry. Koebele and Alexander Craw, employed jointly with the Territorial Board, were consultants.

Their first problem was the sugarcane leafhopper, which then threatened to destroy the sugar industry. The early importations resulted in the establishment of four egg parasites, *Paranagrus optabilis* and *Anagrus frequens* from Australia, *Ootetrastichus beatus* from Fiji, and *O. formosanus* from Formosa. *Paranagrus* and *Ootetrastichus* gave a substantial measure of relief but not complete control. A further search for additional species of greater effectiveness in Australia and Fiji disclosed a bug, *Cyrtorhinus mundulus,* that was predaceous on leafhopper eggs. Its introduction in 1920 finally solved the problem. The leafhopper quickly subsided to a noninjurious level.

The conquest of the leafhopper was followed by that of the New Guinea sugarcane weevil which, while less destructive, caused losses of a million dollars or more each year because the larvae bored in the cane stalks. The search by Frederick Muir through Borneo, New Guinea, and adjoining areas revealed a parasitic fly, *Microceromasia sphenophori,* that attacks the grubs. Air transport was unknown in those days, and the problem of bringing the parasite alive from New Guinea to Hawaii seemed insurmountable. Muir's repeated efforts from 1907 to 1910, including finally the establishment of several relay stations en route, is one of the epics of entomological exploration. The subjugation of the beetle borer quickly followed the establishment of the fly in Hawaii.

While the leafhopper and weevil were the outstanding pests of cane, many others have caused appreciable damage and have necessitated the importation of natural enemies. The outcome has been successful with the oriental beetle, several species of armyworms, the Chinese grasshopper, a mole cricket (*Gryllotalpa africana*), a cane aphis (*Aphis sacchari*), and two species of mealybugs. Many parasites of miscellaneous pests also have been imported, some with conspicuous benefit, such as those against the fern weevil, torpedo bug, a scale on coconut (*Pinnaspis buxi*), the coconut mealybug on avocado, and cockroaches.

The work in Hawaii may be brought up to date by mention of the work on fruit flies, including the oriental fruit fly. First found in the Islands in 1945, it quickly demonstrated its destructive capabilities. Its habits and its large numbers in Hawaii are a serious threat to the fruit industry in California, through the possibility of entry in aircraft or by other means. The importation of natural enemies was undertaken in a cooperative effort of the Hawaii Agricultural Experiment Station, the Board of Commissioners of Agriculture and Forestry of Hawaii, the Hawaiian Sugar Planters' Association Experiment Station, the Pineapple Research Institute, the University of California, and the Bureau of Entomology and Plant Quarantine.

The first shipments of parasites were brought from Malaya and the Philippines by the Board of Commissioners of Agriculture and Forestry in 1948. Since then the exploratory work by the cooperating agencies has extended to South and East Africa, India, Thailand, China, Formosa, Australia, and several islands of the South Pacific. Between 30 and 50 species of parasites have been imported for testing. Many have been released in large numbers. The importation program was completed in 1951. Four or more parasitic species are established in Hawaii. Two of them, originally imported from Malaya, have brought about commercial control on the island of Oahu and prospects of similar control on the other islands appeared excellent.

Many of the introduced parasites and predators I have mentioned have held the pest insects under control for many years and other control measures have not been required. Since 1945, however, complications have arisen because of the new insecticides, beginning with DDT and followed by a series of others, some of which are more toxic than DDT. The use of DDT in the orange orchards of California for control of the citricola scale was followed by widespread outbreaks of the cottony-cushion scale, the first since 1890. This was due to the destruction of the vedalia by the insecticide.

In other instances, the use of the new insecticides against a specific crop pest has upset the natural balance of minor pests of the same crop, likewise apparently due to elimination of their natural enemies. The application of DDT and some other chemicals to vegetable and fruit crops frequently brings heavy infestations of aphids and spider mites—pests that at times become more destructive than the ones against which the insecticide was applied. This upsetting of the natural equilibrium has created a serious situation in pest control and is being investigated. The solution may be found in a combination of remedial measures involving a change in the insecticide used, its formulation, the time of application, or in some other change in current practices.

This account of biological control of insect pests has described only the more important achievements in the United States. The same method has been employed with conspicuous success in other countries, notably Australia, New Zealand, Fiji, and Canada. At least 30 major insect pests have been fully controlled in one or more countries through the use of parasites and predators and substantial reductions brought about in the infestations of a much larger number.

C. P. CLAUSEN *was leader of the division of foreign parasite introduction, Bureau of Entomology and Plant Quarantine, from its establishment in 1934 until 1951, when he retired and became chairman of the division of biological control at the University of California. His training was obtained at the University of California. In 1916–17 he conducted a search for natural enemies of citrus scale insects in Japan, China, Formosa, and the Philippines for the California State Commission of Horticulture. After joining the Department of Agriculture in 1920 he spent the following 11 years in a search for natural enemies of the Japanese beetle in Japan and India and of the citrus blackfly in Malaya.*

For further reading on insect parasites and predators, Dr. Clausen suggests:

Department of Agriculture Technical Bulletins: 86, Imported Insect Enemies of the Gypsy Moth and Brown-Tail Moth, *by A. F. Burgess and S. S. Crossman, 1929; 320,* The Citrus Blackfly in Asia, and the Importation of Its Natural Enemies Into Tropical America, *by C. P. Clausen and P. A. Berry, 1932; 728,* Parasites of the Oriental Fruit Moth in Japan and Chosen and Their Introduction Into the United States, *by G. J. Haeussler, 1940; 938,* Investigations of the Parasites of Popillia japonica and Related Scarabaeidae in the Far East from 1929 to 1933, Inclusive, *by T. R. Gardner and L. B. Parker, 1940; 975,* Field Studies of the Alfalfa Weevil and Its Environment, *by J. C. Hamlin, F. V. Lieberman, R. W. Bunn, W. C. McDuffie, R. C. Newton, and L. J. Jones, 1949; 983,* Biological Control of the European Corn Borer in the United States, *by W. A. Baker, W. G. Bradley, and C. A. Clark, 1949.*

In Hilgardia: The Control of the Citrophilus Mealybug, Pseudococcus gahani, by Australian Parasites, *by H. Compere and H. S. Smith, volume 6, pages 585–618, 1932;* Mass Culture of Macrocentrus ancylivorus and Its Host, the Potato Tuber Moth, *by G. L. Finney, S. E. Flanders, and H. S. Smith, volume 17, pages 437–483, 1947;* Further Tests Using a Polyhedrosis Virus to Control the Alfalfa Caterpillar, *by C. G. Thompson and E. A. Steinhaus, volume 19, pages 411–445, 1950.*

Infectious Diseases of Insects

Edward A. Steinhaus

Like human beings and other animals, insects are susceptible to a variety of infectious agents, which infect and kill hordes of them every year. Most of this mortality goes unnoticed, although at times outbreaks—epizootics—of disease are so spectacular as to claim considerable attention among growers and entomologists everywhere.

The possibilities of using disease agents to help control insect pests have excited entomologists and others periodically since infectious organisms were first detected in insects. As I explain in a later paragraph, however, that is only one of the applications that may be made of our knowledge of insect diseases, because insect pathology has already contributed greatly to other branches of entomology and to medicine, agriculture, and biology generally.

The infectious agents responsible for diseases in insects belong to the same major groups as those that cause diseases in other animals: Bacteria, fungi, viruses, protozoa, and nematodes. In general, however, insects are not very susceptible to those particular micro-organisms that cause diseases of other animals and of plants. Furthermore, most of the micro-organisms that cause fatal diseases in insects are harmless to plants and higher animals.

The resistance shown by insects to pathogens of higher animals is largely a normal or innate one. Nevertheless insects often can ward off infection by virtue of mechanisms of immunity similar to those exhibited by other animals. Antibodies against foreign materials may be produced in the body fluids of the insects, thus giving a humoral immunity against infection. Cellular immunity frequently is evidenced by the activity of the hemocytes, or blood cells, which may engulf foreign particles that enter the body of the insect.

One of the most convenient ways in which to consider the various infections of insects is according to the nature of the etiologic agent, that is, whether it is a bacterial, fungus, virus, protozoan, or nematode infection. To be sure, insects, like other forms of life, are subject to definite metabolic and other noninfectious conditions. Here, however, we are concerned only with true infectious diseases of insects.

EVERY BEEKEEPER is familiar with diseases of the honey bee known under the general name of foulbroods. American foulbrood is caused by *Bacillus larvae*, European foulbrood by *Bacillus alvei*, and parafoulbrood by *Bacillus para-alvei*. Those sporeforming bacteria are true insect pathogens and are not known to be infectious for other animals. Not until their true nature and etiologic role were discovered was it possible to accomplish much in the way of controlling the foulbroods. Although effective control procedures have been realized through strict sanitation and quarantine and such direct therapeutic measures as the use of sulfathiazole, the diseases in some areas still cause losses to beekeepers and agriculture. They and certain afflictions of silkworms were among the first insect maladies to be recorded.

The first widely publicized bacterial disease of a destructive insect was that of grasshoppers, caused by the small, nonsporeforming *Coccobacillus acridiorum* (now *Aerobacter aerogenes* var. *acridiorum*). The bacterium was observed first in Yucatan, Mexico, where it destroyed the hordes of locusts (*Schistocerca*) that were invading Mexico from Guatemala. The infected insects exhibited symptoms typical of dysentery and septicemia and died usually within a few hours.

Great hopes were held at first that the bacterium could be used in controlling grasshoppers. Attempts to accomplish that were made in several countries. Despite the apparent success of early trials, the method was abandoned—in the light of present knowledge it is clear that some of the lack of general success can be ascribed to the failure of most of the users to adhere to the fundamental principles of bacteriology necessary to insure the identity of the cultures used, the maintenance of their virulence, and their application according to the epizootiological demands of the situation.

The most noteworthy and so far the most important of the bacterial diseases of destructive insects are the so-called milky diseases of the Japanese beetle, which are discussed in the next chapter.

Although the examples I have cited indicate to some degree the general types of bacterial infections in insects, they do not indicate the extent to which this group of diseases occurs in nature. Numerous other instances of bacterium-caused diseases have been observed and studied. Nearly all major systematic groups of insects have been recorded as hosts to one or more types of bacterial infection. Furthermore, insect pathogens have been identified as belonging to almost every major group of bacteria, although the small, gram-negative, rod-shaped bacteria and the large, gram-positive, sporeforming bacteria appear to be predominant.

The general characteristics of a bacterial disease of an insect are: As the disease develops, the animal usually becomes less active, has a smaller appetite, and discharges fluids from the mouth and anus. The infection may begin as a dysenteric condition with an accompanying diarrhea, but in most instances the invading bacterium eventually enters the body cavity of the insect and causes a septicemia that terminates in the death of the host. Following death, the insect's body usually darkens to brown or black. That especially is true of larvae and pupae in which the disintegration takes place rapidly, although adults may also show a rapid change in color. The freshly dead insect is usually soft and becomes shapeless. The internal tissues may disintegrate to a viscid consistency, sometimes accompanied by odor, but ordinarily they do not "melt" or liquefy as do insects dying of certain virus infections. The cadaver of the insect usually dries and becomes shriveled, the integument remaining intact. Microscopic examinations of smears or histological sections of an insect dead or dying of a bacterial disease usually show large numbers of the causative bacterium present. If the bacteriological examination is delayed too long, care must be taken to differentiate the true pathogens from similar-appearing saprophytes that may flourish in the tissues of the dead insect.

One of the first diseases of animals to be recognized as being caused by a micro-organism was a fungus disease of the silkworm. As early as 1835 the mycelium and fruiting bodies seen on the cadavers of silkworms were recognized as being similar to those of the molds commonly found growing on bread and other food products. Today hundreds of species of fungi have been reported from insects. Many of them are known to be exclusively insect parasites.

Each of the four classes of fungi (Phycomycetes, Ascomycetes, Basidiomycetes, and Deuteromycetes, or Fungi Imperfecti) contain species capable of infecting insects. In any particular insect the appearance it assumes upon being infected with a fungus varies with the type of fungus. Some specimens dead of a fungus infection (mycosis) may show no marked external signs whatever. Others may be covered with mycelial growth, which makes it difficult to recognize the host insect. Infection usually begins with the penetration of the integument by the germinating hypha arising from a spore or conidium that has lodged on the animal's body. Once within the body cavity, the fungus multiplies rapidly and soon fills the insect. With proper conditions of temperature and moisture, conidiophores then make their way through the body wall of the host to the outside, where fruiting bodies are formed. By this time the insect is a hard, brittle, mummylike object—a condition unlike that seen in typical infections of any other type.

As I have indicated, the first fungus infection of an insect to be well studied was muscardine of the silkworm, caused by *Beauveria bassiana,* a disease that spells great loss to sericulturists. The fungus occurs wherever the silkworm is reared. It causes infection in a large number of insect pests, including the European corn borer and the codling moth.

A closely related species, *Beauveria globulifera,* also rather widespread, causes disease in many insects, including the chinch bug. At one time much thought was given to the possibility of using it to control the chinch bug, but investigation revealed that its spores were almost always present in the areas concerned and that artificial distribution of them would not affect materially the outbreak of disease, which would occur naturally if moisture and temperature were adequate. Green muscardine, caused by *Metarrhizium anisopliae,* is another important infection of insects. In some parts of the world it is responsible for a significant degree of natural control of certain insects.

In Florida, the Orient, and other places, scale insects are found to support the growth of certain fungi. Some of these fungi are true parasites. Others are apparently only secondary parasites, or even saprophytes, which live on the dead tissue of the scales. A great deal of attention has been given these entomogenous fungi in the citrus-growing sections of Florida, where attempts were made to use them in the biological control of the scale insects. Advocates of this method of control relied considerably on the effectiveness of scale fungi of the genera *Sphaerostilbe, Nectria, Podonectria, Aschersonia,* and others. Later work in Florida indicated that many of these "friendly fungi" do not actually parasitize the scale insect but are in fact saprophytes or secondary parasites. On the other hand, it appears that considerable mortality of scale insects does result from the activities of an interesting endoparasitic fungus (*Myiophagus*). Whiteflies on citrus in Florida are hosts to fungi (e. g., *Aschersonia, Aegerita, Fusarium*), which are said by some investigators to be important in the control of those insects.

One of the most important groups of entomogenous fungi from the standpoint of their role in the natural control of insects is included in the order Entomophthorales. Members of the genera *Empusa* and *Entomophthora* are particularly noteworthy. Many insects are susceptible to them. The natural mortality they cause is tremendous. Among their hosts are aphids, leafhoppers, flies, grasshoppers, mealybugs, and various caterpillars, a commonly seen infection of this type is that of the house fly by *Empusa muscae*. The infected flies attach themselves to walls, ceilings, and window panes, where they die of the fungus but remain in a lifelike position, usually with a halo of discharged spores around them.

Other important groups of fungi that contain species parasitic on insects include: *Coelomomyces,* endoparasitic fungi found especially in mosquito larvae in various parts of the world, including the United States; the genus *Cordyceps,* containing about 200 known species, cosmopolitan in distribution, occurring on representatives of several orders of insects, and usually characterized by the presence of a long, stemlike portion bearing a "head" or "club" protruding from the body of the insect host; numerous Fungi Imperfecti infections, which generally have been inadequately studied but which eventually may be revealed as being of great importance in the ecology of many insect species.

LIKE THE VIRUSES affecting other animals and plants, the insect viruses require living tissue to support their growth and are not readily visible with the ordinary light microscope. They cause disease primarily in the larvae and pupae of insects belonging to the orders Lepidoptera, Hymenoptera, and (occasionally) Diptera.

Apparently several kinds of viruses may infect insects—at least several different kinds of response are observed in the tissues of insects suffering from virus infections. The best known group is that in which characteristic inclusions known as polyhedra are formed in the nuclei of the infected cells. The diseases caused by these viruses are known as polyhedroses and the viruses themselves have been placed in the genus *Borrelina*. Under an electron microscope the viruses usually appear as rod-shaped forms (usually about 40 by 300 millimicrons in size) in bundles of several members each. They are situated mostly within the microscopically visible polyhedral inclusions. Among the diseases they cause are the jaundice of the silkworm, *Wipfelkrankheit* of the nun moth caterpillar, and the so-called wilt diseases of the larva of the gypsy moth, the alfalfa caterpillar, the larva of the European spruce sawfly, and others. About 100 different insects have been reported subject to polyhedroses. In most insects suffering from a polyhedrosis, there is a general debilitation, and the integument becomes discolored shortly before death and after. The larva is flaccid and upon death the internal tissues (particularly the fat body and hypodermis) disintegrate, giving the body contents a fluid consistency.

Another group is characterized by the formation of minute granular inclusions in the infected cells of the host. Within each granule is a virus particle. The diseases such viruses cause have been designated provisionally as granuloses, and the agents have been placed in the genus *Bergoldia*. On the basis of the dozen or so examples of this type of infection so far reported, the granuloses may be less virulent and widespread than the polyhedroses. The infected insect (e. g., a cutworm) becomes progressively more sluggish and loses its appetite, and in some species an abnormal white appearance of the diseased insect is apparent. Death may be delayed but usually occurs before pupation.

What may be another type of virus disease has been reported in the larva of a cabbage butterfly of Europe. The virus (genus *Paillotella*) has not yet been demonstrated by such means as the electron microscope. However, the inclusions in infected cells are bizarre, refringent, and irregularly shaped forms originating in the cytoplasm of the host cell. The disease caused is not so destructive to the susceptible insect as are the polyhedroses. So far it has been reported only from France, where it has been seen on only a few occasions.

Not all insect viruses incite the production of recognizable inclusion bodies in the tissues of their hosts. Sacbrood of the honey bee is one of the diseases caused by a virus that does not produce inclusions. Another is a "paralysis" of the adult honey bee. Some investigators believe that certain of the dysenteries in the silkworm have as their primary cause a virus that (when accompanied by the bacterium *Bacillus bombycis*) gives rise to the condition known as "true flacherie" and (when accompanied by *Streptococcus bombycis*) causes "gattine." The accuracy of this etiology, however, remains to be confirmed. Unfortunately none of the viruses infecting insects but not causing the production of inclusion bodies have as yet been conclusively demonstrated except by their infectivity.

THE NUMBER OF PROTOZOAN SPECIES described from insects is great. In most instances the association is a commensal or a mutualistic one, causing the host no essential harm and frequently benefiting it. Many protozoa, however, are parasitic and distinctly pathogenic for their insect hosts.

Although protozoan species pathogenic for insects do occur among the flagellates, amoebae, and ciliates, the most noteworthy infections are caused by certain members of the class Sporozoa. In this class are the well-known gregarines, which, although rarely causing fatal infections, may cause debilitating disease. Somewhat more pathogenic are certain coccidia, which produce slow but frequently fatal infections. Of great general pathogenicity are the microsporidia, which are responsible for a great deal of mortality both in insects reared in insectaries and other means of confinement and in insects as they occur in nature.

Of the many microsporidian infections so far reported, the best known are those causing pebrine of the silkworm and nosema disease of the honey bee. (There are several important genera of Microsporidia, but the best known is that of *Nosema*.) Pebrine has been responsible for tremendous economic losses in the rearing of silkworms for silk production. There is no complete agreement as to the true importance of nosema disease in the economics of apiculture. From the standpoint of the apiary as a whole, the disease is not too serious. Individual bees and sometimes colonies die from its effects, but rarely, if ever, is an entire apiary destroyed. Microsporidian diseases are also found in many destructive insects of economic importance, such as in the European corn borer, imported cabbageworm, codling moth, and others.

Protozoan diseases may be of epizootic proportions, or they appear merely as incidental infections. Unlike most of the diseases caused by bacteria and viruses, those incited by protozoa, with certain exceptions, are slow in developing and may even be chronic in nature. Because of the presence of spores or cysts, the infected insect may take on an opaque, whitish appearance, or other discoloration, or may exhibit no outward symptoms except sluggishness and a diminished appetite. After death the diseased animal may become darkened in color and dry down to brittle remains.

The roundworms known as nematodes are familiar because of the diseases they cause in higher animals and in plants. Many, however, parasitize and destroy insects. The number of nematodes so far reported from insects probably exceeds 1,000 species. Most of the reported hosts are in the order Lepidoptera (approximately 300); the orders Coleoptera, Orthoptera, and Diptera each have at least 100 species as hosts to nematodes.

Nematodes associated with insects may be put in three groups: (1) Nematodes that live in the alimentary tract of the insect. Their life cycles mostly are simple. An example is *Cephalobium microbivorum,* in the gut of field crickets. (2) Nematodes that are more or less closely related to free-living species and often have a combination of saprophagous and parasitic habits. They may live and reproduce in the cadaver of the host, which may or may not have been killed by the parasites. Others of this group may pass through one or more free-living generations which alternate with one or more parasitic generations. An example is *Neoaplectana glaseri* in the Japanese beetle. (3) Nematodes that parasitize the body cavity or the tissues of their host. Those worms are highly specialized, obligately parasitic, and at the most spend only a transitory period in the alimentary tract of the insect. Examples are *Agamermis decaudata* and *Mermis subnigrescens* in grasshoppers.

Of the three groups, the insect pathologist is perhaps the most interested in the last, but the other two have members that are also important from a pathological standpoint as well as from the standpoint of their role in biological control.

The possibility of using pathogenic micro-organisms to control destructive pests has been envisioned for a long time. From time to time efforts to institute the control of certain insects by such measures have been made in various parts of the world, but the reports of the results have been inconsistent. In recent years there has appeared a need to reappraise the possibilities of this method in the light of new techniques and newer knowledge concerning the effect of disease on insect populations.

One of the most successful attempts to control a serious insect pest in the United States by means of an infectious agent has been the application of the bacterial milky diseases against the Japanese beetle. Once the bacterial spores are introduced into an infested area they are able to persist for long periods of time (being periodically revitalized by infecting invading grubs); hence the permanency of the method is one of its outstanding merits. In some areas, effective artificial control of other pests by means of fungi and viruses has also been attained. Dissemination of viruses by means of aircraft to combat certain field crop pests (e. g., the alfalfa caterpillar) has been accomplished and would apparently also be applicable against certain forest insects.

Besides the advantage of permanency in some instances, other advantages of the microbial method include the fact that successful microbial control can be a relatively inexpensive method of reducing populations of destructive insects. Large quantities of most micro-organisms may be produced in a relatively short time and easily distributed as sprays or dusts. Furthermore, microbial control is a "natural" method of control, and therefore may increase its effectiveness by natural means after once having been introduced into an area. Practically all entomogenous micro-organisms are harmless to animals and plants. The potential dangers of some chemical residues to the host plants or to the consumers of the plants ordinarily is not a factor in microbial control. Because most micro-organisms are not appreciably affected by many of the insecticides, the use of these two agencies at the same time is practicable.

In considering the over-all role of micro-organisms in the control of insects and in the suppression of insect populations, one should remember that regardless of man's activities along this line a tremendous toll of insect life is being taken continuously in nature through the pathogenic action of entomogenous micro-organisms. Instances in which nature institutes effective control of an insect species through the agency of disease are common and unceasing. If for no other reason, therefore, it behooves the entomologist and the agriculturist interested in the ecology of insects to be cognizant of those micro-organisms capable of causing disease among these animals and the effect of the diseases on insect populations and activity. Only by including knowledge of this group of enemies of arthropods along with the other more frequently recognized groups can we hope to gain a more complete understanding of insect life.

EDWARD A. STEINHAUS *is an associate professor of insect pathology in the University of California, Berkeley, where he is in charge of the teaching and research program in insect pathology. He is author of the book,* Principles of Insect Pathology, *published by the McGraw-Hill Book Co. in 1949.*

The Laboratory of Insect Pathology is a part of the division of biological control in the College of Agriculture at the University of California, and as such it was the first laboratory of its kind to be organized (in 1945) for the purpose of conducting a full teaching and research program in all phases of the subject. The facilities of the laboratory are available to entomologists, farmers, and others interested in having insect specimens diagnosed as to their diseases.

Specimens (subject to quarantine regulations) submitted for diagnoses should be securely packaged, but should not be placed in alcohol or other preservative. They may be sent by fast mail directly to the Laboratory of Insect Pathology, Division of Biological Control, University of California, Berkeley 4, Calif.

Milky Diseases of Beetles

Ira M. Hawley

Grubs of the Japanese beetle live in the ground, where they may be attacked by several milky diseases, of which the type A, caused by *Bacillus popilliae,* is the most widespread and the most important.

That milky disease was first discovered in central New Jersey about 1933 when men who were conducting field surveys found a few abnormally white grubs. On microscopic examination, the late G. F. White, of the Bureau of Entomology and Plant Quarantine, perceived that the blood of the grubs was teeming with bacterial spores. The spores caused the white appearance and led to the designation milky disease for the ailing grubs.

The spores are spindle-shaped bodies about 1/4600 inch long—so small that several billion may exist in one milky grub. When a healthy grub becomes infected with milky disease, the spores give rise to slender vegetative rods, which grow and multiply in the blood by repeated divisions and in a few days develop into the spore form.

As the disease develops, the blood of a sick grub, normally clear, becomes filled with the bacterial forms and milky in appearance. When affected grubs die, the spores, which had filled the body cavity, are left in the soil. They are taken up by other grubs as they feed on the roots of plants, and they in turn become diseased. As the process goes on the number of spores in the soil increases, more and more grubs are killed, and fewer beetles emerge.

In the rod stage the disease organism is comparatively short-lived, but the spores are long-lived. They resist excessive dryness or moisture, cold, and heat.

They may remain alive in the soil for many years.

Many bacterial pathogens—germs that cause disease—of man, animals, and plants can be grown on artificial culture media and thus made to produce in great numbers the organisms that cause diseases. The culture possibilities of *B. popilliae,* which causes the type-A milky disease, have been intensively studied by S. R. Dutky, the bacteriologist of the Moorestown, N. J., laboratory of the Bureau of Entomology and Plant Quarantine, and by workers in State and private laboratories, but they have found no medium in which the rods will develop into spores.

The rods of type-A bacillus, however, will grow on several culture media and great numbers may be obtained. The rods may be transferred from one culture to another, where they will go on producing more. The milky disease may be started in healthy grubs by the injection of the rods into the blood stream with a hypodermic needle. Of the many ingredients for media tested in culture studies, thiamine and tryptophane have been found to be essential for growth and multiplication of the rod form. Other materials help somewhat. However, some element, which is required to bring about the change from rods to spores, has been wanting in all the many culture media we have tested. Work to find a medium in which spores may be obtained has been in progress since 1934.

Early in the study of the type-A milky disease we learned that it occurred largely in a small area where the Japanese beetle had been longest established in this country. In other words, the beetle had spread faster than the disease. We felt certain that the disease would help control the beetle in places where it did not occur if enough spores could be produced.

Because spores could not then (and still cannot) be obtained in artificial culture media, Dr. Dutky developed a new technique for obtaining spores. In the process, the grub itself is used as the culture medium. Thousands of healthy grubs are dug in the field each fall and stored in cold cellars at the laboratory. They are removed as needed, and each grub is inoculated hypodermically with about 1 million type-A spores from milky grubs. The injected grubs are held individually at a temperature of 86° F. in cross-section boxes with soil and with sprouted grass seed as food for 10 to 12 days. In that time, each grub usually contains 2 billion or more spores. The United States letters patent covering the main features of the process were granted to Dr. Dutky, who assigned them to the Secretary of Agriculture.

Occasionally enough milky grubs are found in a field to justify collecting them for processing, but we seldom find a place with enough diseased grubs in the proper condition to pay to dig.

When the disease has developed to just the proper stage, the grubs are screened from the soil, washed to remove dirt particles, and placed in jars of ice water, which are stored in a refrigerator at about 35° F. The cooling quiets the grubs and prevents deterioration. When enough injected grubs have accumulated, the excess water in the jars is poured off and the grubs are ground up in a meat chopper. Samples are taken of the resulting mixture of spores and grub parts and are checked to see how many spores exist in each unit of the mixture. Enough chalk is added to standardize the mixture at 1 billion spores per gram. Then it is passed through a blower to break up the masses of particles. The mixture is dried by a blast of warm air and a filler, usually talc, is added to standardize the powder at 100 million spores per gram, roughly 2.8 billion spores per ounce. The powder is known as spore dust and it is ready for packaging.

If there were no loss in the making, 23 grubs containing 2 billion spores each would produce 1 pound of spore dust. Spore dust has been held in a dry condition for as long as 10 years without noticeable deterioration and it is always ready to use.

A program to colonize the disease in areas where it did not occur was started in 1939 by workers at the Moorestown laboratory in cooperation with State and Federal agencies. By the close of the 1950 season, more than 166,000 pounds of spore dust had been applied at nearly 122,000 colony sites. Nearly 93,000 acres had been treated in 199 counties in 14 Eastern States and the District of Columbia. At least 15,500 pounds of spore dust were used in treating properties owned or maintained by the Federal Government.

State entomological agencies have sometimes assisted in the production of spore dust by digging and inoculating grubs, which were then shipped under refrigeration to Moorestown, where all the processing into spore dust has been done. The spore dust from the grubs was then returned to the States for distribution. Records of the number of colonized sites in each county were supplied to the Moorestown laboratory. Workers at the University of Maryland have carried on a large-scale program of grub inoculation and distribution of spore dust since 1940.

Because spore dust is difficult to make and costly, it is seldom applied to the soil as a complete coverage. In experimental applications it has been spread evenly over the ground with commercial fertilizer or some other filler and good disease infection has been obtained. There was no evidence that the fertilizer reduced the action of the disease spores. However, spore dust is usually distributed in spots with a modified rotary hand corn planter, which drops about 2 grams of the dust each time it is tripped. In treating a small yard, the powder may be applied in spots with a teaspoon. It is merely placed on top of the ground; the next rain will wash it in.

The amount needed for any area is regulated by the distance between the spots, which are usually 3 to 10 feet apart. When applied with a corn planter at a 3- by 3-foot rate, 20.6 pounds of spore dust will be required to cover an acre. At a 5- by 5-foot interval, 7.0 pounds will be needed. When the spots are 10 by 10 feet, 1.75 pounds are required. The size of the treated tracts has varied greatly. Treatment of at least 2 half-acre plots per square mile is desirable in open agricultural country. In city areas, the treatment of the properties on at least 1 block in 10 is considered good. These rates of treatment are heavier than it has been possible to use in many places. Often the spore dust has been applied in only a few locations where grub counts were highest. In a few places where beetles have been present in destructive numbers, tracts of 100 acres or more have received a complete coverage with the spots close together. That was done to get a quick establishment of the disease.

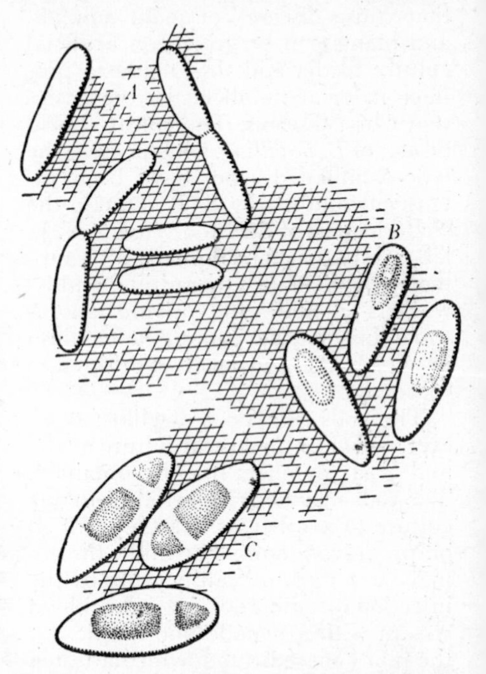

Milky disease spores. A, vegetative rods; B, sporulating rods; C, mature spores.

In colonizing new areas, places are selected for treatment which have a permanent turf and a high count of grubs. Milky disease is not usually applied to fields that might be plowed or cultivated soon after treatment because the spores are scattered and buried before the disease can become established. Furthermore, the grub count is usually low in such places. The rapidity of disease build-up will depend on the number of grubs per square foot, the closeness of the spots in the treated area, and the number and size of treated tracts. Since grubs become diseased largely by feeding in infected soil, some time must elapse before the disease will spread over an entire field or larger area from the first grubs infected. Milky disease will be spread from those initial points by any natural or artificial movement of topsoil containing spores, by the movement of diseased grubs through the soil, and by birds and animals that feed on diseased grubs. It has been shown experimentally that live spores are present in the droppings of birds that have fed on diseased grubs. Spores of the type-A milky disease can withstand wide ranges of soil temperature and moisture conditions, but may lose some of their infective power after direct exposure to the rays of the sun for several days.

The United States Department of Agriculture does not have spore dust for distribution to residents of beetle-infested areas, but two companies have been authorized to make it under license from the Secretary of Agriculture.

Their products may be bought at many of the seed and hardware stores throughout the beetle-infested area. Samples of the spore dust made by the companies are tested by the Moorestown laboratory several times each year to see that a proper standard is maintained. Such samples have always been found to be satisfactory. Spore dust made by the companies has been used to treat small yards, estates, golf courses, parks, and similar areas. In some places garden clubs or other civic organizations have stimulated the purchase and distribution of spore dust. At times State and municipal agencies have purchased spore dust and used it to supplement that supplied by the Moorestown laboratory in cooperative programs.

In some counties the county agents and boards of supervisors have bought quantities of spore dust for sale to farmers at a fraction of the usual retail price. Sometimes the county agents have arranged to have the dust distributed on fields.

Inexperienced observers would probably see little difference in the appearance of healthy grubs and those which have milky disease, especially in the early stages. The hollow body cavity of a beetle grub is filled with blood, which is kept in circulation by the pulsations of the dorsal blood vessel, a tubelike organ that serves as a heart. It runs lengthwise just beneath the semitransparent upper body wall and may readily be seen in a healthy grub. Because of the spores in the blood, it becomes increasingly difficult to see the dorsal blood vessel as the milky disease develops. In the final stage of the disease, the entire grub (even the legs, through which the blood circulates as it does through other parts of the body) has a milky white appearance. If one of the legs is snipped off by pressing it with a fingernail, a drop of blood will be formed on the remaining stump. The drop will be clear and watery in a healthy grub and opaque and white in a milky one. The final test for milkiness is to examine a drop of blood with a compound microscope for the presence of disease organisms.

The female Japanese beetle lays eggs in the ground in summer. The grubs that hatch from the eggs are one-sixteenth inch long at first, but they feed and grow until they are about an inch long. As they grow, they pass through three stages, or instars. The change from one instar to the next is brought about by shedding the outer skin. The grub stage starts in midsummer and continues through the fall and winter and until the change to pupa late the following spring or early sum-

970134°—52——27

mer. During the pupal stage, the insect is inactive and goes through the changes that produce the beetle. The cycle from egg to adult beetle requires nearly a year and is spoken of as one generation or brood of the insect. For example, the eggs laid in the summer of 1951 gave rise to the beetles of 1952, and this constituted the 1951–52 brood.

Grubs of the Japanese beetle may become infected by milky disease at any time during the long span of grub life. In experimental feeding tests, more than one-half of all milky grubs found became diseased in the first and second instars. If a grub becomes diseased in one instar, it seldom lives to change to the following instar, but continues on for some time in a fully milky state before it finally dies. Grubs that become infected in late summer or fall frequently live through the winter with the disease in a dormant state. As the temperature rises in spring, the disease again becomes active. Milky disease has been produced experimentally in prepupae, pupae, and adults of the beetle, but natural infection in these stages is probably not common.

Since grubs contract milky disease and die over such a long period, an inspection of the grubs in the soil will show only those that are milky at that particular time. You will find no trace of the ones that have become infected and died, because their bodies will have decomposed in the soil. The time that must elapse after the grub first takes in the spores until it is fully milky varies with the temperature. At 86° F., grubs will show the first symptoms of milky disease in 6 to 9 days. At lower temperatures it will take longer. Milky disease organisms will not develop at temperatures above 97° or so; therefore they cannot infect man, domestic animals, or wild game, whose body temperatures are higher than that. It also will not develop when temperatures fall below about 62°. The milky disease will not show up in spring-infected grubs until the soil temperature has been above this point for about 2 weeks. You would have to make soil examinations nearly every week during the time grubs are present to get a complete picture of the action of milky disease. You can estimate the mortality due to milky disease by making soil examinations in August, when the soil population is the highest for a brood, and then making later examinations to determine the drop in numbers.

A grub count made in the fall will show the number present just before hibernation. A count in May or June of the following year will show the number present as the time nears for the change to beetles. The number of grubs that are milky is usually highest at that time. The change in the number of grubs per square foot found in examinations in August of one year and June of the next year will give some idea of the number killed by milky disease in any brood. Of course grubs die from causes other than milky disease, and due credit should be given to any other known agent causing death.

Ralph T. White of the Moorestown laboratory has been in charge of investigations of the milky disease under field conditions for many years. I give a few examples of the action of the disease as he found them.

Beetles were so abundant at the Glen Brook Country Club in Stroudsburg, Pa., in 1941 that the grubs caused serious damage to the turf. White uncovered no evidence of milky disease at that time. Using the spot method, plots were treated at 5- by 5-, 5- by 10-, and 10- by 10-foot intervals with the milky disease in October 1941. Soil surveys made all over the course on May 26, 1942, showed an average grub population of 66 per square foot. On the more heavily treated plots the count was 81 per square foot. If there had not been an abundance of rain the turf on the course would have been severely damaged by grub feeding.

When the new brood was in the ground in August 1942 the grub population on the course averaged 88 per square foot. By early June 1943, there had been a drop from 130 grubs per square foot to 31 in the 10- by 10-foot plot, from 53 to 11 in the 5- by 10-foot plot, and from 82 to 11 per square foot in the 5- by 5-foot plot. In two untreated areas, grubs averaged respectively 62 and 66 per square foot in June and there was turf damage there but not in the treated plots. The disease incidence ranged from 30 to 62 percent in treated areas in late June and a few milky grubs were found in untreated areas, showing that the disease had begun to spread. By the fall of 1943, 2 years after the treatment with spore dust, milky disease had spread all over the course and there was no evidence of turf injury. The entire course was examined in June 1949 and the grub population averaged only 1.7 per square foot; 69 percent of all grubs found were milky. In 1952 so many spores were in the soil that turf damage by beetles is unlikely in the future.

On the extensive grounds of the Perry Point Veterans' Administration and Facility at Perryville, Md., the grubs in the soil averaged 37 per square foot in August 1939, and there was marked browning of the grass due to their feeding. A low incidence of milky disease occurred at that time. Soil surveys were made at Perryville several times each year from 1939 through 1949, except during some war years.

In surveys covering six broods, White found reductions of 86.1 to 94.4 percent in the grub populations, due largely to milky disease. At the time of the June examinations, the number of milky grubs varied from 27.7 to 67.0 percent. In computing the figures, all milky grubs were counted as dead, since milky grubs almost always die. The question has often been raised how, with grub mortality approaching 90 percent in each brood as it did at Perryville, it is possible to have enough beetles emerge from the disease-laden soil to produce such high grub counts by August each year. One reason for this is that a female beetle deposits from 40 to 60 eggs in the ground, and if conditions are favorable a few beetles can concentrate many eggs in a small area. Another reason is that so many favored food plants grow at Perryville that beetles move into the area to feed from other places and, as they lay their eggs in the well-cared-for turf, grub populations are high in August each year.

In parts of the District of Columbia, the beetle had become so abundant by 1940 that feeding grubs had injured turf. The disease was well established in one small area and 55 percent of the grubs were diseased. Some disease occurred in a few other places but there was no evidence of it in most of the District. The application of spore dust, started in 1940, was continued. By 1949 a total of 3,784 pounds had been applied to 2,929 acres by Federal agencies. Spore dust also was applied in places near the District by entomological agencies of Maryland and Virginia, and commercially made spore dust was purchased and applied by civic groups.

In August 1941, the grub count in soil surveys made at seven treated places averaged 31.5 per square foot. By June 1942 the count at the same places was 7.0 per square foot; 12 to 70 percent of the larvae were milky. Information is also available from surveys made at 10 widely scattered places twice each year from 1946 through 1949. The grub population at those places averaged 5.0 in June 1947, 5.4 in June 1948, and 1.6 in June 1949. The disease incidence at the time of the surveys averaged 46.0 percent in 1947, 45.5 percent in 1948, and 57.0 percent in 1949. There has been a noticeable reduction in beetles in the District in recent years, as would be expected from the low grub populations, despite weather conditions that favored an increase in numbers. Surveys made in 1948 at several points where no spore dust had been applied showed the disease to be present at all of them. Milky disease probably occurs to some extent wherever there are grubs in this area. The Japanese beetle was present in great numbers in 1951 in places a short distance from the District of Columbia; it was believed that the low populations in most parts of the District could be attributed largely to the high incidence of milky disease there.

THE MORE GRUBS there are to the square foot the faster the disease becomes established and the more rapid the spread. There had been high grub populations in the three locations I have described and the number of disease spores in the soil had become large. Grubs will usually be plentiful in a place where there are many favored food plants on which the beetles can feed and plenty of good turf for egg laying. This was the case at all the places where disease activity has been described. If the conditions are less favorable, there will be fewer beetles, grub populations will be lower, and it will take longer to build up effective numbers of spores in the soil. Therefore, the situation may not always be so favorable as in the instances given. In order to get the disease established as soon as possible, spore dust has sometimes been introduced where the grub population was as low as one or two per square foot. The build-up of disease in such places is likely to be slow. Under highly favorable conditions, good establishment of the disease has been obtained by the second season after introduction. A longer time has been required in less favorable situations.

SINCE THE SPORES can survive under adverse weather conditions, the dust will not have to be reintroduced once the disease has become established in the grub population. Even though unfavorable weather conditions have sometimes reduced grub populations to as low as one grub per square foot, the disease still persisted and became active again as the grub count rose. In some newly colonized places, milky disease is not yet so effective as it eventually will be because of the time needed for it to become generally established. Because of lower temperatures in the northern part of the beetle-infested area, some observers feel that a longer time will be required for the disease to become established there than in warmer places to the south. However, we have every indication that the disease can become established wherever the beetle exists.

Because of the time needed for effective build-up, the use of the disease as an immediate control measure is not advised in situations where beetle grubs are so numerous that turf is being injured. A rapidly acting poison should be used to kill the grubs and protect the grass. The poison will not kill any spores that are present. Spore dust, applied at a heavy dosage to such places, has reduced the number of grubs and checked the injury, but not always in time to prevent additional damage to the grass.

Milky disease organisms probably occurred in our native white grubs before the Japanese beetle was introduced into this country. When the type-A disease was first found in grubs of the Japanese beetle, grubs of many of our native species of May beetles, or June beetles, were examined closely and disease was found in several of them. Apparently several kinds of bacteria caused milky diseases in different kinds of white grubs. The type-A organism may have existed in some of the native grubs and then, with the arrival of the Japanese beetle, found its grubs favorable to its development. As far as we know, only certain species of white grubs develop the milky disease. We have no records of a condition just like it in other insects.

MY DISCUSSION has dealt largely with the important type-A organism because it is the one usually found in field-colonizing work. Another organism sometimes found in grubs of the Japanese beetle is *Bacillus lentimorbus*, which causes the type-B milky disease. Attempts to produce the spore form of this organism in artificial culture, as with type A, have been unsuccessful. Spore dust made of the type-B organism has been tested in field plots, but the results obtained were not so good as those with type A.

BESIDES THE MILKY DISEASE, many biological agents destroy beetle grubs—other bacteria, parasitic fungi, nematodes, parasitic and predaceous insects, birds, and other animals. The amount of summer rainfall is an important factor, for beetles are always reduced in number following summers with low rainfall. Among all of these factors, the milky disease is perhaps the most effective in checking the build-up of the Japanese beetle, as it spreads into new areas, mostly free from its natural enemies. Any agent that slows down or checks this initial build-up makes the pest less destructive. The milky disease is such an agent and this is the reason for colonizing it in newly infested places as soon as the grub population reaches the point where it will support the disease. Diseased spores will then increase in numbers in the soil as more and more beetle grubs become diseased. The number of beetles will decrease again and the Japanese beetle will cease to be the serious pest it has been.

IRA M. HAWLEY *is a native of New York State and a graduate of the University of Michigan. He has a doctor's degree from Cornell University. From 1931 to 1952 he was in charge of biological studies of the Japanese beetle. Dr. Hawley's special interest has been in the seasonal cycle of the insect in different parts of the infested area, its reaction to weather conditions, and its spread and abundance from year to year. He retired in 1952.*

For further reading on milky disease Dr. Hawley suggests Two New Spore-forming Bacteria Causing Milky Diseases of Japanese Beetle Larvae, *by S. R. Dutky, in the Journal of Agricultural Research, volume 61, pages 57–68, 1940, and the Bureau of Entomology and Plant Quarantine publication E–801,* The Effect of Milky Disease on Japanese Beetle Populations Over a 10-Year Period, *by R. T. White and P. J. McCabe, issued in 1950.*

The Vapor-Heat Process

A. C. Baker

The Mediterranean fruit fly invaded Florida in 1929 and spread rapidly across the big citrus region of the State. A campaign to wipe out the Medfly began immediately. It was the first campaign in history that was successful in eradicating a widespread insect pest.

But it was 19 months before the quarantine was lifted. Meanwhile a crop was maturing, which the country needed and on which the economy of Florida depended. A way had to be found to market the crop without risk to the rest of the country. Only embargo had been considered safe against this fly, and fruit from countries where it occurred was excluded.

What should be done? All possible information about the fly was gathered. The cold winters of the Northeastern States made those States seem safe for the shipment of fruit from protective zones—the 9-mile zones surrounding the known infested zones. But the Southern States, from North Carolina and Tennessee westward, and the Pacific States, from Utah and Idaho westward, were looked upon differently. The occurrence of the fly there might mean disaster. Idaho was included as a barrier. It was decided to let no citrus from Florida enter any of those States. In order to open the markets there, a treatment had to be developed that would guarantee fruit free from any living stages of the fly.

Time was short. The new crop was hanging on the trees. To develop a process before the fruit would be ready to move seemed impossible. We had one hope. Larvae of the Mexican fruit fly, which also attacks citrus, had been killed when fruit infested with them had been heated to 110° F. or above.

We had the death points for those larvae. Larvae of the two flies were much alike. What would kill the one should kill the other.

But there was no known way to heat large loads of citrus fruit evenly. Three things we had to do: Devise a method by which carlot loads of oranges and grapefruit could be heated evenly and quickly; work out, with this method, the death points of the larvae; and develop a system that would provide a guarantee equal to that by embargo.

A year or two earlier we had bought for the Orlando, Fla., laboratory of the Department of Agriculture, for a scientific study having theoretical aspects, a large cabinet designed to provide constant temperatures and humidities. A heated mixture could be forced continuously through the cabinet. We made the cabinet ready.

We loaded it with infested fruit. Driving through the fruit was a mixture of saturated vapor, air, and fine water mist. Experiments used the mixture at 110° F., at higher and at lower temperatures. At 110° for 8 hours all larvae were killed. Our experiments continued. We needed to know what would happen to large populations of larvae, to find a source of unlimited numbers of larvae, and to get a place where we could handle them freely without the possibility of jeopardizing the other phases of the work that were wiping out the flies and their larvae from Florida.

Hawaii was the ideal place. The Mediterranean fruit fly was abundant there in many kinds of fruit. Work could go on there without danger. A cabinet was shipped and the mortality phases were transferred to Hawaii.

Experiments had been under way at the laboratory to determine the response of different varieties of citrus to the treatment as at first laid out. The response was good: After the fruit was cooled, the experts could not distinguish treated fruit from untreated fruit. Many other kinds of fruit and vegetables that the fly was known to attack were included in the studies.

The crop was pressing us. No commercial equipment could handle carlot loads on the basis of our laboratory specifications. Engineers with commercial concerns were approached, but in vain. We tried unsuccessfully to treat carlot loads of storage fruit in various ways. The problem was to find a good way to obtain saturated vapor, which on condensing would release latent heat, a kind of hidden heat.

We were able, however, to sterilize well two cars of grapefruit. They were shipped to the New York auction. One sold at premium prices. Sterilized fruit was acceptable to the trade. But to handle the volume we needed standard equipment that would provide saturated vapor uniformly.

Arthur B. Hale, a commercial engineer, standing by and watching a laboratory run, found the solution. In a short time he had mixed water sprays and steam sprays in a metal mixing box. A thermostat to a valve on the steam line controlled the temperature. A multivane blower pulled the mixture across baffles to remove the drops of water. It forced the mixture of air, saturated vapor, and fine mist downward across a spreader in the room and through the load of fruit stacked in the field boxes. A false slatted floor, on guiding studding, directed the spent mixture to a return duct and the mixing box. A drain in the floor carried off the condensate. Standard commercial equipment had been born.

Within a month of our test cars on the auction, sterilized fruit was rolling to market. In November authorization was given to ship to the Southern and Pacific States.

The Texas citrus industry was young in 1927 when the Mexican fruit fly appeared. Soon infestations were occurring each year late in the season. The marketing volume was small, however, and the crop could be moved early enough to avoid serious loss from infestation. Large numbers of the fly moved northward each year to Texas from large wild reservoirs in northeastern Mexico, but fruit of each season's crop was safe to ship throughout the country before the migrations came in.

Because the fly had become a problem to two countries, Mexico and the United States in 1928 joined in a study of it. A cooperative laboratory was established. Mexico provided the buildings and grounds. The United States provided the personnel and equipment. By 1929 the laboratory had developed temperature death points for the larvae of the Mexican fruit fly—information that later proved to be so useful in the work in Florida. D. L. Crawford, working in Mexico as early as 1914, had proposed that citrus be heated, but there was no known way adequately to heat it. The laboratory also had perfected traps and lures for the flies to record the incoming migrations in Texas.

Industry needed a longer marketing season and wider markets. That meant the shipment of fruit while flies were present. The laboratory in Mexico worked out the specifications against the Mexican fruit fly and sterilization was introduced with the crop of 1937–38. It made the late fruit safe. During the years the process has been improved. Time was reduced to a 4-hour holding period at 110° F. and a 6-hour approach to raise the temperature of the load. In 1948 experiments got under way on a new scheme by which the holding period would be eliminated. Fruit has been sterilized by running it up quickly to higher temperatures, then stopping. It has responded well.

The sterilization rooms also have been improved. A ventilating stack was devised through which the air and mist are driven off immediately after sterilization. Automatic temperature recorders now plot on charts the temperatures within the fruit and those of the incoming vapor mixture.

Sterilization in Texas was necessary to expansion. By 1950 half a million tons had been sterilized.

Mexican fruits subject to attack by fruit flies were long excluded from United States markets. Many still are. But with infestation of grapefruit in Texas by one Mexican species and the application of the vapor-heat process there, is was logical to admit Mexican citrus, subject to attack by the same insect, when sterilized by the same process under American supervision and guarantee. In September 1945, therefore, Mexican oranges, grapefruit, and Manila mangoes were authorized to enter the United States under those conditions. Packing plants were built for the Canadian and European trade and sterilization rooms were set up and equipped. Mexican oranges, sterilized by the vapor-heat process, began reaching American markets in 1950.

Hawaiian fruits and vegetables had been excluded for years from mainland markets because of the presence in the Islands of the Mediterranean fruit fly and the melon fly. The major agricultural industries of Hawaii, sugar and pineapples, are processing industries that the flies did not involve. But it was believed there that the opening of mainland markets would stimulate off-season production of fresh vegetables, would foster increased production of certain fruits, and ultimately would result in a profitable export trade. The specifications for Florida against the Mediterranean fruit fly were retested; specifications against the melon fly were developed; and in 1938 mainland markets were opened to Hawaiian fruits and vegetables formerly embargoed. The volume moved after sterilization, however, has been small.

In 1946 the serious oriental fruit fly invaded the Islands. It attacked almost everything, even fruits that the other two flies had left alone. Embargoes were placed on all fruits it infested. The new fly proved to be harder to kill than the other two. New specifications for the process had to be worked out, and because the treatment was more severe, tolerances had to be studied for everything involved. But by 1950 mainland markets were open to sterilized papayas, bell pepper, Italian squash, tomatoes, and fresh pineapples.

The primary aim of the vapor-heat process was to sterilize citrus fruits against fruit flies. The process, though, has been tried experimentally on other things infested by other insects. It has been tested on house plants infested by scale insects, and the results have been promising. Narcissus bulbs infested by mites and the larvae of bulb flies were heated to 111° F. for 2 hours, and the pests were eliminated. The process also increased the growth of the bulbs. Gerbera was cleaned of cyclamen mites by a 30-minute treatment. The process eliminated mites on strawberry plants. Blossoming was a little delayed but growth was excellent and fruit production was heavy and continuous. Experiments with nursery stock looked promising, but difficulty was experienced with the balls of earth in which the roots were held. Since the process influences dormancy it brought astilbe into bloom for earlier marketing.

The vapor-heat process has an unusual feature. When citrus fruit is sterilized, any that is thorn-pricked, bruised, lightly infested, or similarly injured turns brown over the injured spot and is easily culled when the fruit later runs over the graders. Much fruit, so injured, is not detectable when not sterilized. When shipped it breaks down in transit before reaching the market. Sterilization, therefore, reduces transportation losses.

A. C. Baker *is engaged in cooperative research in Mexico for the Bureau of Entomology and Plant Quarantine. The development of the vapor-heat process under his leadership in Florida in 1929 made possible the successful plan for eradicating the Mediterranean fruit fly there while marketing the citrus crop that it attacked. Men working with him also established the specifications for that process for citrus in Texas, for fruits and vegetables in Hawaii, and for oranges, grapefruit, and Manila mangoes in Mexico.*

Cold Treatment of Fruits

Henry H. Richardson

Hundreds of tons of fresh grapes, pears, and other deciduous fruits are imported into the United States in late winter and spring each year to replenish our own supplies. Practically all of it comes from the Southern Hemisphere, where the season is the reverse of ours and where many localities are infested with the Mediterranean and other fruit flies.

Rather than deny ourselves the fruit and eliminate this foreign trade, quarantine treatments have been developed to rid the fruits of the fly maggots that might be present in a few of them. The fruit is given a cold treatment, with regular commercial cold storage or refrigerator facilities. As a result, no live maggots were present in the 285,000 boxes of South African and Argentine grapes, pears, plums, and apples that we imported in 1951, mostly into New York City markets.

The cold treatment was found effective against the Mediterranean fruit fly more than 40 years ago. Exposing the fly larvae, eggs, or pupae to temperatures of 36° F. or below for varying periods will do the job. The first large-scale commercial use of the treatment was in Florida in 1928. A large part of the citrus fruit within the area where a Medfly eradication campaign was being waged was allowed to move to market after holding it at 34° or below for 12 days.

Grapes and other fruits from Medfly-infested areas later were allowed entry if they were treated in approved cold-storage plants on arrival in New York. Finally in 1937 the treatment was approved for application to fruit on shipboard during the voyage.

In order that the period at the

selected temperature can be measured accurately, the fruit must be brought down to the treatment temperature, a process called precooling. Therefore the cold treatment consists of two steps—precooling the fruit to its very center to the desired temperature and holding the fruit at or below that temperature for 12 to 20 days, depending on the species of fruit fly involved and the treatment temperature selected, whether 33°, 34°, 35°, or 36° F.

Precooling must be completed before the shipment leaves the country of origin, so that an inspector of the department of agriculture of that country may so determine it and officially designate the beginning of the second step of the treatment. As the voyage from South Africa or Argentina takes 18 to 20 days or more, the cold treatment fits in very well with shipping schedules. During the voyage a continuous record of the air and fruit temperatures in each compartment is kept by an automatic temperature-recording instrument. On arrival in the United States, officials of the Bureau of Entomology and Plant Quarantine review the temperature charts. If they find no irregularities, they declare the fruit to be cold-treated and release it from quarantine.

The entire procedure always is under careful supervision. Shipments may only be made on ships previously tested and approved by representatives of the Department of Agriculture. Approval is based on proper circulation of air in the refrigerated compartments, adequate cooling capacity and insulation, proper operation of the temperature-recording instrument, and identification of the temperature-sensitive elements that are placed in the compartment. Before the fruit is loaded for the trip, the operation of the temperature recorders is checked and the temperature - sensitive elements are tested to determine whether they register the correct temperature. The elements are at the ends of long extension cords that extend into the compartments. Their correct placement there, in the air stream and in the fruit, is supervised also by the agricultural inspector. When the fruit is properly precooled—that is, all of the fruit-pulp temperatures are down to the desired treatment level—the inspector issues a certificate of precooling, which is forwarded to the port of entry in the United States.

The temperature-recording instruments are mostly of the multiple-point electronic type and usually are accurate down to one- or two-tenths of a degree Fahrenheit. One instrument may record the temperatures from as many as 16 locations. The records are printed one at a time on a roll chart. Each record is identified by a number printed beside it. The instrument may be adjusted to print at 1- or 2-minute intervals, so that each point can be recorded at least once every 16 minutes, or oftener if there are fewer than 16 points. Each sensitive element is labeled with the same code number that is printed on the chart. Usually each compartment has at least four elements, two to measure the air temperature and two for the fruit. The roll chart is about 128 feet long, enough to record the temperatures for a voyage of 30 days.

In South Africa all the fruit is exported by a government control board and consequently is all handled at one point. It is precooled to 30° F. in a dockside cold-storage plant and is transferred to the holds of the vessel so quickly that the temperature rises only 1° or 2°. Thus the cold treatment can be started as soon as the fruit is on board.

Dockside precooling facilities are not available in Argentina. Fruit is usually loaded from refrigerated railroad cars or must be transported by truck from cold-storage plants at considerable distances from the docks. Hence the fruit is only at 38° to 40° by the time it is loaded aboard ship, and precooling must be finished there. The fruit must be stacked in a more open manner to permit air to pass between all fruit boxes to insure uniform cooling. As the process usually takes 2 or 3 days or more, the fruit must be loaded several days before the ship is to leave. All fruit boxes are stamped with an identification mark to preclude mixing treated and untreated fruit. That is necessary because some untreated fruit is imported for treatment after its arrival in New York.

The cold treatment of fruit by itself would be relatively expensive as a method of killing fruit flies. But because imported fruit must be kept under refrigeration anyhow to prevent spoilage, its use during the voyage as a quarantine treatment has proved to be practical. Most modern ships have adequate refrigeration, so that usually it is necessary only to install the temperature recorders and to control the temperatures more carefully. The fact that the fruit is completely clean or disinfested on its arrival in this country removes the risk of disseminating fruit flies.

As a result of the uniform precooling and temperature regulation during the voyage, the fruit arrives in better condition than it used to. The efficiency of the treatment often has been demonstrated upon inspection of cold-treated fruit for other insects. Dead fruit fly larvae have been found—evidence of the hazard involved in the importation of untreated fruit, of the positive effect of the treatment, and the need for continued careful supervision to protect our own fruit industry.

HENRY H. RICHARDSON *studied at Massachusetts State College and Iowa State College and joined the Bureau of Entomology and Plant Quarantine in 1926. He worked on fumigants and other insecticides at the Agricultural Research Center at Beltsville, Md. During the Second World War he served in the Army Sanitary Corps. Since then he has worked at Hoboken, N. J., developing treatments for plants and products regulated by plant quarantines. In 1949 he was sent to Argentina to help that government in the treatment he here describes.*

Traps Have Some Value

Howard Baker, T. E. Hienton

The habits of insects that cause them to hide in sheltered places, that cause them to travel on foot over open spaces toward sources of food, that make them to fold up and drop when disturbed, that attract them to favored food plants, colors, odors, and lamps suggest the use of traps to reduce their numbers and bring them under control.

Traps are devices by which to catch insects unawares. Their possible value in insect control has long been recognized. They used to be the main way to control many pests.

Most traps are only partly effective and continue in use only until more effective treatments are devised or to supplement other methods, but they have contributed greatly to our knowledge of insects. They are a useful tool of research and extension entomologists and often are invaluable in conducting and evaluating the results of large-scale control programs.

Insect traps may be small or large and simple or complex, take any one of a variety of forms, and operate on one of several principles. Most of them combine means or materials that force or draw insects into a receptacle that prevents their escape or holds them long enough to permit destruction. Popular interest in them is great, and research continues to improve them and expand their use.

Traps may be as simple as boards on the ground near plants, a furrow around a field, or a lantern over a tub of water. Or they may be a specific lure, such as an aromatic chemical or lamp, plus a suitable device for capturing or destroying the insects.

Trapping insects under chips, stones, boards, and other materials in appropriate places was an early recommendation for getting rid of insects that naturally hide in such situations. The method recommended about 1840 for the plum curculio required that the trash be cleared a couple of feet from the base of the trees and bark chips, stones, and other similar materials be put in the cleared place as hiding places for the adult curculios, which were then collected and destroyed at regular intervals. The method was less effective than others and was soon dropped.

A somewhat similar way to control cutworms was recorded as early as 1838: Compact handfuls of elder sprouts, milkweed, clover, mullein, or almost any green vegetable were placed in every fifth row and sixth hill, and pressed down with the foot. Regular visits and examinations would expose the worms, which could be killed with a sharp instrument.

Poison was added later to the trap material so that the routine examinations could be dispensed with. Wireworms have also been lured under board traps and killed. Corn was protected from them in the late 1800's by placing small bunches of cut clover poisoned with paris green in water under bits of board at intervals through a cornfield. Large numbers of the parent beetles were killed in this way. Squash bugs, too, hide under such things as trash and boards. They have long been partially controlled in home gardens by trapping the adults under small pieces of board put near the plants. The trapped bugs must be collected and killed each morning.

Joseph Burrelle in 1840 suggested winding something around the trunks of apple trees or placing a cloth in the crotch and then destroying in a hot oven the trapped codling moth larvae. The larvae leave the apples when full-grown and spin their cocoons in protected places on the trees. Before long, others found that more worms could be trapped if the rough bark was scraped from the trees and the ground beneath them cleared of weeds and trash. Thus a larger proportion of the worms was forced to the bands.

Banding materials vary considerably. A hay rope was popular in the 1860's. Heavy wrapping paper, building paper, crepe paper, corrugated paper, flannel cloth, canvas, and burlap came into use later. The bands had to be removed and the worms in them destroyed every 10 days or so during the period they were leaving the fruit. An improvement that came in the 1920's was a band, usually of corrugated paper and coated with beta naphthol in oil, which killed the worms cocooning in them. Under favorable conditions such chemically treated bands often capture 50 percent or more of the worms that develop in the fruit.

Screening or otherwise enclosing packing sheds to trap codling moths that emerge in spring also takes advantage of the habit of codling moth larvae of cocooning in protected places. Worms maturing in apples after they are picked may cocoon in whatever container they happen to be in at the time or in a protected place in the packing shed. If harvesting equipment is stored in the packing shed, one can trap moths as they emerge and keep them from the orchard. Moths so confined are attracted to an incandescent lamp at night and can be killed by an electric-grid trap.

Some insects—among them the plum curculio and pecan weevil—fold up, drop to the ground, and play dead when they are disturbed. For years injury of the plum curculio was reduced simply by jarring the trunk and larger branches of infested trees to dislodge the adult curculios onto a sheet spread beneath the tree. The sheet was a trap from which the beetles were collected and destroyed. For a long time that was the only recommended way to fight the pecan weevil, a serious pest of pecans. It is about 50 percent effective.

Some traps are designed to catch the insects that hop or jump when disturbed. A hopperdozer is one of the best known. It is merely a long, narrow, shallow trough of boards or metal and mounted on runners that can be drawn across a field to catch grasshoppers. A vertical shield, about 3 feet high, at the back of the trough is filled partly with water. Sometimes enough kerosene is added to cover the water with a thin film. The grasshoppers fly up to avoid the hopperdozer, strike the vertical shield, and fall into the kerosene-coated water. One model merely traps the grasshoppers in a screen box and does not require the kerosene-coated water. Up to 8 bushels of grasshoppers an acre have been caught with the machines. Sometimes the back and sides are coated with a sticky material. Such a device catches many leafhoppers when it is run over clover and alfalfa fields. A modified hopperdozer, merely a sticky shield or a box with the inner walls coated with a sticky material, can be used for flea beetles in vegetable gardens.

CRAWLING INSECTS are easy to trap, especially with traps made with a barrier. When chinch bugs, armyworms, wingless May beetles, and such are moving from one field to another they can be halted by deep, dusty-sided furrows plowed across their path. The loose dirt keeps them from escaping. The insects will fall into post holes dug at intervals along the bottom of the furrow. They can be destroyed with kerosene or crushed with a heavy stick. Irrigation ditches sometimes prevent movement of Mormon crickets from range land to irrigated fields. Sticky bands can be used to bar the progress of crawling insects (the fall and spring cankerworms on apple, elm, and other fruit and shade trees, the white-fringed beetle on pecan and other trees, and climbing cutworms on a number of host crops). Also used are chemicals, such as creosote or calcium cyanide, spread or poured along the line of march of chinch bugs and supplemented by a series of post holes on the outer side to capture the repelled bugs.

Small insects that fly or are carried by wind often are caught by a simple trap made by coating with a sticky material a piece of paper, board, wire screening, or the inside of an open-faced box, cylinder, or cone. Sticky flypaper is an example. Sticky traps are useful for studying the flight habits and dispersion of leafhoppers, aphids, psyllids, scale insects, and other insects. For that purpose the traps may be hung on standards in yards, fields, or orchards, in trees, or mounted on a moving vehicle. The color of the coated material may affect the number of insects caught when the trap is stationary. Yellow and other colors to a lesser extent seem to increase the attractiveness of traps to insects during hours of daylight.

Light has been used for a long time to attract night-flying insects to traps. Open flames and lanterns have been superseded by electric lamps. Several hundred kinds of insects are attracted to light at night, among them the codling moth, European corn borer, tobacco and tomato hornworm moths, corn earworm, and cigarette beetle.

Factors like wavelength and intensity of radiation of lamps affect the responses of insects. Ultraviolet, blue, and green generally are more attractive than yellow, red, and infrared. The near ultraviolet, or black-light, region, is very attractive to the European corn borer and the hornworm moth. Attraction of night-flying insects increases with an increase in intensity, although not in the same ratio, up to about one-fourth that of bright sunlight.

In places where night-flying insects are bothersome, yellow and red lights or lamps, which are less attractive to insects, should be chosen in preference to white or blue lamps.

THREE TYPES of electric insect traps are the grid, suction, and mechanical. A lamp usually is used as the attractant with all three types, although baits may also be used effectively with the grid and suction types.

Eighty-five pounds of Clear Lake gnats, attracted by an electric lamp, were caught in a single night in a suction-type trap. Each pound contained about 1 million insects. House and stable flies attracted to a bait in an electric-grid box trap have been destroyed at the rate of 100,000 a day. More than 500 hornworm moths were attracted and captured in 1 night with a mechanical trap.

The grid type is made in several shapes and sizes. The grid itself consists of parallel wires, which are connected alternately to the terminals of a high-voltage, low-amperage circuit. An insect that tries to pass between any pair of wires completes the circuit between them and is electrocuted. A transformer is required to step up the supply-circuit voltage from 110 to 3,500 or more volts on the grid. A flat rectangular type, with vertical or horizontal grid wires, was developed originally for use on window or door screens in restaurants, bakeries, and dairy farms to control flies. It is used in field installations with an appropriate lamp to check time of emergence and heaviness of flight of such insects as the European corn borer and codling moth. Another type for field installations is circular and has a grid that encloses the lamp. A box type of grid trap, rectangular in shape and several inches deep, has a grid on the top of the box and is used principally for fly control where freedom from flies is essential for sanitary reasons.

Suction-type electric traps create an air current that draws insects into the fan and forces them into a porous bag or some such container. The insects are destroyed by pouring hot water over them, crushing them, or chloroforming them. Suction traps are useful for combatting the cigarette beetle in open tobacco warehouses. The tendency of certain moths to fly in circles around a lamp to which they have been attracted is less with the suction type than with the grid type of electric trap.

Mechanical traps include a lamp or another type of attractant. Below it might be a shallow pan that contains a liquid to capture the insects. A more complicated device has an enclosure that insects can enter easily but cannot leave because of baffles around the enclosure.

A trap of this type, developed by engineers in the division of farm electrification, Bureau of Plant Industry, Soils, and Agricultural Engineering, has shown some promise in the capture of hornworm moths. Five of these traps installed on a tobacco farm in Wake County, N. C., captured 12,874 moths in 1 week in September 1951.

Insects that feed on more than one crop may be trapped on one of them in order to protect another. When a few hills or rows of a favored host are planted in or around a main crop in time to attract a mutually injurious insect species, the main crop may not be seriously attacked as long as the trap crop remains attractive. The method is only partly effective at best and may have no value if the insects gathered on the trap crops are not destroyed before they leave it. The method has been suggested for protecting cantaloups and cucumbers from the pickleworm by planting bush squashes every 2 weeks in the cantaloup field; for protecting the seeded main crop from the onion maggot by planting rows of cull onions around the field and at intervals through the field to attract the egg-laying flies; for protecting host crops of the harlequin bug by planting as trap crops strips of mustard, kale, turnip, or radish early in the spring or late in the fall; for protecting peas from the pea weevil by planting border strips of peas in advance of the main crop; and for protecting corn from the Japanese beetle by planting a narrow strip of soybeans around the field of corn.

The trap-tree or trap-log method for trapping bark beetles in forested areas is a variant. Logs are felled to attract injurious bark beetles to a point where they can be destroyed easily. Long recommended in Europe, the method has not been found very effective in the United States.

The attractiveness of favored foods to insects can be utilized to trap many pests. Small paraffin-lined pill boxes or cans baited with sugar solutions or sirups, bacon rind, fat, or meat attract ants. The ants can be destroyed by dropping the container in a pail of boiling water or by adding a poison to the bait. Cylindrical, screen-wire cages baited with stale beer, a solution of one part of blackstrap molasses in three parts of water, milk, or fruit waste have long been used to catch flies. The standard screened cages are 12 to 18 inches in diameter and about 24 inches in height. They have an open-end, screen-wire cone inside that reaches nearly to the top. They are set on 1-inch legs over a shallow pan containing the bait. Similar fly traps baited with meat in water have reduced blow fly populations in large areas in Texas. Nicotine sulfate in the bait kills the flies as they are attracted to it. Flies are also killed on the grids of electric box traps to which they are attracted by a bait, or on electric window screens through which they may attempt to fly.

Fermenting solutions and aromatic and miscellaneous chemicals attract a wide variety of insects to traps. The trap for exposing the baits may be a glass jar, stew pan, tin can, or pail; a sticky-coated baffle or support may also be used. The lure may be a simple fermenting sugar or malt solution; an aromatic chemical such as geraniol, methyl eugenol, oil of sassafras, or terpinyl acetate; and protein material, such as powdered egg albumen, dried yeast powder, or casein; pine tar oil, linseed oil soap, or household ammonia; or a specialized material, such as the sex attractant, identified as gyptol, that is obtained from the terminal segments of female gypsy moths.

Traps based on lures for flying insects have received attention in recent years and some uses have been developed that have had wide acceptance. None, however, gives more than partial control.

In Japanese beetle infested areas in the East, bright-yellow traps hung on standards in sunny places have captured large numbers of the pest. A standard trap consists of an aromatic chemical (a combination of geraniol and eugenol), and bait dispenser (a small bottle with a wick) for holding the bait, and a baffle for deflecting the beetles into a funnel below the baffle leading to a receptacle for retaining the captured beetles. If they are used on a community basis in areas of heavy infestation, such traps may capture bushels of beetles and lower the general level of infestation. Used on an individual basis, however, the usual result is more extensive damage on the property on which the trap is placed.

Apple growers are as familiar with bait traps for the codling moth as the average housewife is with sticky paper to trap flies. The codling moth is attracted to fermenting sugar or malt solutions in wide-mouth glass jars, stew pans, or tins hung in the trees. The traps are more effective when hung in the tops of the trees and when the bait solution is supplemented with an aromatic chemical such as oil of sassafras, bromo styrol, oil of mace, or pine tar oil. Such traps were estimated to have caught nearly 500,000 codling moths in 4 years in traps hung at the rate of one per tree over 35 acres in the Pacific Northwest. Nevertheless, there was just about as much wormy fruit in the baited as in a comparable unbaited area.

A GLASS TRAP, known as the McPhail trap and shaped like an ink bottle, has been popular for exposing baits to attract fruit flies, particularly tropical and subtropical species. Fruit flies gain access to the trap through the partly open concave bottom. Baited with protein lures, this type of trap is useful against several Central American species; baited with a linseed oil soap, it captures large numbers of melon flies; baited with methyl eugenol, it is effective for male oriental fruit flies; baited with a fermenting sugar solution, it is attractive to both sexes of oriental fruit flies.

A small metal cylinder, baited with an extract prepared from the last two abdominal segments of female gypsy moths, is highly attractive to male gypsy moths. The cylinder has a rim at each end to which is attached a screen cone in which there is a hole for the moths to enter. A sticky paper lining prevents their escape. The use of the extract from two tips per trap will catch male gypsy moths, but the extract from 15 tips is necessary to attract the maximum number. The extract is dispensed on a corrugated paper roll suspended by a wire inside the cylinder. The traps are not practical for control, but were used in surveys of approximately 7 million acres for the presence of the gypsy moth in New England, New York, New Jersey, and Pennsylvania in 1950 and again in 1951.

THE INTEREST in traps remains at a high level and efforts to improve their effectiveness and extend their range of usefulness continue. The day may come when traps will be devised that are greatly superior to those we now have; the effort to develop them will be worth while.

HOWARD BAKER *is assistant leader of the division of fruit insect investigations, Bureau of Entomology and Plant Quarantine. He was graduated from the University of Massachusetts in 1923 and joined the Department immediately thereafter. After various field assignments on apple and pecan insects in the East, Middle West, and South, he was transferred to Washington in 1944.*

T. E. HIENTON *is in charge of the division of farm electrification, Bureau of Plant Industry, Soils, and Agricultural Engineering. Between 1925 and 1941 he was in charge of farm electrification investigations at Purdue University, where he conducted research on the development of farm electrical equipment. Dr. Hienton holds degrees from Ohio State University, Iowa State College, and Purdue University.*

Radiant Energy and Insects

Alfred H. Yeomans

Radiant energy can be applied in uncounted ways to kill insects. To prevent damage in storage and the transportation of pests into quarantined zones, it has been tested on fruits, potatoes, grains, wood, textiles, and perhaps other commodities. It has been used to kill larvae of mosquitoes in water. The aim is to kill the insect without harming the material on which it lives and to do it economically.

Radiant energy includes electrical energy of various wavelengths—such as radio, infrared, visible and ultraviolet light, X-rays, and gamma rays. It includes sound waves of various wavelengths, such as audible and ultrasonic. It includes also the energy from various atomic particles such as neutrons, alpha, and electrons.

Its action depends on the structure of matter. All matter, including insects, is made up of combinations of some of the 92 basic elements. Each basic element comprises a particular type of electric solar system called an atom. The systems themselves are composed of elementary particles, some of which have no electric charge or mass. Two of the particles, the protons (which have a positive electric charge) and the neutrons (which have no electric charge) comprise the basic mass of the atomic nucleus. The number of protons determines the type of atom formed. The nucleus is surrounded at a relatively great distance by negatively charged electrons having a definite pattern. Normally the number of electrons equals the number of protons in the nucleus. Atoms can be combined chemically into various patterns of electrical solar systems, or molecules, that form the various materials as we know them.

Living organisms comprise such complicated patterns of these molecules that we do not know everything about their make-up. Nothing is known of the substance that gives life to the combination of molecules forming living organisms.

The energy contained in one atom is tremendous for its size. Some types of atoms can be broken apart and their energy released, such as the explosion of the atomic bomb. The electric solar system of the atom may also be changed less drastically. Radiant energy in various forms and intensities is the means employed to do so. Radiant energy may be used to increase the natural vibrations of the atoms and molecules. The result is increased temperatures of the material. It may be used to cause chemical combinations of atoms that are reluctant to combine. Molecules also may be struck with enough energy to break off electrons and leave fragments called ions.

The molecular structure of an insect is so complex that when radiant energy is applied it is difficult to determine which factors or combinations of factors cause its death. Each type of radiant energy results in a predominant action on the molecule, however. When the energy is intense enough, the insect is killed because it is torn apart physically.

THE USE OF HIGH-FREQUENCY or ultrasonic sound waves, other than the audible ones, is a relatively new science. The first work on it was done in about 1900. Until the First World War it remained a laboratory study, in which small tuning forks, sparks, and special whistles were used to produce the waves. During the war, a narrow beam of high-frequency sound was used to detect submarines. Since then it has been used for underwater signaling, testing for flaws in materials, and removing smoke. It has been used experimentally in television, medicine, biology, and metallurgy. It helps in the agitation of solutions and in making some chemical reactions.

The discovery that ultrasonic signals sent through water killed fish and destroyed other marine life led to research on the effect of ultrasonics on biological organisms. Many types of organisms have been exposed to various frequencies and intensities. Fish and frogs were easily killed, and some insects and bacteria were destroyed. Some of the effects of ultrasonics on biological organisms have been clearly explained. Others have been explained only partly. The biological effects may be due to heat generated by the sound waves or, when the energy is intense, to the shattering or tearing apart of the organism. Less apparent effects are probably due to chemical changes.

The use of sound waves for most insect-control purposes is impractical because of the inefficiency of low-frequency waves and the difficulty in transmitting high-frequency waves through air. The high-frequency equipment available in 1952 could be used only in laboratory tests. Even when a specimen can be exposed in liquid, the high reflecting and absorbing qualities of materials shielding the insect make this method of controlling all but exposed insects impractical.

Sound is a mechanical force produced by rapid vibration in some medium, such as air or water. It travels in the form of waves. Sound waves have three major dimensions, frequency, velocity, and intensity.

The frequency is expressed in cycles or vibrations per second. One kilocycle (kc.) is 1,000 cycles per second. Frequency and pitch are identical in most respects; the notes of the musical scale are defined in terms of frequency. The human ear registers sound from about 16 to 20,000 vibrations per second. Beyond that is ultrasonic sound. The highest frequency so far attained is 500 million cycles.

The velocity of sound waves is determined by the medium in which they travel. Sound travels about 1,000 feet per second in air and about 4,800 feet per second in water, depending mainly on the temperature.

The wavelength can be determined by dividing the velocity by the frequency. In air, at a frequency of 1,126 cycles per second, the wavelength is about 1 foot. At 1,000 kilocycles, the wavelength in air is about 0.0344 inch and in water about 0.145 inch. The cathode-ray oscilloscope is used for making sound waves visible so that they can be studied.

The intensity is the amount of energy in the sound wave. A piano key struck violently or softly produces the same number of vibrations per second but with different intensities. Since it is the energy that does the work, the most effective sound machine is the one that can put the most power into the vibrations it emits. Intensities at low frequencies are measured in decibels and otherwise in watts per square centimeter. There are several instruments for measuring the energy in a sound wave, but it is difficult to obtain a high degree of accuracy in the measurements.

The greatest damage to insects is caused by sound waves having a frequency that produces the maximum absorption in the insect but the minimum in the surrounding materials. The amount of absorption has been found to increase with the square of the frequency of the sound wave, and with the viscosity and heat conduction of the material. The absorption of energy in air is quite high compared to that in water.

L. Bergmann, the German physicist, gives the following values for the distance in air and water in which the sound intensity is reduced to one-half.

	10 kc.	*100 kc.*	*1,000 kc.*
Air.....	220 m.	220 cm.	2.2 cm.
Water....	400 km.	4 km.	40 m.

The absorption in solids depends on the grain or fiber structure of the material. Such fibrous materials as cotton or glass wool have high absorption values.

The generation of heat at the boundary surface of two substances traversed by ultrasonics is especially strong.

When sound waves travel from one type of medium into another, part of the energy is reflected back into the first medium. The amount reflected depends on the density of each material and the velocity of sound. In an air-solid boundary, practically 100 percent of the energy is reflected.

When a sound wave meets an obstacle, the amount of reflection depends on the size and shape of the object. If the object is small compared to the wavelength, some of the wave tends to bend around the object. When sound waves strike an object at an angle, a certain amount of the wave is refracted and the rest is reflected. In liquids and solids, when the angle of incidence is greater than about 15 degrees, all of the wave is reflected.

Thin plates may or may not conduct sound waves, depending on their dimensions and physical properties.

The hard shell of some insects, such as adult roaches, has high reflecting qualities that are difficult to overcome.

When the sound energy is intense enough to cause shattering of the cells of the insect, the maximum bursting action perhaps is obtained by wavelengths shorter than the cell but long enough to produce natural resonance. That would cause the maximum in pressure on different parts of the cell at the same time. Gas bubbles may form which burst with tremendous pressure and disrupt the organism.

One of the earliest practical ultrasonic generators was based on the discovery by Pierre and Jacques Curie in 1880 that a specially cut quartz crystal, when subjected to pressure and tension, will develop electric charges on its crystal faces. Later it was found that this is reversible and that the crystal will expand and contract, thus producing sound waves when an alternating voltage is applied to the surface. It is possible to amplify the vibrations greatly by cutting the crystals properly and backing it in such a way that resonance or natural vibrations amplify the waves. The crystal can also be cut concave to focus the waves. A con-

970134°—52——28

cave crystal has been found to be more efficient than a flat one. At the focal point of converging sound waves, the energy is as much as 150 times greater than at other points. The crystal ultrasonic generator is called the piezoelectric type and is widely used to produce frequencies above 200 kilocycles. With special crystal rods they can also be made to produce lower frequencies. Because of the high frequency, this type of generator is not used to generate ultrasonics in air or other gases. The part of the generator that converts the electrical energy to sound waves, the transducer, is submerged in transformer oil, from which the sound waves are transferred to the testing medium.

Another method of producing ultrasonic waves is with the magnetostriction type of generator, which produces sound waves by the magnetization and demagnetization of a metal rod. When some metals are magnetized and subjected to tension and compression, a voltage is induced in a surrounding coil. The process is reversible; by magnetizing the rod by one coil and impressing an alternating voltage on another coil surrounding the rod, ultrasonic waves can be generated at the end of the rod. The waves generated depend on the frequency and magnitude of the applied voltage. Nickel or nickel alloy are usually used. To be efficient the rod must be designed properly to utilize resonance in amplifying the waves sent out. A circular plate is usually attached to the end of the rod to act as a radiator. The electrical circuit can be very simple. At low frequency it is possible to get large amounts of energy from this type of generator. At high frequency it cannot be tuned sharply and it is too sensitive to temperature. The magnetostriction generator usually is used for frequencies of 5,000 to 60,000 cycles. At that frequency it can be used to generate sound waves in gases and liquids. Magnetostriction and piezoelectric generators operate on a fixed frequency, with the intensity varying with the applied electrical energy. They are usually arranged so that the frequency can be changed by changing the transducer unit.

The siren type of sound generator is used to produce low-frequency sound waves in air. It is not so efficient as the magnetostriction or piezoelectric type, but it can handle a large amount of mechanical energy and the frequency can be changed by changing the speed of the rotor.

A number of exploratory tests of the use of ultrasonic waves on insects have been made at the Agricultural Research Center at Beltsville, Md. A piezoelectric type of generator, an Ultrasonerator, model SL 520, was used. It has four transducer assemblies, each designed to produce a fixed frequency. The frequencies available are 400, 700, 1,000, and 1,500 kc. We used the 400 kc. The maximum power input was 300 milliamperes (ma.) and 1,800 volts or 540 watts. Other tests were run at 200 milliamperes and 1,250 volts or about one-half power. Because of various losses, only about one-half the input power could be applied to the specimen. It is hard to expose test samples to the sound waves without shielding out a good part of the energy with the materials used to hold the samples.

Standing waves usually are set up in the enclosure in which the generator is operating. The position in which the sample is placed in relation to the standing waves is important. The crystal and other parts of the transducer are housed in a battery jar containing about 12 liters of transformer oil. The quartz radiates the ultrasonic waves upward through the transformer oil into a very thin copper cup, 3 inches in diameter and 3 inches deep, which contains circulating water. The test samples were suspended in the water-cooling cup. In the piezoelectric and magnetostriction generators operating in liquid, heat is produced in the liquid by the conversion of electrical to mechanical vibrations as well as by the absorption of the sound waves. Since the effect of temperature is fairly well known in entomology, the first tests were made to learn the other effects of ultrasonics. That was done by maintaining the circulating water at a constant temperature. However, temperature seems to modify other effects of ultrasonics and should be later explored.

We tested newly hatched codling moth larvae. We tried several means of holding them. Paper extraction thimbles or filter paper shielded them too much. Better results were had when the larvae were exposed in small glass vials containing water. In one series of the latter, when the temperature was maintained at about 17° C., and the power at 300 ma. and 1,800 volts with a 400-kc. frequency, the mortality varied from 100 percent at 40 seconds exposure to 25 percent at 10 seconds. When the temperature was increased to 20° C., the mortality varied from 70 percent at 5 seconds to 50 percent at 2 seconds. When the power was reduced to 160 ma. and 1,100 volts and a temperature of 20° C., the mortality was zero at 5 seconds exposure.

Codling moth larvae in apple plugs sealed with wax in test tubes were exposed to 400-kc. ultrasonic waves at 200 ma. and 1,250 volts, and at 300 ma. and 1,800 volts, and there was no mortality when exposure was 15, 30, 60, or 120 seconds. When the wax was not used, there was still no mortality when exposed for 10 minutes at 17° C. or 1 hour at 20°. Codling moth eggs, on paper and 1 to 4 days old, were exposed in the water testing medium to ultrasonic waves at 400 kc., 300 ma., and 1,800 volts with exposure times up to 120 seconds. About 30 percent failed to hatch, as compared with 14 percent of unexposed eggs.

Cabbage aphids, with the usual waxy coating, were exposed on small sections of cabbage leaves. The wetting agent, sodium lauryl sulfate (1–10,000), we used did not entirely prevent the formation of air bubbles on the leaves. A frequency of 400 kc. and a power of 300 ma. and 1,750 volts were used. The mortality varied from 62 percent at 4 minutes exposure to 100 percent at 30 minutes. No wax was visible on the dead or dying aphids, but the surviving aphids had a normal waxy coating. Probably the latter were protected by air bubbles. There seems to be some direct correlation between the mortality and the apparent absence of wax on the aphids.

Bean aphids on bean leaves were similarly exposed. A direct correlation was found between the mortality and the protection of the aphid by air bubbles. All aphids that were thoroughly wet were killed, and many of them were bloated.

Two-spotted spider mites were also similarly exposed. They were more thoroughly wet than the aphids and more than 90 percent were killed at exposures of 4 to 30 minutes. Some of the dead mites were flattened out as a result of the ultrasonic waves.

Third-instar yellow-fever mosquito larvae were exposed to ultrasonic energy with a frequency of 400 kc. At a power of 300 ma. and 1,800 volts, the larvae were all killed at exposures of 7 seconds at 25° C. to 9 minutes at 42°. Many of the larvae were eviscerated after exposure of 3 minutes or more. With a power of 200 ma. and 1,250 volts the larvae had a mortality of 92 percent after 2.5 seconds exposure at 22.2° C. and 100 percent after 20 seconds exposure at 23.5°. When the power was further reduced to 100 ma. and 750 volts, varying the exposure from 2.5 to 20 seconds did not seem to affect the mortality, which was about 35 percent at 21.5° C.

In previous tests on adult yellow-fever mosquitoes, in which low-frequency sound waves in air produced by a siren-type generator were used, there was no apparent effect on the mosquitoes at frequencies of 100 to 21,000 vibrations per second with an energy of 2 watts nor any ill effect at 13,000 and 21,000 vibrations per second at 100 watts energy. The mosquitoes were exposed in 20-mesh copper-screen cylindrical cages 2 inches in diameter and 7 inches long.

Various investigators have studied

the sounds made by insects. Many of them can now be accurately reproduced. It has been suggested that the sounds could be used to attract insects so they can be destroyed.

Radio waves have been used since about 1928 in a number of studies of insects. Most of the work has been with limited power and range of frequencies. The effect of the radio waves on the insect seems to be mainly due to heating. In experiments on bacteria, in which heat was removed as rapidly as it was generated and the temperature could be kept below the thermal death point, there was some evidence that high-intensity electric fields could kill without heat. Because heating would normally first kill the organisms from these high intensities, radio waves have been used only as a means of heating to the temperature required for the death of the insect. For practical purposes, heating with radio waves must be cheaper than the simpler heating methods, much faster, or less harmful to the commodity. In order to use and evaluate radio waves for insect control, some of their properties should be known.

Electromagnetic waves, which include radio waves, can be classified according to their wavelength. The audio waves useful in converting electrical to audible sound waves have a wavelength longer than 20,000 meters. The radio waves useful in transmitting energy over long distances have a wavelength of 20,000 meters to about 1 centimeter. Infrared rays have a wavelength from 1 centimeter to about 1 micron; visible light rays from 1 micron to 4,000 angstrom units, each color having its own wavelength band; ultraviolet from 4,000 to 300 angstrom units; X-rays from 300 to 1 angstrom units; and gamma and cosmic rays below 1 angstrom unit.

Electromagnetic waves are simply traveling fields in which the energy alternately varies between an electric and a magnetic field. These waves can be projected through a vacuum and, like other wave forms, have three major dimensions, frequency, velocity, and intensity.

The frequency is the cycles per second in which a field changes from an electric through a magnetic and back to an electric field. One kilocycle equals 1,000 cycles per second, and one megacycle equals 1 million cycles per second.

The velocity of electromagnetic waves in a vacuum is about 300 million meters per second, which is said to be the speed of light. The permeability and dielectric constant of the material through which the waves travel affect the velocity.

The wavelength is a function of frequency and velocity. In free space, the wavelength in meters can be computed by dividing 300 million by the frequency.

A field of high-frequency radio waves is more useful in heating poor conductors of electricity than in heating good conductors such as metals, which are affected mainly near the surface. If heating of good conductors by electricity is desired, it is more efficient to run alternating current directly through the conductor or to induce an alternating current in the conductor by surrounding it with an alternating current.

Heating nonconductors (dielectrics) in a field of high-frequency radio waves is usually done in an oven whose top and bottom are condenser plates. Oscillating tubes are used to activate one plate with a positive charge while the other is negatively charged and to reverse this charge with any frequency desired. With proper design, an efficient field can be established when specimens are inserted between the plates. To be efficient the frequency must be such that standing waves are not formed on the plates or in the specimen. Also, the plates must be shaped to prevent edge effects, and the specimens must establish a uniform dielectric constant between the plates.

The intensity of the field in radio waves is given in volts per centimeter. The permissible voltage across the electrodes in dielectric heating is limited by the dielectric strength of the material, which sometimes changes with frequency and temperature. When moisture is present steam may be generated. If the conductivity of the material is such that arcing occurs when high voltages are applied, the arcing will char the specimen.

The heat generated in a dielectric specimen placed in an electromagnetic field can be computed when certain electrical properties of the specimen are known. The properties can be measured but differ in various ways with the frequency of the electromagnetic waves and the temperature and moisture content of the specimen. Those factors cause each type of material to have an optimum frequency for efficient heating as well as an optimum frequency for producing a strong field without arcing. Heating has been found to vary directly with the square of the field intensity and with the first power of the electrical properties of the material.

The investigations of high-frequency radio waves of insects have shown that when the insects are imbedded in flour, grain, or similar material no noticeable selective action occurs on the insect. That is probably due to the conduction of heat either to or away from the insect as the temperature varies between the two. It is therefore likely that even though each insect might have an optimum frequency of its own, practical considerations would require the use of the optimum frequency for the material in which it is imbedded.

The electromagnetic waves can be reflected, refracted, and diffracted. The waves can be reflected from any sharply defined gap if its dimensions are at least comparable to the wavelength and of a different dielectric constant from that of the medium.

Infrared rays have been used for heating insects to the death point. If the insects are in grain or other such material, the material itself has to be heated to the required temperature. The infrared rays are readily absorbed by most materials so that the penetration is not so deep as with radio waves. The usual method of producing infrared rays is by means of the red incandescent bulbs that are widely used as heat lamps. In some commercial applications for heating grain to kill insects, the loose grain has been carried on belt conveyors between banks of infrared lamps both above and below the belt. In this way the grain is quickly brought to the required temperature to kill the insects infesting it.

Visible light rays have been used to attract insects so that they could be trapped and destroyed. No other effects have been found that could be used in insect control. They are produced by the common incandescent or fluorescent light bulbs giving a wide range of wavelengths of relatively low intensity. Light and ultraviolet rays, X-rays, and gamma rays are thought to be photons resulting from the collision of two atomic particles, the electron and the positron.

Ultraviolet rays, which have various effects on biological organisms, usually are produced by means of the mercury arc enclosed in quartz. This produces wavelengths from about 2,400 to 4,350 angstrom units. Most of the wavelengths shorter than 3,000 angstrom units can be shielded out by using ordinary glass. The intensity of this type of radiation is given in ergs per square centimeter. The equipment used for biological studies has produced relatively low intensity.

Ultraviolet rays cause excitation of the molecules but not ionization. This excitation sometimes causes chemical changes. The absorption of ultraviolet rays seems to depend on the molecular structure of the material and on its color. The wavelength of about 2,600 angstrom units is the maximum absorption length for one group of acids often found in biological life.

Ultraviolet rays do not penetrate very deeply because of high absorption and some reflection.

G. F. MacLeod, at Cornell University, found that bean weevil adults were not killed when exposed for 20 minutes at 30 cm. to a 5-ampere, 100-volt, 60-cycle Cooper Hewitt burner, but most of the eggs were killed when exposed for 15 minutes.

J. G. Carlson and A. Hollaender, at the Oak Ridge National Laboratory, found that the mitotic ratio of grasshopper neuroblast exposed to ultraviolet rays of 2,537-angstrom wavelength was reduced from 0.97 to 0.58 as the intensity was increased from 750 to 24,000 ergs per centimeter. They also found that the length of exposure time was not important as long as the material received the same total amount of radiation.

SEVERAL FORMS of radiant energy can be projected with enough intensity to cause ionization of molecules on which they impinge. X-rays, one of the widely used forms, are usually produced by impinging high-velocity electrons (cathode rays) against platinum in a vacuum tube. Gamma rays resemble X-rays, but have shorter wavelength and are usually produced by the disintegration of radium. Various atomic particles can be projected against materials with extremely high velocities and thus cause ionization. The particles include electrons, alpha particles, deutrons, (which are the nucleus of "heavy" hydrogen), and neutrons (which can be obtained from atomic piles). The atomic particles can be accelerated to high velocity by such machines as the Betatron and the Cyclotron. These machines use magnets to rotate the charged particles in spiral paths while they are being accelerated by high voltage. The X-rays, neutrons, and gamma rays cannot be bent by magnets. The different forms of radiant energy produce ionization by various methods. The electromagnetic (X- and gamma) rays produce ionization by Compton scattering or the photoelectric effect. They are much less efficient than electrons or alpha particles, which utilize an electric charge to produce ionization. The neutron with no charge produces ionization indirectly by giving high velocity to a nucleus by inelastic collision or by disrupting a nucleus. When ionization is severe, often other side effects, such as secondary X-rays, are produced. The Geiger-Müller counter is one of the methods for determining ionization.

The principal difference in the effects of the various types of ionizing radiation is in the density of the ion clusters and the depth of penetration. X-rays and gamma rays produce very low ion densities but penetrate deeply. The shorter wavelengths penetrate more deeply than the longer wavelengths. The atomic particles produce ion densities in relation to their mass or self-energy and their electric charge. The alpha particles produce much higher ion densities than the smaller electrons, but the penetration is greatest with the small particles. The penetration would depend on the intensity of electromagnetic radiation or the velocity and electric charge of the atomic particles and on the density of the material on which they impinge. The greater the penetration the less dense the ion clusters, but the density of the ionization would not necessarily be uniform along the path of the ionizing radiatron. In the case of the electrons, the maximum ionization occurs at about one-third the depth of penetration. When the velocity of the atomic particles increases sufficiently their mass also increases, which fact agrees with the Einstein theory that mass and energy are the same thing.

The energy unit used in nuclear physics is the electron volt. It is defined as equal to the kinetic energy that a particle carrying one electronic charge acquires in falling freely through a potential drop of one volt. It is often convenient to use the million-times greater unit: million electron volt (mev).

$$1 \text{ mev} = 3.83 \times 10^{-14} \text{ g. cal.} = 1.07 \times 10^{-3} \text{ mass units} = 1.60 \times 10^{-6} \text{ ergs} = 4.45 \times 10^{-20} \text{ kw.-hrs.}$$

Most of the machines used to accelerate particles or produce X-rays are classified according to their potential in volts.

The unit used to express the absorbed energy in ionizing radiation is rep (roentgen-equivalent physical). This replaces the roentgen unit (r) which has been widely used in X-ray work and which is primarily a unit for photon energy dissipated in an arbitrary material, air, where 1 r is about 83 ergs/g. The two are somewhat similar, but the roentgen unit would vary for tissue absorption to some extent with the type of tissue and the amount of radiated energy. One rep equals 83 to 100 ergs/g. tissue.

A dose of 100,000 rep corresponds to a temperature rise in water of 0.2° C. The temperature effects caused by ionizing radiation in the absorber are negligible.

Many experiments have been conducted on the chemical and biological effects of ionizing radiation since 1900, and yet the exact nature of what takes place has yet to be explained. These experiments indicate that doses of radiation required to produce measurable chemical changes *in vitro* often far exceeded those required for profound biological changes *in vivo*.

According to F. G. Spear, of the British Strangeways Research Laboratory, ionization and not excitation has become generally regarded as the link between energy absorption and biological response—there exists in the cell a specially sensitive volume within which ionizations are biologically effective; any ionization outside the sensitive volume is ineffective. It is known as the target or "Quantum hit" theory. Differences in sensitivity to radiation are explained by the chance distribution of ionization in the vital volume of the cell.

One of the methods of producing ionizing radiation has been investigated by the Bureau of Entomology and Plant Quarantine. The method uses cathode rays with ultrashort exposure time to treat food and commodities. The inventors say the ultrashort exposure time of using accelerated electrons destroys biological organisms with the minimum amount of harmful side effects to the material. The reason is that a time element is required for a chemical change but not for a biological change.

All kinds of ionizing radiation can be used under proper conditions for sterilization and preservation. The argument in favor of the electrons is that X-rays and gamma rays are not usable for practical purposes. The biological intensity of penetrating electrons is about 500,000 to 1,000,000 times greater than that obtainable with X-rays. The neutron particles that are easily obtained from the atomic pile cause a high amount of concentrated ionization that leads to greater amounts of side reactions than would be tolerable. The electrons accelerated by tensions up to 10 million volts would cause practically no radioactive byproducts in the irradiated products, but the contrary is true of neutrons.

According to R. D. Evans, a physicist at Massachusetts Institute of Technology, low-energy electrons, when traversing matter, result in elastic scattering by atomic electrons or nuclei. The intermediate-energy electrons result in ionization by inelastic collision with atomic electrons. The high-energy electrons (above 1.5 mev) cause inelastic collision with atomic nuclei and are deflected by the Coulomb field, so that X-radiation, together with ionization, is produced. The proportion of radiative and ionization losses depends on the type of material.

The cathode-ray machine investigated was of 3-million-volt capacity. The electrons were released from a specially designed tube through a window device about 15 cm. in diameter and of very thin aluminum. Each discharge of approximately one-millionth of a second was made by means of a spark gap and the discharges could be produced about once every second. The air scatters the rays slightly after they emerge from the window so that at a distance of 1 foot from the window the rays cover an area of about 1 square foot.

The penetrating range of electrons depends on the accelerating voltage and the density of the target. Electrons of 3 million mev attain a velocity of about 99 percent of light and penetrate into water as far as about 15 mm. with the maximum intensity of ionization at a depth of about 4 mm. and tapering off rapidly below that.

Some foods have been treated with this machine. The red color in meat often turned to dark purple when treated at room temperatures, whereas in such products as strawberries and carrots, a definite bleaching took place. These color changes were eliminated when the food was irradiated below −40° C. Tests have indicated that undesirable side effects could also be eliminated by evacuating the air around the object. Vegetables irradiated with overdoses of electrons showed a partial destruction of the cell walls and oozing-out of the cell contents.

We exposed some wood samples containing powder-post beetle larvae 3 to 7 months old to 1 and 2 impulses at a distance of 10 inches from the window and obtained 100 percent kill. This dosage was computed to be 145,000 and 290,000 rep.

Larvae of the confused flour beetle in an 8-mm. thickness of flour were exposed to one impulse on each side and all were killed. The dosage was computed to be 310,000 rep.

Complete mortality of the following insects resulted from similar treatment: American cockroach egg capsules, with a dosage of 350,000 rep; yellow-fever mosquito eggs, with a dosage of 600,000 and 900,000 rep; black carpet beetle larvae in 6 mm. of dog food, with a dosage of 310,000 rep; and bean weevil adults and larvae in one layer of lima beans, with a dosage of 460,000 rep.

Codling moth larvae buried at various depths in apples were killed when at a depth of 6 mm. with a dosage of 70,000 rep, and when at a depth of 8 mm. with a dosage of 140,000 rep. Death of the codling moth larvae extended over 16 days at a minimum dosage, whereas with an adequate dosage the mortality occurred within several hours of treatment.

Potato tuberworm larvae at depths of as much as 1 cm. in whole potatoes were exposed to a dosage of 350,000 rep. This resulted in 100 percent kill of 5-day-old larvae, 95 percent kill of 3-day-old larvae, and 83 percent kill in 2-day-old larvae. The difference was thought to be due to differences in depth of the larvae in the potato. The 5-day larvae were found at a depth of 4 to 9 mm. where the maximum intensity of radiation would occur. The younger larvae were less than 4 mm. from the surface of the potato.

In experimental work it is often necessary to trace the insect or insecticide. This can be done by using some radioactive material such as triphenylphosphate, and taking readings with a Geiger-Müller counter. The counter can be used not only for tracing but also for determining the amount of insecticide in a particular area.

Radiant energy has been experimented with for detecting the presence of insects in material. When X-rays were projected through material containing insects, the insects could be detected under certain conditions on film.

Reports have indicated that material exposed to "black light," the shorter ultraviolet wavelengths, may cause fluorescence when the light is projected on insects, thus making it possible to detect their presence.

Male screw-worm flies have been sterilized by X-rays and then released with the hope that if this were done on a large scale the normal populations would be greatly reduced.

Many contraptions that supposedly

use radiant energy for insect control have been given wide publicity. Some of them were probably meant to give satisfactory results, but the inventor was not familiar with the possibilities of radiant energy. Others probably were meant to fool the public. Some of these schemes have been investigated. One dubious machine was supposed to project various insecticides by means of radio waves. Another machine was supposed to kill insects in fruit by short impulses of high-voltage electric current. Insufficient time was allowed for heating and the method did not work, and arcing of the electric charges sometimes damaged the fruit.

So, IN SUMMARY, the use of radiant energy for controlling insects is still in the experimental stage and will probably remain so for a long time.

Sound waves do not penetrate most materials that shield the insect. High-frequency waves are difficult to transmit through air, and low-frequency waves do not efficiently produce enough heat to kill the insect. High-intensity waves will shatter the insect and also injure most surrounding materials.

Radio waves kill insects by heat and also penetrate dielectric materials readily, but the cost of operation compared with other methods, such as vapor heat, makes them impractical to use at the present time.

Killing insects by heat produced by infrared waves is restricted not only by the cost of operation but by the poor penetrating qualities of this wavelength.

The chemically active ultraviolet rays have such poor penetrating qualities that their use for most insect problems is impractical.

The ionizing radiation used so far is either very inefficient, as with X-rays and gamma rays, or does not penetrate sufficiently without harming the commodity or material on which the insect lives. The most promising future application of ionizing radiation will be for producing more penetrating electrons or more efficient X-radiation. In any case the high initial cost of equipment must be considered.

THE SUCCESSFUL APPLICATION of radiant energy is so dependent on a knowledge of the fundamentals of life and matter that both must progress together. The work with insects has opened up possible methods of control, however, and with the correlated work on mutations has added to the knowledge of life itself. It is hoped that, with the accelerated development of radiant energy equipment in recent years, increased interest will be shown in applying this energy to a study of insect problems.

ALFRED H. YEOMANS, *a technologist of the Bureau of Entomology and Plant Quarantine, has been engaged in investigating and developing equipment used in insect control. Some of his studies are concerned with such fundamentals as the effect of particle size, which must be considered when developing equipment. He is a native of California and a graduate of Ohio State University.*

For further reference:

L. Bergmann: Ultrasonics and Their Scientific and Technical Applications, *translated by H. S. Hatfield, John Wiley & Sons, Inc. 1946.*

George H. Brown, Cyril N. Hoyler, and Rudolph A. Bierwirth: Theory and Application of Radio-Frequency Heating, *D. Van Nostrand Company, Inc. 1947.*

J. Gordon Carlson and Alexander Hollaender: Immediate Effects of Low Doses of Ultraviolet Radiation of Wavelength 2537 A on Mitosis in the Grasshopper Neuroblast, *Journal of Cellular and Comparative Physiology, volume 23, No. 3, pages 157–169. 1944.*

J. H. Lawrence and J. G. Hamilton: Advances in Biological and Medical Physics, *volume 1, Academic Press Inc. 1950.*

G. F. MacLeod: Effects of Ultra Violet Radiations on the Bean Weevil, Bruchus Obtectus Say., *Annals of the Entomological Society of America, volume 26, pages 603–615. 1933*

F. G. Spear: The Biological Effects of Penetrating Radiations, *The British Medical Bulletin, volume 4, No. 1, pages 2–23 1946.*

Weather and Climate

Harlow B. Mills

Within broad limits, climate governs the general distribution of insects. Weather affects the numbers of insects within their areas of distribution and the fluctuations in numbers around the margins of the areas.

Weather is a snapshot photograph of the atmospheric conditions—winds, temperature, air pressure, precipitation, and humidity—at any one time. Climate is a composite picture of those conditions over a longer period. When we consider weather in relation to insects we are generally considering the effects of extremes of a variable atmosphere. When we think of climate we are thinking primarily of average conditions.

Because weather and climate are expressions of the same phenomena, differing only in time, it often is difficult arbitrarily to divide their effects on the insect populations.

Insects are limited in space and in numbers by many factors, some of which are not directly associated with weather or climate. A parasitic insect may be limited by the absence of its host animal, or a plant-attacking species may not occur in an area because of the absence or rarity of the plant upon which it depends. But in the main an insect is so completely imbedded in atmospheric factors that they must be considered as of great importance in controlling its occurrence and abundance.

Some of the factors composing weather and climate are obvious. Others are neither obvious nor easy to measure. Possibly others are unmeasured or undiscovered as yet. Often the factors work in intricate combination to affect living things.

But some factors are so conspicuous that they can be isolated to show that one cause will produce one effect. In a given area, for example, prolonged spring rains may produce many breeding pools and hence more mosquitoes than a dry spring with a lack of breeding pools. Heavy, pelting rains in the early summer may be the single factor that might end a threat of an outbreak of chinch bugs by destroying the small nymphs. Prolonged high temperatures may allow for an increase of house flies.

Unusually low summer temperatures may greatly reduce the numbers of an insect. That happened in 1950 when prolonged cool temperatures in northern Illinois reduced the second generation of European corn borers by allowing only about 10 percent of the first-generation borers to become pupae and to emerge as egg-laying moths, instead of the 50 to 80 percent that usually furnish the borers of the second generation. Thus, because of an abnormally cool summer in the area in 1950, a second generation of borers and consequent second-generation damage were not important.

Weather effects on insects often act over a short period, and the critical period may be missed in the field and completely hidden in the published weather data. In a day, or a few days, weather factors may reduce a population of insects capable of devastating a crop to one of no economic importance. Often investigators have overlooked this factor of timeliness, although in such insects as chinch bugs and grasshoppers it can be most important.

BECAUSE THEY ARE more easily controlled in the laboratory and measured in the field, temperature effects on insects have been studied more intensively than have the other of the obvious climatic factors. As insects are "cold-blooded," they respond directly to temperature changes—so directly, indeed, that temperatures can be ascertained with considerable accuracy by certain insect activities. For example, various insects' songs can be translated directly and with little error into temperature readings by the use of certain formulas. The snowy tree cricket emits high-pitched, tremulous chirps, each separated from the next by a pause of approximately the same duration. If you count these chirps for a minute, you can determine the temperature in degrees Fahrenheit by adding 40 to one-fourth of the number of chirps per minute. Thus, if there were 120 chirps per minute interval, the temperature would be 40 plus one-fourth of 120, or 70° F.

Insects may be active over a wide range of temperatures. S. W. Frost in his *General Entomology* wrote that certain soldier flies can live in hot springs where the waters are at 122°. J. H. Pepper and I reported in the *Annals of the Entomological Society of America* that the alpine rock crawler came to rest at a temperature of about 38° when given a choice.

Those extreme cases are evidences of insect versatility, but most species are active at intermediate temperatures and are affected by the day-to-day and year-to-year play of more usual and more expected temperatures. Warm and long summers allow the southern house mosquito to move far north, and the reverse situations push it south—a direct expression of the effect of temperature on the distribution of a pest.

Most of the overwintering larvae of the brown-tail moth are destroyed by temperatures approximating −25°; such minimum temperatures rear a wall of cold against northward dispersal. Likewise the average annual minimum isotherm of −15° marks roughly the northern limit of the San Jose scale.

Insects of tropical distribution seldom can withstand freezing temperatures. Those living in cold areas usually can exist under winter conditions only in one stage; the others are susceptible to destruction by low temperatures. Thus only the adults of chinch bugs can live through the winter, only the larvae of the brown-tail moth, only the eggs of the gypsy moth, and only the pupae of the tomato hornworm.

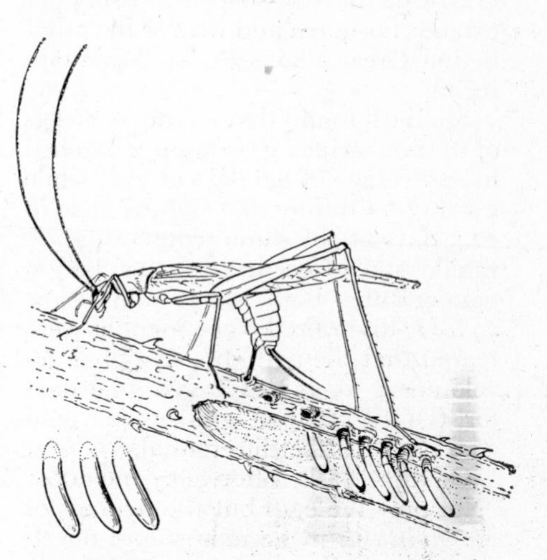

The female of the snowy tree cricket inserting her eggs into a raspberry cane.

The relationship between temperature, rate of growth, and distribution of insects is demonstrated by R. L. Shotwell, of the Bureau of Entomology and Plant Quarantine, who studied the development of several species of grasshoppers from the Great Plains.

The clear-winged grasshopper developed much more rapidly than the others he studied. That may explain why it is an important pest at high elevations and northern latitudes where the growing season is short. The tremendous infestations of this species which have occurred in such high mountain areas as the Centennial Valley of Montana illustrate the point. The lesser migratory grasshopper also has a rapid rate of development and thus a possible adaptation to a short growing season. It inhabits northerly regions and high elevations as well as lower and more southerly areas, where sometimes it has two generations in a season.

An interesting temperature relationship is illustrated by the two-striped grasshopper (*Melanoplus bivittatus*) and the differential grasshopper (*M. differentialis*). The two species are rather closely related in their morphology and habits. Both inhabit the same area, but the two-striped grasshopper extends far north and west of the other in the Great Plains-Rocky Mountain region.

Shotwell found that a sample of eggs of the two-striped grasshopper hatched in an average of 8.6 days at 77°, while a sample of differential eggs hatched in 22.5 days at the same temperature. A similar spread occurred at incubation temperatures both above and below 77°. He discovered when nymphs were reared that the period of nymphal development at 77° averaged 39.2 days for the two-striped grasshopper and 50.6 days for the differential.

On that basis, Shotwell concludes: "Not only the eggs but the nymphs of *M. bivittatus* make more rapid development at all temperatures than do those of *M. differentialis* . . . an earlier hatch and more rapid nymphal development enables *M. bivittatus* to develop in outbreak numbers in latitudes much farther north than those at which *M. differentialis* can do much damage."

What is the significance of these observations?

In the mid-1930's a series of exceptionally long, hot summers enlarged the area where the differential grasshopper could succeed. Making the best of the situation, the species appeared both north and west of its previous range. Many of the extensions of range did not continue, but an invasion into the lower reaches of the Yellowstone River has continued to exist, often in injurious numbers. The populations largely are limited to the more protected river bottoms and make less headway on the exposed uplands. That may not be entirely an effect of temperature, but anyway the two species have been shown to be limited in distribution in certain directions by the prevailing temperatures.

Shotwell's observations show what temperature may do in controlling the distribution of insects. Within the normal area of occurrence, the temperature often affects the numbers of a species by increasing the number of generations in a season and by increasing the number of individuals within any one generation.

This is well illustrated by Dwight Isley, of the Arkansas Agricultural Experiment Station, in his studies on the boll weevil. He learned that when temperatures were increased from 69.8° to 87.8° F., the time required to develop from egg to adult was cut in half. Further, a rise in temperature from 77° to 84° may result in an increase of about 70 percent in the number of eggs laid, and a decrease from 77° to 71.6° may, conversely, result in a reduction of about 50 percent.

RAINFALL in spring, summer, and autumn directly affects the abundance of the hessian fly. James W. McCulloch, of the Kansas Agricultural Experiment Station, found that to be true in four outbreaks of the pest in Kansas. "Three cases . . . were years of excessive rainfall," he wrote. "In the case of the outbreak of 1903 there was a superabundance of rain during the spring months and during the time that most of the injury occurred. The decline of each outbreak was accompanied by a decrease in the precipitation, which was generally much below the normal."

The amount and distribution of rainfall affect the abundance and the number of broods of the pest in a year. In one year, precipitation was normal from April to June and there were two large spring broods. July rainfall was low and fly activity ceased. It began again with increased rain in August and September. It produced a main fall brood and a supplementary fall brood just before cold weather. The following year there were good rains from April through September, and a prolonged midsummer brood appeared between the second spring and main fall broods. There followed a season with little July precipitation. The midsummer brood disappeared, and there was little activity through July and August.

H. H. Ross, of the Illinois Natural History Survey, observed the effect of

Beet webworm.

reduced rainfall on populations of sawflies. From 1928 to the spring of 1930, many species of sawflies were present in large numbers in central Illinois. He made intensive collections in two localities, one a prairie habitat along the railroad right-of-way west of Seymour, the other a wooded flood plain and hillside along Salt Fork Creek south of Oakwood. In the first, he found many species of the sawfly genus *Dolerus* and made daily catches from early April to the end of June of 50 to 500 specimens. At Oakwood, species of *Tenthredo* and *Macrophya* predominated. During May, June, and early July of 1930, excessive drought conditions prevailed throughout the Midwest; there were almost no spring rains. All plants wilted and many died. Insects became extremely scarce. Sawflies completely disappeared near Seymour and Oakwood. Not a single specimen was taken near Seymour until 1934, when one specimen of *Dolerus* was found. Since then there has been a gradual build-up of sawfly individuals in both localities, although never reaching the peak abundance of 1928 and 1929. All the species recorded in 1928 have finally become reestablished near Seymour. Near Oakwood, on the other hand, five of the species recorded as common in 1928 have not been found since. It is interesting to note that the Seymour species were all at or near the southern edge of the species range, and most of the Oakwood species were at the western edge of their ranges. Other North American records of the Oakwood species indicate that this Oakwood area may have been a small "island" on the periphery of the range. If so, the 1930 drought may have brought about a permanent eastward restriction of the range of the affected species. Thus the extremes in weather conditions during the drought weeks of 1930 profoundly affected the distribution and abundance of the sawflies for several years.

Temperature and moisture often act together to limit the numbers or distribution of insects. High temperatures and high humidities encourage the spread of a fungus disease that attacks many species of grasshoppers, for instance, and disease may decimate whole populations, nearly to the exclusion of other limiting factors.

An example of probable temperature and precipitation relationships to the distribution and abundance of an insect is given by J. H. Pepper, of the Montana Agricultural Experiment Station, for the beet webworm. That pest is a Great Plains and intermontane species and feeds on at least 86 species of plants that belong to 33 families. Many of the host plants are spread far beyond the limits of distribution of the insect, and food plants appear to be of no consequence as limiting factors. But when distribution of the webworm is plotted in reference to temperature and rainfall, we can make some correlations that are too close to be mere coincidence.

Eastern distribution of the beet webworm follows quite closely the 25-inch isohyetal line. (An isohyetal line connects points of similar precipitation, as an isothermal line connects points of like temperature.) Something inherent in the physiology of the pests will not allow them to invade indefinitely an area with more than about 25 inches of precipitation annually. Likewise the western edge of distribution is correlated with an annual precipitation of a little more than 10 inches, although this is not so clear-cut as is the evidence for the eastern boundary.

To the south the beet webworm distribution seems to relate to an average annual temperature of about 55°, and the insect does not extend beyond southern Kansas, northern Oklahoma, and New Mexico, areas that are traversed by the 55° annual isotherm.

The physiological mechanisms that keep the beet webworm from moving out of its area to the east and west are unknown, but the barrier to the south seems probably to be associated with a lack of frozen soil in the winter, for laboratory studies have shown that the common natural method of breaking the resting stage of the larvae and inducing them to pupate is their subjection to freezing temperatures.

The eastern, western, and southern barriers appear to be established, but according to Pepper "their northern range extends as far north as the country has been settled and their limits in this direction possibly have not been reached."

Limits of range appear to have been established by climate, but weather may affect numbers within the area of normal distribution, for the data show generally that a rainfall of 1 to 2.5 inches in each month from April to September is necessary for the most favorable conditions of development.

ANYONE WHO HAS FELT the attacks of salt-marsh mosquitoes blown inland from breeding marshes knows about the power of flight and the ability of insects to be carried by wind—two factors that account for their great range.

The direction of distribution of the hessian fly is that of the prevailing winds during the period when the adults emerge. The San Jose scale spreads far more rapidly with the prevailing winds than against them; the wind carries the nymphs as if they were so many particles of dust.

Wind currents, both lateral and vertical, are as much a part of climate and weather as are precipitation and temperature, and their effects on insects vary from the breaking of the resting period, as in some butterflies, to transportation across the face of the earth. Many persons have studied the air as a disseminator of insects. The observations of P. A. Glick were the first extensive explorations of the atmosphere as a distributive medium.

Glick, an entomologist in the Department of Agriculture, developed special traps, which he installed between the wings of a biplane. He made 1,314 flights at Tallulah, La., and 44 at Tlahualilo, Durango, Mexico. In trapping operations that totaled 1,007 hours, he collected 30,033 specimens of insects and arachnids at elevations of 20 to 15,000 feet. The largest number of specimens in a 10-minute trapping interval was taken in May and the smallest in December and January. He captured 18 different orders of insects, spiders, and mites. Among them were 24 species and 4 genera collected for the first time and new to science. Flies were almost three times as abundant in his collections as any other order. Insects were taken at elevations up to 14,000 feet and a spider at 15,000.

The vertical distribution in terms of the average numbers of insects in each 10-minute trapping effort was:

Elevation in feet	*Day collections*	*Night collections*
200	13.03	....
500	....	15.31
1,000	4.70	5.73
2,000	2.41	2.52
3,000	1.35	1.11
5,000	.64	.89

Those figures indicate that above 1,000 feet the atmospheric fauna is relatively static, but below 1,000 feet the number of insects in the air increases at night.

As to whether the insects at higher levels were alive when captured or whether desiccation and low temperatures had destroyed them, Glick wrote: "There is much evidence to support the conclusion that many of the insects taken in the upper air were alive at the time they were collected. Many specimens were alive when removed from the screens. Among the most interesting of these was one mosquito, *Aedes vexans,* and a cicadellid, *Graphocephala versuta,* taken alive at 5,000 feet; a coccinellid, *Coleomegilla floridana,* at 6,000 feet; an aphid at 7,000 feet, and a small dermestid larva, *Trogoderma* sp., at 9,000 feet."

In correlating catch with meteorological conditions, he found that most insects were taken when surface temperatures ranged from 75° to 79° F., when the surface dew point was from 60° to 64°, and when barometric pressures were between 29.85 and 29.89 inches. Most specimens were taken at low elevations when the surface wind velocity was 5 to 6 miles an hour, and fewest during a calm. As might be expected, convection and turbulence are important in populating the atmosphere.

"At an altitude of 200 feet more insects were taken when the air was smooth," he wrote. "At 1,000 feet and up to 5,000 feet more insects were taken when the air was rough or slightly rough. As the air became rougher greater numbers of insects were found proportionately at the higher levels."

He made his largest collections below 5,000 feet at daybreak and at sunset. He got more specimens on moonlight nights than on dark nights.

Glick collected a pink bollworm moth at 3,000 feet, red-legged grasshoppers up to 1,000 feet, the booklouse at 1,000, termites (*Reticulitermes virginicus*) at 3,000, flower thrips at 10,000, chinch bugs at 3,000, cotton fleahopper at 2,000, clover leafhopper at 10,000, cotton aphid at 13,000, red flour beetle at 3,000, spotted cucumber beetle at 3,000, striped cucumber beetle at 11,000, fall armyworm at 2,000, honey bee at 1,000, a crane fly (*Helobia hybrida*) at 14,000, the common malaria mosquito at 1,000, the stable fly at 3,000, and a gnat (*Hippelates texanus*) at 11,000 feet.

More astounding than the variety of insects found in the air, of which I have given only a hint, is that some completely wingless species were taken. Forty bristletails were collected at elevations up to 8,000 feet, 26 springtails

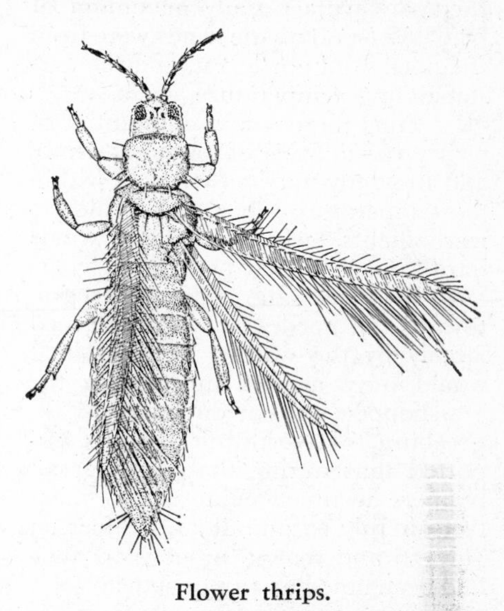

Flower thrips.

at altitudes as high as 11,000 feet, a flea at 2,000 feet, and worker ants and immature stages of a half-dozen different orders at many altitudes.

We have a more specific relationship of wind, temperatures, and insect movements. On July 1, 1938, when the best crops in a decade were in prospect in eastern Montana, a dramatic invasion of lesser migratory grasshoppers occurred. The insects, apparently originating at about the center of the border between the Dakotas, flew northwest into Montana and reached the Saskatchewan border by July 17, causing great destruction to crops.

The general direction of movement was from southeast to northwest. Although the insects had a "flight psychology," they seldom moved in numbers until air temperatures approached 80° F. J. A. Munro and Stanley Saugstad, of the North Dakota Agricultural Experiment Station, noted in connection with this flight that "the winds from the south and southeast, being warmer than those from other directions, were more effective in promoting sustained flights of the insects." They ascertained that in the 29 days following July 17 winds from the south and southeast prevailed and brought with them an average daily maximum of 88.9°. For 11 days the winds were from the north and northwest, and the corresponding temperature average was 79°. Thus there was a differential of nearly 10° in favor of southerly winds, and the daily maxima fell well within the temperature range that would release flights, while northerly winds hardly reached that point.

Very likely the flight direction toward the northwest was governed largely by the warmer winds, which would have assisted in carrying the grasshoppers in that direction. M. B. Freeburg, of Northwest Airlines, reported that during that flight grasshoppers were encountered at 7,000 feet on July 27 and at 11,000 feet on July 26 and that in other years they had been noted up to 13,000 feet.

With proper temperatures, it is obvious that the air could be filled with migratory grasshoppers to a great height above the ground, the direction of movement largely governed by prevailing winds. Winds may not represent the only factor in directional distribution, however, for on some days with northerly winds a few of these insects were seen to rise and unsuccessfully attempt to fly directly into the air currents and in the direction which they had previously followed.

We have a number of instances of the transportation of insects long distances each season through the air—apparently a normal occurrence with some pests. The corn earworm usually cannot withstand northern winters and passes the cold season in the Southern States, whence generally come the moths that produce the larvae that attack corn and tomatoes in the north.

The cotton leafworm is transported long distances through the air. A tropical insect, it winters almost entirely outside the United States. As the season progresses it moves farther and farther north, with successive generations on cotton. In the fall the adults may appear in the Northern States and even in Canada, far beyond the range of their host plant. Winter destroys all stages of the insect in the north, and the country is annually repopulated from the south.

Air currents have many indirect effects on insects. Heavy winds may assist in reducing numbers. Eggs of the corn earworm and the European corn borer are dislodged by wind from the host plants and drop to the ground. Wind movements affect other factors in the weather, changing temperatures, bringing in moisture, and the like.

Charles Macnamara, of Arnprior, Ontario, Canada, has said: "Apparently it is only their lack of chlorophyll and consequent inability to assimilate mineral matter that keeps them [insects] from eating holes in the universe."

The food habits of insects are as diverse as they are important, but what they eat, when they eat, where they eat, and how much they eat is largely controlled by the weather and climate in which they find themselves situated.

So responsive are insects to their meteorological environment that we must have knowledge of its effects if we are to understand, extend, or refine their control. We must know the direct effects of all weather factors and the indirect effects, such as those on hosts, parasites, and predators.

We can consider the climate of an area and fit certain crop practices into the expected climatic performance in order to reduce depredations of pests. We can measure weather and give short-range warnings of things to come. But until we can do something to control weather or can predict it accurately long into the future, we are limited to activities of the kind I have cited in any attempt to manipulate populations of pests by employing the assistance of the many factors that make weather and climate.

HARLOW B. MILLS, *a native of Iowa and a graduate of Iowa State College, is chief of the Illinois State Natural History Survey. Dr. Mills has worked on cotton insects in Louisiana and Texas, cereal insects in Iowa and Montana, and insects affecting livestock in Montana. For 10 years he was head of the department of zoology and entomology in Montana State College.*

Justus Watson Folsom's Entomology with Special Reference to Its Ecological Aspects (*third revised edition, P. Blakiston's Son & Co., 1922*), *Glenn T. Trewartha's* An Introduction to Weather and Climate (*second edition, McGraw-Hill Book Co., 1943*), *and the following bulletins and articles are suggested for further reference:*

P. A. Glick: The Distribution of Insects, Spiders, and Mites in the Air, *U. S. D. A. Technical Bulletin 676. 1939.*

Dwight Isely: Abundance of the Boll Weevil in Relation to Summer Weather and to Food, *Arkansas Agricultural Experiment Station Bulletin 271. 1932.*

Charles Macnamara: The Food of Collembola, *The Canadian Entomologist, volume 56, pages 99–105. 1924.*

James W. McColloch: The Hessian Fly in Kansas, *Kansas Agricultural Experiment Station Technical Bulletin 11. 1923.*

Harlow B. Mills: Montana Insect Pests for 1937 and 1938, *The Twenty-seventh Report of the State Entomologist of Montana, Montana Agricultural Experiment Station Bulletin 366, 1939;* Observations on Grylloblatta campodeiformis Walker, *with J. H. Pepper, Annals of the Entomological Society of America, volume 30, pages 269–274. 1937.*

J. A. Munro and Stanley Saugstad: Grasshopper Migration in North Dakota, *bimonthly bulletin, North Dakota Agricultural Experiment Station, volume 1, No. 1, pages 4–5. 1938.*

James H. Pepper: The Effect of Certain Climatic Factors on the Distribution of the Beet Webworm (Loxostege sticticalis) in North America, *Ecology, volume 19, pages 565–571. 1938.*

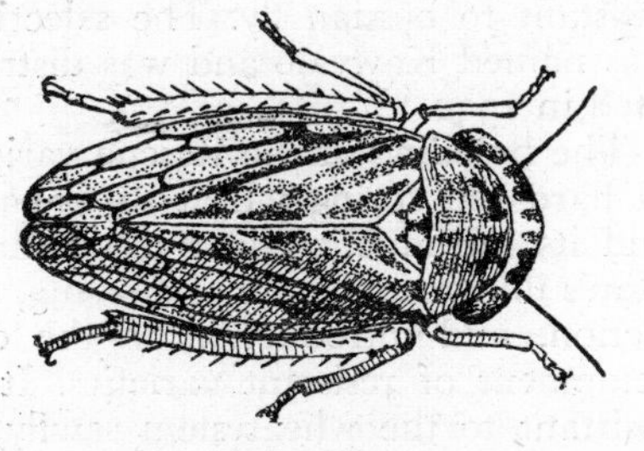

Clover leafhopper.

970134°—52——29

Resistant Crops, the Ideal Way

C. M. Packard, John H. Martin

Growing resistant varieties is the ideal way to protect crops from damage by insects. When a good resistant variety is available, a farmer may not have to change his desirable cultural practices or pay the costs of insecticides.

Farmers, entomologists, and agronomists have been seeking good insect-resistant varieties of crops for many years. The resistance of the Mediterranean variety of wheat to hessian fly was reported shortly after 1819, when it was brought into the United States. Its resistance has been maintained up to now. In recent years exhaustive searches for resistant varieties and the breeding of resistant characters into otherwise desirable varieties have been important phases of over-all crop-improvement programs—a line of research that has been productive and promising.

Records of insect resistance in nearly 100 species of plants were listed in 1941 by Ralph O. Snelling. They included such diverse crops as beans, cabbage, corn, wheat, alfalfa, cane fruits, tree fruits, and forest trees. He also listed examples of resistance to more than 100 species of crop pests, including aphids, beetles, borers, caterpillars, flies, grasshoppers, leafhoppers, sawflies, scales, and wireworms.

The word "resistance" is ordinarily used to mean the ability of a variety to avoid, tolerate, or recover from the attack of an insect to a greater degree than do certain other varieties. Resistance may be due to one or more characteristics in one variety or to entirely different characteristics in other varieties of the same crop. It may range from practical immunity down to moderate susceptibility, and the expression of resistance shown by any plant or variety may be modified by the environmental conditions under which it is grown.

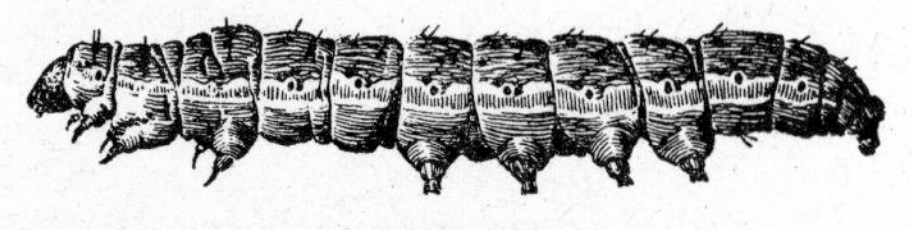

Corn earworm.

Freedom from insect infestation or injury may be due to inherent characteristics of a variety such as hardness or toughness of tissues, hairiness of leaves and stems, or to lack of nutritive value for the insect in its tissues or sap. Hessian fly maggots, for instance, cannot attain normal size or grow at all in certain varieties of wheat even though large numbers of them reach their normal feeding position under the leaf sheaths. Varieties of corn with long, tight husks suffer less injury to the ears by the corn earworm than varieties with short, loose husks. Hairiness of soybeans makes them unfavorable to attack by leafhoppers. The granary weevil destroys the grains of soft varieties of wheat much more rapidly than it does the grains of hard wheat. These are examples of what properly may be considered true resistance.

The ability of vigorous corn hybrids to produce satisfactory yields when attacked severely by corn borers is a good example of insect tolerance. Certain strains of maize grow new roots readily to replace those cut off by the corn rootworm. Some varieties of sugarcane may do likewise after attack by white grubs. The ability to outgrow injury by an insect is a type of tolerance rather than inherent resistance. Nevertheless it is of value in reducing crop losses caused by insects.

The freedom of a variety from infestation may be due merely to the fact that it is in an unattractive stage of growth at the time the insect is laying its eggs or doing its feeding. Early varieties of cotton, or the earliest bolls formed thereon, for example, may escape serious infestation by the boll weevil and pink bollworm. Moderately late planted corn may be much less infested by the European corn borer than very early or very late plantings. The ability to escape insect infestation may be fully as important as actual resistance.

INSECT-RESISTANT VARIETIES are obtained by four general procedures:

1. Introduction of varieties, from foreign countries or elsewhere, which might provide a source of greater resistance than exists locally.

2. Selection of resistant strains from existing varieties.

3. Crossing resistant species or varieties with those not resistant but possessing otherwise desirable characters, followed by the selection of desired recombinations.

4. Grafting otherwise desirable but susceptible species or varieties on the rootstocks of resistant varieties.

Ladak alfalfa, which was introduced from northern India, proved to be resistant to the pea aphid when it was tested in the United States—an example of how resistance to certain insects may be obtained by plant introduction, even though the resistance of the variety may be unknown in its original habitat.

The Kawvale variety of wheat is an example of selection as a method of obtaining insect resistance. A selection from Valley (Indiana Swamp) wheat, resistant to leaf rust, made by the Kansas Agricultural Experiment Station and the United States Department of Agriculture in 1918, was found to be resistant to hessian fly. The selection was named Kawvale and was distributed in 1932.

The breeding of the Rescue variety of hard red spring wheat in Canada and its introduction into the United States illustrate the use of crossing, selection, and introduction in the development of resistant varieties. It is resistant to the wheat stem sawfly, a pest of wheat in western Canada, Montana, and North Dakota. Rescue was developed after many years of intensive breeding by Canadian workers. A small lot of seed obtained from them was increased rapidly by the cooperative efforts of agronomists, entomologists, and growers in the United States and released to farmers. An interesting feature was the production of an extra crop during the winter in Arizona in time to make the seed available for spring seeding in Montana the same year. Rescue is widely grown in the infested areas of Montana, although its susceptibility to some forms of rust makes it less suitable for North Dakota.

The resistance of Rescue is ascribed in part to the fact that its stems are nearly filled with pith. Susceptible varieties have hollow stems that do not retard the activities of the sawfly larvae that develop inside the stems.

The grafting of European varieties of grapes on rootstocks of American varieties is an example of how resistance to a destructive insect may be gained by grafting. A plant-louse called the grape phylloxera, native to the eastern United States, attacks the leaves and roots of grapes. The varieties of grapes native to the East are nearly immune to the root-infesting form, but European varieties are killed or badly injured by it. After the insect was accidentally introduced into France about 1860, it nearly ruined the important grape-growing industry there. The industry was saved, however, by grafting the European grapes on resistant American rootstocks.

A special type of resistance, induced resistance, is listed by R. H. Painter in his book, *Insect Resistance in Crop Plants.* Induced resistance is obtained by applying to the soil fertilizers or insecticidal chemicals, which are taken up by plants through their roots. The ordinary conception of resistance does not include this means of reducing insect infestation, but the effects produced are similar to those resulting from natural resistance. R. G. Dahms, working in Oklahoma, reported that sorghum plants growing in soils low in nitrogen and high in phosphorus or chlorine are less favorable to chinch bug multiplication than soils high in nitrogen and low in phosphorus. Other workers have made similar studies on various crops and insects, but the information we now have does not indicate that a high degree of insect control can be obtained through the use of fertilizers. Several investigators have reported that the addition of parathion or certain other complex organic compounds to the soil makes corn, cotton, and other plants grown thereon practically immune to certain insects for several weeks. Insect control by means of insecticides that are taken up by the plants through their roots is still in the experimental stage, however, and cannot yet be recommended for practical use.

It has long been believed that vigorously growing plants well supplied with all needed food constituents are less subject to infestation or better able to withstand and outgrow injury than poorly nourished plants, but more evidence is needed on the subject. For certain insects the contrary may be true. The European corn borer, for instance, usually chooses the largest and most vigorous plants on which to deposit its eggs.

The discovery and improvement of insect-resistant crop varieties usually is not a simple procedure that the farmer can carry out for himself. Neither is it one that can be expected to solve all crop-pest problems and do away with all need of cultural and insecticidal methods of control. With certain crops and insects where little or no resistance is available, one has to continue using other control methods. The search for the desired resistance may require the testing of thousands of varieties, always with the possibility that none of them will prove to be resistant. Even after resistant varieties have been discovered, they are likely to have some undesirable qualities. In that case it is necessary to improve the resistant variety in other respects or to transfer the resistance to more desirable varieties by the tedious process of artificial crossing and selection. Fortunately, true insect resistance, when found, is transmissible from parent to progeny in accordance with the laws of heredity.

The process of crossing and selection ordinarily requires many years of cooperative teamwork by entomologists, agronomists, and geneticists in order to produce a commercially satisfactory insect-resistant variety. That would be a simple procedure so far as the insect resistance is concerned if readily visible plant characters responsible for or closely associated with it could be used in making the crosses and selections. In most instances, however, it has not yet been possible to find such characters. In an attempt to determine the nature of resistance to the chinch bug in sorghum, for example, the plants have been subjected to 30 or more chemical determinations, numerous studies of their structure, and hundreds of measurements of the growth, survival, and reproduction of the insects when feeding on different varieties. Despite this intensive research over a period of 30 years, it is still impossible to ascribe resistance in sorghum to chinch bugs to any specific plant character or constituent. It is therefore usually necessary to develop special methods of subjecting the varieties or selections to infestation by the insect in order to separate the resistant ones from the susceptible ones.

The problem may be further complicated by the existence of different races or strains of the insect itself in different regions and by the fact that a crop variety may be resistant to one of these races but not to others. The Dawson variety of wheat, for example, is resistant to the hessian fly in California but not to the races of that insect that are found in Indiana. With certain insects it has been shown that a strain capable of attacking and multiplying on a resistant variety of the crop can be isolated artificially in the laboratory. Thus it may be necessary to develop several resistant varieties, because a single one may not be suitable for commercial production in all the different regions where the insect is prevalent or may not even be resistant to all the different strains of the insect that may be actually or potentially present in a single region. The problem of preventing damage by an insect may therefore never be permanently solved by the development of resistant varieties of the crop which it attacks unless completely immune varieties can be discovered or produced. Such are rare.

Still another complication is that resistance to one insect species seldom makes a variety resistant to other species. Exceptions are Atlas sorgo and several varieties of kafir that are resistant to grasshoppers as well as to chinch bugs. In order to determine the resistance of a variety or selection to more than one insect, it must be adequately tested against each one individually. The discovery and breeding of insect-resistant varieties is a slow procedure, but progress can be made more rapidly with crops, such as wheat and corn, that produce seed in a single year than with crops, such as tree fruits, that require several years to reach the seed-producing stage.

AMONG THE MORE STRIKING EXAMPLES of rapid progress after sources of resistance were discovered is the development of wheat varieties resistant to the hessian fly. The fly-resistant variety Pawnee, which was released to Nebraska farmers in 1942 and to Kansas and Oklahoma farmers in 1943, came from a cross between the resistant variety Kawvale and the susceptible variety Tenmarq. The cross was made at the Kansas Agricultural Experiment Station in 1928. Pawnee was produced by 14 years of selection and subsequent testing in the search for desired characteristics. It has good resistance to the races of hessian fly present in central and eastern Kansas. It also has the other virtues of its parents, including high yield, good milling and baking qualities, and resistance to loose smut, stinking smut, and some races of leaf and stem rust.

Wheat growers and millers received Pawnee favorably. By the fall of 1946 it was the predominating variety in central and eastern Kansas. Regardless of other control measures they may apply, by its use farmers can obtain a considerable degree of automatic hessian fly control; they have assurance that the fly will not cause the complete crop failures for which it often has been responsible. Because of its resistance to hessian fly, Pawnee can be sown safely earlier in the fall than can the susceptible varieties. Thus it is available for fall pasturage in localities where the use of wheat as pasture approaches in importance its use as a grain crop. The comparative freedom of Pawnee from fall injury by hessian fly also makes it useful to the farmer who wishes to sow a large acreage, because with reasonable safety he can take advantage of good wheat-seeding conditions that may occur before the so-called fly-free date.

We must mention also the development of the soft white wheat varieties Big Club 43 and Poso 44, which are resistant to the hessian fly. They were released to California growers in 1944 and 1945 after about 15 years of crossing, backcrossing, and selection by workers in the Department of Agriculture and California State Agricultural Experiment Station. The high degree of fly resistance in the soft white winter variety Dawson was bred into the soft white spring Big Club and Little Club types of wheat commonly grown in sections of California where the fly is serious. The varieties selected from these crosses, Big Club 43 and Poso 44, also are resistant to bunt and stem rust. One strain of Big Club 43 is resistant to foot rot. These varieties have largely replaced the ones formerly grown in the Montezuma Hills district of California. Their use has practically solved the fly problem in that area. Wheat is one of the best crops to grow there, but the farmers had turned to other and less desirable small grains because hessian fly and the diseases had made wheat production unprofitable.

The greenbug is a little plant-louse that sometimes causes losses of small grains amounting to many millions of bushels in a single season. I. M. Atkins and R. G. Dahms, working in Texas and Oklahoma, observed marked differences in degree of injury by the greenbug to the varieties of wheat, barley, and oats growing in their experimental plots, where all varieties were exposed to moderate or severe natural infestation. Some varieties of wheat suffered only about one-fifth to one-fourth as much damage as others. Pawnee, a variety resistant to hessian fly, proved to be very susceptible to injury by the greenbug. Among a large number of barleys from world-wide sources several, mostly from the Orient, showed high resistance. None of the few varieties of oats in the tests showed outstanding resistance, but some differences in susceptibility were observed. The greenbug-resistant varieties of barley and wheat discovered in the plots are being used as parents for breeding resistance into new and more commercially desirable varieties. Further effort is needed to find varieties of oats suitable for the purpose.

The resistance of corn to insects has been investigated widely. Corn is subject to the attack of many insect pests. Because no satisfactory control measures are available for a number of them, the development of desirable resistant strains is particularly desirable. Before we had DDT and other insecticides for the European corn borer, the discovery and improvement of resistant varieties or strains of corn offered the most promising means of controlling the insect. The production of highly borer-resistant corn, if possible, would still be the best solution of this extremely serious problem.

Tests of a great many lines disclosed that only about one-half to two-thirds as many borers can survive in the most resistant inbreds as in the most susceptible ones. Among the most resistant inbreds are: Dent type of field corn—Illinois R4, Indiana P8, Iowa L304A, Iowa L317, Kansas K230, Michigan

77, 106, and 285, and Wisconsin CC5; Bantam type of sweet corn—Purdue W675–1, Iowa 461, Michigan 3116, Michigan 1828, and Iowa S5010–9; Country Gentleman type of sweet corn—Iowa 1627 and Iowa 1434; Evergreen type of sweet corn—Iowa S5316–5, Iowa S5328–1, and Iowa S5017–1. When those inbreds are used in the production of hybrids, some or all of their resistance is expressed in their progeny. In some instances in which two resistant lines are intercrossed, the resulting single cross has been infested more lightly than either of its parents. Several of these borer-resistant inbreds are used in the production of commercial hybrids.

The corn earworm is a bad and widespread pest of corn and other crops. Although good insecticidal methods have been devised for its control in sweet corn, no very satisfactory methods of controlling it in field corn are available. Encouraging progress is being made, however, in the search for and utilization of earworm-resistant strains of both field and sweet corn. We mentioned the protection of ears from earworms, weevils, and grain moths by tight husks that extend beyond the tip of the ear. Because little if any additional protection from insects is gained by extension of the husks more than 2 or 3 inches beyond the tip of the ear, there is no advantage in breeding for extreme husk extension at the expense of ear length.

In some strains of corn, characters other than long, tight husks are also responsible for reducing or preventing earworm infestation. Just what these characters may be has not been determined, but they are nevertheless being utilized in the breeding of inbreds and hybrids having earworm resistance along with other desirable qualities such as yield, resistance to lodging, disease resistance, and good feeding value. Some strains of corn come close to being actually immune to the earworm.

Hybrids with considerable earworm resistance, such as the field corn hybrid Dixie 18, especially suited to the Southeastern States, and the sweet corn hybrids Brookhaven, Pershing, Calumet, and Riogold, are grown on some farms. Among the promising earworm-resistant inbreds are the white-capped yellow dent lines L501 and L503 out of Tisdale; the white dent lines L578, F2, F3, K55, T18C, T85A, Ky27, Ky30A, CI.43, CI.61, CI.23, LanLhw, and 38Lhw; and the yellow dent lines L101, Mp2, F6, F44, HK61, 221, R3D, CI.2, 23R7, CI.6, CI.7, Kys, J8–6G, J7–2E, 5675, CI.33, and 317Lh. A number of promising earworm-resistant sweet corn inbreds have also been isolated. The development of desirable earworm-resistant hybrids, well adapted for farm production in the South or in the Corn Belt, however, was still in the experimental stage in 1952.

Various lines of corn are resistant to several other insect pests. Some lines are less subject than others to injury or infestation by the chinch bug, grasshoppers, and the corn leaf aphid. Only rarely has any one line been found resistant to more than one of them. However, lines resistant to the corn leaf aphid are also likely to be resistant to the European corn borer. Resistance to another group of insects, including the corn rootworms and white grubs, apparently due mainly to the larger and more vigorous root systems characteristic of certain strains of corn, has been mentioned.

Some of the insect pests of corn, such as the chinch bug, corn earworm, and corn leaf aphid, also attack sorghums. The chinch bug is probably the worst. Severe infestations in eastern Kansas and Oklahoma almost prohibit the growing of susceptible varieties of sorghum there and have been largely responsible for limiting the eastern extension of the main sorghum-growing region of the South Central States. Among the different varieties of sorghum, the milos are particularly susceptible to chinch bug injury, feterita and hegari are somewhat susceptible, and the kafirs have considerable resistance. Many hybrid selections of sorghum have been tested for chinch bug resistance, and a few strains have been found to be more resistant than either parent. One of the most resistant varieties, Atlas, has become the most popular sorgo in eastern Kansas, eastern Nebraska, and Missouri, partly because of its resistance to chinch bug. The kafir varieties Blackhull, Western Blackhull, and Pink also are resistant. Since 1928, a number of other resistant varieties have been released, including types suitable for combining, such as Combine kafir 44–14, Redlan, Resistant Wheatland 288, and Kaferita 811. A new resistant strain of the susceptible Honey sorgo produces a good grade of sirup and forage. Sorghum varieties that are most susceptible to chinch bug injury also are attacked most frequently by grasshoppers and European corn borer.

Sorghum generally is much less injured than corn by grasshoppers, the southwestern corn borer, and European corn borer. For that reason and also because of their greater resistance to drought, farmers have tended to substitute sorghum for corn when those pests or drought are prevalent. On the other hand, sorghum is perhaps more severely infested than corn by the corn leaf aphid, although varieties of sorghum differ greatly in susceptibility.

The common pea aphid and the potato leafhopper are two of the numerous insect pests of alfalfa. Both are small, pale-green, sap-sucking insects. They are abundant throughout most of the United States. The pea aphid causes the loss of one or more cuttings of alfalfa hay in some area almost every year. Good insecticidal control measures for the aphid on alfalfa have been found, but we think the use of resistant varieties may ultimately be the best way to end the losses. The resistance of the widely grown Ladak variety of alfalfa to the pea aphid was reported by R. H. Painter and C. O. Grandfield in 1935. According to Painter, "Eichmann and Webster suggest the use of resistant varieties of alfalfa for the control of pea aphids on peas. Studies in Kansas and at other stations have resulted in the isolation of several strains much more resistant than Ladak and progress in the control of an insect on two crops by the use of resistant varieties of one may become an actuality in the future." In this connection, we should explain that in some areas spring infestations of pea aphids on peas originate mostly from nearby fields of alfalfa in which they have overwintered.

"The injury and resulting losses caused by the potato leafhopper to alfalfa and red clover in the eastern half of the United States apparently have been far more extensive than has been realized," F. W. Poos and H. W. Johnson wrote in 1936. The statement is still true. They and other workers have found considerable differences in the degree to which the insect injures different varieties of alfalfa, red clover, sweetclover, and soybeans. In red clover and soybeans, the differences are associated somewhat with the hairiness of the different varieties. The possibility of finding and making use of resistance to the potato leafhopper as a pest of leguminous crops needs further investigation.

Resistance in potatoes to several kinds of insects has been reported. Sequoia is resistant to the potato leafhopper and the potato flea beetle. Some other varieties, individual plants within varieties, and other species of plants closely related to the potato are said to be resistant to the leafhopper or moderately so. Extreme differences have been found among potato varieties in resistance to the green peach aphid, which attacks potatoes as well as peaches. Some varieties are less injured by the potato psyllid than are others, and the tubers of some varieties are less subject to injury by wireworms than are those of others.

Cotton has several pests, and varietal resistance to some of them has been observed. Severe damage by leafhoppers was prevalent in South Africa, India, and Australia until varieties highly resistant to them were developed. Resistance to the pink bollworm in certain wild species of cotton has been bred into some cultivated varieties by hybridization and selection. Red-leaved varieties less subject to boll weevil infestation than some of the green-leaved varieties and hairless varieties less infested by plant-lice than hairy varieties have been reported. The available evidence on the relation between hairiness and plant-louse infestation has been conflicting, however. In studies of thrips, some varieties of cotton have shown less injury than others. Early-maturing varieties or the early plantings are more likely to escape severe infestation by the boll weevil and some other insects than late varieties or plantings. Resistance to several other insect pests of cotton has been recorded.

Considerable resistance to the sugarcane borer has been discovered in several varieties of sugarcane. A few of them are in commercial use. Some 25,000 pedigreed sugarcane seedlings, representing more than 225 parent varieties, have been tested for borer resistance in Louisiana or Florida since 1940. Of the commercial varieties, C. P. 34/120, C. P. 34/92, F. 31/962, C. P. 36/19, Cl. 38/32, F. 40/96, and C. P. 28/19 are resistant. C. P. 34/79, which has been released for commercial production in Florida, is highly resistant. A number of promising unreleased varieties have been classified as resistant. Depending on the variety, only about 25 to 80 percent as many of the joints are bored in the resistant varieties as in the moderately susceptible variety Co. 281. Working on Mauritius Island, which is heavily infested with a white grub, W. F. Jepson and H. Evans developed a variety by hybridization that tolerated injury and yielded twice as much as certain more susceptible varieties. One of the helpful measures for the control of the sugarcane beetle and the sugarcane weevil in Louisiana is the planting of vigorous varieties that give the best stands of cane and recover well from beetle injury.

We might cite many instances to show the presence of resistance of one kind or another to insects that attack such crops as fruit, nut and forest trees, small fruits, vegetables, and ornamental plants. The breeding and selection of insect-resistant varieties of those crops, many of which are long-lived perennials, involve greater difficulties than are encountered in the improvement of annual crops. Nevertheless, with the growing interest in insect resistance and recognition of its possibilities, more rapid progress very likely will be made in reducing insect damage to perennial as well as annual crops by this means.

C. M. PACKARD *is an entomologist. He was in the division of cereal and forage insect investigations, Bureau of Entomology and Plant Quarantine, for 37 years and retired in 1950. Until 1937, when he was put in charge of that division with headquarters in Washington, he worked at various field stations on the biology and control of cereal and forage insects.*

JOHN H. MARTIN *is an agronomist with 37 years of service in the Bureau of Plant Industry, Soils, and Agricultural Engineering. His work has included research on the culture, utilization, adaptation, genetics, economics, and improvement of small grains and sorghums throughout the States.*

For further reading on insect-resistant crops the authors suggest:

R. H. Painter's Insect Resistance in Crop Plants, *published by the Macmillan Co. in 1951.*

Ralph O. Snelling's Resistance of Plants to Insect Attack, *Botanical Review, volume 7, pages 543–586. 1941.*

In the Journal of Economic Entomology, volume 34: The Place and Methods of Breeding for Insect Resistance in Cultivated Plants, *by Ralph O. Snelling, pages 335–340;* Breeding Corn for Resistance to Insect Attack, *by J. H. Bigger, pages 341–347;* Breeding Wheat and Alfalfa for Resistance to Insect Attack, *by C. M. Packard, pages 347–351;* Breeding Vegetables for Resistance to Insect Attack, *by S. F. Bailey, pages 352–358;* The Economic Value and Biologic Significance of Insect Resistance in Plants, *by R. H. Painter, pages 358–367.*

Good Farming Helps Control Insects

W. A. Baker, O. R. Mathews

Farmers combat insects when they follow good practices in tillage, crop rotations, planting dates, and field sanitation—cultural methods that help control pests without extra costs in time, money, or convenience. Often they require only minor changes in the usual cropping procedures. They are particularly applicable to cereal and forage crops of too small an acre value to justify repeated sprayings. Some of them also can be applied to insects on vegetables, fruits, forest trees, and other crops.

Delaying the seeding of winter wheat until after the fly-free date gives protection against the hessian fly. Fall seeding is deferred so that the wheat does not come up until the fall flight of the insect is past. Only moderately late sowing should be practiced, however, because wheat sown extremely late is less productive than wheat planted at the optimum time and is more subject to winter injury by ground heaving or soil blowing. Tests as to planting dates have been conducted by entomologists for many years in the principal wheat-growing States. The tests have shown that the safe date for sowing winter wheat to escape fly injury in years of normal rainfall usually coincides nearly with the proper time for sowing in order to secure maximum yields of grain. Growers should consult their county agricultural agent or nearest experiment station to obtain information on safe sowing dates recommended for their immediate localities. The date depends on the latitude, altitude, longitude, weather fluctuations, and other local conditions. It varies considerably in broken or hilly country, even on the same farm—it is considerably later on the southern slope of a hill than on the northern slope.

Moderately late plantings of corn are damaged less than early plantings by the corn rootworm, or budworm, in the Southeast and by the European corn borer in Northeastern and North Central States. Midseason plantings of corn in southeastern Texas can better survive attacks of the sugarcane borer than can early or late plantings. The corn thus escapes the first brood but attains enough growth before the appearance of later broods to withstand the pest more successfully than do late plantings.

Adjusting the time of planting of field dry beans, snap beans, and lima beans in upper New York State so that the beans do not sprout until the larvae of the seed-corn maggot are no longer active in the soil is highly important in avoiding damage by it. Usually that is accomplished by midseason planting, but it is best to delay planting to avoid maggot injury until information is available as to maggot-free dates. Safe dates vary from year to year and the information can be had from county agents.

Grain sorghums planted in late April in southwestern Oklahoma mature with less chinch bug damage than do those planted in early June, although (if there were no insect damage) early June would be a more productive date. In the Gulf coast part of Texas grain sorghums often are planted in late February or March in order to be past the blooming period before many adults of the sorghum midge have emerged. In the potato-growing section of western Nebraska, June-planted potatoes need fewer insecticidal treatments for control of the Colorado potato beetle than early-planted potatoes. In areas in Louisiana subject to heavy damage to sugarcane from wireworms, planting of the cane as early in August as is agronomically practical gives better stands than when the plantings are made in late September or early October.

The proper disposal of crop residues often helps control insects.

The European corn borer survives the winter in the full-grown caterpillar stage, chiefly in the stalks of corn and coarse-stemmed weeds. In late spring or early summer the caterpillars change to moths, which fly to the new corn for egg laying. Complete disposal of the plant remnants in which the borers overwinter, by plowing them under or feeding them to livestock before spring emergence of the moth, is a good way to fight the insect.

The sugarcane borer has similar habits in sugarcane, sorghum, and corn along the Gulf coast, although the warmer climate there causes the adult moths to emerge earlier in the spring. Fall or winter disposal of the residues therefore also helps control the borer.

As to several wheat-infesting insects, among them hessian fly, wheat jointworm, wheat straw-worm, and wheat stem sawfly, plowing under the wheat stubble in summer or early fall prevents their emergence and consequently their ability to infest the new crop and to breed in the volunteer wheat that would otherwise grow in the stubble fields.

Of proved value is the proper disposal of cotton stalks in August for control of the pink bollworm in Texas. Early picking of the cotton and immediate elimination of the stalks greatly reduce the numbers of weevils the following year. Growers of other crops also know how important it is to destroy infested residues as an aid in insect control—sweetpotato weevil in the Gulf States, pepper weevil in California, pea weevil in Idaho, wheat stem sawfly in Montana and North Dakota, and wheat midge in the Pacific Northwest.

Other tillage practices strike directly at the insects while they are in vulnerable locations, particularly during hibernation. In the Lake Erie region, cultivation of vineyards in spring buries and helps destroy overwintering cocoons of the grape berry moth. A shallow covering of soil is enough to prevent the moths from coming out of the ground; it reduces the number of surviving insects so that a shortened spray schedule gives satisfactory control of the moth.

Most species of grasshoppers deposit their eggs in the ground in late summer and fall. The common injurious species spend 6 to 8 months of the year as eggs in the top 3 inches or so of soil. If the soil is plowed at least 5 inches deep some time during the period, preferably in the fall, and the surface layer well compacted by later cultivation, the hoppers hatching from the eggs cannot emerge.

Another method is to deprive insects of their food plants by tillage. The pale western cutworm, a serious pest of small grains in the Great Plains, cannot be controlled by spreading poisoned baits in infested fields, as can most cutworms, because it stays underground day and night and moves from plant to plant by burrowing along just beneath the surface. The worms die quickly after they hatch in the early spring, however, if all newly sprouted vegetation is killed by thorough cultivation as soon as the worms have had a little time to feed. They can survive for some time if they have had no food, but die quickly if they have once fed and then are deprived of food. The infested fields may therefore be kept clean by tillage for about 3 weeks, beginning soon after the worms have hatched, and then sown to spring grains with little subsequent injury to the crop.

The tillage implements used for general farm operations differ widely in their suitability for insect-control practices. We group the implements according to their effect on the soil and their application for insect control.

A. The moldboard plow, which covers residues completely, is effective in several ways. It buries material that would harbor overwintering insects. It may turn up overwintering forms of insects that have burrowed into the soil and expose them to weather and natural enemies. It may bury eggs or pupae so deeply that the young insects or larvae cannot emerge. Plowing is a recommended means of control against pink bollworm, boll weevil, corn earworm, European corn borer, corn root aphid, hessian fly, wheat jointworm, grasshoppers in the cultivated fields, wheat stem sawfly, and others.

B. We list six implements that partly incorporate crop residues in the soil. They are used primarily to prepare the seedbed and control weeds, but they may be effective in exposing eggs of certain insects to drying or to birds.

The one-way or vertical disk plow kills weeds. If the plowing is shallow it may expose some eggs of insects, such as grasshoppers and crickets, in cultivated fields.

The spring-tooth harrow sometimes is used to cultivate alfalfa in the fall and expose eggs of insects like grasshoppers and crickets. But the damage to the alfalfa may be greater than the protection afforded by reduction in insect population.

Field cultivators are used to kill weeds and maintain a surface resistant to erosion. They usually disturb the soil to about the same depth as the spring-tooth harrow.

The disk harrow has an action comparable to that of a vertical disk plow run shallow, but it is not so effective in killing weeds.

The lister is not well adapted to insect control. It does not stir all the soil and does not cover all the residues deeply. Practically all the crop residue is covered in the initial operation, but some of it may be exposed again by later tillage with other implements.

The harrow is used chiefly to kill small weeds or prepare a seedbed on land previously worked with other implements.

The six implements are of use in the control of insects that feed on weeds and volunteer growth to the extent that they destroy or prevent such growth. Some of the insects for which clean cultivation is recommended as a control are pale western cutworm, wheat straw-worm, and certain wireworms.

C. Five implements leave all residues on the surface. They may be of use against insects by controlling weeds and exposing insect eggs, but in most areas that is more than offset by the protection given to overwintering insects. Their use is dictated primarily by the need to control erosion. Among the insects favored by the retention of residues on the surface are the bollworm and the hessian fly. Spider mites and carrot beetle larvae have damaged wheat on straw-mulched land under conditions where there was no injury on land without residues.

The Noble blade is used chiefly for summer fallow tillage. It is an effective weed killer under dry conditions and helps control such insects as the pale western cutworm.

The rod weeder is good for clean tillage for fallow. It makes weed-free land for the control of pale western cutworm.

Sweep implements, with sweeps wider than those of the duckfoot, are used principally to leave residues on the surface for erosion control. They are effective in killing weeds in dry areas. Sometimes wireworms are more destructive to corn when a small-grain stubble mulch had been left on the surface.

The chisel is used for loosening the soil deeply to permit penetration of water, but is of little benefit against insects.

A plow without a moldboard has the same purpose and general effect as the chisel.

Rotation of crops often helps reduce crop injury, particularly by the insects of restricted food habits. White grubs, the larvae of June beetles, feed on roots of crops of the grass family and injure forage grasses and grain crops planted on land that has been in sod. But legume crops are unfavorable to their development. The proper use of legumes in the rotation or in combination with grasses in pastures greatly reduces white grub injuries. The corn rootworm often becomes abundant in fields that are planted to corn for two or three consecutive years. The insect is restricted in food-plant habits, however, and can be eliminated as a serious factor by suitable crop rotations.

EARLY HARVEST of some crops may prevent losses. It is effective against the alfalfa weevil in the Rocky Mountain and Pacific Coast States. In Arizona it helps control lygus bugs when it is combined with a community-wide program of clean mowing or pasturing in the winter and regulation of irrigation during the growing season. Early harvesting of wheat in Montana and North Dakota salvages a large part of the grain that otherwise would be lost when the stems infested by the wheat stem sawfly break over so that the harvester cannot pick up the heads. Early picking saves many ears of corn that would not be recovered by machine pickers in fields where the European corn borer causes stalks to break and ears to drop. The losses increase as picking is delayed. Early harvesting of corn in combination with suitable drying methods may become practical as a means of reducing losses from the corn borer.

All farm operations that promote the growth of crops—good preparation of seedbeds, use of good seed, proper fertilization, regulation of moisture in irrigation, and planting the best-adapted and most vigorous varieties—are of aid in the continual competition between man and insects. Planting new crops at some distance from where they were grown the previous year or out of line with prevailing winds coming from sources of insect infestation aids against some insects. Sufficient separation between fields of small grain and corn retards the movement of chinch bugs from one crop to the other.

CERTAIN PRACTICES can be utilized to advantage in protecting timber from insect attack. Overmature timber is difficult to protect; shorter rotations would cut losses in mature timber. Losses by a spruce bark beetle in Vermont have been avoided by cutting overmature stands of spruce. Vigorous second-growth stands can resist insects better than overmature stands. The mortality due to spruce budworm in spruce and fir stands in New England, the Lake States, and nearby Provinces of Canada is reduced if the trees are in vigorous growth at the time of defoliation. Serious defoliation of hardwood forests in New England by the gypsy moth is limited to areas having a high percentage of certain favored species. Management of the forest to hold the favored hosts to a minimum will prevent damage by the insect. Mixed stands of white pine and hardwood are rarely badly infested by the white-pine weevil, but adjacent pure pine stands are often so heavily attacked that their future value for clear lumber is destroyed. Management practices favoring the increase of hardwood species will aid in preventing losses due to the weevil. Opening of stand through logging favors the subsequent attack on certain trees by such insects as the bronze birch borer in birch, the hemlock borer in hemlock, and bark beetles in pine, which can be prevented by less drastic thinning or removal of the entire stand. Selection of better sites and proper management of tree spacing in new plantations also have great possibilities in protecting our timberlands from insect attack.

W. A. BAKER *is in charge of the division of cereal and forage insect investigations in the Bureau of Entomology and Plant Quarantine. For many years he investigated insects and their control in the field, particularly cereal and forage insects in the Southwest and the European corn borer and its parasites in New England and the Midwest.*

O. R. MATHEWS, *an agronomist in the division of soil management and irrigation, Bureau of Plant Industry, Soils, and Agricultural Engineering, has been engaged in experimental work with tillage and crop production in dry land areas since 1910.*

Economic Entomology

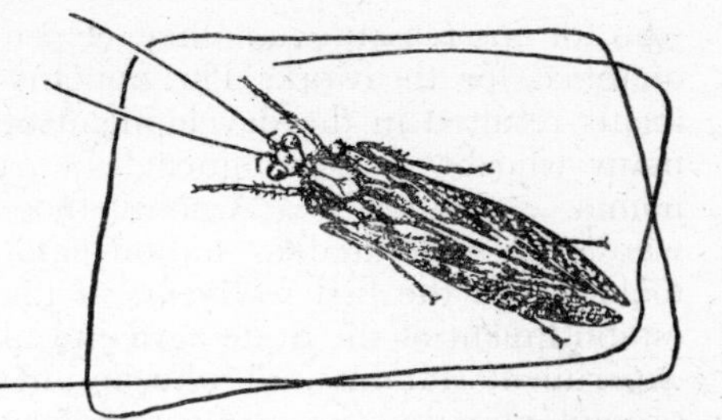

Milestones in Entomology

J. J. Davis

There were men and women in America interested in insects 200 or more years ago. They thought mainly of collecting and identifying insects, for there were few species of economic importance in the beginning of America. The apparent absence of destructive insects in the early days may be attributed to the lack of extensively and intensively grown crops, the absence of introduced insects, and failure to recognize losses.

Problems began to appear towards the end of the eighteenth century. One of the first scientific economic papers by William D. Peck (1763–1822) was "The Description and History of the Cankerworm" in 1795. Peck was referred to as America's first native entomologist, concerned primarily with the economic aspects of insects. In this connection it is interesting to note the titles given by later entomologists to men largely responsible for promoting early entomology: F. V. Melsheimer (1749–1814), "Founder of American Entomology"; John Abbot (1750–1840), "First Great Entomological Artist"; Thomas Say (1787–1834), "Father of American Entomology"; Thaddeus W. Harris (1795–1856), "Pioneer Economic Entomologist"; and Asa Fitch (1809–79), "First Official Entomologist."

Early in the nineteenth century, with the appearance of insects as crop destroyers, agricultural and horticultural societies showed their interest in the control of pests by offering awards for outstanding essays and contributions on specific insects.

Preceded only by Peck as a writer on economic entomology was Thaddeus W. Harris, who in 1841 published his epoch-making *Report on the Insects of Massachusetts Injurious to Vegetation.*

Individual States began to recognize the significance of insects as problems of agriculture and we find the official position of State entomologist established in New York (Asa Fitch 1854), Illinois (B. W. Walsh 1866), and Missouri (C. V. Riley 1868). The reports of the three States represent outstanding and basic contributions to American entomology and the foundation of the science of economic entomology. Other States and the Federal agencies had contributed much up to 1888 with the establishment of the agricultural experiment stations, under Federal aid.

THE FIRST STATE AGRICULTURAL experiment station was established in Connecticut in 1875. Several others were founded before 1888. Some entomological work was conducted there, but the real impetus to economic entomology in the States was the Hatch Act of 1887, which resulted in the organization of the State experiment stations throughout the Nation.

With the organization of the additional stations in 1888, the demand for trained entomologists far exceeded the supply, and many men were appointed who for one reason or another seemed qualified for the work. The appointments resulted in the development of many who became prominent as economic entomologists. Among those who were appointed as station entomologists in the first few years of the establishment of the State agricultural experiment stations and who became prominent in the science of entomology were: J. M. Aldrich (South Dakota 1889), W. B. Alwood (Virginia 1888), C. F. Baker (Colorado 1890), Lawrence Bruner (Nebraska 1888), T. D. A. Cockerell (New Mexico 1893), J. H. Comstock (Cornell 1888), A. J. Cook (Michigan 1888), C. H. Fernald (Massachusetts 1888), S. A. Forbes (Illinois 1888), C. P. Gillette (Iowa 1888), H. A. Gossard (Iowa 1890), F. S. Harvey (Maine 1888), A. D. Hopkins (West Virginia 1888), G. D. Hulst (New Jersey 1888), Otto Lugger (Minnesota 1888), C. L. Marlatt (Kansas 1887), H. A. Morgan (Louisiana 1889), E. A. Popenoe (Kansas 1880), W. J. Sirrine (New York 1894), H. E. Summers (Tennessee 1888), C. H. T. Townsend (New Mexico 1891), J. Troop (Indiana 1888), F. M. Webster (Ohio 1891), C. M. Weed (Ohio 1888), and C. W. Woodworth (Arkansas 1888).

Since the enactment of the Hatch Act of 1887, State-appropriated funds for agricultural research have been augmented by Federal funds on several occasions—the Adams Act, 1906; Purnell Act, 1925; Bankhead-Jones Act, 1935; and Research and Marketing Act, 1946.

Although working independently, the station entomologists have worked closely with the entomologists of the Federal Bureau of Entomology and Plant Quarantine, first, in connection with cooperative projects and second, through the regional field laboratories in most States, which are operated by the Bureau. Thus in discussing the work and accomplishments of the State experiment stations or the Federal Bureau it is quite impossible to separate their achievements. Each is dependent on the other and as a result the accomplishments have been manyfold. To be sure, the individual States have concentrated on local and regional problems, while Federal agencies have stressed problems of more widespread interest and those that may require years for their solution.

ECONOMIC ENTOMOLOGY as a science is young, perhaps only 80 years old.

In the beginning emphasis was given to a study of the life history and habits of insects. It was early recognized that insect controls, whether biological control, legal control, farm practices, mechanical devices, or chemicals, were based on our knowledge of the life history, habits, and structure of the specific insect.

The early entomologists were self-made. They were perhaps first interested in zoology in its broadest sense, or in horticulture, botany, or other cultural or practical sciences, and took up entomological studies because of the relation of entomology to their vocation or avocation.

Early in the nineteenth century a few more or less organized entomology courses were provided in a few institutions. Fitch gave courses at Rensselaer Polytechnic Institute. Peck and Harris conducted some classes at Harvard. However, the first organized courses were in agricultural colleges, beginning with the founding of the State agricultural colleges, known as land-grant colleges, under the Morrill Act in the late 1860's.

Thus, as in the case of State agricultural experiment stations, organized later, it was an act of Congress that launched the widespread establishment of State agricultural colleges and likewise teaching of entomology, with special reference to economic entomology.

The more prominent teachers in the late 1860's and 1870's included Mudge, Riley, and Popenoe in Kansas, Cook in Michigan, Burrill and Forbes in Illinois, C. H. Fernald in Maine and Massachusetts, Comstock at Cornell, and Osborn at Iowa, all at agricultural colleges. H. A. Hagen, educated in Germany, was brought to Harvard in 1870 as professor of entomology and was probably the first regular teacher of entomology in America.

In the beginning there was little demand or incentive for trained entomologists and few students majored in entomology. In fact there were few if any colleges or universities which provided complete curricula in the subject. For the most part the courses were prepared for those majoring in production fields, such as horticulture and agronomy.

With the establishment of experiment stations in most States and the increasing demand for trained entomologists in these stations and in agricultural colleges, one school after another in rapid succession provided special curricula. With the further demand for men in regulatory work, museums, extension, industry, and commercial pest-control work, the training of entomologists became an important phase of instruction in the State colleges. For the most part, the training of entomologists is now largely confined to the State agricultural colleges and universities.

As the importance of entomology as a science became increasingly evident, as the problem of profitable farm production became more and more dependent on preventing insect losses, and as the need for technical studies became apparent, the field of teaching became a major factor in entomological progress. With special curricula for those majoring in entomology, more technical subjects were introduced—specialized courses in morphology, physiology, taxonomy, chemistry of insecticides, and beekeeping. Entomological curricula have provided courses in general education and supporting courses in entomology and related subjects, such as plant pathology. These equip the graduate with a basic knowledge of entomology, which permits him to carry on advanced study. In a few colleges, special 4-year curricula have been provided, such as for commercial pest-control operators who not only need a good basic knowledge of insects but also practical experience in control and certain business fundamentals.

The technical advances in entomology and in all the other agricultural sciences have demanded greater research facilities and a marked expansion in advanced study. Advanced or graduate study is a continuation of the undergraduate professional school, but it is somewhat more concerned with discovering new facts and training students to search for and understand new things.

THE FIRST STATE LEGISLATION to prevent the introduction of plant pests was enacted by the California State Legislature in 1881. This action was taken because the agricultural interests became alarmed by the introduction of such pests as granary weevils, black scale, cottony-cushion scale, grape phylloxera, codling moth, and the San Jose scale, and the fear of introducing other destructive insects. During the next 15 years a few other States enacted similar laws. During the late 1890's many State laws, commonly referred to as nursery inspection laws, were adopted because of the recognition of the seriousness of the San Jose scale and its spread to many States.

From the beginning the State regulatory officer was referred to as State Entomologist. Now the title refers almost exclusively to the plant or nursery inspector, who is sometimes also a quarantine officer; the office is quite different from that of the early entomologists of Illinois, Missouri, and New York, who headed research organizations that were not regulatory.

In the beginning, when only insects were involved, the regulatory officer was usually the State experiment station entomologist. As new plant pests, both insects and plant diseases, appeared and presented a menace, they were added to the list of pests under regulation. Gradually the regulatory operations were transferred to State organizations other than the educational institutions, and the enforcement officer is now more often known as the State nursery inspector, and may be connected with the horticultural board, plant board, department of agriculture, department of conservation, or crop pest commissioner of a State. While the regulatory officer is primarily concerned with the inspection and certification of nursery stock, in most States he also handles greenhouse and other propagation stock and apiaries, as well as handling the enforcement of intrastate quarantines.

In the early years of State nursery inspection, each State enacted regulations without much consideration for the regulations of other States. There was little uniformity of laws. Eventually this resulted in the formation of a joint committee from the American Nurserymen's Association and the American Association of Economic Entomologists, which formulated a so-called model law. This, in turn, brought changes in State laws, until most State regulations now are uniform and reciprocal one with another.

Another major development was the formation of the National Plant Board and regional plant boards, a direct result of a conference of State and Federal nursery inspection officials in Washington, D. C., in April 1924. The purpose was to promote uniformity and efficiency in horticultural and quarantine regulations and State inspection services. The National Plant Board prepared a statement, "Principles of Quarantines," which has had an important part in the history of regulatory organizations.

J. J. Davis *has been head of the department of entomology in Purdue University, the Purdue University Agricultural Experiment Station, and Indiana Agricultural Extension since 1920. He is past President of the American Association of Economic Entomologists, the Entomological Society of America, and the Indiana Academy of Science.*

Surveys of Insect Pests

G. J. Haeussler, R. W. Leiby

Surveys are an intelligence service that provides the entomologist, plant quarantine official, farmer, county agent, and the insecticide industry with essential information regarding the insect enemy. The surveys tell where the enemy occurs, how abundant he is, and what damage he is causing or threatens to do. They are a basis for determining the need and type of action required to combat him.

The many kinds of insect surveys vary according to the objective and the circumstances of the particular problem. Some provide information about a species about which little is known, such as a pest new to an area or the country. Some concern the kinds of insects that attack a given crop, like cotton, or a group of crops, like vegetables or fruits, and are for the purpose of aiding farmers to protect such crops from loss due to insects. Others aid in planning organized control campaigns against specific pests, like grasshoppers, which periodically occur in outbreaks over large areas and require cooperative action by several agencies and organized groups. Some surveys are conducted primarily to obtain data as a basis for determining the need for and as a guide to the enactment of State or Federal quarantine or regulatory measures. Still other surveys are made primarily to provide a record of the occurrence, abundance, and host-plant relationships of all insect species within a given area, such as an entire State. In wartime, surveys are carried on as a defense measure in the event that deliberate attempts should be made to introduce injurious pests from abroad or to spread those of economic importance to new areas.

SURVEYS for a recently introduced or little-known pest are conducted primarily to determine its distribution and behavior, to determine the nature and extent of damage it causes, the manner and rate by which it spreads and to ascertain its potential destructiveness and the need for developing control measures before it can become widely distributed.

An example is the work by the Bureau of Entomology and Plant Quarantine and State agencies in the South to obtain information on the distribution and status of the imported fire ant. This little South American pest, first reported near Mobile, Ala., about 1918, has spread and increased to the extent that citizens in infested areas demanded action to control it. The surveys, started in 1949, have shown the pest to be widely distributed in Alabama and Mississippi and less abundant in Florida, Georgia, Arkansas, Tennessee, and Louisiana. The observations also suggest that shipments of nursery stock may be a common means by which the ant is spread.

SURVEYS OF THE INSECTS attacking a given crop or group of crops have been carried on extensively. During the Second World War supplies of the insecticides for the insect pests of essential crops were scarce, and nearly all the basic materials needed to make insecticides were placed under allocation control. Supplies therefore had to be conserved and the available stocks used only for the most pressing needs on crops having the highest priorities. As a part of the effort to make the best use of insecticides and equipment, the Department of Agriculture in cooperation with other Federal and State agencies and industry instituted special surveys of the insect pests of cotton, truck crops, and fruit and their control requirements.

Whenever possible, a special effort was made to anticipate the development of infestations. Information obtained from the surveys was circulated weekly or oftener to all persons and agencies that needed to plan programs and advise farmers about protecting the crops. It indicated the localities where dangerous numbers of insects were attacking or likely to attack specific crops, the local or regional availability of the necessary insecticides, and the availability of equipment. Extension workers advised farmers promptly as to the situation in local areas by announcements over the radio, in newspapers, and through correspondence. Information from the survey was used by Federal officials to aid industry in obtaining supplies of the basic materials needed to produce additional quantities of insecticides or equipment and guided industry in the distribution of the limited supplies to meet emergency situations.

The emergency situation with respect to availability of insecticides and equipment remained an important problem to the producers of cotton, vegetables, fruits, and other essential agricultural crops, and it has been necessary to continue surveys of this type. For instance, entomologists in New York knew that the Mexican bean beetle entered hibernation in the fall of 1949 in larger numbers than ever. They also knew that because of the mild winter an unusually high percentage of the beetles would probably survive to infest the State's dry bean crop, worth 13 million dollars, in 1950. State workers made surveys in June 1950 to determine whether beetles were present on beans in numbers sufficient to threaten the crop. Counts of the beetles made in 15 counties showed that the insects had survived the winter in such numbers as to necessitate the application of control measures to prevent extensive losses. An intensive control campaign was developed immediately. An evaluation of the results of the control measures instituted because of the survey findings indicated that the growers of dry beans of New York profited by $3,014,094 from an expenditure of $785,162 for insecticides and the labor to apply them.

Several States now conduct surveys

970134°—52——30

of the insect pests of vegetables, fruits, the cereal and forage crops, and cotton and make the results available promptly in periodic reports. County agents, other agricultural advisors, and farmers thus are informed as to the status of insect conditions in their areas. The Bureau of Entomology and Plant Quarantine, through its field offices, assembles the survey data from the various States and summarizes and distributes it in weekly reports that show insect conditions throughout the country with regard to those crops.

The surveys of cotton insects have resulted in a great expansion in the use of control methods. The number of growers applying controls throughout the Cotton Belt has increased more than 100 percent since 1945 as a result of the advisory program made possible because of the survey. The survey of cotton insects has developed into an advisory service for farmers, others associated with cotton production, and the manufacturers of the insecticidal chemicals.

An advisory type of survey, much like those we have mentioned, provides advice to farmers on the timing of insecticide applications. An example is the surveys of the European corn borer, first conducted in 1948 by the State agricultural experiment stations of Illinois, Iowa, Minnesota, and Wisconsin and the Department of Agriculture and later expanded to include 10 other States. Research has shown that the losses caused by the insect can be reduced by the proper use of insecticides, but accurate knowledge of the development of the corn borer eggs and larvae is essential because the period for effective control is short and the timing of insecticide applications is critically exacting. Farmers cannot now determine this development accurately. On the basis of field information obtained by trained personnel, advice is given to farmers every week or oftener by State extension workers over the radio and in newspapers to guide them in carrying out control measures in areas where corn is threatened. A cooperative survey of this type, carried on in 12 States in 1949, helped save some 10 million bushels of corn from loss by the borer. It also helps farmers to avoid unwise use of insecticides and the cost of unnecessary applications by advising them that the degree of infestation in their locality does not warrant treatment or that the time for effective control has passed.

Surveys of pests that occur in periodic outbreaks form the basis for planning regional or national cooperative or volunteer control programs. Grasshoppers and Mormon crickets, chinch bugs, hessian flies, and screwworms are such pests. The surveys vary according to the particular problem, but all are conducted cooperatively by Federal and State agencies. The annual grasshopper survey, for example, is carried on to provide in advance a general picture of the infestation to be expected as a basis for planning control needs for the following season. The knowledge obtained by surveying the population of grasshopper adults and later the eggs is mapped during the winter and enables control agencies to plan their needs for the coming year. The actual grasshopper population is then determined by surveys in the spring after natural enemies and weather have exerted their influence. Further scouting, following the application of control measures, provides information concerning the thoroughness of control coverage, effectiveness of results, and the need for changes in insecticide dosages, application methods, or other procedures.

Surveys carried on in relation to regulatory measures are among the most common types. They furnish a basis for the enactment of State or Federal quarantines against specific pests. Most such surveys are designed to delimit the areas of infestation and may involve inspection of plants, plant products, soil, or other commodities to determine ways by which the particular pest is spread. Examples are the surveys of gypsy and brown-tail moths, the Japanese beetle, white-fringed beetles, the sweetpotato weevil, and the potato tuberworm. Such surveys are usually conducted by the Federal and State units. Special methods and equipment such as traps and lures are often used in the surveys. For instance, traps baited with a material that attracts adult Japanese beetles are placed each summer near airports and other strategic points outside the regulated area to detect new infestations that may get a start from the escape of hitchhiking beetles. For the survey to determine distribution and spread of the pink bollworm, gin-trash machines have been developed; they separate any pink bollworms that may be present in the trash that is regularly removed from seed cotton during the ginning process. Examination of samples thus collected provides a relatively simple and reliable means of detecting the presence of the insect.

A SPECIAL SURVEY for insect pests and plant diseases in the general vicinity of ports of entry was carried on by the Bureau of Entomology and Plant Quarantine in 1943–45. The project, a national defense measure, was undertaken because of the belief that the greatly increased traffic from overseas during the Second World War might have resulted in the entry and establishment of new foreign agricultural pests in the port areas. It entailed intensive inspection of cultivated plants, field crops, orchards, home gardens, ornamentals, and native plants. Special attention was paid wild plants belonging to families closely related to important cultivated crops. The search was concentrated in States along the eastern and west coasts, Gulf coast, and Mexican border. The major effort was in southern California, the Rio Grande Valley, and in States bordering the Gulf of Mexico, where survey crews worked the year around.

Cooperative working relationships were established and maintained with officials of plant boards and departments of agriculture in all States in which the survey was conducted. Upon arrival at a port city, the survey crew first got in touch with local port authorities and county agents. Inspections began near ports and airports, then included gardens in residential areas adjacent to such facilities, and were extended gradually to surrounding agricultural areas until, in general, the entire coast line and the shores of navigable rivers or lakes were covered. All parts of plants were examined for insects, although greatest attention was usually given to foliage and fruits. Nearly 32,000 lots of insect specimens were submitted to specialists for identification. From these, about 3,500 different species of plant-feeding insects and mites were determined. Many others were identified as to family or genus. The survey brought to light at least 41 insects that had never before been recorded in the United States but, fortunately, only a few foreign pests of agricultural importance. Only seven introduced species of insects were found that are recognized as pests of economic importance in their countries of probable origin and which thus might be considered of immediate potential importance to the agricultural economy of the United States. They were all found in Florida and Texas and are known as pests in the West Indies and in countries south of the Mexican border. Among the many specimens collected, the taxonomists also found some 46 species that were new, that is, not known to science, and 82 species which they considered as probably new. Furthermore, the data resulting from this survey established new State distribution records for at least 33 species of insects previously known to occur elsewhere in this country and innumerable new locality records for many others.

A review of the results of this project, which took only 2 years and was carried on in a relatively limited area, demonstrates that we know too little about how many insect pests occur in the United States and that our present knowledge concerning the distribution of most insect pests is still far from complete. Systematic, intensive searches of this type are the only satisfactory means of filling these important gaps in our knowledge of the insects that quietly work away in our gardens, fields, and orchards.

A COMPILATION of the insects known to occur in a given State or locality has value when information is needed promptly about the distribution, seasonal occurrence, host-plant relationships, and economic importance of a species. Such lists can be prepared only from reliable records, maintained through the years, of authentically identified specimens and supplemented by summarizing similar records in the entomological literature. Valuable lists of this type have been published by New Jersey, New York, Connecticut, North Carolina, and Kansas.

A FEDERAL SURVEY of insect pests has been carried on since 1921. The service was established to provide a medium through which all entomologists could keep more closely in touch with current insect conditions throughout the country and to serve as a repository for miscellaneous field observations previously available to only a few persons. Collaborators, chiefly State entomologists and entomologists in the agricultural experiment stations, State universities and agricultural colleges, and Federal entomological workers are encouraged to submit notes or reports on observations regarding the occurrence, abundance, distribution, destructiveness, and host-plant relationships of insect pests throughout the country. Upon receipt in the Insect Pest Survey office, Bureau of Entomology and Plant Quarantine, Washington 25, D. C., the data are analyzed and abstracted, and the information believed to have permanent value is filed so that it remains readily available. A cross-reference index to all of the insects known to affect any given species of plant is maintained. From May 1921 to May 1942, a publication known as the Insect Pest Survey Bulletin was compiled and issued monthly, and an annual summary of insect conditions was published at the end of each year to furnish entomological workers information on the distribution, abundance, and destructiveness of insect pests in the country. More detailed information on the ecology, distribution, and destructiveness of specific pests of major economic importance, such as the European corn borer, Japanese beetle, and others, is published from time to time in the form of special supplements. The activities were curtailed in 1942 because of lack of funds, and publication of the Insect Pest Survey Bulletin was discontinued. Brief monthly and annual statements summarizing available information on the status of a few of the more important economic pests replaced the Bulletin.

In 1951 the agricultural agencies in each State were invited to participate in a plan to make this service more useful to all agricultural workers throughout the country. As a result, since July 1951 information on the status of insects of economic importance is made available every 2 weeks in a statement known as the Cooperative Economic Insect Report and issued by the Bureau.

An adjunct of the service has been the accumulation through the years of an index file of data on the occurrence, distribution, ecology, and host-plant relationships of more than 23,000 species of insects known to occur in this country. Additional data are added to it each year. The records are cataloged so one can furnish promptly information on the occurrence of any specific pest in a given State or county, or its national distribution, in response to the numerous requests received from Federal and State workers. An index file of the host plants from which each insect species has been recorded and of the insects recorded as attacking certain plants of economic importance has also been developed and is kept current.

A good start also was made in recording pertinent data concerning the records of insect pests in foreign countries. There are on file notes on more than 30,000 such species, obtained as the result of reviewing and abstracting the literature published in the Review of Applied Entomology through 1941. The data provide a source of ready reference when needed in connection with foreign plant quarantine activities and are a source of information whenever infestations of new foreign pests are found in the United States. The work was discontinued in 1942 because of the curtailment of funds.

THE COOPERATION of all interested agencies is important to the success of any insect survey, as the pooling of information obtained through individual effort avoids considerable duplication and permits greater and more thorough survey coverage of an area with less expenditure of manpower and funds. Thus, the more effective insect surveys in this country are carried on cooperatively by State and Federal entomological agencies. At times the aid of agricultural officials in foreign countries is sought. The more reliable surveys are made by well-trained workers or by teams of field scouts operating under close supervision of such personnel. Adequately trained workers are thoroughly familiar with the insect or insects concerned and know the essential facts about their life history, food plants, and habits. They know how to search for a pest new to an area, how to measure insect abundance in relation to damage or crop values, and how to determine the degree of destruction likely to result from an infestation of a given intensity. They also know just where to look and what to look for. They know that transportation centers, especially those associated with foreign commerce or the movement of agricultural commodities, are most likely to reveal a new infestation. An effective insect survey requires careful advance planning, with provision to insure the adequate recording of essential data and weeding out of the unessentials that merely serve to clutter up the files.

Surveys are the basis of intelligent insect control programs—whether in one row of bush beans in the home garden or a grasshopper control program in several States. In order to know what action is required and when it should be applied, we must first look the situation over to be sure what pest needs to be combatted and whether it is present in numbers sufficient to warrant treatment. Surveys are the only sure means of providing such information. Regardless of the kind, expense, or trouble, the surveys are essential if we are to keep the upper hand in the constant battle against the insect enemies.

G. J. HAEUSSLER, *a graduate of the University of Massachusetts, joined the Department in 1925. He was engaged for 16 years in investigations on the biological control of fruit insects, and in that connection spent 3 years in southern Europe and 2 years in Japan studying the oriental fruit moth and its natural enemies. He was in charge of the division of insect survey and information, Bureau of Entomology and Plant Quarantine, from 1944 to 1951, when he became leader of the Bureau's division of truck crop and garden insect investigations.*

R. W. LEIBY *is a professor of economic entomology in Cornell University. Formerly he was State entomologist in North Carolina where he did research in economic entomology and later had charge of work on plant quarantines. In North Carolina he was actively interested in insect surveys and contributed to the collection and published list of insects of that State.*

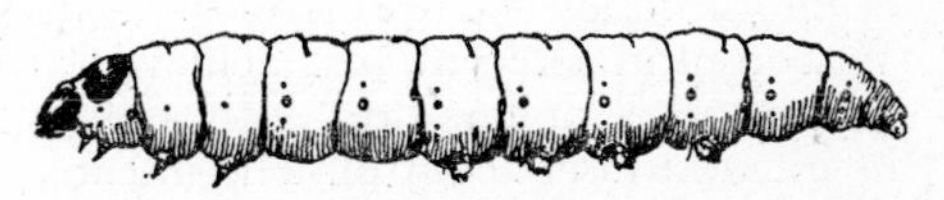

Potato tuberworm.

The Insecticide Industry

Lea S. Hitchner

The insecticide industry of today comprises more than 50 basic producers or manufacturers and more than 500 formulators, remixers, and processors. From their plants throughout the country comes a great variety of insecticides and related products.

The products, except those derived from botanical sources, have their origins in the basic chemicals on which the industry is founded, but the processes that turn the raw materials into the finished products applied by farmers are long, highly scientific, and expensive in capital investment and operating costs.

The industry employs thousands of scientists in the fields of entomology, plant pathology, botany, toxicology, medicine, chemistry, and chemical engineering; thousands of skilled and semiskilled workers in the manufacturing plants; and thousands of men responsible for sales, either as employees of industry or dealers who sell directly to farmers and other consumers.

Demand for the products has climbed to the point where annual sales total at least 200 million dollars, the sum paid for the hundreds of products that industry has developed, produced, and distributed to agriculturists in every State and many foreign lands. The products include insecticides, fungicides, weed killers, rodenticides, defoliants, and plant hormones. Never before has the farmer been so well armed to fight insects and other pests.

Some examples of the effectiveness of the products: Growers of peas in Wisconsin in a recent year achieved a return of 6 dollars for each dollar invested in insect control. The insecticides boosted the yields 15 percent and put nearly 2 million dollars extra in the growers' pockets. In Mississippi at least 75 percent of the 1950 cotton crop would have been destroyed were it not for the control of insects through the use of the industry's products. Insecticides applied in Nebraska to control grasshoppers in 1949 resulted in savings estimated at 2 million dollars. Insecticidal treatment of alfalfa raised for seed production in various States has doubled the yield.

One factor among others responsible for the high productivity of American agriculture is the cooperative attack that is waged on insects and other pests. The agricultural chemicals industry has welcomed the opportunity to cooperate with Federal and State agencies and with farm organizations in this important work and to carry the responsibility for developing, producing, and delivering the necessary pesticides.

Such a responsibility is a heavy one even in normal times. It becomes acutely heavy in times of national stress, when shortages of raw materials, containers, personnel, and transportation may hamper production and distribution.

The industry has come a long way since the 1880's, when its development began to have a real impact on American agriculture. To be sure, the use of chemicals to control insects goes back at least a century, and long before that, man had declared war against the insects that had plagued him from time beyond memory.

Among the earliest records of insect control is the Biblical story of the prophet Amos, who was a "dresser of sycamores." He was one of many who regularly climbed sycamore trees to pinch off the ends of the young fruit, which resembled figs, hoping this would destroy the insect usually found there. For thousands of years the control of insects and diseases was almost entirely guesswork or practically nonexistent, with the exception of mechanical control, like that carried on by Amos, supplemented by a rather haphazard system of crop rotation.

The first record of effective chemical control dates from 1882, when a Frenchman, Millardet, accidentally discovered what is now known as bordeaux mixture. Sixty years ago most of the materials applied for pest control were chemicals, such as paris green and london purple, used primarily in other industries but accidentally discovered to be effective against insects.

PROBABLY THE FIRST insecticide resulting from deliberately planned manufacture was calcium arsenate, destined to become one of the most widely used materials throughout the Nation and to play a special role in the control of the boll weevil in the South.

William C. Piver was typical of the enterprising young businessmen in the industry. Within the first 5 years after his graduation from the University of North Carolina, Piver took part in an early campaign to promote lead arsenate. He conceived the possibility of producing calcium arsenate for use as an insecticide. He reasoned that the arsenical insecticides then in use were effective primarily because they contained arsenic—yet the paris green was expensive because it also contained copper and a large share of the cost for lead arsenate was because of its lead content. He therefore set out to find a way to combine the arsenic with a readily available and inexpensive base, such as lime.

Piver's first experimental apparatus was hidden under his bed in a boarding house because his landlady wanted no poisonous or explosive chemicals in her house. He worked at night, and his progress was slow. He found practically nothing in the technical literature to guide him. But he persevered and he finally produced laboratory amounts of calcium arsenate—but only in pound lots. Then followed further study and research, until in 1912 the first commercial batch of calcium arsenate was produced and shipped in powdered form to a dealer in Houston, Tex. The shipment was intended for the control of the cotton leafworm; the boll weevil was not yet the serious pest it became later in the South.

Supplies of calcium arsenate were also sent to potato growers in Virginia and to apple growers in Nova Scotia. On the basis of results obtained by the Virginia growers, Piver began selling calcium arsenate to potato men in New Jersey. Not all the early results were good.

In 1915, Piver's company had 21 customers; in 1916, 55 customers. By then the boll weevil was serious in cotton. Entomologists accepted the challenge by carrying on extensive experiments with calcium arsenate. In 1918, on the basis of Government tests, a Federal entomologist telegraphed Piver for 40 tons of calcium arsenate—the largest single order he had ever received and a third larger than his highest yearly production. The order nearly floored him. He had to get special permission from his company's board of directors to make up so large a single batch because factory production at that time produced so many failures that the factory back yard was knee deep with the discarded mixes run out from the tanks and dried in the sun. He was "wasting assets of the company," they said, but he won his point. The shipment was made up and sent south. Professional entomologists were quick to realize the potentialities of calcium arsenate as an insecticide.

About the time Piver's company started to manufacture, W. D. Hunter, in charge of southern field crops investigations of the Department of Agriculture, and B. R. Coad, in charge of the laboratory in Tallulah, La., began extensive studies on the use of calcium arsenate for cotton insects. The experimental work continued many years, and much of the development and use of calcium arsenate may be attributed to their efforts.

TYPICAL OF THE DEVELOPMENT of other products by industry is the research in the early 1920's that led to the commercial sale of summer spray oils, now widely used on fruit crops.

The late William Hunter Volck is considered by many as one of the greatest contributors to this field. He first started work on spray oils in 1902 in collaboration with C. W. Woodworth, of the University of California; from then on he continued to study petroleum oil products. Volck developed a series of spray oils, including in 1924 the summer oils, which can be used on foliage. He also developed quick-breaking emulsions and, in collaboration with Hugh Knight and others, summer oils plus poisons and emulsive oil products.

To list all the names of industrial companies, scientists, and university and Government workers who have contributed to the development of petroleum oil pesticides would be to list the names of many of the leaders of research development in the United States. Today approximately 85 million gallons of petroleum oil products are used in agriculture to control pests and weeds.

THE GROWTH OF THE INDUSTRY can be divided into two periods—the first dates from the development of calcium arsenate through the early period of the Second World War, and the second from that time until the present.

During the first period, the industry developed several effective products, adaptable to a wide range of crops and insects—calcium arsenate, lead arsenate, sulfur, nicotine, rotenone, pyrethrum, cryolite, and various copper compounds. The number of manufacturers grew to more than 35, and they hired entomologists, plant pathologists, and toxicologists. Cooperative work between industry and Federal and State entomologists proceeded. Sales of insecticides reached 75 to 100 million dollars annually. The quality of agricultural products was remarkably improved, further concentration of crop production became possible, and the area available for crop production was enlarged.

Many look back on this period as one of pioneer contributions to a more efficient agriculture. Among the early pioneers were A. P. and David Ansbacher and Fred L. Lavenburg, who worked with paris green; James A. Blanchard, also with paris green; B. G. Pratt, miscible oils; and Thomas Grasselli, Arthur Kent, Frank Hemingway, C. D. Vreeland, and George A. Martin, lead arsenate. Besides Piver, Theodore Dosch, Ernest Hart, and Fred Moburg were identified with the development of calcium arsenate; George F. Leonard and Charles Taylor, with nicotine sulfate; William Rose, Edward Mechling, Herbert Dow, Gerald Cushman, R. W. Scott, Arthur Stern, and others, with arsenicals and other products.

The second phase sometimes is called the era of organic insecticides. It was stimulated by wartime research and necessity and resulted in a tremendous increase in the number of products available to growers.

The development of DDT exemplifies the telescoping in a short time the research that might well have taken years. Some authorities have said the major discoveries in curative and preventive medicine during the war were DDT, plasma, and penicillin.

In recognition of his outstanding work in the development of DDT as an insecticide, Dr. Paul Müller of J. R. Geigy, S. A., of Basle, Switzerland, was awarded the 1948 Nobel Prize in Physiology and Medicine. In 1939 the potato crop of Switzerland was seriously threatened by the Colorado potato beetle. The Swiss firm made available to the Swiss entomologists a sample of DDT for testing. Results of the first tests against the Colorado potato beetle confirmed the company's findings and culminated in the control of this destructive insect. The effectiveness of DDT against other destructive insect pests was soon discovered.

A good example of how the insecticide industry developed a product to fill a particular need lies in the story of toxaphene. The toxaphene dusts and sprays are used to kill cotton insects, grasshoppers, and scores of other pests. A chemist of Hercules Powder Co. conceived the idea that insect toxicants might be found in the highly chlorinated terpene products. Chlorinated terpenes of relatively low chlorine content were rather well known, but little was known about chlorinated terpenes of high chlorine content.

By synthesizing a number of different chlorinated terpene materials of varying degrees of chlorination, and submitting them to routine tests against house flies, he discovered that when camphene, a bicyclic terpene hydrocarbon of the formula $C_{10}H_{16}$, was chlorinated to above 60 percent, a unique waxlike product of excellent stability and high insecticidal activity against house flies resulted. When his tests were extended to include agricultural pests, he found that the high activity was even more pronounced.

Formulation of the material into dusts, wettable powders, emulsions, and oil-soluble concentrates became important. A considerable amount of application work was undertaken. It was estimated that 150,000 pounds of toxaphene would be required for extensive field tests. A pilot plant was set up to make it at Brunswick, Ga.

Quantities of toxaphene for commercial consumption first were produced in 1947. Testing has continued since, and the insecticide has been found effective against many pests. Construction was started on another toxaphene-manufacturing unit in the South.

In 1949 at the request of the Department of Agriculture, the trade name toxaphene was released, so that the word could be used commonly for chlorinated camphene having a chlorine content of 67–69 percent.

In the wartime research, many chemicals were screened for efficacy, and several phosphorus compounds were found to have insecticidal activity. Hexaethyl tetraphosphate, tetraethyl pyrophosphate, and parathion were soon on the market. They are effective against many pests not controlled by earlier materials. They therefore have been marketed even though they require special precautions in their manufacture and use.

In the production and marketing of parathion, for instance, a notable job has been done to insure proper handling. The technical material is shipped in welded, specially designed drums. For further protection of the handlers, the drums were reduced from a 500-pound size to 280 pounds as further assurance against accidents. Companies manufacturing the material limited its sale to processors who proved themselves properly equipped to formulate parathion. Their departments of industrial hygiene took an active interest in the handling of the chemical from then on and continued to cooperate with the processors to insure continued safety in handling and distribution.

Beyond that, the companies worked closely with the various Government agencies and devised a model label to be followed by formulators of the finished insecticide. They also prepared manuals for growers and safety precautions in the use of the chemical.

I give only a meager outline of what the insecticide companies undertake to insure safe use of a product. The toxicological studies, laboratory and field tests, chemical analyses, and many other costly and laborious activities are involved. Yet the consumer gets the materials cheap enough to pay him to apply them.

Many of the companies test 10,000 chemicals or more a year in the search for effective new products. Often several tens of thousands of chemicals are screened before one or two of real promise are found. When such a material is discovered, it is scrutinized immediately by a battery of scientists. If it appears that the insects to be controlled and the cost of production will create a new field of use or improve the control resulting from the use of existing products, the material undergoes a series of intensive tests. It may be tested in the manufacturer's greenhouses and experimental farms for its insecticidal effectiveness and for the reaction of the crop being treated. At the same time it is studied by company toxicologists and by toxicological laboratories throughout the country. Entomological and toxicological testing are coordinated so that data showing the insects that are controlled, and precautions to be observed in use, are available at as nearly the same time as possible. Often years are required to obtain adequate data.

Because of the competitive nature of the industry, most of this information is not published. I have no count of laboratories engaged in research on the toxicity of agricultural chemicals. Toxicologists have estimated that there are nearly 25 such laboratories and that their facilities are now being used to capacity.

It is also estimated that 10 to 20 new agricultural chemicals are thoroughly studied for toxic hazards each year in the United States. Not all finally reach the market in quantity. Probably 500 to 1,000 products each year receive some study through the early stages of development but later are abandoned for various reasons. Toxicological research on a chemical that presents no hazards of food residues probably costs not less than 5,000 dollars, but sometimes, when residues of the chemical may occur on food products, the cost often exceeds 20,000 dollars.

A sampling of 20 manufacturers showed that the yearly expenditures for their research, including toxicological studies, is nearly 4 million dollars. Such studies represent fundamental work directed toward the protection of the health of all concerned—workers in the manufacturing plant, farmers who apply the product, and consumers who buy and consume the commodities that have been sprayed or dusted.

For that reason, too, the industry has supported State and Federal legislation to regulate the distribution and use of insecticides, fungicides, and related products.

THE INDUSTRY is regulated at the State and the National level. Many State laws, some of them conflicting, present something of a problem to an industry whose members often sell their products throughout the country. Many States have tried to enact uniform legislation; in that effort, the industry has cooperated with the Council of State Governments, the Department of Agriculture, the National Association of Commissioners, and Federal and State regulatory officials. The combined efforts of those groups have produced the Uniform State Insecticide, Fungicide, and Rodenticide Act, which has been enacted into law in 19 States. Twenty-one States have other pesticide laws. The industry believes public interest will be served by the enactment of a uniform act in more States. The industry also actively supports a proposed Uniform Custom Applicators' Law, which was drafted by the Council of State Governments and other interested groups. Its purpose is to insure the safe application of pesticides from the air and by other means.

THE AGRICULTURAL CHEMISTRY industry has made noteworthy achievements, but it is not content merely to think of them. Its research is being intensified, with increased emphasis on fundamental studies. Substantial capital investments have been made in new plants. Manufacturing and processing techniques are being improved constantly. More efficient methods of distribution are being instituted. Toxicological studies and educational programs more and more seek to safeguard users of its products and the general public.

LEA S. HITCHNER *is the executive secretary of the National Agricultural Chemicals Association, which was founded in 1933 and to which manufacturers of agricultural pest-control chemicals belong. A native of New Jersey and a graduate of the University of Pennsylvania, he has worked in the field of agricultural chemicals since his twenties. A member of the American Trade Association Executives, he is a past vice president of that organization's New York chapter.*

The Industrial Entomologist

Ed. M. Searls

The industrial entomologist, using long-lasting insecticides and exerting full influence on the construction and operation of food-processing plants, has given the world a new conception of sanitation.

Thanks to him, preventive entomology has replaced the older practices of insect control; for the first time in man's history we can speak definitely of insect prevention. Insects used to be thought of in terms of the food they destroyed; now in factories they are considered chiefly as a major index of sanitation.

Industry has become increasingly aware of the need for avoiding and excluding insects. Even factory sites are selected with this in view. Many species of night-flying insects, readily attracted to lights and possibly troublesome in food processing, come from rivers, streams, and ponds. City dumps where refuse accumulates breed many pests and detract from the appearance and desirability of plant sites. Food processing or packing plants today are not built near such places.

Ready transportation is necessary, but smoke, soot, dust, and cinders—as well as insects—are associated with high-speed highways, railroads, and docks. Insect prevention and general sanitation are much easier to achieve when plants are removed from them.

Pest prevention about the plant and on the surrounding grounds is the concern also of the industrial entomologist. There must be no accumulation of waste or debris in which insects might feed and breed.

The influence of the industrial entomologist, working with the plant architect and the industrial engineer, is readily seen in the construction of the newer plants and factories for handling food. The industrial entomologist divides the rooms of a food-processing plant into critical and noncritical. Critical rooms are those where food or food materials are exposed or where containers used for holding food are sometimes open, so that insects or airborne debris might contaminate food. Critical rooms should never open directly to the out-of-doors because there is too much danger of contamination by airborne debris, particularly insect parts, rodent hairs, and feather barbules.

Noncritical rooms are those in which food or food materials are always fully enclosed or in which no food is handled. A noncritical room should always separate a critical room from the out-of-doors.

Most of the insects and other pests of food processing gain entrance through doors and windows. Doors are probably the chief avenues of entrance. Double-swinging, fast-closing doors, properly bumpered to prevent damage, should be used whenever possible in openings to the outside. Single-acting doors or sliding doors may be required by the fire code, but when they open to the outside they should always be supplemented by the double-swinging, fast-closing doors. It is too easy (and sometimes necessary) to block open sliding or single-acting doors and leave them so, thus providing easy entrance for airborne dust, debris, and insects.

Insects enter through unscreened windows left open for ventilation. They even enter through window screens of less than 18 meshes to the inch; 20-mesh screen therefore is much better, because coarser-mesh screen permits the entrance of airborne debris. Consequently artificial illumination and designed air circulation, instead of open windows, screened or unscreened, are earnestly recommended by the industrial entomologist. Apparatus that will keep out insects will usually exclude airborne debris and help prevent unsanitary conditions.

The noncritical room, or vestibule, also serves as a place in which to open materials and supplies used in food processing. Corrugated paper or other types of boxes and packages received from commerce sometimes contain insects and usually contain other debris undesirable in a critical room. Such packages should not be opened or stored in critical rooms.

The location, size, and arrangement of storerooms in food-processing plants have also felt the influence of the industrial entomologist. Too frequently storerooms are the neglected rooms and the source of pests and debris in finished products. Fourteen inches of space all about the walls of a storeroom is recommended to facilitate the detection and destruction of pests in the room. Placing stores on skids 8 to 10 inches high aids in insect prevention and sanitation and adds to the attractiveness of the room. It also facilitates moving of materials. Entomology, sanitation, and efficiency are all one in this case.

IN THE STOREROOM and generally throughout the plant a vacuum cleaner of adequate capacity is a useful tool and one of the finest aids to sanitation.

It is a general rule that where there are no hiding, feeding, and breeding places for insects, sanitation reaches a high plane. The industrial entomologist does not try to kill all the insects that may be found in cracks and crevices in plants. His effort is to have the cracks and crevices closed and to see that conduit switchboxes and similar apparatus do not furnish hiding and breeding places. The sanitation-minded architect and the industrial entomologist avoid false ceilings whenever possible. Those places furnish sanctuary for many pests and are a source of much airborne debris.

Insects are too mobile to be excluded completely even in the most carefully designed plant. After the architect and the plant engineer have done their best, the industrial entomologist has to resort to insecticides. For use in a food-processing plant, insecticides have to be chosen carefully. A guiding factor is the nature of the industry. A few rules apply to all conditions: The desirable insecticide must not have an odor that will be absorbed and retained by the products. It must not corrode equipment. Used with proper caution at recommended concentrations, it must be harmless to personnel. It should be inconspicuous.

Insecticides may be applied as space sprays, residual sprays, or fumigants.

Residual-type sprays combined with proper practices of sanitation and good management and with modern, easy-to-clean equipment have almost completely obviated the need for general space fumigation in food processing. General fumigation is seldom necessary except when insects have gotten out of hand or under unusual circumstances.

Space sprays, the old standbys of industry, do not enjoy the favor they once had. They are usually quite transitory in their insecticidal action and must be constantly repeated where insects find ready entrance. Several hazards accompany the use of space sprays. When they are atomized into a closed space, they must fall mostly on the top of some horizontal surface in the lower part of the room. That may be quite objectionable when food containers are open; their use where food is exposed should be prohibited. Most space sprays contain chemicals that kill insects quickly on contact. Their use must be followed closely with a thorough cleaning of all exposed containers in order to avoid contamination of products by chemicals or dead insects.

Space sprays applied as aerosols are not subject to all of the objections the others have and are often used by the industrial entomologist. Their fine particles usually make aerosols more effective than the others and make possible the use of a much smaller amount. Practically all of the aerosol, except the insecticide, becomes gaseous at atmospheric pressure and there is little danger of damage from precipitated spray material. The same necessity exists for caution in the timing and cleanup after the use of aerosols to remove dead insects as with other space sprays. Insects that fall into containers after the use of an aerosol are just as objectionable as any other dead insects.

Where insecticides are permissible, residual-type sprays have come into use. They are usually more economical in first cost and cost of application and in frequency of use. Residual-type sprays are designed for application only to the places where insects go to rest or roost or hide, of which usually there are relatively few in a processing plant. When the places have been covered with a residue of the insecticide, insects that go to them are killed if the spray material was well selected. The residues often continue to kill for months. They are usually quite effective in preventing insects from breeding. They kill constantly, and insects are not allowed to build up to objectionable numbers. More than any other material in recent years, the residual insecticides have improved sanitation in and about processing plants where food for man or animals or clothing are handled.

Because many insecticides and fumigants are poisonous to humans as well as to insects and because insecticides, like any other material not necessary in the production of food, would be adulterants if permitted to fall into food, only workers trained for the purpose should use insecticides about food-processing plants.

ED. M. SEARLS *is entomologist for National Dairy Products Corporation. He spent 11 years in the Bureau of Entomology and Plant Quarantine and was a professor in the department of economic entomology in the University of Wisconsin. He served as entomologist for the 6th Service Command in 1944 and 1945. He is a colonel in the Air Force Reserves and a member of the editorial board of Modern Sanitation. He received his doctor's degree from the University of Wisconsin.*

Extension Work in Entomology

M. P. Jones

Extension entomology developed from a need to have technically trained entomologists in the State extension services to conduct educational programs in insect control and beekeeping.

The extension entomologist brings to the public useful and practical information and encourages the adoption of recommended practices. The information derives from experiments conducted by the State experiment stations and the United States Department of Agriculture.

Extension entomology grew out of the demands of the public for help in fighting an increasing number of insect pests, the lag between the research worker's discoveries and their application by farmers, and the inability of other organizations to supply the needed help.

The beginning was in 1913. By that year the alfalfa weevil, first noticed in the United States near Salt Lake City in 1904, had spread over Utah and into points in Idaho. Growers of alfalfa knew its destructiveness but were confused as to the character of injury it caused. Hay growers in Idaho were worried about quarantine laws enacted by California and Montana and the threat to their most profitable crop and livestock feed. The University of Idaho decided on a new approach. On April 1, 1913, the State extension service there hired T. H. Parks to devote his full time to extension entomology. The appointment was about a year ahead of the Smith-Lever Act, which created the Federal-State Cooperative Extension Service. Later that year the extension service in New York employed C. R. Crosby as extension entomologist to help combat the insect pests attacking the fruit orchards. The number of such specialists increased gradually between 1913 and 1922 and since 1933. In 1952, 65 extension entomologists were employed in 42 States.

Nine States employed extension specialists in beekeeping in 1952. In most States extension work in beekeeping is handled by the extension entomologists, who also do the extension work in the control of pestiferous spiders, snails, slugs, rats, mice, gophers, birds, and like animals. Their first responsibility is to fortify the 9,000 county agricultural, home demonstration, and 4–H Club agents with current information and why and how it should be put into practice.

The extension entomologist's most effective method of operation is to develop his program in advance of the time when the insects are present and causing damage. Then he can help set up demonstrations of methods, plan for farm tours, and prepare informational materials—exhibits, models and mounted specimens, motion pictures, lantern slides, chalk talks, reports on local conditions, and such. The county agent learns most about the insect and its control from the specialist's visit during an outbreak of insects.

Because too few extension entomologists are employed to serve the agents by visits to the counties, the entomologists have had to rely on such measures as annual refresher courses, which bring together the county agents in a State or district. Because the situation regarding pests and pesticides has been changing rapidly, some extension entomologists issue weekly service letters in which they report on the occurrence, abundance, and development of pests, give information about control measures, and summarize results of experiments by State and Federal research workers.

Pest control now has so many aspects that the specialists and county workers cannot do the job only through direct work with farmers. More and more they work with insecticide and equipment manufacturers, distributors, retailers, commodity production associations, lending agencies, milling and meat-packing industries, canning companies, cotton ginners, oil crushers, other processors of crops and livestock, farm organizations, agricultural consultants, field agents of milk companies, and similar groups.

The groups receive the entomologists' bulletins on pest control and beekeeping and often reprint them in their house organs and periodicals. Specialists appear on their programs and thus project farther the information and recommendations they have. Entomologists in many States arrange conferences with sellers of insecticides. They review the recommendations for the State and discuss the insecticides for which the dealers likely will have a demand. Similar conferences are held with pest-control operators and the operators of aerial and ground equipment who apply insecticides.

Sometimes a critical situation requires concerted action—the sudden outbreak of a pest like grasshoppers and chinch bugs in a region of several States, for example, or the need to warn people of the dangers of careless use of an insecticide or the need (as in 1951) of greater care of stored grain and hence the need for greater efforts against insects in farm grain bins. We call them drives or campaigns, for want of better terms. They are conducted on a regional or State basis. Usually the interested groups in States or counties are organized to share responsibility. An example of such action, which includes extension entomologists and other Government agencies, is the grasshopper control program.

Ever since the first settlers inhabited the Plains States, grasshoppers have threatened crops there. Farmers and ranchers applied the known measures for control with varying results. Later the State colleges and experiment stations offered help. Mechanical devices for destroying the grasshoppers were developed. Some were used extensively, but all turned out to be inadequate. The use of paris green and wheat bran was a long step forward. Many State agencies used the bait in well-organized control programs. But the problem burst beyond State lines. More attention had to be paid to the breeding places of the migratory forms of grasshoppers which began to damage crops far beyond the place where they hatched. As a result, requests were made for Federal help. The early help consisted of providing poison bait to farmers and ranchers, who scattered it on their farms and adjoining property.

The participation of the Federal Government necessitated the establishment of standard procedure in working with the States. Memoranda of understanding therefore were drawn up by State officials and the Bureau of Entomology and Plant Quarantine. The responsibility of each agency was outlined. In each State where grasshoppers were a major problem one person was designated as State leader of grasshopper control—usually the extension entomologist but sometimes the State regulatory official or the head of the entomology department in the State agricultural college. The county agent was in charge of efforts in his county.

A division of grasshopper control was established in the Bureau of Entomology and Plant Quarantine to administer the program. Its headquarters are in Denver, Colo., which is near the center of the "grasshopper country." Another division of the Bureau and State experiment stations have conducted research on grasshopper control and methods of surveys of grasshopper populations. It is possible now to map the grasshopper-infested areas and indicate the relative abundance of the pests in the different areas. State extension services and other agencies have made annual grasshopper surveys. New chemicals were tested against grasshoppers. Some are as effective as poison baits and more practical to use.

As State leader, the extension entomologist has coordinated the efforts of the division of grasshopper control and the county agents. He has assisted in the procurement and distribution of baits to counties. When farmers apply their own baits or insecticides, he and the county agents help farmers to decide on the need for control measures and, by means of farm visits, meetings, demonstrations, publicity, and special service letters, help farmers to decide on the need for control measures and to determine what insecticides to use.

One of the oldest and most highly developed extension programs relating to insects is the spray service for orchardists, especially growers of apples, pears, prunes, and cherries. The type of spray service and its extent depend somewhat on the relative importance of fruit growing in the State or county. Research and extension men from the States and the Department of Agriculture give advice at the meetings on the preparation of bulletins that carry recommendations for the control of fruit insects. Federal employees usually participate only when they are located in the State that has the spray service. Extension specialists in entomology and plant pathology usually publish the recommendations and do most of the field work of the spray service. Sometimes the extension horticulturists or other related specialists cooperate.

The service in a number of States has developed somewhat like this: The extension and research specialists hold a meeting to review the results of experiments and extension experience on pest control. They draft tentative recommendations for control of the various pests. At a later meeting the specialists meet with the county agents to perfect the recommendations. They consider the use of insecticides and fungicides on a farm basis according to the experience of the county agents. The recommendations for a given State are often adjusted to agree with those of adjoining States. In some States the specialists go over the recommendations with representatives of insecticide manufacturers and distributors, who thus get a chance to learn the recommendations first-hand.

Information about the insects, the insecticides to use, and the timing of the applications is then published in bulletins and distributed to fruit growers. During the critical part of the spraying season, the extension entomologist spends much of his time with the county agents and orchardists. The county agents make frequent visits to key orchards to determine the progress in development of the fruit trees and of the insects. The information is relayed to all fruit growers by postal card and radio. In urgent situations, the county agent telephones the information to several orchardists, who in turn telephone their neighboring fruit growers.

Timeliness of applications is important. Proper timing and proper insecticides can reduce greatly the number of applications in a season. The United States Weather Bureau provides special weather reports to aid in the spray programs.

Each week the county agents send to their State extension entomologists a report of the observations in the field. The information from the agents is compiled and distributed to the agents as a weekly news letter, in which the entomologist directs attention to any changes in recommendations, reports on new insecticides, and mentions other matters of timely interest. The county agents and specialists continue to observe spray operations and note the effectiveness of the spray materials. They also hold meetings and arrange tours for fruit growers at various times. Sometimes the fruit is examined to determine the percentage of insect damage.

EXTENSION ENTOMOLOGISTS participate in other work of many types.

When the need for beef and leather became critical during the Second World War, several States were completing campaigns to control cattle grubs. In some of them the extension entomologist, animal husbandman, dairyman, and veterinarian together organized the project and carried it out. Several months before the season began for treating cattle for grubs they worked with county agents, farm groups, and commercial representatives to explain the damage the grubs cause, control methods, and materials to use. They prepared news articles and bulletins. As the time for treating the cattle approached they assisted the county agents in demonstrations to show the methods for mixing and applying the insecticides. Sometimes they used grubby carcasses to show the losses caused by the grubs. The work gained momentum throughout the war. As power sprayers became available, more and more cattle were treated for external parasites—in 1949 about 4 million head in the 29 States that submitted reports. The estimated saving to farmers was almost 14 million dollars.

Another program related to the use of DDT against house flies. Many of the States participated. The work in Iowa is typical. The extension entomologist suggested a State meeting be held. The Governor called the meeting and invited organized groups to send delegates. At the meeting procedure was outlined and discussed. The delegates brought the problem to the attention of the county leaders of their organizations and asked their support. The extension entomologist and others of the extension staff prepared, printed, and distributed suggestions for setting up county, community, and town organizations, recommendations for control, posters and stickers, mats for newspaper articles, and news articles giving information on the progress of the campaign. The county extension agents participated actively in the program, but public-spirited citizens did most of the work and deserved credit for its success.

A drive to reduce losses from pests in cotton was another program.

The efforts in South Carolina illustrate the procedure adopted in several

States. Early in 1950 the chairman of the State agricultural committee called a meeting that about 175 representatives of State and Federal agencies, farm organizations, and commercial and trade groups attended. An outgrowth was the organization of a State cotton committee, of which the director of the State extension service was elected chairman. A committee of extension specialists was formed to give technical guidance. Each county in the State organized cotton committees to handle its insect-control program. The State and county committees held meetings, training schools, demonstrations, and tours, and gave reports by radio and newspapers. The results were considered outstanding, as shown by surveys, but nevertheless some farmers failed to apply the recommended measures. Those who did not apply poison averaged about 90 pounds of lint cotton per acre; farmers who poisoned 10 times or more picked about 460 pounds.

The foregoing are but a few of the problems upon which the public requests the help of the extension entomologist. Others include the many additional pests affecting livestock, field crops, fruit crops, the health of man, vegetables, greenhouse crops, home gardens, shade trees and ornamentals, grain and other products in storage, wood structures, household furnishings, clothing, and pets.

An important phase of extension entomology is the work with young people, particularly 4–H Club members. Many State extension services have issued bulletins, circulars, lesson leaflets, project outlines, and activity manuals on the subject of entomology for the use of 4–H Club members. A Department pamphlet, Miscellaneous Publication No. 318, *4–H Club Insect Manual,* is used widely. Nature study often is conducted at 4–H Club camps. An insect-collecting project has been in operation in Indiana since 1925. About 20,000 persons have participated in it.

Other projects have dealt with the life histories of insects, complete control programs for pests, surveys of the abundance of insects, demonstrations of methods and results, and insect collections. Sometimes the activities are part of a broader project having to do with gardens, cotton, corn, clothing, raising pigs, and so on. Some form of work with insects is being carried on by 4–H Club members in nearly every State.

In some States teams of 4–H Club members are trained to give demonstrations about insect pests and their control. Club members learn to recognize the pest, assess its economic importance, and apply control measures. In Texas, club members learn a certain number of insects; community teams are selected to compete on a county basis, and the county teams compete in a State contest. The teams are judged on oral tests that cover insects found in the contestant's community—the identity of insects, hosts, control methods, and the application of insecticides.

Entomology work with 4–H Club members has developed to the extent that some phase of it is suitable for every club member.

As an added incentive to 4–H work in entomology there has been established a National 4–H Entomology Award. The rewards are medals for the county winners, prizes for State winners, trips to the National 4–H Club Congress for sectional winners, and scholarships for national winners. The rewards recognize excellence in all phases of work relating to insect pests and their control—making collections, conducting life-history studies, carrying out insect-control practices, giving demonstrations relating to entomology, and participating in community-wide control programs.

Extension work in apiculture is as old as the extension service itself. Much of the work now is through county and State beekeepers' associations. The usual extension teaching

970134°—52——31

methods are employed to show the beekeepers how to transfer bees, detect and control bee diseases, and manage the colony for maximum honey production. Management of the colony includes requeening, brood rearing, feeding of bees, swarm control, placement of supers, removal of honey, and provisions of winter stores of food for the bees. Bee management has taken into account the use of bees for pollination—the procurement of bees, the number of colonies needed, and the location of bees in orchards or seed-producing fields. Many thousands of 4–H Club members keep bees as a project. It provides a small enterprise for members who like bees and cannot have livestock or crop projects. John D. Haynie, extension apiculturist in Florida, introduces beekeeping and a taste for honey to 4–H Club members by operating a 4–H Club apiary at one of their camps. The honey produced is distributed to three other 4–H Camps in the State. He uses the apiary to instruct club members in beekeeping practices.

M. P. JONES *is extension entomologist in the Extension Service. Before he joined the Department of Agriculture in 1931, he was assistant extension entomologist in Ohio. He is a native of Ohio and a graduate of Ohio State University.*

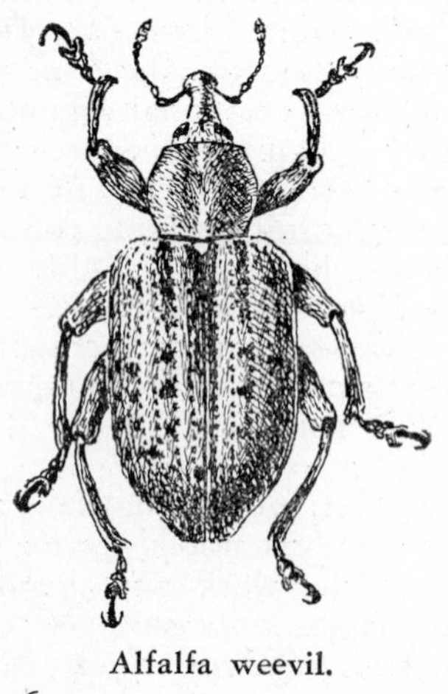

Alfalfa weevil.

Entomologists in Washington

Helen Sollers

One hundred years ago a man by the name of Townend Glover was so fascinated by insects that he made colored plates of every specimen he could get. He spent years making etchings on stone and copper. He also wrote about the insects he saw. He had a dream of a great book which would illustrate all the common insects of North America and help the farmer to identify any pest he found.

He had a counterinterest that interfered with his dream, however. He made almost perfect models of fruits, which he exhibited at State fairs. He displayed the collection also in Washington, hoping that the Government would buy it. While he was in Washington, the Bureau of Agriculture was established in the Patent Office, and Glover was appointed in 1854 to collect information on insects, seeds, and fruits.

Things moved along in the next 8 years. The Department of Agriculture was established, and Glover was appointed the first entomologist in it. He wrote about the destruction of fruit and vegetable crops by insects. He had time to enlarge his agricultural museum. Congress appropriated $10,000 to buy the Glover Museum, which comprised insects, birds, and fruit models. He became curator of the museum.

Glover's heart and time went into the museum, which attracted crowds of people. But what was happening to his dream—his "Illustrations of North American Entomology"? He toiled on plates and his notes in every spare hour. His friends pleaded with him to publish the work. Finally at various times in 6 years he put out four volumes in which he pictured and described grasshoppers, flies, true bugs, and a number of other insects. Fortunate it was that Glover heeded his friends' pleas and realized at least a part of his dream, because time soon ran out and he could produce no more.

CHARLES VALENTINE RILEY took over the post of entomologist in 1878 soon after Glover had retired. He was young and already had made a name for himself as State entomologist of Missouri. His series of annual reports entitled, "The Noxious, Beneficial, and Other Insects of the State of Missouri" were more readable and better illustrated than most of the other articles of his day.

Riley's first stay in the Department was less than a year as he resigned over a misunderstanding. Professor John Henry Comstock of Cornell University took his place. The 2 years that Comstock held office were eventful. New insecticides, such as paris green and london purple, were discovered; pyrethrum was being used in the United States for the first time. Great advances were made in other insecticides and in machinery for applying insecticides. Comstock, a practical man, helped place economic entomology on a sound footing in the United States.

A change of administration in 1881 sent Comstock back to Cornell and placed Riley in charge of the new division of entomology, which had been established in 1879. Riley was an active man and did four important things for entomology. He started to build an organization which grew into the Bureau of Entomology and Plant Quarantine. His studies of the grape phylloxera helped the Europeans to bring this dangerous pest under control. He saved the citrus industry in California by bringing the Australian lady bird beetle to control the white scale, which was ravaging the citrus trees—the first time an international experiment on natural control had been sucessfully carried out. Largely because of his efforts, the United States Entomological Commission was founded in 1877.

The job of the Commission (attached to the United States Geological and Geographical Surveys of the Territories) was to find out how to control the hordes of grasshoppers which had descended upon the crops in the West and Midwest and to prevent their recurrence. Three men, C. V. Riley, A. S. Packard, and Cyrus Thomas, made up the Commission. The results of their important work is published in several reports and bulletins on grasshoppers, armyworm, cotton worm, and several other insects. In 1880 the Commission became a part of the Department of Agriculture. In June 1881 its activities ceased.

A NEW ERA for entomology began when Leland O. Howard stepped into the position of chief of the division of entomology in 1894. Howard was an intellectual giant with ideas to promote. He wrote about insects, talked about them, and conducted campaigns against them. All this he did in such a clear and simple manner that he even got the children interested in killing flies. Americans began to wake up to insect problems. But Howard meant to keep them awake. For 33 years he hammered away to make our people aware of the seriousness of insect damage—sufficiently aware to spur them into action. His books, *The Insect Menace, Insect Book,* and *Fighting the Insects,* challenged the people of the world to take up the fight against the insect horde.

Howard had another idea. He was interested in the natural control of insects—controlling insects by other insects. Riley had pioneered in the field, but Howard really developed it. Summer after summer he sailed to Europe to consult famous entomologists and to arrange for shipment of parasites and predators left behind when the gypsy moth and brown-tail moth got into this country.

Actually he knew more about the subject than the Europeans because for years he had studied parasites and their hosts from a world viewpoint. Added to that he had described many of the parasites himself. Howard's personality won him many friends. The friends helped him to establish a regular plan of shipping parasites and predators from several European countries into the United States.

Following the First World War an incident happened that Howard termed a parasite introduction of a reversed kind, that is, from America to Europe, instead of from Europe to America. The woolly apple aphid is native to the United States, but in some way it got into England and then into France and was called "the American blight." A minute parasite was the chief reason the woolly apple aphid was not a very serious pest in our country. The French wanted the parasite. Howard himself took a direct part in the experiment. He put the precious packages of parasites in the refrigerator room of the boat. Arriving in London late at night, he laid the packages on the window ledge outside his room. The next 3 days the parasites rested in a fish monger's cold room.

Then the great day arrived. Dr. Paul Marchal, who wanted the parasites for France, hastened with Howard from the station in Paris to the laboratory. Here, made ready for the occasion, was a pear tree well infested with woolly apple aphids and covered with gauze. Everyone gathered around and the packages of parasites were opened and one by one their contents emptied on the white paper. To everyone's amazement not a live parasite could be seen. Failure stared at them. However, they put the gauze back over the tree and Howard and Marchal went to the south of France. By the time they reached Montpellier a telegram arrived telling them that all the parasites were not dead as they had supposed but 10 had emerged from the dead aphids. Soon 200 emerged and by the time Howard got back to Paris these had multiplied to millions in Marchal's experimental garden. The parasites passed the winter and helped to settle the problem of the French fruit growers.

Howard had a third idea to advance. Little work had been done in the field of insects in relation to disease. He believed house flies carried diseases, and he fought to make people believe that the flies in their houses could do them harm. He inaugurated antifly campaigns. "Swat the fly" stirred peoples' interest in insects throughout the country. Europeans also caught the idea and started campaigns of their own. His book, *The Housefly—Disease Carrier,* boosted the fly crusades everywhere. It was even translated into Russian, Hungarian, and Spanish. In Hungary it was used as a reader in the public schools.

Then came the mosquito crusade. Shortly after malaria and yellow fever were discovered to be carried by mosquitoes, Howard's book, *Mosquitoes—How They Live; How They Carry Disease; How They Are Classified; How They May Be Destroyed,* came off the press. The moment was ripe for such a book. Yellow fever was the scourge of Havana and Panama. The control measures presented in Howard's book were put into immediate action and helped to rid both places of the disease. But Howard was not satisfied with this book. It did not contain the facts that mosquitoes carry malaria and yellow fever. He then embarked on a more ambitious scheme—an extensive monograph of *The Mosquitoes of North America, Central America, and the West Indies.* This four-volume work helped sanitarians, doctors, and biological workers the world over. Co-authors with Howard were H. G. Dyar and F. Knab.

Dr. Howard won numerous awards, medals, and honorary memberships in societies. He was a member of practically every entomological society in the world. Howard's ideas helped entomology to grow. As Riley's assistant he had learned the technique of organization but improved on it so well that, 10 years after Riley resigned in 1894, Howard headed a Bureau instead of a division. The Bureau of Entomology to Dr. Howard was a dream fulfilled.

One of the men in the new Bureau was Charles L. Marlatt. For many years he had observed pest after pest reaching our shores and settling here. By 1900 such invaders as the codling moth, the hessian fly, the San Jose scale and horn fly helped themselves to a good share of our food supply. Several attempts had been made to keep the pests out, but Marlatt could see that the problem was not solved. His plan was to put up a legal fence.

The first step in this direction was the passage of the Insect Pest Act of 1905. It prohibited shipping live insects into this country, mailing them, or sending them from State to State. The Act helped, but it did not go far enough. Marlatt wanted a law to keep bugs from entering the United States on their host plants or in any other way. He prepared such a law and labored for 3 years to get it passed.

FINALLY IN 1912 he saw the Plant Quarantine Act become a reality. For the first time a plant quarantine had police power behind it. Imports of nursery stock, plants, and plant products could now be restricted or stopped to prevent new diseases and insect pests from entering the United States. The Act also made possible the control of insect-infested products moving across State lines into uninfested areas.

The Federal Horticultural Board was established in 1912 and Dr. Marlatt, father of Federal quarantines, became its chairman. The Board made investigations concerning foreign and domestic insect pests before it could propose quarantine action. It also held hearings to find out the need for plant quarantines and had the authority to enforce them. In 1928 the Board became the Plant Quarantine and Control Administration.

During the time that Marlatt served on the Board, he was also Howard's associate chief and in 1927 became chief of the Bureau when Howard retired.

QUARANTINE WORK had another leader to sponsor its cause. A westerner by the name of Lee A. Strong studied all phases of quarantine work. He took an active part in setting up a system that helped the whole country work together on quarantine matters. Lee Strong did another thing for entomology. When he became chief of the Bureau of Plant Quarantine he could see quarantines ought to be closely tied up with the research and control activities of the Bureau of Entomology. He visualized several agencies being put into one strong organization.

In 1933 he became chief of the Bureau of Entomology. The following year the merger he had worked for took place. Strong had brought the Bureau of Plant Quarantine, the insecticide division of the Bureau of Chemistry and Soils, the work on plant diseases conducted by the Bureau of Plant Industry, and the Bureau of Entomology into one unit, the Bureau of Entomology and Plant Quarantine. He kept strengthening the organization throughout his term of office.

Suddenly one night in 1941 Strong died. P. N. Annand, who had risen rapidly in the Bureau, became chief. Annand was a research man and under his direction during the Second World War a notable piece of research on insecticides took place—the development of DDT at the Orlando, Fla., laboratory of the Bureau. Many other insecticides, insect repellents, and improved methods of applying them also were discovered or developed during the period. Dr. Annand died in 1950 after serving 9 years. Avery S. Hoyt succeeded him. The Bureau has 200 field laboratories and offices, each located in the midst of the insect problem with which it deals. Most of the laboratories are in rented quarters so they can move as the insects move. The work of the Bureau lies in three main fields, research, quarantine, and control. It has five regional offices and ten research divisions.

Exciting events in entomology were taking place in other parts of the Government service.

Back in 1884 anybody who even suggested that an insect or tick could cause disease was looked upon as a queer person. Theobald Smith shared these views but in a few years he changed his mind.

The great Robert Koch in Germany was looking at the tiny microbes that carry disease. Smith wanted to look at microbes and he wanted to study under Koch. But Germany was a long way off for a man with no money. He had an M. D. degree but he was not interested in practicing medicine. He found just the job he wanted in the Bureau of Animal Industry. He went to work in a hot attic of a Federal building. His nights were his own, and in the long hours he absorbed everything Koch wrote about microbes.

Little did Smith know, as he poured over those books, that he was to solve the riddle of Texas fever. It was an odd disease. Southern stockmen bought healthy northern cattle, brought them to the South, and in a month the cattle got sick and died. Southern cattle came North, grazed with the northern cattle; in a month the fields were red with the blood of northern cattle. The southern cattle stayed healthy all the time regardless of the locality. The stockmen were in a panic. The Bureau of Animal Industry put Theobald Smith and F. L. Kilborne to work on the mystery.

Smith decided that he would move right out into the field with the disease. As he prepared for the summer work, Kilborne tossed out the idea that ticks might be causing Texas fever. Smith did not close his mind to this theory, especially when Kilborne told him that the cattlemen were saying, "No ticks—no Texas fever."

In the summer heat of 1889 Kilborne set up open-air enclosures in fields to run the tests. In the first fenced-in field he put four tick-laden cows from North Carolina and six healthy cows from the North. Then just to see if ticks had anything to do with it, Kilborne picked by hand all the ticks off three other North Carolina cows, which he placed in the second field with four healthy northern cows. In a month all the northern cows in the first field were burning with fever, but those in the second field remained healthy.

Now another man by the name of Cooper Curtice played an important but less glamorous part in the story of Texas fever. His job was to study the life cycle and habits of cattle fever ticks. Smith and Kilborne needed the facts he gathered to continue their experiments with ticks on cattle.

Smith looked at the blood of the dying cows and he spied some pear-shaped organisms. He examined the blood of many cows with Texas fever and every time he found the same pear-shaped objects. Could these be the germs of Texas fever? He was not sure. He looked at thousands of blood cells and made test after test with cattle and ticks in the fenced-in fields.

But he wanted more proof. He raised cattle ticks in his laboratory and in the summer of 1890 decided to put a number of the baby ticks on a cow in a box stall. Day after day he took blood from the cow. One day he found the cow hot with fever. He took a sample of her blood and found it thin and dark. He rushed to his microscope and there before him were the little pear-shaped organisms. His picture was complete. Texas fever had survived in these tiny baby ticks. Now he saw why there was a 30-day lapse before the northern cattle got the disease. It took just this length of time for the parent tick to drop off the animal, for the eggs to be laid, and for the young ticks to hatch, crawl up a cow's legs, and attach themselves to the body. The southern cattle became immune to the disease when they were calves.

For the first time in the history of man, a tick was proved to be a disease carrier. Theobald Smith's discovery started a chain of events in which certain ticks, insects, and mites were labeled disease carriers, and opened up a whole new field of entomology—medical entomology.

The Bureau of Animal Industry made use of this discovery and with the help of cooperating States wiped Texas fever out of the United States, except for a long, narrow strip next to the Rio Grande River in Texas. This is known as a buffer zone and will remain that way until Mexico eradicates the disease. The Bureau is making splendid headway in eradicating the destructive scab mites of livestock and is continuing the fight against other animal pests that cut our meat, milk, and wool supply.

About 10 years after Theobald Smith's discovery, Walter Reed was called upon to fight a disease of humans. Yellow fever was raging in Cuba at the time the United States Army ordered Maj. Walter Reed to Quemado de Güines. Cubans and American soldiers were dying every day. Reed had studied microbes but he could find none in the bodies of the victims.

The Commission, consisting of Jesse Lazear, James Carroll, Aristides Agramonte, and Walter Reed, did not know what to do next. They had time on their hands, time enough to hear the voice of Carlos Finlay, ringing out, "Yellow fever is caused by a mosquito." Finlay was considered a fanatic in Cuba but the Commission had tried everything else and acknowledged that Finlay might be right. Anyway they talked to him and raised adult mosquitoes from the little black eggs he gave them.

Walter Reed decided to test the mosquito theory. First he needed guinea pigs; animals he had tested did not get yellow fever. He needed humans. His own commission accepted the challenge: One of the deadliest mosquitoes was put on the arm of James Carroll. A few days later Carroll had yellow fever and nearly died, but he was proud to be the first experimental victim of yellow fever.

Still another man got the disease from one of Lazear's laboratory-raised mosquitoes. Then Lazear himself must take the chance. But he did not use one of his own mosquitoes; he let a stray mosquito from the yellow fever ward in which he was working suck his blood. In 5 days he had a chill. In 6 days he was dead.

The Army gave Reed money to pay men to be guinea pigs and to find out if a mosquito really did carry yellow fever. He set up a camp of seven tents and two small houses. Each volunteer soldier was locked up in one of the shelters for days or weeks to make sure he did not get yellow fever before one of Reed's mosquitoes bit him. Six more men got yellow fever from his mosquitoes. Walter Reed wanted to test one more theory.

Everyone was saying that bed linens and household effects of yellow-fever victims were dangerous. Even houses were burned down to get rid of the disease. Reed got piles of bed linen soiled with blood and discharges from dying men in the yellow fever ward. He put these bedclothes in a little house, especially built, and raised the temperature to over 90. Into this house went three brave Americans who slept in this stench for 20 nights and then were quarantined in a tent to wait the attack of yellow fever. But they continued to be healthy.

Then Reed wondered if the men were susceptible to yellow fever. To test this he put three of his yellow fever mosquitoes on their arms and in a few days they had yellow fever.

They never found the microbe of yellow fever, but they did find that it was a virus too small to be seen.

The Gorgas Memorial Laboratory and the Health Department of the Panama Canal Zone, with help from the United States, continued the fight against yellow fever, which now exists only in small areas in Africa and Tropical America, where it exists in the jungle mosquitoes and monkeys.

They have also continued the fight against malaria and other insect-borne diseases.

THE SECOND WORLD WAR increased the interest of the Armed Forces in entomology. The Army, in a cooperative arrangement with the Bureau of Entomology and Plant Quarantine, has done research work on insects affecting troops. During both World Wars attention was given to louse control and other insects that attack man.

The Army also worked on insect damage to food, clothing, and military supplies. The Navy Medical Corps has published much information on mosquitoes and their relation to disease. They have made a number of improvements in ways of applying insecticides from the air and in dispersing aerosols in aircraft.

Entomologists of the United States Public Health Service work on insect-borne diseases, such as malaria, yellow fever, plague, Rocky Mountain spotted fever, and several fly-borne diseases. They are also concerned with the biology of the insect involved in these diseases. The Hamilton, Mont., laboratory conducts work on ticks; the vaccine for Rocky Mountain spotted fever was discovered there. The Communicable Disease Center is concerned with plague, disease transmission by insects, ticks and mites, testing insecticides for their long lasting action and the development of equipment. Studies of malaria transmission and the effect of insecticides on man, are some of the activities of the National Institutes of Health.

The Public Health Service has been studying the malaria problem for many years. In 1945, using DDT, it started an eradication program with the help of various State Departments of Health in the Southern States.

Another Government agency that works on mosquito control is the Tennessee Valley Authority, which has prevented outbreaks of malaria along its hundreds of miles of reservoirs.

The Fish and Wildlife Service works with the Bureau of Entomology and Plant Quarantine, Tennessee Valley Authority, and the United States Public Health Service in studying the relation of mosquito control to wildlife. The Service also makes studies of insect enemies of game animals incidental to its routine work.

Entomology enters the work also of the Food and Agriculture Organization and the World Health Organization of the United Nations. They have a number of projects on insects in various parts of the world. The control of malaria-carrying mosquitoes, the protection of stored cereals against insects, and grasshopper control are problems vital to the welfare of many countries.

WORK ON several basic entomological problems is done in the Bureau of Plant Industry, Soils, and Agricultural Engineering of the Department of Agriculture—breeding plants resistant to insects, special light-trapping devices, and equipment for applying insecticides.

The insecticide division of the Livestock Branch, Production and Marketing Administration, makes the use of insecticides safer and more effective by seeing that packages are properly labeled. This important work is done under the insecticide act of 1947, which requires all insecticide products to meet the claims of their labels.

The capstone of a large part of the entomological research is the insect collections in the United States National Museum. There specimens are studied and identified, for on proper identification rests any successful control action. Taxonomists of the Museum and the Bureau of Entomology and Plant Quarantine cooperate so closely that they function as one unit.

HELEN SOLLERS, *an entomologist in the Bureau of Entomology and Plant Quarantine, is engaged in research on insects of medical and veterinary importance and prepares bibliographies on mosquitoes. She joined the Bureau in 1937.*

Insects, Man, and Homes

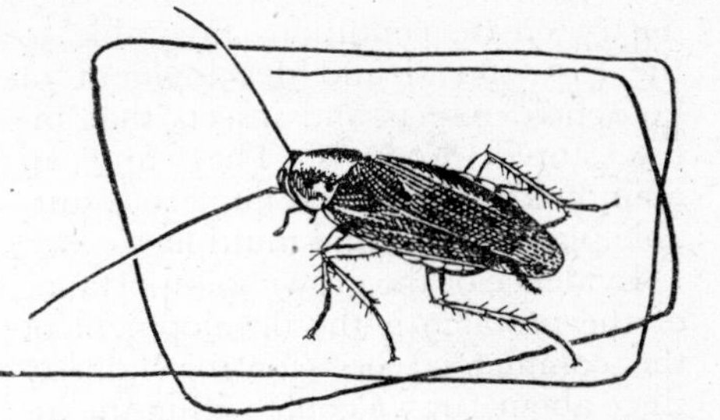

Household Insects

L. S. Henderson

The many kinds of pests that invade households cause trouble in numerous ways.

Termites, carpenter ants, powder-post beetles, and other wood borers attack buildings and the wood in furniture.

Clothes moths, carpet beetles, silverfish, roaches, and crickets damage clothing, rugs, and upholstery.

Various kinds of weevils, beetles, moths, mites, psocids, flies, roaches, and ants infest food. Flies, mosquitoes, fleas, lice, mites, and roaches may carry diseases.

Scorpions, wasps, and some kinds of ants may sting us. Bed bugs, lice, fleas, mites, mosquitoes, punkies, sand flies, ticks, and black widow spiders may bite or suck blood from us or our household pets.

Some pests may cause no particular damage but are a nuisance just by their presence in homes—house spiders, millipedes, centipedes, drain flies, some kinds of ants, springtails, and psocids.

Some, such as bed bugs, silverfish, clothes moths, brown dog ticks, and some kinds of roaches, and ants, spend their entire lives in homes or other buildings.

Others normally live out of doors and invade homes only in search of food. Boxelder bugs, cluster flies, clover mites, elm leaf beetles, lady beetles, and wasps often enter homes in the fall to find a protected place in which they can spend the winter. They do not multiply in houses and do no feeding during the winter. On warm days some may become active and find their way into rooms. All of them will go outside if they can when warm weather arrives in the spring.

A number of kinds of insects are not usually household pests but may enter homes occasionally, sometimes in tremendous numbers. When conditions happen to be favorable for them to live there, or under some unusual circumstances, pillbugs, black widow spiders, scorpions, earwigs, psocids, thrips, springtails, millipedes, or ground beetles may become a serious problem. In addition there are myriads of kinds of beetles, moths, flies, wasps, leafhoppers, and other outdoor insects which may accidentally get into homes or be attracted there by lights.

Commercial establishments often encounter serious problems from the same insects that are household pests. Offices, stores, restaurants, warehouses, factories, and food processing or packaging plants all suffer losses caused by insects. Personnel are annoyed or disturbed, records are destroyed, food is contaminated, or raw materials and finished products are damaged.

As THE NUMBER of homes in the United States becomes greater and greater, as our population becomes increasingly urban, and as industry and production continue to expand, the household-insect problems become more prevalent and more acute. Heavy concentrations of population and industry create conditions favorable to the easy spread and development of household insects and insects that infest stored products. They find an abundance of food and numerous suitable places to live and multiply.

Evidence of the growing importance of the problem is the development of the commercial pest-control industry since about 1935. People within the industry state that 50 million dollars is a conservative estimate of the annual volume of pest-control services rendered. More than 700 firms are organized in the National Pest Control Association, whose major aims are to improve service and business practices. Several universities conduct instructional conferences and short courses, which many pest-control operators attend year after year. "Pest Control," a periodical containing technical information, is published primarily for the industry. The association and some of the firms employ entomologists as technical directors and advisors. Pest-control service is now available in many communities from experienced and reliable firms.

Early recommendations for controlling household insects leaned heavily on the use of kerosene, turpentine, bichloride of mercury, white arsenic, and gum camphor. Poison baits were used commonly. Ants were attracted to bits of sweetened sponge and dropped into boiling water. The value of heat was early discovered for killing insects in some commodities and buildings. The "curious effect" of Persian insect powder (dried and powdered pyrethrum flowers) on roaches was referred to in a publication as early as 1864—about 50 years later the value of pyrethrum extracts in insect sprays was fully realized.

Shortly after the turn of the century, fumigants began to receive attention. New and more effective fumigants were discovered. Techniques were developed for fumigating warehouses, mills, factories, and homes. Commodities were fumigated in atmospheric vaults and vacuum chambers. Since 1946 the use of DDT, chlordane, and lindane residual sprays has reduced the amount of fumigation done.

Since 1920 much has been learned about the biology and habits of clothes moths and carpet beetles. Mothproofing solutions were studied for several years. Thorough treatment of fabrics with common silicofluoride solutions now available in stores was found to give a worth-while degree of protection. Commercial treatments applied at the factory in the hot dye bath gave more complete and longer lasting protection and withstood more laundering and dry cleaning.

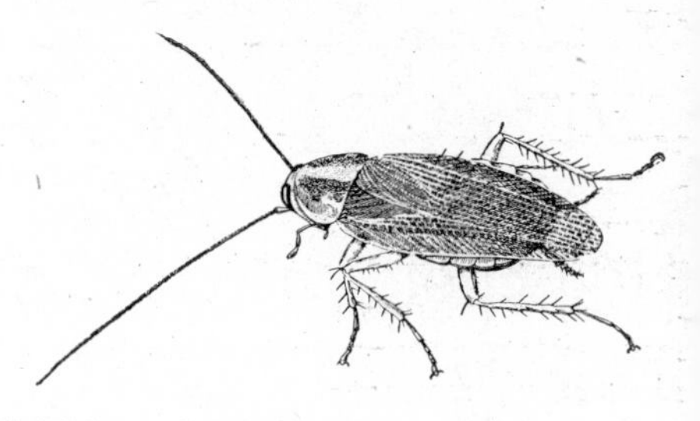

German cockroach.

An investigation of cedar chests and other cedar products was ended in 1922. It was found that storing woolens in chests made of the heartwood lumber of eastern red cedar seven-eighths inch thick gave good protection against clothes moths if no large larvae were put in with the woolens. They could be removed by sunning and brushing or by dry cleaning. Small larvae and adults were killed quickly in the cedar chests. Thin cedar veneers and cedar oil were found to be relatively ineffective against clothes moths. These facts, and other results of the research, were then made available to the public in bulletins.

Between 1920 and 1940, great emphasis was placed on the development of more effective space sprays and contact sprays. These insecticides had to be used repeatedly and frequently against insects as hard to control as roaches, bed bugs, carpet beetles, and brown dog ticks.

DDT, first brought to this country in 1942, was rapidly developed for the control of bed bugs, mosquitoes, flies, and roaches, which are of importance to the Armed Forces. By 1946 DDT was available to the general public and immediately received extensive use in homes.

THEN A WHOLE new trend began in the field of insect control—a parade of synthetic chlorinated organic insecticides with residual properties—toxaphene, chlordane, methoxychlor, TDE, benzene hexachloride, lindane, aldrin, and dieldrin. Some had undesirable physical, chemical, or toxicological properties that made them unsuitable for use in homes. Some turned out to be less effective than DDT against household insects; others were more effective than DDT against some species or for specific uses. Confusion existed for a time when the products were new, and answers were sought to questions as to which should be used for which purpose. A more orderly condition now exists as the various insecticides find their proper places.

Aerosol bombs were bought eagerly when they became available to civilians and were often ineffectively or wastefully used. Many people did not understand their proper uses and limitations; they thought all one had to do was open the valve and release the entire contents in a closet or kitchen to kill all the clothes moths or roaches. In time they learned that the aerosol spray is not a fumigant but a highly effective form of space spray made up of extremely small particles. There was also a mistaken belief that since many aerosols contained DDT an effective residual deposit should remain after their use. A more recent development is a sprayer resembling an aerosol container, which produces a mist spray with particles larger than the aerosol particles. This type of sprayer is designed to apply a surface spray of a residual insecticide. Mothproofing solutions for application to fabrics are also available in this kind of sprayer.

Another development is the finding of more effective synergists for pyrethrum. Sesame oil previously was used to increase the killing effect of pyrethrum; now materials like piperonyl butoxide or *n*-propyl isome are available and are more effective.

THE CONTROL of household insects cannot be reduced to such simple terms that a single insecticide or method of application will suffice for all purposes or under all conditions. The developments since 1942, however, make the job much easier than it used to be.

A few basic principles of control should be understood.

Good housekeeping and thorough sanitation are of paramount importance in controlling or preventing infestations of many kinds of household insects. These practices remove insects, disturb them, or make conditions unfavorable for them. The removal of garbage, bits of food, lint, scraps of waste fabrics or other materials, and other accumulated matter reduces the available food supply of insects and deprives them of some possible hiding places. If such things are allowed to remain, a few or many insects may develop there and spread to places where they will cause damage or annoyance.

A doctor diagnoses an illness before he decides what medicine to use or how it shall be administered. When you encounter insects or insect damage it is just as important to know or find out what kind of insect is involved so you can decide how best to control it. Different insecticides may have to be used against different kinds of insects. Almost certainly the method of approach and the manner or places in which an insecticide is to be applied will have to be decided on the basis of the particular pest involved.

If you do not recognize the insect, send specimens to your State entomologist, agricultural experiment station, the entomology department of a university, or the Bureau of Entomology and Plant Quarantine, Washington 25,

D. C. Send several specimens if you can. Kill or stun them with a fly spray if you can't catch them easily. Put them in a small bottle or vial of 70 percent alcohol or rubbing alcohol. You can pick up tiny insects with a moistened camel's-hair brush or on the damp tip of a small twisted paper swab and transfer them to the vial. Pack this vial in a small box so it does not get broken in shipping. If you just place insects in an envelope, they are likely to dry up and be crushed in the mail beyond the point of recognition even by an expert. Be sure to enclose your name and address. It will help to write, request an identification of the insects, and send any information you can about where the insects were, their abundance, a description of the damage, or any other details that seem important. Most of the places named can send you bulletins on at least the major pests, in which you will find control recommendations and answers to many of the questions you might ask.

After you know what kind of insect you are dealing with you will know or can find out what it feeds on, where it lives or hides, and what its habits are. Then you may have to seek out the source of the infestation and destroy the food supply of such insects as fruit flies. Or you may have to correct a faulty condition which is responsible for a termite infestation. If the insects are ants rather than termites, you would decide to use an insecticide. If an insecticide is required, you will be able to decide which insecticide to use, whether a powder or liquid, and if liquid, whether to apply it as a space spray, aerosol spray, contact spray, or residual spray. You will select the type of equipment according to the form of insecticide and where it is to be applied. And most important of all, you will decide where to apply the insecticide to be most effective against this particular pest. Remember that proper application of a moderately effective insecticide will give better results than poor application of the best of insecticides.

Roaches can be controlled effectively in homes with a spray containing 2 percent of chlordane. It is important to apply the spray in places where the roaches hide or live.

American and oriental cockroaches live primarily in warm, moist locations, as in steam tunnels, boiler rooms, storerooms, basements, and under unexcavated parts of buildings. During warm weather they may also live under porches, around foundations, or in outbuildings.

German cockroaches live right in or near the places where you find them, usually in the kitchen or bathroom. Brown-banded roaches live in these places and also all over the house. You may find them in furniture, closets, or other protected places.

When insecticides are being applied in the kitchen, precautions should be taken not to contaminate food, dishes, or utensils. Such things should be removed from cabinets or shelves before spraying into the surrounding cracks or hiding places of roaches. If it is necessary to spray close to food or utensils, one of the less toxic insecticides—those that contain various combinations of pyrethrum, synergist, or rotenone—should be used. Such sprays will have to be used more frequently than chlordane sprays.

Pantry pests include several kinds of weevils, beetles, and moths that infest flour, meal, cereals, spices, and other dry foods in the home. When they cause trouble, find the infested products and destroy them. Clean the shelves thoroughly and spray the surfaces inside the storage area with 5 percent DDT. You can destroy all stages of these insects by heating most dry foods in the oven for one-half hour at 140° F. Store uninfested or heat-treated foods in containers with tight-fitting covers.

Silverfish live in bookcases, around closet shelves, and behind baseboards and window or door frames. In the summer they may be in storage attics where books and papers are present. In the winter they may be in a warm furnace room. Silverfish feed on starchy materials, wallpaper, paper, and books. They sometimes cause serious damage to rayon.

A 10 percent DDT powder can be applied in the cracks and in places where a dust deposit is not objectionable. In other places, or on surfaces where the dust would not adhere, a 5 percent DDT spray should be applied.

ANTS are usually best controlled with chlordane insecticides. Treat the nest if you can locate it with 5-percent powder or 2-percent spray applied into and around the opening of the nest. If ants are getting into the house from outside, they can usually be kept out by spraying porch landings, building supports, foundations, or the sides of the house up to the window level. If the ants are of the kind that nest within the partitions or other places in the house, it is usually impossible to locate the nest. Apply a 2 percent chlordane spray into the openings from which these ants emerge, and onto surfaces immediately surrounding the openings.

CLOTHES MOTH larvae feed on articles that contain wool, mohair, feathers, down, fur, or hair. They usually spend all their time right on the article upon which they are feeding.

Good housekeeping will help control clothes moths by disturbing or killing them and by removing waste material and lint upon which they might feed. Closet walls and shelves should be sprayed once or twice a year with 5 percent DDT. Moths or larvae that crawl over the treated surfaces will be

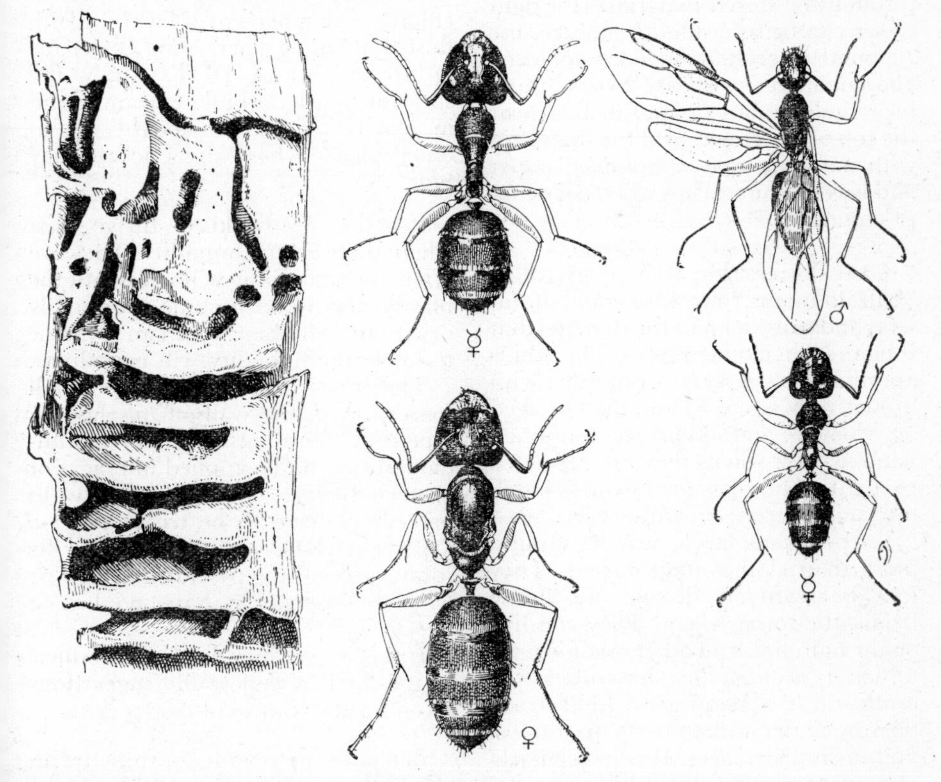

The carpenter ant constructs extensive galleries in dead wood where it rears its young. Here are shown large and small neuter workers, a winged male, and an apterous egg-laying female.

killed. Aerosols or household fly sprays will kill the moths or exposed larvae that are hit with the spray. They have little or no lasting effect, however, and should be used at frequent intervals if they are to be of much value.

Woolen articles such as clothing, blankets, rugs, or furniture upholstery can be protected from clothes moth damage by treating them with a spray containing 5 percent of DDT or methoxychlor. Silicofluoride solutions also give good protection and can be bought in stores under such names as Berlou, Guardex, Larvex, Perma-Moth, Per-mo, and Ya-De.

If articles to be stored are not mothproofed, they should be put in a tight container with paradichlorobenzene crystals or naphthalene flakes. A pound of crystals or flakes is enough for a trunk and they should be scattered through the stored material. If a tight closet can be set aside for storage, use 1 pound of crystals or flakes for each 100 cubic feet of space. Expose them in a shallow pan or muslin bag near the top of the closet. Seal the door shut with masking tape or gummed paper and leave it shut except when necessary to enter.

CARPET BEETLES, sometimes called "buffalo moths," are very common insects and cause a lot of the damage that is blamed on clothes moths. The adults are small beetles, black or mottled with brown and white. They do not feed on woolens and often are found on window sills, where they are attracted to light. They lay eggs which hatch into small, fuzzy, brown larvae.

Carpet beetle larvae wander around more than clothes moth larvae. They may be scattered all over the house from attic to basement. They can live on the hair, lint, and other organic matter that accumulates in corners, in cracks in the flooring, behind baseboards, under radiators, in partitions, and in similar places. It is particularly important to clean thoroughly as many such places as possible. Then apply a spray containing 2 percent of chlordane or 0.5 percent of lindane. Use these sprays only in closets, around baseboards, and along the edges of rugs or floors. To protect rugs, clothing, blankets, and upholstery, use the same things as recommended for clothes moths.

HOUSE SPIDERS cause no real damage but are annoying because of the webs they spin in corners and under furniture. Vacuum cleaning removes the webs, spiders, and their egg cases. If they continue to recur, apply a spray containing 2 percent of chlordane or 0.5 percent of lindane around windows, doors, or other places where the spiders might get in. Use the same spray in corners or under furniture where the spiders might live.

HOUSE CRICKETS can be controlled with sprays containing 2 percent of chlordane or 5 percent of DDT, or with dusts containing 5 percent of chlordane or 10 percent of DDT. Apply the spray or powder around entrances and in closets, around baseboards or in other places where the crickets may hide.

PSOCIDS or booklice thrive best where there is high humidity. They are often abundant in new homes until the plaster and wood become thoroughly dried out. Anything that can be done to lower the humidity will be helpful.

The insects live in cracks, wall spaces, or on the walls themselves. A 2 percent chlordane or 0.5 percent lindane spray can be applied in cracks or protected places. Where entire walls or ceilings have to be treated, use a 5 percent DDT spray. Household fly sprays will kill the psocids that are hit with the spray, but have no lasting effect.

If psocids get into dry food products in the kitchen, follow the suggestions given for the control of pantry pests.

BED BUGS are readily controlled with a 5 percent DDT spray. It should be applied lightly but thoroughly to infested mattresses, bed frames, and the wall surfaces in the immediate area of the bed. Upholstered furniture should also be sprayed if it becomes infested.

WASPS, HORNETS, and yellow-jackets may nest around homes during the summer, or they may have nests in the ground in lawns or gardens. A chlordane or DDT spray or powder applied into the nest will kill the insects. Wait until dusk or after dark to use the insecticide. The insects are all in their nests then, and are quiet so you can avoid being stung.

A DDT spray on screens, porches, and around windows and doors will help prevent wasps from getting into the house. Some kinds of wasps find their way into attics or walls of homes to spend the winter. Plugging up possible entries around eaves, window frames, or other places will help keep them out. Chlordane or DDT sprays or dusts can be used to kill those which get in.

TERMITE control may be relatively simple in some cases, or it may be rather difficult. The control measures required will vary with the circumstances relating to an infestation. Sufficient detail cannot be given here to provide satisfactory directions for control. If you have a termite infestation, study a good bulletin before trying to do the work yourself, or call in a reliable pest-control operator.

Subterranean termites live in nests in the soil and must maintain contact between the soil with its moisture and the wood where they are working. The basic principle of all termite control is to break the line of contact between soil and wood. This can be done by several means, including structural changes, mechanical barriers, and soil poisons.

FRUIT FLIES or vinegar gnats live in ripe fruits, jelly, garbage, rotting vegetables, around cracked or leaking fruit jars, or wherever they can find fermenting plant material. Prompt garbage disposal and keeping the garbage in tightly covered containers will help to prevent the production of large numbers of these flies. Treating screens and porches with a 5 percent DDT spray will aid in preventing them from getting into the house. Aerosols or fly sprays can be used to kill the flies that are present in a home. If the flies are developing inside the home, satisfactory control will not be obtained until the source of infestation is discovered and eliminated or destroyed.

L. S. HENDERSON *is the assistant leader of the division of stored product insect investigations in the Bureau of Entomology and Plant Quarantine. He holds two degrees from the University of Kansas. An employee of the Department of Agriculture since 1938, he conducted research in tests on insecticides and the control of household insects until 1946, when he became an assistant leader of the division of insects affecting man and animals. He was assigned to his present position when the new division was established in October 1951.*

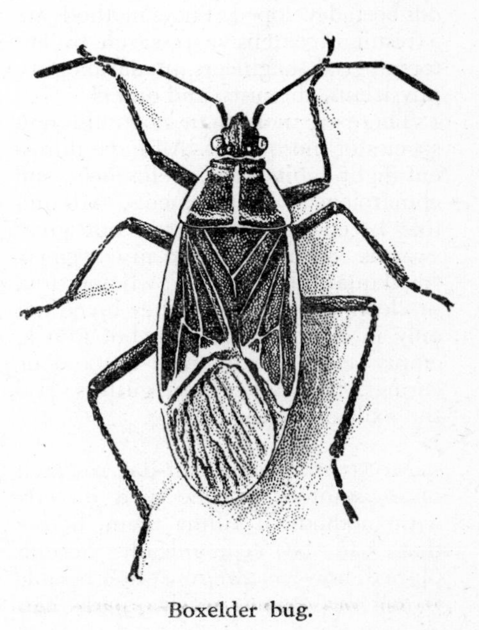

Boxelder bug.

Mosquitoes

Harry H. Stage

Mosquitoes have annoyed man and undermined his health for centuries. These voracious bloodsucking pests occasionally become sufficiently numerous to kill livestock. They have prevented industrial and agricultural development in many parts of the world. Merely as annoying pests they have kept large areas from becoming summer resorts. But all those losses are slight, compared to the damage done to human beings by mosquitoes as carriers of malaria, yellow fever, dengue, filariasis, and encephalitis. Practically every school child learns about the relationship of mosquitoes to malaria and yellow fever. There are few insects that have been studied more or about which more has been written, but only within the last 50 years have economical and effective control methods been developed. These methods are a result of extensive research by entomologists, engineers, malariologists, physicians, chemists, and others.

There are more than 2,000 different species of mosquitoes. All have different flight habits, food preferences, and climatological requirements. Mosquitoes breed only in water, but great swarms can be produced in extremely small quantities of water, whether foul or clean, salt or fresh. They breed not only in extensive marshes but also in empty cans, abandoned automobile casings, tree holes, rain gutters, and the axils of some plants.

MOST OF THE present-day research on mosquitoes is concerned directly with methods of killing them. Before that can be economically accomplished, however, we must first be able to tell the various species apart. The problems of classification have led to a great deal of biological work, with implications that go far beyond the immediate practical objectives. Perhaps the biological studies may seem to place an undue emphasis on morphology and taxonomy in entomological writing, but without it how could we refer with precision to a single mosquito species of a total of 2,000, around the world, having definite relationships? In all languages the name *Culex pipiens,* for example, can refer to only one species of living thing.

Taxonomic research on mosquitoes began with Linnaeus, the father of systematic zoology. In 1735 he named the first genus of mosquitoes *Culex,* and his tenth edition of *Systema Naturae* published in 1758 was the beginning of the systematic naming of animals. In that work we find the genus *Culex* with six included species, but only one of these—*Culex pipiens*—is recognized as a valid species of mosquito today. In 1818 J. W. Meigen described the genera *Aedes* and *Anopheles,* and in 1827 J. B. Robineau-Desvoidy added the genera *Sabethes, Psorophora,* and *Megarhinus.* Late in the nineteenth century there were more attempts at classification, led by F. Lynch-Arribalzaga, who recognized all the old genera and proposed a number of new ones.

When the importance of mosquitoes as disease transmitters became known, late in the 1890's, the systematic study on the classification of mosquitoes was accelerated considerably. The leading research worker on classification of mosquitoes at this period was F. V. Theobald, who, from 1901 to 1910, published a five-volume monograph on the Culicidae, a family which included all mosquitoes known to him. Many new genera and species were described and given scientific names, but their classification was based on superficial adult characters, which subsequent research has shown to be unreliable. Somewhat later, in 1912, H. G. Dyar, F. Knab, and D. W. Coquillett published larval characters and adopted much sounder adult characters. Dyar continued his research on mosquito classification, and in 1929 the Carnegie Institution published his *Mosquitoes of the Americas,* which revised the previous volumes by L. O. Howard, Dyar, and Knab, included many new species, and also increased the geographic scope of Dyar's knowledge to the entire Western Hemisphere.

The present classification of mosquitoes was rather firmly established by F. W. Edwards in Wytsman's *Genera Insectorum* in 1932. The family Culicidae, as established by Edwards, consisted of 39 genera and some 1,400 species. New genera and a number of new species have been described since then, and many changes in names have been made. During the Second World War military entomologists discovered more than 200 new species of mosquitoes, mostly in the Pacific area.

The classification of mosquitoes now is probably in the best condition of any comparable group of insects, since it is based on intensive studies of the morphology of adults, eggs, larvae, and pupae, as well as on biological information. There have been major publications on the mosquito faunas of Surinam, Australia, India, the Philippines, Ethiopia, Egypt, and the Americas, and more are in progress. Much remains to be done in describing species from out-of-the-way places, in describing presently unknown larvae and pupae, and particularly in clarifying the status of closely related species, such as the *Culex pipiens* and *Anopheles maculipennis* complexes.

Research on the biology and life history of mosquitoes was started about 1670 by Jan Swammerdam, of Holland. In 1691 P. Bonanni of Italy studied and described the life history of the common European mosquito, *Culex pipiens.* About 25 years later René de Réaumur of France studied the same mosquito, and his account of the development of the species remained valid until 1886, when the Department of Agriculture published Howard's first full life history of an American *Culex.*

W. Raschke, a German, studied the larva of a European *Culex* in 1887, and in 1890 an Englishman, C. H. Hurst, wrote on the pupal stage of *Culex.* Both Raschke and Hurst included observations on the physiology of the respiratory tubes, the gill flaps, and the tracheae, by which mosquito larvae breathe.

By 1892 Howard had worked out the life history of the southern house mosquito. In 1896 he published illustrations of the egg, larva, pupa, and adult of the northern house mosquito, the common mosquito around Washington early in the summer and therefore a ready subject for Howard's interest. His research was followed shortly thereafter by the first complete history of the common malaria mosquito.

The Department of Agriculture published Howard's *Notes on the Mosquitoes of the United States* in 1900. In it he described the anatomy and biology and suggested practical controls, which served as background and guide for W. C. Gorgas and J. A. Le Prince in their clean-up of mosquitoes in Havana. The following year Howard published *Mosquitoes—How They Live; How They Carry Disease; How They Are Classified; How They May Be Destroyed,* a book of 241 pages containing a chapter on the taxonomic characters of several of the common mosquito genera and an extensive account of the remedies suggested against mosquitoes. Howard stated that the results of this research appeared "at the psychological moment," and the book was widely distributed to members of the Army Medical Corps. Its recommendations were soon put to use by the authorities responsible for the construction of the Panama Canal.

G. M. Giles, an English naturalist for the Indian Marine Survey, in 1900 published a handbook on mosquitoes, which contained the results of a great amount of research on the life history and on the conditions affecting their abundance. In 1902 he published an

970134°—52——22

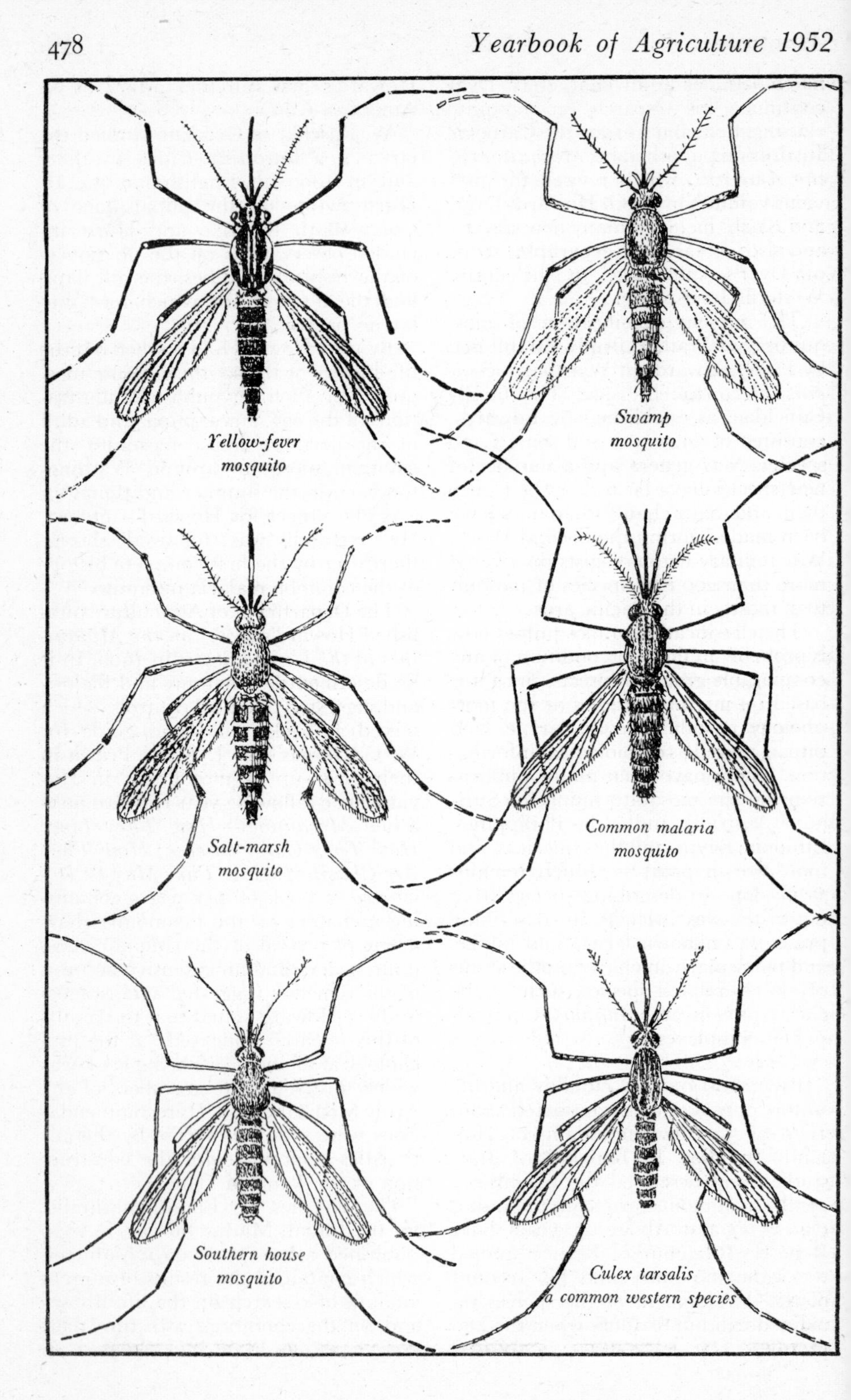

Yellow-fever mosquito
Swamp mosquito
Salt-marsh mosquito
Common malaria mosquito
Southern house mosquito
Culex tarsalis
a common western species

enlarged edition of more than 500 pages.

A few years later Howard, stressing the lack of information which his papers and books disclosed, obtained a grant from the Carnegie Institution of Washington to finance the preparation of an extensive monograph, *Mosquitoes of North and Central America and the West Indies,* by himself, Dyar, and Knab. Much study and research went into the preparation of two volumes, which appeared in 1912, followed by another in 1915 and one in 1917. The four volumes were an outstanding contribution to research on the biology of mosquitoes in the Western Hemisphere.

John B. Smith, of the New Jersey Agricultural Experiment Station, in 1904 published a monumental report on his investigations on the habits and life history of New Jersey mosquitoes. This report was revised by Thomas J. Headlee in 1915, 1921, and 1945. In his third revision Headlee stated that most of the chapter on biology first published in 1904 was used in the last edition because the research work by Smith and his assistants was so fundamentally sound that it still served as the principal basis for modern mosquito-control procedure.

Although biological research on mosquitoes has been somewhat hampered by the complex problems of classification, a voluminous literature has been accumulated on the life history and biology of these insects, albeit the original reports are scattered through a wide range of scientific periodicals in several languages.

It was not until 1949 that a detailed volume appeared on mosquito biology, or *The Natural History of Mosquitoes,* as Marston Bates, the author, preferred to call it. Reporting on his own research, and compiling thousands of notes and reports by other scientists in all parts of the world, Bates prepared one of the very few volumes on the biology of a family of insects. His work and endless research provide a detailed summary of the known behavior of the adult stage, the process of egg laying, the time and place of flight, longevity, seasonal distribution, sexual behavior, food preferences, distribution, egg development, larval reactions to physical and chemical environment, the habitat of the larvae, and the classification of the multitudinous number of larval habitats. Despite all this knowledge on the biology of mosquitoes, the author concluded that the detailed and minute information necessary to make clear-cut definitions of habitat characteristics for some 2,000 species of mosquitoes was still lacking.

Three highly significant pieces of research on the biology of mosquitoes have appeared since the volumes by Howard, Dyar, and Knab. S. B. Freeborn and R. F. Atsatt determined in 1918 that mosquito larvae for the most part are killed by toxic properties in petroleum oils that penetrate tracheal tissue, rather than by suffocation brought about by the layer of oil on the water.

N. H. Swellengrebel and A. de Buck in Holland in the early 1930's found that two Dutch malaria-carrying mosquitoes belonged to two distinct species; that is, the adult feeding preferences, mating habits, and larval habitat were completely different, although the morphological structures of the two species were almost identical. The thorough research performed by these scientists showed that the species were definitely separated by sterility barriers.

The necessity of a low oxygen concentration for the hatching of *Aedes* mosquito eggs was reported by C. M. Gjullin, C. P. Hegarty, and W. B. Bollen in 1941. They found that any method, chemical or physical, caused hatching when the oxygen content of the water was reduced. They concluded that bacteria or other organisms stimulated *Aedes* eggs to hatch by reducing the oxygen content of the water flooding *Aedes* eggs, which are normally laid on "dry" ground. This contradicts the earlier belief that heat, cold, or drying, by causing a so-called conditioning or incubation period, was a necessary prelude to hatching.

The great importance of a thorough knowledge of the biology or life history of mosquitoes may be illustrated best in actual mosquito- or malaria-control operations. For example, it would be useless to attempt malaria control in Trinidad by destroying malaria-carrying mosquito larvae in ground pools, streams, and puddles, because the larvae of the principal malaria vector on Trinidad are found only in water in the axils of certain air plants growing in high trees. Mosquito annoyance within 20 or 30 miles of a salt marsh cannot be reduced by the simple operation of destroying larvae appearing in rain barrels, discarded tin cans, and other containers around the home. Many other facts based on differences in the biology of mosquitoes must be known before a successful control program can be conducted.

Disease transmission by mosquitoes has furnished the incentive for intensive research in many parts of the world, and the unfolding of these stories of disease prevention by the control of the mosquito carriers, little by little, down through the years, has been a drama in medical entomology.

Two medical men, Josiah Nott of Mobile, Ala., and Louis D. Beauperthuy of the West Indies, 100 years ago argued that mosquitoes were instrumental in carrying yellow fever. Somewhat later Dr. Carlos Finlay of Havana conceived the idea independently that mosquitoes carried yellow fever. In 1877, however, when Sir Patrick Manson's research proved that the southern house mosquito developed filarial worms within its stomach after biting a human patient in whose blood there were embryo filarial worms, evidence was given of the mosquito's part in disease. Sir Patrick later observed these worms developing within the stomachs of test mosquitoes, and finally he traced their migration through the stomach walls into the abdominal cavity and then up into the thoracic muscles. G. C. Low, of London, in 1899 found the worms in the mosquitoes' proboscises, where they were ready to flow with the saliva into the victim's blood and thus complete the cycle. Here, then, were the first proofs of a mosquito sheltering in its stomach a parasite of man's blood without harming the parasite or being harmed by it.

Notwithstanding Sir Patrick's research, little attention was paid to his next theory that mosquitoes might also suck out malaria parasites, as well as filarial worms, in man's blood. But a Scots army surgeon, Ronald Ross, began his own research on malaria in 1895. Apparently Ross, who was working in India at that time, was the only person actively conducting research on the mosquito-malaria relationship. After more than 2 years of energetic research involving many mosquito dissections, Ross on August 20, 1897, found a malaria parasite growing within the stomach wall of an *Anopheles* mosquito. That discovery was confirmed by B. Grassi in 1898 and by R. Koch in 1899.

A year later Ross added an even more significant discovery, when he demonstrated the life cycle of bird malaria, which is transmitted by *Culex* mosquitoes. To Ross then must go the credit for proving the complete cycle of malaria—from an infected bird to a *Culex* mosquito and back to another bird. Although this tremendous and fundamental research should have been carried forward by Ross, he was soon ordered to another assignment, where he was able to continue his human malaria research only on his own time. His work was duly recognized, however, for he was awarded the Nobel prize in 1902 and was knighted somewhat later for his important discoveries.

Ross's research on bird malaria was soon confirmed by several other scientists. In 1898 A. Bignami, an Italian, succeeded in experimentally infecting a man with malaria by the bite of an *Anopheles* mosquito. Dramatic confirmation of malaria transmission was furnished by Sir Patrick Manson in

1900, when his son in London deliberately allowed himself to be bitten by infected *Anopheles* mosquitoes sent up from Italy by Professor G. Bastianelli. Fifteen days later Manson's son developed malaria.

Although Dr. Finlay advanced the mosquito-yellow fever relationship as early as 1881, his research was discredited until 1900, when the Army Yellow Fever Commission, headed by Walter Reed, and his associates James Carroll, Jesse W. Lazear, and A. Agramonte, announced the results of their experiments in which yellow fever had been caused by the bite of an infected *Aedes aegypti* mosquito. Carroll and Lazear permitted themselves to be bitten by mosquitoes that had previously fed on a yellow fever patient. Both men suffered attacks of yellow fever and Lazear died, a martyr to scientific research.

T. L. Bancroft, working in Australia, published evidence in 1906 that infected *Aedes aegypti* carried dengue. *Aedes albopictus* and *Armigeres obturbans* mosquitoes have since been found capable of transmitting the virus of dengue fever. Research on this virus, however, has been greatly limited because no very suitable experimental animal is known with which experiments can be conducted.

Mosquitoes were first associated with animal viruses in 1900 through research by Reed, Carroll, Agramonte, and Lazear, but the causative agent of yellow fever was not positively known as a virus until W. A. Sawyer, S. F. Kitchen, and their associates in the Rockefeller Foundation published a report of experiments in 1930. Since that time research has added much information on several mammalian viruses that are transmitted by mosquitoes. R. A. Kelser's experiments, the results of which were published in 1933, first proved that mosquitoes could transmit western equine encephalomyelitis. After results of extensive laboratory and field investigations by W. M. Hammon, W. C. Reeves, and others were published in 1940, *Culex tarsalis* was first named as the culprit that carries sleeping sickness in horses. Additional encephalitides and other species of mosquito carriers have since been incriminated.

The few pieces of research that I have mentioned are examples of many discoveries in which mosquitoes had a major part in diseases affecting man and animals. Until 30 or 40 years ago, practically all such discoveries were made by medical men, but they illustrated the value of entomological knowledge. A new concept of this science was thus created and greatly accelerated research in medical entomology. The field is a fertile one, and entomologists with broad training in the biological sciences are greatly needed. Research on mosquitoes and disease challenges the keenest intellects.

OIL APPARENTLY WAS the first material used to control mosquito larvae. Before 1800 its use on water was recommended in Europe and America. Dr. Howard, then a boy 10 years old, in 1867 tested the use of coal oil against mosquito wrigglers in a horse trough. Mrs. C. B. Aaron, in her Lamborn prize essay, published in 1890, gave the results of her research on killing mosquito larvae with kerosene. Between 1892 and 1896 Howard put this information to practical use in ridding two localities of the mosquito nuisance.

Howard in 1892 and Ross in 1900 recommended the use of kerosene and paraffin oil on infested water and suggested that men be employed to drain, fill, and oil mosquito-breeding puddles. These practices were shortly carried out as part of a malaria-control program in western Africa.

A. Celli and O. Casagrandi in 1899 published a pamphlet, *On the Destruction of Mosquitoes—A Contribution to the Study of Culicidal Substances.* A wide variety of available substances was tested by these Italians, but only two—paraffin and an aniline product which they called Larycith—acted as poisons. Used at the rate of 1 part to

7,000 parts of water, Larycith killed all larvae within 24 hours and was considered harmless to man, animals, and plants. It was cheap and more permanent than paraffin.

In 1900 several communities had begun to use oils as mosquito larvicides.

The beginning of a long and persistent fight against mosquitoes in New Jersey was made by John B. Smith in 1900. Mosquito-control experts in New Jersey, led first by Smith and later by T. J. Headlee, have since done a monumental piece of research on perfecting control methods against the salt-water species in that State.

Howard's first public address on mosquito extermination was made in New Jersey in May 1901. This talk was the real beginning of a wide-scale concerted effort against mosquitoes in the United States. As the New Jersey Mosquito Extermination Association got under way in 1912, the managers of the abatement districts began to emphasize the need for an effective larvicide that could be safely used where fish, warm-blooded animals, and plants were involved.

D. L. Van Dine in 1903 outlined 21 simple rules, based on Howard's research, to be followed in controlling mosquitoes in Hawaii. The rules were published on placards in five languages and included practical suggestions on the use of coal oil on water containing mosquito wrigglers.

The next important killer for mosquito larvae was the so-called Panama Canal Larvicide, developed in 1904. It was made by mixing 150 gallons of crude carbolic wood resin (grade E) and 30 pounds of commercial sodium hydroxide in 6 gallons of water. A spray was made by diluting this concentrate, 1 part to 5 parts of water.

M. A. Barber's and T. Haynes' discovery of the value of paris green against *Anopheles* larvae in 1921 revolutionized malaria control. Within 5 or 6 years practically all malaria-control organizations in the world were using this relatively cheap but effective anopheline larvicide. In 1923 W. V. King and G. W. Bradley tested its application by means of an airplane. From that time until the development of DDT in 1942, paris green was the standard larvicide used against malaria mosquitoes. Scientists around the world tried to incorporate paris green with other materials so as to make it effective against other species of mosquitoes, but they met with little success.

J. M. Ginsburg, a biochemist of the New Jersey Agricultural Experiment Station, started to conduct research with mosquito larvicides in 1926. Annual papers reporting the results of his studies have added greatly to our knowledge. In various parts of the world researchers slowly began to study oil combinations for control of mosquito larvae. In 1924 A. S. Hurwood, of Australia, combined 70 parts of kerosene and 30 parts of residual oil to make a durable spreading film. In 1927 Ginsburg found that these desirable properties of a mosquito oil could be increased considerably by adding crude cresylic acid. In 1930 Ginsburg first published a report on the use of pyrethrum-oil emulsion as a mosquito-control agent. This well-known New Jersey mosquito larvicide has remained the one safe material for use on fishponds and ornamental pools.

The addition of a 4-percent emulsifying agent to Diesel oil in 1943 by E. F. Knipling, C. M. Gjullin, and W. W. Yates not only increased the efficiency of the oil when it was applied as an emulsion against the larvae, and particularly against the pupae, but also greatly reduced operating costs. Only 6 gallons of oil in emulsion form per acre of water surface was required, instead of the 20 to 60 gallons per acre previously recommended.

Research in medical entomology was greatly accelerated during the Second World War, and much of it was directed against the disease-carrying species of mosquitoes. For the protection of the Armed Forces, the military agencies needed a mosquito larvicide more effective than the arsenicals and petroleum oils that were in wide use.

At the request of the U. S. Army, the Bureau of Entomology and Plant Quarantine organized a laboratory at Orlando, Fla., early in 1942 to conduct research on better methods for controlling disease-carrying mosquitoes and a more satisfactory repellent for preventing mosquito bites. The entomologists and chemists assigned to the project contributed all of the early recommendations to the military on the use of DDT as a mosquito larvicide. From 1942 until the research at the laboratory was reduced in 1945, more than 6,000 chemicals were evaluated as mosquito larvicides.

C. C. Deonier, R. W. Burrell, E. Nottingham, J. D. Maple, J. H. Cockran, H. A. Jones, P. M. Eide, C. B. Wisecup, and others in 1945 published reports on their preliminary field studies with DDT as a mosquito larvicide. Properly formulated DDT was found to be at least 25 times more toxic to anopheline mosquito larvae than paris green. When an oil solution containing 5 percent of DDT was applied at the recommended dosage of 0.1 to 0.4 pound of DDT per acre of water surface, it was not hazardous to plants, fish, or warm-blooded animals. As soon as DDT in oils, emulsions, or dusts was found to be effective against mosquito larvae in the laboratory and under field conditions, entomologists at the Orlando laboratory cooperated with the Tennessee Valley Authority in the summer of 1943 to test its value when dispersed by aircraft against *Anopheles* larvae. Because of their physical properties, the DDT dusts were difficult to apply with available equipment; in those tests DDT showed very little practical superiority over paris green. In the fall of 1943 the Orlando entomologists tested DDT sprays from aircraft against salt-marsh mosquito larvae. Special equipment to disperse sprays was designed by C. N. Husman, of the laboratory. In the spring of 1944 A. W. Lindquist and Husman first tested the use of small aircraft against mosquito larvae in the jungles of Panama. These tests were followed by others in January 1945, in which Army and Orlando entomologists worked together. Large airplanes were used. Excellent results were obtained with dosages as small as 1 to 2 quarts per acre.

Sprays containing DDT now are widely used as mosquito larvicides. Of the new hydrocarbon insecticides, it is considered the most effective and the safest.

Research on the control of mosquito larvae by fish, drainage, the building of dikes, and the filling in of low places has been carried on by engineers, entomologists, and others in many parts of the world. In some places those methods have given permanent control, although first costs have been high.

Managers of mosquito-abatement districts in California, Illinois, Florida, Virginia, New York, New Jersey, and other States have made significant contributions in modifying existing power shovels, cranes, trench excavators, marsh plows, and hand tools. Probably nowhere else in the world has so much study and time been spent on developing mechanized equipment for use on salt marshes as in New Jersey.

Mosquito control is big business. The mosquito-abatement district managers across the United States have encountered difficult problems involving areas of enormous extent. They have met these problems with amphibious full-track, 3/4-ton "weasels," small and large aircraft, insecticidal fog applicators, hydraulic spray equipment, power shovels, "swamp angels," and "skeeter-eaters."

Extensive research has been carried out on the manipulation of water levels as a means of reducing mosquito populations and thereby preventing malaria. In 1882 C. V. Chapin, of Rhode Island, wrote about the malaria outbreaks adjacent to impounded water along railroad embankments. The building of the Hales Bar Dam for the development of hydroelectric power on the Tennessee River in 1912 created a malaria epidemic focus which lasted for more than 35 years. Malaria epidemics followed other impoundments, and some resulted in lawsuits instituted by residents who had contracted the disease.

The program of regional development undertaken by the Tennessee Valley Authority in 1933 afforded a unique opportunity for the study of water manipulation as applied to the control of *Anopheles* mosquitoes. More than 10,000 miles of shore line was involved in an area of widely varying topography. This research was combined with that of the Public Health Service in 1947 in a manual, *Malaria Control of Impounded Water*. A sustained increase in the efficiency and economy of control practices on impounded water has been aided greatly by the combination of knowledge, experience, and research effort expressed in the manual.

Before we had DDT we knew of no effective and economical way of killing adult mosquitoes in large areas out of doors. In 1893 it was reported that the Chinese burned pine sawdust, brimstone, and arsenic in incense pots to kill mosquitoes indoors. Late in the 1890's the Italians, Celli and Casagrandi, recommended dinitrocresol, known to them as Larycith III. By 1900 the burning of pyrethrum powder was generally known and effective within doors. General Gorgas banished yellow fever and greatly reduced malaria within a year in Havana by destroying adult *Aedes aegypti* and *Anopheles* mosquitoes. A considerable part of this accomplishment was effected by burning pyrethrum and sulfur within homes.

In 1910 Howard compiled a list of materials for use as smudges and fumigants. Somewhat later a number of household sprays for killing mosquitoes and other insects were advocated. During the early 1930's several workers in New Jersey tested the use of pyrethrum sprays against mosquito annoyance at out-of-door gatherings. These pyrethrum and kerosene sprays were fairly effective for several hours.

B. DeMeillon in 1936 and P. F. Russell and F. W. Knipe in 1939 reported their experiments in Africa and India, respectively, where the number of malaria cases was reduced by killing adult mosquitoes with sprays. In 1940 F. L. Soper and D. B. Wilson showed how they had been able to exterminate *Anopheles gambiae* in Brazil, partly at least, by using a spray containing pyrethrum, carbon tetrachloride, and kerosene. This eradication of an insect from a country is one of the most interesting chapters in medical history.

In 1940 W. N. Sullivan, L. D. Goodhue, and J. H. Fales published their first report on a new method for dispersing insecticides in air. This method suggested to Goodhue an entirely new and revolutionary approach to insecticide dispersal. The aerosol bomb they developed provided in a small package the most effective means known for killing adult mosquitoes within enclosures—the release of the aerosol for a few seconds in 1,000 cubic feet of air space will kill all the mosquitoes in it.

When in June 1943 it had been shown that very small quantities of DDT sprays applied from the ground were effective against adult mosquitoes, the Orlando entomologists immediately started tests with aircraft. Aircraft had not previously been employed for controlling adult mosquitoes. If usable, this could be the means for reducing the adult mosquito population within a matter of hours, thereby immediately checking the spread of malaria and dengue among our military forces in various places. Special spray equipment was designed by Husman and the initial tests made against salt-marsh adult mosquitoes on the Florida Keys in November 1943. The results indicated that practically all adult mosquitoes could be killed by spraying 2 or 3 quarts of a 5 percent DDT oil solution per acre over dense vegetation. In December of the same year, the first tests were made with large combat planes, using Chemical Warfare Services M-10 tanks. Similar tests were followed in Panama in April 1944 where Lindquist and Husman practically eliminated the adults of *Anopheles albimanus* in jungle forest at 0.4 pound of DDT per acre with a 10 percent DDT spray.

Their early research established the value of DDT aerial sprays for controlling adult mosquitoes and stimulated world-wide investigations by the Allied Forces. Airplanes became one of the most effective ways of controlling mosquitoes and mosquito-borne diseases wherever our troops were located.

Early in 1943, A. W. Lindquist, J. B. Gahan, B. V. Travis, F. A. Morton, Wisecup, Eide, and others at the Orlando laboratory found that the new DDT insecticide possessed unusual residual properties. Following intensive laboratory tests, their first field tests were made near Tallahassee, Fla., in August 1943. DDT applied in sprays on the interior sufaces at the rate of about 200 milligrams per square foot protected buildings for at least 70 days against infestations of the common malaria mosquito, the most important vector of malaria in the Southeastern States. Here was born the most important method yet devised for controlling malaria. The Orlando entomologists recommended this method of mosquito control to the Armed Forces who were experiencing many cases of malaria in various parts of the world.

In 1944 the Orlando entomologists tested two formulations under practical conditions near Stuttgart, Ark., a rice-growing area heavily infested with *Anopheles* mosquitoes. In two areas, each 9 miles square, the interior of every outbuilding was sprayed with an oil solution containing 5 percent of DDT. The experiments confirmed the Tallahassee tests and recommendations were made for using 5 percent DDT sprays at the rate of 200 milligrams per square foot. The information was sent to our allied countries. Further large-scale tests were started by C. B. Symes, A. B. Hadaway, and G. Giglioli, in January 1945 in British Guiana, and by Gahan in New Mexico in April. The experiments were aimed at two very efficient but different vectors of malaria and were successful.

This research has been of great benefit to practically all peoples of the globe. In 1950 more than 800,000 homes in the Southeastern States were treated by Federal and State public health agencies employing DDT residual sprays. Elsewhere the World Health Organization reports a total of about 50 million persons as now being protected against malaria by this residual insecticide alone.

Military pickets, night laborers, explorers, and other personnel working in areas heavily infested with mosquitoes have sought constantly for some means of protecting their persons from mosquito bites. In 1910 Howard listed several essential oils for this purpose. Of these, the oil of citronella was the most widely known repellent. It was effective for a few minutes to an hour, but some people preferred the stings of mosquito bites to the odor of citronella.

The first extensive research on mosquito repellents was begun by Phillip Granett of New Jersey in 1935. In 1940 he had developed a repellent that was greatly superior to all others. Unfortunately, however, this material, after being tested on experimental animals, was declared unsafe for use on humans.

When the United States entered the Second World War the need for a mosquito repellent became acute. The military services were particularly insistent on knowing of a good protective agent against mosquito bites. With funds allotted by the Office of Scientific Research and Development, the Department of Agriculture initiated an extensive research program in April 1942 at the Orlando laboratory. Many industrial companies and manufacturers cooperated in the investigations. Subsequently more than 10,000 synthetic organic chemicals in various formulations were tested against hungry mosquitoes by Travis, Morton, and their associates on the skin and clothing of men. Promising materials were also tested for their toxicological effects by the Food and Drug Administration.

Three materials and combinations of them were recommended to the military services—dimethyl phthalate, Rutgers 6–12 (2-ethyl-1,3-hexanediol), and indalone (*n*-butyl mesityl oxide oxalate). These and a mixture of them, commonly known as 6–2–2, were standard insect repellents in 1952.

HEALTH CONDITIONS in many parts of the world have been revolutionized by mosquito control. Vast regions are now healthier, safer habitations for men as a result of the tremendous amount of research that has been carried on during the past 75 years. Today more than 25 million people of the United States live in areas where mosquito-control programs are in progress.

One of the world's most effective malaria-carrying species of mosquito was eradicated from Brazil between the time of its discovery in March 1930 and November 1941. Other eradication projects have been undertaken.

Still, mosquito research is far from finished. Each year, workers all over the world add hundreds of articles on mosquito investigations to a considerable bibliography already available. All this information is immediately put to practical use by the 250 separate local, city, county, State, and Federal mosquito-control agencies.

HARRY H. STAGE *is assistant leader of the division of insects affecting man and animals, Bureau of Entomology and Plant Quarantine. After completing work at Syracuse University in 1917 and subsequent mosquito control work in the Navy in the First World War, he was employed as entomologist of the St. Louis Southwestern Railway Lines and actively participated for 10 years in malaria control in the area served by that railroad. From 1931 to 1940 he was in charge of the Bureau's northwestern laboratory on mosquito investigations. Since 1940 he has traveled extensively in the Arctic and the Tropics on various kinds of mosquito-control research.*

The Control of Insects Affecting Man

E. F. Knipling

We have known for half a century that insects, ticks, and mites are the transmitting agents for malaria, typhus, bubonic plague, yellow fever, tick fevers, dysenteries, typhoid, and many other dangerous diseases. The role of insects as carriers of human diseases is discussed by F. C. Bishopp and C. B. Philip in another chapter of this book.

As scientists gathered more and more information on the relation of insects and diseases during the last decade of the nineteenth century and the early years of the twentieth century, entomologists, parasitologists, and medical doctors investigated ways to control insects that attack man, but the world did not seem concerned enough to support research adequately, and progress was slow.

As late as the First World War, louse-borne typhus caused millions of illnesses and deaths among Europeans. Nevertheless no intensive effort was made to develop effective and practical ways to control the lice. By the time the Second World War began no substantial improvements had been made in the methods.

Malaria, the most important of the diseases of man, could be controlled if enough manpower, materials, and equipment were used. But the control methods were costly and weeks or months of intensive effort were required to achieve substantial reduction in the incidence of the diseases.

Such slow methods could not protect troops when they invaded malarious areas and moved quickly from one region to another for combat or training. Nor did we have positive and practical ways to kill flies, fleas, ticks, mites, and other disease vectors, especially under wartime conditions.

As we entered the war, men in the Armed Services, including Colonel W. S. Stone and General J. S. Simmons, of the office of the Surgeon General, and others in civilian institutions, including F. C. Bishopp of the Department of Agriculture and G. K. Strode of the Rockefeller Foundation, recognized the need for developing better ways to combat the vectors of malaria, typhus, yellow fever, and plague. They encouraged such research as an important part of our national preparedness program. Entomologists, chemists, and insecticide-equipment engineers were available to undertake the emergency research programs.

Special research was started in 1942 in laboratories of the Department of Agriculture at Orlando, Fla., and Beltsville, Md. The Office of Scientific Research and Development and the Department of Defense provided most of the funds for the investigations. The Rockefeller Foundation, which had sponsored many important projects having to do with insects that transmit diseases to man, also started investigations on specific problems. The War Department organized a special commission, the United States Army Typhus Commission, to develop means for controlling typhus diseases. About 25 specialists were assigned to the various problems in 1942; in 1943, as the casualties due to insect-borne diseases mounted in combat areas, the research programs were expanded. The United States Public Health Service, the Tennessee Valley Authority, and several colleges undertook investigations on insect problems of most importance to the war effort. Insecticide industries facilitated the programs of the various institutions. The Army and Navy and their growing numbers of entomologists, medical officers, and engineers performed large-scale tests and conducted independent research. Great Britain, Canada, and Australia were among the Allies that conducted research on the insects.

The results of the work during and after the war have greatly improved the health and welfare of mankind. Perhaps no science has done more for man in the past decade than medical entomology. Let us review some of those accomplishments.

In dealing with insect problems, it is important to know how to distinguish one species from all other forms: One species of *Anopheles* may be indistinguishable from another, except by the mosquito taxonomist. Yet it may be a dangerous transmitter of malaria; the other may seldom attack man. A small mite or chigger may look like six related species, yet that species may transmit typhus. Its relatives may be unimportant. The time required for eggs of the human lice to hatch is significant to the investigator who is attempting to develop control measures—for his goal would be a treatment that destroys the lice present at the time of treatment and also remains in the clothing or hair long enough to destroy those that hatch from the eggs.

A knowledge of the kinds of animals that an insect, mite, or tick will attack may make it possible to destroy the alternate animal hosts and so help control the parasite. The investigators who during the past 100 years have studied the taxonomy, life history, ecology, and habits of insects have paved the way for the more rapid advances in control methods that have been made during recent years.

Three kinds of lice attack man—the body louse, the head louse, and the crab louse.

The body louse is the principal vector of typhus. Closely related to the head louse, it lives and hides in the clothing and lays its eggs in the seams and folds of garments. People who have several changes of clothing and practice reasonable sanitation need not worry about body lice. But less fortunate people, especially during wars when clothing, fuel, food, soaps, and housing facilities are limited, are vulnerable to louse infestations. Combat troops who are in campaigns for weeks without clean clothing often become heavily infested with lice.

When a high proportion of people become lousy, conditions favor typhus. Civilian refugees and troops often are crowded together in vehicles and living quarters. Lice from one infested person readily spread to others. Then when one case of typhus occurs, a chain reaction is set in motion. An explosive epidemic is the result.

Many methods were advocated for controlling the body louse—the use of dry heat, exposure of infested clothing to cold temperatures, washing garments in hot water, steam sterilization, and use of naphthalene, creosote, and rotenone. But all methods known before 1942 were impractical or so ineffective that there was little hope of preventing typhus disasters of the kind that have occurred so often in the past.

Entomologists and chemists, assigned that year to the problem of improving methods for controlling lice, planned their research with a single aim: To develop a simple method of fumigating clothing to destroy lice and eggs. Randall Latta of the Department of Agriculture discovered that methyl bromide is highly effective for the purpose. Fumigating vaults, easily constructed and readily transported, were designed and set up near combat areas. They made it possible to treat hundreds of pounds of clothing in a few hours. Even more mobile equipment, later developed, consisted of small, light, airproof bags large enough to hold one person's clothing. A 20-cubic-centimeter ampule of methyl bromide broken in the bag would release enough gas to destroy lice and the eggs in an hour or less.

The methods were a vast improvement over heavy steam-sterilization or laundry equipment. Yet they did not seem to be the most practical solution to the louse problem because deloused individuals were again subject to reinfestation immediately after clothing had been treated: Sorely needed was a louse-killing powder that the soldier could carry in his pack and use when he became infested with lice or was exposed to conditions where he might be infested.

The entomologists at Orlando and the staff of the Rockefeller Foundation in New York worked on the problem. Their aim was to develop a powder that would kill all the lice when dusted into the clothing and destroy the louse eggs attached to the clothing. It had to remain effective long enough to kill lice that might crawl on the person from others.

Several problems had to be solved first. People infested with body lice are rare in the United States; so it seemed futile to try to develop a good louse-killing substance by experimenting on persons naturally infested. Furthermore it would be risky to apply materials of unknown toxicity to human subjects. It would be difficult to check results.

The plan therefore called for evaluation of new materials under controlled laboratory conditions. Only the most promising treatments would then need to be tried on the naturally infested persons.

The first problem therefore was to develop a method for rearing lice by the thousands in the laboratory so that the insects would be available for tests. That was accomplished by G. H. Culpepper. At that time feeding lice on human beings was the only way known to grow them in the laboratory. The lice, kept comfortable on patches of cloth in an incubator set at 86° F., were placed on the backs of human volunteers twice each day so they could get their blood meals. Culpepper had trouble finding persons who were willing to make their living by allowing 25,000 to 50,000 lice to feed on their backs at one time.

The millions of lice and eggs thus grown were used by entomologists and chemists to find the chemical which would accomplish the objectives.

Thousands of substances were tested against the lice and their eggs. First they dipped an ordinary patch of cloth, 1 inch square, in an acetone solution of the test chemical. After the acetone evaporated, leaving the chemical on the cloth, they placed the patch in a small beaker and put 10 lice on it. If the lice were not killed in 24 hours, we felt certain the chemical would not be satisfactory if a person's garments were similarly treated. But if it did kill all the lice, the same treated patch was retested each day or at intervals of several days to determine how long it would continue to kill.

The few chemicals, about 3 or 5 of every 100 tested, that killed lice and remained effective for several weeks were given a second test to determine if they would kill the lice when they were made into a dusting powder and actually applied on man. This test involved treating garments that were placed on the arms or legs by taping both ends to the skin. Before taping the garments on the men, 20 lice were placed in each garment and given every opportunity to live as they normally would except that they were exposed to the test substance. If any lice survived for 24 hours, the test material was discarded. If all lice were killed, new lice were added every day to determine how long the treatment remained effective. Many chemicals used as 5-percent dusts killed the lice the first day or two, but very few remained effective for longer than a few days.

The third step was designed to try the most promising materials under almost natural conditions. Human subjects, the same ones who fed the lice and those on which the arm and leg tests were conducted, were used in the tests. The men lived in barracks. They wore clothing of the kind issued to troops. About 500 lice from the laboratory colony and about 1,000 louse eggs of different ages were placed in the clothing. The underwear was then dusted with the test materials to determine if it would kill the lice, the eggs, and the newly hatched lice.

Within 6 months after starting the project, we developed a good formula. It killed lice of all kinds quickly and would usually remain effective for 1 week. The material was called MYL powder. It contained 0.2 percent pyrethrins, 2 percent of *n*-isobutyl undecylenamide (a substance which made the pyrethrins more effective), 0.25 percent Phenol S (a substance which prevented deterioration of the pyrethrins), and 2 percent of 2.4-dinitroanisole (a chemical among the hundreds tested which proved most effective in killing the louse eggs). The powder was tested by the Food and Drug Administration and found safe to use on man.

The men at Orlando who developed the treatment—R. C. Bushland, G. W. Eddy, H. A. Jones, L. C. McAlister, and others—felt confident it would work as well in protecting our troops from lice as it did on the research subjects. The powder was issued to troops in 2-ounce cans and proved highly successful.

To find out whether it would also work on civilians who wore different types of clothing, W. A. Davis at the Rockefeller Foundation conducted experiments in Mexico. MYL powder proved effective. It practically eliminated lice from people and demonstrated that typhus among the people in small villages could be controlled.

The United States Army Typhus Commission tested MYL powder in North Africa. Results among civilians were variable, possibly because of the nature of the clothing worn and because improperly mixed commercial louse powders were used. The Rockefeller Foundation found the MYL provided excellent control of lice among prisoners. Tests conducted by the British among prisoners in Africa gave results that were generally in line with those obtained in the laboratory at Orlando.

Although the MYL powder was good, the research on lice at Orlando was expanded in 1943. Pyrethrum was in short supply, and we wanted to develop a material that killed lice and protected individuals from louse infestations for at least 3 weeks—the maximum time that might be required for louse eggs to hatch.

Tests were continued with hundreds of new chemicals. Among them was DDT, whose Swiss discoverers had reported to be effective against lice. Tests by the entomologists proved that DDT has a high degree of toxic action to lice and—of even greater importance—its effects last for weeks. Of the thousands of formulas previously tested, including the MYL louse powder, none lasted longer than 8 days. When humans wore garments treated with 10 percent DDT, all lice in the clothing were killed after 8 days. Even in garments that had been worn for 30 days, only an occasional louse survived. Even more startling: Garments dipped in a 1- or 2-percent emulsion of DDT repelled lice for at least 6 months if unwashed or for four launderings. DDT was also incorporated in a special liquid preparation for controlling head lice, crab lice, and the itch mite.

The work at Orlando on DDT as a louse insecticide was recorded by Bushland, McAlister, Jones, and Culpepper in the Journal of Economic Entomology for April 1945 and by Eddy in the Journal of Investigative Dermatology for February 1946.

As to louse-killing properties, DDT was the immediate answer to the louse problem. But was it safe? No adverse effects had been noted by the scientists who worked with it at Orlando. The late H. O. Calvery of the Food and Drug Administration and P. A. Neal of the Public Health Service conducted repeated laboratory tests from which they concluded the treatment was safe. They interpreted their laboratory data on experimental animals in terms of probable hazard when the materials were applied as directed. They reasoned from reports of insecticidal efficacy that DDT would save many lives. Their data on toxicity indicated that, even without the safety margin allowed in the directions for use, humans would not be harmed by the DDT. Since then DDT has been applied to millions of people and millions more have been exposed to DDT when applied in their homes. Millions of deaths or illnesses due to insect-borne diseases have been avoided. There is still no authentic case of death due to DDT when used as an insecticide.

While the laboratory studies were still under way at Orlando, field testing of DDT was carried out by workers of the Rockefeller Foundation, the United States Army Typhus Commission, the United States Army, and by the British. The research men in their field studies simply applied DDT to crowds of people with ordinary hand dusters. Their field results confirmed the data obtained at Orlando.

The Geigy Company of New York, who furnished us the original sample of DDT, began commercial production of DDT early in 1943. The first DDT produced for the Army was allocated for louse control. It was issued to troops in 2-ounce cans; thousands of pounds of DDT in bulk were shipped to North Africa.

In the fall of 1943 a typhus epidemic threatened in Naples, Italy. Thanks to the foresight of Colonel W. S. Stone and others, the Army was prepared. Enlisting the aid of experts of the Rockefeller Foundation, headed by F. L. Soper, the United States Army Typhus Commission and the Medical Department of the North African Theatre of Operations started a program, the first of its kind, to stop the epidemic, which by December was becoming serious. Thousands of people were dusted with the MYL and DDT powders. In only a few months, an epidemic of typhus among crowded people in a war-torn area was brought under complete control.

Even though DDT seemed to be the answer to the louse problem and typhus, intensive research on new insecticides continued during 1944 and 1945 and to a lesser degree during 1946 to 1950. Benzene hexachloride, toxaphene, chlordane, and a number of pyrethrum preparations were found to be excellent louse killers. These materials had no particular advantage over DDT, however, so they were not developed for actual use in louse control.

In 1951 entomologists in the Army and Navy experienced difficulty in controlling body lice on Korean and Chinese prisoners of war. They concluded that lice in Korea were resistant to DDT. Therefore, the body louse, in the face of man's effort to destroy it, has demonstrated an ability to become immune to DDT. G. W. Eddy, who had contributed so much during the war in developing control measures for lice, was called upon to assist in finding ways to control the Korean lice. Traveling under orders issued by the Department of the Army, he went to Korea to test other louse powders. Within a few weeks he found that the DDT-resistant Korean lice could be controlled with lindane, several new pyrethrum formulas similar to the MYL louse powder, and toxaphene. Toxicologists of the Army environmental health laboratory approved the use of 1 percent lindane and the pyrethrum powders. These materials are now controlling the lice in Korea. Research is continuing, however, in a search for other ways to control lice. Entomologists are fearful that the most intimate parasite of man, like the house fly, might develop in time a resistance to the substitute louse killers.

The ordinary house fly transmits many kinds of diseases and parasites. It feeds on almost every kind of filth and lives in close association with man and man's habitations. For a long time investigators have sought ways to get rid of the dirty pest. Entomologists and medical authorities long have advocated sanitation practices to destroy the breeding places and the use of screens and other mechanical devices to exclude flies from buildings.

Chemical methods directed at the immature as well as the adult stages have received most attention in research. Insecticides applied as sprays or dusts in homes have been used successfully for many years. Pyrethrum sprays and methods for their application were developed during the early part of this century and soon were employed in almost every home.

In view of the known value of pyrethrum as a fly killer and the public demand for fly insecticides, research from 1930 to 1940 was directed toward the development of substitutes as effective but more economical than pyrethrum, the improvement of pyrethrum itself, and more effective ways to apply the sprays. The Hercules Powder Co. and the Rohm and Haas Co. developed organic thiocyanate sprays, which were also widely used, especially during the Second World War, when pyrethrum was scarce. Materials were also developed which would increase the efficacy of pyrethrum. Craig Eagleson of the Department of Agriculture discovered that sesame oil would increase the fly-killing power of pyrethrum. The DuPont Company found that *n*-isobutyl undecylenamide, an organic chemical, also would increase the efficacy of pyrethrum.

L. D. Goodhue and W. N. Sullivan of the Department in 1940–41 discovered a new method of applying fly sprays—the liquefied gas dispersal system, later perfected as the aerosol bomb. The Armed Services used millions of the bombs primarily against flies and mosquitoes. The first bombs contained pyrethrum and sesame oil. DDT was added later. After the war, aerosol bombs contained pyrethrum and other insecticidal materials came into extensive use by the public to control house flies and other flying insects.

The most spectacular advance was the development of DDT as a residual treatment. R. Weismann, of Switzerland, had noted the unusual residual properties of DDT when flies rested on surfaces treated with it. A. W. Lindquist, A. H. Madden, H. G. Wilson, and H. A. Jones at the Orlando laboratory independently discovered the remarkable residual properties of DDT when used as a surface treatment. The applications continued to kill flies for months. Dairy installations, one of the most difficult places to control flies, remained practically free of flies for months after one thorough treatment. The Armed Services used DDT residual sprays successfully in many parts of the world.

When the war ended, the public purchased DDT by the millions of pounds for controlling flies. In 1945–47 it was used almost everywhere where flies were a problem. People organized community-wide fly-control programs. Results were spectacular, and there was talk of eradicating the house fly entirely.

But in late 1947 reports were received that flies were not being killed by DDT. Could flies be developing resistance to DDT? Actually, that possibility was considered even before we had any evidence of it. A. W. Lindquist and H. G. Wilson of the Orlando laboratory in 1946 started exposing flies to DDT in the laboratory. They killed about 90 percent of a group of flies with DDT. The survivors were allowed to reproduce. The offspring were then treated with DDT in order to kill the most susceptible ones. After repeating this procedure for several generations, we had evidence of resistance to DDT among the flies. We hoped, however, that resistance would not become great enough to result in DDT failure in actual control practice. But by 1948 failures were being reported from many places. Intensive studies followed by several investigators. (The problem is discussed in detail by W. N. Bruce on page 320.)

When DDT had unquestionably failed to control flies in many areas, the substitute insecticides, previously judged as good although inferior to DDT, were reexamined by the University of California, the Bureau of Entomology and Plant Quarantine, the Public Health Service, the University of Illinois, and other research institutions. These substitutes included methoxychlor, chlordane, TDE, toxaphene, technical benzene hexachloride, and lindane, the pure gamma form of benzene hexachloride. Newer compounds, including dieldrin and aldrin, were investigated extensively. But all investigators have come to the conclusion that the house fly in time can survive the most deadly chemicals that chemists and entomologists have been able to devise so far.

Entomologists thus have suffered a stinging defeat in their war on the house fly. They did not lose all the ground they won, because there are fewer flies today than before we had DDT, but they have had to include in their recommendations for fly control the sprays and aerosols employed before residual treatments were developed. Such sprays and aerosols have been improved through the development of pyrethrum synergists, such as piperonyl butoxide and *n*-propyl isome, products developed, respectively, by the U. S. Industrial Chemicals Co., Inc., and S. B. Penick & Co.

Chemists and entomologists set out to find new materials to which flies cannot develop resistance, to test chemicals in combination with DDT with the hope of blocking the resistance mechanism developed by the fly, and to determine whether any factor of physiology enables flies to develop such high degrees of immunity to a normally deadly insecticide.

I believe that in the not too distant future we shall find a weapon by which we can regain the ground we lost. If the resistance problem is solved for the house fly, it may mean much to insect control in general, for it is known that other important insects have developed resistance to insecticides now employed for their control. If the problem is not solved, we might expect increasing difficulty in controlling certain important insects during the next 5, 10, or 50 years. The problem is truly a challenge to the entomologists, insecticide chemists, and insect physiologists.

Many people in States east of the Rockies and south of a line running roughly through Maryland, Ohio, and

Iowa have at one time or another become infested with chiggers. The chigger, or red-bug, is the larval stage of a small mite. It is no larger than the point of an ordinary pin. Its bites cause intense itching for several days; scratching them can bring secondary infections. In some parts of the world chiggers transmit a disease similar to and as deadly as the typhus carried by lice.

We knew relatively little about chiggers in 1940, but since then many investigators have studied their taxonomy, life history, relation to disease, and control.

Most of the research on control has been carried out by the Orlando laboratory, where intensive studies were started during the Second World War and continued since with funds provided by the Department of Defense. The Army Typhus Commission during the war conducted investigations on taxonomy, biology, and control in areas in the Pacific where mite typhus plagued troops. The Chemical Services, Department of the Army, gathered valuable information on the biology of the chigger mites.

For many years sulfur, dusted in infested parts of the body or applied in socks and clothing, was used against the mites. Sulfur is not a very good miticide, however, and men at Orlando in 1942 sought to develop a more effective and practical method of coping with them. A material that could be carried and applied by the soldier to prevent chigger attacks was particularly desired.

The first problem was to develop techniques for testing the material. No methods for rearing chiggers in the laboratory were then known, but the entomologists assigned to the problem, A. H. Madden and A. W. Lindquist, found an abundance of chiggers for test purposes along lakes and swamps in Florida.

Boys were employed to test the effectiveness of various treatments. In clothing treated with different chemicals, they exposed themselves for 2 hours or more in places where chiggers were known to be numerous. They were examined several hours later, and the chiggers on them were counted. To compare the effectiveness of the treatments, at least one boy in each test wore untreated clothing; it was not uncommon for them to become infested with as many as 200 chiggers. Because some of the experimental materials turned out to have little value, some of the boys who wore treated clothes also became heavily infested. They suffered nothing more than several sleepless nights, however.

Within a few months, several good materials were discovered. The most effective and practical material developed first was dimethyl phthalate. Rings of it on the socks near the shoe top, on the bottoms of trousers and shirts, and around the belt line were almost 100 percent effective in keeping chiggers away.

With that, the research on mites was stopped. But in 1943 the Armed Forces were encountering a high incidence of mite typhus among troops in the Pacific and in Burma. General S. Bayne-Jones and Col. J. F. Sadusk of the Army Typhus Commission urged further research at Orlando.

The Commission also sent research teams to the Pacific and Burma. Among them was Capt. R. C. Bushland, who had worked on lice at Orlando before entering the service. Assigned the problem of developing a field method of impregnating the clothing of troops with dimethyl phthalate, he developed a soap-emulsion treatment, which was used extensively and successfully by the Armed Services in 1944 and 1945.

The expanded research program at Orlando, closely coordinated with research by the Army Typhus Commission and also the Chemical Warfare Service, was carried out under the direction of F. M. Snyder. The objective was to develop miticides that when impregnated into clothing would be effective even though the clothing were laundered, a shortcoming of dimethyl

970134°—52——33

phthalate. Several thousand chemicals were screened by simple laboratory methods; about a dozen promising materials were selected for further study. Benzyl benzoate was among the more effective materials. Clothing treated with it would still protect individuals after two launderings.

In the meantime, Australian scientists had developed dibutyl phthalate, which was comparable in effectiveness to benzyl benzoate, although somewhat less effective than the latter against mites in Florida. Benzyl benzoate was shown to be as effective as dibutyl phthalate in tests conducted in New Guinea by the Typhus Commission. A combination of the two materials was finally issued for use by our troops because of short supply of benzyl benzoate. During the closing months of the war and since, several miticides were found which were so effective and persistent that treated clothing would still protect persons from chigger attack after laundering six to eight times.

The development of several effective miticide treatments permitted troops to go into areas where mites and mite typhus were prevalent with assurance of almost complete protection from them.

Studies also were conducted to develop chemicals that would destroy mites in infested areas, particularly around camp sites. J. P. Linduska of the Orlando laboratory demonstrated in 1945 that benzene hexachloride was effective when applied at the rate of several pounds per acre. C. N. Smith of the Department's laboratory in Savannah, Ga., also demonstrated the efficacy of benzene hexachloride when so used. Since the war, men at Orlando have found that chlordane, toxaphene, or benzene hexachloride, applied at the rate of 2 to 4 pounds per acre as a dust or spray, will destroy chiggers and keep the infested areas practically free of the mites for 2 months or longer.

TICKS ARE AMONG the most difficult of the arthropods to control with insecticides or repellents. Until recent years, no satisfactory method had been developed to protect individuals from their attack or to control the ticks in infested areas.

In 1942 and 1943 the Orlando laboratory investigated many repellents for application to clothing. Dimethyl phthalate and indalone were found to be of value for this purpose.

Following the war, a special effort was made by the Orlando laboratory under the direction of W. V. King, with financial support from the Department of Defense, to develop more effective treatments. At the Public Health laboratory in Montana, which also carried out studies on the problem, J. M. Brennan discovered the tick-repellent value of *n*-butyl acetanilide.

The tick-repellent work at Orlando is closely coordinated with similar studies under way at the same laboratory on mites, fleas, and mosquitoes. Under the direction of C. N. Smith, an all-purpose repellent was developed. It consists of 30 parts benzyl benzoate; 30 parts *n*-butyl acetanilide; 30 parts of 2-butyl-2-ethyl-1,3-propanediol; and 10 parts of an emulsifier. Clothing dipped in a 5-percent water emulsion of the repellent protects individuals from ticks, chiggers, and fleas and helps prevent annoyance by mosquitoes.

Research on ticks has also included investigations on materials which will destroy ticks in infested areas. Smith found that DDT dust or sprays applied at the rate of about 2 pounds per acre would destroy the ticks. Further research by W. C. McDuffie, C. C. Deonier, M. M. Cole, and J. A. Fluno of the Orlando laboratory has shown that DDT, chlordane, and toxaphene are about equally effective against the American dog tick and the lone star tick. R. D. Glasgow and D. L. Collins of New York State Science Service have demonstrated the effectiveness against ticks of DDT sprays and aerosols applied to vegetated areas. Studies by the State Board of Health and the State Conservation Commission of

Massachusetts also demonstrated that ticks can be controlled by applying DDT to roadsides, pathways, and other places where ticks concentrate.

FLEAS ARE RESPONSIBLE for transmission of bubonic plague and endemic typhus. Flea-borne typhus, known as endemic or murine typhus, is prevalent in the United States.

Before the development of DDT, methods for controlling fleas were not satisfactory. Investigators at Orlando demonstrated that DDT, applied as a dust or spray to infested buildings and grounds, would completely eliminate infestations of the common cat and dog fleas. Army personnel employed DDT effectively for controlling fleas during the Second World War.

The Public Health Service has shown that the oriental rat flea can be controlled effectively by applying DDT dusts in buildings, runways, holes and other places frequented by rats. DDT thus applied has reduced the number of cases of endemic typhus in the southern United States.

A number of the new insecticides—chlordane, toxaphene, lindane, heptachlor, dieldrin, and aldrin—are effective as dusts against fleas.

Although the application of DDT to infested buildings and on animals has provided an effective insecticide for controlling fleas and flea-borne disease, the insecticide is of little immediate value in protecting individuals from attacks by the insects. Extensive studies have been conducted at Orlando to develop flea repellents for treatment of clothing for individual protection. Among the most effective of the materials tested are benzyl benzoate and undecylenic acid. The all-purpose tick repellent also is an effective treatment against fleas.

THE BED BUG does not transmit diseases, although it is one of the most widely distributed of the parasites that attack man. It is killed easily with many contact insecticides, but because of its habit of hiding in well-protected places it is difficult to eliminate from infested quarters with such treatments. The fumigation of quarters with hydrocyanic acid gas was used extensively, but it is almost impossible to reach all hiding places with sufficiently high concentrations of the gas to eliminate an infestation.

Because bed bugs were considered one of the more common and annoying pests in military installations, investigations of its control were made at Orlando.

The entomologists assigned to the project, A. W. Lindquist and A. H. Madden, decided that to be really effective an insecticide would have to kill the bed bugs on contact and remain indefinitely as a lethal residue. Therefore the idea of a residual-type treatment for controlling the insect was under investigation early in 1942, before DDT became available. They tested several hundred insecticides in the laboratory. Pyrethrum and a synergist, *n*-butyl undecylenamide, was the most effective treatment developed during the early months of their research. Special cages that had good hiding places were heavily infested with bugs from the laboratory colony. The surfaces were then treated with pyrethrum spray. Bed bugs were placed in the cage every week thereafter. The residual deposit of pyrethrum and synergist killed the bugs for 3 or 4 weeks. Unfortunately, though, all available supplies of the insecticide were required for controlling mosquitoes, lice, and other more important insects.

When DDT became available, it was tested immediately as a residual treatment. Bed bugs added to the test cages were killed week after week. Homes infested with the bugs were then treated by spraying the beds and walls of sleeping quarters. Each week the beds were examined, but no living bed bugs were found. As a further check, 25 bugs from the laboratory colony were placed on the beds each week—by the following week, only dead bugs could be found.

Colonel J. Q. A. Daniels, medical

officer of the Army air base at Orlando, was having difficulty controlling bed bugs in the barracks. Under his direction, a large-scale test was carried out. In April and May 1943 more than 100 barracks containing about 6,000 beds were thoroughly treated with DDT. Close checks on results were made for at least 6 months without finding any bed bugs. The tests not only demonstrated the value of DDT against the bed bug but were of even greater importance in establishing the potential value of the principle of residual treatment against more important insects, particularly mosquitoes and flies.

THE SCIENTISTS who have taken part in research on the control of the mosquitoes, lice, mites, fleas, ticks, bed bugs, and flies have vastly improved the health, welfare, and comfort of mankind. The methods they have developed for destroying these vectors of diseases, I believe, will make serious epidemics of typhus, malaria, and plague a thing of the past. But the job of teaching people how to profit by the advances is far from complete, even though organizations such as the World Health Organization are disseminating information about these significant developments.

E. F. KNIPLING, *a graduate of Texas Agricultural and Mechanical College and Iowa State College, is in charge of the division of insects affecting man and animals of the Bureau of Entomology and Plant Quarantine. He has been with the Department of Agriculture since 1931. During the Second World War, Dr. Knipling was in charge of the laboratory at Orlando, Fla. The laboratory was awarded the Distinguished Service Award of the Department of Agriculture in 1947. The Army awarded Dr. Knipling the Medal for Merit and the United States Typhus Commission Medal, and the King of England awarded him the Medal for Services in the Cause of Freedom for the contributions he made at Orlando.*

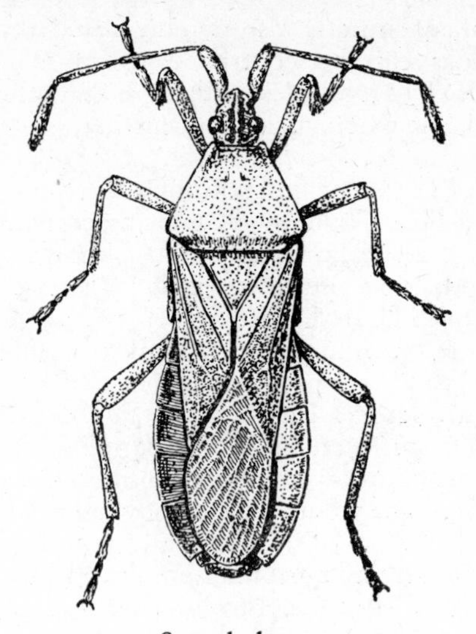

Squash bug.

Tomato hornworm.

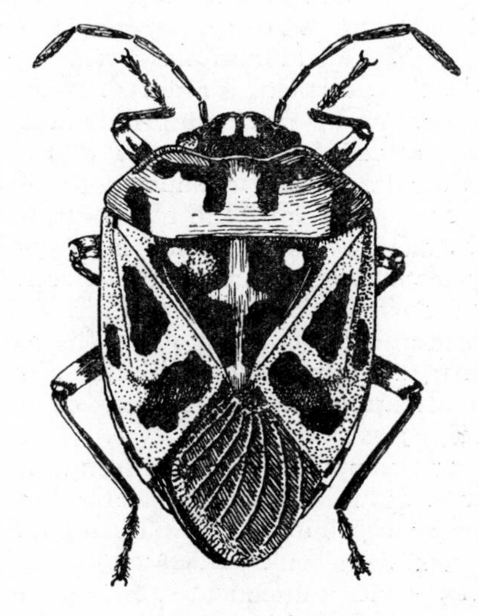

Harlequin bug.

Insects on Cotton

Progress in Research on Cotton Insects

C. F. Rainwater

Cotton is a plant that nature seems to have designed specifically to attract insects. It has green, succulent leaves, many large, open flowers, nectaries on every leaf and flower, and a vast amount of fruit. All seem made to order for insects, some beneficial to man and some—the boll weevil, bollworm, pink bollworm, cotton leafworm, cotton aphid, cotton fleahopper, tarnished plant bug, rapid plant bug, conchuela, southern green stink bug, spider mites, grasshoppers, and thrips—notoriously obnoxious.

The cotton leafworm was the first insect of major importance to deprive the early cotton grower of a substantial part of his crop. Records dating from the eighteenth century show that in some years it destroyed 25 to 90 percent of the cotton. Many early planters were keen observers of insects and accurately recorded descriptions of them, the type and amount of damage they caused, the time they appeared in various localities, data on life history, and the effect of predacious insects on them.

The bollworm became notorious early in the nineteenth century. It and the cotton leafworm often destroyed the crop completely in some localities. Many early writers and researchers could not differentiate between the bollworm and the cotton leafworm, and the estimates of damage by the two insects no doubt were often wrong.

Research by individual cotton planters was the chief source of information concerning cotton insects during the first half of the nineteenth century. The information was disseminated largely through individual correspondence and newspapers. The significance of some of the research and its accuracy is shown by the fact that it was a planter who first reported that the bollworm of cotton and the corn earworm are the same insect.

As the country grew and as cotton production increased, other insect pests appeared to plague growers. Stink bugs and aphids were known in 1855 to be serious pests of cotton. Planters often found it unprofitable to grow cotton because of insects. It became evident that the Government must take a hand in the study and control of the insects. Consequently the Congress ordered a special investigation of cotton insects in 1878.

The early studies were directed very largely at determining the life history and habits of the species that were then causing damage, the effects of their natural enemies, and cultural methods of control. The investigations provided much of the background for later control efforts.

The first successful control measures were cultural methods. Even today they are recognized as of fundamental importance. The early planting of early fruiting varieties of cotton, frequent cultivation, clean culture, cleaning up debris and fence rows around fields, and fall and winter plowing were early recognized as valuable aids in the control of the insects that attack cotton.

Artificial methods of control also received the attention of early research workers, both professional and laymen. They tried different kinds of attractants and repellents, poisoned baits, fires in the fields at night to attract insects, mechanical devices for dislodging and collecting the insects from the plants, and hand picking of the insects from the plants.

Plant breeders contributed a great deal to the research during the early 1900's. They undertook studies to develop varieties of cotton that could better withstand insect attack, varieties that were fast growing and early maturing so that the crop could be produced and matured before insects had time to build up to their maximum numbers, and more prolific varieties that could produce additional fruit after part of it had been destroyed. Indeed, plant breeding still has a vital part in research on the control of cotton insects.

Research on the chemical control of cotton insects really began in earnest in the early 1900's. Various chemicals were applied as sprays in the hope of finding effective controls. As early as 1905 paris green was recommended as a spray to combat some of the insects. London purple and arsenate of lead also came into general use then. The methods of application were crude; that probably accounted largely for the failure to get effective control. One method, for example, was to stir the chemical in water and sprinkle it over the tops of the plants with a cedar bough. Another method was to drive small holes into wooden buckets or kegs and allow the solution to trickle through them on the plants. Nevertheless, sprays came into fairly general use during the period.

The part of the agricultural engineer was first realized fully during the early 1900's. The development of machines for applying sprays is one example of their early work. Various attachments were constructed and fastened onto the plow to knock the insects and the infested squares from the plant and collect them in some sort of container whereby they could be buried, burned, or otherwise destroyed. One widely recommended device was a chain drag, which pulled infested squares from under the plant and deposited them in the middle of the row so they would be exposed to the sun and the larvae in them would be killed.

The first arsenate of lead ever used in dust form for insect control was in 1908. From then until 1916, hundreds of experiments were conducted with dusts of lead arsenate, paris green, and london purple. Against the cotton leafworm and certain other insects, the dusts were highly effective, but they never proved entirely satisfactory against the boll weevil or the bollworm. Emphasis continued to be placed on cultural methods of control for most cotton pests.

Of great importance was the discovery in 1916 that calcium arsenate dust was highly effective against some cotton insects. For the next three decades, however, research on the control of cotton insects was largely devoted to developing dusts and dust mixtures and methods of applying them. It was demonstrated during this period that insect pests of cotton could be economically controlled and that cotton production could be made profitable even under conditions of heavy attack.

Meanwhile, another serious insect menace appeared. The pink bollworm, the most serious insect pest of cotton known in many parts of the world, was discovered in Texas in 1917. Many people realized that our cotton industry might be doomed if it were allowed to spread as the boll weevil had done. Research efforts were doubled therefore as to the biology, ecology, and control of the pink bollworm. The research provided the basis for the successful fight to prevent its spread to the principal cotton-producing areas through quarantine regulations and control efforts.

During the 1920's research on cotton insects reached its peak. The boll weevil had completed its spread eastward and northward until it had invaded the Cotton Belt from Texas to Virginia. Every State in the Cotton Belt was searching feverishly for more effective controls against cotton insects. A shortage of cotton after the First World War sent prices up, and prosperity was in the grasp of any farmer if he could produce cotton despite the insects. Intensive cultivation created new insect problems—insects that had previously been confined largely to other plants were being forced onto cotton as new land was being brought into cultivation and as the intensity of cultivation increased. The cotton fleahopper, plant bugs, thrips, aphids, spider mites, and stink bugs all were recognized as serious pests of cotton. The primary emphasis of research was on control. Calcium arsenate was then a proved insecticide against the boll weevil, bollworm, and cotton leafworm. Methods of applying it by ground machines and airplanes were perfected. Millions of pounds were being used annually. Nicotine controlled the cotton aphid. The first combination insecticide, calcium arsenate and nicotine, simultaneously controlled the boll weevil-bollworm-cotton aphid. Sulfur was found to be effective against the cotton fleahopper and other plant bugs, as well as against spider mites. So, despite the increased complexity of the insect problems, research demonstrated that insects could be effectively and economically controlled and that cotton could be profitably produced despite the insects.

From 1930 until 1945 the primary emphasis was on developing new methods or improving existing methods of control. The different methods were thoroughly tested under various climatic conditions. Plant bugs were causing serious losses in the irrigated localities of the Southwest. A mixture of 7.5 percent paris green and 92.5 percent sulfur was developed to fight them.

Thus through a half century control measures had been developed for all of the principal insect pests of cotton. The threat that the cotton industry in the United States might be doomed because of insects no longer existed. The insects had not been eradicated; in fact, they were far more numerous at the end of this period than they were at the beginning, but we had learned how to cope with them. Our success in controlling them only made conditions more favorable for their rapid increase when control was relaxed. It was inevitable that the fight against cotton insects would have to be continued. The cotton planter had become resigned to the fact that insect control was just as important a part of his normal farming operations as the selection of good seed, proper fertilization, or proper cultivation.

In 1945 a new era in the research began. The development of the new and more powerful organic insecticides opened up new avenues. But it likewise created new research problems.

The first experiments with the new organic insecticides proved that they were not cure-alls. DDT was the first to be tested extensively, followed by benzene hexachloride, toxaphene, and chlordane. These were found to be highly effective against certain insect pests of cotton and were adopted in the control recommendations of many States. But not one of these individually controlled all the major pests. Certain combinations were developed, such as 3 percent gamma isomer of benzene hexachloride-5 percent DDT-40 percent sulfur, 20 percent toxaphene-40 percent sulfur, and 10 percent chlordane-5 percent DDT.

The synthesis of new organic compounds was greatly accelerated, and thousands were tested for insecticidal efficacy during the late 1940's and early 1950's. Aldrin, dieldrin, parathion, and tetraethyl pyrophosphate were included in the official recommendations of some States. Others, notably heptachlor, EPN (O-ethyl O-*p*-nitrophenyl benzenethiophosphonate), methyl ester parathion and a sterio isomer of dieldrin, showed considerable promise in later tests. Again, however, none satisfied the requirements for an all-purpose cotton insecticide. The most effective combinations have to be worked out for each State or area.

Certain organic insecticides can kill insects developing inside of plant tissue as well as those that feed on the exterior parts. Heptachlor, chlordane, aldrin, dieldrin, and (to a lesser extent) benzene hexachloride are known to kill boll weevils developing inside of punctured squares when applied to cotton under field conditions. This property may prove to be extremely important in fixing the ultimate value of the poisons used against cotton insects and may have far-reaching effects in developing better controls.

The organic insecticides in general lend themselves readily to incorporation into emulsifiable concentrates through the use of proper solvents and emulsifiers. Properly formulated, they can then be diluted with water and applied as low-gallonage, low-pressure sprays. The trend in the use of insecticides for cotton insect control now is toward such sprays. In 1950 and 1951 millions of gallons of sprays were applied to cotton. Recent experiments have shown that as little as 1 gallon per acre of a concentrated spray containing the required amounts of the insecticide, or insecticides, may be enough. Since sprays can be applied under conditions that would render dusts ineffective, this research represents a distinct achievement. Many farmers apply concentrated sprays to cotton at the time they cultivate the crop, and thereby reduce the cost of application. Combination sprays have been developed for the simultaneous control of most cotton insects. They may be applied effectively by ground equipment and airplanes.

The development of proper schedules for applying insecticides to cotton has done much to lower the costs. Early season control programs that have been developed for many areas have been so successful as to make unnecessary additional applications later. Considerably smaller amounts of the insecticide per application are needed in the early applications. Killing off many insects of minor importance helps the plants to grow faster, so that the crop is usually matured earlier and the farmer has a better chance to get it properly harvested. Both dusts and sprays have been successfully used in early season control, but sprays appear to be preferable to dusts largely because they can be applied directly onto the small plants by the use of proper spray equipment, whereas with dusts there is some unavoidable wastage. Ground machines are also preferable to airplanes for applying sprays to cotton in the early season for the same reason.

The need for research stems from the fact that the value of the cotton destroyed by insects has averaged more than 100 million dollars annually since 1929, climaxed by an all-time-high loss of more than 900 million dollars in 1950. The value of the research is shown by the thousands of farmers who have followed recommendations and have increased their yields three, four, and five times over comparable areas in which no control was used. Net profits due entirely to insect control of 150 to 175 dollars an acre and net returns of from 20 to 28 dollars for every dollar spent for insecticides have frequently been obtained by cotton farmers who followed research findings and recommendations. The difference between a profit and a loss on any given acre of cotton often depends entirely on whether the insects are controlled.

C. F. Rainwater *was reared on a cotton farm in southern Mississippi. Since graduating from Mississippi State College in 1931 he has been engaged in research on cotton insects in Louisiana, Florida, South Carolina, and Texas. Since 1948 he has been in charge of the basic cotton insect research laboratory at College Station, Tex.*

The Boll Weevil

R. C. Gaines

The boll weevil, undoubtedly a native of Mexico or Central America, is about one-fourth inch long and a third as wide. The amount of food the developing larva gets in the square (flower bud) or boll (fruit) causes differences in the size of the weevils. The color varies from light yellow to gray or nearly black, depending on its age.

The boll weevil was identified first by the Swedish entomologist Boheman from specimens he got from Mexico. We know little about its spread through Mexico. It crossed the Rio Grande River near Brownsville, Tex., in 1892 or so. By 1894 it had spread to six counties in southern Texas. It advanced 40 to 160 miles a year and by 1922 it had infested more than 85 percent of our Cotton Belt.

It is possible to produce cotton in the infested part of the Cotton Belt because about 95 percent of the hibernating adults die and many that actually survive the winter emerge and die before cotton produces squares in which eggs may be deposited. Even after egg deposition and weevil development have started, heat, dry weather, insect parasites and predators, and birds help materially to check the rapid multiplication. Without such natural interference, offspring of a single pair of boll weevils could amount to several millions in one season.

Much attention has been given to the possible control of the boll weevil with parasites. About 80 percent of all the parasites reared in the different States have been *Bracon mellitor*. Other species of importance are *Triaspis curculionis*, *Eurytoma tylodermatis*, *Catolaccus hunteri*, *Zatropis incertus*, *Eupelmus cyaniceps amicus*, and *Myiophasia globosa*. About 6 percent of the boll weevil larvae were parasitized. Occasionally parasitization has run as high as 30 percent. In a few localities it has remained as high as 20 percent throughout the season. *Bracon kirkpatricki*, from Kenya Colony, and *Triaspis vesticida* and *Bracon vesticida*, from Peru, have been released in cotton fields, but we have no evidence that any of them have become established in the United States.

The damage caused by the boll weevil varies greatly from year to year. During 1950, for example, boll weevil damage was greater than for any year since 1921 and 1922 over the Cotton Belt as a whole and was the greatest ever recorded in Arkansas, North Carolina, and Virginia. The supply of feeding and breeding material, which is affected by weather conditions during the late summer and early fall, determines the number and condition of boll weevils for hibernation. Low temperatures in winter greatly influence the survival and emergence during the following spring and summer. The effect of rainfall and temperatures is most important throughout the period of cotton production. Each of these factors constitutes a separate study. At Tallulah, La., a greater correlation occurred between the number of days on which there was 0.3 inch or more of rainfall from June 21 to August 19 and the percentage of increase in yield in experimental plots where boll weevils were controlled than between any other two variables.

Research to reduce the losses caused by the boll weevil was started by the Department of Agriculture in 1894. It has been continued up to now, except during 1898–1900, when Texas made a special appropriation and all the work was handled by the State entomologist. Research has also been conducted by the various States in the cotton-growing area. Starting in 1947, a conference of Federal and State workers concerned with studies of cotton insects has been held in November or

December of each year. The conference reports bring together the results of research and are a basis for control recommendations.

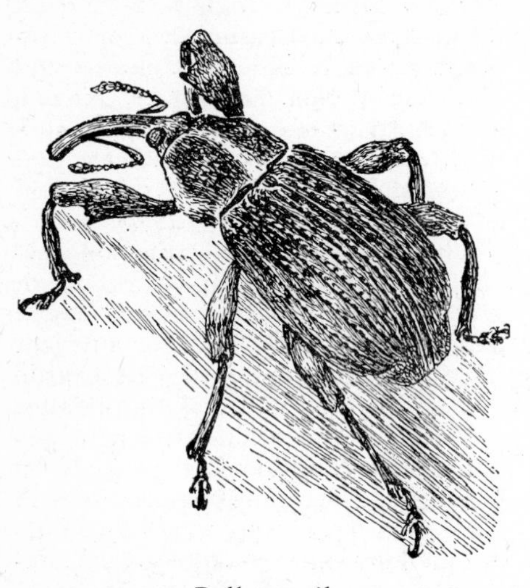

Boll weevil.

Indirect or cultural practices are of vital importance. Successful control cannot be accomplished unless full advantage is taken of every possible indirect method. The control program must be based on a combination of the different methods rather than an attempt to concentrate all efforts on direct control. Some of the most important cultural practices are preparation of seedbed, early planting, seed treatment, planting of a recommended variety, soil improvement and fertilization, frequent shallow cultivation, clean-up of favorable hibernation quarters, and early destruction of cotton stalks.

Early destruction of cotton stalks, one of the first recommendations made by entomologists, is a sound practice. It removes the food from boll weevils, stops late-season breeding, and causes the adults to enter hibernation in a more or less starved condition, which increases winter mortality. The earliness of stalk destruction has a bearing on the effectiveness. In a long series of experiments at Tallulah, La., no survival occurred when the weevils were placed in cages during the first week in September, while the highest survival was in cages installed during the latter half of October and first half of November. That is the time when frost normally kills cotton and the weevils enter hibernation.

The stalk-destruction program practiced in the Rio Grande Valley of Texas and Mexico for control of the pink bollworm has greatly reduced the crop losses from the boll weevil there. More than 1 million acres of cotton in Cameron, Hidalgo, and Willacy Counties in Texas and the adjacent area in Mexico were in this clean-up program, which calls for the completion of cotton planting by March 31 and destruction of the stalks by August 31. Immediately thereafter the debris is plowed under and seedling and sprouted cotton plants are eliminated so as to create a host-free period between crops.

The program has reduced the infestation and increased the yield of cotton in this area. Records of infestation of squares were made in June in the three counties from 1944 through 1950. In 1944 and 1945, before the program was started, the infestation averaged 38.5 percent. In 1946 to 1950, following the clean-up, infestation averaged 10.5 percent. The average lint yield per acre was 213 pounds in the three counties for the 5 years before the clean-up and 342 pounds for the 5 years afterwards.

Chemical defoliation of cotton plants causes boll weevils to leave the treated fields almost immediately. Proper defoliation checks the growth of the cotton plant and accelerates the opening of bolls. The crop may be harvested earlier so that the cotton stalks can be destroyed earlier.

Direct control of the boll weevil with insecticides is used if natural conditions and indirect methods or cultural practices fail. Treatments should be started while cotton is in the presquare stage, in fields where weevils are unusually abundant, in order to kill overwintered insects. The boll weevil on fruiting cotton is hard to poison because the immature stages develop within the cotton square or boll. No poison has been very effective against those stages in the field in normal weather. The adults must be poisoned. Because they feed sparingly on external plant tissue, it is difficult to do so. The number of applications required varies greatly from field to field and year to year. Applications are started when 10 to 25 percent of the squares have been punctured, depending on the locality and type and fertility of soil. Applications must be repeated at intervals of 4 or 5 days because the plants grow rapidly and the poisons break down chemically and may be removed from the plants by wind, dews, or rains.

MANY INSECTICIDES and mixtures of insecticides have been tested.

Years ago calcium arsenate was tried and found so effective that it remained the No. 1 boll weevil poison until the organic insecticides became available in 1947 and 1948.

Calcium arsenate usually causes an increase of the cotton aphid. After several years of experimentation, a mixture of calcium arsenate containing 2 percent of nicotine in alternate applications was recommended in 1940. The mixture was very effective against the boll weevil and cotton aphid when properly applied, but the supply of nicotine was so limited that the program could not be put into effect in all of the areas where it could have been used successfully. In South Carolina, where the calcium arsenate residue in some soils caused injury to crops, the arsenic was reduced by using a mixture of calcium arsenate and lime. In some parts of Texas, where insects in addition to the boll weevil were involved, a mixture of calcium arsenate and sulfur was used.

DDT will not control the boll weevil. It often makes conditions favorable for the increase of cotton aphids and spider mites by reducing the numbers of their natural enemies. Since it is effective against the bollworm it has become essential in mixtures of insecticides now in general use on cotton.

Benzene hexachloride, first tested against cotton insects in 1945, was found to be effective against the boll weevil and other cotton pests. It failed to control the bollworm and spider mites, and often encouraged an increase in the number of those pests. Of the many combinations tested, a mixture containing 3 percent of the gamma isomer of benzene hexachloride, 5 percent of DDT, and 40 percent of sulfur was one of the best. The benzene hexachloride kills the boll weevil, cotton aphid, tarnished and rapid plant bugs, cotton leafworm, thrips, southern green stink bug, garden webworm, fall armyworm, cotton fleahopper, and grasshoppers. DDT kills the bollworm, pink bollworm, plant bugs, fleahoppers, and thrips. Sulfur prevents the development of injurious spider mite infestations. The extent to which sulfur is used primarily to control spider mites is shown by the fact that approximately 200 million pounds were dusted on cotton in 1950.

The benzene hexachloride in the mixture is a fast killer and kills as a vapor, by contact, and as a stomach poison. Alternate applications of this fast killer (which has a short residual effect) and calcium arsenate (a slow killer with long residual effect) make an effective control program.

Toxaphene has given excellent control of the boll weevil. It also controls many other cotton insect pests. Like DDT and benzene hexachloride, it may cause an increase of spider mites. In areas where mites are a problem, at least 40 percent of sulfur should be added.

Chlordane has given promising results in some tests against the boll weevil. But dusts containing as high as 10 percent of the material have given varying results. Chlordane encourages the increase of bollworms and spider mites. When used in low concentrations it also causes an increase of the cotton aphid; therefore it has not been used extensively against the boll weevil.

Aldrin has been tested throughout the Cotton Belt. It is a good boll weevil poison if enough of it is used. Used alone, it will not control the bollworm and may cause an increase in the number of spider mites. Aldrin will not control heavy infestations of cotton aphids and in some instances it has caused an increase of aphids. DDT should be added to an aldrin mixture for control of bollworms, and sulfur should be added to prevent an increase of spider mites.

Dieldrin is a good boll weevil poison if used in sufficient quantity. DDT should be added to the dieldrin mixture to aid in the control of the bollworm; sulfur should be added to prevent an increase of spider mites.

Heptachlor has given excellent control of the boll weevil. DDT should be added to heptachlor mixtures for control of the bollworm, and sulfur should be added to prevent an increase of spider mites.

Each of these insecticides has its place in the boll weevil control program. Some are more effective in certain areas and under certain conditions than others. Intensive experimentation is necessary to determine the exact conditions and locations under which they may be most effective. In recent large-scale experiments, however, aldrin, benzene hexachloride, calcium arsenate, chlordane, dieldrin, heptachlor, and toxaphene all gave satisfactory boll weevil control when properly applied as needed.

EQUIPMENT AND METHODS for applying poisons to cotton for control of the boll weevil differ greatly. Dusting has long been more popular than spraying. Spraying cotton with the arsenicals has not proved profitable. However, experiments conducted in many areas in 1949 and 1950 indicated that some of the organic insecticides applied as spray emulsions at low pressure and volume per acre were effective against the boll weevil.

Hand gun, saddle gun, one-mule and wheel-barrow-type machines, traction-power cart machines, power-operated machines, and airplanes are the types of dusting machines in general use. Each type has its place. The sprayers in use are of two general types—ground and airplane.

The cotton grower now has a wide selection of insecticides or combinations of insecticides which can be used to control the boll weevil, including dusts and sprays, which appear to be about equally effective. More important than this or than the method used are the proper time of starting applications, the correct interval between applications, favorable weather conditions, complete coverage, and the continuation of applications until the crop has matured.

R. C. GAINES *is an entomologist in the Bureau of Entomology and Plant Quarantine. He was graduated from the Alabama Polytechnic Institute in 1920 and has been in the Bureau since September 1, 1920. In January 1931 he was put in charge of the laboratory of the division of cotton insect investigations in Tallulah, La.*

For further reading:

P. N. Annand: Recent Developments in the Control of Cotton Insects, *A Report to the Cotton Subcommittee on Agriculture, by the Bureau of Entomology and Plant Quarantine, Agricultural Research Administration, United States Department of Agriculture. 1948.*

R. C. Gaines: Relation Between Winter Temperatures, Boll Weevil Survival, Summer Rainfall, and Cotton Yields, *Journal of Economic Entomology, volume 36, pages 82–83, 1943;* Machinery for Dusting Cotton, *with D. A. Isler, U. S. D. A. Farmers' Bulletin 1729. 1934.*

W. D. Hunter and B. R. Coad: The Boll-Weevil Problem, *U. S. D. A. Farmers' Bulletin 1262. 1922.*

U. C. Loftin: Living with the Boll Weevil for 50 Years, *Report of the Smithsonian Institute for 1945, pages 273–292. 1946.*

J. L. Webb and F. A. Merrill: Cotton or Weevils, *U. S. D. A. Miscellaneous Publication 35. 1929.*

Reports of the Chief of the Bureau of Entomology and Plant Quarantine, Agricultural Research Administration, 1936 to 1951.

The Pink Bollworm

L. F. Curl, R. W. White

The pink bollworm first appeared in the United States in 1917 near Hearne, Robertson County, Tex.

The first published record of the pest was in a report in 1842 by W. W. Saunders, of the Entomological Society of London, who received specimens from cotton plantations in India. It has since spread over most of the cotton-producing countries. Severe depredations were reported in 1904 in what was then German East Africa. The pink bollworm is believed to have been introduced into Egypt from India about 1906 or 1907. It was found in 1909 in the Hawaiian Islands, where it caused such severe damage that cotton production was abandoned.

Cotton is grown commercially in 60 or 65 countries, 8 of which—the United States, India, China, the Soviet Union, Egypt, Brazil, Mexico, and Argentina—produce more than nine-tenths of the world crop. The pink bollworm is said to be generally established in all of them except the United States and Mexico. The losses of cotton it has caused have averaged 15 to 25 percent in India and Egypt. In China it has caused greater losses than all other cotton insects together. In 1933 it was so bad in Russia that Russian entomologists came to the United States to study methods of control. An average annual loss of 20 to 25 percent is reported in Brazil, with a high point of 60 to 70 percent in the 1949–50 cotton crop.

The pink bollworm was brought into Mexico in 1911, and an average loss in yield in the Laguna region of 15 to 20 percent can be attributed to it. It reached the United States in infested cottonseed moved from the Laguna to some oil mills in Texas and soon thereafter it was found in nearby cotton fields. The commercial damage in the following 35 years has been negligible because vigorous measures were adopted immediately—first, an effort to eradicate it and later, when that was found to be an impossible goal, a program designed to suppress infestation and prevent its spread. Despite the low intensity of infestation in most of the affected areas, however, the pink bollworm has inflicted heavy damage in certain localities and on individual farms. Fields in Presidio County, Tex., suffered total damage in 1931, for example, and in 1939 several thousand acres in Cameron County, Tex., suffered commercial loss.

In 1943 a number of fields in southwestern Louisiana showed 25 to 30 percent damage to the bolls from pink bollworm attack. In 1950 in a 400-acre field in Nueces County, Tex., 54 percent of the bolls had been made nonpickable by the pink bollworm. Others showed damage from 30 to 40 percent, and all bolls in one small field of late cotton were completely ruined by the pink bollworm.

Quarantines and control measures were in effect in 1951 in five States—Arizona, New Mexico, Oklahoma, Texas, and Louisiana—because of earlier findings there of the pink bollworm. It also occurs in wild cotton and dooryard cotton plants in southern Florida.

The adult of the pink bollworm is a small brown moth about four-fifths of an inch from tip to tip of the extended wings. By day the moths are inactive and are seldom seen even in a heavily infested field. The female moth begins laying eggs a day or two after she emerges and continues for 4 or 5 days or longer. The moths normally live only 10 days or so.

The eggs are small, white, and oval and have a finely wrinkled surface. A moth usually produces about 200 eggs; most of them are deposited on the base of maturing green bolls under the calyx. Early in the season, in the absence of the favored boll, or later, after a saturated infestation has been reached in bolls, eggs are often deposited on the squares. The eggs hatch within 4 or 5 days in the summer, and the tiny larvae bore into the boll or square.

The newly hatched larva is glossy white, has a dark brown head, and bears but little resemblance to the full-grown worm. The mature larva is about one-half inch long. Rather wide, splotchy stripes of a deep pink give it a pink appearance. Larvae of the summer broods usually complete their growth in 8 to 12 days. In the summer most of them cut holes through which they leave the boll, dropping to the ground to pupate in the surface trash or cracks in the soil. Pupation may occur within the boll in areas of considerable rainfall.

Resting-stage larvae, which are those going into natural or forced hibernation, act differently. Cool weather, lack of humidity, lack of food supply, or other unfavorable conditions may cause a large percentage of the larvae to go into this resting stage. This cycle, particularly if entered into late in the season after cold weather begins, ordinarily lasts until the following spring when cotton is again fruiting. Larvae have been known to remain in hibernation for more than 2 years. Extremely dry weather in late summer or early fall seems to cause more than the usual number of larvae to enter this stage. If the dry weather is followed by considerable rain, many of the inactive larvae go into pupation and emerge as moths. This trait is a factor in control—the cotton stalks are destroyed soon after harvest so that those moths will find nothing upon which to deposit their eggs when they emerge.

The pupal stage lasts 8 to 10 days in the summer, but is usually longer in the cooler weather of spring and fall. The pupa is whitish, with faint markings of pink when first formed; it turns to a mahogany brown as it dries and to a darker brown before emergence. It is about one-fourth inch long. It is covered with velvety hairs; practically no other pupae of similar size have such a pronounced pubescence. The hind end of the pupa is short, stout, hooklike, and up-pointing.

Under the best conditions during the summer breeding season, the pink bollworm can complete its life cycle in 22 or 23 days. In areas with long growing seasons, seven or eight generations are possible in a single season. The average number of generations in most of the cotton-producing areas of the United States is four or five if there are no cultural controls such as shortening of the season through a mandatory planting period and the destruction of stalks to stop breeding of the insects.

THE PINK BOLLWORM affects the cotton yield in several ways. In severe infestations, damaged squares and small bolls may be shed, leaving no visible evidence of reduced yield on the plant itself. The preferred food of the larva is the kernel of the seed. Usually the tiny larva, upon entering a boll, travels a short distance just under the inner surface of the covering, making a typical path commonly referred to as a mine. It soon leaves the lining of the boll and cuts through the immature lint to a seed. It devours the inside of the seed; then the small worm proceeds to the next seed, ruining the lint as it passes through it. Many larvae are heavy feeders and eat out all the seed of a lock or cell of the boll before they reach maturity.

If only one to three pink bollworms feed to maturity in a boll, several of the locks may escape damage; others may suffer partial damage but still be worth picking. In heavy infestations the entire boll may be so damaged that pickers leave it on the plant. Such damage is recognized readily, but partly damaged locks are picked. They lower the grade and staple of the lint because of the staining and cut fibers caused by the feeding of the worm as it passed from one seed to another.

There is also the added loss of oil content of the seed produced from heavily infested bolls. Hollowed-out seeds contain no oil. Naturally in extremely heavy infestation the greatest loss is the reduced yield of pickable cotton. Although the pink bollworm may completely ruin a boll, the damage is more clean-cut than the damage done by some other insects, such as the boll weevil. In passing from one lock to another, the larva usually cuts a round hole in the partition wall; the hole is easily recognized as the work of the pink bollworm.

After finding the first infestation of pink bollworms in Texas in 1917, a zone in which no cotton could be grown was established in 1918, 1919, and 1920 for a short distance around the known infested spot. A regulated area of much greater size was established around the noncotton zone. The entire section was declared free of infestation and all controls were removed following inspection in 1923.

Later in 1917 infestation was found in other Texas counties—Galveston, Fort Bend, Brazoria, Harris, Chambers, Liberty, Hardin, Jefferson, Newton, Jasper, and Orange. Cotton production was not extensive there. Noncotton zones, field clean-up, and regulatory measures were invoked in an effort to eradicate the pest. Inspections were negative from 1921 through 1926, and all restrictions were removed in 1927. Reinfestation occurred in 1943 in Liberty, Chambers, and adjacent counties, but was eradicated by enforcement of a small noncotton zone and a larger regulated area. The area was again released from quarantine in 1947. Brazoria, Chambers, Fort Bend, and Liberty Counties became infested again in 1950, and Harris County in 1951.

The pink bollworm was found in several southwestern parishes in Louisiana in February 1920, but was wiped out by setting up a noncotton zone and a regulated area. Inspections through 1924 showed no infestation, and all restrictions were removed.

Reinfestation occurred there again in 1943 but was eliminated and the area was released from quarantine after inspection of the 1946 crop. Unfortunately the tremendous spread of the pink bollworm during the 1950 crop season involved southwestern Louisiana for the third time, and vigorous counter measures were initiated.

The Shreveport area of Louisiana became infested in the fall of 1920 because of movement of seed from southwestern Louisiana before discovery of infestation there. Through a noncotton zone, regulatory, and clean-up measures, the infestation was eradicated. All restrictions were removed after negative inspections in 1925.

Infestations were found in Ellis and Grayson Counties, Tex., in 1921; each resulting from movement of cottonseed from Carlsbad, N. Mex., before an infestation was detected. Field clean-up, noncotton zones, and regulated zones were used to end the infestations. The quarantine was removed in 1926.

An infestation in the Salt River Valley of Arizona was found near Gilbert in Maricopa County in October 1929. Later in the season infestation was found in a cotton field in Pinal County. One of the largest noncotton zones ever established was set up in Arizona to aid in eradication, and all of the Salt River Valley was placed under regulation. After several years of negative inspection, the quarantine was removed in 1934. Infestation reappeared in the late fall of 1938. A vigorous eradication program, involving field clean-up and heavy frequent applications of insecticide, was inaugurated in 1947, following a heavy build-up in a limited area in 1946. Inspections were negative during the 1947, 1948, and 1949 crop seasons. The area was released from quarantine for a second time on January 10, 1950.

Inspections were negative in 1951 in Arizona except in Cochise, Greenlee, and Graham Counties. This resulted in release from quarantine of additional Arizona counties of Pima and Santa Cruz early in 1952.

An infestation was discovered in northern Florida and in southern Georgia in 1932–33. The source was from moths spreading from heavily infested wild cotton on the southern tip of the State. Control work on the wild cotton of southern Florida reduced the infestation to a low point. Field clean-up, early maturity of the crop, and other regulatory measures, including heating of the seed as ginned, eliminated infestation, and there has been no recurrence of the outbreak in northern Florida and southern Georgia since the area was released from quarantine in 1936.

Three principal methods of inspection are used to determine the presence of the pink bollworm—inspection of cotton blooms, bolls, and gin trash.

During the early part of the cotton-growing season there are no bolls for the pink bollworm to enter and feed on, and the moths that come from over-wintering larvae often deposit their eggs on half-grown cotton squares, or flower buds. The larvae that hatch from the eggs enter the squares and reach maturity at about the time the flower opens. To protect itself from the heat of the sun and from predators, the larva seals the tips of the flower petals together with a fine web; such flowers have a distinctive rosette appearance. An inspector, walking through a cotton field at this stage of its development, can detect easily the abnormal blooms on plants. That method of inspection is used only in areas already known to be infested to determine the degree of carry-over from the previous year.

Green cotton bolls are inspected by making longitudinal cuts midway between the sutures, or lock divisions, and peeling back the boll covering, or hull, without disturbing the contents of the lock. If no larvae or evidence of insect injury is noted on the surface of the developing cotton lock, the inside surface of the removed hull is examined for the characteristic mines left by the young larvae in entering the boll. If a mine is noted, the small larva usually is found in the corresponding part of the developing cotton lock. In nearly mature green bolls, the presence of pink bollworm infestation often can be determined by looking for exit holes in the boll wall—these smooth, round holes are about the size of the lead in an ordinary pencil.

After frost has stopped further growth of the cotton, the open mature bolls are examined for exit and partition-wall holes, lint discoloration, and other evidence of insect injury. If such evidence is found, the cottonseeds are cut with a pocket knife. Pink bollworms may be found inside the seeds. Boll inspection is used to determine the bollworm population per acre and may also be used to determine the presence or absence of the insect where cotton acreage is small or isolated and no gin trash is available.

Gin-trash inspection is the most rapid and effective method of inspection.

When the seed cotton is brought to a ginning plant, it is first put through cleaners to remove dirt, sand, and leaf particles. Many of the pink bollworms inside the seeds of the cotton locks are shaken out during the process and are discharged with the trash. Samples of the trash are collected from a large number of gins in an area under inspection and are taken to a central location and put through a special inspection machine, which was developed by men in the Department of Agriculture. It uses two screen drums and air suction to eliminate about 99 percent of the dirt and leaf particles; any pink bollworm larvae and other insects are left in the rest.

Inspection of limited amounts of gin trash is conducted annually in the regulated areas to determine the status of the infestation. More extensive inspections are made in the nonregulated parts of the affected States and in the other cotton-growing States in an effort to discover incipient infestations promptly.

THE FEDERAL QUARANTINE is designed primarily to prevent the spread of the pink bollworm across State lines. Suppression of an infestation and the prevention of spread within a State also are important. A State quarantine therefore is a necessary complement to the Federal order. The quarantines regulate the movement of cotton and its products that can harbor and spread infestation. The shipment of some products is prohibited entirely—primarily gin waste and entire cotton plants. Seed cotton may move only to adjoining regulated areas or designated gins for ginning. Cottonseed and cotton lint must be treated under supervision of an inspector in such a way as to kill all pink bollworms; after that, the products may move under certificate from regulated to free areas.

The character of treatment required varies with the degree of infestation present at the originating point of the products.

The principal method of treating cottonseed to control pink bollworms is to heat the seed to 150° F. for 30 seconds or more. That does not injure the seed for planting. When the seed is properly handled after heating, there is no injury to the oil or products manufactured from it. Another treatment is methyl bromide fumigation at atmospheric pressure. A third method involves fumigation with hydrocyanic acid gas under vacuum. The heat treatment is the only procedure that can be used as a part of continuous ginning.

Approved methods for treatment of lint cotton includes passing the lint between steel rollers that are set to crush all pink bollworms in the lint as it is carried in a thin sheet from the gin stands to the press box; fumigation of the baled cotton with hydrocyanic acid gas under vacuum; and standard or high-density compression of the baled cotton.

Sanitation at gins, oil mills, and other points where untreated cotton and its products may be stored is required. Gins have to dispose of gin trash, cotton burs, and other waste, which is separated from the seed cotton or snapped cotton in ginning. Many gins burn the trash, burs, and waste in incinerators. Others haul the material to a burning ground or dump, where the ginners are held responsible for complete destruction. Some gins have equipment to steam-treat burs so they can be used for feed or fertilizer. An important phase of an inspector's duties is to see that waste material does not become mixed with treated products before it is disposed of.

COTTON PLANTS will grow and produce squares, blooms, and bolls an average of 8 to 10 months of the year in parts of Arizona, southern Louisiana, southern Texas, and northeastern Mexico. Often in the lower Rio Grande Valley of Texas and nearby areas of Mexico cotton plants remain alive throughout the year; if such plants are not destroyed they will provide food for the pink bollworm and other insects. It is therefore essential, under those conditions, to require a host-free period as a control measure.

The procedure that has been adopted in the lower Rio Grande Valley works about as follows. Growers are placed under individual permits, which authorize them to plant cotton during a specified time. An added stipulation is that the cotton plants must be destroyed by midnight August 31 in such a way as to prevent subsequent growth. The grower or owner of the land is expected to keep his fields entirely free of cotton plants during the host-free period, beginning September 1 and ending at planting time in late January or early February of the following year. That often means the land may have to be plowed three or four times to destroy seedlings, which come from shattered locks of seed cotton or plants which sprout from old roots of the previous crop. Texas regulations also require the ginners in the lower Rio Grande Valley to collect

970134°—52——34

$10 from the growers for each bale of cotton ginned. The money is placed in an escrow fund and returned to the grower upon compliance with the stalk-destruction regulations. If any grower fails to place his cotton field in a host-free condition on schedule, the State has authority to use his escrow funds to do the job.

INSECTICIDAL CONTROL of the pink bollworm was never successful on a field scale until the development of DDT. It now appears that insecticidal control will prove a valuable supplement to the cultural controls, which involve planting the cotton within a short period, using quick-maturing varieties, destroying the stalk early, and maintaining a host-free period. Large-scale field tests, using DDT in approved amounts at weekly intervals during the period in which the crop is susceptible to pink bollworm attack, show as much as 65 to 70 percent control.

The discovery of heavy infestations in wild cotton and ornamental or dooryard cotton in southern Florida led to a program of eradicating all wild and dooryard cotton plants there. From its inception in 1932 through June 1947, infestation was cut from 40 percent in many sections to less than 0.1 percent. Early in this period, the migration of pink bollworms from the wild cotton to cultivated cotton in northern Florida and southern Georgia was stopped, the incipient infestation in the two areas was ended, and the quarantine was removed.

Federal funds were lacking from July 1, 1947, through June 30, 1949; in that time the wild cotton plants, although present in greatly reduced numbers, fruited and much of the benefits of the eradication work was lost. In the absence of a host-free period, seven or eight generations of pink bollworms were produced each year, and infestation began to climb rapidly in some localities. The work was resumed in July 1949 in time to prevent a new spread from wild cotton to cultivated cotton; inspections in northern Florida and southern Georgia were negative in 1949, 1950, and 1951.

The aim of the program is the complete eradication of all cotton plants in southern Florida. In the meantime, infestation has to be kept at a very low level to prevent natural spread. The various areas are covered from two to four times during the period—late September to May—when weather conditions permit work in the jungle-like swamp, and existing cotton plants are destroyed. The procedure establishes a host-free period that is effective in holding down infestation. The presence of a single plant in the heavy undergrowth may permit pink bollworm infestation to persist from year to year.

Past experience indicates that infestation would build up sufficiently in 4 or 5 years, in the absence of a vigorous eradication program, to spread the pink bollworm once more to cultivated cotton in northern Florida and southern Georgia.

THE BUREAU of Entomology and Plant Quarantine, through its pink bollworm control organization, cooperates closely with the Mexican Government. The interest of the United States is primarily the prevention of long-distance spread into the uninfested areas of this country. If that is to be accomplished, infestation in Mexico, particularly in border areas, must be held to a very low level. The cooperation consists mainly of technical assistance to officials of the Mexican Department of Agriculture. Regional agricultural committees, farm organizations, and banks also participate in the work. The control programs in Mexico closely parallel those in the United States. Stalk-destruction dates in the lower Rio Grande Valley and adjacent Mexican territory are established annually after conferences among officials of the two Governments.

Regulatory requirements in the two countries are similar and awareness of needs and results is growing. A program that combines sanitation at gins and other processing plants, treatment of cottonseed, cultural practices, and insecticidal applications has been developed; larger yields of cotton per acre have been achieved by it.

The tremendous increase in cotton acreage in the Matamoros region adjacent to the lower Rio Grande Valley makes a continuation of the cooperative program essential. Otherwise much of the work along the border in the United States would be nullified, because the areas are actually one continuous region whose principal crop is cotton. The pink bollworm does not know what an international boundary is.

L. F. CURL, *formerly leader of the division of pink bollworm control, is now regional director for several insect control programs of the Bureau of Entomology and Plant Quarantine in the Southwest and Mexico. He is a native of Arkansas and a graduate of Mississippi State College.*

R. W. WHITE *is in charge of the pink bollworm control project, in which he began work in 1920. He is a native of Texas and a graduate of Cornell University.*

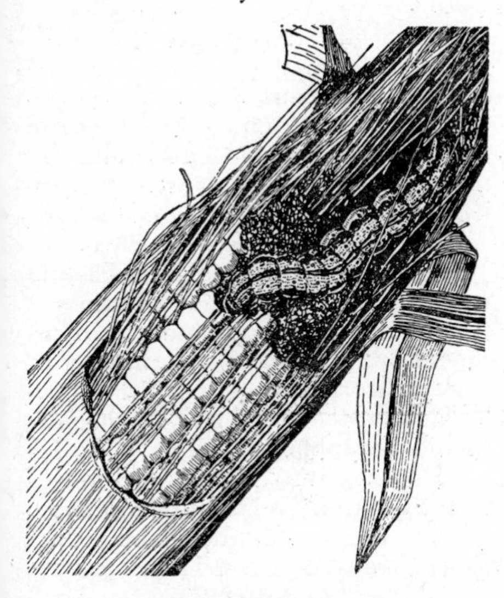

Corn earworm in an ear of corn.

The Bollworm

K. P. Ewing

The bollworm has been known since 1796 as a widely distributed and destructive pest. Unlike the boll weevil and the cotton leafworm, which attack cotton only, it feeds on many cultivated and wild plants—corn, grain sorghums, tomatoes, peas, alfalfa, lespedeza, beans, soybeans, flax, peanuts, and other commercial crops. It has several common names. On cotton it is called the bollworm; on corn, the corn earworm; and on tomatoes, the tomato fruitworm.

It has four stages in its life cycle—egg, larva, pupa, and adult.

The eggs are white, ribbed, dome-shaped, and about half the size of a pinhead. They are laid singly and mostly on the tender growing tips of succulent cotton plants. Sometimes they are deposited on squares, bolls, and stems. In hot weather they hatch in 3 days. A female usually lays about 1,000 eggs.

The larva is the destructive stage. After the egg hatches, the young larva feeds on the nearest tender growth for a day or two and then moves toward the center or bottom of the plant, eating out the squares and tunneling into and eating the contents of the bolls. In color and markings, the larvae range from a pale green through rose and brown to almost black.

The full-grown worm, about 1½ inches long, enters the ground to pupate, and overwinters in this stage. The moths emerge in the spring over a period of a month or two; the number at any one time depends on the locality, temperature, and rainfall. The adult is a yellowish or brownish moth with a wing spread of about 1½ inches. The first-generation moths oviposit on such host plants as clovers, alfalfa, bluebonnets, winter peas, and young corn. The second generation usually comes along in time to infest corn ears. The third and succeeding generations are the ones that ordinarily attack cotton. Often they overlap.

The bollworm is troublesome in Texas, Oklahoma, Louisiana, Arkansas, and Mississippi. Sometimes it reduces the yields in every cotton-growing State. It is hard to control, for it is difficult to kill with insecticides after it has entered the bolls. If control measures are not applied when the larvae are small, considerable loss usually can be expected even when insecticides are used. The presence of an injurious infestation of the bollworm often is not detected until it is too late to get maximum control from the use of insecticides. Many growers therefore fear the bollworm more than any other cotton pest.

At least two other insects, the tobacco budworm and the yellow-striped armyworm, often cause damage to cotton similar to that caused by the bollworm and are often mistaken for it. Some of the failures of the recommended insecticides to control the bollworm may be due to the mistaken identity of the insect against which the control was directed.

Natural enemies often are important in its control or in the reduction of the damage it causes. A heavy egg deposition or hatch of young larvae often fails to develop into a damaging infestation because of parasites and predators. Among the more important predators are *Orius insidiosus* and several species of Coccinellidae and Chrysopidae.

Laboratory tests in 1941 disclosed that 12 species of predaceous insects commonly found on cotton readily fed and survived on bollworm eggs. The populations of beneficial insects vary from field to field and season to season and therefore cannot always be depended on to control developing bollworm infestations.

Insecticides used against other cotton insects also kill the beneficial insects that attack the bollworm. Their use immediately before the time the bollworms usually appear often causes increased infestations of bollworms unless insecticides are also applied later. In Texas, early season applications of insecticides for control of cotton insects are coming into general use. It is recommended that when possible the last of these be timed to come at least a month before the normal occurrence of bollworm infestations. If no insecticides are used on cotton during this period, the beneficial insects will have a chance to reestablish themselves so they can effect some control of the bollworm when it appears.

Cultural practices of use against the bollworm are deep plowing in fall or winter; early planting or use of early maturing varieties of cotton; and thorough preparation and cultivation of the soil to hasten maturity of the crop. The use of trap crops, especially corn, to prevent infestations on cotton has been suggested, but they are not very successful in actual use, partly because farmers hate to destroy the crops early enough to prevent maturity of the worms.

Severe infestations do not occur every year, but some areas, such as central Texas, usually have infestations of some degree annually. The causes are complex and the infestations are therefore impossible to predict. Most localities have a fairly well-defined period when infestations normally occur. Just before that time, growers should inspect their cotton several times a week until the crop matures. They should apply an insecticide when they find bollworm eggs and 4 or 5 small larvae per 100 terminals. Insecticides should be applied at 4- or 5-day intervals until infestations are brought under control. Important are proper timing of the applications and proper coverage of the plants. The worms are easily killed when they are hatching.

Paris green, calcium arsenate, and lead arsenate were used for many years. Cryolite and basic copper arsenate had limited use. Calcium arsenate was fairly effective when heavy dosages were applied at the time the worms were hatching, but was not very effective against heavy infestations of medium or large worms; when heavy aphid populations followed its use, bollworm infestations often increased and yields were reduced.

DDT is the most effective chemical so far used for the bollworm. DDT does not control the boll weevil, the cotton leafworm, or the cotton aphid, however. Because one or more of them often occur in damaging numbers at the time the bollworms occur, it is desirable to use an insecticide that will kill two or more of the insects at once.

A dust mixture containing 3 percent of the gamma isomer of benzene hexachloride, 5 percent of DDT, and 40 percent of sulfur, commonly called 3–5–40, was developed in 1946 for cotton insects. It is one of the best all-purpose insecticides for use on cotton insects.

Another combination of those insecticides, a mixture containing 2 percent of the gamma isomer of benzene hexachloride, 10 percent of DDT, and 40 percent of sulfur (2–10–40), has given excellent control of several pests; in heavy dosages of 15 to 20 pounds per acre it is preferred for extremely heavy infestations of medium- to large-size bollworms.

Toxaphene controls the bollworm, boll weevil, cotton leafworm, cotton fleahopper, fall armyworm, cutworms, thrips, and cotton aphid. It is not recommended as a "knockout" against aphids, but when it is used regularly it will prevent their build-up. As a dust it is used in a mixture containing 20 percent toxaphene, an inert diluent, and 40 percent sulfur and applied at the rate of 10 to 15 pounds per acre, depending on the severity of the infestation.

Other chlorinated hydrocarbons, such as chlordane, aldrin, and heptachlor, which are effective against the boll weevil, are ineffective against the bollworm. Their use alone where bollworms are a problem may result in increased infestations of the latter. In those areas they should be used in mixtures with DDT.

Dieldrin is ineffective against the bollworm at the dosage (0.15 to 0.25 pound per acre) that kills boll weevils. At a higher dosage, 0.5 pound per acre, it is effective but, to lower costs, when boll weevils and bollworms occur simultaneously, DDT should be added and the lower boll weevil dosage applied.

In experiments conducted in 1945, we found that DDT in xylene emulsions applied at rates of 0.8 and 1.6 pounds of DDT per acre, and at a total volume of 3 gallons per acre at each application, gives satisfactory control of bollworms. Because no satisfactory spray material for the boll weevil had been developed at that time, the discovery was not considered highly important. Growers still required dusting equipment to control the boll weevil, and DDT could be applied as a dust for bollworm control, using this equipment.

With the development of toxaphene for boll weevils, more effort was expended to develop spray applications for all cotton insects. Experimental work in 1948 and 1949 developed spray emulsions for this purpose. They have come into common use on many cotton farms. The emulsions are applied as low-volume sprays through ground machines and by airplane. DDT applied as an emulsion gives as good or better bollworm control than if the same quantity is applied as a dust. Its use in spray mixtures with other insecticides, which will control boll weevils and other insects, has become popular. Sprays may be applied under weather conditions in which the effective application of dust materials would be impossible.

K. P. Ewing *is an entomologist in*

the Bureau of Entomology and Plant Quarantine. He was graduated from Mississippi Agricultural and Mechanical College and has been in the Bureau since 1920. In 1933 he was placed in charge of a new laboratory of the division of cotton insect investigations at Port Lavaca, Tex.; in 1939 he became head of the division's new laboratory in Waco, Tex. The laboratory received the Superior Service Award of the Department of Agriculture in 1949.

For further reading:

F. C. Bishopp: The Bollworm or Corn Ear Worm as a Cotton Pest, *U. S. D. A. Farmers' Bulletin 1595, 1929;* The Cotton Bollworm, *with C. R. Jones, U. S. D. A. Farmers' Bulletin 290. 1907.*

K. P. Ewing: Some Factors Influencing Bollworm Populations and Damage, *with E. E. Ivy, Journal of Economic Entomology, volume 36, pages 602–606, 1943;* Early-Season Application of Insecticides for Cotton-Insect Control, *with C. R. Parencia, Jr., Bureau of Entomology and Plant Quarantine publication E–792, 1949;* Cotton-Insect Control with Benzene Hexachloride, Alone or in Mixture with DDT, *with C. R. Parencia, Jr., and E. E. Ivy, Journal of Economic Entomology, volume 40, pages 374–381. 1947.*

E. E. Ivy, in Journal of Economic Entomology: Tests with DDT on the More Important Cotton Insects, *volume 37, page 142, 1944;* A Chlorinated Camphene for Control of Cotton Insects, *with C. R. Parencia, Jr., and K. P. Ewing, volume 40, pages 513–517, 1947;* DDT for Bollworm Control During 1944, *with C. R. Parencia, Jr., R. W. Moreland, and K. P. Ewing, volume 38, pages 534–536. 1945.*

R. W. Moreland and J. C. Gaines: Insecticide Tests for the Control of the Bollworm in 1936, *Journal of Economic Entomology, volume 32, pages 104–106. 1939.*

L. D. Newsom and C. E. Smith: Destruction of Certain Insect Predators by Applications of Insecticides to Control Cotton Pests, *Journal of Economic Entomology, volume 42, pages 904–908. 1949.*

C. R. Parencia, Jr., in Journal of Economic Entomology: Late-Season Control of Boll Weevil and Bollworm with Dusts and Sprays, *with K. P. Ewing, volume 43, pages 593–595, 1950;* Control of Bollworm and Cotton Flea Hopper by DDT, *with E. E. Ivy and K. P. Ewing, volume 39, pages 329–335. 1946.*

Charles V. Riley: Fourth Report of the United States Entomological Commission, *United States Department of Agriculture, 1885.*

Vegetable weevil.

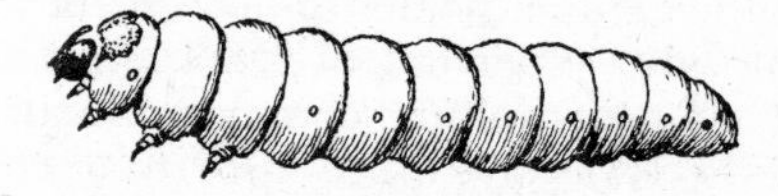

Squash vine borer.

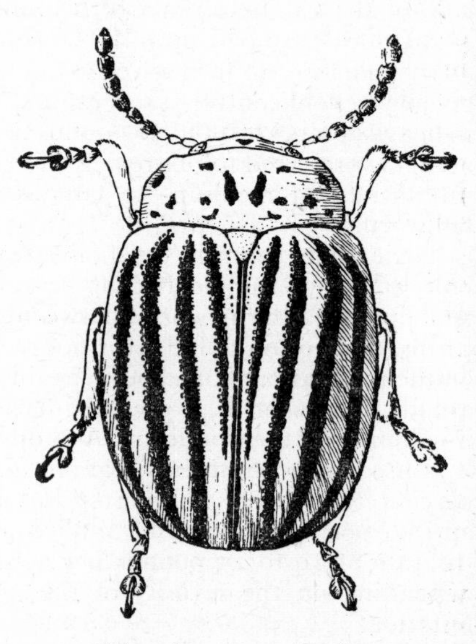

Colorado potato beetle.

Insects and Vegetables

The Potato Psyllid

R. L. Wallis

Psyllid yellows, a disease of potatoes and tomatoes, is due to a substance injected into the plants by the nymphs of the potato psyllid (*Paratrioza cockerelli*) while feeding. The disease, if not controlled, will completely destroy the crops in years when psyllids are abundant. The psyllid is a native of the Western States. It originally subsisted on wild plants of the nightshade family. Soon after people began growing potatoes and tomatoes in the West the potato psyllid adapted itself to those crops and became a pest of economic importance.

The potato psyllid does not injure crops every year. Sometimes it causes total crop failures. In other years the psyllids are so few as to be difficult to find, except at the higher elevations where the cooler climate is more favorable for their development. In 1911 and 1912 a reduction in the potato crop in Colorado to only 35 to 95 bushels an acre was due to the potato psyllid. Earlier the injury to tomatoes was thought to be caused by the direct feeding of the psyllid rather than the disease it transmits. Other epidemics of the psyllid yellows have occurred in 1927–28, 1929–33, 1938–39, and 1949, with a varying degree of injury in the intervening years. Considerable injury is done to potatoes in years of light infestation even though the symptoms of the disease or the effect of direct feeding by the insects are not readily apparent.

The injury to potatoes by psyllid yellows results in an excessive root growth, the production of a large number of small tubers, and a reduction in quality. If infection is severe, all the tubers may be below marketable size. They cannot be stored successfully because their rest period is shortened and they will sprout early. They may even sprout in the ground before harvest.

The first visible symptoms of infection on the above-ground part are an upward curling of the base of the younger leaflets near the top of the plant. As the disease progresses, most of the leaflets turn slightly yellow and the curled parts have purple edges. The leaves finally become leathery, the plant is stunted, and it turns brown and dies. If infestation is light, the plants show no symptoms of disease but the tubers are noticeably smaller in size and yield and the storage qualities of the tubers are poorer.

The injury to tomatoes causes a reduction in the yield and quality of the fruit. Young plants that are attacked may fail to produce any fruits or set only a few, small, yellowish, coarse, and rubbery fruit with a low content of juice.

The symptoms on the tomato plant are a thickening and upward curling of the older leaves. Some purpling of the veins is evident. The leaves are lighter green than normal. The new leaves at the tips of the branches are much smaller in size and give the appearance of a sparsely foliated and stunted plant.

The potato psyllid occurs throughout the continental area west of the 100th meridian, except in Washington, Oregon, and most of Idaho. It has occurred east of that area in the lower Rio Grande River Valley in Texas in small numbers, and in eastern Nebraska and eastern North Dakota to the extent of causing slight injury in some outbreak years.

The greatest injury is caused in Colorado, southern Wyoming, western Nebraska, southeastern Montana, and Utah, particularly at the higher elevations where average summer temperatures range below 70° F. At the lower elevations the July temperatures are usually above 70° and psyllid infestations are retarded in their development. In Texas, New Mexico, and Arizona the insect may cause considerable damage to early spring crops.

THE ADULT or parent potato psyllid is a tiny, delicate insect. When full-grown it is about one-tenth of an inch long. The transparent wings are held at rest in a raised rooflike position over the body. The newly emerged adult is green but after 2 or 3 days becomes black. Its white markings give it a grayish appearance. It has two white marks—a broad transverse one on the first abdominal segment and an inverted V-shaped one on the last abdominal segment. It has strong hind legs, which aid it in taking a quick flight or jump and give it the common name of jumping plant-lice. Mating may take place within a few hours after emergence, and egg laying begins in about 5 days. The females deposit the eggs mostly on the edges or under sides of the leaves in the shady parts of the plants. Egg deposition takes place most freely at temperatures of about 80°. Few eggs are laid at temperatures of 60° or 100°. Each female deposits about 300 eggs during a lifetime at the rate of about 15 a day.

The bright-yellow, oval eggs are about one thirty-second inch long. One end of the eggshell lengthens into a stalk about the length of the egg. It is attached to the leaf and supports the egg. The eggs hatch in 4 to 15 days, depending on the temperature. The flat, scalelike nymph has a row of short hairs around the entire margin of the body. It is roughly elliptical in shape, about one one-hundredth of an inch wide when first hatched, and about one-twentieth of an inch wide when fully grown. In their development the nymphs pass through five stages, becoming progressively larger each time. In the first, they are orange or pale yellow but later they become light green. They complete their nymphal development in 12 to 21 days.

DURING FEEDING the nymphs inject into the potato plant a substance that disturbs the proper relation between the foliage of the plant and the tubers. Tubers developing on the stolons of infected plants cease normal growth. From the eyes of the undersized and immature tubers, short sprouts soon appear. Other small tubers may form on the sprouts. If the psyllid yellows infection continues, the abnormal growth may proceed until a chain of several tubers occurs on one stolon, none of which will be of marketable size. Tubers that have been checked in their growth by drought or by other causes not due to disease and then start growing again ordinarily produce knobby potatoes totally unlike those formed by potato plants infected with the psyllid yellows.

The potato psyllid restricts its feeding almost entirely to the plants of the nightshade family, to which the potato and tomato belong. Its preferred host plants are the ornamental plant known as Chinese lantern (*Physalis francheti*) and horsenettle (*Solanum carolinense*). They feed in considerable numbers also on buffalo-bur (*Solanum rostratum*), several species of groundcherry (*Physalis*), and matrimony-vine (*Lycium*), as well as potatoes and tomatoes. Potato sprouts growing in cull piles bulk large in the spring build-up of psyllid populations in the potato- and tomato-growing areas. Adults have been collected from members of several other species of plants, but only on two species, field bindweed (*Convolvulus arvensis*) and sweetpotato, have occasional eggs and nymphs been found, indicating that the insect can adapt itself to those species when other food plants are not available.

Because of an incorrect identification of the insect, people long believed that the potato psyllid passed the winter in the northern part of its range on cedar trees or other evergreens. Further investigations disclosed, however, that the psyllid on evergreens in the northern areas in winter is a different species. Extensive surveys have revealed no positive evidence that the potato psyllid overwinters in areas where subzero temperatures occur. The surveys have shown, however, that the potato psyllid passes the winter in southern Texas, southern New Mexico, and southern Arizona in an active condition on wild host plants, principally species of wild matrimonyvine. The insect increases in numbers during the spring, but completely disappears therefrom in June, coincidentally with its movement northward, and returns to its southern range in October or November. In the more temperate areas farther north, wild plants also serve as a source of subsistence for psyllids that come from the south in early spring. Late in the spring they move into potato and tomato fields.

A study of the potato psyllid in its overwintering area in southern Texas and southern New Mexico showed that small numbers appeared in the area in November and persisted in the territory bounded, roughly, by Crystal City, Tex., on the south, San Angelo, Tex., on the east, Big Spring, Tex., on the north, and Las Cruces, N. Mex., on the west. It increased in numbers during the late fall and early winter but ceased breeding temporarily during January under the influence of the relatively low temperatures normally prevailing then. In winters when temperatures are above normal, however, such as occurred in the winter of 1949–50, breeding activities continued throughout the winter, as evidenced by the abundance of eggs, nymphs, and adults during this period. In winters of below-normal temperature—such as the winter of 1950–51—the wild plants on which they feed are killed. So are the psyllids. As a result, none could be found on potatoes and tomatoes in northern sections in the summer of 1951.

The movement of the potato psyllid for long distances depends on wind currents. P. A. Glick, of the Bureau of Entomology and Plant Quarantine, has captured this psyllid at elevations of 4,000 feet and in considerable numbers up to 2,000 feet. Prevailing winds during most of the year in the plains east of the mountains from southern Texas and southern New Mexico to northern Colorado are from the south. In Wyoming and Nebraska prevailing winds are from the northwest. That may account for the generally lower populations in the North Platte Valley in Wyoming and Nebraska. When wind currents blow from the south for several days in the spring the movements of the potato psyllid into the North Platte Valley are much faster. Conversely, when the psyllid is moving in Colorado and wind directions are northwest in Wyoming and Nebraska, it reaches those areas in small numbers. The northern Colorado potato-growing area is the center of the summer population—an indication that unfavorable wind currents north of that point greatly retard movements beyond that area.

Three main influences govern outbreaks in the northern potato and tomato districts of Colorado, Wyoming, Nebraska, and Montana—the number of psyllids that move into those districts in the late spring from the southern breeding areas; the direction and velocity of the wind currents, which may aid or limit the movement and the distribution of the moving psyllids in the cultivated districts; and temperature conditions, which may favor or retard the rate and magnitude of the psyllid infestation on the potato and tomato crops. Temperature is probably the most important natural factor. Psyllid populations increase most rapidly at average temperatures between 60° and 70° F. Conversely, temperatures above 70° for only a few days cause a heavy reduction in numbers.

Early crops of potatoes are subject to severe injury because they make the major part of their growth in the spring and early summer during the seasonal period when favorable temperature conditions for psyllid development normally prevail. Temperatures favorable to potatoes are likewise favorable to psyllid development. By the time that high temperatures occur in July the fully grown plants of the early potato crops are large enough to afford considerable shade and thus to protect the psyllids from temperatures above 70°. The later potatoes are planted in the season the less injury they suffer from psyllid infestation. In areas above 6,000 feet elevation the temperatures are low enough so that psyllid infestation can develop uninterruptedly throughout the growing season.

Control can be achieved with chemicals if they are applied properly. A dust containing 5 percent of DDT in sulfur applied at the rate of 25 to 35 pounds per acre, or 2 pounds of 50 percent DDT in 100 gallons of water applied as a spray at the rate of 100 to 125 gallons per acre, is effective. Because the nymphs inhabit the under sides of the potato or tomato leaves, those parts must be covered thoroughly with the insecticide—the duster or sprayer nozzles should be directed upward at a 45° angle from near the ground level and from each side of each row of the plants. On sprayers, a third nozzle should be directed downward on the center of each row of plants; a pressure of 350 pounds or more is necessary to force the spray into the foliage and attain a thorough covering of the leaves.

The first application should be made when the plants are about 6 inches high, except that on early potatoes the first application should be made when the plants are 3 or 4 inches high. When the infestation is light (3 or 4 psyllid adults in 100 sweeps of a standard insect net 15 inches in diameter) two or three applications at intervals of 10 or 14 days will be enough to obtain control. In epidemic years five applications at intervals of 10 or 14 days are needed. In years of heavy infestations it will be necessary also to continue insecticide applications after the vines have grown so large that no open spaces are left between the rows. This may be accomplished, without much injury to the plants, by the use of vine lifters on the spray or dust equipment.

The control of psyllids can be materially aided by the elimination of the spring host plants in both the northern potato and tomato areas. It is impractical to control wild *Lycium* in the southern breeding areas, since it is so abundant and widespread. But cultivated *Lycium* in the northern potato areas, if removed, would eliminate it as a plant on which psyllids collect and breed before the potato crops are growing. It can be easily killed with a herbicide containing 2,4-D. It is hard to kill by grubbing because new plants appear from any roots remaining in the soil.

Potato sprouts in cull piles are also a source of spring breeding of the potato psyllid before potato or tomato crops are growing. These potatoes sprout early and produce a dense growth where the psyllid is protected from adverse weather conditions. The plants developing from the sprouts die in July because of the lack of moisture and plant food. The psyllids then are forced to move to other hosts, particularly early potato crops. The menace caused by the growth of the potato sprouts can easily be prevented by spreading the tubers when they are dumped, so that the piles are not more than one tuber deep. Killing the growing sprouts with chemicals or plant-growth regulators is too expensive and slow to be of much benefit in preventing the spring breeding of psyllids.

Late planting of potatoes, where practicable, will avoid serious injury by the potato psyllid—only 30 to 40 percent as many adults of the psyllid are found on potatoes planted after June 10 in western Nebraska as on those planted before May 20.

Parasites and predators have some effect in keeping psyllids in check. The hymenopterous parasite, *Tetrastichus triozae,* has been found parasitizing many psyllid nymphs, in some seasons, particularly in the fall of the year, but their build-up in numbers is too late in the season to be of much benefit in controlling the psyllid. Another hymenopterous parasite, *Metaphycus psyllidis,* is reported to be effective in keeping psyllids in check in southern California. The larvae and adults of the convergent lady beetle and closely related species are predators on psyllid nymphs. The larvae of several species of *Chrysopa* are predaceous on the psyllid adults and nymphs. The bigeyed bug, *Geocoris decoratus,* as well as *Nabis ferus,* are also predators of psyllid adults and nymphs.

R. L. WALLIS *is an entomologist in the division of truck crop and garden insect investigations, Bureau of Entomology and Plant Quarantine. He was graduated from the Colorado State College of Agriculture in 1927 and has been in the Bureau since 1928. He has worked on the gypsy moth in New England, bean insects in New Mexico and Colorado, and potato insects in Colorado, Wyoming, and Nebraska.*

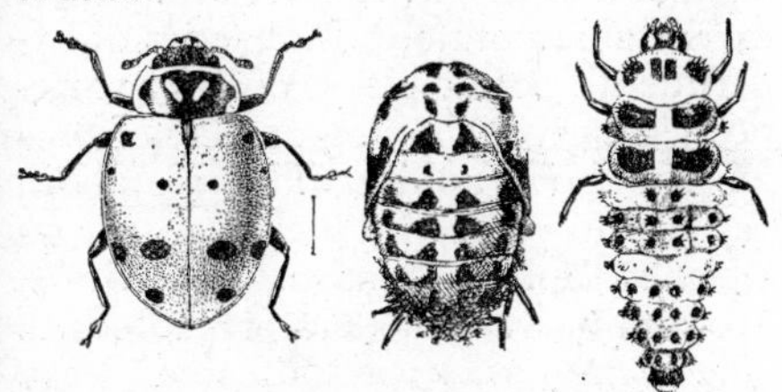

Adult, pupa, and larva of the convergent lady beetle.

Potato Aphids

W. A. Shands, B. J. Landis

Four species of aphids commonly attack potatoes: The buckthorn aphid, the green peach aphid, the potato aphid, and the foxglove aphid.

All attack potatoes in New England, but only the green peach aphid and the potato aphid are pests of potatoes in some areas of the Western States. In the wingless form the aphids usually are green or yellowish green. The winged form may vary from green tinged with brown to completely black. They reproduce rapidly under favorable conditions. A few aphids per plant may increase to such a degree that they cover the leaves of the plant in a few weeks.

All four species can transmit potato virus diseases when they feed. The winged aphids can infect more plants over a wider range than the wingless forms. The greatest spread of some of the virus diseases follows the periods when large numbers of aphids fly into, within, and between the potato fields in midsummer. Most important among the diseases are spindle tuber, mild mosaic, rugose mosaic, and leaf roll, the worst. Under natural conditions leaf roll is spread only by aphids.

All these diseases affect yields. If all plants in a field are diseased, the marketable yields may be reduced 20 to 100 percent. Spindle tuber causes the tubers to become elongate with growth malformations about the eyes. Leaf roll disease causes an internal dark netting—net necrosis—within the flesh of some varieties; the defect in even a small percentage of the tubers lowers the market grade of the entire crop.

Virus diseases of the potato first attracted attention in Europe about 1770. The progressive deterioration of potato crops was generally regarded then as a weakening or running out of the seed stocks. Before 1913 no distinctions were draw between leaf roll and other potato virus diseases; in 1920 scientists learned that aphids transmit leaf roll. In 1937 a serious outbreak of the green peach aphid in Maine was accompanied by an unusual spread of leaf roll. Yields were reduced and few seed stocks were sufficiently free of the disease for further propagation. Because nearly half of the certified seed stocks in the United States were grown in Maine at that time, many eastern gardeners, truck farmers, and potato growers could get no good planting stock.

In 1940, men in the Department of Agriculture began to cooperate with those of the Maine Agricultural Experiment Station, which had been engaged in aphid research for many years, in an investigation of the aphid problem on potatoes in northeastern Maine. Their studies of the biology and control of aphids in large measure have led to the production of better seed potatoes and increased yields of table-stock potatoes.

In 1938 leaf roll occurred in damaging amounts in Washington. Until that time the green peach aphid had not been recognized as an important pest of potatoes in that State. Widespread losses from 1941 to 1949 were accompanied by unusually large populations of the green peach aphid. In 1947 the Department, the Washington Agricultural Experiment Station, and the Washington Department of Agriculture began an investigation of aphids on potatoes in central Washington.

Climate determines the period during which potatoes can be grown and also whether other host plants, which are essential to the survival of the aphid, may occur in the region. Aphids generally require more than one kind of host plant, cultivated or wild, for existence. In areas where climatic conditions are unsatisfactory for the growth of the host plants aphids are not usually a factor in potato production. In Maine the climate favors the growth of host plants of the green peach aphid, the potato aphid, the buckthorn aphid, and the foxglove aphid. In Washington the buckthorn aphid is not a pest of potatoes because of the lack of its primary host plant, and the foxglove aphid has shown little inclination to adopt the potatoes to gain a beachhead.

These species are not all equally important in spreading the virus diseases, but all have been reported to be carriers of leaf roll. The potato aphid is of little moment as a carrier of leaf roll, but it transmits mild mosaic and it can spread spindle tuber from plant to plant. The buckthorn aphid transmits leaf roll but is of minor importance in its spread because of its sedentary habits. The foxglove aphid is an important vector of leaf roll but has a relatively limited occurrence on potatoes, except in Maine. The green peach aphid is the most important vector of leaf roll and also transmits rugose mosaic, mild mosaic, and spindle tuber. In Maine and Washington the greatest spread of leaf roll has occurred in seasons when the green peach aphid was abundant. Considerable variation in the annual abundance and the relative numbers of the various kinds of aphids present on potatoes has been observed. Without regard to their ability to carry disease, the buckthorn aphid in Maine and the green peach aphid in Washington usually are the most abundant species on potatoes.

A reduction in yield from aphid feeding in Maine results chiefly from a reduction in the number and size of marketable potatoes. In a series of experiments, potato plants of three varieties were given varying degrees of protection from aphids. The Katahdin variety proved to be the most susceptible to aphid damage. The Green Mountain was moderately affected. The Chippewa was affected least. From the standpoint of plant appearance, Kennebec seemed to be suscepible to aphid damage in 1950, but at harvest we found that the yield was reduced only to a degree comparable to that in Chippewas. Protection from aphids increased the yield of No. 1

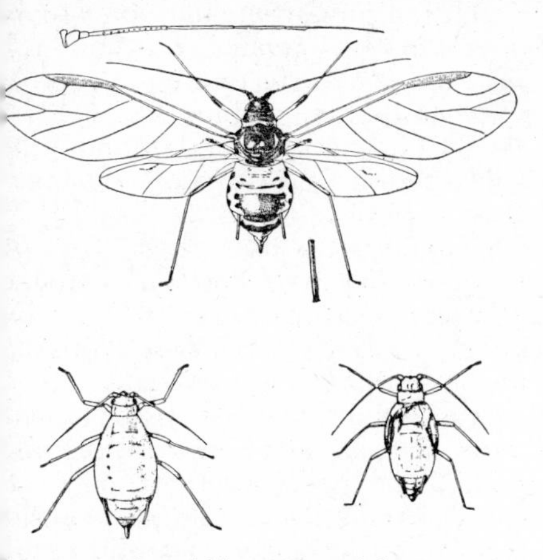

Green peach aphid. Winged form at top; wingless form below at left; last instar nymph at right. (All about 15 times natural size.)

grade potatoes considerably. Increased yields of the Green Mountain could be attributed about equally to an increase in the number of tubers reaching grade size and to an increase in the size of tubers within that grade. In Chippewa about 25 percent of the increase in yield was the result of the increase in numbers of tubers that reached the grade size and 75 percent to the increase in size.

Greater direct losses from aphid feeding occur in Washington in the White Rose variety than in the Russet Burbank. Both are susceptible to leafroll infection, but the greater losses occur in Russet Burbank. White Rose is grown mainly for an early crop, Russet Burbank for a late crop. The amount of damage in the late crop depends largely on the amount of leaf roll and the number of aphids that develop in the early crop.

Studies with the Green Mountain, Katahdin, and Chippewa varieties in Maine showed that leading factors in the rate of leaf roll spread in plots of the three varieties were the numbers of aphids feeding on the plants and the amount of leaf roll present in the planting stock. In Green Mountains and Chippewas the amount of leaf roll spread was in proportion to the size of population of wingless and winged aphids allowed to develop within the plots, but in Katahdins, leaf roll was spread principally by winged aphids that developed elsewhere and flew into the plots.

In the Southern States, the females of the green peach aphid propagate by depositing young aphids, most of which develop into wingless females during much of the year, on various host plants. Winged females, however, are produced at intervals; they serve primarily as a means of transfer to progressively younger crops. In Maine and Washington, where winter temperatures prevent aphid development, the aphids survive the winter in the egg stage. In Maine some of the winged females produced in August, September, and October fly to primary hosts, where wingless females capable of laying eggs are produced. Males appear from August to November and fertilize the females. The females then lay the overwintering eggs on the buds and bark of the trees.

The aphid eggs hatch in late February and March in Washington. In Maine they hatch in late April and early May. From then until the following fall, all the individuals produced are females.

Starting with the eggs that hatch in the spring, several generations of the green peach aphid are produced on the peach or wild plum trees. In Maine some of the aphids of the second generation and most of those of the third generation are winged; they leave the wild plum trees and relocate on summer host plants, such as weeds and potatoes, where successive generations, mainly wingless, are produced until fall. In Washington, however, the winged forms appear first in the third generation on peach trees, and the production of winged aphids continues through each successive generation until fall.

In Maine when the spring migrations start before potatoes are up, as frequently happens, the migrant aphids land chiefly on weeds, where they continue to breed. Winged aphids developing here soon infest potatoes. If diseased potato plants are present, the aphids become infected and carry the disease from plant to plant as they breed and feed through the season.

In Washington the winged spring migrant aphids fly to weeds and various spring crops, including potatoes, where wingless aphids are produced. In July and August large numbers of the winged aphids appear and fly to younger plants, including late-crop potatoes. Winged and wingless forms are produced on the potato crop until fall. As in Maine, most of the leaf roll spread occurs in summer during the period when winged aphids are dispersing.

Aphids can overwinter in the egg on only a few kinds of plants. Although the green peach aphid propagates abundantly on the pin cherry (*Prunus pensylvanica*) and the common chokecherry (*P. virginiana*) during the fall in northeastern Maine, colonies of the aphids have never been found on them in the spring. In this region the Canada plum (*P. nigra*) is the only recognized primary host. The buckthorn aphid overwinters primarily on the alder buckthorn (*Rhamnus alnifolia*). The potato aphid overwinters chiefly on wild roses, of which the most important in northeastern Maine is *Rosa palustris*. The foxglove aphid is known to overwinter on common foxglove (*Digitalis purpurea*), which is rare in northeastern Maine—the aphid propagates locally on some unrecognized host or utilizes foxglove in areas far removed from the potato districts and later flies into potato fields.

In Washington the peach (*Prunus persica*) is the principal primary host of the green peach aphid. The wild rose is a primary host of the potato aphid but is never abundantly populated.

The aphids may utilize many kinds of plants as secondary hosts, none of which can support greater populations or occurs in greater concentration than the potato. Second to potatoes as summer hosts of aphids are weeds—chiefly, in northeastern Maine, the wild radish (*Raphanus raphanistrum*), bird rape (*Brassica campestris*), bristlestem hempnettle (*Galeopsis tetrahit*), curltop ladysthumb (*Polygonum lapathifolium*), lambsquarters goosefoot (*Chenopodium album*), sheep sorrel (*Rumex acetosella*), and oxeye daisy (*Chrysanthemum leucanthemum* var. *pinnatifidum*). The green peach aphid propagates abundantly on all except sheep sorrel and oxeye daisy, but wild radish and bird rape are the most important. The potato aphid propagates most abundantly on lambsquarters goosefoot, hempnettle, and curltop ladysthumb. The foxglove aphid propagates most abundantly on hempnettle, curltop ladysthumb, and bird rape. The buckthorn aphid propagates on all of the weeds mentioned as aphid hosts.

The most important weed hosts of the green peach aphid in Washington are lambsquarters goosefoot, tumble mustard (*Sisymbrium altissima*), amaranth (*Amaranthus*), shepherdspurse (*Capsella bursa-pastoris*), a low-growing nightshade (*Solanum villosum*), and the cultivated sugar beet (*Beta vulgaris*).

Weeds in Maine ordinarily appear earlier in the spring than potatoes. Spring migrations of aphids often start before potatoes are up and the winged aphids begin to propagate on the nearest available host plants. Weeds growing in crops are soon subjected to severe competition from the crops, especially close-growing ones such as oats, English peas, clover, and potatoes. Under those conditions, winged aphids soon mature on the weed hosts and the aphids fly to potatoes or to othe weeds growing in more favorable locations. A large percentage of the young aphids deposited by winged migrant potato aphids on weeds in oat fields in Maine are destined to become winged adults. Summer dispersal forms of this aphid therefore are on the wing within 2 weeks after the spring migration begins. By contrast, the summer dispersal forms of the green peach aphid normally start to mature on weeds in oats about 3 weeks after the spring migration. The spindling, small-leafed plants that are able to survive in close-growing crops usually do not support large numbers of aphids and are suitable as hosts for a relatively short time. The importance of weeds in this kind of environment lies chiefly in the fact that winged aphids that develop on them move to and infest potatoes early in the summer. Frequently this is an outstanding initial infestation source of potatoes by the green peach aphid.

Weeds that grow in wasteland have less competition than those in close-growing crops; the larger plants can support greater numbers of aphids. The period of aphid propagation is longer and the numbers of winged and wingless aphids produced is much greater than for those in close-growing crops. In central Washington, where irrigation is necessary for the production of crops, the time during which aphids are produced on weeds in wasteland and in the foothills depends upon the time and abundance of rain in the spring. In northeastern Maine we find considerable year-to-year variation in the use of various weeds as hosts. For example, the oxeye daisy and sheep sorrel were major hosts of the buckthorn aphid in 1942 but have been utilized much less since then. Oxeye daisy is a favored host in years when the spring migration of the buckthorn aphid starts early and the plant is in the bud stage when the migration begins. Since 1942 hempnettle, curltop ladysthumb, and the wild radish have exceeded oxeye daisy or sheep sorrel as hosts of the aphid.

Many factors affect the importance of weeds in wastelands as secondary hosts of the aphids in Maine. Weeds germinating early in July produce more aphids than earlier germinating ones. On the other hand, small numbers of winged aphids produced early on the early weeds augment the aphid populations on potatoes in time to influence materially the peak numbers to develop on potatoes; those that develop on late weeds do not reach potatoes in time to influence appreciably the population trends on potatoes. The smaller and younger weeds produce winged aphids in a shorter time after being infested than larger and older weeds. Soil moisture and air temperature influence the time, rate, and the extent of development of weeds and aphids. Other factors include the relative numbers of spring migrants coming from primary hosts, the relation of time of spring migration to the time of weed germination, and the relative abundance of each kind of weed.

FLIGHT HABITS of the aphids have been studied in Maine for several years. One type of trap used in the studies has an opening 19½ inches wide. The traps are placed 12.5 feet above ground and are in use from early spring until late fall. Frequently they have detected the spring and fall movements of the aphids before the migrations were detected from examinations of plants. They show the time and duration of aphid flights, the numbers involved, and the proportions of the various aphids. The records are of value in the timing of aphicides and have other uses, such as indicating when to kill tops of potatoes grown for seed.

In a year of heavy aphid migration, a maximum daily catch of 23,641 winged aphids of the species that affect potatoes was recorded from a single trap. Since the general use of aphicides on potatoes began, however, fewer winged aphids have been collected in the traps and the duration of aphid flights also has been less than before.

A series of the traps was placed at

heights up to 30 feet. Many aphids were taken at 30 feet—about as many as at 5 feet, but the bulk of the green peach aphids was collected at 15 and 20 feet, and the potato aphid at 20 and 25 feet. The bulk of the buckthorn aphids was taken at 10 and 15 feet.

In central Washington we learned that there are three periods of flight of the green peach aphid. Parts of the periods overlap, however, and at least a few winged aphids may be found on potatoes throughout the growing season. The spring migration starts during the first week of May and continues to be fairly heavy until the first week of June. The extremely heavy summer dispersal starts during the last few days of June or the first half of July and continues in considerable volume until some time in August. The fall migration starts about September 15 and continues at a moderate rate until frost kills potatoes and other tender host plants. Winged and wingless aphids have been found on rutabagas as late as November 17.

In Maine the several species of aphids do not begin their fall migration at the same time. Winged buckthorn aphids start returning to overwintering hosts from August 10 to 15 and the flight has continued in some years as late as October 12. The potato aphid begins its fall migration August 20 to 25 and winged aphids have been taken in traps as late as October 8. The green peach aphid usually begins its fall migration August 28 to September 15. Winged aphids have been taken as late as October 16. The foxglove aphid seldom produces fall migrants in northeastern Maine.

Surveys of the abundance of aphid eggs on primary hosts were made in the spring and fall for 10 years in Maine. Great variation in the abundance of eggs on the host plants was observed from year to year—from none to several hundred per 6 inches of twig. Ordinarily many of the eggs laid in the fall shrivel and die during the fall and winter. Birds destroy others. We noted some relation between the number of viable eggs found in the spring and the size of the aphid population that develops on the primary hosts.

In years of heavy fall migration of the green peach aphid to peach trees in central Washington, a maximum average of 20 aphid eggs per 6 inches of twig was found in some orchards. Collections of eggs made during the winter failed to show that any of these were parasitized.

NATURAL CONTROL by insect parasites and predators, fungus diseases, and weather operate in various combinations to reduce aphid populations or retard their propagation. These beneficial influences rarely control the aphids to a point where some damage does not occur, however. Before the time when aphicides were generally applied to potatoes, the differences in yields that occurred from year to year were ascribed largely to differences in the effectiveness of the natural controls.

Several kinds of insect parasites attack aphids in Maine and Washington. They exert a restraining influence, but they seldom eradicate the aphids. In Maine we have seen instances where parasites have controlled the buckthorn aphid on its primary host in the spring. Ordinarily the potato aphid is parasitized to a greater extent than the other aphids on potatoes in Maine. In 1950, for the first time, parasitized buckthorn aphids were found occasionally on potatoes throughout the summer.

The larvae and adults of lady beetles are the most abundant and effective predators of aphids in Maine and Washington. *Hippodamia convergens*, *H. parenthesis*, and *Coccinella transversoguttata* are most abundant in central Washington. Other predators are the larvae of syrphid flies (Syrphidae) and of lacewings (Chrysopidae). Sometimes syrphid larvae become abundant enough to reduce the populations of aphids on the summer hosts and (when lady beetles and other predators also are present in large numbers) the aphid populations on potatoes have been virtually obliterated. However, that has never been observed until large populations of aphids have developed.

Fungus diseases sometimes help control the green peach aphid, the potato aphid, and the foxglove aphid in Maine, but rarely in central Washington. The diseases are most effective late in the summer and at times have practically eradicated populations of these aphids in Maine. Under favorable conditions the diseases take their toll of aphids within a few days. In Maine the most abundant disease is *Empusa aphidis*. Less abundant are *Empusa sphaerosperma* and *Entomophthora coronata*.

WEATHER is the major natural agency of control but is seldom so bad that infestations of aphids are completely eliminated. Its effects, rather, are to assist or hinder in varying degrees the aphids in reaching their greatest productivity. The spring migrant aphids ordinarily leave the primary host soon after they mature. Wet, cool, and windy weather prevents the migration, and many aphids die on the primary host when there are several consecutive days of unfavorable weather. In Washington, periods of dry, hot weather also are responsible for the death of large numbers of winged and wingless aphids.

Wind direction and velocity during the spring migration influence the degree of successful transfer of aphids from primary to secondary hosts—particularly true of the small buckthorn aphid, which ordinarily is most abundant on potatoes near its primary host but may be irregularly distributed and of variable abundance in fields far removed from the primary host.

Heavy, gusty, beating rains dislodge many aphids from the plants, kill them outright, or entangle them with mud. Such developments early in the summer delay the time when the aphids reach their greatest abundance. That can be a big factor in determining the maximum number of aphids that may develop on a potato plant and also the length of time during which the plant will be infested with large numbers of aphids. A delay in Maine in the time of development of large numbers of aphids on potatoes, especially during the time when the tubers are growing rapidly, can greatly influence the yields.

BEFORE the Second World War, some nicotine and rotenone were used on potatoes against aphids. Both were expensive.

The first use of DDT on potatoes in Maine and Washington gave promising results. In 1946 most of the potato acreage in Maine received 2 to 10 applications of fungicidal sprays containing DDT. In 1947 practically the entire potato acreage in the Yakima Valley, Wash., was dusted with DDT. The use of DDT or some other aphicide has since become standard practice. The number of applications to potatoes has increased each year, until in 1950 an average of eight was made in Maine and four in Washington.

The increased use of insecticides on potatoes in Maine has meant large increases in yields. In the 10 years before 1946, the average yield was 277 bushels an acre. In 1946 it was 355 bushels and in 1950, 480 bushels. These increases largely have been due to better control of aphids.

Ordinarily the insecticides are applied with ground machinery and in spray or dust form with or without fungicides, as conditions may require. In Maine both spraying and dusting are effective. In Washington dusting is preferred because it is faster.

EITHER EMULSIFIABLE DDT concentrates or DDT wettable powders can be used in preparing sprays for potatoes. For DDT concentrates, a sufficient amount of the material is mixed in 100 gallons of spray to provide a half pound of DDT in the spray mixture. For wettable DDT powders, enough of the powder is washed

970134°—52——35

through a screen into the spray tank to provide 2 pounds of DDT in the spray mixture. DDT deteriorates rapidly in alkaline mixtures but may be used with bordeaux mixture if the spray is applied immediately after the DDT is added. DDT is compatible with neutral copper compounds, organic fungicides, and oil solvents. The sprays are applied at the rate of 125 gallons an acre.

In Maine the effectiveness of DDT dusts has been increased by the addition of a small amount of a relatively nonvolatile oil. Nonoiled dusts should contain 5 percent of DDT; if approximately 4 percent of oil is added during the mixing, the amount of DDT required may be reduced to 3 percent. A DDT-impregnated dust mixture is satisfactory when it contains 2 percent of DDT and 4 percent of oil. DDT may be included in non-oiled copper-lime dust mixtures only if the dusts are applied immediately after mixing. Dusts are applied at the rate of 30 to 35 pounds per acre depending upon the size of the potato plants.

PARATHION and some of the other organic phosphates are proving to be powerful aphid killers, but they must be handled and applied with great caution. Excellent control of the aphids can be obtained by applying sprays containing in each 100 gallons of the mixture as little as one-half pound of a 15 percent parathion wettable powder or one-half pint of a 25 percent parathion emulsifiable concentrate. The aphid-control value of some organic phosphates is reduced when put into an alkaline spray mixture such as bordeaux.

Trials conducted in Washington have shown that dusts containing 5 percent of DDT and at least 50 percent of dusting sulfur are superior to 5 percent of DDT dusts without sulfur against the green peach aphid. In 1950 and 1951 a dust containing 5 percent of DDT, 50 percent of sulfur, and 0.5 percent of parathion was more effective than a DDT-sulfur dust and is recommended for the control of aphids on potatoes.

The aphid killers are most effective when the potato foliage is completely covered by the spray or dust. For that, efficient, well-adjusted machinery is needed. In spraying, best coverage is obtained with a spray boom equipped with the dropped type of nozzles. In dusting, one or two nozzles should be directed on each row and set in such a way that the dust will be driven into the plants from the top or from each side of the row. A trailing apron, 6 to 15 feet long, of canvas or duck cloth, and attached to the duster boom, confines the dust about the plants momentarily and improves the coverage of the plants.

IT IS BEST to start the applications as soon as the potato plants appear above ground. In Maine applications should be made every week. In Washington applications seldom can be made more frequently than every 8 to 12 days because of conflicts with irrigation of the crop. The use of vine-lifter attachments enables one to continue applications without damage throughout the growing period.

Besides using aphid killers, it is well to kill the weed hosts that grow in crops and wasteland. Aphids do not carry leafroll and other virus diseases unless they feed on diseased plants. The use of the best seed potatoes available, early roguing out of all diseased plants, early harvesting of seed potatoes, and effective aphid control should prevent severe outbreaks of leaf roll in the future.

W. A. SHANDS, *an entomologist of the Bureau of Entomology and Plant Quarantine since 1929, since 1940 has studied the seasonal movements and habits of aphids that attack potatoes in Maine and the development of control measures. Previously he engaged in investigations on the beet leafhopper in Utah, Colorado, and Arizona and tobacco insects in North Carolina and was assistant leader of the division of truck crop and garden insect investigations in Washington, D. C. He is a graduate of Clemson Agricultural College and did graduate work in the University of Minnesota.*

B. J. LANDIS, *entomologist of the Bureau of Entomology and Plant Quarantine since 1928, has conducted investigations on the habits and control of aphids, flea beetles, and other insects affecting potatoes in Washington since 1940. He also has studied the Mexican bean beetle and other insects affecting vegetables in Ohio and in Mexico, insects affecting raspberries and blackberries, and the European earwig. He is a graduate of Miami University. He did graduate work at Ohio State University.*

For further reading on the potato aphids the authors suggest:

Bureau of Entomology and Plant Quarantine publication ET–196, An Aphid Trap, *by W. A. Shands, G. W. Simpson, and F. H. Lathrop. 1942.*

In Agricultural Engineering: An Improved Sprayer Boom for Potatoes and Other Row Crops, *by John W. Slosser, volume 26, pages 453–455. 1945.*

In the Journal of Agricultural Research: The Production of Alate Forms of Myzus persicae on Brassica campestris in the Greenhouse, *by W. A. Shands and G. W. Simpson, volume 76, pages 165–173. 1948.*

In the Journal of Economic Entomology: Brassica campestris L. and Raphanus raphanistrum L. as Breeding Hosts of the Green Peach Aphid, *by W. A. Shands, T. E. Bronson, and G. W. Simpson, volume 35, pages 791–792, 1942;* Control of Aphids on Potatoes in Northeastern Maine, *by T. E. Bronson, Floyd F. Smith, and G. W. Simpson, volume 39, pages 189–194, 1946.*

Maine Agricultural Experiment Station Bulletins: 469, Maine Potato Diseases, Insects, and Injuries, *by Donald Folsom, G. W. Simpson, and Reiner Bonde, 1949; 470,* Progress on Some Important Insect and Disease Problems of Irish Potato Production in Maine, *by G. W. Simpson and W. A. Shands, 1949; 480,* Control of Aphids on Potatoes with DDT when Used With Fungicides, *by W. A. Shands, G. W. Simpson, P. M. Lombard, R. M. Cobb, and P. H. Lung. 1950.*

Maine Agricultural College Extension Bulletins: 333, Weeds and the Aphid-Leafroll Problem in Potatoes, *and 361 (revised),* How to Use DDT on Maine Potatoes, *by G. W. Simpson, W. A. Shands, and O. L. Wyman. 1945 and 1952.*

Sweetpotato Weevil

R. A. Roberts

The sweetpotato weevil occurs in parts of Alabama, Florida, Georgia, Louisiana, Mississippi, South Carolina, and Texas. Very likely it is of Asiatic origin. Our first record of it in this country was in 1875 in Louisiana.

The adult weevil is about one-fourth inch long and resembles a large ant. The head, snout, and wing covers are a dark, metallic blue. The prothorax and legs are reddish orange. The adult has well-developed wings and is capable of limited flight. The small eggs are yellowish white. The larvae are white, legless grubs about three-eighths inch long. The pupa is white and somewhat smaller.

The adult places its eggs in small cavities, which it punctures in the stem of the plant near the ground or directly into the sweetpotato. The eggs hatch in about a week. Then the grubs feed in the vine or potato for 2 or 3 weeks. The pupa is formed within the vine or stem or within the potato and this stage lasts a week or longer, after which the adult emerges. The adult may live for several months. The time required for the development of all the stages varies according to the season or the conditions under which potatoes are stored. In a year six to eight generations may be produced.

The adult weevils damage sweetpotato plants by feeding on leaves, vines, and roots and by pitting the potatoes with feeding and egg-deposition cavities. The larvae, which feed in both the vines and the potatoes, do the most injury. Men of the Louisiana State University and the State Extension Service estimated the loss to the commercial crop of sweetpotatoes in Louisiana in 1946 to be nearly 3 million dollars.

In 1950 this loss was reduced to 250 thousand dollars. Growers of sweetpotato plants in Georgia in 1945 had losses of about 1 million dollars. Eradication measures have prevented subsequent severe losses to these plant growers. The weevils even in light infestations can cause great damage because they can impart a bitter taste to the sweetpotato after only slight feeding and thus destroy much of its value.

CONTROL OR ERADICATION depends on strict adherence to the recommended procedures and constant care by the grower to prevent reinfestation. The principle of control is to deny the weevil the host plants in which to feed. Strict sanitary, cultural, and storage practices are required. The use of insecticides to destroy and prevent weevil populations helps.

In areas of noncommercial sweetpotato production where weevil infestations are light and where nonplanting zones can be established, the weevil can be eradicated if it is deprived of its food for about a year. If weevils are found on a property no sweetpotatoes should be bedded, grown, or stored within a zone extending ½ to 1 mile from the point of infestation. The procedure has resulted in eradication of the weevil when practiced on a single farm or on a community basis.

When a nonplanting zone is established, all remaining sweetpotatoes in the zone should be disposed of by February 1 (or earlier, if possible) by dehydration, feeding to livestock, or burning. The place where the potatoes were stored should be thoroughly cleaned and the debris burned. Thereupon the storages should be dusted with a 10 percent DDT dust at the rate of 1 pound to each 1,600 square feet of surface area. A spray may be used, consisting of 8 pounds of 50 percent DDT wettable powder to 100 gallons of water, applied 1.5 gallons to each 1,000 square feet. The treatment will eliminate any remaining weevils.

Potatoes still in the ground when the infestation is found should be removed from the premises at harvesttime and disposed of in such a way as to prevent infestation of other properties. None should be stored within the restricted zone. Before the potatoes are plowed out, vines should be cut off at the surface of the ground and burned when dry. All potato roots, crowns, small sweetpotatoes, and scraps in the field should be destroyed by cultivation and by grazing livestock on the field after harvest. The old potato field should be plowed at least twice during the winter in order to expose any roots or potatoes missed. No volunteer sweetpotato plants should be permitted in the field or elsewhere on the property. These may be grubbed out or destroyed with a weed killer.

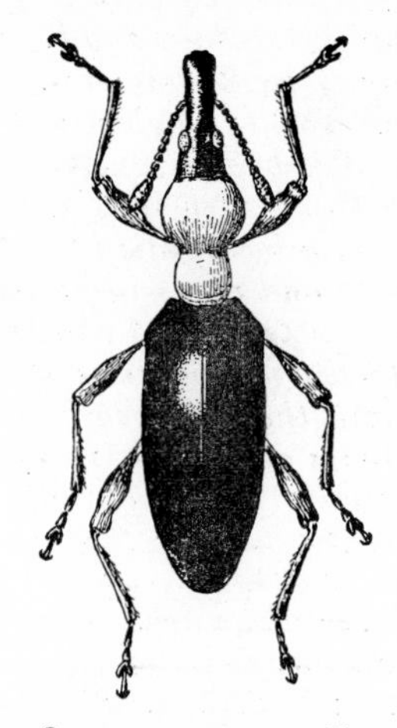

Sweetpotato weevil.

After the end of the 1-year nonplanting period, potatoes may be grown again. In the new plantings in zones that have been out of production, it is important that weevil-free planting stock be used.

In areas generally infested with weevils and in places where the extent of commercial potato production does not warrant the establishment of nonplanting zones, effective control can be had by following recommended control, cultural, and sanitary practices.

Planting stock of either plant slips or seed potatoes should be obtained from sources certified as weevil-free or from known weevil-free areas. If seed is selected locally at harvesttime in generaly infested areas, however, the potatoes should be treated thoroughly with 10 percent DDT dust applied at the rate of 1 pound to 6 to 8 bushels of seed. The treatment will prevent the establishment of infestation within the seed and kill any already existing weevils if they emerge from the potatoes.

Sweetpotato parts and scraps should be removed from the field after harvest. Storage banks or houses should be cleaned and sprayed with DDT as soon as potatoes are removed. Fields previously planted to sweetpotatoes should be plowed at least twice during the winter and all volunteer sweetpotato plants destroyed.

The sites for seedbeds should be located on land that was not planted in potatoes the previous year. Fields to be planted in potatoes should be removed as far as possible from the seedbed and be located preferably on land which had not been planted to potatoes the previous season. Plants and tubers in the seedbed or mother rows should be destroyed as soon as sufficient plants have been produced.

The storage of sweetpotatoes in commercial kilns used to be a problem because of the spread of weevils from infested potatoes to noninfested potatoes in storage and the dispersal of large numbers of adult weevils at the end of the storage period from the kilns to adjacent planted fields. A new treatment for stored table-stock potatoes does much to solve the problem. Visibly infested potatoes are culled out and the potatoes to be stored are then dusted with 10 percent DDT dust. An inexpensive duster, operated on the principle of an air blower, is used that can treat a crate at a time at the rate of about 600 crates an hour. Only one-twentieth of a pound of dust is applied to a crate. The treatment will not destroy weevils already in the potatoes, but it will kill all adults upon emergence and prevent any spread of the infestation. It is desirable also to dust or spray the kiln with DDT before the crated potatoes are stored.

SWEETPOTATO WEEVILS also develop in certain morningglories and related plants of the genus *Ipomoea*. The insect-host relationship is not entirely clear, but apparently the wild seaside and marsh morningglories are important as hosts. Certain of the cultivated morningglories may have to be considered in eradication projects that involve urban districts. The weevil breeds in the seaside morningglory (*Ipomoea littoralis*), but chemical weed killers will control the plant. Infestation of the marsh morningglory (*Ipomoea sagittata*) is rarer, but the species may harbor the weevil enough to permit reinfestation of potatoes grown following the termination of a nonplanting period in an eradication area. These two wild morningglories are found only in limited sections of the sweetpotato-growing areas, mostly in the coastal and tide-marsh margins. In controlling the plants with a herbicide, it is desirable that DDT be included in the spray. The DDT will kill any weevils present or those that might emerge from the plants before the action of the herbicide is complete.

THE SUCCESS OF A CAMPAIGN against the weevil depends largely on the cooperation of every grower, packer, and storage operator. Programs to inform all individuals of the aims of the campaign in areas of commercial potato production in Louisiana have helped greatly in getting full support. The keystone of the endeavor is a county or parish committee of growers, storage operators, dealers, representatives of civic and other organizations, and public officials. The committees sponsor meetings of growers and school groups to discuss the problem and methods. Exhibits and publicity material are presented by Extension Service specialists, county agents, and State and Federal agricultural workers.

For some years the States infested by the weevil have maintained quarantines to prevent spread of the pest to weevil-free areas within the infested States as well as to noninfested States. The enforcement of the quarantines is primarily a responsibility and function of State plant quarantine officials but the Bureau of Entomology and Plant Quarantine aids in the enforcement as a means of assistance in the eradication and control work. The quarantines of infested States and noninfested States regulate the movement of sweetpotato plants and parts thereof (including vine cuttings, slips, and potatoes), other species of *Ipomoea,* and other plants that may be found to be hosts of the sweetpotato weevil.

Fumigation with methyl bromide or another approved treatment is required for the movement of table-stock potatoes from any of the infested areas to any of the States maintaining quarantines. The sweetpotato-producing States have additional regulations pertaining to the certification and movement of seed potatoes and plants.

From the beginning of the cooperative Federal-State eradication and control work, Federal inspectors have assisted the States in enforcing the nonplanting restrictions and in carrying out other control and eradication measures. Between 1937 and 1951, control and eradication work was done in 106 infested counties in 7 States. Of the 16,169 infested properties found in the counties, 12,327 were freed of weevils. In 1951, there remained 3,842 infested properties in 73 counties of the 7 States. No weevils were known to be present in the other 33 counties.

R. A. Roberts, *an employee of the Bureau of Entomology and Plant Quarantine, holds degrees from Texas Agricultural and Mechanical College and Iowa State College. He has conducted research on insects and has worked on cooperative Federal-State insect control projects since 1926.*

The Pea Weevil

T. A. Brindley
Joseph C. Chamberlin

The pea weevil depends entirely on edible and field peas for its existence. It occurs nearly everywhere peas are cultivated.

It is a pest in all pea-growing areas of the United States and Canada. It is especially abundant in places where peas are grown for the dry seeds. In some localities—the upper Snake River Valley of eastern Idaho and parts of Montana, among them—it is held in check by the long, cold winters. Heavy and long continued rains, such as occur in parts of the coastal areas of Oregon and Washington, also reduce winter survival.

Until 1920 or so the pea weevil was considered primarily a pest of dry or seed peas and, indeed, the main limiting factor in their production. In vain attempts to evade its ravages, the industry moved steadily westward from one growing area to another, until the now great pea-growing areas of the West—principally Idaho, Oregon, and Washington—were reached. When the production of green peas for processing was begun, the problem became even more acute because the weevily or "wormy" peas are unfit for human use.

To meet this challenge and to assist the new industry in controlling weevils so as to prevent the contamination of canned or processed products, the agricultural experiment stations of Oregon, Washington, and Idaho and the Department of Agriculture in 1930 began a cooperative research program to develop a solution.

The damage done by the pea weevil is due entirely to the feeding of the grubs or larvae within the growing seeds. Almost always a single larva completes its development in one seed, but so many eggs are laid that every pea may be infested. In the Willamette Valley of Oregon infestations in 70 to 90 percent of the total crop have been observed and an average loss of 30 to 70 percent may occur annually if steps are not taken to control it. In other sections, such as the Palouse area of eastern Washington and northern Idaho, the damage is less, although infestations of 5 to 50 percent have been recorded.

THE PEA WEEVIL is one of several types of weevils of the family Bruchidae, which exist by feeding on seeds of leguminous plants. The adult is small, generally mottled, grayish or brownish gray, and about one-fifth of an inch long. It has a small head with short threadlike antennae, a "round-shouldered" oval body, and long hind legs. The weevils are active insects, running and flying quickly during warm weather but in a rather clumsy fashion. When disturbed they often fall to the ground and play dead.

The life history of the pea weevil is simple. The winter is passed in the adult stage. The weevils fly into the pea fields at the end of the hibernation period at a time that coincides rather closely with the blossoming period of the peas. Mating follows a relatively brief period during which the weevils feed on the nectar and pollen of the pea flowers and to some extent on the petals or foliage. The female does not produce viable eggs unless she has fed on pollen. By the time the pea pods have dropped their blossoms, she is ready to lay eggs. The orange- or lemon-colored eggs are oval and less than one-sixteenth inch long. They are laid singly or sometimes in pairs, one above the other, on the outside of the pea pod, to which they are firmly attached by means of a transparent gluelike substance. Within a few days the darkening head of the developing larva may be seen through the translucent shell. Hatching time varies with temperature, being shortest during warm periods. The incubation period may be as short as 4 days or as long as 2 weeks or more. It averages about 9 days.

The tiny grub when fully developed cuts its way through the thin eggshell. Then it eventually finds its way through the young pea pod into one of the embryonic peas within it. Several grubs may enter a single pea but usually only one grub lives to complete its development. The hole made by the larva in entering the pea soon heals, but its site is usually visible as a tiny dark spot or "sting."

Once safely within the pea the larva soon molts. Having no further need for them, it then loses its legs and the peculiar comblike structure on the back of the first segment of the thorax, which no doubt helped the newly hatched grub in getting from the egg into the pea. The larva is now white or creamy yellow, except for the strong, dark-brown, jawlike mouth parts. For the rest of its larval life it eats and grows rapidly and does most damage to the pea. The endosperm and often the germ of the developing seed are almost completely eaten. Infested seed either die or at best produce weakened sprouts.

The larval stages, four in all, take 4 to 8 weeks (depending on temperature) to reach maturity. Development proceeds fastest in warm weather.

The full-grown larva cuts through or nearly through the seed coat, leaving a circular cap or "window" through which the future adult may easily force its way. Afterwards the larva becomes nearly inactive for a short period—the prepupal stage. Then it molts, giving rise to the pupal stage, which averages 12 to 14 days. The pupa looks like the adult. During the prepupal and pupal stages, by a process as mysterious as the development from egg to larva, the internal tissues regroup themselves to form the adult. The adult beetle is first soft and pallid, but the skin soon hardens and within hours assumes the normal adult colors. The size of the adult varies with the amount of food it had during the larval stage. Because no one larva feeds in more than a single seed, the size of the pea affects somewhat the size of the emerging adult. Small or undeveloped peas may be entirely consumed except for the seed coat; from them come dwarfed adult weevils. The normal adult is strong, vigorous, and well provided with relatively enormous stored energy in the form of fat. That is important because no further feeding occurs until the following spring.

ENVIRONMENTAL FACTORS as well as available food supply govern the abundance of the pea weevil. Among them are suitable climatic and cropping conditions for development and successful hibernation.

The pea weevil in its spread to new areas has mostly left behind the parasitic and predatory insects that presumably evolved along with it in its native habitat. Or possibly such natural enemies as did succeed in accompanying it found the new conditions unsuitable to their survival. In any case, the pea weevil in this country is practically free from the attack of parasitic insects. Attempts to introduce parasites have not been successful.

Beginning with the emergence of the adult weevils from the peas, there are four critical periods to consider: The period during the summer-to-fall emergence of the weevil with the succeeding dispersal flights to hibernation quarters; the hibernation period; the period of dispersal flights in the spring from hibernation quarters to the pea fields; and the period of oviposition.

The adult weevil appears about the time the pea in which it feeds becomes fully developed. Under some conditions many peas shatter from the pods and become scattered over the ground. Additional peas are lost by shattering during the harvesting process. Weevils from any of the infested peas begin to emerge within a few weeks. The rate of emergence is stimulated by moisture from heavy dew or rainfall. The emerging weevils take flight and drift about with the prevailing winds until by chance they arrive at locations which offer more or less suitable shelter in which to pass the winter. These seemingly indirect flights of the pest may take it 3 miles or more from the place it emerged from the pea. In Northwestern States, fall emergence flights start about mid-July and early August and continue until early October.

The adult weevil is a daytime flier and its critical activities are governed by temperature. Flights rarely start earlier than 8 a. m. and continue later than 4 to 6 p. m. Peak flights occur near or shortly after noon. The minimum observed temperature at which summer and fall flights take place is 60°–61° F.; peak flights occur mostly at temperatures between 66° and 79°.

The number of weevils coming from shattered peas in unharvested, abandoned fields or from volunteer pea stands in other crops is large, but still is smaller than the number present in the harvested seeds. The weevils in green peas are destroyed in processing and therefore do not contribute to weevil populations.

If the peas are stored in tight sacks or other tight containers, many weevils may remain in the dry seed and emerge only in limited numbers or not at all until the seeds are planted. Then, activated by the soil moisture, the weevils emerge from the seed and soil. If infested peas are kept in dry containers long enough, many adults never emerge at all but die in peas. In a few cases, weevils kept under such conditions have survived two full winters before finally succumbing.

The fall migration period is one of peril to the pea weevil. Many are destroyed by predatory insects, animals, and birds. The greatest danger, however, results from various farming operations. Livestock and poultry foraging in the field after harvest may destroy weevil-inhabited peas in large numbers. Deep plowing and packing the soil immediately following harvest kill many weevils. Finally, the treatment of the dry peas by fumigation, heat treatment, or other methods shortly after harvest takes an extra toll.

It would almost seem that man might spell the doom of the insect by applying cultural practices and fumigation. But that has never been the case, for enough weevils invariably escape to perpetuate the pest—mainly because of the practical impossibility of securing community-wide adherence to the needed practices and because cultivation and fumigation are not completely effective under the conditions that obtain in pea production. Such practices are nevertheless of great help in reducing subsequent infestations and are a vital part of any good control program.

The hibernation shelter of the weevil might be almost any crevice in natural or artificial objects or debris of any kind into which the insect can crawl and be protected from the weather. The most favored quarters are those that are nearest the place where the weevils came into being. Checked and split posts, old sheds, barns, warehouses, or other structures offer favorable situations; so do crevices in the bark of trees, brush piles, weedy or brushy field edges, moss and lichens on trees, and forest litter. In some places such as the rolling, treeless areas of eastern Washington and northern Idaho, no hibernation quarters may be nearby, and many of the insects fly far up the mountain slopes, where they find suitable quarters under the bark of trees or in the forest duff, especially in the ponderosa pine groves.

The greatest hazard to which weevils in hibernation are exposed is the weather itself. Natural predators such as birds also take a toll. The lack of adequate protection afforded by the different types of shelter or the lack of sufficient snow cover may expose the weevils to lethal zero or subzero temperatures or to excessive moisture, and result in their wholesale destruction, especially where the exposure lasts long. A few weevils may survive short exposures to temperatures as low as 15° or 16° below zero, but none can survive a full winter's exposure to a constant temperature as high as 12°. These facts no doubt account for the absence of the weevil from certain high mountain valleys and northern Canada and Alaska—even in places where peas flourish in the warmer periods of the year.

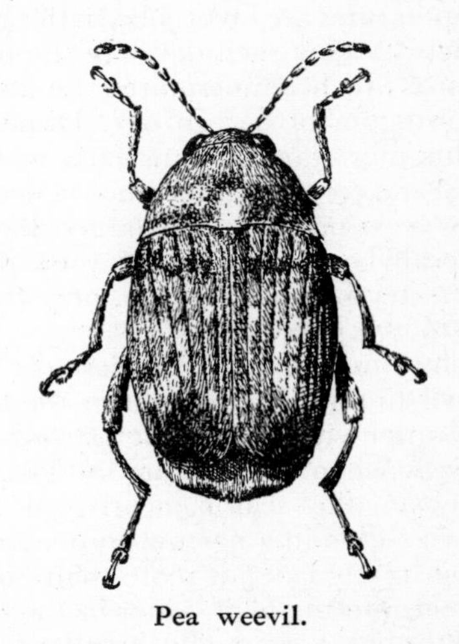

Pea weevil.

The fluctuating mortality of hibernating weevil populations explains the year-to-year variations in the numbers of weevils that occur in the pea fields. Annual fluctuations are especially marked in climatic zones having extreme year-to-year differences of winter weather. Such conditions characterize many agricultural areas of the northern Mountain States.

The weevil, like other animals that are inactive in winter, enters the winter with a store of fat. During hibernation the fat reserves are depleted gradually and reach their lowest ebb the following spring. In a test in the mild Willamette Valley, fatty materials, which accounted for 35 percent of the total dry body weight at the time of entrance into hibernation, gradually decreased to only 22 percent by late May. The weevil influx into the pea fields was at its height at that time.

THE SPRING FLIGHTS from winter quarters coincide with the blossoming of the earliest peas. Activity and dispersal begin only after spring temperatures have accumulated to a certain point. Thus no flights occur in very early spring even on warm, sunny days that later in the season would be accompanied by many flights. Once the movements start, however, flights occur on days during the hours when temperatures are favorable. In the Willamette Valley such days are the ones during which temperatures rise above a minimum of 62° to 63°. Dispersal flights may start there as early as late April and continue into June—a period of 6 weeks or more. The largest flights generally occur during May on days when temperatures reach or exceed 70° to 75°.

The instinct or tendency of the weevil to settle from flight at the first encounter with a pea plant is strong, especially when the peas are in blossom. Early in the season nearly all the weevils settle in a narrow border zone, which rarely extends more than 40 or 50 feet into the field. Later in the season the zone gradually broadens because of the gradual dispersal of the weevils within the field. The original pattern of distribution, however, tends to be maintained to the last—that is, a reduction in weevil numbers will be found from field edge to center even late in the season. In areas where pea fields of 100 acres or greater exist and populations of the insect are relatively low, the centers of the fields may not become infested during the entire season.

The pea grower has taken advantage of these facts by limiting his early-season control operations to the infested field edges—if the beetles on the borders are killed the crop is protected.

The pea weevil is less prolific than some other insects but enough to maintain itself as a plague. Males and females are present in nearly equal numbers. Only fertilized eggs hatch. The number of eggs laid by one female ranges from fewer than 100 up to more than 700. When weevils are present in large numbers, practically no pods escape their egg-laying activities. Weevils will lay eggs on any green pod, but they favor the younger pods.

Cool weather retards both egg laying and the hatching—in cool spring weather, 150 weevils, say, would produce the same number of offspring as 100 weevils would when temperatures are higher. Late-planted fields may therefore be damaged more seriously than early fields by a relatively smaller number of weevils. After egg laying has been completed the adults die. None survive to do damage a second season.

THE ONLY EFFECTIVE METHOD we can recommend for controlling infestations is dusting the infested parts of the pea field with insecticides. Dust mixtures that have been found effective are 0.75 percent rotenone, 5 percent DDT, and 5 percent methoxychlor. The materials are applied to peas at the rate of 20 pounds per acre. How to use them depends on the nature of the crop.

The insecticide selected for use on canning and freezing peas depends on whether the green vines are to be used for livestock feed after harvest. If they are, dust mixtures containing rotenone or methoxychlor should be used. If not, DDT can be applied. The insecticides should be applied with a hooded dusting machine.

Peas to be harvested for processing green should be dusted during the interval between the appearance of the first blossoms and the appearance of the first pods. The adult weevils thus are killed before they can lay eggs on the pods. This period from first blooms to first pods ranges from 2 or 3 days in hot weather to more than a week in cool, cloudy weather.

If rotenone dust has been used, the action of sunlight reduces its effectiveness; hence not many of the weevils that enter the field 24 hours after the application are killed. To protect peas from reinfestation, therefore, it may be necessary to dust a second or third time. The period between successive applications of rotenone ranges from 2 or 3 days to more than a week, depending on when additional weevils enter the field.

DDT and methoxychlor are more

persistent. Fewer treatments are needed with them and the interval between treatments may be longer.

The longer the application is delayed, the more weevils are likely to fly into the field and the more will be killed by the insecticide, but the consequences may be serious if dusting is delayed beyond the date when the first eggs of the season are laid. A delay of even 1 or 2 days after small pods have appeared may result in the peas becoming infested to such an extent as to render them unfit for canning or freezing. Generally it is much better to start dusting a little early.

Rain and wind sometimes interfere with the correct application of the dust. The use of dusting equipment may be impractical in muddy fields. Windy weather may make dusting ineffective. Dusting should not be attempted when the wind velocity exceeds 12 miles an hour. Rain, wind, and cool weather cause the weevil to be relatively inactive. Most of the eggs are deposited at 70° or higher, and none below 65°.

Since power-dusting equipment cannot operate effectively on muddy fields, peas grown in irrigated areas should not be watered until after dusting has been completed. Under normal conditions and proper culture, no damage to the peas should result from the delayed irrigation.

THE GROWER of green peas should try to eradicate the weevil from his fields. The control requirements for dry peas, on the other hand, are less rigid, because the processors can remove small numbers of weevil-infested peas during the cleaning. Furthermore, the relatively low per-acre value of dry peas restricts the extent of dusting that is economically justified.

In general, only one application of rotenone, DDT, or methoxychlor is recommended for dry edible peas. It should be timed to avoid as far as possible a considerable amount of oviposition by the pea weevil. If the weather is unfavorable, dusting should be delayed until conditions are better. The temperature should be above 65°, with indications that it will go higher, since weevils are usually inactive at temperatures below this level. It is extremely important, however, to remember that if dusting is delayed because of unsatisfactory weather the grower should be prepared to treat his peas immediately as soon as conditions become favorable. Otherwise, enough eggs may be laid to produce a serious infestation. A 5 percent DDT dust, applied at 15–20 pounds per acre, is most commonly used for the control of the pea weevil on dry peas and seed. If the vines are to be used for cattle feed, 0.75 percent rotenone dust, or methoxychlor, at 5 percent, should be used.

THE BULK of a seed-pea crop is produced by the pods set during the peak of the blooming period; the very earliest and the last two or three pods contribute relatively little to the total yield. In such instances, we may sacrifice those sets (the earlier through weevil infestation, the latter through lack of maturity) without too serious a loss in yield. Also, the weevil larvae developing from eggs laid after the midseason period are usually too small, at the time of early harvest, to have affected seriously the viability of the infested seed. If promptly fumigated by such materials as methyl bromide, chloropicrin, carbon disulfide, or other suitable fumigants, such seeds are acceptable to the trade on the basis of actual germination tests. The single insecticidal treatment, which is all that is ordinarily justified in such cases, should therefore be delayed until after the first large influx of weevils, which generally comes shortly after the first pod or two has set. Besides eliminating the initial infestation, the residual effectiveness of the DDT will then suffice to control subsequent influxes until near midseason or later.

When DDT is used for pea weevil control on Austrian winter field peas, it should be applied at the rate of 15 to 20 pounds of the 5-percent dust per acre. We emphasize that early harvest and prompt fumigation are essential to success with this program. Peas infested by large larvae as a result of early infestation are lighter and are readily removed in the cleaning process.

IT IS IMPORTANT to know when and where to dust. Since the pea weevil populations are generally not distributed uniformly throughout a field but are most often concentrated in a narrow zone around the edges, especially those edges close to favorable hibernation quarters, it is often unnecessary to apply the dust mixture to an entire field, particularly if it is large.

The parts of the field that might require dusting can be determined only on the basis of actual weevil-population surveys made by the grower or control operator. Such surveys are most quickly and accurately accomplished by the use of an insect-collecting net. A 15-inch collecting net is commonly used. In heavily infested areas, particularly where peas are grown for canning and freezing, it is often necessary to dust the entire acreage of small fields, that is, those that do not exceed 8 to 10 acres.

A method of determining the weevil infestation is:

Sweep the field soon after the first blossoms have appeared and before dusts have been applied. Go into the field in several places on each of the four sides, or, if the field is irregular in shape, sweep at intervals around it. Each stroke across the upper part of the vines is considered a sweep. Hold the net at such an angle that weevils knocked off the vines will fall into it. Take a step or two between each sweep. Make two or more 25-sweep collections at each place swept and count the weevils in each collection. Work toward the center of the field until no more weevils are found. In a field of seed peas, sweep toward the center of the field until the weevil population drops below the number for which it is considered profitable to dust, as we explain later. On a rough map of the field mark the locations where the weevils were collected. To keep track of the locations, it is helpful to step off the distance from the edge and sweep at 100-foot intervals. For instance, if weevils are found 200 feet from the edge of the field, walk another 100 feet and sweep again. If this method is followed, it is easy to mark the distance on the map.

Pay particular attention to the places most likely to be severely infested. Examine the edge nearest extensive timbered or brushy areas, ravines, and gullies running into the field; the vicinity of sheds or trees; and areas where the first peas blossomed, if the bloom is spotted. Check on the effect of the dusting operations in a similar manner 18 to 24 hours after dusting. If many weevils are found, it may be necessary to dust again within 3 or 4 days. We stress again that the green-pea field must be kept practically weevil-free, but in seed peas a light infestation is not so important. A more thorough check therefore is needed on the green-pea field, both before and after dusting.

GROUND AND AIRPLANE dusters have been used to apply insecticides. Power dusters should be provided with a box-type hood or a canvas trailer so as to confine the dust to the vines for a brief period before it is dissipated or the wind carries it away. The nozzles or hollow perforated boom for dust distribution should be so constructed as to distribute or blow the dust across the entire swath so that it can circulate freely through and around the vines before exposure to the effects of wind. The dusters are of many sizes and designs. Most have provision for telescoping, trailing, or dismounting the booms or hoods to facilitate movement from field to field. Some have special elevating devices for adjustment to the height of the vines. Those that cover swath widths greater than 30 or 40 feet (up to about 60 feet) have caster wheels at the ends of the booms or hoods to permit them to follow uneven field contours with efficiency and without damage to the equipment. Some are mounted in trucks. Others are on trailers that are pulled by tractors, jeeps, or horses. Sometimes the dusting machine is driven from a power take-off by the tractor itself; others are driven by separate engines. Providing they distribute the dust fairly uniformly at the required rates, all have been reasonably satisfactory.

Dust applications from the ground should not be made when winds exceed 10 or 12 miles an hour. Rotenone dust applications are most effective when temperatures reach or exceed 70° and should not be made at other times. That is because rotenone is effective only on immediate contact, and during cool weather weevils remain inactive and more or less concealed in places not reached by the dust.

Airplane dust applications have proved reasonably effective if properly made and supervised. Good applications to field margins are especially important, but that often is dangerous to do with airplanes and may not be too effective, especially if the fields are small, irregular, or obstructed by trees, power lines, or buildings. Ground equipment is recommended for such. In general, dust applications by airplane should be at rates about 50 percent greater than with ground equipment. Dust deposits from airplanes are largely concentrated in a narrow swath or zone, the effective width of which does not greatly exceed 25 to 30 feet. Airplane applications are also much more limited by wind than are ground applications. Such applications are effective only when made under nearly windless conditions—where velocities do not exceed 2 or 3 miles an hour.

One of the greatest advantages of aerial application is the absence of crop damage by the equipment itself. With truck- or tractor-drawn ground dusters covering a swath width of 30 feet, the damage may amount to as much as 3 or 4 percent of the value of the crop in the part of the field actually treated. Light equipment and the use of dusters covering greater swath widths would substantially reduce the injury.

T. A. Brindley, *entomologist in the Bureau of Entomology and Plant Quarantine, devoted 20 years to a study of the biology, ecology, natural enemies, and control of the pea weevil and other insects affecting peas in the Pacific Northwest and in adjacent regions. He is a graduate of Iowa State College and pursued graduate studies there. Since 1950 Dr. Brindley has been coordinator of research in cooperative investigations in Iowa on the European corn borer between the Bureau of Entomology and Plant Quarantine and the Iowa Agricultural Experiment Station.*

Joseph C. Chamberlin, *entomologist for more than 20 years in the Bureau of Entomology and Plant Quarantine, has done research on several of the more important insects affecting truck crops, including the pea weevil, pea aphid, and beet leafhopper in the Western States. He investigated the insects of Alaska in 1943–45. During recent years Dr. Chamberlin has worked with agricultural engineers to develop and improve aircraft for the application of insecticides to peas and other crops. Dr. Chamberlin holds degrees from Stanford University.*

For further reading:

T. A. Brindley: Some Notes on the Biology of the Pea Weevil Bruchus pisorum L. (Coleoptera, Bruchidae) at Moscow, Idaho, *Journal of Economic Entomology, volume 26, pages 1058–1062, 1933;* The Pea Weevil and Methods for Its Control, *with J. C. Chamberlin, F. G. Hinman, and K. W. Gray, U. S. D. A. Farmers' Bulletin 1971, 1946;* Effect of Growth of Pea Weevil on Weight and Germination of Seed Peas, *with F. G. Hinman, Journal of Economic Entomology, volume 30, pages 664–670, 1937;* Influence of Specific Gravity on the Separation of Weevil-Infested Peas, *with H. J. Shipman, Seed World, volume 39, number 5, pages 8–9, 1936.*

J. C. Chamberlin and K. W. Gray: Suggestions for the Control of the Pea Weevil in Oregon With Especial Reference to Peas Grown for Processing, *Oregon Agricultural Experiment Station Circular 126, 1938.*

F. H. Chittenden: Insects Injurious to Beans and Peas, *Yearbook of Agriculture for 1898, pages 233–260. 1899.*

The Pea Aphid

John E. Dudley, Jr.
William C. Cook

The pea aphid is a small, light-green insect less than one-quarter inch long. Its food is the sap it sucks from the plants on which it lives. Except for size, adults and young look alike. It was first recorded in the United States in 1879 on peas in Illinois. It is now found in every State and in several Provinces of Canada wherever peas or its other food plants are grown. In 13 States it is a serious pest nearly every year.

Peas are the most widely distributed and the most favored food plants of the pea aphid. It attacks all peas, whether grown as green peas for market, for canning, for seed, as field peas, as a cover crop, or sweet peas grown for their flowers. The country's commercial planting of peas for canning and freezing in 1951 amounted to 445,860 acres. Peas are grown for canning and freezing in at least 31 States. The Great Lakes States and Washington and Oregon are the centers of the industry. In them also are large acreages of alfalfa and clover, perennial crops that are a reservoir for the aphid during the months when peas are not growing.

Next to peas the aphid likes alfalfa best. Serious infestations may develop on alfalfa in some States, notably Kansas and California. About 18 million acres of alfalfa were grown in the United States in 1949. The pea aphid also feeds on vetch and red clover, alsike clover, crimson clover, and sweetclover, but they seldom are damaged seriously.

THE PEA APHID spends the winter in the egg stage in the Northern States. In the Pacific Northwest it may overwinter in an active stage. In the South it remains active most of the winter. Tiny black eggs, glued to the stems and fallen leaves of alfalfa and clover and protected most of the time by a blanket of snow, remain throughout the winter in the North. In April or early May, depending on the latitude, the eggs hatch into young aphids, called nymphs, which feed upon the newly sprouted alfalfa and clover. They molt four times before becoming adults. After one or two generations of aphids have been reared on alfalfa and clover, a large proportion of the next generation will develop wings and fly to peas in late May and early June. They are weak fliers, but wind currents may carry them far, perhaps 50 miles. Arriving in pea fields, the winged aphids commence at once to produce young, most of them wingless. In a season 14 or 15 generations may be produced.

BECAUSE PEAS are more succulent and tender than the crops the aphids have left and the temperature is likely to be rising, reproduction on peas is rapid. Female aphids can produce young without fertilization; in spring and summer all aphids are females. In warm weather a female may produce 10 to 14 young a day—on one acre of peas there might be millions of aphids which came from eggs laid the previous autumn on alfalfa and clover and which can quickly ruin the crop if insecticides are not applied promptly. As the peas approach maturity and become less favorable for feeding, winged forms again appear. Most of them die, but some find their way to later planted, more tender peas or go back to alfalfa and clover. Some aphids remain on alfalfa all summer.

In October the forms change. Some of the aphids then born become males. Others become egg-producing females. Some are winged. Others are wingless. After the males and females have mated, fertile eggs are laid, which overwinter on alfalfa and clover. Thus the yearly cycle is completed.

The aphid sucks the sap from the

leaves, stems, blossoms, and pods of plants. The injury they do to alfalfa and clover is not conspicuous unless the plants are small and suffering from drought or the infestation is heavy. Occasionally a heavy infestation has destroyed the entire spring growth of alfalfa. A few aphids may kill small pea plants. A heavy infestation on more mature plants may reduce yield and quality or even destroy the crop. The plants become stunted and produce fewer and smaller pods than uninfested plants. Aphids frequently attack the pods and cause them to curl, shrink, and be only partly filled with peas. The deformed pods are low in market value and do not shell out in the viner.

The aphid also transmits several virus diseases of peas. One is the yellow bean mosaic. In the Pacific Northwest alfalfa is the reservoir for the virus; it is spread to peas by winged aphids. In years of heavy migrations from alfalfa severe epidemics often cause great damage to peas. Another virus carried by the aphid is enation mosaic, which roughens or toughens the pods. In late-planted peas it is more destructive to the crop than the yellow bean mosaic because infected pods become too tough to be shelled in a viner, and the result is that half the crop often is lost.

Two other virus diseases sometimes are found in peas. One causes a wilting of the growing tips and the other a bronzing of leaves and stems.

Devastating infestations of the pea aphid do not appear without some warning. The number of eggs laid on winter hosts and the early spring population of nymphs in alfalfa and clover make possible an estimate of the infestation that may be expected in peas. Seasonal weather conditions are the main determining factors. Warm, sunny weather stimulates rapid reproduction. Cool, rainy weather slows it down or even stops it for a while.

To know when to begin control operations, growers have to keep a close watch of the pea fields. They can determine how many aphids are present by several methods. A common way is to sweep the plants with an insect net that has an opening about 15 inches in diameter. The number of aphids captured in one sweep of the net is counted. After many such counts from sweeps in different parts of the field, the average number per sweep is determined. When an average of 35 aphids per sweep has been found, it is time to apply insecticides.

More than 70 species of predatory and parasitic insects, which vary greatly in abundance from season to season, attack the aphid. Now and then in sections with warm, humid weather, a fungus disease may attack the aphids and kill a high percentage of them in a short time. The disease is of small account in dry climates. All these natural checks on aphids usually come too late to prevent damage to the pea crop.

The first attempts at commercial control of the pea aphid in the United States were made in Maryland about 1900 by W. G. Johnson, of the Department of Agriculture. He experimented with sprays of kerosene and fish oil soap and with tobacco dust. He concluded that sprays were not practical for use on large acreages. Then he developed brushes of pine boughs, which, attached to a cultivator, knocked the aphids off the plants.

Research on methods of control began in 1922 by the Maryland Agricultural Experiment Station, the Department of Agriculture, and the Wisconsin Agricultural Experiment Station. Gradually, as the aphid became a widespread menace, 12 State experiment stations initiated experiments. The work has involved tests with mechanical devices, insecticides, parasites, predators, and cultural methods.

Cultural methods have included heavy pasturing of alfalfa fields with sheep or cattle in fall or early spring, cutting as soon in the spring as a hay crop could be obtained, clipping the tender alfalfa tops, and regulating the time of irrigation in reference to the infestation. All gave varying degrees of control, but all had disadvantages and generally fell short of preventing aphid damage to the hay crop. Efforts to breed alfalfa plants resistant to aphids have been carried on in Kansas, California, and Wisconsin. Research in Wisconsin has shown that some varieties of peas—Onward, Pride, Yellow Admiral—are partly resistant.

About a million coccinellids, or lady beetles, collected in great masses from hibernation in the mountains of California, were liberated in the middle of a large alfalfa field in California. Several hundred thousand were shipped to Wisconsin and liberated in a field of peas. In both instances the beetles soon took wing to scatter far and wide without appreciably reducing the aphid infestation.

Burning alfalfa fields in late fall or early spring was tried by igniting the stubble and weeds and later by spraying the fields with fuel oil before firing them. Neither way achieved complete combustion, and enough unburned areas were left to allow the surviving aphids to build up again. Machines called stubble burners were developed and tested. They burned oil and produced a hot flame, which consumed all the green foliage—both alfalfa and weeds—as they were driven through a field. They destroyed practically all living aphids and their eggs but also killed the aphid's natural enemies. New growth appeared soon after the burning, winged aphids flew in from nearby unburned fields, and the aphids were able to reproduce so rapidly that in a short time the field again became critically infested.

Dragging alfalfa with brush, platform, or chain drags, cultivating it with a spring-tooth harrow, and rolling with a field roller have been tried in several States. But the consensus is that even when the operation is repeated several times during the season too many aphids are left unharmed and reproduction goes on. An aphid-collecting machine, called an aphidozer and tested in several States, consisted of a hopper and revolving brushes mounted on wheels and pulled by a horse or mule. It collected bushels of aphids from an acre of peas, but it had the same fault as most other mechanical devices—it had no residual or lasting effect and left too many aphids on the plants to continue reproduction.

INSECTICIDES are the answer to the control problem on peas grown for processing. Many types of insecticides have been tested, but for one reason or another all but three or four have been abandoned for commercial or experimental use. Insecticides may be applied with ground equipment or by aircraft.

The most common methods with ground equipment are the power duster; the high-gallonage power sprayer, which applies 100 gallons or more of dilute spray per acre; the low-gallonage weed sprayer, which applies about 25 gallons per acre; and the mist blower, which applies about 10 gallons per acre. The power duster is the most common way because it is rapid and causes a minimum of damage to the peas. Few canners use the high-gallonage sprayer; it is slow and costly and is apt to damage the plants. The low-gallonage sprayers are used experimentally and commercially but need further improvements.

Aircraft apply insecticides as dusts or concentrated sprays. Both methods are fast and do no mechanical damage to the peas. Dusting by airplane is the most common method, although the application of concentrated sprays is increasing. Canners have been quick to adopt the use of aircraft because of the rapidity with which large acreages with threatening aphid infestations can be treated.

Each type of control has its advantages and disadvantages but, everything considered, more effective aphid control may be expected when ground rather than airborne equipment is employed. In either case the degree of control depends on the use of efficient equipment and thoroughness and timeliness of application.

Wind is the primary factor in determining whether ground equipment or aircraft should be employed. The higher the wind velocity the less effective will be the control, regardless of method of application, but very low wind velocity is particularly important where aircraft are employed. Wind of even 3 or 4 miles an hour is apt to make dusting by air unprofitable because most of the dust may drift away before it hits the plants. When aphid control is imperative, aircraft sprays can be applied effectively in winds of 3 to 7 miles an hour. Normally periods of little air movement may be expected an hour or two before sunrise, and 1 to 3 hours before dark.

Effective treatment with ground equipment, on the other hand, is possible with considerably higher wind velocity. By attaching an apron or trailer 25 feet long to the boom, one can get satisfactory results in winds of 10 to 12 miles an hour. Spraying without an apron can be effective in winds of like velocity.

The size and shape of individual fields and the amount of acreage needing immediate treatment also influence the method of application. The larger and more open the field the more efficient will be treatment by aircraft because of the time spent in turning at the ends and in going from field to field. Ground equipment is likely to be more efficient than aircraft in small, hilly, odd-shaped fields and in those bordered by trees, buildings, or high-power lines.

When treatment is advisable early in the growing season before peas have blossomed and while the aphid infestation is still light, ground equipment may be preferable. On the other hand, if the crop is nearing maturity, with a growth of tall, heavy plants, or if the ground is wet, aircraft application is particularly desirable.

Experiments at Forest Grove, Oreg., during 1950, revealed the principal causes for the unequal distribution of sprays from airplanes as ordinarily used for the control of the pea aphid on peas and for other insects on low-growing crops. In flights made at a height of about 2 feet above the soil surface, with the wheels touching the pea vines, the spray deposits were effective for insect control over a swath about 50 feet wide. Similar results were obtained from flights at the 10-foot level. The spray was deposited unevenly over this swath, however, and under some conditions caused plant injury in spots where the insecticide was applied too heavily and relatively inferior insect control in spots where the application was too light. In experiments designed to correct this uneven distribution of the spray, separate flights were made with all nozzles closed except in groups of three, representing a 1-foot segment of the boom. Knowledge gained during these experiments has provided criteria for determining the most efficient nozzle spacings, minimum spray boom lengths, effective swath width, and a basis for improvements in airplane sprayers and dusters.

Nicotine in sprays, dusts, or vapor has been more widely used for years than any other insecticide.

As a spray it is always combined with a soap or an emulsifiable oil. As a dust it is generally combined with hydrated lime or other powdered carriers. A cloth apron or trailer some 50 feet long is used so that the dust will circulate and settle on the plants and little will be blown away. Under favorable weather conditions, high kills of the aphid can be obtained with both sprays and dusts.

About 1940 a machine was devised which vaporized highly concentrated nicotine by passing it through the exhaust pipe of a gasoline engine. The vapor was expelled under a gasproof cloth trailer 100 feet long. Kills of nearly 100 percent were obtained, but the operation was slow and costly.

Nicotine has little residual value (at most only a few hours after application) and is effective only when the air

970134°—52——36

temperature is rather high, preferably in the 70's or 80's.

Rotenone was first used against the pea aphid as a spray about 1922 in Maryland. The value of the finely powdered root in dusts or sprays was shown in 1935 in experiments in Wisconsin. The dusts and sprays did not kill aphids as rapidly as nicotine, but they had a residual value and continued to kill for several days if the weather was favorable. Many tests were made subsequently with different diluents and by adding oils and conditioning agents to improve the performance of the mixtures. Rarely did rotenone give a very high degree of control, such as 98 percent, but the more effective combinations often gave satisfactory commercial control, particularly in humid localities.

DDT, properly formulated, is much better than rotenone. It gives both high initial kill and has good residual properties. In the eastern and central parts of the country a 1.5 percent DDT dust dissolved in a nonvolatile solvent gave 95 percent control of the aphid. In eastern Oregon and Washington, however, it has been necessary to use a dust containing 5 percent of DDT. This higher concentration of DDT affords a longer residual action and protects the late-planted peas from a reinfestation caused by aphids that fly in from other peas or alfalfa.

Aerosols began to be used against the pea aphid in 1944 in Maryland, Wisconsin, and Virginia. Concentrated insecticides in solution are introduced into a steel cylinder of 2- to 4-gallon capacity, and some liquefied gas under high pressure is added. Released through a valve, the liquefied gas volatilizes and disperses the insecticide as a mist. Excellent kills were reported, but the method is less commonly used than dusting or spraying.

Three canneries in Wisconsin used airplanes in 1942 and seven in 1943. By 1948, aircraft—either airplanes or helicopters—were employed by 102 out of 109 factories for applying insecticides to all or part of their canning-pea acreage. The aircraft applied 81 percent of the dusts and sprays used. Eighty-two of the factories used only DDT; 19 used a combination of DDT and rotenone.

By 1948, then, people considered DDT the nemesis of the aphids, but that hope was dispelled. DDT in minute quantities was found occasionally in the body tissues and milk of cattle fed treated pea vines before or after the vines had been made into ensilage. The possible danger to people from consuming meat or milk that might contain DDT discouraged the use of DDT against the pea aphid, and by 1951 only a small amount was used in Wisconsin, and that early in the season before peas had blossomed so sufficient time would elapse before harvest for nearly all of it to dissipate.

New phosphate compounds became available for testing in 1947 and they soon revealed a power to control the aphid just as well as DDT. They caused a high initial kill—100 percent in some plots. Parathion, the phosphate most commonly used in 1951, is highly poisonous to man and animals if it touches the skin, is inhaled, or is taken into the mouth. Applied to plants in the field as a spray or dust, however, it breaks down into relatively harmless compounds. If it is applied 10 to 14 days before harvest it is not a hazard in canned peas or on the ensilage. Consequently it has no long residual value, although tests in greenhouses indicate that it maintains its toxicity for at least a week when it is applied to peas growing in pots. Several years of work with parathion indicated that it is just as good under field conditions as any other material in preventing a build-up of the aphids that were not killed immediately after the application.

In Wisconsin in 1948 only a few growers of peas for canning used parathion but in 1949 parathion and other phosphates accounted for 63 percent of the acreage treated and in 1950 they were used on 81 percent of the treated acreage.

The extent and cost of control of aphids on canning peas alone are indicated in figures supplied by canners in Wisconsin, where an average of 37 percent of the Nation's pack is produced. Infestation was severe in Wisconsin in 1948. Aphid control was carried on by 109 of the 122 pea-canning factories, which treated 90,000 or 71 percent of the State's 126,000 harvested acres of canning peas. Dust was applied in the amount of 4,502,269 pounds. Only a few acres were sprayed. Materials cost nearly 295 thousand dollars. As the cost of application equals the cost of insecticides, the total cost was nearly 600 thousand dollars.

In 1949, the aphid was less serious, and 105 of the 121 factories growing peas treated 76,800 acres, 63 percent of the harvested acres. Dust in the amount of 2,442,990 pounds was applied and about 27,000 acres were sprayed; the estimated total cost was nearly 480,000 dollars. In 1950, 100 factories treated 63,935 acres, 54 percent of the 118,100 harvested acres. The dust used amounted to 2,031,033 pounds; 11,620 acres were sprayed. The total cost was set at 236,888 dollars.

The amount of dust applied has averaged 35 to 40 pounds an acre whether the application was made by aircraft or with ground equipment. Concentrated sprays generally are applied by aircraft at the rate of 3 to 5 gallons an acre. Dilute sprays applied with ground equipment have averaged 100 to 125 gallons an acre.

JOHN E. DUDLEY, JR., *a graduate of the University of Wisconsin, was an entomologist in the Bureau of Entomology and Plant Quarantine from 1911 to 1951, when he retired. His first assignment was with the gypsy and brown-tail moth laboratory in Massachusetts. Since 1918 he had been in charge of the truck crop and garden insect investigations laboratory in Wisconsin.*

WILLIAM C. COOK *has been an entomologist in the Bureau of Entomology and Plant Quarantine since 1930. Before that time he was employed by the Montana Agricultural Experiment Station for work on cutworms. Since 1943 he has been stationed at Walla Walla, Wash., studying wireworms and the pea aphid. He holds degrees from Cornell University and the University of Minnesota.*

For further reading:

R. A. Blanchard: Control of Aphids on Alfalfa in the Antelope Valley, Calif., *U. S. D. A. Circular 307, 1934;* Burning for the Control of Aphids on Alfalfa in the Antelope Valley of California, *with H. B. Walker and O. K. Hedden, U. S. D. A. Circular 287, 1933;* Alfalfa Plants Resistant to the Pea Aphid, *with John E. Dudley, Jr., Journal of Economic Entomology, volume 27, pages 262–264, 1934.*

T. E. Bronson, J. E. Dudley, Jr., and R. Keith Chapman: Liquefied-Gas Aerosols for Pea Aphid Control, *Journal of Economic Entomology, volume 42, pages 661–663. 1949.*

L. P. Ditman, E. N. Cory, and Castillo Graham: Studies on Pea Aphid Control, *Journal of Economic Entomology, volume 32, pages 537–546, 1939;* Pea Aphid Studies in Maryland, *with Albert White, Maryland Agricultural Experiment Station Bulletin A24, 1943.*

J. E. Dudley, Jr.: The Pea Aphid on Peas and Methods for Its Control, *with T. E. Bronson, U. S. D. A. Farmers' Bulletin 1945, 1943;* Pea Aphid Investigations, *with Ed. M. Searls and Alfred Weed, Transactions of the Fourth International Congress of Entomology, Ithaca, August 1928, volume 2, pages 608–621, 1929.*

R. D. Eichmann and R. L. Webster: The Influence of Alfalfa on the Abundance of the Pea Aphid on Peas Grown for Canning in Southeastern Washington, *Washington Agricultural Experiment Station Bulletin 389. 1940.*

C. L. Fluke: The Known Predacious and Parasitic Enemies of the Pea Aphid in North America, *Wisconsin Agricultural Experiment Station Research Bulletin 93. 1929.*

K. W. Gray and Joe Schuh: Pea Aphid Control in Oregon, *Oregon Agricultural Experiment Station Bulletin 389. 1941.*

C. D. Harrington, Ed. M. Searls, R. A. Brink, and C. Eisenhart: Measurement of the Resistance of Peas to Aphids, *Journal of Agricultural Research, volume 67, pages 369–387. 1943.*

W. G. Johnson: Notes upon the Destructive Green Pea Louse (Nectarophora destructor, Johns.) for 1900. *U. S. D. A. Bulletin 26, new series, pages 55–58. 1901.*

The Beet Leafhopper

J. R. Douglass, William C. Cook

The beet leafhopper is the only known carrier of curly top, a destructive virus disease of sugar beets, beets, beans, tomatoes, spinach, melons, other crops, ornamental flowering plants and many weeds. The insect favors arid and semiarid localities of the western United States, northern Mexico, and southwestern Canada. Its breeding grounds are abandoned and overgrazed lands on which weed hosts occur. Such areas are also reservoirs for the virus.

Curly top has been given many common names—on sugar beets it has been called California beet blight, western blight, blight, curly leaf, and curly top; on tomatoes, tomato blight, yellow blight, summer blight, western blight, western yellow tomato blight, tomato yellows, and tomato curly top; on beans, bean blight.

How serious it can be is shown in records for southern Idaho, where growers of sugar beets in 1924 abandoned 11,442 out of 22,418 acres they planted. In 1934 they abandoned 18,635 out of 21,389 planted acres. The average yields of the harvested fields were 5.51 and 4.88 tons an acre for 1924 and 1934—far below the 16-ton average in years of little leafhopper exposure. Factories were dismantled and moved to other places, only to be dismantled and moved again when it was found that they had been relocated in areas infested by the beet leafhopper.

A leafhopper can pick up the virus from a diseased plant and transfer it to a healthy plant in 4 hours. Once a leafhopper has become infected with the virus of curly top, it remains infective, but it cannot transmit the virus through the eggs to its progeny.

Serious losses to cantaloups and muskmelons have been reported in Arizona, California, Idaho, and Utah. In 1945, N. J. Giddings, a specialist on curly-top virus, found that flax from the San Joaquin Valley, Calif., was infected with curly top. Later tests indicated the possibility of serious injury to flax during seasons of high infestations.

The beet leafhopper, commonly called the whitefly in the West, is slightly more than one-eighth inch long. It is gray to greenish yellow. It is a sun-loving, dry-climate insect and often breeds on many species of introduced weeds established on nonagricultural and deteriorated range lands. It feeds by sucking juices from its host plants. Rarely does it become numerous enough to cause great direct damage by its feeding. It is important then only because it carries curly top.

The virus of curly top survives the winter in both the beet leafhopper and its winter host plants. The leafhopper transmits it during feeding. It is carried from the winter hosts to other weed hosts and cultivated susceptible crops, principally during the spring movement. Some of the crops in their seedling stage are very susceptible to the disease. Infected plants often die. The percentage of the spring-generation leafhoppers carrying the virus has varied from year to year, with a low of 4 percent and a high of 80 percent.

Varieties of sugar beets that are resistant to curly top have been developed. We have no commercial varieties of tomatoes that are resistant. Serious losses occur during years of leafhopper outbreaks in parts of California, Colorado, Oregon, Utah, and Washington. In southern Idaho and some other areas, tomatoes are not grown for commercial use, because the crop is practically a complete loss in years of drastic exposure to curly top.

Most varieties of snap beans are susceptible. Southern Idaho produces approximately 80 percent of the national requirement of garden seed beans. The area is free from bacterial blight and other seed-borne bean diseases. During years when large spring movements of hoppers coincide with the "crookneck," or seedling, stage, field after field of the most susceptible varieties of beans in southern Idaho have been so seriously damaged by curly top that it has been necessary to plow them under. Losses to less susceptible varieties have also been high. In the past, serious losses occurred in most of the varieties of the field, or dry, beans. The Idaho Agricultural Experiment Station has developed resistant varieties of Great Northern and pinto beans.

THE EARLIEST VISIBLE SYMPTOMS of curly top in beets are the clearing of the tiny veinlets and the inward rolling of the lower and outer margins of the youngest leaves. As the disease gets more severe, the curling and distortion of the leaves increase, vein swelling occurs, and numerous papillae, or wartlike bumps, appear on the under sides of the leaves. A general stunting often ends in the death of the plant in the most severe cases. The diseased leaves are dark, dull-green, thick, crisp, and brittle. The roots show marked symptoms. The disease causes the death of the lateral rootlets and the beet then sends out a large number of new lateral rootlets, which look hairy or woolly. A cross section of a diseased root often shows dark concentric rings alternating with light circular areas. A longitudinal section shows the dark discoloration extending lengthwise throughout the beet.

In beans the first symptoms are the most pronounced on the trifoliate leaves, which become slightly puckered, curl downward, turn yellow, and die. They and the primary leaves are thicker than normal and brittle and break off readily. The infected young plants soon die. Plants infected later in the season may drop their blossoms, become chlorotic, and die. Affected plants are decidedly dwarfed and have short internodes, which give them a bunchy appearance. Plants infected late in the season do not always develop typical symptoms of the disease and generally grow to maturity.

In tomatoes the first reliable symptom is a general drooping, but not wilting, accompanied by yellowing of the young leaves and purpling of the veins. The plant is abnormal—often silvery—in color. The leaves thicken and become leathery and brittle. The entire plant turns yellow and usually dies. In seriously diseased plants the blossoms may drop and no more fruit is set. Fruits that are already formed turn yellowish red, ripen prematurely, and are stunted and of poor quality.

In squash the symptoms are somewhat similar to those in the other susceptible commercial crops. If the young seedling is infected by virus-carrying leafhoppers as soon as it emerges above the soil, it may die before its true leaves appear. In the older infected plants, new growth is stunted, internodes are shortened, and the leaves may roll upward at the margins. An upward bending of the tip of the runner is characteristic. Blossoms may drop and not set fruit, and the fruits already formed are stunted. There are no distinctive color differences by which a diseased plant may be identified. Wilting is not characteristic of curly-top infection in squash plants.

Infected cantaloups show no reliable symptoms. Infected seedlings become severely stunted and usually die. In the older infected plants, new growth is stunted, internodes are shortened toward the end of the runners, and the leaves may become puckered with the margins turned down. The flowers become dwarfed and often become dry before the petals expand. Yellowing occurs in severe cases.

Spinach affected by curly top undergoes stunting, shows crinkling and curling of the leaves, and acquires a more leathery texture and, in severe cases, yellowing of the leaves.

Considerable variations may occur in the symptoms of the infected plants, depending on the strains of the virus. The length of the incubation period and the severity of the disease that develops depend on the age and condition of the plant, its resistance, virulence of the virus, temperature, relative humidity, and light intensity. High temperature, low relative humidity, and high light intensity all increase the severity of the disease and the rate of development. Irrigation does not check the disease. Serious epidemics of curly top are dependent on several contributing factors—magnitude and time of the movement of spring-generation leafhoppers, percentage of leafhoppers carrying the virus of curly top, size and condition of susceptible plants at the time of infection, and weather conditions.

The first variety of beets resistant to curly top, U. S. 1, was developed by the Bureau of Plant Industry, Soils, and Agricultural Engineering and was released to growers in 1934. Since then, other resistant varieties have been released. Each is an improvement in resistance and adaptation. The development of varieties of sugar beets resistant to curly top has greatly lessened the losses to the crop. Eubanks Carsner and F. V. Owen have told the story in *Science in Farming,* the 1943–1947 Yearbook of Agriculture, of the research that made this possible.

The development of resistant varieties of sugar beets has made it profitable to grow beets again in areas of the western part of the United States that are affected by the beet leafhopper. Even the resistant varieties are susceptible to curly top in the early stages of growth, however, although they are far more resistant to injury than the nonresistant varieties previously grown, such as Old Type. Although the threat of failure to the beet crop has been greatly lessened, curly top has not vanished, as serious losses from curly top have occurred in California, Idaho, Nevada, and Utah in recent years when large spring movements of beet leafhoppers have coincided with the susceptible seedling stage of the plant. Although the losses have been local in extent, they have dealt hard blows to growers in affected areas. There is also the possibility that new and possibly more virulent strains of the virus of curly top will have to be dealt with.

Since the beet leafhopper survives only in a dry climate, it has probably reached the limits of its economic distribution in North America. The general climatic condition, rather than its host plants, is the limiting factor in restricting further geographical distribution of this insect, as its summer, winter, and spring breeding host plants are found growing abundantly outside of its economic range.

In only two instances has the insect been reported in the Eastern States. D. M. DeLong found it reproducing on purslane sesuvium (*Sesuvium portucastrum*) at Miami, Fla., in 1921. In 1936 he and K. J. Kadow collected it from horseradish at Collinsville, Ill.

An occasional outbreak of the insect and the curly top disease may be expected in areas removed from its normal range. Such outbreaks have occurred in the past in the Big Horn Basin, Wyo., and near Billings, Mont. Those outbreaks evidently followed long-distance migrations of the leafhopper into the areas, followed by favorable weather conditions for the insect for a few years. Because the disease depends on the vector for its spread, it is limited to the region infested by the beet leafhopper.

THE BEET LEAFHOPPER passes the winter in the adult stage, chiefly in uncultivated and overgrazed areas where mustards or other suitable host plants grow. The insects are active and feed during the winter whenever the temperature permits. The female develops its eggs in late winter. Egg-laying usually begins about the time the host plants begin spring growth. The eggs are laid inside the tissues of the leaves and stems of plants. A single overwintered female has been known to deposit 675 eggs. The average is between 300 and 400. The eggs hatch in 5 to 40 days, depending on the temperature. The young leafhoppers, the nymphs, emerge from the eggs and immediately begin to feed by inserting their beaks into the plant tissue and sucking the juices. The tiny nymphs are white, but in a few hours they darken considerably. As they grow they shed their skins five times, becoming larger after each molt. The older nymphs are usually spotted with red and brown. After the fifth molt, they become adults and have wings.

The time required for nymphal development from the time the insect hatches until it is adult is 3 to 6 weeks. Development from egg to adult takes 1 to 2 months. The generations overlap considerably. All stages may be found in the same breeding area at the same time in summer. The beet leafhopper breeds continuously during the warm months, and nymphs may be found at any time during the growing season. In the Central Columbia River area of Oregon and Washington, on the Snake River Plains of southern Idaho, and in northern Utah, three generations are produced each season. In the warmer regions in Arizona and California, five or more generations may develop.

The first, or spring, generation is produced on spring weed hosts, chiefly mustards, that are rather short-lived and mature and dry about the time the spring-generation leafhopper reaches the adult, or winged, stage. When weather conditions are favorable for flight, the leafhoppers move to their summer hosts, the progress of which coincides with the maturation of the insect. They travel with the wind and infest practically all host plants in their path. Most of the favorable summer host plants are weeds.

The infestation of crop plants is incidental to the general movements of the leafhopper, as they do not actively seek these out but infest any favorable host in their path. The leafhoppers moving into the cultivated areas alight first in the fields nearest the spring breeding grounds and gradually move farther into the cultivated lands. Consequently beets, beans, tomatoes, and other susceptible crops nearest the breeding grounds are more heavily infested than those farther away and are, therefore, more seriously affected with curly top. Of the cultivated plants, beets are the only important breeding host. Spinach and Swiss chard are less favorable. During the spring migration, the leafhopper will feed on beans, cantaloups, squash, tomatoes, and other crops but will not reproduce on them. It is during such feeding that the plants are infected with the virus of curly top.

The wild host plants of the beet leafhopper usually occur in large patches scattered over definite areas. Such areas, where large numbers of favorable host plants combine with favorable climatic conditions, are very productive of leafhoppers. It is difficult to trace the flights of such tiny insects, and much remains unknown about their movements. Yet it is known in a general way that leafhoppers from any one breeding ground infest the same cultivated areas year after year.

All the breeding grounds, except the ones along the Rio Grande in New Mexico and Texas, are west of the Continental Divide. All are in areas with a mean annual rainfall of not more than 12 inches. In all except the Arizona and Rio Grande areas, the summers are dry, and the heaviest rainfall is in winter or spring. In southern Arizona and New Mexico and in southwestern Texas, there is an appreciable winter rainfall, with another rainy period late in the summer. The quantity and distribution of rainfall in all breeding grounds are such that practically all agriculture depends upon irrigation. The summers are hot and dry in all breeding areas, but the winter climate varies greatly. In the central Columbia River breeding areas of Oregon and Washington and on the lower Snake River Plains of Idaho and eastern Oregon and in western Colorado, northern Nevada, and northern Utah, heavy snows and subzero temperatures are not uncommon. In the southern breeding areas, the moisture falls as rain, and the winters are short and cool.

The six most important breeding areas of the beet leafhopper are: Area 1, San Joaquin Valley in California; area 2, lower Colorado River drainage area; area 3, the Rio Grande area of southern New Mexico and western Texas; area 4, scattered breeding areas of western Colorado, Nevada, and Utah; area 5, the lower Snake River Plains of Idaho and eastern Oregon; and area 6, the central Columbia River of Oregon and Washington.

The important breeding areas that affect agriculture in the Great Valley of California lie along the foothills on the west side of the San Joaquin Valley. The largest overwintering and spring breeding grounds are in the eastern foothills of the Coastal Range, while the summer breeding grounds are in the Valley.

The lower Colorado River drainage breeding areas lie in southwestern Arizona, southeastern California, southern Nevada, and southern Utah. These are the most extensive spring breeding areas in the United States, and leafhoppers moving from them affect agriculture in Arizona, Utah, and western Colorado.

The breeding areas of western Colorado, northern Nevada, and northern Utah are small, localized, and scattered, and leafhoppers from them affect adjacent agricultural crops. The most important is within the Great Salt Lake Basin.

In Idaho and eastern Oregon, the breeding grounds are on the Snake River Plains at elevations below approximately 4,500 feet. Some summer reproduction occurs above this elevation, but these areas are generally repopulated each spring. The spring movements generally progress eastward across the Snake River Plains.

The breeding areas of Oregon and Washington lie in the dry sagebrush plains of the Columbia Basin from the Grand Coulee to central Oregon. Leafhoppers from those places infest sugar beets and other susceptible crops in the Yakima and Walla Walla Valleys and other smaller irrigated areas. In certain seasons they may be blown down the Columbia Gorge into the Willamette Valley.

Because the leafhopper does not hibernate during the winter but must feed when temperature permits activity, it requires a sequence of host plants. The principal plants on which it overwinters and produces one or more spring generations in the major breeding areas are mustards. The principal spring host plants in the various breeding areas are: Area 1, peppergrass (*Lepidium nitidum* and *L. latipes*), desert plantains (*Plantago insularis, P. fastigiata,* and *P. erecta*), and filaree (*Erodium cicutarium*); area 2, peppergrass (*Lepidium lasiocarpum*), patata (*Monolepis nuttalliana*), and desert plantain (*Plantago fastigiata*); area 3, perennial peppergrass (*Lepidium alyssoides*); area 4, filaree, blistercress (*Erysimum repandum*), and African mustard (*Malcolmia africana*); area 5, flixweed (*Descurainia sophia*), green tansymustard (*D. pinnata* ssp. *filipes*), perfoliate peppergrass (*Lepidium perfoliatum*), and tumblemustard (*Sisymbrium altissimum*); area 6, filaree, tumblemustard, flixweed, and green tansymustard.

Russian-thistle (*Salsola kali* var. *tenuifolia*) is the most important summer weed host of the leafhopper in the western United States. Other important summer host plants in various breeding areas are: Area 1, bractscale (*Atriplex bracteosa*) and fogweed (*A. expansa*); areas 2 and 3, chinchweed (*Pectis papposa*), *Tidestromia languinosa,* and *Trianthema portulacastrum;* area 3, *Acanthochiton wrightii;* areas 4, 5, and 6, smotherweed (*Bassia hyssopifolia*). In California, Idaho, Montana, Nevada, Utah, and Wyoming, the recently introduced halogeton (*Halogeton glomeratus*), which is poisonous to livestock, is also a summer host. Siberian mustard (*Chrispora tenella*) and kochia (*Kochia scoparia*) have invaded the breeding areas of southwestern Idaho, which emphasizes the fact that the beet leafhopper and curly top problem are not static and that the host-plant complex for both leafhopper and curly top is constantly changing.

With the maturing and drying of the summer hosts in the fall, the leafhoppers move to their winter hosts. If the summer weed hosts dry before the winter hosts germinate, the leafhoppers may be forced to feed on perennial plants and shrubs, the only available green vegetation, until the winter annuals germinate. These temporary food plants differ in the various breeding areas, as follows: Area 1, desert saltbush (*Atriplex polycarpa*), spiny saltbush (*A. spinifera* and *Lepidospartum squamatum*); area 2, creosotebush (*Larrea tridentata*), bur-sage (*Franseria dumosa*), mesquite (*Prosopis juliflora*), and spurges (*Euphorbia* spp.); area 3, creosotebush, saltbush, and snakeweed (*Gutierrezia* spp.); area 4, sagebrush (*Artemisia tridentata*), rabbitbrush (*Chrysothamnus* spp.), and snakeweed; areas 5 and 6, sagebrush and rabbitbrush. If the summer hosts dry before the winter hosts germinate, there may be a heavy mortality of the insects. If the winter hosts germinate before the summer hosts dry or are killed by frost, the mortality is greatly reduced and high leafhopper populations enter the winter.

Of the 16 important spring and summer weed hosts of the beet leafhopper listed for areas 1, 2, and 3, only filaree and Russian-thistle are introduced species; in areas 4, 5, and 6, only green tansymustard is a native. The others are introduced plants that have become established on abandoned, waste, and deteriorated range lands.

Evidently the geographical distribution of the beet leafhopper was once confined to the warmer arid regions of the southwestern United States but has spread northward as its introduced weed hosts became established. It is of interest to note that the first curly top outbreak in California occurred after Russian-thistle had become established in the State. Later investigations have shown that the outbreaks are influenced by the acreage of Russian-thistle in the San Joaquin Valley of California, Snake River Plains of Idaho, the central Columbia River area of Oregon and Washington, and to a lesser degree in Arizona, Colorado, New Mexico, Texas, and Utah.

After fields are abandoned or range is overgrazed, a succession of plants takes over. First come annual weeds, which have little forage value, followed by some annual grasses. Then, if no further disturbance occurs, this condition is followed by native perennial grasses and shrubs. The order of these changes in southern Idaho is: First, Russian-thistle; second, mustards; and third, downy chess, an introduced annual grass that is not a host of the beet leafhopper. Our observations indicate that range fires generally have their origin in areas where downy chess forms the plant cover or where it has entered deteriorated sagebrush areas to such an extent that it will carry fires. During the fire season, it is the greatest range fire hazard in the Intermountain Region; it will burn like tinder. If it is burned under favorable conditions, it may reseed itself and again form the cover, but under unfavorable conditions, such as wind erosion and trampling by livestock, mustards, principally tumblemustard, and Russian-thistle may appear. The shift from mustards and Russian-thistle to downy chess and then back to these weeds may continue in an endless cycle. On burned areas, mustards are generally first and then downy chess, but with further disturbance either Russian-thistle appears or the ground may become bare. Mixed stands of Russian-thistle and mustards are the most important combination of weed hosts for leafhopper reproduction, since the leafhoppers can overwinter and reproduce their spring and summer generations in the same area.

THROUGHOUT THEIR GEOGRAPHICAL range, many leafhoppers are destroyed each year by parasites and predators, which attack the leafhopper in all its stages and are evidently a factor in reducing the population in the breeding grounds. Large numbers of eggs are destroyed by minute parasitic wasps that develop within them. The nymphs and adults of the beet leafhopper are attacked by three groups of internal parasites—the big-eyed flies (Dorilaidae), the parasitic wasps (Dryinidae), and the twisted-winged parasites (Strepsiptera). The flies and wasps deposit their eggs in or on the leafhopper, and the resulting larvae develop within or partly within its body. Upon reaching maturity, the larvae work out of the leafhopper, causing its death. The twisted-winged parasites develop differently, as the female remains within the body of the leafhopper during its entire life and gives birth to living young. These tiny larvae crawl away, attach themselves to the first leafhopper they find, and bore into its body. They seldom become of any real importance, because the chances of their finding leafhoppers in which to develop are slight. The tendency of the beet leafhopper to move about from host to host during the season apparently reduces the effect of these parasites.

Several species of predacious bugs, one being a big-eyed bug (*Geocoris pallens*), destroy large numbers of leafhoppers by sucking out their body juices. Spiders, lizards, and birds reduce the number of the insects. The grazing of livestock, principally sheep, destroys many eggs in the plants which they eat.

Reducing curly top infection in susceptible crops by controlling the leafhopper with insecticides is a difficult problem, because continuous infection of the crops occurs by reinfestation during the susceptible period.

Applications of DDT will reduce beet leafhopper numbers and have a good residual toxicity, but it will not prevent the feeding of all leafhoppers that reinfest the fields. In instances where reinfestation occurs over a 2- to 3-week period, applications of DDT and other insecticides to tomato plants have not reduced the incidence of curly top. Double-hill planting of tomatoes has given limited protection against curly top under moderate to high infestations of the leafhopper in Utah. In other instances where reinfestations do not usually occur, such as in fields of sugar-beet seed, a single application of DDT in the fall has effectively reduced curly top.

Other control methods have been developed. First, the major host plants of this insect were determined and methods for their replacement by nonhost perennial grasses were studied. The replacement of weed hosts by perennial grasses may best be accomplished by reseeding the abandoned and burned areas. If native perennial grasses are still present, protection against excessive grazing will accomplish the same purpose. Because the perennial grasses remain green until late in the season, they do not constitute a fire hazard when compared with downy chess.

The second method is the chemical control of the beet leafhopper in weed-host areas.

J. R. DOUGLASS, *a South Carolinian, obtained his entomological training in Clemson Agricultural College, Kansas State Agricultural College, Cornell University, and Ohio State University. He has been with the Department of Agriculture since 1921. From 1923 to 1934 he was in charge of the Estancia, N. Mex., laboratory, investigating insects affecting beans in the Southwest, and since 1935 he has been in charge of the Twin Falls, Idaho, laboratory.*

WILLIAM C. COOK *is a graduate of Cornell University and has a doctor's degree from the University of Minnesota. He has been an entomologist in the Bureau of Entomology and Plant Quarantine since 1930. Before that time he was employed by the Montana Agricultural Experiment Station for work on cutworms, especially the pale western cutworm. He served from 1930 to 1943 in California, studying the beet leafhopper. Since 1943 he has been stationed at Walla Walla, Wash., studying wireworms and the pea aphid.*

Insects on Fruit

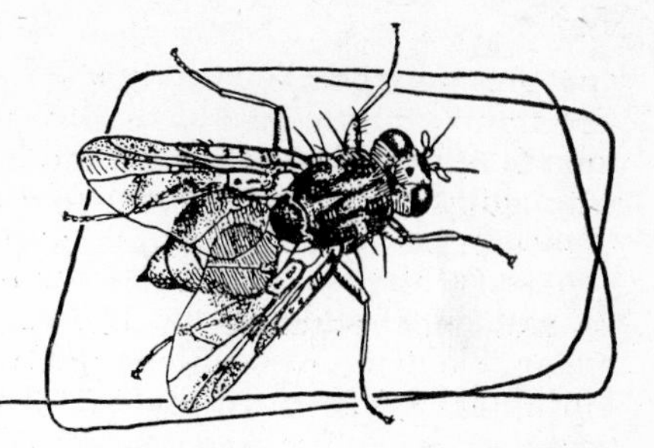

The Oriental Fruit Fly

Walter Carter

While making routine observations on the Mediterranean fruit fly in May 1946, Mabel Chong, a member of the Territorial entomology staff of Hawaii, noticed a stranger in the collection. The strange fly was *Dacus dorsalis,* the oriental fruit fly. It soon became evident that the newly arrived immigrant was thoroughly established on the principal Hawaiian Islands.

Within 2 years it became a major pest of almost every economic variety of fruit in the Islands. It was also found in many wild fruits and berries. It even invaded fruit stands inside stores and laid its eggs in imported fruits. Some garden flowers, including orchids, attracted hordes of the flies.

It is an attractive, clear-winged fly about the size of a house fly. Its body is light brown with bright-yellow markings on its middle section, or thorax. The female has a long egg-laying organ protruding from the end of the abdomen.

The fruit is "stung" with this ovipositor and eggs pass through it into the tissues below the surface. The eggs are laid in groups. Many different females may use the same sting hole for oviposition.

After about 2 days, depending on temperature, the eggs hatch. White, legless maggots emerge and begin to feed on fruit, in which decay soon starts. The maggots pass through three growth stages in about 10 days before they leave the fruit and enter the soil to pupate. They rarely pupate on the fruit if it remains on the tree. The pupa is enclosed in a brown cylindrical puparium. This stage of the insect's life, a quiescent one, lasts 8 to 12 days. Lowered temperatures markedly affect the length of the pupal stage. The adult fly, which emerges, is not sexually mature, but at the temperatures normally prevailing becomes so in 6 to 10 days. The adult life of the fly is conditioned by so many factors that it is difficult to set a normal longevity. Flies maintained at high levels of nutrition and fully active live much shorter lives than those kept at lower temperatures and on a low-grade diet. A fully active female probably has a normal life of about a month.

The losses the flies cause are of three kinds. The first is reduction of grade caused by the stings, which spoil the appearance of the fruit. This can occur in many fruits that are not favorable for complete development of the fly. Second, the entire fruit can be lost from damage by maggots and resulting decay. The third, an indirect loss, comes from quarantining any infested area to prevent dissemination of the fly.

Action against the fly was promptly taken by Territorial and private agencies. Since control of insect pests by means of parasites and predators has become traditional in Hawaii, the biological method received first attention. Work was started by the Territorial Board of Agriculture and Forestry in 1947 and extended in 1948. A cooperative project added the resources of the Hawaii Agricultural Experiment Station, the Bureau of Entomology and Plant Quarantine, and two private research institutions, the Experiment Station of the Hawaiian Sugar Planters' Association and the Pineapple Research Institute of Hawaii.

Agricultural interests in California had become thoroughly alarmed, and in 1948 a committee from the California legislature visited Hawaii. The committee returned to California convinced that the situation presented grave implications to the agriculture of the mainland.

In the meantime, the depredations of the fly reached a climax of economic loss when the flowers of the orchid *Vanda Miss Joaquim* were found infested with eggs. Shipments of this flower and, as a precaution, all other *Vanda* flowers were stopped by embargo. The orchid industry had begun to assume considerable importance in Hawaii, and its abrupt cessation pointed up the necessity for more scientific work on the problem of the fruit fly.

Congressional appropriations were made available on July 1, 1949, in addition to funds from the Research and Marketing Act. The Bureau of Entomology and Plant Quarantine proceeded to assemble its enlarged staff in Hawaii. California made an appropriation for research in Hawaii and in California, and enlarged contributions from Territorial agencies also became available for a concerted attack.

When a new insect arrives in an area and follows the typical pattern of such arrivals in a favorable environment and without hindrance from parasites, a research program must attack the problem from all practicable angles. The approach to the problem in Hawaii appeared to offer five possibilities: Biological control, chemical control, area control, ecology-biology, and commodity treatments. A group began work on each aspect. Later a project in insect physiology was set up.

By far the greater part of the cooperative investigations are for the benefit of mainland agriculture. We hope the biological-control project will give immediate relief in Hawaii, but even that project, by reducing fly numbers, will help reduce the opportunity for chance migrants to reach the mainland. It will also provide a reservoir of beneficial insects in local fruit, which will be available for use should a mainland infestation be discovered.

Commodity treatments also have an immediate value to Hawaiian economy, although few commodities are of sufficient quantity or quality for export. The success of these treatments no doubt will influence the future production of such agricultural commodities as papayas, since before the first approved commodity treatment there was little incentive for small farmers to produce for export. The greatest value of commodity treatments, however, will be to any infested mainland area whose fruits would have to be treated before shipment.

The chemical-control project is designed primarily as a proving ground for old and new insecticides against this one insect. Its data will be essential to orchardists and other producers on the mainland, should the fly reach there.

Area control is primarily for the development of large-scale emergency techniques, equipment, and methods of application to meet a mainland infestation.

The chief purpose of the ecology-biology project is the study of the effect of climate on the insect to permit a carefully based prediction of the possible distribution of the fly on the mainland. Should an infestation develop, the data will help in establishment of safe areas, thus contributing immeasurably to the free movement of commodities.

The term ecology-biology requires some explanation. Ecology is primarily concerned with the study of the insect in its natural environment or surroundings. Biology is intended to cover the detailed life history of the insect as studied in the laboratory. All ecology is biology and all good biology recognizes the necessity for interpretation of data in terms of the insect's environments.

In nature, the fly feeds on "honeydew" deposited by other insects and on decaying fruit that has been broken down by micro-organisms. Slight changes in composition of the insect's diet, particularly in protein and vitamin constituents, may profoundly affect egg-laying capacity. For example, flies fed a diet of macerated papaya, honey, and yeast in a laboratory laid a total of 655 eggs, as against 21,538 eggs from the same number of flies fed the same basic diet plus a source of protein and vitamins. One female in the latter group produced 3,062 eggs. Diet also affects the length of time necessary for the fly to develop its eggs. In the basic-diet group, this was from 21 to 71 days; with the fortified diet, from 6 to 14 days.

California fruits have been tested as hosts of the fly. This study is of critical importance if the significance of an incipient infestation in California is to be properly evaluated.

For example, some varieties of plum are very susceptible, others not at all. Cotton bolls, in the young, firm stage, are susceptible. Citrus fruits strongly attract egg-laying females, but very little larval development takes place in them; perhaps the rag of the citrus interferes with the progress of the maggot into the flesh. Apparently citrus is not a good host and is not likely to be responsible for the development of sizable fly populations. Apples also become heavily infested but are poor hosts for larvae, maybe because they rot slowly.

The ideal host is one that is fleshy and succulent, with a firm but not too thick epidermis, and developed beyond the early immature stage. Bruising and damaging sometimes makes a poor host into a good one. More than 150 Hawaiian hosts have been recorded. When large numbers of flies are present, the pressure to lay eggs is terrific. Eggs are laid in strange places: A ping-pong ball punctured with a few pinholes; a knothole in a wall; even on an entomologist's thumb. Host records, therefore, require careful evaluation, especially if serious economic consequences might result.

The orchid *Vanda Miss Joaquim* and its record as a host is a striking example of the necessity for careful evaluation. Eggs have been found on these flowers and, under very special circumstances, larvae have developed. As a result, an embargo against the flowers coming into the mainland was placed by the Bureau of Entomology and Plant Quarantine. Later, flowers were allowed to come in after being fumigated. A subsequent study has shown that the commercial flower does not present any hazard as it is only in unopened buds, kept in a saturated atmosphere and allowed to rot, that larvae could develop. When this was learned, the requirement of fumigation was discontinued.

Guava is the most important host fruit in the Islands. It covers many thousand acres of gulch land and is responsible for the greater part of the fly infestation. It fruits heavily, and the two main fruiting seasons a year give a carry-over of late fruit to connect them up. It is an ideal host fruit, and in the absence of parasitism or other interfering factors, enormous populations can build up. A biological control for guava fruiting would be of importance in the control of the oriental fruit flies, but recent build-up of parasite populations has reduced the need for such drastic action.

The mountain masses in Hawaii offer an opportunity to study the insect in a wide range of conditions. Field ecological stations have been established on the islands of Maui and Hawaii at altitudes from 40 feet, with the mild and equable climate typical of the lowlands, up through the more temperate regions where deciduous fruit and citrus are common, to the high, wind-swept mountain slopes at 9,200 feet, where only alpine plants and low-growing shrubs exist.

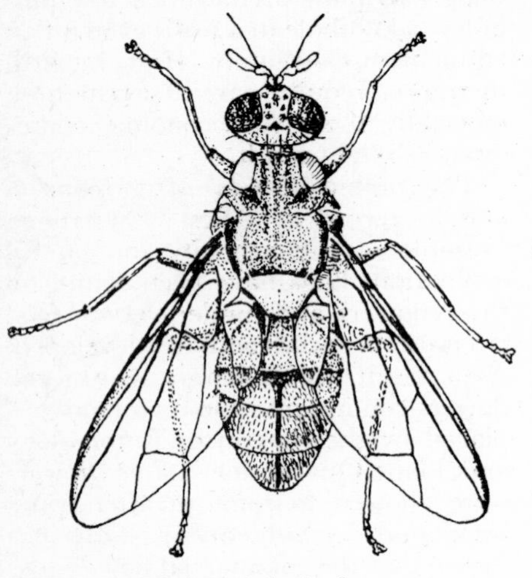

Oriental fruit fly.

Rainfall varies greatly between stations, from less than 20 to more than 300 inches annually. In more than one station heavy mountain fogs roll in regularly each day.

Temperature and host availability stand out in these studies as two major limiting factors. Above 3,500 feet altitude, low-temperature effects are noted. Activity of the flies is greatly reduced at the higher, cooler stations, but they live longer than at the lower, warmer stations.

At Haleakala (9,200 feet), the larval period is extended to 31 days as against 28 days at Pohakuloa (6,500 feet) and 10 days at Hilo (50 feet). Pupae are highly susceptible to low temperatures. No emergence takes place at the higher stations unless the temperature goes above 61° F. (This is in contrast to the Mediterranean fruit fly, which has a threshold temperature for emergence of 56°.) Ability to deposit eggs is also materially affected by temperature. It is not attained at all at the higher altitudes in winter and, even with richly fortified diets, the period before egg laying begins is greatly extended in summer. Many areas on the mainland have far more rigorous temperature conditions than those recorded in Hawaii.

Host availability can limit the development of large populations of flies at altitudes where temperatures are favorable. The ideal situation for the fly is a succession of hosts throughout the season—a break in the sequence of hosts means that only the individuals able to live over until a new host is available can infest the later appearing host. Host availability affects the size of fly populations in Hawaii, but at the lower elevations enough incidental hosts are always available to permit the fly to carry on.

The ideal way to determine whether the fly will survive weather conditions in various places on the United States mainland would be to take colonies of flies there and study them in those specific environments. That obviously is impossible. In order to determine the survival possibilities for the fly in any of the more likely mainland fruit-growing areas, a unique method has been developed. It permits the duplication of mainland temperatures and humidities in a cabinet so large that the flies can be maintained under suitable conditions for their survival if the climate will permit it. These bioclimatic cabinets, as they are called, have been in operation since 1951. The data obtained in the first studies indicated that it is possible to map the possible and probable distribution of the fly on the United States mainland. Should an incipient infestation develop in any of those areas, the maps would be of great value in determining safe areas. Thus the need for quarantine treatment might be met.

CONTROL OF INSECT PESTS by other insects is standard practice in Hawaii, where notable successes have been achieved.

The techniques are highly specialized. First it is necessary to determine the native home of the insect pest because that is the most likely area in which to find its insect enemies. The next step is exploration. Explorers must have scientific training, skill, and the ability to get along with people. They must accustom themselves to unusual and often inadequate food. They are exposed to many tropical diseases.

Collections of fruit fly pupae, made in the native habitat, are rushed by air to Honolulu, where they are put in quarantine rooms without delay. There, under rigid inspection, they are held for the emergence of fruit flies and parasites.

The habits of the parasites are then subjected to an intensive study. Their ability to attack the fruit fly, and not other parasites, must be determined. That is a critical operation, for slight variations in technique often spell the difference between successful breeding and failure. The taxonomist assumes an important role, because many of the parasite species are alike in appearance but unlike in habits. One species therefore must be separated from another so that only pure cultures are studied.

When it is determined that they are primary, or capable of parasitizing only the fruit fly, they are released for the laboratory rearing of large numbers, which in turn are liberated in the field among heavily infested fruits. Close watch is then kept of the points of liberation, and the recovery of the parasites later is proof of their establishment in the field.

Exploration was begun in 1947, when the Territorial Board of Agriculture and Forestry arranged with Leopoldo B. Uichanco of the College of Agriculture in the Philippines to send fruit fly material to Hawaii. Later Q. C. Chock, an entomologist on the staff of the Territorial Board moved his headquarters to the College at Los Banos while he explored the area for additional material. He succeeded in getting a predaceous beetle (*Thyreocephalus albertisi*) to Hawaii, where it was successfully bred and liberated in the field.

Noel L. R. Krauss, also an entomologist with the Territorial Board of Agriculture and Forestry, was sent to Malaya in May 1948. In the following 11 months he sent to Honolulu 85 shipments containing nearly 340,000 fruit fly puparia. From these emerged some 19,000 adult fruit fly parasites of about 14 species.

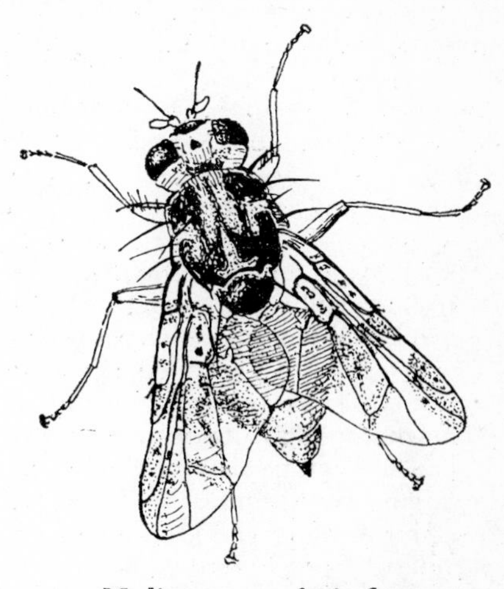

Mediterranean fruit fly.

The initial successes greatly encouraged extension of the work. Exploration has been extended to every tropical area in the world.

Results have been good. More than 2 million puparia in 465 shipments have been received and reared. From them some 106,000 parasites of at least 40 species have been obtained. Many of the parasites could not be reared on the oriental fruit fly, and some that have been released have not yet been recovered.

The successful species thus far came from Malaya in the early collections made by Krauss. Four species are well established, and the evidence from the field is clear that they are materially reducing the numbers of fruit flies and the numbers of infested fruit. It is still too early to know at what levels fruit fly populations will be stabilized or what the relative role of the introduced parasites and already established biological-control factors such as ants will be.

The chemical-control project has for its objective the control of fruit flies by means of insecticides, which may be used as sprays against adult flies or as residual sprays to kill flies that might emerge later. Information obtained would be primarily for use on the mainland.

Another direct approach is the use of soil insecticides, which would take advantage of the habits of the fly in entering the soil toward the end of the larval stage.

Indirect methods of chemical control to be developed include the use of lures and repellents, which would attract the flies to poisoned sprays or deter them from settling on fruit.

The methods available to this project are well standardized, but under Hawaiian conditions the standards have had to be modified.

Orchards, as generally understood, are rare in Hawaii. It is almost impossible to find well-ordered ranks of evenly spaced trees. A banana plantation has been used successfully for insecticide experiments despite close planting, awkward ditches, and narrow roads, which made a tractor standard equipment for pulling out stalled spraying machines. The nearest approach to a formally designed orchard experiment was made possible by bulldozing trails through an area of wild guava so that a series of plots could be set up.

Testing new insecticides has been an important preliminary to field experiments. Usually one adds a measured amount of the insecticide to a small piece of blotting paper in the bottom of a small screen cage. The flies are then introduced into the cage and are exposed to the chemical when they walk over it or come in contact with its fumes.

More than 250 compounds, many of them newly synthesized by the division of insecticide investigations at Beltsville, Md., have been tested. The new organic insecticides have proved very useful in the studies; all the successful ones are in that class.

DDT, parathion, dieldrin, aldrin, and Dilan are effective in varying degrees. DDT, because of its long residual toxicity, is probably one of the most practical. Parathion is outstanding and is so toxic to flies that its residues, although small, still function the third week after spraying.

Diet seems to affect the resistance of the flies to insecticides. Flies fed a rich protein-vitamin diet can resist even the most toxic materials. Flies fed an ordinary fruit pulp-sugar-water diet showed 66 percent mortality after 48 hours of exposure to parathion, 1 part to 200,000 parts of water, but only 1 percent of the protein-fed flies died.

Some insecticides are more toxic than others to the fruit fly parasites. This is significant in Hawaii, where the beneficial insects are so important, and would require similar consideration if it ever becomes necessary to try to establish the parasites on the mainland.

Lures have been developed that will attract the male fly for long distances. One of them is a clear liquid, methyl eugenol. More than 1 million male flies were caught in 45 traps from July to September, 1950. Some of them were attracted to the lure from a distance of a half mile. Use of the lure, poisoned with parathion, is an effective way to rid an area of the male flies.

The female fly is attracted to fermenting baits, such as a sugar-yeast combination. New lures six times more effective than the old standard lure have been developed, first from protein hydrolysate and later by using vitamin B complex. The next step is to test the constituents of the complex to increase further its effectiveness if possible and to reduce costs. An effective eradication program or an orchard spray program, in the event the fly ever becomes permanently established, would benefit immeasurably from lures that could be added to poison sprays.

The area-control project is closely related to chemical control. Area control theoretically would best follow a well-developed chemical control, but delay could not be permitted if large-scale control methods were to be available for early mainland use. Area control has only one purpose—to develop techniques and methods whereby an incipient infestation could be contained and eradicated.

In Hawaii, it is possible to develop techniques and methods only because no attempt at eradication is feasible. Even an operation covering a whole island would not eradicate the fly, because of its ability to travel long distances.

Data on fly movement have been obtained by releasing and later trapping marked flies. A spot of color was dabbed on the thorax of flies, which had been chilled to permit easy handling. Marked male flies have been recovered 20 miles from their point of liberation. Flies have crossed an ocean strait 9 miles wide. They evidently move back and forth over each island and possibly over more than one island. They can be carried on the outside of fast-moving vehicles for great distances. Such mobility would complicate quarantine and control measures should an infestation occur on the mainland.

Aerosol spraying would be an ideal method for controlling the insect in urban areas, which in Hawaii are rich in host fruits. Tests with light doses of DDT applied in this way have been promising, having reduced adult fly populations by 98 percent. The tests were made in villages on the windward side of Oahu, which are relatively free from reinfestation, each entire village being used as a sample control area.

The first step taken in area control was to determine the various types of areas, since control would differ, depending on whether the area was purely urban with fruit fly hosts in home gardens, or urban with wild hosts nearby, or extensive wild-host areas. After 18 months of intensive study of type areas, it was decided to increase the size of field experiments so that they would serve as control-demonstration plots.

Control operations over the wild-host areas, which are mostly covered with guavas, have had to be by airplane. Here again, the habits of the fly have complicated the technique. Airplane application deposits most of the insecticide on the upper surfaces of the leaves; the fly spends most of its time on the lower surfaces. Addition of sugar to a DDT emulsion resulted in bringing the flies to the top surfaces of the leaves and greatly increased control.

Lanai Island is well suited for area control. It has approximately 89,000 acres, including a low, tree-covered mountain range, a town full of host trees, large areas devoted to pineapple plantings, and almost-desert slopes. The movements of the flies have been followed carefully. The host fruits, wild and cultivated, have been mapped and their seasonal sequences plotted. Wild-host areas, principally guava on the lower mountain slopes, have been aerially surveyed to determine the feasibility of defoliation techniques that will eliminate the current crop of fruits. Guava areas on the island have been divided into three plots of approximately 500 acres each to provide three separate experiments. Guavas elsewhere were too scattered for effective spraying, and were either temporarily grubbed out or treated with a defoliant spray to knock off the current crop.

The central town of Lanai was also divided for experimental purposes. One-half was treated with a fog sprayer, and the other with dilute spray. Strict sanitation was practiced, and all fallen fruit collected and disposed of.

Two other small and isolated areas on the island were used for some other experiments. Subject only to limitations imposed by weather, the operations proceeded at the same time so that actually a huge control program, organized on an experimental basis, was under way. Upon completion of

970134°—52——37

the actual operations, studies to evaluate the results were conducted for several months.

ONE MAJOR SOURCE of loss that can result from infestation is the embargo that must be placed promptly on the movement of commodities out of an area infested with fruit flies. Hawaiian agriculture has experienced many of these embargoes.

The effect of an incipient infestation on the economy of a large fruit-growing area in California, if shipments out of the area were suddenly stopped, would not be difficult to visualize. Authorities in California have been so alarmed at the prospect that a staff of investigators has started work on the problem in that State.

The immediate answer is the development of commodity treatments. They can be studied only in Hawaii, where infested fruits can be used. The limiting factor in the rapid development of treatments is the fact that a treatment that will kill the pest is likely to damage the commodity. Therefore two aspects must be studied. One is the effect of the treatment on the insect eggs and larvae, and the other the tolerance of the commodity to the treatment.

Tolerance varies greatly between different fruits. The tolerance of the huge list of California fruits cannot be judged by the way tropical fruits in Hawaii react. The California staff, therefore, is testing the tolerance of those fruits to treatments developed in Hawaii.

The procedure to be followed before any particular fruit or vegetable can be shipped from Hawaii is exacting. First, it must be effective. In fact, treatments which have been permitted are usually more severe than the statistical chances of infestation would seem to make necessary. Second, it must be practical so as not to impose too great a burden or expense on the shipper. Third, it must leave no harmful or objectionable residue on the fruit.

Vapor-heat treatment, the most widely used, consists of heating the fruit for 8¾ hours at 110° F. in a saturated atmosphere. Some fruits require a period of heating at somewhat lower temperatures and at reduced humidity in order to tolerate the long period at 110°, so that the entire process takes more than 16 hours. Therefore it is not deemed the most practical method for treating large quantities of fruits, especially as it requires specially designed rooms and equipment. In Hawaii the vapor-heat method has been approved for papayas, zucchini, bell peppers, pineapples, and tomatoes.

FUMIGATION with toxic gases offers the best solution for large-scale operation because, with a suitable gas, freight cars could be treated and sealed off so that part of the treatment could actually take place en route and involve a minimum of interference with commerce.

Methyl bromide can be used to fumigate the fresh fruits and vegetables that will tolerate it. The standard dose is 2 pounds of the fumigant for each 1,000 cubic feet of space. Many commodities will not tolerate methyl bromide. In Hawaii it has been used only for fresh pineapples.

New fumigants are being sought. Two other bromine compounds, ethylene dibromide and ethylene chlorobromide, may soon be available as permitted fumigants. They are so toxic to fruit fly larvae and eggs that greatly reduced dosages can be used. This lowers the hazard of injury to the fruits.

Hundreds of other compounds are being tested for their toxicity to eggs and larvae. As rapidly as the tests are completed, the data are sent on to the California workers for inclusion in their tolerance tests.

Low temperature is a third possible method of treatment. These tests take longer than others, because of the prolonged development time for the insect at low temperatures. The results, however, are gradually accumulating and offer promise for some commodities which are normally stored at low temperature.

The index of infestation is determined by making systematic collections of fruits and vegetables in the field, holding them in specially designed boxes, and recording the average number of flies emerging from each host.

Theoretically the severity of infestation in commodities for export determines the degree of treatment, but a valid procedure for determining incidence of infestation is difficult to achieve. In actual practice, commodity treatments are determined on such an extreme safety factor that the indexes of infestation up to now have not really functioned in establishing these treatments. One example illustrates the difficulties. A year's collection of papaya for index-of-infestation purposes showed one larva in about 4,000 mature green papayas, which is the stage used for commercial shipping. From a recent collection, however, a single mature green fruit yielded 68 oriental fruit fly pupae. With the tremendous reduction in populations of the fly now being recorded, however, it should be possible to make practical use of the index in establishing treatment levels.

WALTER CARTER *is a graduate of Montana State College and holds advanced degrees from the University of Minnesota. After 5 years with the Bureau of Entomology and Plant Quarantine, in charge of entomological work on beet leafhopper, he joined the staff of the Pineapple Research Institute of Hawaii as the head of its entomology department in 1930. Since then he has had wide experience with tropical entomology, including membership in an international commission to the Gold Coast of West Africa. In 1949 his services were made available to the Bureau of Entomology and Plant Quarantine by the Pineapple Research Institute to organize and direct the research on oriental fruit fly. He returned to full-time duty with the Institute on July 1, 1951.*

The Mexican Fruit Fly

P. A. Hoidale

The Mexican fruit fly is an international traveler that pays no attention to boundary lines and is as unwelcome abroad as at home. Each fall and winter large numbers of the flies move from northeastern Mexico to southern Texas and infest grapefruit and oranges in groves in the Rio Grande Valley. Shipments of infested fruit can easily spread the fruit flies over wide areas and cause infestations in fruit-growing regions. It is therefore imperative that every precaution be taken to prevent their spread from the rather isolated infested area in southern Texas.

The Bureau of Entomology and Plant Quarantine is charged with that responsibility. Over a period of several years, through its quarantine regulations, it has supervised the movements of citrus fruit from the lower Rio Grande Valley of Texas to the rest of the country. Although many thousands of carloads of fruit are shipped from that area annually, the Mexican fruit fly has not been able to spread outside the regulated area. The area regulated in Texas on account of the fly consists of the southern part of Jim Wells County and all of Brooks, Cameron, Dimmitt, Hidalgo, La Salle, Webb, and Willacy Counties.

The Mexican fruit fly is the principal citrus-infesting fruit fly native to Mexico. Entomologists first believed it was a native of the Tropics and had spread northward, but research has indicated that its original home was in northeastern Mexico in the States of San Luis Potosi, Tamaulipas, and Nuevo Leon. With the coming of modern transportation and through its own migratory habits, it has spread throughout most of Mexico to southern Texas and as far south as Panama. It destroys large quantities of fruit in Mexico and Texas annually and is a serious threat to other American fruit-growing sections. Not being a tropical insect, it can stand freezing weather and still live and infest fruit. It can adapt itself to a dry country as well as to rainy areas, mountains as well as the coastal plains.

The adult fly is a brightly colored insect with beautifully marked wings. It is considerably larger than a house fly, but the female particularly is noticeably different from flies of that group. The ovipositor sheath of the Mexican fruit fly is nearly as long as its thorax and abdomen. The ovipositor proper is a sharp, needlelike organ, capable of depositing eggs even beneath the thick rinds of citrus fruit. When the gravid female is ready to lay her eggs she selects suitable fruit on the tree and deposits 1 to 10 or more eggs in the pulp of the fruit. The incubation period of the eggs, length of larval life, and days spent in the pupal stage vary with the temperature, variety of fruit, and other factors. The shortest period from egg to adult appears to be about 36 days, while the maximum is close to 150.

Besides tropical fruits like the sapodilla, white sapote, and mangoes, the fly infests oranges, grapefruit, apples, peaches, pears, pomegranates, quinces, and yellow chapotes in the field. The yellow chapote, *Sargentia greggi,* is the wild host of primary importance in Mexico. It abounds along the mountain ranges in San Luis Potosi, Tamaulipas, and Nuevo Leon. It is a close relative of citrus and resembles an orange tree in size, shape, and color of foliage. The mature fruit is nearly the size of an olive and is single-seeded. The seed constitutes most of the fruit, which is said to be edible but is of small economic importance in Mexico. The plant is generally distributed for a distance of over 200 miles along the mountains wherever moisture conditions are favorable. It provides an important reservoir from which flies originate and migrate to establish infestations in Texas citrus groves.

In southern Texas, the flies begin to move into the groves in numbers in the late fall. The influx of flies continues during the winter and the infestation builds up to its height in late March and April. Then it begins to diminish. By early summer infested fruit is difficult to find. Some infestation may be present throughout the summer, if fruit is left on the trees, but it frequently happens that no infestation can be found in a grove in June that was heavily infested in April. The operation of a large number of traps over a period of years has established that there is a general exodus of flies from the groves in Texas in the late spring. We do not know just where the flies go. That they may leave the groves in search of their preferred wild host, the yellow chapote, is one possibility, but it may be that the flies do not prefer an environment where there is no opportunity for oviposition and that the harvesting of the fruit causes them to move out in search of a place to lay their eggs. Because the flies do not move into the groves until late fall and as they leave in the late spring, Texas citrus plantings are relatively free of infestation over a large part of the year.

The fruit flies prefer heavily foliaged groves in which to rest as well as to infest fruit. No grove is immune to infestation, but larvae are rarely found in fruit on young trees or trees with sparse foliage. Flies apparently prefer to lay their eggs in fruit on the lower branches. Few larvae are ever found in fruit high in the tree or on outer exposed branches. Flies do not normally infest fallen fruit.

TRAPS ARE SET in groves in the Rio Grande Valley primarily to determine when the migration period begins and ends. Traps do not control the fruit fly, but trapping records form an excellent basis for forecasting the probable amount of larval infestation that can be expected and when the first-treatment period will begin. The records of their operation also have been beneficial in working out the life history of the fly in Texas. Without them it is doubtful if its migatory habits would have been known.

Fruit flies are attracted to various lures for feeding purposes, but no substance has been found that is outstandingly attractive to either sex of the Mexican fruit fly. As a result of work done by A. C. Baker and others, the lure that was found to be the most practical for use in Texas groves comprises 6 pounds of brown sugar dissolved in 5 gallons of water. Traps are filled with the bait as soon as the mixture is made. It is not necessary to wait for fermentation to take place, although fermentation apparently enhances its usefulness.

The trap used in Texas, an adaptation of a Mexican house fly trap, is made of glass. It is somewhat bottle-shaped, with a concave bottom which forms a receptacle for holding the bait. The insects enter through a large opening in the center of the bottom. They are removed through a small opening in the top.

The fruit flies most frequently are trapped in heavy shade. More of them are caught on the outer rows of the grove than in the center. Traps set in trees planted along irrigation canals and close to windbreaks usually take more flies than those set in trees with sparse foliage, where they are exposed to high winds.

Traps are usually set in groves in groups of 20. They are placed about shoulder high and as near the center of the tree as possible. They should not be in contact with foliage but be visible from all sides. They are set out in the grove with at least one line of them near an outer row. They are examined and rebaited once a week. One inspector can examine and rebait approximately 200 traps daily. About 8,000 traps are in constant use in the Rio Grande Valley.

Citrus fruit grown in the Rio Grande Valley is inspected in the field before it is certified for shipment. Because the northward movement of flies from Mexico to Texas blankets the whole citrus area, all groves in Texas are considered to be infested with the Mexican fruit fly and all the fruit produced in the area is subject to inspection and treatment and certification before shipment.

The field inspection of citrus fruit consists of examining the fruit on the tree for off-color and cutting all fruit on the tree or the ground that shows any signs of insect injury. Grapefruit usually shows no outside evidence of being infested other than taking on a slight orange color. Oranges, however, may develop an enlarged brown spot, which shows where the larvae have worked within a segment. Newly hatched larvae are hard to find, but their presence frequently is betrayed by small brown spots in the rag underneath the skin on each end of the fruit. Examination includes cutting off a small part of each end of the fruit. If no telltale signs of infestation are visible, no further examination is made. If the small brown spots are visible, larvae, with rare exceptions, are found within the fruit. Fruit in which the female fly has laid her eggs soon falls from the tree, and the larvae complete their development before going into the soil to pupate. Before leaving, the larvae burrow through the fruit and make it wholly unfit for food.

Fruit-sterilization methods have been developed that will prevent the shipment of infested fruit and still permit the movement of Texas citrus fruits without danger of establishing infestations elsewhere.

When the first infestation was discovered in a grapefruit planting near Mission, Tex., in April 1927, the presence of such a dangerous fruit pest in American groves was viewed with great concern by many growers. Quarantine measures were promptly promulgated to control the shipment of fruit and to eradicate the pest. It was hoped that eradication could be effected within a few years, but the migratory habits of the fly were not known at that time. It was soon found that there was no way of preventing flies from moving into Texas citrus groves from northeastern Mexico and that eradication was impossible. Research efforts were then directed toward developing ways and means of treating Texas fruit which would permit it to be shipped safely to other fruit areas.

One method of sterilization consists of lowering the inside temperature of the fruit to 32°–33° F. and holding it there for 18 days, or keeping the temperature at 33°–34° for 22 days. Either will kill any larvae in the fruit.

The second method is more economical and more widely used in Texas. Known as the vapor-heat process, it involves raising the inside temperature of the fruit. Larvae can be killed much more quickly with high temperatures than with low temperatures. In order to treat large quantities of fruit properly, specially designed rooms are necessary; the rooms also can be used during the regular packing-house procedure for the coloring of fruit. Treatment consists of forcing a large volume of air, saturated water vapor, and water in the form of a fine mist through the load of fruit, at a temperature of not less than 110°. After the inside temperature of the fruit has been raised to that point, it is maintained there for the duration of the holding period. The process is then reversed and a large quantity of dry air is forced through the load of fruit in order to reduce the temperature as rapidly as possible and permit the fruit to be packed for shipping.

P. A. Hoidale *began his career in the Department of Agriculture with the Bureau of Plant Industry in April 1915. In 1917 he transferred to the Federal Horticultural Board in the control of the pink bollworm. When the Mexican fruit fly was first found in the Rio Grande Valley, he was placed in charge of the control project.*

Spider Mites, Insects, and DDT

Howard Baker

As recently as 1944, apple growers throughout the United States feared that the codling moth would put them out of business. Other insects and mites were of comparatively little concern. Today the situation is reversed. The codling moth has been reduced to a pest of minor importance and a number of other insects and mites have become problems. DDT is primarily responsible for this reversal: It brought the codling moth under control, but factors associated with its use have been responsible for some measure of the resurgence of other pests.

Others had had similar experiences. Cotton growers saw the cotton aphid increase following applications of calcium arsenate to control the boll weevil. Pecan growers have seen the black pecan aphid increase following application of bordeaux mixture to control pecan scab. Citrus growers found more scale insects and mites after the use of sprays to control diseases or to correct nutritional deficiencies.

Never before, however, have so many pests with such a wide range of habits and characteristics increased to injurious levels following application of any one material as has occurred following the use of DDT in apple spray programs.

Losses due to the codling moth reached alarming proportions during the 1930's and early 1940's. Fortunate indeed was the grower who could hold them down to 10 or 20 percent of his crop. Much larger losses were not unusual. Despite the use of stronger spray mixtures and more frequent and heavier applications, control became more and more difficult. The harder the orchardists fought the codling moth, the harder it was to control and the greater the injury it caused. The codling moth was so all-important that other pests received but scant attention. That was the situation when DDT was introduced to a discouraged industry.

First tested by a few growers on a large scale in 1945, DDT became generally available to the industry in 1946. It promptly proved its worth in checking the codling moth and soon displaced lead arsenate or other materials in most apple-insect spray programs. Timely, thorough applications of 1 or 2 pounds of a 50 percent DDT wettable powder per 100 gallons of spray in an average of three to six cover sprays, depending on the region, brought the codling moth under control. Growers who had become accustomed to losses of 15 percent or more of their crop are now dissatisfied with losses of more than 1 or 2 percent. Many have losses of less than 1 percent.

DDT also controls other insect pests on apples. It is effective against most leaf-feeding insects that attack apples and pears, such as tent caterpillars, fall webworms, Japanese beetles, casebearers, leafhoppers, and, to some extent, aphids. Some pests it does not control, at least not when used in ordinary, practical amounts. Some other pests seem to be even more serious following the use of DDT than when it is not used. Various species of orchard spider mites, the red-banded leaf roller, and some scale insects, pests formerly serious only occasionally or in restricted areas, have threatened to cause or have caused serious injury more often than formerly and on a more general scale. Additional insects, for instance the woolly apple aphid, plum curculio, and yellow-necked caterpillar, have also increased in numbers in some places.

Why is this?

Several reasons have been advanced. Research might uncover others. The effect of DDT on the natural enemies of injurious species and the tendency to omit materials, such as lead arsenate and mineral-oil emulsions, from standard DDT spray programs are the two reasons most commonly advanced to explain the situation.

Many orchard pests are normally greatly reduced in numbers and held in check by natural enemies, particularly parasitic and predacious insects and predacious mites and spiders, that feed on and destroy them. DDT is highly toxic to many of these natural enemies. It kills them off at a much higher rate than it does some of the injurious species on which they prey. That is one reason why such pests as orchard spider mites, red-banded leaf roller, and woolly apple aphid are apt to develop in injurious numbers when DDT is used in the spray program. Not all outbreaks of these and other species are associated with the use of DDT—other factors are involved, factors that we do not fully know or understand yet.

DDT is less effective against some insects than materials it has displaced in apple spray schedules—materials such as lead arsenate and mineral-oil emulsions, or their substitutes, that had a wider range of usefulness than to control only the codling moth. This has led to increases in importance of some of the insects that were controlled through their use. It accounts somewhat for the increase in injury caused by such insects as the plum curculio, red-banded leaf roller, and San Jose and Forbes scales.

DDT AND THE changes in the comparative importance of the insects and mites infesting apples that have occurred following its use have profoundly affected apple spray schedules and the trend of research to develop the simplest possible spray program. Attention used to be focused on finding and developing a material that would control the codling moth better than lead arsenate. Now it is directed toward working out a complete spray program that will take care of all pests that may be present. This means finding and developing materials that can be used with DDT or substituted for it to control such pests as mites, leaf rollers, curculios, aphids, and scales, as well as the codling moth. A great deal of progress has been made.

VARIOUS SPECIES OF MITES, formerly serious pests only occasionally or in restricted areas, came into the limelight along with DDT and have since caused, or threatened to cause, serious injury each season in all important orchard areas. The most important are the European red mite, two-spotted spider mite, and Pacific mite. The clover or brown mite has increased in Colorado and other western fruit-producing areas, and several new or little-known species of *Tetranychus* and other spider mites have become more important. For example, at least 11 species of mites in 1952 were known to infest orchards in the Yakima Valley of Washington; three of them were recognized in that area for the first time in 1950.

Orchard spider mites may be divided roughly into two groups for control purposes—those that overwinter in the egg stage on the trees and those that overwinter as adults in trash, under bark scales, and in other protected places, mostly on the ground. The European red mite and clover mite are in the first group. Most of the others, if not all, are in the second group.

Dormant sprays are quite effective against the overwintering eggs of mites. They delay or obviate the need for summer sprays to control the species that overwinter in this stage, depending on the timeliness and thoroughness of their application and whether weather conditions during the growing season are favorable for mite activity and development. Mineral-oil emulsions diluted to provide 3 or occasionally 4 percent oil in the dilute spray are most commonly employed in dormant sprays applied to control mites. Lime-sulfur is occasionally used; it has some value but is less effective than oil and is not generally recommended unless needed for some other purpose. Some dinitro insecticides also have shown promise for use in dormant sprays against mite eggs, but they are more likely to injure the trees than oil if used carelessly and not strictly according to directions.

Another material that has given good, early-season control of the species of mites overwintering in the egg stage is parathion. One pound of a 25 percent wettable powder per 100 gallons of spray in the calyx application has given as good control of these species as a 3 percent dormant oil. Parathion cannot be used safely on all varieties so early in the season; it may cause serious injury to McIntosh and related apples and increase russeting of other varieties, such as Golden Delicious and Jonathan.

Dormant sprays are of little value against the two-spotted spider mite, Pacific mite, and other species wintering as adults. With some of these species, this is partly because they feed on other hosts before moving into the apple trees.

Recent research has aimed to develop safer, more effective materials for use in summer applications. Such materials have been badly needed to combat the mite species against which dormant sprays are ineffective as well as to control midseason or later outbreaks of the species against which dormant sprays are used. Summer-oil emulsions, 1 to 1.5 percent, and various forms of sulfur were formerly commonly employed for the purpose but sometimes caused injury and were not always as effective as desired.

The first promising substitute that came into wide use against mites was the dicyclohexylamine salt of dinitro-*o*-cyclohexylphenol (DN-111). Its tendency to cause injury when high temperatures prevail and its failure to be fully effective against the European red mite at safe strengths limit its usefulness.

Many materials have been tested in summer sprays against mites. A few have proved their worth in enough tests to justify recommending them. The most promising ones include parathion, tetraethyl pyrophosphate (TEPP), 2-(*p-tert-butylphenoxy*)-1-

methylethyl 2-chloroethyl sulfite (Aramite), O-ethyl O-*p*-nitrophenyl benzenethiophosphonate (EPN), and 1,1-bis(*p*-chlorophenyl)ethanol (DMC).

Some growers prefer to include these materials in one or more of the regular cover sprays applied to control the codling moth in order to prevent the development of mite infestations. Other growers prefer to withhold their use, unless needed for other purposes, until mites show up in sufficient numbers to require control. In the latter case, two applications about 7 to 10 days apart may be required. Both systems have many advocates and both have advantages and disadvantages. Only further research will prove which is superior.

Just when marked progress was being made in developing effective treatments for mite control the problem of resistance attracted attention. Early in 1951 recommended quantities of parathion did not control the European red mite in Washington. Later in the season other species of mites, including some not previously suspected of being present, were not controlled satisfactorily and other promising new materials were not as effective as they had been earlier. Still later reports indicated that mites were becoming harder to control in other areas—West Virginia and New Jersey. Possibly the orchard mites were developing resistance to insecticides. That is not altogether surprising, because a resistant strain of the two-spotted spider mite has been reported by greenhouse workers. It is apparent that the problem of orchard mites is far from solved: We have to reexamine spray schedules; find insecticides that do not lead to increases in mite populations to replace materials whose use seems to favor such increases; determine the factors that affect the development of mites; and put forth further efforts to find materials that will hold in check all species of mites.

THE RED-BANDED LEAF ROLLER is perhaps second only to mites among the pests that have increased in importance in apple orchards following the use of DDT. It has long been widely distributed on many hosts, but is ordinarily heavily parasitized. Rare indeed was the orchardist who knowingly had to contend with it until a few years ago. Now it is a problem pest throughout the Midwest and East, where in 1947 and 1948 particularly it caused severe damage in many orchards. A study of the problem showed that including lead arsenate in the first two or three cover sprays usually takes care of this leaf roller for the season. Later studies revealed the value of TDE, parathion, and EPN in controlling it. TDE is particularly effective and valuable to combat infestations during the summer whenever outbreaks threaten. Now the red-banded leaf roller is a pest growers need no longer fear but one they must plan to take care of.

THE WOOLLY APPLE APHID, a pest widely distributed throughout all apple-growing areas in the United States, has been held in check by the parasite *Aphelinus mali*. This aphid is the insect that lives in the little cottonlike masses that are often seen around pruning wounds and other scars on the trees and in the axils of leaves on new growth, particularly on water sprouts. It may also occur on the roots of the trees. A particularly important pest in the Pacific Northwest because of its connection with spread of the perennial canker disease, it is only in that area that it has increased to serious proportions following the use of DDT. Presumably because of the effect of DDT on the *Aphelinus* parasite, the woolly apple aphid is once again a pest to be reckoned with in that area.

Formerly controlled with nicotine sulfate when the parasite did not take care of it, it can now be checked by including materials such as benzene hexachloride, parathion, or TEPP in an early cover spray, or controlled later with either of the latter two materials. Benzene hexachloride may impart an off-flavor to the fruit if used after the early part of the season.

THE PLUM CURCULIO, an important fruit pest east of the Rocky Mountains, is most commonly associated with stone fruits, particularly peaches and plums. On apples it seldom caused serious injury when the regular spray program included lead arsenate to control the codling moth. Ordinary dosages of DDT do not control it effectively. Its jump in importance to apple growers dates from the time they changed their spray programs from lead arsenate to DDT. The best answer has been to include lead arsenate in the early-season part of the spray program, especially in the calyx and first-cover spray. For heavy infestations a special application between the calyx and first-cover spray is often desirable. Other materials show promise, but none seems to be superior to lead arsenate for use against plum curculio on apples.

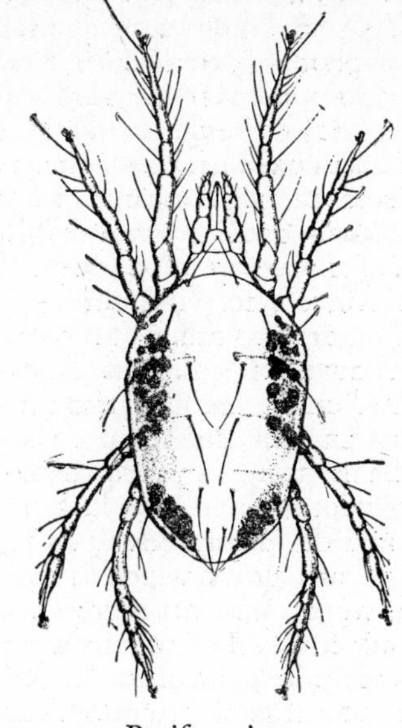

Pacific mite.

APPLE GROWERS have known the San Jose scale for many years, but few were familiar with Forbes scale, which is like it in appearance and habits. Many growers in the Midwest now are concerned with both species. Long held under control by the use of dormant- and summer-oil emulsions, the scales are growing in importance as the use of oil in the regular spray program steadily declines.

Dormant-oil emulsions at ordinary strengths, usually 3 percent oil in the dilute spray, are highly effective against the San Jose scale but do not seem to be so effective against Forbes scale. It appears that former wide use of oil in summer cover sprays may have had more effect in scale control than was generally recognized.

Our experimental work has shown that dormant sprays may not be necessary to control either one of the scales if a material such as parathion is included in the regular spray schedule. The minimum effective dosage of parathion has not been determined, but one-fourth pound or more of 25 percent parathion per 100 gallons in six applications or one-half pound in three applications have given complete protection in tests in Indiana. A single summer application of one-half pound of 25 percent parathion per 100 gallons has given partial control of Forbes scale on apples.

I HAVE DISCUSSED only the pests that have created serious problems for years and in important producing areas following the use of DDT. Others, such as the yellow-necked caterpillar in West Virginia, Virginia, and Maryland and mealybugs elsewhere, have appeared for a season or two in limited sections, presumably (but not necessarily) because of a direct or indirect effect of the use of DDT. In general, effective treatments have been developed promptly or adjustments made in the spray program to control such outbreaks, and they have not proved too serious. Other ordinarily minor pests no doubt will appear in outbreak proportions from time to time and require temporary or continuing adjustments to take care of them. But the apple grower must be ever on the alert and his spray program must be a flexible one.

The reader should not conclude that increases in importance of previously minor pests following the use of DDT have been confined to apples or that DDT is the only one of the newer insecticides whose use has led to such developments. For example, the use of DDT has been associated with increases of mites on peaches, grapes, pecans, shade trees, and cotton; mealybugs on grapes; aphids on cotton; the red-banded leaf roller on peaches and grapes; and cottony-cushion scale on citrus. On the other hand, the use of materials such as methoxychlor has been followed by more mites on apples and peaches and aphids on cotton. The use of parathion has been followed by increases of the soft scale on citrus. But all in all DDT on apple trees has been more to blame than the others for outbreaks of pests that used to be of little importance. Despite the problems its use has created, DDT has been a great benefit to apple growers; advantages resulting from its use far outweigh its disadvantages.

Howard Baker *is assistant division leader of the division of fruit insect investigations, Bureau of Entomology and Plant Quarantine. He was graduated from the University of Massachusetts in 1923 and joined the Department immediately thereafter. After various field assignments having to do with apple and pecan insects in the East, Middle West, and South, he was transferred to Washington in 1944.*

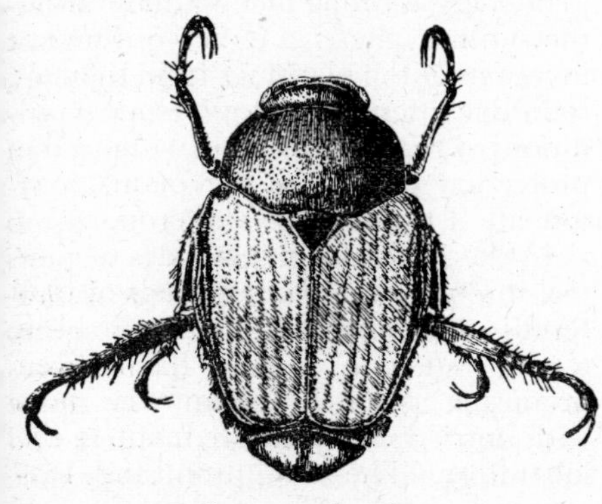

Japanese beetle.

The Japanese Beetle

Charles H. Hadley
Walter E. Fleming

Harry B. Weiss, who since became director of the New Jersey Division of Plant Industry, found a few shiny, metallic green beetles in a nursery near Riverton, N. J., in 1916. He did not recognize them at first, nor did anyone else, but they were finally identified as Japanese beetles, *Popillia japonica.* That was the first record of their occurrence in the United States. Entomological literature contained little information about them other than that they were common on the main islands of Japan and were not considered a serious pest. We knew little about their habits in Japan and nothing to indicate whether they would become serious in the United States. We did know that related beetles had caused considerable trouble in the Old World and in the other Pacific islands that they had invaded.

Apparently the beetle had come to the United States with plants before restrictions were established by the Plant Pest Act of 1912.

The adult Japanese beetle is plump, shiny brown and green with 12 white spots, and about one-half inch long. It is seen only in the summer and may feed on 275 kinds of plants.

Its white grub stage is in the ground, where it feeds on the roots of plants. The beetle does damage estimated at 10 million dollars a year to farm and orchard crops, residential and public ornamental plantings, lawns, and golf courses.

Men in the Department of Agriculture began an investigation in 1917 to get information about its development and habits in its new home. By the end of that year it was obvious that the beetle had found ideal conditions for its rapid multiplication and was capable of causing great losses to many economic crops and plants. In 1918 the Department and New Jersey authorities undertook to exterminate it, but the infestation was so well established that it could not be eradicated by the control measures then known and with the funds available.

Scientists then began work to find measures to reduce damage and prevent its spread. They set out to get full knowledge of the insect's life history and habits in its new surroundings; develop measures whereby farmers, home owners, and others could prevent material damage to crops and plants by the insect in any of its stages; develop practical and economical methods for insuring freedom from infestation of commercially grown nursery stock and agricultural products so as to prevent spread of the insect throughout the United States by the movement of those products; and to hasten natural control of the insect by the introduction and dissemination of its insect enemies from the Orient and by the practical utilization of microscopic organisms such as bacteria, fungi, and others found to attack the beetle in any stage of its growth.

Detailed information was obtained on the seasonal cycle, behavior, and reactions of the Japanese beetle to climatic conditions in both the older area of infestation and in the more recently infested northern, western, and southern areas. This information was used as a basis for the development of methods of dealing with the insect.

Each year a natural outward movement of the beetles from the margins of the area of general distribution occurs. Federal and State entomological workers make surveys each season to determine the relative abundance of the beetle in different parts of the area of general distribution.

The amount of summer rainfall is the main climatic influence on year-to-year changes in the numbers of beetles. Rainfall in June, July, and August in most of the East is normally about 12 inches. When it is below 8 inches there is such a high mortality of eggs and small grubs that beetles are less abundant the following year. A comparison of the climates in Japan and the United States indicates that the beetle probably will be able to develop in most of the States east of western Kansas. In some States farther west, summer rainfall is probably too low for survival, except in irrigated lands where adequate soil moisture is maintained. In areas where crops are grown under irrigation, no beetles would develop in nearby unwatered areas. In northern New England and some other cold parts of the country, summer temperatures may be too low for the beetle to become established. In most of the area now infested by the beetle, few die during the winter because a snow cover usually prevents soil temperatures from falling to the point where hibernating grubs would be killed. If the insect should be introduced into certain parts of the northern interior of this country, where the snowfall is normally lighter, the beetle grubs might be destroyed.

Protection of fruit and foliage from attack by the adult Japanese beetle involves killing the beetles that are on the plants and keeping the beetles that fly to the plants from establishing themselves there. The Japanese beetle attacks orchard crops, small fruits, field crops, shade trees, and ornamental plants. It is a strong flier, so that during the summer there may be continuous invasions of the plantings from the surrounding infested territory. Under conditions of heavy infestation without the protection of sprays, the plants may lose all of their leaves and crop.

In the search for insecticides to control the beetle, many hundreds of materials and formulations have been tested, but only a few have given promising results. Preliminary tests with untried materials are made in the laboratory. The few promising materials found in this manner are tried on a small scale in the field and compared with one of the best sprays recommended for the protection of plants. If favorable results are obtained in the small tests, the material is used in different localities in commercial orchards, vineyards, and cornfields and is also applied to shade trees and ornamental shrubs.

Before 1943 no material had been developed that destroyed the beetles on the plants and then remained effective for several weeks. Sprays containing soap, or soap and pyrethrum, kill many of the beetles that are thoroughly wetted during the application, but the plants soon become reinfested. Repeated applications of the sprays necessary to control the beetles have injured the plants.

Whitewashing by several applications of a lime-aluminum sulfate spray before beetles become established on the plants produces a nonpoisonous coating that repels beetles in lightly or moderately infested areas. It is inadequate when the beetles are abundant. The residue from it is objectionable on ornamentals and is hard to remove from fruit at harvest.

Lead arsenate at the rate of 6 pounds to 100 gallons of water kills few beetles, but the deposit repels beetles that come to the plants later. Lead arsenate cannot be used in midsummer on peaches because of injury to the tree or on other fruits that ripen shortly after spraying because of the excess residue at harvest. A spray of 3 pounds of derris or cube to 100 gallons of water kills many beetles by contact, but the residue keeps beetles away for only 7 to 10 days. It can be used safely on all crops and ornamentals, but the period of protection it affords is short and the results vary from year to year because of the variations in the composition of the natural product.

DDT so far is the most effective material for killing beetles on plants and protecting fruit and foliage from later attack. Dusts containing DDT generally are not satisfactory because their poor adhesive qualities require repeated applications at relatively short intervals. DDT in the form of a wettable powder or an emulsion, mixed with water at the rate of 1 pound of DDT to 100 gallons and applied by a hydraulic sprayer, will kill beetles on early-ripening apples, early-ripening peaches, cherries, nectarines, plums, and grapes and prevent the reestablishment of the insects on the plants. One application is usually enough to protect the plants until the crop is harvested. After harvest a second application may be necessary to protect new growth. A single application usually protects the foliage of fruit ripening in the late summer or early fall. One or two applications have given protection to shade trees and ornamental shrubs throughout the summer. On small plantings of corn, the injury to the developing ears can be prevented by applying the spray or by dusting with a 10-percent dust when 25 percent of the ears are in silk and repeating the operation 3 days later.

Concentrated sprays of DDT applied by airplane or mist blower are effective in controlling the beetle in large acreages of corn and in large-scale spraying of shade trees and ornamentals but have not given satisfactory control in orchards. Sprays containing 1.5 pounds of DDT in the form of an emulsion or a wettable powder in 5 gallons of water have been used with no injury to the plants. Oil solutions containing 1 pound of DDT per gallon have caused some injury to the foliage of trees, shrubs, and corn.

Several chlorinated hydrocarbons and other new insecticides have been tested as substitutes for DDT since 1943. The preliminary results of tests in the laboratory and field with some of the materials are summarized. A mixture of piperonyl cyclonene, pyrethrins, rotenone, and cube resins causes temporary paralysis but kills few beetles and gives little protection to plants. Ryania, chlordane, toxaphene, aldrin, and dieldrin are of little value. Benzene hexachloride gives protection to plants for only a few days. The results with parathion and the oxygen analog of parathion were similar to those obtained with benzene hexachloride. TDE and the ethoxy analog of TDE are slightly inferior to DDT.

Methoxychlor is practically as effective as DDT in protecting orchard crops, corn, shade trees, and ornamentals. Because it is definitely less poisonous than DDT to man and warm-blooded animals, there is an advantage in using methoxychlor on forage crops, on fruits that ripen early in the summer, and under other conditions where the use of DDT is not desirable.

Poisoning the sap of a plant is a novel method for protecting it from attack by beetles. In preliminary tests, octamethyl pyrophosphoramide was applied in water to soil at rates up to 200 pounds per acre. The material did not injure the plants, and a sufficient amount was absorbed by them to reduce slightly the feeding by the beetles. Although the protection afforded in this preliminary test was not adequate, the method seems to have possibilities.

Many different types of traps have been devised, and several hundred kinds of baits have been prepared and tested. The most effective trap is one painted a primary yellow color and baited with a mixture of geraniol and eugenol or with a mixture of anethole and eugenol. Although the attractant draws beetles from the surrounding area and thereby increases the number in the immediate vicinity, it is estimated that not more than 25 percent of the beetles are captured. Traps cannot be considered a satisfactory measure for protecting plants from attack, but they are of considerable value in determining the presence of beetles in localities outside of the known infested areas. Thousands of traps are used annually by the Department of Agriculture in scouting for new infestations.

Turf in lawns, parks, and golf courses can be protected from damage by the grubs by grub-proofing, which was developed at the Japanese Beetle Laboratory about 25 years ago. Many grubs in the turf may destroy the grass in a short time. Tests have been conducted continuously to develop better materials for grub-proofing and to determine how long different treatments are effective in different types of soil under various conditions.

Several fumigating methods, such as treatment with dilute emulsions containing carbon disulfide, methyl bromide, or ethylene dibromide, are effective, but have to be applied annually. Other materials have been developed that remain effective for a number of years.

Lead arsenate at the rate of 435 pounds an acre has been used for grub-proofing turf since 1929. Among the various arsenicals tested, it is the least detrimental to grasses. Such grub-proofing is effective for 5 years or more. Lead arsenate, however, has several objectionable features. It is a slow-acting poison. Its effectiveness and lasting qualities vary greatly in different soils because of its reaction with the different soil constituents. It reduces the effectiveness of certain fertilizers. Finally, it sometimes makes difficult the establishment of newly seeded grass.

DDT and chlordane are effective and practical. Like lead arsenate, they kill the grubs while they are feeding on roots or burrowing in the soil. They kill the newly hatched grubs faster than the older and larger ones. They work best at high temperatures and have little or no effect at temperatures below 50° F., when the grubs are practically inactive. DDT and chlordane are not affected by the common fertilizers and soil conditioners. Neither seems to interfere with the actions of fertilizers on plants. The common grasses are tolerant to both materials.

DDT applied at the rate of 25 pounds an acre to established turf kills grubs about two times faster than lead arsenate at the rate of 435 pounds an acre. Equally good results are obtained with DDT applied as a dust or as a spray. Either a wettable powder or an emulsion can be used in preparing the spray. When DDT is applied late in the fall or in the spring, it can be expected that about one-third of the fully grown grubs in the soil will be killed before changing to beetles in June. Both treatments, however, will practically eliminate by mid-September all grubs of the next annual brood that hatch during the summer. The number of years that one application of DDT will be effective in grub-proofing turf has not been determined. The oldest experimental treatment, applied in the spring of 1944, has eliminated eight annual broods. More recent applications at various localities in New Jersey, Connecticut, Massachusetts, and North Carolina have shown no sign of reduced effectiveness.

DDT has largely replaced lead arsenate for grub-proofing because it kills grubs faster, is less influenced by soil conditions, remains effective just as long, and is less likely to injure grasses. In 1952 it was cheaper than lead arsenate.

Chlordane at the rate of 10 pounds an acre kills grubs twice as fast as DDT at the rate of 25 pounds an acre. A treatment applied in September, while the fully grown grubs are active, will kill more than 90 percent of them within 3 weeks. When the treatment is applied in late fall or early spring while the grubs are inactive, however, few grubs will be killed until late in the spring. The period during which one application of chlordane will be effective has not been determined. The oldest experimental treatments, applied in the spring of 1947 in New Jersey, Connecticut, and Massachusetts, have eliminated five annual broods. Since chlordane kills grubs faster than DDT, it is more effective in reducing populations of grubs in the spring and fall. When a dense infestation is discovered during those seasons, damage to turf can be stopped faster by an application of chlordane than by using DDT. Both materials are now used extensively for grub-proofing.

Of numerous other organic compounds that have been tested as grub-proofing materials since 1946, the best results have been obtained with aldrin and dieldrin. Either, at the rate of 3 pounds an acre, kills grubs 1.5 times as fast as 10 pounds of chlordane and 4 times as fast as 25 pounds of DDT. The common grasses are tolerant to them. The tests have not been under way long enough to determine whether the effects of aldrin or dieldrin last long enough to justify recommending them for grub-proofing.

Isolated infestations of the beetle in localities remote from the generally infested area can be controlled and the normal rapid increase in the population greatly retarded by treating the soil with DDT at the rate of 25 pounds an acre. This has been demonstrated with such an infestation in North Carolina, where about 250 acres were treated in 1945. The number of beetles was reduced to a low level and it has not increased very much since that time. In contrast, the infestation in a nearby untreated area increased rapidly and spread over the countryside. Either DDT or chlordane may be used for the treatment of isolated infestations.

Chemical treatments for fruits and vegetables have been developed to permit their shipment to areas where the beetle does not occur. The shipper may choose the treatment that is best suited to his needs and is least likely to cause damage to the commodity. Carbon disulfide, vaporized at the rate of 10 pounds to each 1,000 cubic feet in a closed chamber, was the first method developed for killing adult beetles in packages of blueberries, blackberries, raspberries, and strawberries. Because of the explosion hazard, this material has been replaced by ethylene oxide or methyl bromide, which are not explosive at the strengths employed and are equally effective for the fumigation of fruits and vegetables. A DDT treatment has now superseded the fumigating procedures for potatoes and sacked onions because it is cheaper and more easily applied under commercial conditions. Refrigerator cars are treated by blowing 1 ounce of 10 percent DDT dust per 2,500 cubic feet into the loaded cars. Trucks with tightly enclosed bodies are treated by applying 1 ounce of the dust before and after loading.

Methods have been developed for the treatment of soil about the roots of plants so that the nurseries and greenhouses within the infested area may continue to conduct business in other parts of the country. All of the immature stages of the beetle in soil, compost, and decomposed manure used for potting plants are destroyed by fumigating with carbon disulfide or methyl bromide in a closed chamber, by mixing flakes of naphthalene throughout the material, or by heating the mass to 130° F. and maintaining it at this temperature for 30 minutes. During the seasons when only the grubs are present, the soil may be fumigated with chloropicrin or with a mixture of ethylene dibromide and ethylene dichloride. With these treatments, screening is necessary when beetles are around, to prevent reinfestation. Mixing DDT, chlordane, or lead arsenate with the potting medium will destroy the infestation present at the time of application and will destroy any infestation which may be introduced during the following 2 years.

One of the first treatments to be used to destroy infestation about the roots of plants before digging in the field was the application of a dilute emulsion of carbon disulfide. Later, emulsions of methyl bromide or of ethylene dibromide-ethylene dichloride were developed and replaced the carbon disulfide. The treatments have been satisfactory and practical at the smaller nurseries but are generally impractical at the wholesale establishments. The application of lead arsenate at the rate of 1,000 pounds to the acre was developed for the treatment of the larger fields. The soil is analyzed each year and the lost insecticide is replaced. DDT at the rate of 25 pounds an acre (or chlordane at the rate of 10 pounds an acre) has replaced lead arsenate for the treatment of nursery stock.

When the stock is grown in the field in uncertified plots, the infestation may be destroyed by immersing the roots in water at a temperature of 112°, or by dipping the roots in dilute emulsions of carbon disulfide, ethylene dichloride, or ethylene dibromide-ethylene dichloride, or by fumigating them with methyl bromide in a closed chamber.

The use of these methods by nurserymen and others for treating fruits, vegetables, and nursery stock to satisfy the requirements of the quarantine because of the Japanese beetle is discussed in more detail in the chapter "Off Limits for Beetles," page 574.

The fact that the beetle, although common in Japan, was not a pest of much importance, suggested the existence of insect or other enemies which kept it under control. A search for enemies of the beetle in Japan and elsewhere was carried on from 1920 through 1933. It was found that a relatively large number of insect parasites and predators attacked the various stages of the Japanese beetle and related species. About 49 species of insect parasites and predators were shipped to the Department's laboratory in New Jersey from Japan, Korea, Formosa, China, India, Australia, and Hawaii. Some parasites were released immediately in the beetle-infested area. Others were used for further study or reared to provide additional parasites for subsequent release.

Five species of imported insect parasites have become established in the beetle-infested area. Two of these, the spring Tiphia (*Tiphia vernalis*) from Korea and the summer or fall Tiphia (*Tiphia popilliavora*) from Japan, are well established and are one of the important causes of a decline in Japanese beetle numbers in the older infested area. Both parasites are wasps that attack the grub of the Japanese beetle. The wasp lays an egg on the body of the grub. The maggot that hatches from the egg feeds on the grub and destroys it. The first colonies of the spring Tiphia were released in 1926 in New Jersey; by 1951 a total of 2,018 colonies had been released in 14 States from New Hampshire to North Carolina and westward to Ohio. State authorities, using wasps collected locally from the sites of earlier releases made by the Department, released several hundred additional colonies. The fall Tiphia was first released in 1921 in New Jersey; by 1951, 767 colonies were released in nine States.

Surveys were made between 1935 and 1951 to determine the distribution of the spring Tiphia. By the close of the 1951 season the parasite was generally distributed over an area of some 5,300 square miles in eastern Pennsylvania, Delaware, and southern New Jersey. It also occurred at many scattered points in the beetle-infested territory outside of this area. Because the wasp attacks only the grub stage of the beetle in the ground, any estimate of the effectiveness of the parasite must be based upon the actual number of parasitized grubs in proportion to the total number of all stages of the beetle found in the ground at the time of the survey. The surveys disclosed a range of parasitization from 19 to 61 percent, with a general average of about 43 percent. The spring Tiphia is the most effective of the introduced insect parasites of the beetle, but the other established parasites are also contributing to the reduction of the beetle population.

The native insect parasites and predators of white grubs occurring in the area infested by the Japanese beetle have been studied to find out to what extent they attack the beetle. Occasionally grubs have been found parasitized by native Tiphia wasps. A species of *Ptilodexia,* a fly known as a parasite of white grubs, was found attacking Japanese beetle grubs to an extent that suggested that it may ultimately be of importance in biological control. With this exception native parasites and predators appear to play at best only a minor part in the control of the beetle.

Early observations indicated that the grubs were subject to several diseases. About 25 different soil microorganisms can cause some stage of the Japanese beetle to become diseased. Among these are bacteria, fungi, protozoa, nematodes, and viruses. The bacteria causing the milky diseases of the Japanese beetle grubs were found to be the most important of the organisms. These are sporeforming bacteria, *Bacillus popilliae* and *B. lentimorbus.* The former, the more important, causes the type-A milky disease. A more complete discussion of the milky disease begins on page 394.

Another disease found in Japanese beetle grubs is the blue disease, socalled because of the bluish tint of infected grubs. Its causal organism is believed to be a virus. The disease seems to be very potent and may lend itself to large-scale utilization in much the same manner as the milky disease.

Several species of nematodes, tiny microscopic worms commonly found in the soil, cause considerable mortality among the grubs and are an important factor in biological control. Their effectiveness depends much more on favorable climatic and soil conditions than do the milky diseases, however.

Several species of fungi attack the Japanese beetle. The most important is the green muscardine fungus, *Metarrihizium anisopliae.* It is widespread and under favorable conditions is important in the biological control of the beetle.

CHARLES H. HADLEY *was an entomologist in the division of fruit insect investigations of the Bureau of Entomology and Plant Quarantine. He was in charge of Japanese beetle investigations, with headquarters at the Japanese Beetle Research Laboratory at Moorestown, N. J., until he retired in 1952.*

WALTER E. FLEMING *is also an entomologist. He succeeded Mr. Hadley at Moorestown and is in charge of the station.*

970134°—52——38

Off Limits for Beetles

William Middleton
Timothy C. Cronin

Three years after the Japanese beetle was discovered in New Jersey, the Department of Agriculture of that State instituted a quarantine to try to prevent the spread of the beetle. The effort was not successful. By 1919 the beetle had begun its relentless march. In its new home it found many plants it could feed on, extensive turfed areas to breed in, and none of the natural enemies that held it in check in its native Japan.

So the United States Department of Agriculture invoked a Federal quarantine.

The action was taken under the Plant Quarantine Act of 1912, which authorizes the Secretary of Agriculture to quarantine any State, territory, or district when he determines that a quarantine is necessary to prevent the spread of a dangerous insect or plant disease and to cooperate with any State, territory, or district in connection with any quarantine they enact.

Federal quarantines apply only to interstate movement of regulated articles, and hence entire States are quarantined. If it is necessary to prevent or retard the spread of a pest into an uninfested part of a State under Federal quarantine, authority to control movement within the State must be used—the Secretary designates the regulated area within the State and a State official issues a quarantine paralleling the Federal instrument as to area, articles, and conditions.

The Secretary's original quarantine order against the Japanese beetle became effective June 1, 1919. It was under the direction of the Federal Horticultural Board, with the Federal Bureau of Entomology and the State of New Jersey as cooperators. The quarantine prohibited the movement of ears of green corn, unless inspected and certified as beetle-free, from three townships in Burlington County, N. J., where the beetle was first found in this country.

As the beetle continued to spread naturally and more was learned about it, changes were made in the areas regulated and additional materials were restricted. In 1920 the area regulated by Federal quarantine was extended to include a small part of adjacent Pennsylvania, and the movement of general farm products, nursery and greenhouse stock, and soil was restricted. In 1924 Delaware was placed under quarantine. In 1926 the quarantine was extended to New York and Connecticut. Meanwhile further changes were made in the regulations pertaining to the movement of materials and in quarantine procedures; under some conditions the shipping of some articles were prohibited entirely. By 1937 the Federal quarantine had been extended to include all the States under regulation by June 30, 1951.

On March 30, 1951, a public hearing was held in Washington, D. C., to determine whether the quarantine should be revoked or continued and extended to other States. The hearing was attended by many State officials and spokesmen of industry. Opinion was unanimous against revocation of the quarantine. The Federal quarantine therefore was extended to include North Carolina, as of August 14, 1951.

The District of Columbia and 15 States were under Federal quarantine in 1952. Entirely under regulation were Connecticut, Delaware, Maryland, Massachusetts, New Jersey, Rhode Island, and the District of Columbia. Maine, New Hampshire, New York, Ohio, Pennsylvania, Vermont, Virginia, West Virginia, and North Carolina were partly regulated. The area under Federal quarantine regulation totaled about 172,000 square miles, about one-twentieth of the total area of the United States. Some localities were under State regulation in Ohio, North Carolina, Virginia, West Virginia, and Missouri.

The regulations of the quarantine in 1952 prohibited shipping live beetles to nonregulated destinations, and regulated the shipments of commodities and materials that might harbor the insects—soil, peat, compost and manure, nursery and greenhouse stock, and fresh fruits and vegetables. There also were provisions for cleaning and treating vehicles and aircraft to kill or remove the beetles before the conveyances reached nonregulated areas. There were various exemptions, conditions that determine the applicability of the quarantine restrictions, and methods of compliance.

THE PROBLEM of preventing spread of the beetle and at the same time permitting movement of regulated articles is complex. Because in the beginning little was known about the insect or its control, the first quarantine measures contained few practical methods of permitting movement of regulated materials. Such an embargo type of quarantine produced complaints and demands by shippers of plants and farm products for every possible easement, including extension of regulated areas to which unrestricted shipments could be made. The needs of shippers were viewed sympathetically even at that time, but there was some resistance to rapid expansion of regulated areas, because of a desire to avoid quarantine and a hope for retardation of spread.

The conflicting interests had to be considered in the development of a sound policy. The immediate policy was to extend the regulated areas and to find out more about the beetle itself. Large areas in quarantined States were placed under regulation because relatively small numbers of beetles were found in scattered localities. A force of Federal and State entomologists and other workers cooperated with quarantine officials and industry in the research; the nature and the amount of the information required made extensive study necessary. Desired changes in the quarantine procedures and methods of compliance consequently were delayed. The basic needs were to determine the hazards of artificial spread, the methods of determining the presence and distribution of the insect, and safe, effective, and cheap methods of control and certification.

Early in the development of the quarantine the regulations divided certification activities into two parts. One phase dealt with grubs, eggs, and pupae, which were found about plant roots and in soil. That was a year-round problem. The other involved only the adult beetle, which might be transported with farm products and flowers—a problem only when adults were present. That division of activities persisted, but the part dealing with the adult beetle was divided later to include a study of dissemination by vehicles, including aircraft.

The affected producers and shippers of plants and farm products were handicapped by quarantines, but most seriously affected were the nursery and greenhouse establishments. They were under regulation throughout the year and in the entire regulated area. Among them were large commercial organizations, which produce many varieties of plants under different conditions, as well as small specialists. They had shipped their products throughout the country. Certification of plants at first was almost entirely on a free-from-soil basis, but that was not always practical. Hence alternative methods under the varying conditions were needed.

A practical certification treatment requires a minimum of chemical, time, equipment, and labor, and reasonable temperature limitations. The procedures also have to be adaptable to the routine work in the industry. In the early period, the development of treatments was limited by the quarantine requirement that complete insect mortality occur before certification, a requirement that narrowed the margin of safety between insect mortality and plant injury. Few effective insecticides were available.

During the next years, treatments with carbon disulfide, lead arsenate, heat, paradichlorobenzene, and naphthalene were approved. Many plant producers used the treatments, but the regulated establishments were still under a handicap in competing with unregulated establishments.

Beginning in the late 1930's, the development of insecticides having residual action made it possible to authorize more practical treatments as a basis for certification. The development had an important effect on the quarantine program. It made available to large and small plant producers and shippers alternative methods of treating their products. While there is no cure-all treatment, they now have a choice of 16 low-cost and effective treatments, which may be applied safely to most regulated articles. Treatment may be done before or at shipping time. Methyl bromide, ethylene dichloride, ethylene dibromide, DDT, and chlordane are some of the chemicals used. All treatments for certification must be applied under the observation of a quarantine inspector. The establishment provides all material and labor and assumes all risk of injury. Before subjecting large numbers of plants to treatment, a plant owner is urged to treat sample quantities to ascertain plant tolerance.

An accompanying table shows the quantities of plants, potting soil, and plant-growing areas treated for quarantine certification from 1924 through 1950. It illustrates the volume of materials certified after treatment with the newer chemicals since the late 1930's. In 1950 more than 400 commercial plant growers in 15 States and the District of Columbia used one or more of the treatments to make plants eligible for shipment under quarantine certification. Although the treatments were used for the purpose of certifying material under the quarantine, growers who found it necessary to use them had important side benefits—including control of injury by the Japanese beetle and of many other insects, weeds, and fungi. For example, chlordane soil treatment is reported to control the Taxus weevil; DDT and methyl bromide, many other soil-inhabiting insects; chloropicrin, fungi; and carbon disulfide, weeds.

Special quarantine regulations are required for farm products. They apply only during the summer in areas where the abundance and activity of the adult beetles present a hazard of spread through movement of those commodities. In general, only commercial shipments are involved. Coincidental with the development of treatments for plants and soil, practical methods of treating the commodities for shipment under certification were developed. Methyl bromide fumigation was the treatment most generally used in 1951.

Before these later, more efficient, treatments became available, certification methods required the services of many inspectors for volume plant inspection on a piece-by-piece basis or treatment and for other certification activities. Because of the progress in methods, materials, and equipment, industry generally has found the quarantine regulations less burdensome, and fewer men are needed for inspection services.

So today, despite a larger regulated area, more establishments, a larger volume of certification, and higher costs, reasonable protection is being given to uninfested parts of the United States. Present operations permit the decentralization of the inspection force, which is distributed at convenient locations on a work-load basis.

Wider knowledge of the quarantine, more efficient and less expensive methods of certification, and increased understanding of quarantine objectives have eased the problems of quarantine enforcement. All certification treatments and inspection are under direct observation of inspectors, however, and checks for compliance are made on a

Quantities and Values by States of Materials Certified July 1950 Through June 1951

States	Materials certified: Plants	Farm products	Cut flowers	Soil	Value of certified articles
	Number	*Cars and trucks*	*Packages*	*Pounds*	*Dollars*
Connecticut	7,130,796	......	......	171,283	515,373
Delaware	11,730,189	531	75	10	2,476,347
District of Columbia	12,304	152	1,667	2,450	312,487
Maine	69,843	......	......	....	9,563
Maryland	13,087,235	915	1,340	4,543	1,926,465
Massachusetts	618,278	......	......	10,827	213,773
New Hampshire	463,863	......	......	....	36,362
New Jersey	6,050,797	853	285	3,823	2,355,886
New York	31,453,123	67	4	2,837,759	1,089,581
North Carolina	1,086,183	98	1,407	50	122,780
Ohio	19,686,525	......	......	94,357	3,047,905
Pennsylvania	11,841,263	427	2,913	641,421	1,987,937
Rhode Island	468,601	......	......	100	238,732
Vermont	14,494	......	......	....	7,082
Virginia	11,521,799	1,337	3,783	224,433	1,866,911
West Virginia	1,073,030	74	......	14,780	220,452
Total	116,308,323	4,454	11,474	4,005,836	16,427,636

regular schedule the year around at mail, express, and freight terminals. Special and seasonal checks also are made as required, especially on highways.

In the late 1930's it was recognized that the beetle could be transported long distances quickly in airplanes to nonregulated areas from eastern airfields where beetles occurred. Surveys then showed that beetles were numerous enough to require protective action at only a few airports. Inspectors stationed at those fields, working with airfield personnel, could check the hazard of spread. Plane openings were kept closed except during actual loading. Beetles were removed from passengers and cargo. The interiors of planes were examined and beetles removed.

Such surveillance had to be extended later to more fields, but even so it became inadequate when beetles increased in numbers at airports. Efforts were intensified to find sprays that could be applied to interior spaces and surfaces of the aircraft to kill the beetles. Satisfactory special DDT-pyrethrum residual and space sprays applied from bomb-type containers were developed for use as an adjunct to inspection. Those procedures are being continued at the principal military and commercial airfields in the heavily infested sections of the East. Since the program was started, thousands of beetles have been killed by inspectors and military and commercial personnel. During the 1951 season, more than 3,000 residual and 12,000 space applications were made.

As evidence of the effectiveness of the treatments, dead and dying beetles have been taken from treated planes at destinations in this country and abroad. Further evidence is the generally negative results of special annual trapping at the main airports in the unregulated parts of the United States. Research workers have started tests to find an acceptable, one-shot spray that can be applied, after preflight closing, to plane interiors, including occupied passenger compartments.

In addition to airplane treatments, DDT foliage sprays and traps have

Chemicals Used at Plant-Growing Establishments in Japanese Beetle Quarantine Treatments, 1924–50

Chemical	*Period of use*	*Plants*	*Potting soil*	*Surface*
		Number	*Cubic yards*	*Square feet*
Carbon disulfide	1924–50	262, 639	52, 714	457, 213
Lead arsenate	1924–50	4, 335, 425	162	38, 442, 721
Naphthalene	1929–50	....	557	500, 576
Paradichlorobenzene	1934–42	692, 676	....	....
Methyl bromide	1939–50	15, 192, 561	383	....
Ethylene dichloride	1942–50	6, 826, 024	....	....
Chloropicrin	1943–50	....	446	....
Ethylene dibromide	1945–50	3, 522, 333	242	102, 999
DDT	1946–50	40, 975, 031	3, 765	63, 459, 413
Chlordane	1948–50	720, 833	180	6, 619, 966
Ethylene-dibromide-chlordane	1948–50	731, 214	....	....
Total	....	73, 258, 736	58, 449	109, 582, 888

been used at many airfields to reduce beetle population.

Despite the opportunities available for dissemination of the beetles by soil, plants, plant products, vehicles, and aircraft, the spread does not seem to be in proportion to the hazard involved—as indicated by results of annual surveys and the absence of reported beetle occurrence by nonofficial observers, the Japanese beetle is well known generally because of the wide publicity given it, and it is not likely to become very abundant in an area without being recognized.

West of the Mississippi no beetles have been collected over the years through 1951 except for two beetles at Fort Madison, Iowa, one beetle at Kansas City and one at the Olathe Air Base, Kans., one at the airport at New Orleans, one at the Kansas City Airport, one near the Los Angeles Municipal Airport, and annual collections at St. Louis.

By 1951, east of the Mississippi, at least one beetle in at least one locality has been found in every State, except Alabama, Mississippi, and Wisconsin.

A table gives by States the number of localities surveyed and the results through 1950. No surveys of this type are conducted in the States or portions of States under regulation.

Included in an annual trapping-scouting program to determine the distribution of the beetle, several hundred plant-growing establishments outside of the federally regulated areas have had special scouting. Those nearer to the regulated areas and isolated control localities are given much closer scouting. Where beetles are found, such premises are placed immediately under State quarantine agreement, paralleling Federal quarantine regulations, and under Federal supervision.

Although the early efforts at eradication were not successful, interest in control continued. In 1927 State officials, in cooperation with the Federal Government, began the general practice of applying control treatments at isolated infestations to delay extension of quarantine regulations and prevent the increase of beetles. Surface-soil treatments for this purpose with carbon disulfide emulsion were only partly successful. Interest continued, however, and cooperative research developed lead arsenate surface-soil treatments and baited traps. They proved to be practical, effective aids to control. They made it possible to suppress the insect at isolated infestations.

By suppressing beetle population and (where desirable) using State quarantines under Federal supervision, the extension of Federal quarantine regulation could be deferred safely. Thus a new policy was justified and established. Later, these control efforts were made more effective and less costly by

Summary of Trapping-Scouting Program by States

	Number of localities—		
	Surveyed	*Negative*	*Positive*
Unquarantined States:			
Florida	105	99	6
Georgia	220	208	12
South Carolina	154	145	9
North Carolina	320	242	78
Tennessee	131	125	6
Kentucky	100	93	7
Indiana	113	96	17
Illinois	146	133	13
Michigan	91	73	18
Quarantined States, surveys in unregulated area:			
Maine	52	40	12
New Hampshire	17	16	1
Vermont	57	50	7
New York	381	314	67
Pennsylvania	20	12	8
Virginia	137	91	46
West Virginia	109	86	23
Ohio	479	418	61

the use of DDT soil and foliage treatments with more efficient applicators. There has been some use of chlordane for soil treatment.

Since 1934, when the first large-scale control programs were begun in St. Louis, Mo., and Indianapolis, Ind., the effects of this policy through 1951 have been shown in two ways: First, Federal quarantine has been extended to only two States, Ohio and North Carolina; secondly, control treatments have been applied at many isolated infestations and other beetle-collection locations which are not under Federal quarantine regulation.

A few examples of the results of the program at important isolated infested locations illustrate its effectiveness. More than 1,300 beetles were taken in St. Louis in 1934. Lead arsenate surface-soil treatment was applied to about 450 acres. Beetle collections in that treated area were reduced to 14 in 1936, and none has been taken in it since. In a localized infested area in Chicago in 1936, 1,400 beetles were found, and lead arsenate surface-soil treatment was applied. Only 41 beetles were taken in the same area in 1938 and none since 1940. At Highland Park, Ill., 5,000 beetles were taken at one site in 1941. Timely applications of lead arsenate were made, and by 1945 only five beetles could be found in the treated area and none since. More than 3,000 beetles were taken in one area in Detroit in 1947. Lead arsenate soil treatments and DDT foliage treatments apparently controlled this infestation because only 21 beetles were taken in Detroit in 1950. A small infestation at Dahlonega, Ga., has been held in check for several years by soil and foliage treatments.

Most of the remaining isolated control areas perhaps should not be classed as infested because of the small numbers of beetles that have been found. Treatments have been applied at many of these places and they have not become new sources for spread.

All control treatments against this insect in which the Bureau participates are limited to isolated areas not under Federal quarantine regulation. The treatments are on a cooperative basis. State and local governments and sometimes civic groups usually supply the insecticide and labor. Supervision, special equipment, and operators are assigned by the Bureau.

Control or suppression within the Federal quarantine regulated areas is the responsibility of State and local governments and individuals. However, the Bureau has cooperated by helping to establish parasites and disease, conducting research in cooperation with various States to develop methods of control, especially with newer insecticides, and preparation of leaflets, bulletins, and circulars on these modern controls.

William Middleton *is an entomologist in charge of the Japanese beetle control and gypsy moth certification work of the Bureau of Entomology and Plant Quarantine. He is stationed at the headquarters of the project in Hoboken, N. J.*

Timothy C. Cronin *is an entomologist assigned to the same project as assistant to the leader.*

Dates of Federal Quarantine and Extension of Regulated Areas by States

State	*1919*	*1920*	*1921*	*1922*	*1923*	*1924*	*1925*	*1926*	*1927*	*1928*	*1929*	*1930*	*1931*	*1932*	*1933*	*1934*	*1935*	*1936*	*1937*	*1938*	*1939*	*1940*	*1941*	*1942*	*1943*	*1944*	*1945*	*1946*	*1947*	*1948*	*1949*	*1950*	*1951*
New Jersey	q	r	r	r	r	r	r	E	.	.	.	.	.	.	.	.	:	.	.	.	.	.	.	.	.	.	.	.	.	.	.	.	.
Pennsylvania	.	q	r	r	r	r	r	r	r	.	r	r	.	r	r	.	.	.	.	r	.	r	r	.	.	.	.	.	.	.	.	.	r
Delaware	.	.	.	.	.	q	r	r	.	.	r	r	.	E	.	.	.	.	.	.	.	.	.	.	.	.	.	.	.	.	.	.	.
New York	.	.	.	.	.	.	.	q	.	r	.	r	.	r	r	.	.	.	r	r	r	.	r	r	r	.	.	.	r	.	.	r	r
Connecticut	.	.	.	.	.	.	.	q	r	.	r	E	.	.	.	.	.	.	.	.	.	.	.	.	.	.	.	.	.	.	.	.	.
District of Columbia	.	.	.	.	.	.	.	.	.	.	E	.	.	.	.	.	.	.	.	.	.	.	.	.	.	.	.	.	.	.	.	.	.
Maryland	.	.	.	.	.	.	.	.	.	.	q	r	.	r	r	.	.	.	r	.	.	r	r	r	r	r	.	.	r	r	E	.	.
Virginia	.	.	.	.	.	.	.	.	.	.	q	r	.	r	r	.	.	r	.	r	r	.	r	r	r	.	.	r	.	r	r	r	.
Massachusetts	.	.	.	.	.	.	.	.	.	.	.	q	.	r	E	.	.	.	.	.	.	.	.	.	.	.	.	.	.	.	.	.	.
Rhode Island	.	.	.	.	.	.	.	.	.	.	.	E	.	.	.	.	.	.	.	.	.	.	.	.	.	.	.	.	.	.	.	.	.
New Hampshire	.	.	.	.	.	.	.	.	.	.	.	.	.	.	q	.	.	.	.	.	.	.	.	.	.	.	.	.	.	.	.	.	.
Vermont	.	.	.	.	.	.	.	.	.	.	.	.	.	.	q	.	.	.	r	.	.	.	.	.	.	.	.	.	.	.	.	.	.
Maine	.	.	.	.	.	.	.	.	.	.	.	.	.	.	q	.	.	.	r	.	.	.	.	.	.	.	.	.	.	.	.	.	.
West Virginia	.	.	.	.	.	.	.	.	.	.	.	.	.	.	q	.	.	.	r	r	.	r	r	r	r	r	.	.	r	.	r	r	r
Ohio	.	.	.	.	.	.	.	.	.	.	.	.	.	.	.	.	.	.	q	r	r	r	.	.	.	.	r	.	.	.	.	r	r
North Carolina	.	.	.	.	.	.	.	.	.	.	.	.	.	.	.	.	.	.	.	.	.	.	.	.	.	.	.	.	.	.	.	.	q

q = Initial quarantine action.
r = Extension of regulated area.
E = Entire State under regulation.

Insects on Field Crops

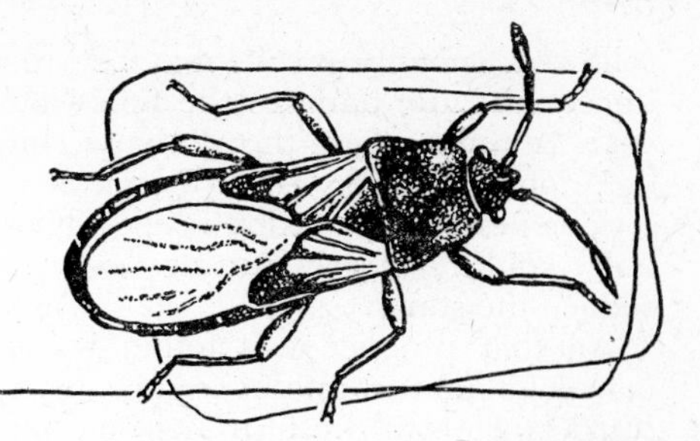

Cereal and Forage Insects

C. M. Packard

For many years the available methods of controlling the insect pests of cereal and forage crops have consisted mainly of modifications in cultural practices to prevent or reduce infestations. Such measures as rotation of crops, thorough and timely tillage, variations in time of planting or harvesting, destruction of crop residues, weeds, trash, and volunteer crop plants, and fertilization to promote rapid, vigorous crop growth can usually be applied for the control of insects with little or no addition to the cost of crop production. Low cost of application is particularly important with respect to cereal and forage crops, which generally are of such low value per acre as to make the use of expensive methods of control impractical.

More recently, increases in yields per acre and market or farm value of cereal and forage crops have raised the permissible limit on expenditures for control of the insects that attack them. Also, more efficient insecticides and insecticide application equipment than were formerly available have now been discovered or devised. In 1950, for example, the average acre-value of corn in the United States was $42 higher than it was in 1940, the acre-value of No. 1 baled alfalfa hay increased $10 or more, that of alfalfa seed increased about $33, and that of red clover seed increased approximately $14. Furthermore, properly applied insecticidal treatments costing about $3 to $6 an acre have produced returns in increased yields amounting to several times their cost.

On the other hand, cultural control measures still continue to be the best if not the only methods of control for some of the insects. Because the general subject of cultural control methods has been discussed in another article (p. 437), only those that have been worked out and recommended during the past few years are mentioned here.

THE ALFALFA WEEVIL, an immigrant from Europe, is prevalent in the Rocky Mountain and Pacific Coast States. Its control by early cutting of the first and second alfalfa crops of the season is a development in cultural control. Early cutting means harvesting when most of the alfalfa plants in a field are in the flower-bud stage of growth, when there is only a sprinkling of first bloom and only the earliest shoots of the next crop have appeared at the crowns. Clean cutting at that time and prompt removal of the hay leave the weevil larvae on the bare field where nearly all of them, together with eggs and pupae, die of starvation or exposure to heat. Thus, the growth of the second-crop shoots is unhindered by the weevil and comparatively few adults of the new generation will be produced to carry the species over winter.

To keep the alfalfa weevil under control by this means, the first and second crops should be cut early every year even though they are not actually being injured. If this practice is not followed, enough weevils may be produced to cause damage the following year. In areas where the alfalfa weevil does not occur or never becomes a serious pest, early cutting is not advisable; continual early cutting tends to reduce the stand.

Another practice was found to be beneficial in the alfalfa-seed-growing districts of southwestern Arizona for the control of lygus bugs, the little greenish-brown sucking bugs about three-sixteenths inch long and winged when full-grown. They greatly reduce yields of alfalfa seed and hay. Under Arizona conditions they can be fairly well controlled by a community-wide program of cleanly mowing or pasturing off all growths of alfalfa and weed hosts in the winter, early cutting of the first crop of alfalfa for hay in all fields within a 10-day period in late April, growing the second crop for seed and starting it as nearly as possible on the same date in all fields, and regulating irrigation so as to avoid extremely succulent vegetative growth of the seed crop. This system kills off most of the overwintering lygus bugs, and during the growing season prevents the survivors or their progeny from multiplying by moving back and forth among fields in different stages of growth. Thus the insect is kept under control by starvation. This method is less practicable in other areas where there is greater diversity of crops and a larger proportional acreage and variety of wild host plants.

THE WHEAT STEM SAWFLY has caused serious losses of wheat in Montana and North Dakota. It is a little, wasplike insect. In its worm stage it mines up and down within the growing wheat stem. In making its overwintering cell in the base of the stem, it cuts a groove around the inside at about ground level. As the heads become heavy with grain, the infested stems break over in the wind and fall to the ground, so that the harvester cannot pick up many of the heads. The only methods yet developed for reducing the losses are cultural. They consist of early harvesting before many of the stems have fallen; shallow cultivation of the stubble as soon after harvest as possible to throw it out on the surface of the ground where many of the sawfly worms that overwinter in it will die from lack of moisture; plowing the stubble under deeply where wind and water erosion is not a serious factor, so that the sawflies cannot emerge from it the following summer; rotation of wheat with crops that the sawfly does not attack, such as barley, oats, flax, corn, or mustard; and, in areas to which it is suited, the use of the Rescue variety of wheat, which is resistant to the sawfly. For most effective results these control measures must be applied throughout whole communities.

Cultural measures have been found helpful in the control of the wheat midge in the Pacific Northwest. Fall-sown wheat grown on uplands matures early enough to escape infestation by the midge, but spring wheat becomes infested unless it is sown very early. If sown by the first week in April it usually escapes injury. Either winter or spring wheat sown on low, wet peat land, however, may mature so slowly that it becomes infested. The stubble of infested wheat should be turned under if possible, to bury the midges that overwinter in it so that they cannot emerge the following June to infest the new crop.

The pale western cutworm is a serious pest in the small-grain areas of the southern Great Plains. It is of long-standing importance in the spring-wheat region farther north. It works mostly underground and therefore cannot be controlled satisfactorily with the poison baits that are effective against most species of cutworms. In the spring-wheat region it can be controlled by early spring starvation of the newly hatched worms. That is accomplished by thorough cultivation of the wheat-stubble fields to destroy all green vegetation early in the spring as soon as the weeds and volunteer grain show 1 to 2 inches of growth, followed by a delay of 10 days before seeding to a spring grain crop. In the southern Great Plains, however, where fall-sown wheat is the chief crop, the starvation method of control is not feasible except possibly where a spring grain crop such as barley is to be sown on wheat-stubble land.

Under the conditions prevailing there, winter wheat sown on land that has been cleanly fallowed during the preceding summer and that had been planted during the previous year to a row crop such as sorghum, almost always escapes serious injury. Alternation of winter wheat with clean summer fallow also is an effective way to prevent injury. In applying this method, the stubble of the year's crop is left undisturbed until the following spring, when the ground is cultivated and kept clean throughout the summer until wheat-seeding time the following year. The spring cultivation should start as early as possible without incurring danger of spring soil blowing, preferably before April 15. From the standpoint of soil conservation, subsurface cultivation to produce a trashy mulch may be more desirable than clean fallow, but its effectiveness as a substitute for clean fallow in controlling the pale western cutworm has not been determined.

Rotation of crops is a good way to control the so-called white-fringed beetles, which are several closely related South American insects and are abundant in some parts of the Southeastern States. Their larval (grub) stages attack many summer crops, especially peanuts, soybeans, velvetbeans, crotalaria, corn, cotton, and vegetables. The adult beetles feed on the legumes, cotton, and various broadleaved vegetable crops, shrubs, flowers, and weeds. On the other hand, grasses and winter grains are unfavorable to both larvae and adults. Although these insects can be controlled by insecticides, the crop losses they cause can be prevented by the following cultural practices:

1. Plant oats or other small grains for grain and grazing on the heavily infested portion of the farm.

2. Do not plant more than one-fourth of the cropland each year to such summer legumes as peanuts, soybeans, velvetbeans, or other plants that are favorable food for the adult beetles. Do not plant them on the same land oftener than once in 3 or 4 years.

3. Do not intercrop corn with peanuts, soybeans, crotalaria, or velvetbeans, and do not permit broadleaved weeds, such as cocklebur, to grow among the corn.

4. Fertilize cotton and corn heavily with a commercial fertilizer, and use a winter-grown manure crop that can be turned under before the cotton or corn is planted.

Most of us are familiar with the large, white grubs with brown heads and curved bodies that live in the soil and feed on plant roots. They are pests of bluegrass, timothy, corn, and several other crops. When they are full-grown they turn into the large, brown beetles commonly known as May beetles or June beetles. They often ruin bluegrass pastures in the Northeastern and North Central States. Grub populations can be reduced on infested farms in those States by planting deep-rooted legumes such as sweetclover, alfalfa, and red clover (which are unfavorable to them) in rotation with the more susceptible crops. The legumes are most effective if they are planted in the years of major beetle flights, which come in 3-year cycles and have been determined in advance for the infested areas.

More recently, a system of renovating hillside bluegrass pastures badly infested with white grubs has been developed by the Wisconsin Agricultural Experiment Station, based on the knowledge that both the adult beetles and the grubs are partial to grasses but do not like legumes. The sod is thoroughly torn up with a disk, springtooth harrow, or field cultivator during late fall or early spring, treated with lime and fertilizer in accordance with need as shown by soil tests, and sown in the spring with a seed mixture consisting mainly of legumes. These soon provide good pasture and are gradually replaced by the original bluegrass.

It is possible that a successful soil treatment with DDT or one of the other new insecticides eventually will be developed for control of white grubs as pests of cereal and forage crops.

CULTURAL METHODS of control often are of limited value. Also, they must be applied before or at the time a crop is sown and before it becomes infested. Some farmers therefore tend not to use them; they do not like to make changes in their established routine to forestall insect infestations that may or may not attack their crops at some future time. What they want is some control measure that can be applied immediately if or when their crops are actually being injured. With the advent of new and more efficient insecticidal chemicals and the currently higher yields and value of some cereal and forage crops it has been increasingly possible to meet this need through the use of insecticides.

BECAUSE ALL insecticides are more or less poisonous to man and other warm-blooded animals, as well as to insects, the usefulness of most of them on cereal and forage crops is limited. When these crops are treated according to recommendations with any of the insecticides mentioned in the following discussions, the amount of insecticide residue that remains on them at harvesttime is too small to be appreciably toxic to animals fed on hay, forage, or silage made from the crops. On the other hand, these feeds may retain very small amounts of the insecticide and when fed to farm animals may cause the deposition of very small quantities of it in their body tissues, milk, or eggs. What effects, if any, the consumption by man of extremely small quantities of these insecticides in meat, milk, eggs, and other foods may have on human health is still in doubt. Therefore, except as otherwise indicated in this article, forage, hay, or silage from crops that have been treated with any of these insecticides should not be fed to dairy animals or poultry, or to meat animals being finished for slaughter.

DDT and toxaphene in sprays or dusts are two of the best insecticides yet tried for the control of the true armyworm, fall armyworm, and army cutworm, but some investigators have reported poor results. Also, the advisability of using them on grain and feed crops is still questionable because of the residues of insecticide that may remain on them at harvesttime. These insects are really cutworms that appear in great numbers some years when weather conditions are favorable to extensive outbreaks. The true armyworm and army cutworm are partial to small grains, grasses, and corn, but the fall armyworm also attacks peanuts and other legumes. Excellent control has been obtained by application of a spray made from factory-prepared concentrated solutions of toxaphene or DDT which are emulsifiable with water. Toxaphene has been successfully applied by airplane at the rate of 1.5 to 2 pounds per acre in 2 gallons of spray. A spray containing 1.5 pounds of DDT in 5 gallons of spray per acre has also given satisfactory control when applied by airplane or with ground equipment. Dusts containing 20 percent of toxaphene or 10 percent of DDT, applied at the rate of 20 pounds per acre, have also given good control under some conditions.

The broadcasting of poison bran bait as commonly applied for cutworms and grasshoppers is another of the good methods of control for armyworms. It has been used for many years. It is less likely than dusts or sprays to leave a residue of insecticide on the crop.

According to Connecticut Agricultural Experiment Station workers, "Thirty pounds of 10 percent toxaphene dust or 10 percent chlordane dust per acre applied to the surface of the soil at least a week before planting gave excellent control of cutworms on tobacco. Toxaphene emulsion, at the same rate of active ingredient per acre was equally effective."

Similar results on vegetable ground with 5 percent DDT or 5 percent chlordane dust at 30 to 40 pounds per acre have been reported by the Minnesota Agricultural Experiment Station. These treatments would appear promising for cutworm control in young corn. In fact, the application of 1 to 2 pounds of toxaphene per acre in two or more gallons of spray with conventional weed sprayers, as recommended by the Iowa Station, has successfully controlled cutworms on hundreds of acres of young corn in Iowa.

CHINCH BUGS are little black sucking insects that attack corn, sorghum, small grains, and grasses grown for forage or lawns in the Central and Eastern States. They are about one-eighth inch long when full-grown, with white wings folded on their backs to form a sort of X. When newly hatched, they are smaller than a pinhead, red, and wingless, but their wings develop and they lose their red color as they mature. They often become extremely abundant in small grains. When these ripen the young bugs migrate in enormous numbers on foot to adjacent fields of young corn, sorghum, and other crops belonging to the grass family. Barriers of one kind or another are widely used to prevent these migrations.

Chinch bug barriers are made in several ways, but the best of them include a narrow band of a repellent or insecticidal chemical on the surface of the soil. For many years repellents such as coal-tar creosote have been used for this purpose, either directly on the ground or on a fence about 2 inches high made of stiff, heavy paper. More recently insecticidal dusts containing 4 percent of dinitro-*o*-cresol, 10 percent of DDT, or 1 percent of benzene hexachloride, applied in a narrow band on smooth, hard-packed soil or in a truck-wheel track, at the rate of 1 to 2 pounds per rod, have been found very satisfactory. The dust line should be patrolled every day to remove leaves or other debris that may have been blown onto it, and to repair any breaks made in it by wind, water, or soil cracks. Lines that have been destroyed by heavy rain should be completely renewed.

Although rather expensive, several of the new insecticides have been recommended as dusts or sprays for application to valuable small plantings of corn and other grains being grown for seed, or to limited areas of corn that have been invaded by chinch bugs from adjacent small-grain fields. Being sucking insects that do not eat plant tissues, chinch bugs cannot be killed by merely spraying or dusting the plants, but must be actually hit with the insecticide. Satisfactory control of the adults on corn has been obtained with toxaphene applied in a spray or dust at the rate of 1½ pounds per acre. One of the best dusts yet found consists of 4 percent by weight of sabadilla powder in pyrophyllite, used at the rate of 50 pounds or more per acre.

Good protection of lawns against chinch bugs has been obtained with a dust containing 5 percent of chlordane by weight applied at the rate of 5 pounds per 1,000 square feet. For more convenient and uniform application this quantity of the dust may be mixed with 2 or 3 pounds of sand or 10 pounds of fine-grained fertilizer and spread with a fertilizer or lime spreader. If no device for settling the dust is attached to the spreader, a broom or the back of a rake may be used. The treatment should not be applied when the grass is wet. Mowing the lawn just before or just after treatment is helpful in perfecting coverage and settling the dust.

THE GREENBUG is a little green plant-louse that frequently does extensive damage to small grains in the spring and early summer in the Central and Southeastern States. No satisfactory control measure for it was known before 1949. Experiments and large-scale use in 1949 and 1950 showed that excellent control can be obtained with parathion at temperatures above 45° F., and with tetraethyl pyrophosphate at temperatures above 70°. These insecticides were used with good effect in 1949 on some 60,000 acres of badly infested small grains in the North Central States and in 1950 on upwards of 650,000 acres in the South Central States. The best results were had with oil or water sprays made from factory-made emulsifiable solutions containing 15 to 25 percent of parathion and applied by airplane or power ground equipment at the rate of 3 to 4 ounces of parathion in 2 to 5 gallons of spray per acre. Tetraethyl pyrophosphate was used at the rate of 4 to 5 ounces per acre in the same gallonages of spray. Both of these insecticides are very toxic to man and contact of any kind with them must be avoided. They should not be applied with hand equipment. They disappear from the plants quite rapidly. However, treated small grains should not be pastured or cut for hay or grain during the first 2 weeks after treatment with parathion or for 3 days after treatment with tetraethyl pyrophosphate.

For white-fringed beetles excellent insecticidal control methods have been worked out. Adult beetles that are injuring ornamental shrubs and flowers may be killed with cryolite or DDT applied as a dust or spray. An undiluted full-strength cryolite dust or a 3 to 5 percent DDT dust is applied at 7- to 10-day intervals. As a spray, cryolite is used at the rate of 1.5 ounces to 1 gallon of water. For a DDT spray, 1 ounce of 50 percent DDT wettable powder, or 2 ounces of 25 percent DDT wettable powder, are mixed with 3 gallons of water, and applied at 10- to 15-day intervals.

Field infestations of white-fringed beetle larvae can be controlled by treating the soil with DDT. One application of 10 pounds of DDT per acre gives good control for several years. The DDT is applied evenly over the soil surface in a dust or spray and mixed thoroughly into the upper 3 or 4 inches of soil with a disk harrow. A good method of applying the DDT is to mix 20 pounds of 50 percent DDT dust thoroughly with 500 pounds of pulverized dry sandy soil or sand—enough for treating 1 acre—and spread the mixture by hand or with a rotary or spreader-type fertilizer distributor. Even distribution can be obtained by spreading half of the mixture in one direction and the other half at right angles to the first. For garden plots, 1 ounce of 50 percent DDT mixed with a suitable quantity of dry sand is enough for 140 square feet.

For protection of row crops such as corn, cotton, soybeans, and peanuts, DDT is applied in the drill rows at planting time in the spring. The DDT is mixed with soil or sand as previously described and applied by hand or with a fertilizer distributor (at the same depth as the seed is to be planted) at the rate of 2.5 to 5 pounds of DDT per acre.

In experimental trials other new chemicals are showing promise as soil insecticides for control of the white-fringed beetle.

Growers of sweet corn in the home garden or for the market usually have trouble with the corn earworm, especially in the warm climate of the Southern and Pacific States, where this insect is a limiting factor in sweet-corn production. A good method of control is to inject a few drops of refined white mineral oil, preferably containing 0.2 percent of pyrethrins, into the base of the silk mass at the tip of the ear with an oil can or medicine dropper about 4 days after the silk first appears, at which time the oil will not interfere with pollination.

A spraying method better suited for application to large commercial plantings also has been developed. The spray consists of 3 quarts of factory-made 25 percent DDT emulsifiable concentrate (5 pints of 30 percent DDT concentrate can be substituted) and 2½ gallons of white mineral oil of 65 to 95 seconds Saybolt viscosity, mixed thoroughly with enough water to make 25 gallons. For a small batch the quantities may be reduced to one-fourth pint of the 25 percent DDT concentrate, three-fourths pint of the oil, and enough water to make a gallon. The spray is applied to the tips of the ears 1 day after the first silks appear and again 2 days later. A third application 2 days after the second usually increases control. Only enough spray should be applied to wet the silks. Twenty-five gallons of the spray is enough for 1 acre of corn, and 1 gallon will take care of a plot about 17 by 100 feet. Any good hand sprayer is satisfactory for treating garden sweet corn. For commercial acreage a high-clearance power sprayer is used, with nozzles fixed in suitable positions to spray the tips of the ears, and adjusted to wet them adequately but not excessively with a fine spray.

A similar spray, but with only 1¼ gallons of mineral oil in a 25-gallon lot, can be applied to the entire plants to reduce "budworm" damage by the earworm and fall armyworm to sweet corn before tasseling and silking.

THE CORN FLEA BEETLE causes direct injury to field and sweet corn and also is a carrier of the destructive bacterial wilt (Stewart's disease) of corn. This shiny black beetle is not much larger than a flea and jumps like one when disturbed. It is especially injurious to very young sweet-corn plants, which it often infests in great numbers. Experiments have indicated that it can be readily controlled in home-garden plantings, with attendant reduction of the wilt disease it carries and material increase in yields, by applying a dust containing 1 or 2 percent of DDT to the young plants. Good control also has been obtained in home gardens with a light application of a fine, mistlike spray containing DDT applied with a small plunger-type hand sprayer. The spray is made by thoroughly mixing 6 tablespoonfuls of a ready-made emulsifiable liquid concentrate containing 25 percent of DDT (usually obtainable in seed stores) with 1 quart of water. The spray may burn the plants more or less if applied so heavily as to leave droplets on them. One or two additional applications may be necessary if the plants become reinfested.

Some of the other new insecticides tested against the flea beetle on young sweet corn have shown considerable promise. In one trial on 8 acres of sweet corn plots, very good control was obtained by applying a concentrated solution of DDT as a very fine mist with a power blower at the rate of 2 pounds of DDT per acre. This treatment did not injure the plants.

THE ALFALFA CATERPILLAR could be controlled very easily by treating the infested stand with about one-fourth pound of DDT per acre in a dilute dust or spray if it were not for the residue problem. Even with such a light dosage, tiny amounts of DDT remain in the hay and appear in the milk, eggs, and meat of animals to which the hay is fed. The use of DDT on alfalfa therefore can be recommended only where the crop is being grown for seed; the threshings should not be fed to dairy animals, poultry, or meat animals that are being finished for slaughter.

The California State Extension Service in 1951 recommended methoxychlor sprays, applied at the rate of three-fourths pound of the active ingredient per acre for the control of the alfalfa caterpillar. Methoxychlor does not cause a residue hazard when it is used at the dosages recommended herein on alfalfa grown for hay.

This velvety green caterpillar, which is nearly 2 inches long when full-grown and of importance only in the Southwestern and Pacific Coast States, is kept under control much of the time by its insect enemies and a wilt disease. With their help, most of the losses it causes can be prevented by cultural measures systematically applied throughout whole communities. Alfalfa growers in some California districts have found it profitable to employ entomologists to watch their fields during the growing season and advise them concerning the application of measures for the control of the caterpillar and other alfalfa insects.

Good control has been obtained by University of California research workers from the experimental spraying of infested fields with laboratory-prepared suspensions of the virus that causes the wilt disease of the alfalfa caterpillar. This method appears promising.

SEVERAL SPECIES of *Lygus,* as I mentioned, often are abundant in alfalfa and greatly reduce the yield where the crop is being grown for seed. DDT and toxaphene have been found very useful in controlling them. Recommendations issued in 1951 by the Utah State Agricultural College are:

"1. Dust the alfalfa seed field when the plants are in bud stage, using 20 to 25 pounds of 10 percent DDT dust per acre. *Or,* spray the field, using at least 1.5 pounds of actual DDT per acre. Either treatment will eliminate lygus nymphs for the first 3 weeks and, in addition, will often keep the population so low during the rest of the seed period that a second treatment is unnecessary.

"2. If, 3 or 4 weeks after the bud stage treatment, lygus nymphs begin to become numerous, apply 20 pounds of 10 percent toxaphene dust per acre. *Or,* 1½ pounds of actual toxaphene as a spray may be used if a spray treatment is preferred. Make the application when bees are *not* working in the field. Put on the dust or spray before 7 a. m. or after 7 p. m. If applied as directed, toxaphene is not too harmful to bees for use on alfalfa in bloom. Most other insecticides will kill many bees even though applied at night.

"Do not feed forage or chaff treated with DDT or toxaphene to dairy animals, animals being fattened for slaughter, or poultry."

IN ADDITION to the cultural method of controlling the alfalfa weevil I mentioned earlier, the new insecticides have led to improvements in its control. A new departure is to kill off the overwintered adults early in the spring before they have had a chance to lay eggs for a new generation. This is done by applying 1.5 to 2 pounds of chlordane per acre in a spray when the first spring growth of alfalfa is only 1 to 2 inches tall. As little as one-fourth pound of dieldrin per acre applied in a spray at that time has given even better results and is now being recommended by State Agricultural Experiment Station and United States Department of Agriculture entomologists.

When seed is to be grown the additional weevil control needed is provided by the application of DDT for control of lygus bugs as already described.

In field plot tests promising results have been obtained with extremely small dosages of aldrin, heptachlor, lindane, or chlordane, but none of these chemicals can be used safely on alfalfa to be cut for hay.

When the crop is to be used for hay the grower may prefer to control the weevil by killing the larvae after they become abundant on the first cutting of the season. If so, for maximum benefit the crop should be treated before many of the plants have started to turn gray. A dust or spray containing 2 pounds of calcium arsenate, 1 to 2 pounds of methoxychlor, or one-fourth pound of parathion per acre is then used.

Parathion-treated hay must be left at least 14 days before cutting. When calcium arsenate is used the crop should be allowed to stand at least 10 days.

If parathion is used it should be applied only by airplane or power ground machine, not with hand equipment, and in strict observance of the directions and warnings given on labels and otherwise by the manufacturer.

THE PEA APHID is a serious pest of alfalfa as well as peas. This little, pale-green plant-louse often multiplies to enormous numbers on alfalfa early in the spring and ruins the first hay crop of the season in one area or another practically every year. Before we had the new insecticides certain cultural measures of a preventive nature were the only known methods of control. Several of the new insecticides are useful in suppressing infestations when actually in progress. The use of DDT as already described for the control of lygus will give good control of the pea aphid.

Parathion may be used as a 1-percent dust at 35 to 40 pounds per acre, if applied by ground dusters. *This dust should not be applied by airplane.* Excellent control may also be achieved with 1 pound of wettable 25 percent parathion powder in 100 gallons of water per acre. Alfalfa that has been treated with parathion should not be cut or pastured for at least 14 days. *Do not apply parathion to alfalfa fields in blossom.*

Tetraethyl pyrophosphate (TEPP) is extremely toxic to aphids. One pint of 40 percent emulsifiable TEPP in 10 gallons or more of water is applied per acre. The spray should be used immediately after it is mixed because it loses its strength in an hour or two. It should be applied after 7 p. m. if the alfalfa is in bloom, in order to avoid killing bees essential to cross-pollination. Large fields may be treated by airplane when the wind does not exceed 4 miles an hour.

The garden webworm may become extremely abundant on alfalfa in late summer or early fall. This small, yellowish-green, black-spotted worm encloses the foliage in webbing, inside of which it feeds on the leaves. It can be controlled on alfalfa grown for hay by cutting the alfalfa as soon as it comes into bloom and the young shoots of the next crop have begun to appear on the plant crowns. Keeping weed growths cleaned up in fields, fence rows, and other uncultivated areas also helps to prevent the infestation of alfalfa from these sources. Where alfalfa is being grown for seed, however, prompt cutting is not feasible, and the use of an insecticide is the only alternative. The garden webworm is much easier to control with an insecticide if it is applied before the larvae become half-grown, because by that time they feed largely within their webs, which keep the insecticide off the foliage.

Newly seeded fields of alfalfa that become infested can be protected by dusting them with calcium arsenate at 10 pounds per acre or spraying them with 4 pounds of this insecticide in 100 gallons of water per acre.

Preliminary tests conducted by experiment station workers in Kansas and Oklahoma indicate that toxaphene is satisfactory for controlling this pest. Toxaphene is less toxic to bees than some other insecticides. Nevertheless, if the alfalfa is in bloom it should be applied only before 7 a. m. or after 7 p. m., when bees are not active in the field. Toxaphene as a spray at the rate of 2 pounds, or as a dust at the rate of 3 pounds, per acre should give adequate control if applied when the worms are small.

These insecticidal treatments are recommended for use only on alfalfa being grown for seed, where no part of the crop is to be used for feed or pasture.

The two-spotted spider mite, clover mite, and other mites occasionally damage seed alfalfa during the blooming period. A way to prevent the damage is to apply dusting sulfur to the crop just before it blooms. A single application of 20 to 25 pounds of sulfur per acre will usually suffice. It can be applied as a diluent of DDT where DDT is being applied for lygus control, or by itself if the DDT is being applied as a spray.

Some of the miticides recently put on the market by insecticide manufacturers have shown promise for use on alfalfa. For information concerning these the grower should consult his State agricultural experiment station.

970134°—52——39

THE POTATO LEAFHOPPER does much damage to alfalfa and peanuts and could as well be called the alfalfa or peanut leafhopper. It is a pale-green, soft-bodied, wedge-shaped winged insect only about one-eighth inch long when full-grown. It often becomes extremely abundant on these crops and sucks the sap out of the leaves, causing them to turn reddish yellow and die.

In experimental trials favorable results have been obtained with several of the new insecticides for leafhopper control on alfalfa and peanuts. On alfalfa excellent control was obtained with one-half pound of methoxychlor per acre in spray or dust form applied midway in the development of the crop.

On peanuts in Virginia, three applications of a dust containing 90 percent of sulfur and 1 percent of DDT gave good control of the leaf spot disease as well as the leafhopper. The first application was made about July 10 and the other two applications at 3-week intervals. To avoid possible residue hazards, the total amount of this dust applied during any one season should not exceed 80 pounds per acre.

SEEDLING PEANUTS are subject to injury by the tobacco thrips, an extremely small yellowish insect that becomes numerous within the folds of the young leaflets, causes them to crinkle, shrivel, turn black, and die, and retards the early season growth of the plants. Several of the new insecticides, especially DDT, aldrin, and dieldrin, have given good control as dusts and sprays in experimental trials, and it is hoped that one or more of these can be recommended when more information has been obtained on dosages required and possible residue hazards.

SPITTLEBUGS have been abundant in the Eastern and North Central States. These insects produce little masses of white froth around themselves and the stems of alfalfa, clover, and other plants from which they suck sap through their sharp beaks. The young bugs begin feeding very early in the growing season and cause surprising losses in yield.

Several of the new insecticides have been effective against these insects, one of the best being lindane at one-fourth pound per acre in a water emulsion or a wettable powder suspension in water. The emulsions have been successfully applied in 10 to 20 gallons of spray per acre with the low-pressure power weed sprayers now in common use. These sprayers must be cleaned very thoroughly of all weed killer with a solution of 1 gallon of ammonia in 100 gallons of water before they are used for applying insecticides. Emulsions or suspensions can also be applied in more dilute form with high-pressure sprayers such as are used for treating vegetable and fruit crops.

Good control has been obtained with a 5 percent benzene hexachloride or toxaphene dust applied by airplane or ground equipment at the rate of 20 to 30 pounds per acre. One pound of methoxychlor per acre in a spray suspension or emulsion was also effective, even when applied in as little as 5 gallons of spray per acre.

For best protection the insecticide must be applied before the new growth is more than 8 inches high and before many of the young bugs have become enveloped in froth. It has been suggested that the second crop can be protected without causing a residue hazard by spraying or dusting the stubble as soon as the first crop can be removed from the field and before the second crop has attained much growth.

When used as recommended, methoxychlor can be safely applied to crops being grown for hay or forage, but lindane, benzene hexachloride, and toxaphene should be used only on crops being grown exclusively for seed. If applied to crops grown for hay or forage they may contaminate the meat, milk, or eggs of animals fed thereon. Benzene hexachloride or lindane should not be applied to fields that will be planted to potatoes, other root crops, or peanuts, as they may cause an off-flavor in such crops.

Although more expensive than the above-mentioned insecticides, a 0.75 percent rotenone dust at 25 to 40 pounds per acre has been recommended and can be safely used for spittlebugs on crops grown for hay, forage, or food.

THE ADULTS AND LARVAE of the clover root borer, a beetle that burrows in the roots of red clover, kill many of the plants and thus rapidly deplete stands. No satisfactory method of preventing the damage has been available. However, several research workers have succeeded in greatly reducing infestations by treating the clover with a dust containing benzene hexachloride, chlordane, aldrin, parathion, or certain other new insecticides in the fall or spring to kill the adults during their spring flight period. Some of the treatments also gave good control of spittlebug infestations. From the results to date it appears that the insecticidal control of the clover root borer will be practical, but at this writing further information is needed on possible residue hazards involved, before definite recommendations can be made.

TWO SPECIES of grayish weevils only about one-tenth inch long, called clover seed weevils, attack the florets or immature seeds of alsike, ladino, and red and white clover being grown for seed, and seriously reduce the yield. Most of the damage is done by the larvae working deep in the blossoms. These weevils originally came from Europe and no satisfactory method of controlling them was known until very recently. Experiments have shown that one treatment with 20 pounds of 5 percent DDT dust evenly applied by airplane or ground machine when about 20 percent of the clover heads have withered and turned brown will control them in most seasons under Oregon and northwestern Idaho conditions. To avoid killing honey bees and other pollinating insects, the dust should be applied early in the morning or late in the evening when those insects are not working on the blossoms.

Favorable experimental results have been obtained by workers in the New York Agricultural Experiment Station with a dust containing 1 percent of parathion.

A little weevil, known as the vetch bruchid, infests the seeds of the hairy, woolly podded, and smooth vetches but not those of common vetch. Because of its winter hardiness, hairy vetch is a valuable winter cover crop in the South. This weevil, which undoubtedly came into this country in seed imported from Europe, ruined the production of hairy vetch seed in the Eastern States. Before DDT came along it had also nearly ruined the production of this seed in Oregon and southern Washington, the only area from which it could be obtained in quantity during and after the Second World War. In tests of various insecticides it was shown that good seed crops can be obtained if hairy vetch is treated by airplane or ground machine with a 3 percent DDT dust at the rate of 25 pounds per acre as soon as the first pods appear outside the fading hairy vetch flowers. The general use of this method of control has enabled Oregon growers to continue the production of hairy vetch seed.

THE SOUTHERN CORN ROOTWORM is the larva of the spotted cucumber beetle. It is a white worm about three-quarters inch long when full-grown, with a brown head and tail-plate. The worms live in the soil and attack the underground parts of many kinds of plants, including corn and peanuts. Cultural methods of preventing the damage they do to those crops have never been very satisfactory, but it has been found that they and some other soil-inhabiting insects can be destroyed by treating the soil with new insecticides. Benzene hexachloride and lindane are effective against them but cannot be recommended for use as soil insecticides because they are likely to impart a disagreeable odor or flavor to the crop or to succeeding crops.

The Louisiana and South Carolina Agricultural Experiment Stations have conducted extensive tests with soil insecticides for the control of the southern corn rootworm, the sand wireworm and the seed-corn maggot as pests of corn. Following successful results with chlordane, they recommended it in 1950 for the purpose, with certain reservations, and it has been quite widely used by Louisiana and South Carolina farmers. The chlordane is applied in the drill rows at corn-planting time, at the rate of 1 to 2 pounds per acre, either mixed thoroughly with the fertilizer, with old sawdust, or with sand. One of the reservations is that chlordane should never be mixed with fertilizer containing lime or any other alkaline material. More information is needed on the possibility of injury of one kind or another, such as adverse effect on flavor, from the use of chlordane or other organic insecticides on food and feed crops. Attention is also called to the precaution that if fertilizer is to be the carrier of the chlordane or other organic insecticide the mixture should be used within 2 or 3 weeks after processing. There is a possibility that deterioration of the insecticide may result from longer storage.

A single application to the soil surface of 2 pounds of aldrin or 25 pounds of toxaphene per acre is recommended for control of the southern corn rootworm on peanuts. Aldrin is applied as a 2.5- or 5-percent dust and toxaphene as a 10- or 20-percent free-flowing mixture.

VARIOUS SPECIES OF WIREWORMS are pests of cereal and forage crops in different parts of the country. These are small, yellowish or brown worms about 1 inch long and are immature stages of click beetles. They live in the soil and injure plants much as the southern corn rootworm does. As I mentioned in the discussion of that insect, it is known that material damage to corn by certain species of wireworms can be prevented by the use of chlordane as a soil insecticide.

British and Canadian workers have reported good protection of small grains and corn from wireworms by treating the seed uniformly and thoroughly with a dust containing from 20 to 40 percent of purified gamma benzene hexachloride (BHC). This can also be combined with a fungicidal dust for protection of the grains from certain fungus diseases as well as wireworms. Only dusts containing purified gamma BHC should be used because the crude BHC is harmful to germination. Depending on the quantity of seed to be sown per acre, enough of the dilute dust is applied to the seed to provide 1 ounce of actual BHC per acre. Not more than 1 ounce of this ingredient should be used per bushel of seed. The seeding rate of grain should be reduced about one-fourth in fields where, in the past, a heavier than normal rate has been used to overcome the effects of crop thinning by wireworms. Otherwise the stand may be too heavy for best yields, especially in dry years. The seed grain should not be treated more than a week or two in advance of seeding, or germination may be lowered. Planting of treated seed in dry soil should be avoided.

THE RED HARVESTER ANT and the mound-building prairie ant are prevalent in the Southwestern States, where numerous bare spots in fields of alfalfa and other crops indicate the location of their large colonies and the damage they do. Similar bare spots in Texas and Louisiana may signify the presence of Texas leaf-cutting ant colonies. All three of these species are pests in dooryards and farmyards as well as in crops.

The harvester ants clear all vegetation from the ground around their nests, and use the seeds for food. The leaf-cutting ants also denude the ground around their nests but carry the foliage to their nests to serve as the medium on which to grow a mold which they use for food.

When properly and persistently applied, various insecticides have been used effectively against all three species for many years, although complete eradication of colonies is very difficult. More recently dieldrin, chlordane, and methyl bromide have been added to the list of chemicals found useful against them. One of the most effective and easily applied insecticides is a dust containing 2 percent of dieldrin. For a medium- or large-sized colony spread about one-half pound of the dust thinly in a continuous band 4 to 6 inches wide to form a circle 5 to 6 feet in diameter around the entrance tunnel of the nest. For small colonies with a cleared area less than 6 feet wide, place the band of dust around the edge of the cleared area and reduce the dosage proportionately. In irrigated areas apply the dust as soon as possible after the surface of the flooded land has dried.

In the larger colonies new entrances may be opened outside the dust ring. Treat these entrances individually or include them in the same ring with the original entrance when making the next application. Inspect all treated colonies every 2 or 3 weeks, and re-treat those showing activity, until all are inactive. Inspections can then be made less frequently.

Apply the dust on warm days when there is little wind, and renew the band if it becomes broken or washed away. In handling dieldrin special care must be taken to observe the safety precautions given on page 271 or on containers.

A 5 percent chlordane dust applied in the manner just described for dieldrin dust will give fairly good control. It does not remain effective as long as dieldrin and more applications usually are necessary to subdue the ant colonies. A 10 percent chlordane dust sifted thinly over the cleared areas surrounding colony entrances has given good results in trials conducted in the Rio Grande Valley by the Texas Agricultural Experiment Station.

Methyl bromide has also given good control of ant colonies in moist soil. This fumigant is a liquid sold in cans which forms a heavy poisonous vapor when released, and must not be inhaled. It is injected into the nest openings with a mechanical dispenser that can be attached to the can. Apply 2 fluid ounces of the fumigant per colony and pack the soil tight over the entrance hole to prevent the gas from escaping. Methyl bromide is also sold in small glass ampules that can be inserted and broken in harvester ant nests with a special applicator.

THE SUGARCANE BORER damages sugarcane, corn, and sorghum in the Gulf States in much the same way as the European corn borer injures corn in the Northern States. The yellowish white, brown-spotted larva is about 1 inch long when full-grown and turns into a small straw-colored moth. Although it is able to survive only in tropical and semitropical regions, it is one of the worst insect enemies of sugarcane, corn, and sorghum along the Gulf coast and in Florida, where it produces several generations a year.

For about 10 years a full-strength cryolite dust has been widely and profitably used against the sugarcane borer in Louisiana. Four applications are made at weekly intervals while the first- or spring-generation borers are hatching from eggs laid on the cane leaves by the moths. The dust is applied with airplanes or ground equipment at the rate of 10 pounds per acre, very early in the morning while the air is still and the plants are wet with dew. Where it is used to control the second or midsummer generation the same number of weekly applications are made by airplane, the stand of cane by that time being too tall and thick for the use of ground equipment. For several reasons first-generation dusting is preferable.

After several years of testing, a dust containing 40 percent of ryania was recommended in 1950 for use against the sugarcane borer. It is applied at the same dosage and in the same way as cryolite.

AMONG THE ENEMIES that attack sugarcane underground are wireworms and several small soil-inhabiting insects and related animals. The losses they cause can be much reduced by deep drainage of the soil, by the planting of varieties that give thick stands of cane and recover well from injury, and by planting the cane in late summer rather than in the fall in order to promote rapid vigorous growth and the production of good stands of cane before cold weather. Because of the difficulty of completing the planting of large acreages before fall, the application of these cultural control measures is not always practicable. Investigations have shown that stands can be increased equally well by applying a 1 percent chlordane or toxaphene dust at the rate of 400 pounds per acre on the seed cane as it is placed in the furrows at planting time, and then covering it with soil in the usual way. This method of control would enable the grower to plant his cane in the fall with confidence that insects and related pests will not prevent the development of a good stand.

PROGRESS is being made by entomologists and chemists in the Department of Agriculture, State experiment stations, and industry toward practical control measures for a number of other insect pests of cereal and forage crops that have not been mentioned.

A few figures will show the importance of the investigations to the production of staple food and feed crops. A billion dollars a year is a conservative estimate of the annual losses caused by the insect pests of these crops during production and storage. The annual losses caused by only a few of the insects, including the corn earworm, European corn borer, chinch bug, hessian fly, and grasshoppers, during the growth of the crops they attack, total some 300 million dollars. That is less than 3 percent of the farm value of the crops. The additional losses caused by the insect pests of grains and cereal products while in farm and commercial storage are estimated to be in the neighborhood of 600 million dollars a year. A billion dollars worth of staple foods saved from destruction of insects would feed a lot of ill-nourished or starving people.

C. M. PACKARD *is an entomologist. He was in the division of cereal and forage insect investigations, Bureau of Entomology and Plant Quarantine, for 37 years and retired on September 30, 1950. Until 1937, when he was put in charge of that division with headquarters in Washington, he worked from various field stations on the biology and control of cereal and forage insects.*

For further reading on cereal and forage insects, Mr. Packard suggests some publications of the Department of Agriculture:

Bureau of Entomology and Plant Quarantine publications—E–519, Control of the Pale Western Cutworm in the Southern Great Plains Region, *by H. H. Walkden, 1940; E–546,* An Experimental Cooperative Community Program for the Cultural Control of Bugs of the Genus Lygus on Alfalfa Crops in the Mohawk Area of Arizona in 1939 and 1940, *by Loyd L. Stitt, 1941; E–780,* DDT Sprays for Control of the Corn Earworm and the Budworm in Sweet Corn, *by R. A. Blanchard, W. A. Douglas, G. P. Wene, and O. B. Wooten, 1950; EC–14,* The Wheat Stem Sawfly and Its Control, *by E. G. Davis, J. A. Callenbach, and J. A. Munro, 1950.*

Circulars—494, The Texas Leaf-cutting Ant and Its Control, *by E. V. Walter, Lee Seaton, and A. A. Mathewson, 1938; 732,* The Wheat Midge in the Pacific Northwest, *by Max M. Reeher, 1945; 850,* White-fringed Beetles and How To Combat Them, *by H. C. Young, B. A. App, J. B. Gill, and H. S. Hollingsworth, 1950; 878,* Pests of Sugarcane and Their Control, *by J. W. Ingram, E. K. Bynum, W. E. Haley, and L. J. Charpentier, 1951.*

Farmers' Bulletins—1094, The Alfalfa Caterpillar, *by V. L. Wildermuth, 1922; 1668,* The Red Harvester Ant and How to Subdue It, *by V. L. Wildermuth and E. G. Davis, 1931; 1780,* How to Fight the Chinch Bug, *by C. M. Packard and Curtis Benton, 1937, revised 1951; 1798,* Control of Common White Grubs in Cereal and Forage Crops, *by P. Luginbill, 1938; 1850,* The Armyworm and Its Control, by *W. R. Walton and C. M. Packard, 1947, revised 1951; 1930,* Prevention and Control of Alfalfa Weevil Damage, *by J. C. Hamlin, W. C. McDuffie, F. V. Lieberman, and R. W. Bunn, 1943; 1990,* Habits and Control of the Fall Armyworm, *by Philip Luginbill 1950.*

Leaflet 284, Protect Your Garden Corn From Earworms, *1950.*

Mr. Packard also suggests the Clemson Agricultural College (S. C.) Extension Circular 352, Use of Insecticides with Fertilizer for Controlling the Sand Wireworm and the Southern Corn Rootworm on Corn for 1950, *by H. A. Woodle and W. C. Nettles, 1950; and the following State Agricultural Experiment Station publications:*

Connecticut (New Haven)—Circular 168, Chinch Bug Control, *by J. C. Schread, 1949.*

Oklahoma—Mimeographed Circular M–190, Insecticides for Greenbug Control, *by R. G. Dahms, 1950.*

Oregon, Circulars of Information—372, Control of Weevil in Hairy Vetch Grown for Seed, *by L. P. Rockwood, M. M. Reeher, D. C. Mote, E. C. Anderson, and H. A. Scullen, 1946; 485,* Control of Clover Seed Weevil, *by M. M. Reeher, L. P. Rockwood, E. A. Dickason, and D. C. Mote, 1950.*

Utah—Circular 125, Growing Alfalfa for Seed in Utah, *section on harmful insects, by F. V. Lieberman, S. J. Snow, C. J. Sorenson, and H. F. Thornley, 1950.*

Wisconsin—Research Bulletin 159, White Grubs in Cereal and Forage Crops and Their Control, *by T. R. Chamberlin and C. L. Fluke, 1947.*

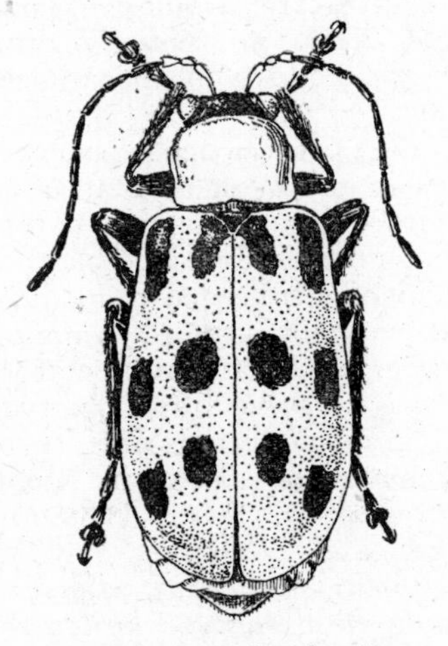

Spotted cucumber beetle.

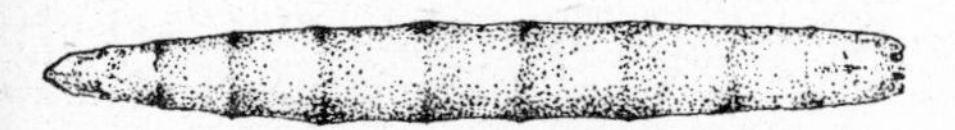

Carrot rust fly maggot.

Grasshoppers

J. R. Parker

Grasshoppers have caused concern among men since the beginning of recorded history. They have brought fear and famine at one time or another to every continent. A description of their ravages is given in Joel 2: 3—"The land is as the Garden of Eden before them, and behind them a desolate wilderness, yea, and nothing shall escape them."

Grasshoppers are recorded as having injured crops in New England in 1797. In 1818 hordes of them destroyed the crops of early settlers in the Red River Valley in Minnesota. During 1874 to 1877 the Rocky Mountain grasshopper, or locust, as it was then called, increased to such numbers that its depredations were considered a national calamity. Great swarms originating in the plains east of the Rocky Mountains in Montana, Wyoming, and Colorado migrated to the Mississippi Valley and Texas, devouring crops wherever they paused in their flights. Damage to crops amounted to 200 million dollars. Congress recognized the seriousness of the outbreak and on March 3, 1877, created the United States Entomological Commission and authorized it to investigate the grasshopper problem.

Grasshoppers still destroy crops somewhere every year and during outbreaks cause losses totaling millions of dollars. Overgrazing by grasshoppers is one of the fundamental reasons for loss of productive grasslands in many States. Grasshoppers contribute to soil erosion and dust-bowl conditions, particularly when drought and mismanagement of the land also occur.

Grasshoppers are found all over the United States, but serious outbreaks seldom develop in the East. Local outbreaks have occurred in New England, New York, Virginia, Georgia, Florida, Alabama, and Mississippi, and grasshoppers are numerous enough to cause some damage in most Eastern States every year. Outbreaks are mostly in the western two-thirds of the United States. They occur most frequently in the Northern Great Plains, including eastern Montana, North Dakota, South Dakota, Nebraska, and Kansas.

Every State within the region subject to outbreaks has more than 100 kinds of grasshoppers. Some are rare and others fairly common. Only a few ever become abundant enough to injure crops seriously. At least 90 percent of all grasshopper damage to crops is caused by five species, the lesser migratory grasshopper, the differential grasshopper, the two-striped grasshopper, the red-legged grasshopper, and the clear-winged grasshopper.

The lesser migratory grasshopper, the two-striped grasshopper, and the red-legged grasshopper are found throughout the grasshopper country. The differential grasshopper seldom moves farther north than the southern borders of North Dakota and Minnesota. The clear-winged grasshopper is confined largely to States bordering the Canadian boundary from Michigan to Washington, but in the mountainous West it extends south to New Mexico, Arizona, and southern California.

The lesser migratory hopper normally selects well-drained, light soil and sparse vegetation. The differential, two-striped, and red-legged grasshoppers prefer moist, heavy soil and lush vegetation. The clear-winged grasshopper adapts itself to many conditions but is most common in mountain meadows, grassy openings in timbered land, and well-sodded, closely grazed pastures on the open plains. Under outbreak conditions all five species spread far from favored habitats and feed on a variety of crops and vegetation.

Of the five species, the lesser migratory grasshopper is the most widely distributed and most destructive. It is a strong flier. Adults sometimes gather in great swarms, which migrate hundreds of miles and destroy crops and range plants wherever they pause in their flight. In most respects it resembles the Rocky Mountain locust, or grasshopper, which ravaged Western States years ago. The latter has longer wings and stronger power of flight, characteristics that several species are known to develop during periods of great abundance. It was called a locust because its habits were similar to those of Old World locusts.

In most parts of the world the word "locust," or its equivalent, designates grasshoppers that migrate in swarms—the same species may be a grasshopper during its periods of small numbers and a locust when it becomes extremely abundant. Everyone understands the term "grasshopper" as commonly used in the United States. It is less confusing to use the term than to change to locust when the same grasshoppers fly in swarms. The periodical cicada and its relatives are popularly known as locusts. They are entirely different from grasshoppers in appearance and habits.

Of the 142 species collected on range plants in the Western States, only a few are known well enough to have common names. Considerable training in taxonomy is needed to identify the adults correctly. Often it is impossible to recognize the immature stages. On the basis of surveys and observations made in range districts since 1936, the most abundant species in Montana, North Dakota, South Dakota, Nebraska, and Wyoming have been *Melanoplus mexicanus, Ageneotettix deorum, Amphitornus coloradus, Phoetaliotes nebrascensis, M. angustipennis, Phlibostroma quadrimaculatum, Opeia obscura, Trachyrhachis kiowa, M. infantilis, Aulocara elliotti, M. gladstoni, Mermiria maculipennis, Cordillacris occipitalis, Melanoplus femur-rubrum, Encoptolophus sordidus, Metator pardalinus,* and *Drepanopterna femoratum.*

Mention also should be made of the long-winged plains grasshopper and *Melanoplus rugglesi,* both of which are migratory and highly destructive during outbreaks. The adults fly in swarms and oviposit in well-defined egg beds. The young hoppers march in bands.

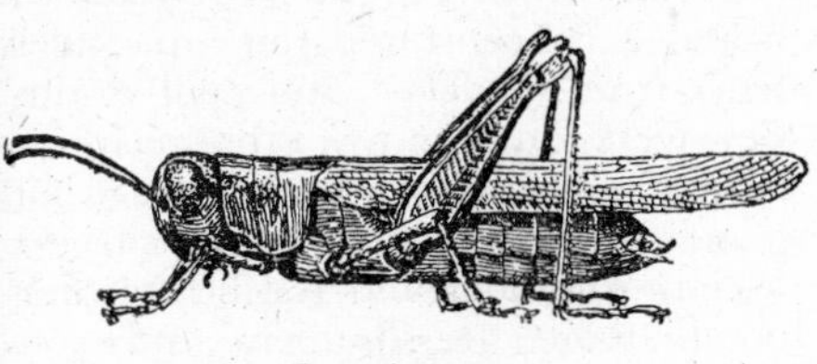

Grasshopper.

Outbreaks of the long-winged plains grasshopper have occurred in Colorado, New Mexico, Oklahoma, Texas, and western Kansas. Outbreaks of *M. rugglesi* have occurred in Nevada, southeastern Oregon, and northeastern California. The Mormon cricket, a long-horned grasshopper or katydid, should also be listed as a pest in the Rocky Mountain and Plateau States. It is normally confined to range vegetation in foothills or mountains, but large bands sometimes migrate long distances and attack crops.

Within the regions where conditions are most favorable for grasshoppers are the principal wheat, barley, and flax areas in the United States. In them also are extensive acreages of corn, oats, rye, and alfalfa. Grasshoppers relish all those crops.

Damage even in average years is more serious than most of us realize. The grasshoppers may eat only a small part of the host plants, but they attack them at vulnerable points. They bite off grain heads and flax bolls and may injure the rest of the plant only slightly. They go for corn silks; if the silks are eaten in the early stage, pollination is prevented and the ears do not fill. Grasshoppers prefer the flowers of alfalfa and sweetclover to the foliage, and heavy losses consequently befall beekeepers and seed growers. Small numbers of hoppers can greatly reduce cotton yields by cutting the seedlings and later the bolls.

Damage in outbreak years has varied from partial to complete destruction of crops over large areas. Estimates by entomologists and county agents in 23 States put the total of losses at $789,374,140 in the 25 years between 1925 and 1949.

The Forest Service reported that in 1934 grasshopper damage to range vegetation in Colorado, Montana, Nebraska, North Dakota, South Dakota, and Wyoming amounted to $2,455,000. Similar damage continued in 1935. In 1936 the Wyoming State entomologist estimated grasshopper damage to forage in Wyoming at $1,480,351. The figures cover only the normal annual value of the forage and do not include such indirect losses as the forced sale of unfattened animals and breeding livestock. As I said before, overeating of grasslands by grasshoppers, particularly in drought years, hastens soil erosion. Reseeding is prevented, vegetative cover often is completely removed, and the soil is exposed to washing and blowing. Areas so affected for several seasons may remain depleted for years.

The division of cereal and forage insect investigations is responsible for grasshopper research conducted by the Bureau of Entomology and Plant Quarantine. Most of the work is centered in its field station at Bozeman, Mont. Staff members of the station study grasshoppers in many States, but most of their work is done in Montana, North Dakota, South Dakota, and Wyoming, where grasshoppers are a serious problem nearly every year.

Research on grasshoppers also is carried on at other field stations of the Bureau. Stations at Manhattan, Kans., Sacramento, Calif., and Forest Grove, Oreg., have included grasshopper investigations in their work programs. In 1950 work on grasshoppers was done at Tempe, Ariz., and Tifton, Ga. Staff members of the Tempe station test new insecticides and carry on field research during the long period of grasshopper activity that prevails in Arizona, March to December.

The research has two main aspects. One has to do with the recognition, distribution, seasonal development, and habits of grasshoppers, and with ecological studies—the effects of meteorological factors and natural enemies upon their abundance. The second division pertains to the immediate control of grasshoppers by insecticides, cultural methods, or other means. These are termed control investigations. No clear-cut distinction actually exists between the two aspects. The objectives are the same, and one depends on the other.

Permanent study areas were established in Arizona, California, Kansas, Minnesota, Montana, North Dakota, and South Dakota, beginning in 1936. Each area included at least 8 square miles of typical farm land. All had histories of grasshopper outbreaks. Maps were made to show the locations of crops, idle land, and native vegetation. Air and soil temperatures and precipitation records were kept. Annual adult, egg, and nymphal surveys were made on each quarter section for 10 years.

The studies produced data on the seasonal development, preferred habitats, food preference, egg-laying habits, and population records of grasshoppers. Information on the effects of parasites, predators, disease, and meteorological factors also was obtained. I cite some of the findings.

Ten-year averages were established for egg hatching, nymphal, adult, and egg-laying periods of the main economic species. On such information is based the timing of control operations and autumn egg surveys. If control begins before the hatching of the major species is completed, it may have to be repeated. If it is continued after egg laying is well under way, it has little effect on preventing grasshopper damage the following year. If the fall egg surveys are made before peak egg laying is completed, a false picture of the next year's potential infestation is obtained. O. L. Barnes used the data from study areas in Arizona in making recommendations for the timing of grasshopper surveys in that State.

In Montana and North Dakota, where the lesser migratory and two-striped grasshoppers are the dominant economic species, eggs were found most heavily concentrated in roadsides, fence rows, idle land, and small grains. Few were found in row crops or fallow land. Knowledge of where eggs are laid is indispensible in making egg surveys. Weedy roadsides and fence rows harbored more grasshoppers and contained more than twice as many eggs as similar places that were covered with solid stands of grass. E. G. Davis used that information as the basis for recommending the regrassing of weedy roadsides and fence rows to reduce grasshopper damage in nearby crops.

One of the study areas in Montana was in the Centennial Valley in Beaverhead County. The clear-winged grasshopper, the dominant species there, in some years completely destroyed the hay crop. The studies disclosed that this species concentrated its eggs in the roots and crowns of white bunchgrass associations (*Poa* and *Puccinellia*), which occur in well-defined patches throughout the native hay lands, constitute only a small fraction of the total hay acreage, and are easily recognized by their light color. Landowners were asked to bait the white bunchgrass whenever they saw grasshoppers in more than ordinary numbers. No outbreaks have occurred since.

Data from Montana and North Dakota provide estimates of what happens to the yearly potential grasshopper population. Females of the more important species lay approximately 200 eggs. Males and females are about equal in numbers. If the same level of population from one year to another is maintained, 198 (99 percent) of the eggs, young grasshoppers, or adults must perish sometime between the completion of egg laying and the beginning of egg deposition the following year. During the 10-year period, approximately 20 percent of the eggs were destroyed by predators, 60 percent of the young grasshoppers died during or shortly after the hatching period, and disease and parasites killed 5 percent of the older nymphs and adults.

Weather conditions during and following the hatching period may start or end outbreaks. If it is warm and dry, the death rate may decline below the 60-percent average and allow grasshoppers to develop in outbreak numbers. If it is cold and wet, mortality may increase to such an extent that few survive.

OUR KNOWLEDGE of grasshoppers on crops has been greatly furthered by seasonal studies in typical agricultural areas. R. L. Shotwell and I have described the 1931 outbreak of the two-striped and differential grasshoppers in South Dakota and northeastern Nebraska, which destroyed 75 percent of the crops on 17,000 square miles and 25 percent on an additional 13,000 square miles. Shotwell has published a bulletin on the histories and habits of grasshoppers that attack crops in the Northern Great Plains. C. C. Wilson reported his observations on the devastating grasshopper, an important economic species in California.

Surveys of numbers of adults and eggs have been conducted by State and Federal entomologists for many years and are of importance in planning control operations. Surveys have evolved from reconnaissance (which merely delineated areas of greatest abundance) to the present standardized type, in which infestations are classified according to the number of adults per square yard and the number of egg pods per square foot of soil.

One of the problems in connection with annual grasshopper egg surveys on the permanent study areas, as well as in State surveys, was the number of samples needed to rate accurately the fields and field margins and the number of stops needed per section, county, or other area unit. Special surveys designed to answer these questions were conducted in Montana in 1939 and 1940 and in South Dakota in 1942. The results of the studies were published by Davis and F. M. Wadley. They concluded that five 1-square-foot samples in each field and two similar samples in its margin should be taken and that no fewer than 10 field stops should be made in a county or group of counties.

RANGE GRASSHOPPER studies have been conducted as a major project since 1936. They include yearly observations at 10 permanent range stations in Montana, 3 in Wyoming, and 2 in South Dakota; adult and egg surveys of the western range region extending from Montana and western North Dakota to Wyoming and western Nebraska; and seasonal observations in places where significant range grasshopper activities are in progress.

State and county distribution of 142 species of grasshoppers found on the western range has been mapped. Adult and egg surveys conducted since 1941 have recorded over-all population trends and the dominant species for each year. Egg-laying records, including the number of pods laid and the number of eggs per pod, have been made for 29 species. Egg pods, nymphs, and adults of the more common species have been photographed or described.

Studies of seasonal development in Montana and Wyoming have shown wide differences among the complex of species found in any locality. Some are early; others are intermediate; and the rest are late in hatching, reaching the adult stage, and egg laying. Differences of 4 to 5 weeks have been found between early- and late-developing species. Knowledge of the seasonal development of the dominant range species is essential to the proper timing of control operations and surveys.

We divide range grasshoppers into two groups on the basis of food preferences—those that feed on grass and those that feed on forbs (which are range herbs other than grass). Of 40 species under study for three seasons in southeastern Montana, half were grass feeders and half were forb feeders. Those that prefer grasses will starve if restricted to forbs, which they refuse to eat in quantity. Forb feeders starve on grass unless it is tender and succulent. Several grass-feeding species would not eat bran bait. *Trachyrhachis kiowa* and *Opeia obscura* ate no bait. *Phlibostroma quadrimaculatum, Amphitornus coloradus,* and *Metator pardalinus* ate it sparingly. When those species predominate, baiting is ineffective.

Egg predators and parasites of nymphal and adult range grasshoppers have been investigated. Two species of nemestrinid flies, *Trichopsidea* (*Parasymmictus*) *clausa* and *Neorhynchocephalus sackenii,* not previously reported as common parasites of grasshoppers in the United States, were discovered in southeastern Montana in 1949. Females lay their eggs in cracks in wooden fence posts and trees and do it fast. One female laid 1,000 eggs on a single post in 15 minutes. Another confined in a pill box laid 4,700 eggs in 7 hours. The eggs hatch in 8 to 10 days. The tiny maggots are scattered by the wind. When a maggot finds a grasshopper, it bores into the abdomen and lives on its contents. Eventually it kills the grasshopper. Nemestrinid maggots differ from the better known sarcophagid parasites in having long breathing tubes, which they attach to the grasshopper's air circulating system to get their own fresh air. Nemestrinid flies are particularly destructive to the important range species *Metator pardalinus;* 80 percent of the adults of this species were found parasitized in some localities in 1950. The remarkable number of eggs laid by nemestrinid females and the ease of obtaining them suggests the possibility of gathering large quantities for distribution in grasshopper areas where parasites are not abundant.

Many observations have been made to determine the damage done to range vegetation by known numbers of grasshoppers. During drought years, infestations of 20 to 50 per square yard frequently have destroyed 75 to 100 percent of available forage by midsummer. From outdoor cage experiments conducted in range areas for several years we learned that an adult grasshopper of the larger range species ate 30 milligrams of vegetation (dry weight) a day. In earlier laboratory experiments we found that the relatively small, lesser migratory grasshopper ate 24 milligrams a day. A cow requires 20 pounds of vegetation (dry weight) a day. From these data we calculated that 301,395 adult range grasshoppers and a cow would eat equivalent quantities of forage a day. This number of grasshoppers distributed over 1 acre would average 62 per square yard, or 31 per square yard over 2 acres. The fact that such populations are common during outbreaks shows the stiff competition between grasshoppers and livestock for range vegetation. The same data show that infestations of only 7 grasshoppers per square yard on an acre will eat one-tenth as much forage as a cow. Control measures are seldom employed against such numbers of grasshoppers even though they lower the livestock-carrying capacity of the range.

Many long-time residents in western range districts have commented that range grasshopper outbreaks in their neighborhood always started in certain relatively small places and then spread to surrounding land. Fifteen potential outbreak localities in eastern Wyoming were selected for study. They have been under observation since 1941. Yearly population records have been made for each area and for the range adjacent to it.

Those studies showed that trends during low years were not necessarily uniform; that is, some areas were slowly declining while others held their own, and still others built up slightly and declined again. Build-ups tended to accompany an expansion of the infested area involved, while declines accompanied a contraction of infested areas. During 1946 and 1947, gradual increases occurred at about the same rate both within hold-over areas and outside them, but independently of each other. The increases continued in 1948 and 1949, and the hold-over areas with their greater populations were the first to reach damaging levels. When they did, there was a tendency for local migrations and light flights to take place—some of them to the outside. Drought tended to stimulate both migrations and flights. It was evident, however, that with a continuation of favorable years, outside populations could, and in some cases did, reach damaging levels without contributions from the hold-over areas. Over-all populations built up through slight to moderate increases of most major species rather than by large increases of a few species.

The results of the studies are disappointing to those who hoped that widespread outbreaks of range grasshoppers could be prevented by prompt use of control methods on a few small areas whenever numbers approached outbreak proportions. They do show that prompt control in hold-over areas is highly desirable, but they also indicate that similar action may be needed in many other places when conditions become unusually favorable for grasshoppers.

Poison bran bait was the most commonly recommended method of controlling grasshoppers in the United States for more than half a century. State and Federal entomologists have devoted many years in experimentation to improve the effectiveness of the bran, arsenic, sugar, and water mixture first used by D. W. Coquillet in California in 1885. Molasses, citrus fruits, lemon and vanilla extracts, apple flavoring, beer, vinegar, saccharin, salt, calcium chloride, amyl acetate, geraniol, soap, and other materials have been used to attract grasshoppers to poisoned bran and induce them to eat it more readily. It is generally conceded now that those materials add little to the attractiveness and palatability of bran and are not worth their cost.

Extensive tests have also been conducted to find substitutes or diluents for bran in grasshopper baits. Materials tested included sawdust, cottonseed hulls, rolled wheat, ground wheat screenings, citrus meal, chopped and ground alfalfa, ground flax fiber, ground peanut shells, bagasse, pear and apple pomace, peat moss, ground beet pulp, ground corncobs, chopped cornstalks, cornmeal, soybean meal, pea bran, oat hulls, and low-grade wheat flour. Of all the materials tested none was eaten more readily by grasshoppers than coarse wheat bran; most were decidedly less palatable.

Substitutes most closely approaching the palatability of bran were rolled wheat, apple and pear pomace, citrus meal, and chopped alfalfa. Sawdust, ground or chopped cornstalks, and cottonseed hulls were effective bran diluents. Mixtures of low-grade flour and sawdust and mill-run bran and sawdust were nearly as effective as coarse bran and sawdust in wet baits.

Arsenic in some form was the toxic agent in grasshopper baits until 1943, when it was replaced by sodium fluosilicate. By 1950 sodium fluosilicate had been largely superseded by chlordane, toxaphene, and aldrin.

The Bureau of Entomology and Plant Quarantine and State research staffs have given attention to the improvement of grasshopper baits. From 1921 to 1938, particular attention was given to testing the value of attractants, bran substitutes and diluents, and to determining the temperatures and time of day most favorable for bait spreading. More recent accomplishments were the replacement of arsenic by sodium fluosilicate, and later by chlorinated hydrocarbons, as bait toxicants, and the development of dry bran baits.

Research on the effectiveness of sodium fluosilicate was conducted in Arizona, California, Colorado, Minnesota, Montana, North Dakota, Oklahoma, and South Dakota from 1931 to 1942. It was found that sodium fluosilicate-bran baits under most conditions killed as many grasshoppers as arsenic baits and killed them faster. In experiments conducted by the veterinary science departments of the University of Nevada and Montana State College in 1939, 1940, and 1941, it was demonstrated that grasshopper baits containing sodium arsenite were approximately eight times more toxic to sheep than baits containing sodium fluosilicate. The experiments also indicated that sodium fluosilicate bait is extremely distasteful to sheep, horses, cows, and rabbits, and is not readily eaten by chickens, ducks, quail, or pheasants. In no instance was enough eaten voluntarily to cause ill effects.

In nearly all cases, sodium fluosilicate bait has been superior to sodium arsenite bait for grasshopper control on range grass and in most dry-land crops. Some failures have occurred in green crops such as alfalfa, but that was also true with sodium arsenite baits.

Tests to determine the effectiveness of chlordane, toxaphene, and aldrin were started in 1946 and continued through 1950. Baits containing them were found to kill grasshoppers faster and for longer periods than sodium fluosilicate. Chlordane at ½ pound, toxaphene at 1 pound, and aldrin at 2 ounces consistently gave as good or better kills than 6 pounds of sodium fluosilicate per 100 pounds of bran. The chlorinated hydrocarbons are soluble in kerosene and, when dissolved, are easily applied to the bran as a spray. Because of their higher, quicker, and longer killing action, small bulk and ease of mixing, chlordane and toxaphene in 1949 and aldrin in 1951 were recommended as bait toxicants. They now have largely replaced sodium fluosilicate in wet baits and are used exclusively in dry baits.

Before 1932, all grasshopper bran baits in general use contained water. Such wet baits have several limitations. To get best results, one has to apply them just before or during the period of the most active feeding, which is limited usually to a few hours each day. Wet bran flakes become hard and curled after drying and are then less palatable to grasshoppers than flakes that have never been wet. Sawdust or other diluent must be included to prevent lumping during mixing and spreading operations. Wet bait molds and cakes if stored for more than a few days. Water in baits doubles their weight.

Research to eliminate these disadvantages was begun in 1932. The first step was to leave out the water, molasses, and sawdust then commonly used in wet baits. Bran was thoroughly mixed with dry sodium arsenite or sodium fluosilicate. Two gallons of lubricating oil per 100 pounds of bran were then added to stick the poison onto the bran. Oil baits with sodium fluosilicate as the toxicant were found to be as effective as wet baits and have been widely used, particularly to control Mormon crickets. Oil baits containing arsenic were usually less effective than wet baits made with the same poison. Dry bran bait came into its own after the appearance of chlordane, toxaphene, and aldrin. Bran can be thoroughly impregnated by spraying it with low-volume kerosene solutions of any of these insecticides without materially affecting the palatability of the bran or the toxicity of the insecticide.

After 2 years of tests with ground equipment on small plots, 6,850 acres of heavily infested range in Montana and Wyoming were treated in 1948 with chlordane- or toxaphene-impregnated bran applied by airplane. The results were so good that similar bait was used almost exclusively in the large-scale campaigns conducted in Montana and Wyoming in 1949 and 1950.

Dry bait can be spread without regard to feeding periods of grasshoppers. In good weather the bran flakes remain effective for days. Those that are not eaten one day may kill grasshoppers the next. It is easier to mix and can be stored for months. It does away with the purchase and transportation of sawdust. It scatters more evenly from an airplane and weighs only half as much as wet bait.

Some insecticide dusts are excellent grasshopper killers, but in general the same insecticide is more economical and more effective when it is used as a spray. From 25 to 50 percent more insecticide per acre is needed with dust, and the cost of the diluent is an added expense. Anyone who has seen airplane dusting knows why higher acre dosages are needed. Dusts are lighter than sprays and more of the poison floats away in the breeze. Dusts are more easily removed from vegetation by wind and rain and, therefore, kill for a shorter period. Dusts are more likely to kill bees and other beneficial insects.

Paris green and sodium arsenite sprays were used against grasshoppers years ago but were given up because the poisoned vegetation endangered livestock. The recent development of insecticides that can be used at very low dosages and yet are highly toxic to grasshoppers and easily formulated as sprays aroused new interest in this method of control. The results have been so good that it now looks as though poisoned bait, the standard method of control for half a century, will be superseded by sprays.

Success with the best baits depends on the habits of the grasshoppers. If they do not eat the bait they are not killed. In sparse vegetation during dry weather kills sometimes reach 90 to 95 percent. In succulent vegetation like irrigated alfalfa they seldom exceed 75 percent and are generally lower. Certain range species gorge themselves with bait. Others hardly touch it. Some refuse it entirely. When bait-feeding species predominate, kills on the range may reach 90 or 95 percent. If many nonbait feeders are present, kills are much lower. Kills of 75 to 95 percent prevent serious damage to most crops and range, but they frequently allow grasshoppers to survive in such numbers that control must be repeated the next year. In seed alfalfa and flax almost perfect control is needed to prevent injury to blooms, seed pods, and bolls, which can be severe when only a few grasshoppers are present.

Grasshoppers have little chance of surviving the new sprays, which kill both by contact and as internal poisons. Even if they escape being hit by the spray the first meal of treated vegetation will be their last. Kills with the best sprays usually reach 90 percent in 3 days and continue for 1 or 2 weeks. Populations of 25 to 100 per square yard have been reduced to less than 1 grasshopper in 10 square yards. Such kills give complete protection to crops and range. If spraying is done early enough to prevent egg laying no further control will be needed for several years unless grasshoppers move in from untreated land.

Sprays have other advantages over baits. Standard acre dosages applied as sprays have controlled infestations regardless of the number of grasshoppers per square yard. Bait application must be varied according to numbers present, which can be determined only by time-consuming surveys of the area to be treated. Use of too much bait is wasteful and expensive; too little is still more expensive if re-treatment becomes necessary. Spray materials are more stable in price than bran and cost less to transport and store. Bran for bait is in direct competition with bran for livestock and frequently soars to high prices when large quantities are needed for grasshopper control. Loading planes with sprays takes less time than with bait. A plane loaded with spray can cover more acres than the same plane loaded with bait. The overall cost of spraying is less than baiting.

Of the various new insecticides tested against grasshoppers as sprays, chlorinated hydrocarbons have given the best results and are lowest in cost on a per-acre basis. Chlordane spray was first used in grasshopper control programs in 1947, toxaphene in 1948, and aldrin in 1950. Acre dosages are: Toxaphene, 1 to 1½ pounds; chlordane, ½ to 1 pound; and aldrin, 1 to 2 ounces.

Almost complete destruction of grasshoppers by spraying half a gallon of kerosene containing 2 ounces of poison over an acre seems almost incredible but that is what aldrin does.

Before new insecticides are recommended for general use in grasshopper control they are subjected to extensive tests. Preliminary screening is done in winter with laboratory-reared grasshoppers. The first step is to administer carefully measured quantities of the new insecticide to individual grasshoppers and compare the results with those of a standard chemical for which effective individual and acre dosages have been established. Materials that show slight killing action are discarded. Those that show promise are used in laboratory dusting and spraying experiments. Contact action is tested by treating the grasshoppers and holding them on untreated green plants; stomach action is determined by placing untreated grasshoppers on sprayed or dusted plants. Baits are tested by exposing measured quantities to grasshoppers in screen cages. Laboratory results sometimes agree closely with those obtained later in the field but not always. How the insecticide performs outdoors is most important but laboratory tests are of great value as indicators of the most promising dosage levels for initial field trials.

Field tests, using ground equipment, are made on small plots (1.5 to 5 acres) under a wide variety of conditions. Insecticides outstanding in small plot tests are next applied by ground equipment and airplanes on 10- to 40-acre plots, and finally on large tracts.

When the Bureau of Entomology and Plant Quarantine is convinced that an insecticide it has tested is worth recommending for general use, its findings are reported to the State Leaders' Advisory Committee on Grasshopper Control at its annual meeting in Denver, Colo. Data available from State and commercial organizations are also considered. If agreement is reached on formulations and acre dosages, the insecticide is recommended for general use the following year.

Thereafter the insecticide is given farm-scale testing. That is done to compare it with insecticides previously recommended and to test it under the special conditions in the various representative agricultural districts. Blocks of grasshopper-infested farms growing the typical crops of the district are used. The intensity of infestation is determined by surveys of eggs and young grasshoppers in the spring before control is started and by surveys of eggs and adults in the fall after control is completed. Control measures are applied to all economic infestations within the block, regardless of their location. Records are kept of quantities of insecticides used, cost of application, kills obtained, and crop damage. The areas are rechecked to find out if control one year prevents damage the following year.

Such tests have been conducted in corn and small grains in South Dakota, in seed alfalfa in South Dakota and Nebraska, and in flax and small grains in North Dakota. Results proved that crop protection is attainable at reasonable cost by correctly timed applications of new insecticides: One year's effort in treating all economic infestations within a block of farms will eliminate or greatly reduce the need for grasshopper control for several years thereafter. Farmers have shown keen interest in these tests, have commented favorably on them, and have been quick to adopt the control measures.

J. R. PARKER *is in charge of research on grasshoppers and Mormon crickets at the Bozeman, Mont., field station of the Bureau of Entomology and Plant Quarantine. Dr. Parker represented the United States at the International Conference on Locusts and Their Control in Cairo, Egypt, in 1936, and was a consulting delegate to the Second Inter-American Conference on Agriculture at Mexico City in 1942. In 1952 he received the Department's Distinguished Service Award for his work on grasshopper and locust control.*

For further reading:

O. L. Barnes: Time Schedules for Grasshopper Surveys in Arizona, *Journal of Economic Entomology, volume 37, pages 789–795. 1944.*

D. W. Coquillet: Report on the Locusts of the San Joaquin Valley, California, *U. S. Commissioner of Agriculture, Annual Report, 1885, pages 289–303. 1886.*

E. G. Davis: Reducing Grasshopper Damage by Regrassing Weedy Roadsides and Fence Rows, *U. S. D. A. Circular 813, 1949;* Grasshopper Egg-Pod Distribution in the Northern Great Plains and Its Relation to Egg-Survey Methods, *with F. M. Wadley, U. S. D. A. Circular 816. 1949.*

E. J. Hinman and F. T. Cowan: New Insecticides in Grasshopper Control, *Bureau of Entomology and Plant Quarantine publication E–722. 1947.*

J. R. Parker: Some Effects of Temperature and Moisture Upon Melanoplus mexicanus Sauss. and Camnula pellucida Scudder (Orthoptera), *Montana Agricultural Experiment Station Bulletin 223, pages 92–96, 1931;* Grasshoppers and Their Control, *U. S. D. A. Farmers' Bulletin 1828, 1939;* Tests of Insecticides for Grasshopper Control, 1947, *Bureau of Entomology and Plant Quarantine publication E–774, 1949;* Tests of Insecticides for Grasshopper Control, 1948 and 1949, *Bureau of Entomology and Plant Quarantine publication E–807, 1950;* Toxicity of Sodium Fluosilicate to Livestock, Poultry, and Game, *with George G. Schweis, Journal of Economic Entomology, volume 37, pages 309–310, 1944;* Devastation of a Large Area by the Differential and the Two-striped Grasshoppers, *with R. L. Shotwell, Journal of Economic Entomology, volume 25, pages 174–187.*

R. L. Shotwell: Methods for Making a Grasshopper Survey, *Journal of Economic Entomology, volume 28, pages 486–491, 1935;* Some Problems of the Annual Grasshopper Survey, *Journal of Economic Entomology, volume 31, pages 523–533, 1938;* Life Histories and Habits of Some Grasshoppers of Economic Importance on the Great Plains, *U. S. D. A. Technical Bulletin 774, 1941;* The Comparative Effectiveness of Poisoned Bait and Sprays for Grasshopper Control in Lyman County, S. Dak., 1947, *Bureau of Entomology and Plant Quarantine publication E–771, 1949.*

W. W. Stanley: Outbreak of Grasshoppers in Tennessee During 1932, *Journal of Economic Entomology, volume 26, pages 300–301. 1933.*

970134°—52——40

The Mormon Cricket

Claude Wakeland, J. R. Parker

Since the days of the early settlers the Mormon cricket, a large wingless grasshopper, has remained a periodic scourge and persistent threat to agriculture in Intermountain and Far Western States. A native, dry-land insect of the West, naturally inhabiting high, rugged terrain in mountainous country, Mormon crickets are feared in cultivated areas because of their sudden, devastating migrations and the severity and extent of their attacks.

Mormon crickets increase to large numbers at irregular intervals in more well-defined areas than do most range grasshoppers. The outbreak centers or hold-over places are mostly in areas remote from crops. When conditions are favorable, the crickets become very abundant, form in bands, and migrate long distances from the hold-over areas by walking and jumping.

They are voracious feeders on nearly all plants. Probably their greatest damage is to range forage. They feed on more than 250 species of range plants and on all cultivated crops they come in contact with. The insect shows preference for some kinds of plants and for certain plant parts. In general, flower and seed parts are severely attacked. The preferred range plants are those with large or fleshy succulent leaves, such as balsamroot, mustard, dandelion, bitterroot, and young Russian-thistle. All crops in outlying dry farm areas, which are in the path of migrating Mormon cricket bands, may be attacked, but the greatest financial loss occurs in small-grain crops, principally wheat. Alfalfa, sweetclover, and truck crops, especially young sugar-beet plants, are among its preferred foods.

Tender garden crops often are completely destroyed. Headed grain crops may be stripped of the kernels. Very important, but inadequately measured, is the destruction of seed on forage and browse plants—such destruction adversely affects the establishment or maintenance of range cover.

Laboratory experiments were conducted by Frank T. Cowan and H. J. Shipman to determine the quantity of food consumed by Mormon crickets, which in reality are nonflying range grasshoppers. They found that an adult ate an average of 100 milligrams of food (dry weight) a day. At that rate, 96,800 crickets, or 20 per square yard over an acre, would eat 20 pounds of forage a day, which is the same as the average daily consumption of a cow.

Losses to agriculture chargeable to Mormon crickets during the past 100 years undoubtedly amount to millions of dollars. In 1938 alone the insect was estimated to have caused an average measurable loss of 15 percent on almost 13 million acres of range land and to have damaged crops from slightly to severely on 235,000 acres of croplands.

The extensive infestations of the late 1930's were reduced to a point where in 1949 the insects invaded and damaged only 230 acres of crops and caused slight injury to range plants on 200,000 acres of range.

During the 1930's Mormon crickets reached the largest outbreak proportions on record. A survey in the fall of 1938 revealed damaging populations in Colorado, Idaho, Montana, Nebraska, Nevada, North Dakota, Oregon, South Dakota, Utah, Washington, and Wyoming. No survey was made then in California, but large numbers of crickets were known to be there.

Measures to control Mormon crickets have evolved through progressive stages as rapidly as research has led the way. Early operations to halt migrating bands involved the use of trench barriers, wood-metal barriers, metal barriers, oil-on-water barriers, and dusting the insects with sodium arsenite dust. Dust was applied by means of hand dust guns and later by power dusters.

Sodium fluosilicate in poisoned bran baits was tested in grasshopper control in 1933 but was not used extensively against Mormon crickets until 1939. Early trials with baits containing arsenic were failures; before 1939 dusting with mixtures of sodium arsenite and hydrated lime was the most effective known method of control. Dusting was expensive and arsenic was dangerous to the operator, to livestock, and to green plants. In 1935 attempts to find a cheaper and less dangerous method were started by Cowan. He learned that tiny amounts of arsenic were highly repellent to Mormon crickets and that mixtures of bran and sodium fluosilicate were readily eaten and highly toxic.

Bait composed of mill-run bran, sawdust, and sodium fluosilicate has superseded sodium arsenite dust. It is applied by ground spreaders and by airplanes. Mormon crickets are controlled also with a bait composed of pure bran impregnated lightly with an oil solution of chlordane or toxaphene. Each improvement in control methods has meant increased effectiveness, less work, or lower operational costs.

According to records of several years, the cost of control with sodium arsenite was $2 an acre with hand machines and $1.50 with power dusters. The average per-acre cost of baiting in 1941 through 1949 was 85 cents or 65 cents less than the cost of power dusting. In the 9 years, 2,649,160 acres were baited. This represents a saving of $1,721,954 from the use of bait rather than power dusting with sodium arsenite.

Several different baits are used with good results. Steamed, rolled wheat impregnated with a solution of 1 pound of toxaphene in one-half gallon of oil to each 100 pounds of wheat is one of the easiest baits to handle. The material, spread at the rate of 3 to 5 pounds to the acre, gives almost complete control. Large, flaky bran, 100 pounds, impregnated with a solution of 1 pound of toxaphene or one-half pound of chlordane in 1 gallon of oil and spread at the rate of 10 pounds an acre, also results in satisfactory control.

Baits are applied by aircraft or

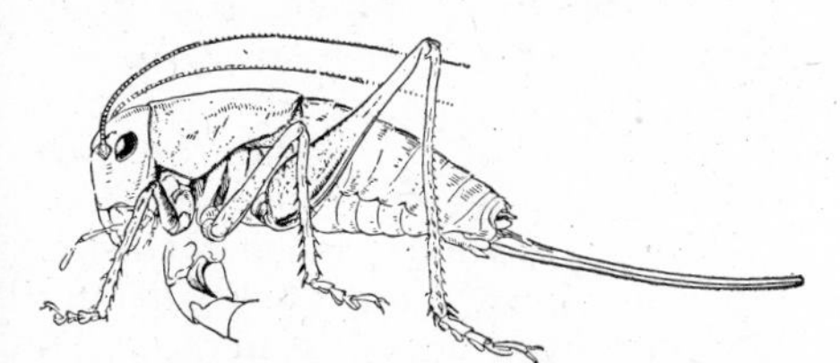

The female of the Mormon cricket is a wingless katydid whose long ovipositor is a ready tool for inserting the eggs deep in the ground.

ground equipment. Airplanes equipped for spreading bait for grasshoppers are usually used. On small infestations bait broadcasters or blower spreaders are commonly used. The bait also may be spread by hand.

Because the crickets ordinarily feed heavily while migrating, bait is spread in strips across the front of an advancing band, or uniformly in hold-over areas where crickets are not migrating. More than 95 percent of the crickets in a band are commonly killed in this way.

Entomologists have started experiments with new chemicals in the hope of finding better methods of control.

The more important hold-over areas in the Rocky Mountain States have been mapped and are surveyed each year. Poisoned bait is applied whenever dangerous numbers are found. Baiting relatively small acreages within the hold-over areas, in recent years, has held range damage to a minimum, prevented crop damage, and eliminated the extensive control operations formerly conducted after Mormon crickets had spread from the hold-over areas to much larger acreages.

Organized control over nearly two decades has reduced the infestations chiefly to hold-over areas and has eliminated the possibility of current heavy crop damage.

Present control operations are aimed principally at preventing populations from again building up in local areas to the point where major outbreaks could occur. Since 1945 control has been accomplished mainly against range infestations distant from cultivated lands. Control work was done in Colorado, Utah, Montana, Nevada, Oregon, and Washington in 1950 and 1951.

Other areas of infestation in Utah and other States were reported and examined late in the season. Those infestations are developing in areas that for several years have been suspected of being particularly favorable to the crickets. Many are on public lands used for grazing and some are in remote mountain or desert locations where the land has little value to humans but provides conditions favorable to survival of the insects. Infestations may build up there and the crickets emigrate, over a period of years, to nearby crop or grazing lands to become the "seed" from which a destructive outbreak can grow when climatic and biological factors are favorable.

The increased populations of crickets that were noted in several States in 1950 have developed in areas in which severe outbreaks were experienced in 1937 and 1938. Where feasible, measures were taken to control the infestations.

The later developments indicate, to those familiar with the earlier, widespread outbreaks of Mormon crickets, that similar infestation conditions may be near at hand if control at the source is neglected. Control of small outbreaks when they start depends on annual surveys to determine the extent and intensity of infestations. Trained men make such surveys by searching out cricket concentrations and recording pertinent data, such as size of bands, location, and intensity, factors that govern the need for control.

Prevention of another large-scale outbreak of Mormon crickets is feasible. Between 1938 and 1949, the infested area was reduced from nearly

19,000,000 acres to 116,000 acres. By directing control against small concentrations of the insects in known infested areas, we can continue to decimate them so that they have no opportunity to band, migrate, and coalesce into large bands that grow to outbreak proportions. Mormon crickets increased in numbers in several States in 1950 and showed a banding and migrating tendency they had not exhibited in recent years. Unless many small bands are consistently controlled when they are found, another widespread outbreak may be in the making.

CLAUDE WAKELAND *holds degrees in entomology from Colorado Agricultural and Mechanical College and Ohio State University. Since 1938 he has been a member of the Bureau of Entomology and Plant Quarantine as project leader for Mormon cricket control, leader of the division of grasshopper control, and entomologist.*

J. R. PARKER *is in charge of research on grasshoppers and Mormon crickets at the Bozeman, Mont., field station of the Bureau.*

For further reading on Mormon crickets, the authors suggest Mormon Crickets and Their Control, *by F. T. Cowan, H. J. Shipman, and Claude Wakeland, U. S. D. A. Farmers' Bulletin 1928, 1943;* Nature and Extent of Mormon Cricket Damage to Crop and Range Plants, *by Ralph B. Swain, U. S. D. A. Technical Bulletin 866, 1943;* Quantity of Food Consumed by Mormon Crickets, *by Frank T. Cowan and H. J. Shipman, Journal of Economic Entomology, volume 40, pages 825–828, 1947.*

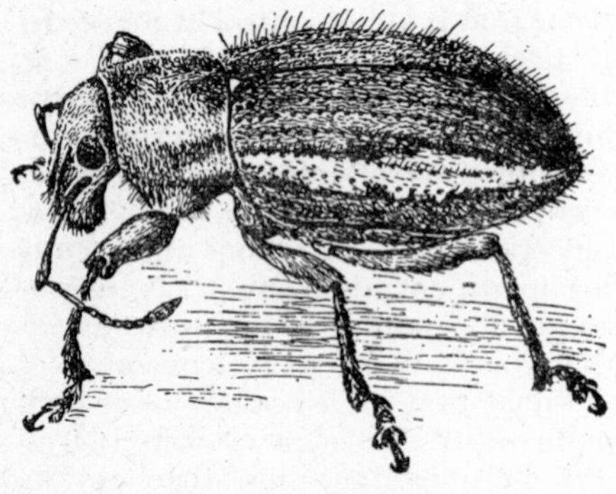

White-fringed beetle.

White-Fringed Beetle

R. A. Roberts

The name "white-fringed beetle" is applied commonly in the United States to a group of species and races of beetles belonging to the genus *Graphognathus.* They are believed to have been brought accidentally from South America to the United States. They were first found in Okaloosa County, Fla., in 1936 and before long were discovered in adjoining counties in Alabama.

In 1937 their larvae did serious damage to cotton, corn, peanuts, and velvetbeans in the infested area. Entomologists and officials from several States who visited the area concluded that white-fringed beetles were a serious threat to a wide range of cultivated crops elsewhere in the United States. Representatives of the State Plant Board of Florida, the Alabama Department of Agriculture and Industries, and the Bureau of Entomology and Plant Quarantine agreed that a cooperative Federal-State program to attempt the control of the white-fringed beetle should be started immediately.

The beetles were found in Louisiana and Mississippi in 1937. In 1942 some were collected in North Carolina at Wilmington. In 1946 infestations were discovered in Georgia near Eastman, Fort Valley, and Macon. Inspections during 1946 of properties landscaped with ornamental plants obtained from nurseries in the infested area in Georgia disclosed many additional infestations in that State, as well as two in Alabama and one in South Carolina. In 1948 the beetle was found in Tennessee. On January 1, 1952, nearly 340,000 acres (including 100,000 acres of farm land) were known to be infested.

The adult beetle is a little less than

half an inch long and brownish gray. It gets its name from the lighter band along the margins of the wing covers. Because the wing covers of the adult are fused together and the underwings are rudimentary, the beetle cannot fly. All adult beetles are females. A few days after emergence, after having fed on foliage, each can lay viable eggs. The beetles live 2 or 3 months. Under favorable conditions a female averages 600 to 700 eggs. The eggs are cemented in small masses to plant stems, sticks, debris, or soil particles. They begin hatching in about 15 days. The larvae enter the soil where they feed on plant roots. The larvae or grubs usually occur in the top 9 inches of soil but sometimes go deeper. They are white, legless, and about a half inch long when fully grown. The insect passes the winter in the ground in the larval stage. In the spring the matured grub forms a cell in the soil in which it pupates. The pupa transforms to an adult beetle, which then returns to the soil surface. One generation of the insect is produced each year.

WHITE-FRINGED BEETLES seriously damage many field crops and garden, ornamental, and wild plants. Most of the damage is caused by the larvae feeding on plant roots. The adults do some damage by feeding on foliage. The larvae eat parts of the soft outer tissues of the root and may completely sever the main root. The beetles feed on at least 385 species of plants. Some of the common host plants are peanuts, velvetbeans, soybeans, lespedeza, clover, alfalfa, cotton, corn, blackberry, strawberry, white potato, chrysanthemum, dahlia, cocklebur, coffeeweed, gallberry, and beggarweed.

When an abundance of favored host plants is available, the beetles build up rapidly to heavy populations, as when lightly infested fields are planted during the summer to such crops as peanuts and velvetbeans, which furnish good food and shelter. A farmer can prevent a rapid increase by the summer planting of small grains or other crops that are not preferred food plants of the adult beetles and give less cover.

DDT MIXED in the soil will eliminate or reduce the beetle populations materially. DDT applied to cropland at the rate of 10 pounds of the technical grade per acre in an emulsion spray or an equivalent amount (such as 20 pounds of 50 percent DDT wettable powder) in a water suspension spray will control the pest. The DDT also may be broadcast as a dust at the rate of 20 pounds of 50 percent DDT powder or its equivalent per acre. Regardless of how applied as a soil treatment, the DDT must be cultivated thoroughly into the top 3 inches immediately after application. The treatment will give adequate control of the insect for at least 5 years. Between 1946 and 1951 about 45,000 acres of farm land were so treated.

A similar treatment is recommended for nurseries, except that the dosage is increased to 50 pounds of technical grade DDT or its equivalent per acre. The higher dosage of DDT insures the elimination of larvae and permits the certification of plants for movement from regulated areas without further treatment. Applications of DDT are made to vegetation in the environs of the nursery regularly in spring and summer. Between 1948 and 1951 approximately 2,500 acres of nursery land in the infested areas were soil-treated with 50 pounds of technical grade DDT per acre or its equivalent.

TO CONTROL THE BEETLES in margins of treated fields, in fence rows, or on adjacent border lands, a foliage spray is applied. One pound of technical grade DDT per acre in an emulsion or 2 pounds of 50 percent DDT per acre in a water suspension spray is applied. Applications are made at intervals of 2 or 3 weeks during the season when adult beetles are present. Foliage sprays should be repeated yearly as long as beetles are present in the non-soil-treated lands in the environs of those which have been soil-treated. DDT also is applied as a foliage spray in city and rural areas where the beetles threaten to spread. Such areas usually include industrial sites, processing plants, mills, gins, railroad rights-of-way, roadsides, vacant lots, school yards, or cemeteries. In 1950 approximately 40,000 acres in the infested areas received foliage applications.

Because of the relatively heavy dosages of DDT, no applications are made on any crop used for human food or for animal forage or to any pasture used for grazing by dairy or beef cattle.

The DDT sprays or dusts may be applied by several types of equipment. For soil treatments, a tractor-mounted power sprayer with nozzle outlets on a boom located close to the ground has been successful in dispensing concentrated sprays. DDT dust may be mixed with sand and broadcast by hand. Dilute dust may be spread on the soil surface by drill or spreader-type fertilizer distributors. Concentrated foliage sprays have been applied by power sprayers that have special oscillating discharge nozzles. This type of sprayer may be mounted on a tractor or a jeep. Turbine blowers mounted on trucks or jeeps also are used. Airplanes have been regularly employed in making foliage applications.

Home owners with gardens or flower beds infested with white-fringed beetles may apply a simple treatment. A 10 percent DDT dust, which may be bought at seed stores, may be applied to the soil at the rate of 1 ounce to 27 square feet of soil surface or 1 pound to 432 square feet. It should first be mixed with moist sand and then broadcast on the plot. Even distribution is important to get effective control. The insecticide should be worked into the soil with a potato fork or another tool. The dust may be applied at any season, but to be immediately effective the application should be made in the fall when the beetle larvae are small.

White-fringed beetles are spread in farm and industrial commodities or through the movements of man and his belongings, or incidentally by automobiles, trains, and other public carriers. Since all beetles are females, each potentially able to start a new generation, spread can result from the movement of a single egg, larva, pupa, or adult.

Soon after the discovery of the beetle in the United States, Federal and State quarantines were promulgated to regulate the movement of many articles known to be potential carriers of the insect in one or more of its stages—certain agricultural crops, nursery stock, forest products, grass sod, scrap metal, and soil. The quarantines, which have been revised from time to time, provide three conditions under which certificates may be issued for the movement of regulated articles: That they have been inspected and found to be free of white-fringed beetles; that they have been treated, processed, fumigated, or sterilized in an approved manner; or that they have been grown, stored, manufactured, or handled in a manner which would prevent them from becoming infested.

Effective methods have been developed for treating regulated articles. Nursery stock may be bare-rooted when such a procedure will not result in injury to the plants. Stock that cannot be bare-rooted may be fumigated with methyl bromide at atmospheric pressure or under partial vacuum. Plants that will not tolerate methyl bromide fumigation may be treated by soaking or dipping them in a solution of pyrethrum-piperonyl butoxide. Peanuts may be shelled to eliminate egg masses attached to the outside. Unshelled peanuts may be fumigated with methyl bromide. Peanut hay may be fumigated with methyl bromide or passed through a hammer mill to destroy any eggs present. White potatoes may be fumigated with methyl bromide to make them safe for movement.

Some crops, such as white potatoes, small grains and legumes for seed, including lupine and soybeans, that are grown and harvested under specified conditions in fields soil-treated with 10 pounds of DDT per acre may be certified for movement without further treatment. Materials to which beetle eggs might be attached—building timbers, junk, and scrap metal, for example—may be treated with spray consisting of 1 pound of technical grade DDT in 7½ gallons of kerosene. Lumber, poles, and pulpwood may be stored by stacking them off the ground in order to prevent the beetle from depositing eggs on them. Under such conditions of storage and when weeds and other vegetation are controlled on the storage premises, the materials may be certified for movement without further treatment.

R. A. ROBERTS, *an employee of the Bureau of Entomology and Plant Quarantine, is a graduate of Texas Agricultural and Mechanical College and holds a master's degree in entomology from Iowa State College. He has been associated with research problems with insects and with cooperative Federal-State insect control projects since 1926.*

Sixteen insects that attack cereal and forage crops are illustrated in the section of color drawings. Opposite the drawings are descriptions and life histories of the insects and recommendations for their control.

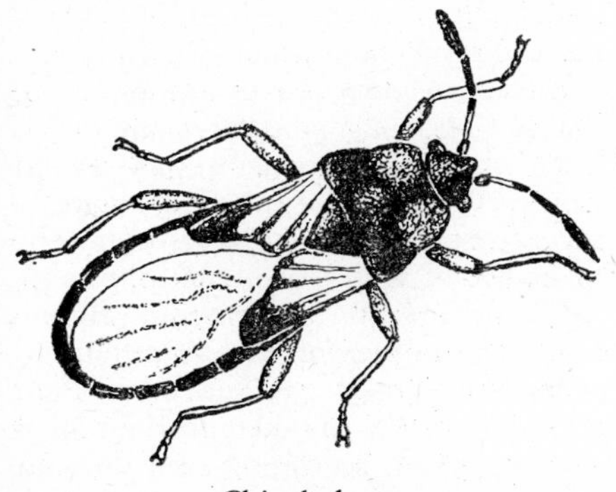

Chinch bug.

The Chinch Bug

Claude Wakeland

The chinch bug is widely distributed in the United States but rarely is it abundant enough to cause serious crop losses except in Illinois, Indiana, Iowa, Kansas, Missouri, Ohio, Nebraska, Oklahoma, and Texas. It occasionally damages crops in Michigan, Minnesota, Wisconsin, South Dakota, North Carolina, and South Carolina. The chinch bug increases rapidly under favorable weather conditions. In outbreak stages it is one of the most completely destructive insects to corn and sorghum plants in the United States.

Chinch bug adults in the fall fly from cultivated crops to bunchgrasses, where they rest during the winter. In spring they fly to fields of small grain in the cooler areas of their habitat or directly to corn and sorghums in the warmer areas, such as in Texas and southern Oklahoma. After reaching cultivated fields, they mate and lay their eggs on the leaves of the plants or on the soil near the bases of the plants. After the eggs hatch, the young bugs feed on the plants and, in grainfields, most of them crawl to nearby crops such as corn and sorghum when grain plants lose their succulence or begin to ripen. A second generation usually is produced while bugs infest corn or other susceptible crops, and the adults from this generation fly to bunchgrasses for the winter.

The bug feeds by sucking the juices of plants. When the insects crawl from grainfields they concentrate on the outer rows of young corn or sorghum plants, which soon wilt and die. As the outer rows are killed, the bugs migrate inward until an invaded field becomes infested throughout. Chief reliance for protection of cornfields from bugs invading them from grain fields is placed upon the use of barriers to intercept migrations or to kill migrating bugs before they can reach susceptible crops.

When the overwintering adults fly directly from bunchgrasses to corn, the entire cornfield may be infested more or less uniformly. An economical and practical control has not yet been established to cope with that situation.

Chinch bugs feed successfully only on plants of the grass family. In years of severe infestations, when their normal food plants become scarce, they may try to feed upon legumes or other nongrass plants, but only rarely in numbers sufficient to cause injury.

Particularly susceptible among the small grains are barley, spring and winter wheat, rye, and oats. Barley is especially preferred and so is a hazardous crop to grow during a period of chinch bug outbreaks.

Most favored of the larger crop grasses are corn, sorghums, broomcorn, Sudangrass, and millet. Young corn plants are choice food for the bugs.

Chinch bugs also feed upon many forage and wild grasses, including foxtail, timothy, crabgrass, kafircorn, quackgrass, and ticklegrass. Bentgrass, bluegrass, and other lawn grasses may be attacked.

Conditions permitting, the most economical and effective way to prevent losses from chinch bugs is by crop rotation and by the location of susceptible crops with relation to small-grain fields. The first generation of chinch bugs, except in the southern part of their habitat, depends at first on small grains for its food; second-generation bugs feed mainly on corn and sorghums. Eliminating or reducing acreages of grain crops or avoiding planting susceptible crops near small-grain fields materially scales down losses due to chinch bugs.

Legumes and other practically immune crops may be substituted to advantage for small grains or corn and sorghums during years of threatening outbreaks. Crops that may be grown without danger of serious injury by chinch bugs include alfalfa, beans, buckwheat, alsike clover, red clover, sweetclover, cowpeas, field peas, flax, lespedeza, peanuts, potatoes, pumpkins, rape, soybeans, squash, sugar beets, sunflowers, velvetbeans, vetch, and other field, garden, and truck crops not belonging to the grass family. During years of severe infestations, the farm cropping scheme should be so adjusted as to avoid, or reduce to a minimum, the planting of corn or sorghums next to small-grain fields. If it is impracticable to substitute immune crops for grains, injury may be lessened by planting some of the least susceptible or resistant varieties.

Hybrid corns and sorghums have been developed that have some resistance to second-generation bugs. Ruined fields of corn, sorghums, or small grains should be disked or plowed to destroy the bugs and replanted with an immune crop. Early planting of grains, corn, and sorghums helps to reduce injury. Chinch bugs are attracted more to thin stands of grain than they are to rank growth. All tillage, fertilization, and seeding practices that promote a vigorous growing grain crop therefore tend to lessen damage. Small-grain fields, with a dense growth of clover, which causes a damp, shady condition, also are unattractive to the bugs.

In preparing to combat chinch bugs, surveys in the fall give a pretty good idea of how many to expect the following season and where they are most likely to be found.

Surveys, cooperative among State and Federal agencies, are made in November and December in several Central States. The bugs hibernate in several species of bunchgrasses, the principal of which are little bluestem, big bluestem, and broomsedge. By examining samples of the grass clumps hibernating bugs are detected, their abundance determined, and their locations mapped. Entomologists familiar with the insects make a survey each year in the areas suspected of harboring infestations. In each county they visit they collect five samples of bunchgrass at widely separated points. Each sample consists of a bunch of grass, including the crown, from 3.5 to 4.5 inches in diameter. If possible, the samples are from places near corn or sorghum fields because those plants are among the insect's favored food plants. Bugs avoid clumps of grass containing ants; so, before a sample is taken, an inspection is made to ascertain that no ants are present. The sample is cut from the sod clump with a tiling spade and is trimmed with shears. It is then placed in a double paper bag on which the location, date, and other pertinent details are written. A group of samples is taken or mailed to the State college or university, where students or staff members count the numbers of bugs contained in each sample. The number in the sample is converted on the basis of the number of bugs per square foot. Each sample is rated according to the following table:

Classification	*Number of bugs per square foot*	*Rating*
Noneconomic	0–250	1
Light	250–500	2
Moderate	500–1,000	3
Severe	1,000–2,000	4
Very severe	2,000 or more	5

A rating is given to each county. It is based on the number of bugs present and the percentage of land under cultivation in the county. The reason for considering the percentage of cultivated land is that the greater the percentage of land that is farmed the less area there is to support protective cover for chinch bug hibernation and the fewer chinch bugs there will be in comparison to the crops that might be fed upon.

Having this information for infested counties, entomologists then proceed to plan their battle against the insects. They make estimates of needs for barriers for the next year on the basis of what would be considered the potential requirements. In doing so they realize that the hazards of prophecy are probably at their maximum when chinch bug infestations are being forecast and that weather conditions during the following crop season may produce an outbreak as serious as the potential or reduce the threat to noneconomic importance.

Barriers are used to protect susceptible crops from attack by bugs that migrate from small-grain fields. Three types of barriers are effective: Creosote line barriers, creosote paper barriers, and dinitro-*o*-cresol dust barriers.

A creosote line barrier is made by plowing a furrow with a moldboard plow around the field to be protected. The soil is thrown toward the corn. A narrow line of creosote is then poured on the smooth ridge of soil thrown up by the plow and on the side of the ridge toward which the bugs will approach. Post holes about 2 feet deep are dug in the trench next to the creosote line and several feet or yards apart. The spacing of the post holes depends on the abundance of the migrating bugs. Creosote repels chinch bugs. As they encounter the creosote, their direction of march is diverted as they seek to get around the line. They fall into the post holes, where they may be killed by pouring a small amount of kerosene or dinitro-*o*-cresol dust over them. Ordinarily 1 gallon of creosote is used for erecting and maintaining 1 rod of barrier.

The creosote-treated paper barrier is made by plowing a shallow furrow and digging post holes as for the creosote line barrier. A strip of tough paper 4 or 5 inches wide is placed against the vertical side of the furrow and the soil then tightly packed against the lower edge of the strip so it is in an erect position with the upper edge protruding 2 or 3 inches above the ground level. The paper used is cut and rolled and then thoroughly soaked in creosote. The Iowa Agricultural Experiment Station developed a machine for plowing the furrow and placing the paper at one operation. Farmers in Iowa and elsewhere have made similar machines. About one-half the creosote is required for a paper barrier as for a line barrier, but savings in the cost of creosote are more than compensated for in the cost of the paper and barrier construction.

Dinitro-*o*-cresol dust makes an effective barrier. It is prepared by mixing thoroughly 4 pounds of dinitro-*o*-cresol and 96 pounds of pyrophyllite dust. The mixed dust is applied in a strip 2 inches wide along the field that is being invaded. This barrier is easily disturbed by winds and the feet of animals. Its advantages are the saving of time in applying it and the fact that it kills the bugs that crawl through the dust in the barrier line. From 1 to 2 pounds of mixed dust is required to erect and maintain 1 rod of dinitro-*o*-cresol dust barrier.

Regardless of the kind of material used to construct a barrier, additional material must be applied to maintain an effective barrier for 10 days or 2 weeks or until the invasion ceases.

Direct control of chinch bugs by the application of sprays or dusts to infested crops may be practical now in some instances, using the newer insecticides. Insecticides have not been tested extensively against field-wide infestations, because infestations of chinch bugs have been nearly noneconomic since the chlorinated hydrocarbons became available.

Populations of chinch bugs fluctuate from year to year, as indicated by the fact that nearly 9,000,000 rods of barrier were constructed in 1934 and only 94,000 rods in the following year. Another year of high populations was 1940, when 2,221,000 rods of barrier were used to protect crops. After a survey in 1944, it was estimated that 7.5 million rods of barrier would be needed in 1945. Only 273,000 rods of barrier were constructed, however, because weather unfavorable to chinch bugs abruptly reduced their numbers.

CLAUDE WAKELAND *is an entomologist in the Bureau of Entomology and Plant Quarantine.*

The European Corn Borer

Wm. G. Bradley

A research worker of the Massachusetts Agricultural Experiment Station in 1917 discovered several pinkish-brown worms on sweet corn in market gardens near Boston. Specialists examined the larvae and found them to be a species that was a pest of corn in Europe. A bit of sleuthing disclosed that they had sneaked into this country a few years earlier in broomcorn imported probably from Italy or Hungary for use in broom factories in Medford, Mass.

Sometimes quickly, sometimes more slowly, the insect, the European corn borer, spread outward from its original point of infestation. By 1952 it had been found in 37 States east of the Rocky Mountains, in which are most of our main corn-growing sections. The losses it caused in field corn were estimated at 314 million bushels in 1949.

From studies of the biology and habits of the insect we learned that two strains of the borer now exist in the United States. The single-generation, or univoltine, strain passes through one life cycle a year. The multiple-generation strain has two or more complete cycles every 12 months, depending on environment.

The multiple-generation strain flourishes in nearly all of the infested area, although its proportion to the single-generation strain varies in different localities, reaching its maximum in the southern sections and diminishing toward the north.

Observation of hundreds of species of plants in the field and tests in experimental plots on plants from many parts of the country showed that the borer can live on more than 200 different kinds of wild and cultivated plants. Corn, however, is infested and injured by the larvae, or borers, to a greater extent than any other crop. The borer injures field corn (both dent and flint), sweet corn, popcorn, and corn planted for fodder or silage. In the western part of the Corn Belt, corn is practically the only cultivated plant that is infested or injured to any extent. Broomcorn, soybean, millet, oats, potato, pepper, sorghum, and some large-stemmed flowering plants may be attacked when they are grown near corn or in years when corn matures late.

In the East, where the multiple-generation strain predominates, it commonly infests many other plants, including vegetables, field crops, flowers, and weeds. Many of them serve as shelter for the borers, rather than as food, and are infested sometimes by the borers which "overflow" from corn and other favorite host plants growing nearby.

THE EUROPEAN CORN BORER is essentially a boring insect and its greatest injury results from the tunneling and feeding of the larvae within the stalk, ears, tassel, midrib of the leaf, brace roots—practically all parts of the corn plant except the fibrous roots. The larvae also feed to some extent upon the leaf blades in the whorl, tassel buds, husks and silks of the ear, and behind the leaf sheaths.

The character of the injury depends on the stage of development of the corn plant when it is attacked. Soon after hatching, the borers begin migrating to various parts of the same plant or to other plants nearby. The developing whorl is a favorite feeding place for newly hatched larvae. If the attacked plant is just developing a tassel, some of the small borers enter the tassel buds and feed within; others eat the surface of the tassel buds and protect themselves with a slight silken web. If the infestation occurs at the time of pollen shedding, accumulations of the pollen at the ligules supply favorable material on which the larvae feed. Later they tunnel within the tassel stem and its branches, often causing it to break over. These broken tassels, with bunches of sawdustlike borings at the breaks, are the outstanding signs of infestation in fields of growing corn, although many infested plants may not show this particular injury. The borers may continue tunneling downward into the main stalk, or they may leave the upper part of the plant and enter it or neighboring plants at points lower down. Some of the newly hatched borers, instead of feeding upon or within the tassel buds and tassel stalks, enter the stalk directly at some lower point.

The borers usually enter between the leaf sheath and stalk or between the stalk and the base of the partly developed ear if the plant has advanced to that stage of development. As they gradually increase in size, they make larger tunnels and work upward or downward. Small holes in the stalks, with bunches of sawdustlike borings at or below them, indicate the section in which the borer is at work.

At any stage of their development the borers may enter the ear directly at its tip, base, or side; or they may enter it indirectly through the short stem, or shank, by which the ear is attached to the stalk, in which case the shank is often so weakened by the injury that it breaks over. Frequently the ear is entered at its tip by small borers, which feed first upon the silks or the tender portion of the husk and then work their way down into the cob and grain.

The injury to stalks and ears may be increased still further by disease organisms, which often follow the work of the borers and gain entrance through lesions made by borers.

THE EUROPEAN CORN BORER passes the winter as a fully grown borer, or worm, inside its tunnel in the stalk, stubble, or ear of corn, or in some weed or other plant. The presence of the borers may be detected by small holes on the surface of the infested plants which are usually plugged with castings. When you split open the stalks or stubs, you usually find the borers inside. They are then nearly an inch long and one-eighth inch thick. The head is dark brown or black. The upper surface of the body ranges in color from light brown to dark brown, or it may be pink. Each division of the body bears a row of small, dark-brown spots; several narrow dark-brown or pink lines extend lengthwise of the body. The under side of the body is flesh-colored and is without markings.

As soon as warm weather begins, in April or May, the borer may leave its winter shelter and bore into more suitable places to pass the resting stage.

In May or early June it cuts a small circular opening from its tunnel to the surface of the plant to provide an exit for the future moth. It then closes the hole with a thin webbing of silk and retreats into its tunnel to a point near the last feeding or shelter place, where it usually spins a thin cocoon. Inside the cocoon the borer changes into the resting stage, or pupa, which is shuttle-shaped, light brown to dark brown, and one-half to five-eighths inch long. After 10 to 14 days the skin of the pupa case splits, and the moth, or adult, comes forth and (under average weather conditions) is present in the fields from June to September.

The females begin to lay their eggs soon after they emerge. The moths remain quiet during the day, hiding in patches of weeds and grass or underneath the leaves of other plants. Evenings and sometimes through the night when the weather is good, they fly from plant to plant and lay their eggs in flat, irregular masses. A female lays up to 1,900 eggs; the average is about 400. The moths live 10 to 24 days. An egg mass usually contains 15 to 20 eggs; as many as 162 have been found in a single mass, although eggs deposited singly may be observed. The masses are laid mainly on the under surface of the corn leaves, although they are sometimes laid on the upper surface, on the stalk, or on the husk. Each egg is about half the size of an ordinary pinhead; in the masses the eggs overlap like fish scales. The egg is nearly flat and is white when first laid, but later changes to pale yellow and becomes darker just before the young borer comes out.

The eggs hatch in 4 to 9 days, depending on the temperature. The newly hatched borer, about one-sixteenth inch long, has a black head and a pale yellow body, which bears several rows of small black or brown spots. During its growth the borer molts or changes its skin five or six times, gradually increasing in size with each change until it becomes full-grown.

Borers of the single-generation strain become full-grown in August if weather conditions are normal. They continue to feed, or bore, however, at intervals until cold weather stops their activities in October or November. They remain in a dormant condition throughout the winter within their tunnels in the cornstalks, stubble, cobs, or other plant remnants.

Soon after they discovered the borer in the United States, investigators tried to establish biological controls like the ones that exist in its native haunts.

During the investigations, which started in 1919 and have continued since, more than 23 million borer larvae and pupae from Europe and 3 million from the Orient were brought to the United States. From them the natural enemies were reared. Other parasites were collected and forwarded to this country in the cocoon or pupal stages. Of the 24 species included in the importations, 21 were numerous enough to permit colonization over the borer-infested area in this country. The number of parasites available for colonization obtained from host larvae and pupae or parasite cocoons and pupae shipped from Europe or the Orient exceeded 2.5 million; it was increased by breeding in laboratories and by domestic field collections. About 8.5 million adults from all sources were released in fields.

Entomologists set loose adult parasites at selected localities throughout the infested area where the borer was sufficiently abundant to support a parasite population. The scientists conducted surveys in the vicinity of these localities to determine which species

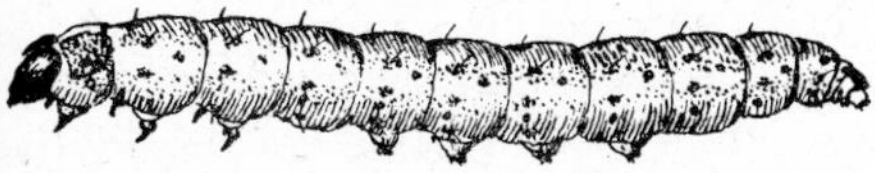

European corn borer.

became established and to get information on their biology as an aid in increasing their distribution within previously colonized areas and in colonizing areas newly infested by the natural spread of the borer. The species known to have become established in the United States and the number of adults of each that were released are: *Lydella stabulans grisescens* (*838,966*); *Horogenes punctorius* (*198,145*); *Macrocentrus gifuenis* (*2,610,654*); *Sympiesis viridula* (*394,382*); *Chelonus annulipes* (*401,983*); and *Phaeogenes nigridens* (53,234).

To determine the effects of the parasites, scientists developed special sampling designs and techniques. Among them were polar coordinate designs suitable for studying extent of establishment, rates and direction of dispersion, and other pertinent points. These designs consisted of sections to aid in randomizing samples in concentric rings about a central circle surrounding the release point. The number of sections in each ring and the width of the ring were varied to suit the objectives sought.

The studies showed that the parasites have spread at varying rates from the many release points. From the older colonies in the East where they have been present 20 years or more, some species have been found at distant points. In the North Central States, where colonization is more recent, some establishment and dispersion of a number of the species have occurred. It is hard to evaluate accurately the economic benefit derived from the parasites, but in many sections parasitization of more than 50 percent of the borers has been observed; average parasitization over considerable areas is high enough to indicate that many borers are being killed by the parasites.

Twenty-nine species of insects indigenous to the infested area parasitize the borer. None has been numerous enough to have a great effect on the borers. Scientists have tried to supplement the natural occurrence of *Trichogramma minutum,* a parasite that occasionally destroys a high percentage of the later portion of the second-generation eggs, by rearing a stock supply of parasites in the laboratory and releasing them when first- or second-generation eggs were present. Neither permanent nor appreciable temporary benefit resulted from the efforts.

Predators exert some influence on the borers.

Birds, particularly the downy woodpecker (*Dryobates pubescens medianus*) and the red-winged blackbird (*Agelaius phoeniceus phoeniceus*), and insect predators, particularly the lady beetles *Ceratomegilla fuscilabris* and *Hippodamia convergens,* have been frequently observed removing large numbers of borer larvae and egg masses from corn plants. No predators have been imported for testing against the corn borer.

The only disease organism that has been observed to kill the corn borer in the field in the United States is *Beauveria bassiana* and then only under circumstances directly traceable to infection originating in the laboratory. *B. bassiana* is an insectivorous organism that probably was brought into the United States on imported larvae. Field recoveries of this disease have been made immediately following its dissemination, but evidently no lasting effect has resulted from efforts to establish it as a natural control.

THE DISPOSAL of host plants in such a way as to destroy the borers infesting them is a logical and effective way to combat the borer. We have conducted a great deal of research to determine the best ways to do that. By the use of traps, for catching surviving borers, consisting of a rectangle of boards set on edge in the test ground and lined on the inside with strips of corrugated paper, the most efficient equipment was developed and information on the number of borers killed as a result of being buried at various depths in many types of soil was obtained. Because of the ability of the borer to reproduce at a very high rate and because of the mortality caused by many natural factors it is doubtful if disposal of host plants will prove highly beneficial unless a thorough community-wide effort is made. Because most of the mechanical methods of control are actually good farm practices, however, it is wise to follow them.

Feeding infested plants to livestock is one way to fight the corn borer. Their food value is not noticeably reduced unless they are severely infested. Infested corn plants can be fed as silage, direct from the field, or as finely shredded or cut fodder. Properly done, any of these methods destroys nearly all the borers in the plants.

Any infested corn that is put in the silo should be cut close to the ground. Borers that escape the silage cutter are destroyed in the silo.

Infested cornstalks must be cut into pieces not longer than a half inch so that nearly all the borers may be killed. This precaution is particularly important if the silage is not placed directly in the silo or is not fed soon after it is cut.

If cutting and shocking in the field is done, the corn should be cut low and early. Low cutting also helps in doing a clean job of plowing later and makes other clean-up methods easier.

In general, the proportion of borers living in the stalk below any given height increases as the season advances.

If infested cornstalks are fed directly without previous cutting or shredding, the uneaten parts should be collected and destroyed unless they are trampled completely by livestock and thoroughly mixed with the manure of the feed lot.

Shredding or cutting corn fodder into fine pieces, as is ordinarily done by husking and shredding machines, kills 95 to 98 percent of the borers and makes the fodder more acceptable to livestock. Most of the borers that escape death in the machine perish during the general practice of storing the shredded material, feeding it to livestock, and using the residue as bedding, which is finally trampled into the manure.

Stalk cutters, which break up the stalks in the field, probably do not kill on an average more than 60 percent of the borers present, but they promote more rapid rotting of the stalks and make clean plowing easier.

EFFECTIVE PLOWING to control borers depends on turning under the corn remnants and other trash so completely that none of it remains on the soil surface. The material plowed under should not be dragged to the surface by later cultivation before the moths emerge, and the ground should be cultivated or pulverized to close all large cracks and crevices.

Plowing infested material under does not itself kill the borers. Most of the borers crawl up to the surface sooner or later. If the plowing has been clean, however, most of the larvae coming to the surface die because they are exposed to natural enemies like birds, ants, ground beetles, and insect parasites and predators. But if the plowing is not done clean, the borers, when they reach the surface, bore into any fragments of a corn plant or weed that may be left there and with that protection they can complete their development to the moth stage.

The depth of plowing for corn borer control is not important if all infested material is covered completely to such a depth that it will not again be brought to the soil surface by later cultivation or weathering and thus become a shelter for the borers that crawl on the surface. To insure proper coverage, however, and to reduce the possibility of the plowed-under material being again dragged to the surface, plowing to a depth of 6 inches or more should be done if soil conditions permit.

An effective plow attachment to aid in turning under trash consists of three No. 9 gage wires. The wires, about 12 feet long, are attached to the framework of the plow, and the outer ends are left loose. The loose ends are caught by the furrow slice as it is turned over. Thus the wires are held tightly to the top of the furrow slice by the weight of the soil on the buried ends of the wires and so turn all trash to the bottom of the furrow.

Disking cornstalks or high stubble in preparation for seeding to small grain or other crops is objectionable from the the standpoint of corn borer control, except when it is followed by clean plowing. Disking allows a very high percentage of borers to survive and the shade given later by the growing grain protects the borers in the trash left on the surface.

Rolling, soil packing, disking, or other similar types of cultivation are of practically no value in combatting the borers.

INSECTICIDES are effective for protecting corn from damage by the borer.

Research has been directed toward finding more efficient and economical insecticides. In recent years nozzles have been developed and tested to deliver sprays with droplets of satisfactory size and under efficient pressures to be carried from the nozzles to the whorls, leaf axils, and other parts of the plants where the borers feed. Chemists have produced new and highly toxic insecticides and formulations have been modified to permit practical low application rates with freedom from nozzle clogging and with the ability to penetrate into the concealed plant parts where the larvae feed and to remain on the plants for several days. In the search for new insecticide material research workers have attempted to keep the toxicity to plants and warm-blooded animals as low as possible.

EACH YEAR several hundred compounds have been developed by the division of insecticide investigations and tested to determine their effectiveness in controlling the borer. Many of these materials are powders ground from parts of plants from foreign lands. In this work extremely accurate tests are conducted in the laboratory to find the most promising insecticides. These are next given further tests in small plots in the field and those found effective are then given large-scale field tests.

Because the borer feeds in concealed places and because of the growth characteristics of the corn plant, application equipment differing greatly from that used on row-crop pests had to be designed.

State agricultural agencies in most of the infested States have established services whereby the progress of corn and borer development is followed, and they can furnish reliable advice on timing of application, as well as on other problems relating to corn borer control.

Corn should be planted at the time which normally will allow it to produce its maximum yield in the locality in which it is grown as recommended by the State agricultural agencies. Avoiding early planting protects against heavy infestation by first-generation borers as well as the danger of poor germination and possibly frost damage in spring. Avoiding late planting protects against damage from second-generation borers and from the possibility of early frost damage and soft corn in the fall.

No strain of corn has shown complete immunity from corn borers. Some strains have inherent characteristics that enable them to resist or tolerate the borers better than others. The number of borers per plant at harvest, as compared with the number of corn borer eggs originally on the plants, is much smaller in some strains of corn than in others. Also some strains of corn will stand up better than others under an attack by a given number of borers. Plant breeders are taking advantage of the information obtained relative to the resistance of commonly used corn inbreds and those recently developed on the basis of borer resistance to provide growers with hybrids which can be expected to produce a satisfactory yield in the borer-infested localities.

Research to determine these points involved the study of thousands of lines of corn obtained from all parts of the world. Observations were made on such widely divergent material as open-pollinated varieties from Mexico and South America, areas in which corn was thought to have had its origin, open-pollinated corn grown for years under corn borer conditions in Europe, lines developed by breeders to provide resistance to other insects, germ plasm brought down from corn grown originally by the Indians in the United States, hundreds of lines developed by breeders searching for improved agronomic characters and many others.

In order to determine accurately the relative differences in resistance between the various lines of corn it was necessary that each should be infested with borers as nearly uniform as possible. To obtain this objective and to insure that tests could be made even in years of low natural borer infestation, many thousands of corn borer eggs are produced each year under laboratory conditions and placed on the test plants by hand. To promote the success and efficiency of this method many pieces of equipment and specific techniques were developed. Moths reared in large emergence cages are induced to lay eggs on wax paper. Egg-cutting machines capable of turning out 10,000 masses on wax-paper disks per day were utilized. Storage conditions for ovipositing moths and eggs were studied and improved in order to increase the efficiency of this research.

No one of the methods discussed gives all the control needed, but crop losses from corn borers can be cut by their use. The amount of benefit obtained will depend on favorable or unfavorable weather, how many of the control methods are used, and how well these are carried out.

While the grower has at hand means of saving his corn from serious injury, it should be the objective of research to reduce the threat so that no additional control methods would be necessary, other than those which would be followed in sound farm practice in the absence of the borer, or to reduce the cost in labor, money, and equipment of recommended control measures enough to promote their universal adoption.

To further the first of these objectives continued search should be made in all the corn-growing areas of the world to find and utilize germ plasm of high resistance to the borer. Incorporation of this material into agronomically desirable hybrids for use within the infested area would bring about substantial savings without seasonal outlays of funds for direct control measures.

Although the outlook for biological control seems encouraging, continued search should be made in those parts of the world where the borer is present but in which no investigations on parasites have been conducted. A more thorough study of predators and their utilization should be made and the role of such beneficial insects in the countries in which the borer is indigenous should be studied. An efficient combination of parasites, predators, and disease organisms would aid materially in reducing borer damage.

Research with respect to the second objective would involve the development of more efficient insecticides, application equipment, and application methods. More infallible and practical means of determining whether or not to treat and when to treat would be a distinct advance. Some studies have been made on systemic poisons. A number of systemic poisons have been tested both in the laboratory and in the field by mixing the materials in various dosages with the soil in which corn is grown. High mortality of larvae feeding on corn so treated has been produced. This work should be continued as it points to the possibility of a control measure which can be utilized with little additional cost to the farmer.

WM. G. BRADLEY *was entomologist in charge of the European Corn Borer Research Laboratory of the Bureau of Entomology and Plant Quarantine at Ankeny, Iowa. After graduation from Louisiana State University, he was assistant entomologist at the Louisiana Agricultural Experiment Station. In 1952 he went to the Dominican Republic to work on the Point IV program.*

For further reading:

W. A. Baker and W. G. Bradley: Insecticidal Treatments for the Control of the European Corn Borer, *Bureau of Entomology and Plant Quarantine publication E–718 (revision), 1947;* The European Corn Borer: Its Present Status and Methods of Control, *U. S. D. A. Farmers' Bulletin 1548, revised 1948.*

G. A. Ficht: Relative Resistance of Selected Strains of Corn to European Corn Borer, *Journal of Economic Entomology, volume 29, pages 687–691. 1936.*

F. G. Holdaway, L. K. Cutkomp, and A. W. Buzicky: Fighting the European Corn Borer in Minnesota, *University of Minnesota, Agricultural Extension Service, Extension Bulletin 257. Revised 1949.*

L. L. Huber, C. R. Neiswander, and R. M. Salter: The European Corn Borer and Its Environment, *Ohio Agricultural Experiment Station Bulletin 429. 1928.*

Marion T. Meyers, L. L. Huber, C. R. Neiswander, F. D. Richey, and G. H. Stringfield: Experiments on Breeding Corn Resistant to the European Corn Borer, *U. S. D. A. Technical Bulletin 583. 1937.*

L. H. Patch: Survival, Weight, and Location of European Corn Borers Feeding on Resistant and Susceptible Field Corn, *Journal of Agricultural Research, volume 66, pages 7–19, 1943;* Resistance of Dent Corn Inbred Lines to Survival of First-Generation European Corn Borer Larvae, *with Ray T. Everly, U. S. D. A. Technical Bulletin 893, 1945;* Strains of Field Corn Resistant to the Survival of the European Corn Borer, *with J. R. Holbert and R. T. Everly, U. S. D. A. Technical Bulletin 823, 1942.*

970134°—52——41

Insects That Attack Tobacco

D. J. Caffrey

Tobacco is subject to damage by several species of insects from the time the seedlings develop in the plant bed until the crop is harvested, during the time it is in storage, and after the manufactured products have been prepared and offered for sale.

The insects that attack the seedling tobacco or the growing crop include hornworms, flea beetles, aphids, cutworms, green June beetle larvae, tobacco budworms, and wireworms.

Others, less widely distributed, are webworms, thrips, grasshoppers, mole crickets, vegetable weevils, midge larvae, slugs, and suckflies.

The cigarette beetle commonly infests practically all types of tobacco in storage. Stored tobacco of the flue-cured domestic and imported Turkish types used in making cigarettes is also menaced by the tobacco moth. All kinds of tobacco products—cigars, cigarettes, smoking and chewing tobacco, and snuff—may be mutilated and contaminated by the cigarette beetle.

Despite many years of research and the development of fairly good remedies, insects continue to cause impressive losses—an estimated loss of 100 million dollars annually to the growing crop and 5 million to 10 million dollars to the stored and manufactured product in recent years. One appreciates the losses when he remembers that tobacco has been a commercial crop in the United States since 1612, it had a farm value of more than 1 billion dollars in 1950, and in that year was grown on 1,593,900 acres through the Southern, Central, and Eastern States.

In plant beds the tobacco seedlings are attacked commonly by flea beetles,

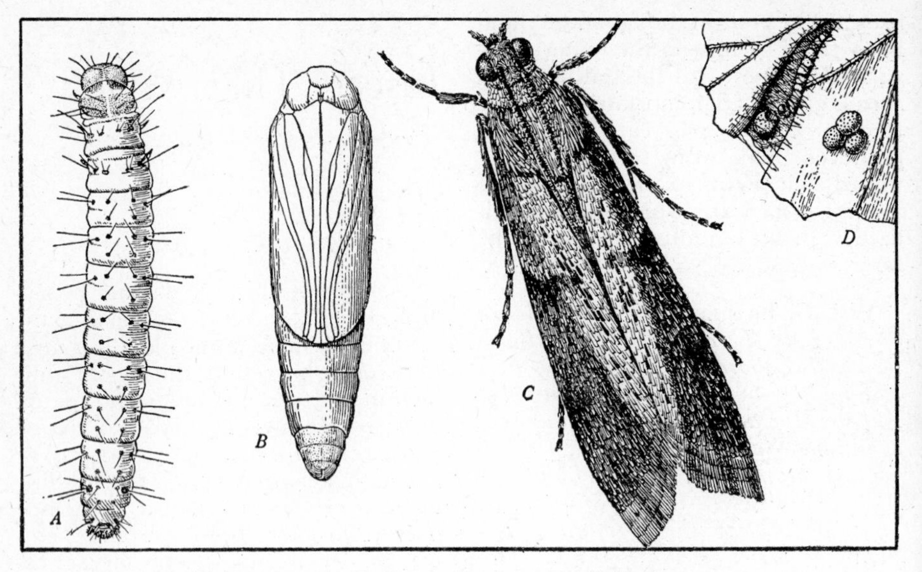

Tobacco moth. A, Larva; B, pupa; C, adult; D, eggs.

larvae of the green June beetle, and aphids; more rarely, by cutworms, mole crickets, black European slugs, vegetable weevils, grasshoppers, and the larvae of midges.

Flea beetles (principally the tobacco flea beetle and the potato flea beetle) are serious pests of seedling tobacco in many districts. Their depredations often lead to the total destruction of the young crop. A way to combat them is to construct the plant beds with tight side walls and a tight cloth cover, which keeps out the flea beetle adults. If that is not enough, dusts or sprays containing DDT, cryolite, or rotenone are effective.

The larvae of green June beetles cause damage in plant beds by burrowing in the soil, uprooting the small seedlings, or covering them with soil. The burrowing also causes an excessive aeration of the topsoil, which often leads to the drying out and death of the seedlings. The pest can be controlled by the use of a poison bait, consisting of parathion, or barium, sodium, or potassium fluosilicate mixed with wheat middlings and scattered on the plant bed. Equally effective results are had by applying a dust mixture or a drench containing parathion (or a dust mixture containing lindane) to the plant-bed surface. Ordinary gasoline may also be effective against the larvae when it is applied to the plant-bed soil through holes large and deep enough to enable the level of the gasoline poured into each hole to remain at least 2 inches below the soil surface. This procedure keeps the gasoline away from the roots of the small tobacco plants, which it would injure. After the gasoline has been applied the holes are plugged with lumps of moist soil.

In many districts aphids (principally the green peach aphid) have become a major pest of tobacco. Some infestations start in the plant bed and, if they are not controlled, may be carried on the seedlings to the fields in which they are transplanted. The plants in the plant bed therefore should be inspected frequently to determine if aphids are present. A dust mixture containing parathion will control them. Because aphid infestation in the plant bed may originate from certain weeds and such cultivated crops as collards, broccoli, or turnips, it is important during the early stages of the tobacco crop to remove weeds from the plant bed and its vicinity and locate the plant bed at some distance from cultivated crops infested with aphids.

Several species of cutworms may do extensive damage to plant beds in a short time. Some species overwinter in the soil as larvae. When temperatures are favorable they feed voraciously on the small plants. Even plant beds that are sterilized by burning or steaming should be examined carefully for cutworm damage. If the damage continues, a bait containing paris green or sodium fluosilicate in wheat bran should be applied evenly over the bed. Baits containing toxaphene or chlordane and dust mixtures containing DDT applied to the surface also have given good results.

In the South, mole crickets often cause serious losses by uprooting and covering the seedlings with soil. The bait of paris green or sodium fluosilicate in bran or a spray containing parathion will get rid of them.

The black European slug frequently invades tobacco plant beds. It devours the seedlings, particularly along the margins of the bed. It can be controlled by hydrated lime or air-slaked lime applied just inside the plant-bed walls. A poisoned bait containing metaldehyde or a dust mixture containing parathion, applied to the surface of the bed, also is good.

The vegetable weevil feeds in both the adult and larval forms on seedlings. Dusts containing DDT or lead arsenate control the pests and prevent their spread through fields when the seedlings are transplanted.

Several species of grasshoppers and midge larvae (Tendipedidae) sometimes infest the plant beds. The grasshoppers can be controlled by the bait mentioned for cutworms or mole crickets or by a dust containing toxaphene applied to the plant-bed surface. Midge larvae sometimes are abundant enough to cause damage by burrowing and aerating the soil so that the plants dry out. DDT, applied to the soil surface as a dust, is a good remedy.

Newly set tobacco plants are often damaged severely by flea beetles, cutworms, wireworms, aphids, and (less commonly) by webworms.

Flea beetles often are particularly destructive during the wilting stage, before the plants are established in their new environment. Much damage can be avoided by making applications of dust mixtures or sprays containing DDT or cryolite to the plants before they are taken from the plant bed. The beneficial results of those insecticides usually last 7 to 10 days and their use then makes it unnecessary to apply special insecticides later. But if one has to fight the beetles on the newly set plants in the field, dust mixtures containing DDT or cryolite can be used to advantage. All surplus plants in the beds should be destroyed as soon as transplanting has been completed in order to eliminate them as a source of breeding and food material for flea beetles, which may be in nearby tobacco fields. The surplus plants can be destroyed by plowing or harrowing the plant beds thoroughly.

Several species of cutworms attack newly set tobacco plants. The most effective insurance against them is to apply a poisoned bran bait containing paris green or sodium fluosilicate before the plants are set in the field. As many cutworms are active at night, broadcasting the bait over the field in the late afternoon has given best results. Even with this precaution, damage after plants are set sometimes occurs in spots in the field. That problem can be solved by scattering a small amount of the bait next to the plants in the affected parts of the field—but in doing so one has to be careful to put the least possible amount of the poisoned bran on the plants because any bait that lodges on the tobacco leaves may cause injury.

Several species of wireworms have been considered among the most important pests of newly set tobacco plants. Chlordane or parathion, mixed in small amounts with the water used during transplanting, are effective against them. Ample transplanting water should be used in order to insure a good distribution of the insecticide ingredients in the soil immediately surrounding the transplants. Large, stocky transplants should be used because they suffer less damage than smaller plants do.

Aphids, which ordinarily do not seriously damage tobacco in the transplanting stage, can be reduced by applying a dust mixture containing either parathion or tetraethyl pyrophosphate immediately before the plants are pulled for transplanting. Such applications usually protect the plants from aphids while they are being set and are becoming established in the field.

Sod webworms, sometimes known as tobacco crambids, feed on the roots and bases of the newly set plants. An efficient remedy consists of a bait containing paris green, oil of mirbane (nitrobenzene), and cornmeal, applied to the plants immediately after transplanting or as soon as damage is noticed in the fields.

GROWING TOBACCO PLANTS are commonly injured by hornworms, tobacco budworms, aphids, and flea beetles. More rarely, the growing crop is attacked by thrips, grasshoppers, and suckflies.

Hornworms are the most widely distributed and destructive. Lead arsenate was used extensively for many years although it had several objectionable features. Scientists have tried to find a substitute that will control the pests without leaving a poisonous residue, will not injure the plants, and will not lower the quality of the cured tobacco.

They found that paris green is fairly effective although it injures tobacco under some conditions and contains arsenic. Cryolite is also fairly effective and has been used by some growers. DDT is effective against the tomato hornworm on tobacco but not against a closely related species, the tobacco hornworm, which is the predominant species in the South. Encouraging results have recently been obtained in

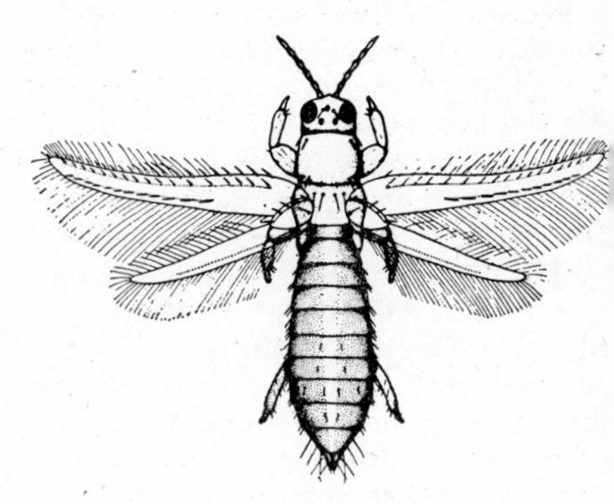

Tobacco thrips.

controlling both species by applying dust mixtures or sprays that contain TDE.

Considerable research has been devoted to methods for luring, trapping and poisoning the parent moths of the hornworms. Used alone, that practice is not completely satisfactory, but it has some value as a supplement to other methods, such as hand-picking or using insecticides.

The tobacco budworm is widespread and destructive in the South. In early days growers used the "little boy-big boy" team to fight it—the little boy placed in the growing bud of each infested tobacco plant a small handful of warm surface soil; it caused the budworm to leave its place of concealment in the folds of the expanding leaves of the plant. The big boy followed closely and killed the budworm before it could move out of danger. In later years, the budworm could be thwarted by applying a pinch of cornmeal and lead arsenate to the growing bud—an effective method that left only a little poison on the harvested product. But it took too much time and labor. Now growers use a dust mixture containing DDT, which is as effective as the poi soned bait and can be applied without too great an outlay for labor. DDT can be used on maturing plants or the seedheads of tobacco plants, when the poisoned bait cannot be used.

Since 1946 tobacco in most of the producing regions has been subjected to an outbreak of aphids, principally the green peach aphid. They have reduced the yield and quality of the tobacco by sucking the juices from the plants and have contaminated the product with insect remains and a sticky material known as honeydew, which they secrete and which cannot be removed from the harvested tobacco without injuring the product for market. Extensive research on the habits of the aphids and methods of control and tests of the newer insecticides disclosed that a satisfactory control may be achieved by the timely use of dusts or sprays containing parathion or tetraethyl pyrophosphate. Many growers have used those materials, but further research is needed to determine their ultimate effect on the tobacco plant and the extent of their toxicity.

Although flea beetles are controlled successfully in the plant bed and on the newly set plants, heavy infestations are sometimes encountered on plants in the field. The infestations are occasionally severe near harvest and require the application of insecticides, particularly on the types of tobacco grown for cigar wrappers, since a few holes made by the beetles ruin tobacco leaves for cigar making. Rotenone was found to be an excellent remedy. More recently, dusts or sprays containing DDT were shown to be effective against flea beetles and useful against other species of leaf feeders, including the tobacco budworm, which sometimes injures the plants during the same period. Dusts or sprays containing cryolite are fairly effective.

Tobacco thrips mar leaves used for cigar wrappers. Often they are associated with flea beetles. A dust mixture containing pyrethrum and rotenone will control thrips on tobacco leaves and reduce damage by flea beetles.

The suckfly attacks tobacco grown for flue-curing in many parts of the South. Periodically it becomes abundant enough to cause serious damage in fields of late-planted tobacco. In growing tobacco shortly before harvest, its feeding may reduce the weight and thickness of the cured leaves. Unsightly specks of excrement on the under surfaces of the leaves and an abnormal change in their condition prevent proper coloration and curing and a consequent loss in quality. A dust mixture containing parathion or sprays containing parathion or tetraethyl pyrophosphate are effective against the suckfly.

Mole cricket.

Several species of the grasshoppers sometimes despoil the growing tobacco crop, particularly along the margins of fields. The pests can be checked under field conditions by the poisoned baits which I mentioned for use against them in plant beds or by a dust mixture containing toxaphene applied to the weeds growing along the margins of tobacco fields which normally harbor the grasshoppers before they invade the tobacco.

Insects infesting stored tobacco and tobacco products affect a large industry concerned with the curing, fermentation, and manufacture of those products in the United States. The insect enemies take a large toll each year, but it should not be inferred that tobacco products from the factories of American manufacturers are likely to be insect-infested or that they were made from infested tobacco. Precautions are taken to eliminate insects from tobacco warehouses and factories. The industry makes a constant effort to keep its stocks free of insects. Most tobacco must be held in storage for 2 years or longer so that it will slowly ferment or age under natural conditions of temperature and moisture. Therefore manufacturers must carry large stocks of tobacco in storage to fill trade and manufacturing requirements. In August 1950, for example, 3,155,000 million pounds of unmanufactured leaf tobacco were in storage in the United States and Puerto Rico.

Years ago the cigarette beetle was the principal pest affecting stored tobacco, but beginning in 1930 the tobacco moth assumed importance as a pest of flue-cured and imported Turkish tobaccos used for cigarettes in some parts of this country. Specimens of the cigarette beetle were found in alabaster vases in the tomb of Tutankhamen, indicating that the species was present in Egypt at least 3,500 years ago. Research in the second decade of this century demonstrated that fumigation of tobacco with hydrogen cyanide gas would control the cigarette beetle in closed tobacco warehouses as well as in vaults and in vacuum chambers. Continued experience of the industry showed, however, that hydrogen cyanide gas, directed against both the cigarette beetle and the tobacco moth, was not effective under practical conditions in some closed warehouses, because of the leakage of the fumigant from inadequately sealed structures. Further research developed methods for sealing ventilators in the walls of such warehouses with suitable paper and glue, for sealing sliding doors with a dough made of asbestos, calcium chloride, and water, and for sealing cracks or crevices in the walls and around the eaves with elastic roofing cement applied with a pressure gun. These methods of sealing warehouses before fumigation were successful and were widely adopted by the tobacco industry in this country and abroad and also by other industries.

The efficiency of such fumigation was further improved by the development of a suction light trap, which attracted and captured the adult insects and thus indicated the most efficient time of fumigation by providing a continuous index of insect abundance and activity. One of these traps is installed for each 75,000 to 100,000 cubic feet of space in a tobacco warehouse. The traps are operated during the part of the year when insects affecting stored tobacco are active—in the latitude of eastern South Carolina from about April 1 to December 1. As soon as the average catch in each of the suction light traps rises above an established danger point—usually 50 cigarette beetles or tobacco moth adults a week—the warehouse should be fumigated. Visual inspection cannot be depended upon for detecting the need for fumigation, because the feeding activity of the insects in the tobacco within hogsheads and bales often proceeds to a danger point before external indications of injury are noticeable.

As one part of the method of evaluating the efficiency of different fumigants and fumigation schedules, a hollow steel spike was developed for placing test lots of insects at different depths in hogsheads and bales of tobacco before fumigation. After fumigation, the spikes are removed and the insects in them are examined to determine the mortality obtained during the fumigation process. Thus one can determine, without disturbing the tobacco, the depth to which fumigation is effective and the percentage of insects killed at various depths in the tobacco. Its use also led to more effective dosages of the fumigant and duration of exposure periods. The development of fumigation in vacuum chambers also increased the facilities for the control of insects in tobacco being shipped into or out of this country. Large vacuum chambers result in superior penetration of the poison gas into the tobacco containers.

A fumigant consisting of a mixture

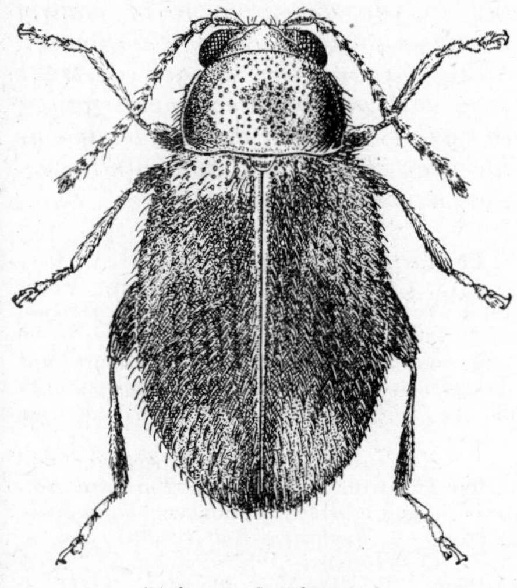

Tobacco flea beetle.

of ethylene oxide and carbon dioxide is useful against the cigarette beetle and the tobacco moth under vacuum conditions, particularly in the case of manufactured cigars and cigar tobaccos. This fumigant has the advantage of not leaving any objectionable odor but it is not effective at temperatures below approximately 60° F.

Methyl bromide is a satisfactory fumigant in closed tobacco storages, but under some circumstances obnoxious odors develop. Methyl bromide is more dangerous to handle than the other commonly used tobacco fumigants.

A chemical consisting of equal parts of acrylonitrile and carbon tetrachloride is an effective fumigant for insects affecting stored tobacco in closed storages. It has not been widely adopted because of the possible fire hazard involved, but it promises to become an effective substitute for hydrogen cyanide gas.

Aerosols containing DDT, pyrethrum or lindane have given a moderate degree of success, and research on this method of insecticide application is being continued.

The problem of protecting tobacco in open storage has been studied. In that type of storage, the fumigation methods used in closed storages obviously are impracticable. Several years ago a method was devised for the treatment of the interior of open-storage warehouses by applying pyrethrum dust with special equipment directed against the adults of the cigarette beetle and the tobacco moth. The treatment proved helpful, but the dust deposits that accumulated as the result of repeated applications were objectionable. Recently a finely divided pyrethrum-oil spray has been found more effective than pyrethrum dust against the adults of insects affecting tobacco in open-storage warehouses. Special equipment had to be developed to apply the spray to the interior of the warehouses, and the successful accomplishment of this project has led to the widespread adoption of spraying as a standard procedure in the control of insects in open warehouses.

Until recent years most of the research on the control of insects in stored tobacco dealt with the cigarette type of tobacco, since this type is held in storage for aging longer than the other types. Beginning in 1948, however, emphasis was shifted to the cigar type of tobacco, for which cyanide fumigation is objectionable in some respects, and to the adaptation of fumigation and spraying procedures to factory conditions. Greater emphasis also has been placed on studying methods for protecting cigarettes, cigars, and other manufactured products from insect damage.

The problem of devising materials for covers or liners of containers for stored tobacco, or manufactured products, that would exclude or repel insects has been given some attention. Various types of paper and plastic substances have been tested to line hogsheads prior to packing the tobacco therein. Similarly, many different coverings, including paper impregnated with a pyrethrum-piperonyl butoxide combination have been tested as coverings for cigarettes and cigars. None of these materials has been completely successful.

In many areas the tobacco moth periodically infests harvested tobacco in packhouses on the farms. Many of the infestations were originally caused by adults of the tobacco moth which bred in and escaped from nearby open-storage warehouses. The screening of these open-storage units so that the moths cannot escape and gain entrance to tobacco packhouses has aided greatly in solving this problem, as has the elimination of, or screening of, grains or feedstuffs stored nearby, which also function as breeding sources. Packhouse sanitation, including the disposition of scrap tobacco and similar trash, also aids greatly in reducing the local population of the tobacco moth, and minimizes the likelihood of infestation of the harvested tobacco stored in the packhouse. The application of pyrethrum dust to the interior of infested tobacco packhouses was found to be effective in killing the adults.

Special studies on the effect of cold storage or cool storage disclosed that this common commercial practice is of value in preventing or checking an insect infestation in stored or manufactured tobacco. Conversely, many factory processes, particularly in the instance of domestic cigarette types of tobacco, involve a redrying operation of the stored tobacco. The machines used in this operation subject the tobacco to high temperatures. A study of this treatment revealed that all insect infestation is killed in the presence of the high temperatures used in the operation. The redried tobacco is subject to reinfestation, however, when held in an infested factory or storage warehouse and may later require fumigation.

D. J. CAFFREY *joined the Bureau of Entomology and Plant Quarantine in 1913. He is well known for his research in the field of cereal and forage insect investigations, particularly on the European corn borer, range caterpillar, clover seed chalcid, alfalfa caterpillar, and wheat straw-worm. He initiated many of the fundamental studies leading to the development of control measures for the European corn borer. Since entering the division of truck crop and garden insect investigations in 1934 as assistant division leader, he has been closely identified with the research on tobacco insects.*

For further reading:

F. S. Chamberlin: Control of the Vegetable Weevil in Tobacco Plant Beds, *Journal of Economic Entomology, volume 37, pages 293–294, 1944;* Insect Pests of Cigar-Type Tobaccos in the Southern Districts, *with A. H. Madden, U. S. D. A. Circular 639, 1942.*

S. E. Crumb: Tobacco Cutworms and Their Control, *U. S. D. A. Farmers' Bulletin 1494, 1926;* Tobacco Cutworms, *U. S. D. A. Technical Bulletin 88, 1929.*

L. O. Howard: The Principal Insects Affecting the Tobacco Plant, *U. S. D. A. Farmers' Bulletin 120. 1900.*

A. C. Morgan: Methods of Controlling Tobacco Insects, *Bureau of Entomology Circular 123, 1910;* The Tobacco Budworm and Its Control in the Georgia and Florida Tobacco-Growing Region, *with F. S. Chamberlin, U. S. D. A. Farmers' Bulletin 1531, 1927;* Arsenate of Lead as an Insecticide Against the Tobacco Hornworms in the Dark-Tobacco District, *with D. C. Parman, U. S. D. A. Farmers' Bulletin 595, 1914.*

A. H. Madden and F. S. Chamberlin: Biology of the Tobacco Hornworm in the Southern Cigar-Tobacco District, *U. S. D. A. Technical Bulletin 896. 1945.*

K. B. McKinney and Joe Milam: The Green June Beetle Larva in Tobacco Plant Beds, *U. S. D. A. Farmers' Bulletin 1489. 1926.*

G. A. Runner: The Tobacco Beetle: An Important Pest in Tobacco Products, *U. S. D. A. Bulletin 737, Professional Paper, 1919;* The Tobacco Beetle and How to Prevent Damage by It, *U. S. D. A. Farmers' Bulletin 846, 1917.*

M. C. Swingle: Low Temperature as a Possible Means of Controlling the Cigarette Beetle in Stored Tobacco, *U. S. D. A. Circular 462. 1938.*

W. H. White: Cutworms in the Garden, *U. S. D. A. Leaflet 2. 1927, slightly revised 1943.*

C. B. Wisecup and N. C. Hayslip: Control of Mole Crickets by Use of Poisoned Baits, *U. S. D. A. Leaflet 237. 1943.*

Insect Pests of Stored Grains and Seed

R. T. Cotton, Wallace Ashby

The inauguration of the Government grain-loan program under the Agricultural Adjustment Act of 1938 brought a large increase in the stocks of grain carried as reserve supplies and in the length of time such stocks were held. On October 1, 1941, for example, the carry-over of corn was 646 million bushels—nearly four times more than the 1928–32 average of 163 million bushels. Much of the extra corn was shelled and stored in farm-type bins, a method of storage previously unused in the United States. Although the reserve supplies of corn, wheat, and sorghum grain since 1940 fell at times as the result of increased world requirements for grain as human food or animal feeds, the years since 1948 again brought a marked increase in the quantity of grain in reserve. Every conceivable type of storage structure was pressed into service.

To meet the many problems that arose in the storage of these large reserves, State and Federal agencies started a research program to determine the best type of storage structures to use and the most efficient insect-control programs to follow. Studies were made of the changes in the condition of the grain during extended periods of storage, the insects involved, their origin, the factors favoring or deterring their abundance, temperature changes in the grain and their effect on insect abundance, methods of drying and cleaning grain, and the effectiveness of various fumigants in controlling insect infestations. Observations were made in hundreds of bins of corn, wheat, and sorghum grain in various parts of the country, in special storage sites, and under laboratory conditions.

The scope of the work is constantly changing to meet the need for information on special types of storage, to evaluate the usefulness of new fumigants, sprays, drying, cleaning and grain-handling equipment, and storage structures, and to make adjustments for shortages of insecticides or structural material.

INSECTS are one of the most important hazards to the safe storage of grain—but the investigations have demonstrated time and again the basic truth that the factors favorable for preserving the keeping quality of grain are unfavorable for the development of insects.

The insects that attack stored grain are rather general feeders, but some of them definitely prefer certain grains. In the commercial corn area—Illinois, Iowa, Nebraska, Minnesota, and South Dakota—the six species most commonly found in stored shelled corn and constituting more than 98 percent of the insect population were the saw-toothed grain beetle, flat grain beetle, red flour beetle, foreign grain beetle, larger black flour beetle, and hairy fungus beetle. The first three comprised the greater portion of the insect population. In the South, where field infestation is common, the rice weevil is by far the most abundant species and constitutes the largest proportion of the insect population of stored corn.

In the Great Plains hard winter wheat region, seven species constitute more than 90 percent of the insect population of wheat in farm storage—the flat grain beetle, saw-toothed grain beetle, lesser grain borer, red flour beetle, long-headed flour beetle, cadelle, and rice weevil. Their abundance varies with climatic conditions. In the northern parts of the region, the hardier species, the flat grain beetle and the saw-toothed grain beetle, predominate. In the southern part, the lesser grain borer and the rice weevil become increasingly abundant. Along the eastern seaboard the Angoumois grain moth is occasionally one of the common pests of stored wheat, although ordinarily the flat grain beetle and the rice weevil are the main species there. Found in greatest abundance in rough rice in storage are the Angoumois grain moth, rice weevil, flat grain beetle, lesser grain borer, and red flour beetle.

The moths that attack grain and seed are not among the most abundant species, but they occasionally appear in tremendous numbers wherever grain is stored. They confine their activities largely to the surface grain, where the caterpillars spin silken threads that mat the kernels together and form a silken web over the tops of bins. The Indian-meal moth, the chief offender, attacks all types of grain. It and the almond moth are also troublesome in seed stores and hybrid seed-corn establishments.

INSECTS DESTROY at least 5 percent of the world production of cereal grains. A survey in 1947 by the Food and Agriculture Organization of the United Nations indicated that in 29 countries the total loss of cereals was 25,750,000 tons, of which 50 percent could be attributed to insects.

Weevils, flour beetles, and many other bran beetles devour at least their own weight of food each week. Their larvae destroy many times their own weight of food during the 3 or 4 weeks they are developing. Loss of stored wheat in the Great Plains region may be as high as 10 percent in a season. Corn in storage in the deep South may be destroyed at the rate of 9 percent a month.

Insects may do other kinds of damage. Many species feed almost entirely on the germ of the grain, so that its viability is reduced and much larger amounts of infested than uninfested grain must be used for seed. They frequently cause grain to heat. A musty odor may result; deterioration and rotting of surface grain may be caused by the translocation of water vapor from the heated area to the cooler surface grain. A lowering of the grade may be caused by off-odors or insect damage. Finally, the milling quality of infested grain is reduced by the presence in the kernels of immature stages of weevils, which are hard to detect and cannot easily be removed during the milling process.

MANY PEOPLE still believe that insects are generated spontaneously in grain—probably because most of the insect pests of stored grain are so small that they remain unobserved until they have multiplied to such large numbers that the grain may suddenly seem alive with them.

The sources of insect infestations vary with crop and region.

In all grain crops in the South infestation begins in the field. The farther north the crop is grown, the less the degree of field infestation, until in the Great Plains and northward field infestation is almost negligible. Corn grown in the Corn Belt is comparatively free from field infestation except in the southern parts of Ohio, Indiana, Illinois, Missouri, and Kansas. Along the eastern seaboard, wheat may be infested to some extent in the field by the Angoumois grain moth, but in the main wheat-growing regions small grains are seldom infested in the field by this moth or by other stored-product pests. Leguminous seed—beans, peas, cowpeas, chickpeas, and others—are invariably infested with weevils in the field, so that the seed grower always must be prepared to prevent further damage in storage.

Besides field infestation, infestation in stored grain and seed originates in storage facilities or from nearby stores or accumulations of feed, grain, or other infested dry food products.

In the South, to minimize field infestation, early harvest is imperative. In the Gulf States, when harvest is delayed until October or November, 60 to 90 percent of the ears of corn in the field may be infested by the rice weevil and many ears almost completely destroyed. We know of no practical method of destroying insect infestation in grains and seeds in the field; hence harvest must be prompt so that control measures can be applied in storage before serious damage occurs. Prompt harvesting of small grains is desirable wherever the Angoumois grain moth occurs. It helps to prevent infestation by the moth in the field and in the bin, because the soft-bodied moths cannot make their way far below the surface of binned grain to lay their eggs. The use of combine harvesters reduces damage to grain from the insect because the unthreshed grain does not stand in shocks or lie in the mow, where the moth can continue to breed in the entire mass.

THE INSECT PESTS of stored grains and seed depend on their food supply for water. Seed or grain that is low in moisture is unfavorable for their development. The true grain weevils cannot breed in grain that has a moisture content below 9 percent, and their breeding is greatly restricted in grain unless the moisture content is above 11 percent. The bran beetles, of which the red flour beetle and the saw-toothed grain beetle are examples, do not breed in clean seed unless the moisture content is 11 percent or above or the temperature is above 80° F. If the seed contains floury dust or broken kernels, however, the beetles can breed in it regardless of the moisture in it. Moisture and temperature requirements of stored-grain insects are closely related. Up to certain levels their rate of development rises with the increase in temperature and the moisture content of the food.

Molding in bins causes considerable loss because the grain was not properly dry when stored or because water or snow leaked into the bin during the storage period. The percentage of loss is heaviest when temperatures are high.

Under storage conditions similar to those in Nebraska, wheat, oats, shelled corn, and like grains not intended for planting can be stored for a year with very little loss if the grain moisture content does not exceed 13 percent. Soybeans, which contain a high percentage of oil, are more difficult to store, and their moisture content should not exceed 11 percent for long-time storage. If the grain or seed is to be planted, the moisture content should be 1 or 2 percent less than we have indicated. The warmer the climate, the lower the moisture content at which it is safe to store grain or seeds.

Ear corn, since it is harvested in cool weather, can be stored safely in well-ventilated cribs in the Northern States with as much as 20 percent moisture and usually will dry to safe moisture levels by late spring.

The moisture-content requirements for long-time farm storage of grains and seeds are lower than those set by the United States official grain standards. The official standards are used primarily in marketing grain after it leaves the farm and enters commercial channels, where much of it is processed in a few weeks. Also, commercial handlers have better facilities than farmers for caring for grain. The bins in most large elevators have electric thermometers that enable the operator to read on a central instrument board the temperature of the grain at several places in each bin. The elevators have driers, conveyors, and elevator legs that make it easy to move the grain from one bin to another to break up hot spots or to mix damp grain from one bin with dry grain from another and thus reduce the average moisture content to a safe level for short-time storage.

Farmers hesitate to dry grain to safe moisture contents because in many markets they lose money if they have fewer pounds to sell even if part of that weight is water. Removing moisture from grain does not result in any loss of the dry matter, which is the valuable part. In fact, after a few months of storage, dry grain retains more of its original dry matter than moist, since the moister the grain the more dry matter is burned up by respiration of the kernel and by mold activity.

In Iowa 29 cribs were filled in November with corn having kernel moisture contents ranging from 15 to 26 percent. After 8 months of storage in ventilated cribs, the average loss of dry matter from the kernels was almost 5 percent, the loss being greatest in the moistest corn. One crib was filled with ear corn having 24.5 percent kernel moisture. When emptied in June, the corn had dried to 13.1 percent moisture—but besides the loss of water the kernels had lost 13 percent of the original dry matter.

Some elevator operators recognize the greater value of dry grain and pay a higher price for grain that is drier than the official grain standards require. More grain dealers might well follow that practice.

SAFE STORAGE is aided by freedom from cracked kernels and foreign material, which provide food for insects and fill up the spaces between kernels and interfere with the natural movement of air through the grain. In one test with shelled corn, in which air under pressure was used, 5 percent by weight of cracked corn, chaff, and other foreign material reduced air movement by 19 percent. Because the kernels continually give off heat and moisture by respiration, slowing down of air movement through the bulk of grain tends to develop hot spots and caked grain. Even the slow air movement in clean grain due to convection currents helps keep it in good condition.

Cleaning is best done when small grain, soybeans, or other seeds are combined or corn is shelled by properly adjusting the sieves and air blast of the machine. It can be done later with a fanning mill or by gravity flow over screens. A rod-bottomed section for an elevator spout to remove shelled corn and similar material when cribbing ear corn is illustrated in Farmers' Bulletin 1976, *Handling and Storing Soft Corn on the Farm.*

TO BE SATISFACTORY, a bin must hold the grain without loss of quantity; exclude rain, snow, and ground moisture; afford reasonable protection against thieves, rodents, birds, poultry, insects, and objectionable odors, such as might be caused by fertilizers, chemicals, dusts, gasoline, or kerosene; permit effective fumigation to control insects; and provide reasonable safety from fire and wind damage.

Many farm storages do not meet those requirements. A survey of 7,000 farms in Georgia, for example, disclosed that 74 percent of the storages visited could not be fumigated effectively, 96 percent were not rodentproof, and fewer than half gave good protection from the weather.

An examination by agricultural engineers of buildings used to store wheat and shelled-corn storages in six Midwestern States showed the importance of good foundations, floors, walls, roofs, well-constructed doors, and ventilator and roof-hatch openings in protecting grain. Even small leaks around a bolt without a lead washer in a metal roof may cause spoilage of 2 or 3 bushels of grain. Loose knots, split boards, or open joints in single-walled wood bins may allow leakage enough to spoil several bushels. Improperly flashed doors are other spots where leakage may occur. Floors that are too close to the ground may be flooded during heavy rains or by water backed up by snow and ice. Sometimes the top of the foundation is higher than the bin floor and catches water that finds its way into the grain. Concrete floors in damp locations should be raised well above the ground and protected by a vapor barrier (such as a layer of composition roofing under or on top of the concrete) to prevent rise of water vapor, which condenses in the grain and may cause serious spoilage.

SMALL GRAIN or shelled corn may be dried in batch or continuous driers before it is placed in the storage bin. Such driers consist of a ventilated container for the grain, a power-driven fan, a source of heat (usually an oil burner or a gas burner), and necessary handling devices and controls. Batch or continuous driers of a size to keep up with a small-grain combine or a corn picker-sheller combination may cost $1,500 or more, depending on capacity, percentage of moisture to be removed, and the amount of construction done at home. They are rather expensive for the average farm, but they are good investments for farms that have large acreages of grains or seeds in areas where the grain cannot safely be left on the stalk until it is thoroughly dry. They could be used to advantage by groups of farmers.

The development of artificial drying methods and equipment suitable for farm use makes it possible to shell ear corn immediately after it is picked or to use the picker-sheller, a machine that leaves the cobs in the field. Corn can be shelled when the moisture content of the kernels is 25 percent or slightly more, although it must be dried immediately before placing in storage. Since shelled corn occupies only half as much space as ear corn, the cost of drying equipment may be offset by the saving in building cost. The method of field shelling, drying, and storage in bins instead of cribs may have special value in the South, where it is difficult to build cribs that can be ventilated well enough to dry the corn and then closed tightly enough for effective fumigation.

Drying grain in the bin is less efficient than drying with special driers, but the cost of equipment is usually lower. The ordinary method with small grains is to place a perforated or screened floor about a foot above the regular floor of the bin. Parallel rows of 8- by 8- by 16-inch concrete blocks may be laid on the floor, spaced 12 to 16 inches apart in each direction, and a 2- by 6-inch plank laid on top of each row of blocks. Special perforated and corrugated or ridged metal sheets are then laid over the 2 by 6's, thus making a continuous perforated floor. Air forced under the floor of the bin passes up through the grain. Hardware cloth supported on 2 by 4's, and covered with fly screen may be used instead of the perforated sheet metal.

The drying air may be heated or unheated. Drying with unheated air is slow, except when the atmospheric humidity is low and the temperature is above 60° F. For reasonably rapid drying, the air temperature should be above 80° and the relative humidity below 60 percent. In climates where atmospheric conditions at harvesttime are favorable, a heavy-duty electric fan or blower may give sufficient drying capacity, but under unfavorable conditions a unit that provides heated air is needed.

The best results are had when the thickness of grain on the perforated floor is not more than 2 or 3 feet. If air under sufficient pressure is available, drying can be done at depths of 6 or even 10 feet, depending on the moisture content of the grain and the resistance it offers to passage of air. For example, air passes through shelled corn and oats much more easily than through wheat. The wetter the grain the thinner the layers should be. From 5 to 10 cubic feet of air per minute per bushel of grain are needed when drying at temperatures between 60° and 130° F., which are about the limits for farm drying. Detailed information about equipment and methods for drying shelled corn and small grain in bins are described in Farmers' Bulletin 2009, *Storage of Small Grains and Shelled Corn on the Farm.*

Ear corn may be dried in almost any type of crib. One way to distribute the drying air is by using a large canvas on the side of the crib to form an air duct. Methods of drying corn are described in Farmers' Bulletin 2010, *Storage of Ear Corn on the Farm,* and Circular 839, *Mechanical Drying of Corn on the Farm.*

Ventilation is desirable to cool grain in large bins or flat storages in autumn and thus prevent "migration of moisture" from the warm interior to the cool top layers of grain. If the grain in large bins is not cooled rapidly, convection currents are set up by the temperature difference between the warm grain in the central part of the bin and the cool grain around the edges. The upward air currents at the center of the grain mass carry moisture to the cool top layers of the grain, where it condenses and may cause molding. The condition is particularly bad when insect infestation is present on account of the warmth and vapor given off by their respiration. Winter cooling of the grain helps to destroy insects in it. The amount of air needed to cool grain is much less than to dry it, and comparatively small fans and air ducts are adequate.

To preserve grain from insect damage, one must think first of prevention of destructive outbreaks.

Most of the insect pests of stored grain and seed have short generations, a high rate of reproduction, and long-lived individuals—characteristics that cause great fluctuations in numbers. Under favorable conditions, outbreaks are apt to occur suddenly.

The immediate causes of such outbreaks are the factors that affect the rate of egg laying, the rate of development, the death rate, or the longevity of the insects. The more important factors are moisture, temperature, food supply, and human activities. We cannot do much to alter the weather or change the existence of large supplies of food, but we can make grains less susceptible to insect attack by the use of efficient cleaning and drying equipment and by the application of fumigants and good storage management practices.

After prompt harvest, followed by drying when necessary, grain and seed should be stored in clean, insect-free, weather-proof storage on premises from which nearby sources of insect infestation have been eliminated. Steel bins that are easy to clean and can be made tight by calking are best for storage of small grains, shelled corn, or other seed.

Wooden bins should be thoroughly cleaned and the walls and floors treated with a residual spray before they are refilled. This will kill most of the insects that emerge from burrows and cracks in the woodwork. Steel bins should be thoroughly cleaned. It is not necessary to spray the entire bin, but it is advisable to spray around the door frame where insects may be concealed. Wooden-crib elevator bins should also be sprayed.

For spraying bins use 2.5 percent of DDT, TDE, or methoxychlor by weight as emulsions or water suspensions, or 5 percent of piperonyl butoxide and 0.5 percent of pyrethrins by weight as an emulsion. The sprays should be applied at the rate of 2 gallons per 1,000 square feet of surface area. They may be applied safely and easily with an ordinary garden sprayer or a power sprayer.

Farm-stored small grains should be fumigated within 2 weeks after placing in the bin in the South and within 6 weeks in the central part of the United States. In the North, fumigation after storage may not be necessary but is good insurance against infestation. Fumigants and dosages recommended for small grains in farm storage are given in the chapter, "Fumigating Stored Foodstuffs," page 345.

In the Northern and Central States, one fumigation will probably be enough. Properly applied, the fumigant will destroy insect infestations present and will protect the grain from serious insect invasion until fall. Winter weather will then cool the grain to levels where insects are inactive.

Farm-stored grain should be inspected periodically to detect dangerous insect infestation. In Northern and Central States during the warmer months and in the South throughout the year, grain that has been in storage a month or more should be inspected every 2 to 4 weeks and refumigated if serious infestations are found.

The need for refumigation will depend on circumstances and the insect involved. In general, if living specimens of the rice weevil, granary weevil, or lesser grain borer are present, or if enough bran beetles are present to cause the grain to be graded weevily (five beetles per quart), the situation calls for immediate application of remedial measures. Similarly, a surface infestation of moths, as indicated by the presence of webbing, is dangerous.

Rice is commonly infested in the field by the rice weevil and other insects. Hence it must be fumigated soon after it is put in storage. The fumigants and dosages recommended for small grains can be used. Rice is high in moisture content at harvest. It must therefore be dried after it is threshed if it is to be stored in bins on the farm.

Rice that is harvested with a binder is shocked and allowed to dry in the field until the grain moisture is approximately 14.5 percent. Then it is threshed from the shock and put in burlap bags for storage in warehouses. Rough rice in warehouse storage can be fumigated efficiently with hydrocyanic acid or methyl bromide at a dosage of 1.5 pounds per 1,000 cubic feet of space, provided the warehouses are made tight enough to hold the fumigant for 24 hours.

Soybeans stored in farm-type bins rarely become seriously infested with insects. Occasionally small infestations of bran beetles occur in high-moisture soybeans. If serious infestation should develop, the beans can be fumigated in the same way and with the same dosages recommended for small grains.

Field corn is usually stored on the ear for the first season because of its high moisture at harvest. With the exception of corn grown in the South and in the extreme southern part of the Corn Belt, field infestation is inconsequential and is killed out by winter temperatures that readily penetrate corn stored in slat cribs. During mild winters the Angoumois grain moth may survive in cribbed corn as far north as southern Indiana, Ohio, Illinois, Missouri, and Kansas, but in severe winters the moth will die.

Slatted crib bins afford no protection to corn from insects. In summer, therefore, a certain amount of infestation of ear corn is likely to develop. For corn that is fed or disposed of during the summer no treatment is required.

Corn that is to be stored for an additional year or longer should be shelled and put in bins as soon as the moisture in the kernels is down to a point as low as it is likely to go. In most seasons that is about the middle of May. Ear corn that is infested by the Angoumois grain moth will be seriously damaged unless it is shelled before the moths begin to emerge in the spring. As soon as the corn is shelled and binned it should be fumigated if infested. It should also be inspected every 2 to 4 weeks during warm weather, as recommended for small grains, and fumigated or refumigated if necessary.

In the area south of the Corn Belt, corn is more likely to become heavily infested in the field by the rice weevil and other insects. Where field infestation is light, ear corn should be fumigated as soon as possible after harvest. The cribs should be lined on the inside with roofing paper, fiber-reinforced paper, or other material to make them tight enough for fumigation, and also be provided with ventilators on the sides and gable ends that can be opened after the fumigation to facilitate drying.

In the South where field infestation is heavy, corn should be harvested as early as possible after maturity and promptly dried, shelled, cleaned, stored in tight bins, and treated with fumigants. Thereafter it can be handled as recommended for shelled corn in other regions.

In the warehouse storage of bagged grain or seed, the warehouse has to be of modern construction, easily cleaned, and tight enough for fumigation. Much can be done to improve the condition of old, poorly constructed warehouses. Every effort should be made to eliminate dead spaces in walls and floors where accumulations of grain and seed offer food and housing for insects.

Double, hollow walls and partitions should be eliminated. If floors are of wood, see that all cracks are filled or kept clean of dust or accumulations of grain. Mop boards should be removed and openings where floor and walls meet should be filled with an elastic cement, such as a good calking material or a good grade of roofing cement. All cracks around posts and in walls should be similarly filled and the walls painted.

Old wooden floors and badly worn concrete floors are difficult to keep clean. They can be renovated by laying quick-setting plastic preparations over the old ones. Light and ventilation should be adequate. Most insect pests of stored grain seek dark corners in which to hide.

Strict sanitation in the warehouse is imperative. Bagged grain and seed should be stacked on racks or lift platforms, if possible in piles at least 12 inches from the walls of the warehouse and far enough apart to allow inspection and cleaning. Floors and walls should be sprayed periodically with a residual spray as a preventive measure—a help in preventing trouble from migrating insects. If the warehouse is filled or partly filled with bagged grain, the stacks of grain must be covered during spraying operations to prevent contamination.

FUMIGATION OF GRAINS and seed on the farm where infestations often originate is important, but it is no less important to fumigate them in the elevator or warehouse. Much of the grain and seed produced goes directly to such storage without temporary storage on the farm. In the rush of the harvest season it is difficult to be sure that some old stocks of infested grain are not mixed in with uninfested grain as it is put into elevator storage. Furthermore, many country elevators that handle grain between the farm and the terminal elevators have wooden crib bins that are a continuous source of infestation. It is just as important to clean up the premises of country elevators and spray empty wooden bins with residual sprays as it is on the farm. The same sprays and dosages recommended for farm bins should be used. At times when most bins are empty the entire elevator can be fumigated. A close and continuous check should be kept on all grain stored in elevators, and it should be fumigated at the first sign of trouble. As a precautionary measure it is desirable to fumigate all new stocks of grain received from farm storage.

Many fumigants and fumigant mixtures that are difficult and dangerous to use in farm storage are suitable for elevators, and different methods are available for applying them. Automatic applicators controlled by the flow of the grain now eliminate the possibility of inaccurate dosages and relieve the operator of the discomfort and danger of applying liquid fumigants by hand. Mixtures of carbon tetrachloride with carbon disulfide, ethylene dichloride, propylene dichloride, trichloroethylene, chloropicrin, ethylene dibromide, various combinations of those chemicals, and calcium cyanide are being used successfully.

The ease with which grains are handled in elevators makes it simple to use cleaning or drying machinery to turn it during periods of cold weather, and thereby improve its condition or cool it to temperatures where it will be safe from insect attack.

Fumigation of seed may be done in bins, vaults, and warehouses, or under tarpaulins. Hydrocyanic acid can be used at the rate of 1 pound to 1,000 cubic feet of space. No damage to germination need be feared under normal conditions. For treating binned seed a 3 to 1 mixture of ethylene dichloride and carbon tetrachloride is recommended at a dosage of 5 gallons per 1,000 bushels of seed. The mixture does not appear to injure germination of bulk seed regardless of the seed moisture, the dosage, or the exposure period.

The vapor from naphthalene and paradichlorobenzene crystals is toxic to insects, and they have been used extensively for the protection of seed. The recommended dosages vary greatly. A popular dosage is about 1 ounce of the crystals per bushel, although much heavier dosages are sometimes recommended. The maximum weights of naphthalene and of paradichlorobenzene needed to saturate the atmosphere at 77° F. are 0.04 and 0.5 pound respectively for 1,000 cubic feet of space. Thus the small dosage recommended is more than sufficient to provide a saturated atmosphere.

Little injury to germination of seed corn need be feared from naphthalene vapors if the moisture content of the corn is below 12 percent. Paradichlorobenzene vapors cause serious injury to germination even in very dry seed, however. Seed treated with either chemical is rendered unfit for animal feeds, since an obnoxious odor and taste are imparted to the flesh of animals and poultry fed treated grain and to the eggs laid by poultry so fed.

Hybrid seed corn or other seeds must be fumigated carefully in order not to injure the viability. If seed moisture is more than 12 percent, or if the dosage or the exposure period is excessive, many fumigants will cause such injury. Exposure periods should not exceed 24 hours. If bulk seed is treated, provision must be made to aerate it after 24 hours unless the fumigant is known to be harmless under all conditions. Most bulk seed absorbs and retains fumigants for long periods; therefore, unless it is aerated, the exposure period is automatically extended and serious germ damage will result.

The entire warehouse can be fumigated satisfactorily if it can be made gas-tight. If it is not full enough to make it worth while, individual stacks can be fumigated under gas-tight tarpaulins. For grains other than seed, methyl bromide is the best fumigant to use; if the temperature is 70° F. or above, a good kill can be obtained with a dosage of 1 to 1.5 pounds per 1,000 cubic feet of space. At temperatures below 70° the dosage can be increased at the rate of one-half pound per 1,000 cubic feet of space for every 5° drop.

970134°—52——42

To fumigate corn or milled rice in warehouses, hydrocyanic acid can also be used at a dosage of 1.5 pounds of liquid hydrocyanic acid per 1,000 cubic feet. That dosage is also safe to use for the fumigation of seed of all kinds.

Mixing seed with dust is simple and economical. It gives long-time protection against insects and does not affect the viability of the seed.

Many dusts have been used. Some are active insect poisons. Others apparently affect the insects physically rather than chemically. In the following discussion, we designate the poisonous dusts as chemically active; those that appear to have only a physical effect on the insects we refer to as chemically inert.

Chemically inert dusts are thought to be effective by causing breaks in the waterproof fatty covering of insects so that the dusted insect dies as a result of the evaporation of excessive amounts of body moisture. Because of their mode of action, the effectiveness of inert dusts declines as the moisture content of the seed increases over 12 percent.

Inert dusts that have been used successfully for treating seed include finely divided silica gel, rock phosphates, precipitated chalk, magnesium oxide, and aluminum oxide. Dusts with a particle size of 1 micron or less can be used at the rate of 1 part per 1,000 parts by weight or approximately 1 ounce per bushel.

Pyrethrin powder has often been recommended for mixing with seed. Finely ground dusts impregnated with pyrethrins and piperonyl butoxide also have been advocated for this purpose; they show promise as preventives of insect infestation.

Poisonous dusts are effective regardless of the moisture content of the seed. Because surplus seed stocks often are fed to animals, however, the dusts have not been popular. Outstanding among them are lindane and DDT. Lindane is effective at a dosage of 1 part per million and DDT at the rate of 15 parts per million. Both are best used in combination with a carrier such as pyrophyllite or similar chemically inert dust. The carrier increases the volume and therefore insures thorough distribution over the seed. A dust containing 3 percent of DDT is effective when mixed with seed at the rate of one-half ounce per bushel. No damage to seed viability has been observed as a result of treatment with either compound at recommended dosages.

The practice of treating many types of seed with disinfectant dusts to protect it from fungus diseases is being amplified by the incorporation of small percentages of DDT to insure protection from insects.

Dusts may be applied by any method that will insure a uniform coverage. To treat bulk seed, a seed-treating machine is satisfactory. Operators applying the dusts should be equipped with adequate respirators. Because of the poison hazard involved, seed that has been treated with DDT, lindane, or a fungicide should not be used as food for man or livestock.

Grain is transported to mills and terminal elevators chiefly by railways. Boxcars used for the purpose are so constructed that grain and grain dust invariably accumulate in cracks in the floor, at the junction of the walls with the floor, between the ends and the wooden-end linings, and sometimes between the side walls and the inner grain linings of the cars. Such accumulations of grain and dust become infested, and the infestations are difficult to remove or destroy by ordinary methods. Consequently they are dangerous sources of infestation to other, later shipments of grain or milled cereal products. Obviously it would be desirable to prevent the contamination of the cars by shipping only insect-free grain or other products. While much is being done to reduce infestation in grains and grain products, it is doubtful whether we shall ever reach the stage where total elimination of insect infestation in these products will be possible.

Changes in the construction of boxcars would help reduce the opportunities for insect colonies to become established in them. The removal of the bottom board on the inner grain linings on the sides of the cars facilitates cleaning and prevents the accumulation of grain and waste material between the linings and the side walls. The placing of layers of resilient insulating material between the end linings and the corrugated ends of the cars would help eliminate space in which grain and dust could accumulate. Fibrous glass shows promise of being useful for this purpose. The impregnation of such insulating materials with DDT would probably add to their efficiency in preventing the establishment of insect infestations.

As remedial measures where infestations do occur, cars should be thoroughly cleaned out with compressed air after each use. The application of a residual spray (with a knapsack sprayer, a power sprayer, or an aerosol-type generator) also is helpful. Residues from it do not appear to be a hazard to shipments of grain or milled cereals. In most cases, cars are lined with paper before loading with milled cereals.

Grain and grain products are so attractive to insects that they have to be packaged in containers that afford them the greatest protection from infestation during later storage.

Most insects that infest cereal products have comparatively weak mouth parts and cannot cut through substantial wrappers. Many can thrust their ovipositors through the meshes of fabric bags and lay their eggs directly in the cereal products within the bags. The immature stages of many insects also can crawl through the meshes and through needle holes along the seams and at the top or bottom where the bags are sewn. The more closely woven fabrics offer the greatest resistance to penetration. Bags made of paper, paper laminated to cloth or back-filled fabrics, and cartons of fiberboard offer more resistance to insect penetration than ordinary cotton or jute bags. Unless such containers are adequately sealed, however, small flat beetles, such as the saw-toothed grain beetle and the larvae of other beetles and moths, may easily penetrate through minute openings where the seals are imperfect. Most commercial methods of sealing bags and cartons are inadequate. If bags are closed by sewing, the sewed ends must be protected by the use of a gummed strip that will cover all needle holes. For fiberboard cartons the application of a wet-wrap cover offers the best protection. Experimental work with insect repellents for incorporation in the adhesives used to seal fiberboard cartons and paper bags may help solve the problem.

Impregnation of fabric and paper bags with pyrethrins or pyrethrins and synergists has been found to afford considerable protection against penetration by insects. In fabric bags this protection is more efficient when the weave is close enough to offer some mechanical resistance against penetration. More powerful insecticides such as DDT, benzene hexachloride, and chlordane also are effective in resisting penetration when used to impregnate bags, but (because of the danger of contaminating the food) are not practical for use in insect-proofing bags intended for packaging food. Insect-repellent chemicals may offer the best means of providing an insect-proof container. Packages impregnated with them are particularly useful in resisting the invasion of certain insects that have wood-boring habits.

The cadelle, probably the most troublesome of the boring insects, feeds on a wide variety of stored commodities and is widely distributed. It is primarily a pest of grain and flour and is commonly found in railway boxcars, ships, warehouses, farm granaries, and other places in which foodstuffs are stored or transported. The larva bores into woodwork to form a sheltered place in which to hibernate or to transform to the pupal or adult form. It has jaws powerful enough to cut through many types of packages. It will cut through a multiwall paper bag or metal-foil-wrapped carton overnight.

Termites also burrow through cartons and other packages that are stored in warm, damp locations, or in warehouses with wooden floors that are infested. The larvae of many insects, when fully grown, have the urge to migrate in search of pupation quarters.

THE STEADY RISE of population in this country and the increasing demand placed on us to share our food supply with people of other nations makes it imperative that we conserve as much as possible of our harvested crops.

More pest-free storage, on and off the farm, is needed for handling crops at harvesttime and to carry over reserves from year to year.

We cannot in the foreseeable future expect research concerned with the control of insects in stored grain to be completed, but on the other hand, we are more than holding our own against these pests. As we learn more and more about sprays, fumigants, control of grain moisture, and the habits and weaknesses of the insects themselves we are better able to meet their threats.

R. T. COTTON *has been an entomologist in the Bureau of Entomology and Plant Quarantine since 1919 and has been in charge of field research on the control of the insect pests of stored grain and milled cereal products since 1934. He has specialized on fumigation and other methods of controlling the insect pests of stored foodstuffs. Dr. Cotton holds degrees from Cornell University and George Washington University. In 1940 he was given a Modern Pioneer award in recognition of achievement in science.*

WALLACE ASHBY, *a native of Iowa and graduate of Iowa State College, is an agricultural engineer in charge of research on farm buildings and rural housing in the Bureau of Plant Industry, Soils, and Agricultural Engineering.*

Pests on Ornamentals

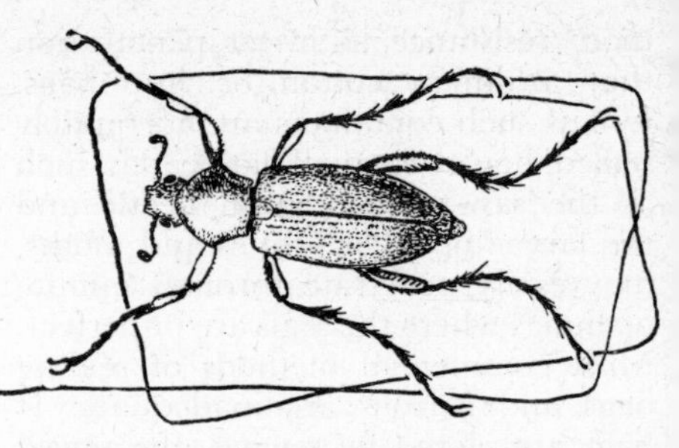

Insect Pests of Flowers and Shrubs

C. A. Weigel, R. A. St. George

Many kinds of insects beset flowers and shrubs about the home and in greenhouses. The injury they do depends on their feeding and egg-laying habits. Some insects feed on the seed as soon as it is planted. Others attack the young seedling as it breaks through the ground. Still others infest the flowers, leaves, stems, or roots.

Injury to the leaves may consist of mining the interior, skeletonizing the surface, and eating part or all of the foliage. Injury to the terminal shoot may be caused by external feeding, by the chewing of holes through the surface, and by tunneling extensive mines in shrubs between the bark and wood or even in the wood itself. Such injury may cause the stunting or death of the terminal growth beyond the point of attack. Certain insects also hollow out the interior of terminal buds and shoots of hardy shrubs. A few make pits in the surface of the bark of the main stem after settling there and feeding for a while. One other type of injury consists of the removal of the cell sap by the feeding of certain insects or mites on the stem, foliage, or other parts of the plant; the part attacked may have a stippled appearance. Injury to the roots may consist of feeding on the young rootlets and—on shrubs--of chewing through the bark surface or boring direct into the wood. Further injury consists of the formation of galls, which may occur on any part of the plant.

The effect of the various kinds of injury depends largely upon the intensity of insect infestation and the vigor of the plants. It may range all the way from making the plants only slightly less attractive in appearance to seriously weakening, stunting, or killing them. The maximum effect of such injury is apt to be most marked during or immediately following periods of drought or transplanting operations, when it is difficult for the plants to get adequate moisture and food.

Because insect enemies of flowers and shrubs are of many kinds, it would be difficult for the average person to identify them without first knowing the different groups involved. We therefore group them as leaf-chewing insects, sucking insects, leaf-mining insects, gall-forming insects, tip- and stem-infesting insects, and soil- and root-infesting insects. We give a few examples of each group and an account of the injury they cause, their habits, and control.

To control insects outdoors, insecticides are usually applied as sprays, dusts, or baits. In the greenhouse they may be sprays, dusts, baits, fumigants, and aerosols, although aerosols have been made so effective that they have nearly replaced other methods in greenhouses.

Leaf-chewing insects bite off the foliage and chew and swallow the plant tissue. Therefore they generally are controlled by a stomach poison. Chief among them are caterpillars, sawflies, and beetles: The bagworm, cutworms, the fall webworm, the juniper webworm, the eastern tent caterpillar, sawflies, the catalpa sphinx, the rose chafer, the rose curculio, cucumber beetles, the Japanese beetle, blister beetles, flea beetles, and the imported willow leaf beetle.

The bagworm is a caterpillar that lives in a silken, cocoonlike bag, to which are attached bits of leaves from the host plant. It gradually increases the size of the bag as it grows. By late summer it is about 2 inches long. At that time it attaches itself to a twig. The female is wingless and remains in the bag, where she lays a mass of eggs. The winter is passed in the egg stage. The eggs hatch in May in the South and late May or early June in the North. Bagworms prefer to feed on arborvitae and juniper but also infest many other evergreen and deciduous trees and shrubs.

Treatment: Destroy all mature bags in the spring before growth starts in order to kill the overwintering eggs. If that is not done, spray with lead arsenate soon after the caterpillars hatch (about June 1 in Washington, D. C.), using stronger dosages for the larger caterpillars. A 2-percent emulsion of chlordane or parathion as a wettable powder is also effective. DDT is inferior to arsenate of lead against bagworms, particularly the more mature larvae.

Cutworms are seldom seen. They usually remain hidden under clods of earth or in the topsoil by day. Evenings they emerge to feed. They cut off small plants at or near the ground line, climb the plants, and feed on the foliage or bore into the developing flower buds. Plants are usually ruined overnight. One cutworm can kill several plants.

Cutworms are smooth, plump caterpillars, gray or brownish, and 1 to 2 inches long when full-grown. They hatch from eggs laid by brownish moths late in the summer. By late fall they are nearly full-grown and bury themselves in the ground for protection during the winter. Among the several species, the variegated cutworm probably is the most serious, both under glass and outdoors.

Treatment: Poison bait consisting of a mixture of sodium fluosilicate or paris green mixed with wheat bran is a standard remedy. The moist bait is scattered thinly over the infested area late in the evening when the caterpillars are active. DDT in dust or spray mixtures is said to be superior to baits in greenhouses.

Poisonous caterpillars occasionally eat and injure garden plants, shrubs, and trees. Most caterpillars are not poisonous, although several species have stiff, poisonous hairs or spines that may cause a painful, burning sensation when they come in contact with tender skin.

The saddleback caterpillar, the best known, attacks several kinds of flowers and shrubs. It is brown at each end; the middle is green with a purple center that resembles a small saddle. Poisonous caterpillars are seldom found in greenhouses.

Treatment: Spray the leaves with DDT or lead arsenate. If only a few caterpillars are present, they may be picked by a gloved hand.

Sawfly larvae injure roses by skeletonizing the foliage or chewing large, ragged holes in the leaves. Three species are concerned. They are often called false caterpillars or slugs. The adults are small, wasplike insects. The females deposit their eggs in slits "sawed" in the leaves.

A common species is the bristly roseslug. The young larvae skeletonize the leaves on the under side and give a glazed appearance to the foliage. As they increase in size they eat large holes and often leave only the larger veins. Full-grown slugs are about one-half inch long and are dirty, yellowish green with a darker green stripe on the back. The body bears stiff hairs, from which the name is derived.

Treatment: Spray or dust with DDT or lead arsenate. If diseases or mites are present, add sulfur to the mixtures. Nicotine sulfate and derris are effective against the young slugs. Frequent spraying or washing of plants with a stream of water under pressure will keep them free of the slugs.

The spotted cucumber beetle is typical of several species that attack flowering plants. It feeds on the leaves, buds, and flowers. Its chief injury consists in eating holes in the blossom petals. If many beetles are present, their excrement often discolors the blossoms. Injury is likely to be most serious in late summer or early fall. At that time many of the more favored host plants have matured or become unpalatable and the beetles migrate to asters, dahlias, and other late-season flowers. The beetles are about one-fourth inch long and yellowish green, with 12 black spots on the wing covers. They winter in the adult, or beetle, stage. The eggs are laid in the ground in the spring. Newly hatched larvae feed on the roots of various garden plants and weeds for about a month before the adults emerge.

Treatment: Spray or dust the plants with DDT or chlordane every 2 or 3 weeks. Repeated applications are recommended because the beetles are apt to be present in the surrounding area and thus are likely to be a recurrent problem.

The rose chafer is an outstanding pest of the blooms of the rose, iris, and peony. It also attacks the flowers of many other plants. It is a long-legged, yellowish-brown beetle about one-third inch long. It often appears in swarms rather suddenly in June or early July and continues its ravages for a number of weeks.

Treatment: If only a few plants are involved, shake the beetles into a pan of water, covered with a film of kerosene or other oil, early in the morning before they become active. Otherwise, DDT or chlordane as a dust or spray is recommended.

Sucking insects get their food by inserting their mouth parts through the surface of the plant and drawing the sap into their bodies. They are usually controlled by contact poisons, which destroy them by affecting the nervous systems, corroding their bodies,

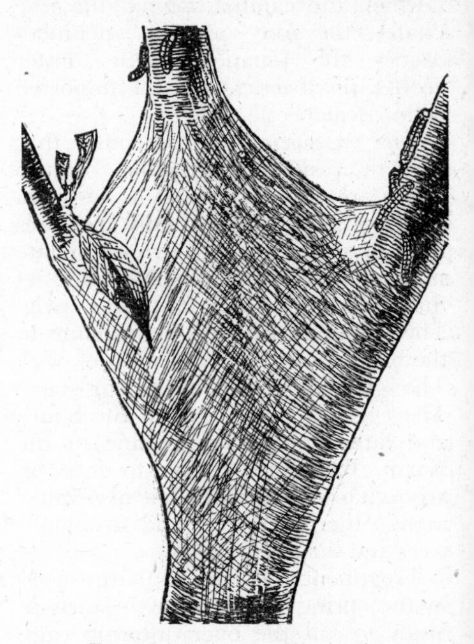

Eastern tent caterpillar nest.

or suffocating them. This group includes aphids, leafhoppers, treehoppers, scale insects, mealybugs, thrips, lace bugs, psyllids, plant bugs, spittlebugs, chermids, and spider mites.

Aphids, or plant-lice, infest all sorts of plants, including annuals, perennials, and shrubs. Usually they do not kill the plants but frequently reduce plant vigor, curl or distort the leaves, harden the buds, or cause malformation of the flowers. They usually occur in colonies or clusters on the new growth, at the base of buds, or on the under sides of the leaves. Infested plants often are visited by large numbers of ants and other insects that feed upon the honeydew excreted by the aphids—a sweet, sticky, liquid excretion that often coats the leaves or objects immediately below the aphids and gives them a varnished or sooty appearance, which results from a sooty mold that develops on the honeydew.

Aphids are soft-bodied insects, whitish, greenish, or blackish. They have pear-shaped or nearly globular bodies and comparatively long legs. They are usually not over one-eighth inch long. Many are smaller. Most are without protective covering, but some of the woolly aphids are covered with white waxy threads.

Some species attack the roots of asters. Others infest flowering bulbs, such as tulip, iris, and crocus. Certain aphids carry plant diseases. The green peach aphid is a vector of carnation mosaic, lily mottle virus, pansy and viola flower breaking, and mosaic diseases of gladiolus and several other plants.

Treatment: Spray or dust infested plants with nicotine sulfate, rotenone, or pyrethrum. Chlordane, in the form of dusts or sprays, is effective; so is spraying with tetraethyl pyrophosphate or lindane.

To control root-infesting aphids this procedure has been reported to be effective: Make a shallow trench around the base of the plants. Into it pour enough chlordane emulsion to soak the ground and reach the infested roots. Then replace the soil in the trench.

To control aphids under glass, use a spray or dust, or fumigating may be done with hydrocyanic acid gas or nicotine smokes. But aerosols containing tetraethyl dithiopyrophosphate, parathion, or DDT are more effective and easier to apply and have largely replaced the older methods.

To control aphids on dormant bulbs, such as tulip, gladiolus, iris, lily, and crocus, immerse the infested material in a hot water bath.

Fumigation with hydrocyanic acid gas or methyl bromide in a special chamber designed for the purpose also is effective but must be done with great caution.

Thrips attack foliage, buds, flowers, and bulbs of ornamental plants outdoors and in greenhouses. Certain species carry virus diseases of flowering plants. Some thrips feed on and destroy other insects and therefore are very beneficial.

The gladiolus thrips is an outstanding pest. It causes the usual type of thrips injury and also feeds on the

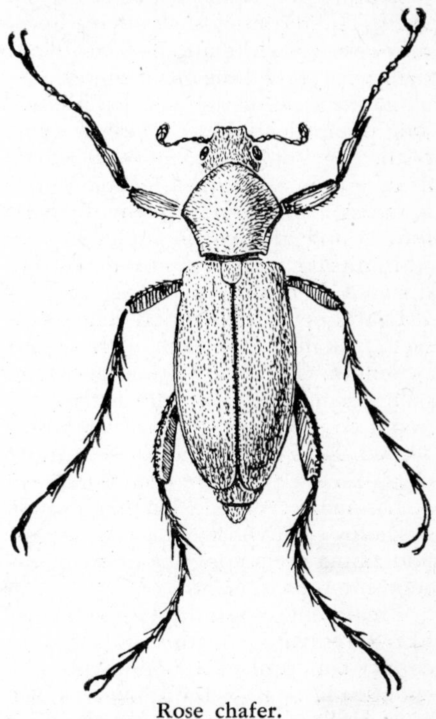

Rose chafer.

gladiolus corms in storage. The fed-over spots become russetted. The infested leaf sheaths become brown and the leaves silvered. The bud sheaths dry out and appear straw-colored. The flowers have whitish streaks. In severe cases the spikes never show color but turn brown and appear blighted. The adult of this thrips is a tiny insect with a brown body and a white band at the base of the featherlike wings.

Treatment: The harvested gladiolus corms should be allowed to dry for about a month and then treated with DDT. Small lots may be treated in tight paper bags and larger quantities in trays. If treatment is delayed until late in the storage period, dipping in a Lysol solution (1 tablespoonful in 1 gallon of water) just before planting is recommended. To control thrips on the growing gladiolus and other plants, spray or dust with DDT on the first sign of injury. Chlordane, parathion, and toxaphene are reported to be quite effective.

Leafhoppers injure plants in various ways. The draining of the plant juices may cause a whitening and curling of the leaves and killing of the tender tips, as in the case of the rose leafhopper. The potato leafhopper causes a dying of the edges of dahlia and other leaves, a condition known as hopperburn. Some species transmit plant diseases; for example, the six-spotted leafhopper transmits the virus of aster yellows from diseased to healthy plants.

Leafhoppers are slender, delicate insects, usually one-eighth inch or less in length. They vary from brown to pale green. They are very active and hop a considerable distance when disturbed. Eggs are laid in the leaf tissue or stalks. Two or more broods may occur annually. Aster, calendula, dahlia, gladiolus, hollyhock, marigold, rose, and zinnia are among the many plants they commonly attack.

Treatment: Standard insecticides like pyrethrum, nicotine sulfate, and copper-containing compounds are used extensively against leafhoppers. DDT and chlordane are more effective, however.

Lace bugs attack such plants as azalea, chrysanthemum, firethorn, and rhododendron. There are several species, but their appearance and the type of injury they cause are similar. The common azalea lace bug is typical. It winters in the egg stage on the leaves. About midspring the eggs begin to hatch. The immature insects, the nymphs, are small and shiny. The adults are about one-eighth inch long. Their thin, lacelike wings lie flat over their oval bodies. In summer both nymphs and adults suck the juices from the under sides of the foliage. That causes the upper surface of azalea leaves to have a spotted or mottled discoloration and an unhealthy look. The lower surface becomes spotted with many flattened specks of blackish, shiny excrement.

Treatment: The usual treatment is to spray the under sides of the leaves with nicotine sulfate or pyrethrum when the nymphs first appear in the spring. A spray made of white-oil emulsion and derris powder or of white-oil emulsion and nicotine sulfate also is effective. DDT used in the form of an emulsion, wettable powder spray or dust, or as an aerosol is good. Parathion or lindane wettable powders also may be used as a spray.

The boxwood psyllid causes a characteristic cupping of the terminal leaves as the result of its feeding. It is a small, grayish-green, sucking insect related to aphids. The nymphs are covered with a whitish waxy material and appear in early spring. Plants are seldom injured seriously, although their appearance may become unattractive. Severe infestations may retard growth.

Treatment: Spray with DDT, parathion, or a nicotine sulfate and soap solution or pyrethrum at the first evidence of leaf cupping or occurrence of the psyllid. A second or third spraying, at intervals of 10 days, may be necessary for a heavy infestation.

Recent research indicates that if control measures are directed toward the adults, rather than the nymphs, the plants will be free of insects the following spring and the cupping injury will be avoided. Such application kills the adults before they can lay eggs and thus eliminates the nymphs, which otherwise would be present to cause injury. The same insecticide as used for the nymphs should be applied about the middle of June in places that have a climate like that of Washington.

Plant bugs are sucking insects that injure many plants. The principal species are the phlox plant bug, tarnished plant bug, four-lined plant bug, and yucca plant bug.

The phlox plant bug feeds in all stages on the upper surfaces of the more tender leaves and buds of perennial phlox. Injured leaves show white or pale-green spots on the upper surfaces. Often the plant becomes stunted, and the blossom head loses its symmetry. Sometimes the entire plant is killed. The adult bug, not over one-fourth inch long, is very active and may be recognized by its dull orange or reddish wing covers and a black stripe on the back. The adults from the summer brood lay their eggs in the fall in the phlox stems behind the leaf petioles, and the winter is passed in the egg stage. Near Washington, D. C., overwintering eggs begin to hatch early in May, and the nymphs develop to adults in a few weeks. Two or more generations develop. By midsummer all stages of the insect are present.

Treatment: The standard treatment in the past was to dust the plants with sulfur alone or mixed with pyrethrum every 10 days. Dusting or spraying with DDT is much more effective. In the fall the old stems, which contain the overwintering eggs, should be cut off and burned to prevent reinfestation the next spring.

Scale insects are of two general groups, the soft scales and hard scales. The soft scales are usually half-round and rubbery. The hard scales vary in shape and have a shieldlike covering. Scale insects usually are less than one-fourth inch long and of different colors. They may be found on any part of the plant. The young are referred to as crawlers and are active for only a short time after birth, when they infest the new growth and settle down for the rest of their lives. As a result of their feeding, copious amounts of honeydew are excreted by the soft scales. On this sticky exudation a sooty mold develops, giving the foliage, grass, and the other materials it covers a blackened appearance. The honeydew attracts ants, wasps, flies, and other insects. Many species of scales attack plants grown under glass and out of doors.

Among the soft scales of economic importance, especially in greenhouses, are the soft scale, hemispherical scale, and tessellated scale. Some of the important hard scales attacking outdoor plants are the San Jose, oystershell, euonymus, and rose scales.

Treatment: Apply miscible oil or oil-emulsion sprays in the early spring to outdoor plants while they are dormant. Two applications of a summer oil, one just at the time the young are hatching and another 10 days later, are effective. DDT and parathion also can be used. In greenhouses, spray with a light oil emulsion, DDT, or parathion, when the crawlers are active. Fumigation with calcium cyanide or application of DDT, TEPP, and parathion aerosols are also widely practiced.

Spider mites, not really insects but relatives of the true spiders, feed by sucking juices from the leaves and other tender parts. The result is a stippled appearance of the foliage, which later turns pale and brown. Some species spin a fine web. Under a lens they seem to be minute, reddish, greenish, or yellowish spiderlike animals. Sometimes only the shed skins or the globular eggs or eggshells are present.

Some species winter in protected places, as among the buds or crowns of perennials and weeds, and attack the new growth as soon as it starts in the spring. Others hibernate in the egg stage on the bark and under the bud scales of trees and shrubs. In greenhouses the mites may develop rapidly.

The two-spotted spider mite is the species most frequently encountered on plants under glass and in the open. The cyclamen mite, broad mite, bulb scale mite, bulb mite, and spruce spider mite also are serious pests.

Treatment: For light infestations, frequent washing of the plants with a forceful stream of water has value but does not give complete control. Spraying with white-oil emulsions, alone or combined with rotenone or thiocyanate, is effective on outdoor and greenhouse-grown plants. Only one application every week or 10 days is usually needed. Spraying with tetraethyl pyrophosphate gives good results. Dusting with sulfur is effective in summer but in extremely hot weather it may burn the leaves of tender plants. Several commercial preparations that also are effective are mentioned in the chapter on spider mites, page 652. Aerosols containing tetraethyl pyrophosphate, tetraethyl dithiopyrophosphate, or parathion are practical and effective against red spiders in greenhouses.

Leaf-mining insects feed on the plant tissue between the upper and lower leaf surfaces and cause the formation of blotchlike or irregular serpentine mines. Typical of the insects that produce the blotchlike mines are the boxwood, burdock, and arborvitae leaf miners. The columbine and holly leaf miners make serpentine mines.

Some forms, like the azalea and lilac leaf miners, after mining the inner tissue of the leaves for a short period, abandon the mine, roll or tie the leaves together, and feed on, or mine, the opposing leaf surfaces. Others, like the greenhouse leaf tier (also called the celery leaf tier), have the latter habit, but do not mine the interior of the leaves.

The boxwood leaf miner is a very small fly whose larvae, or maggots, feed inside the leaves. Their mines appear as blotches or blisters on the lower leaf surface. When they are numerous enough, they kill the leaves and thus disfigure the plant. The tiny yellowish-orange maggots require a year for development, from the time of hatching in late spring until the following spring, when they transform to pupae within the mines. The orange-colored, gnatlike flies emerge from the leaves over a period of about 2 weeks, usually starting during the first or second week in May around Washington, D. C., and deposit their eggs in the under side of the new leaf tissue. Emergence starts earlier farther south and later in States to the north.

Treatment: Just before the adults appear in spring, spray the under side of the leaves with parathion wettable powder or with DDT or chlordane in the form of an emulsion or a wettable powder. It is advisable to add a spreader-sticker to the DDT or chlordane spray to cover the shiny or waxy surface. One thorough treatment should suffice for the season.

The greenhouse leaf tier typifies the caterpillars that roll, fold, and tie together the leaves and terminal growths. It feeds on the inner surface of the folded leaves. Sometimes it eats into the bud and flowers. It is chiefly a greenhouse pest. It also attacks many

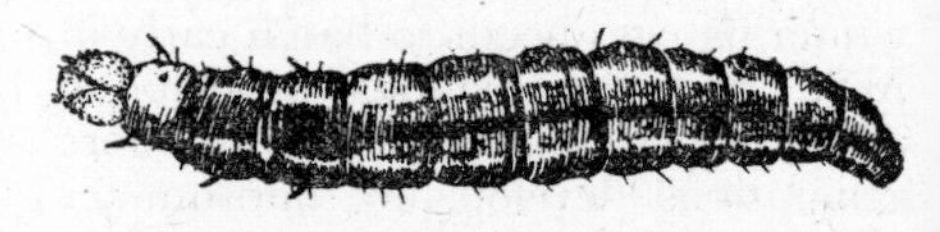

Greenhouse leaf tier.

flower-garden plants. The full-grown caterpillars are yellowish-green and about three-fourths inch long. The adult is a small, tan-colored moth.

Treatment: Dust heavy infestations with pyrethrum, making two applications at 30-minute intervals. Spraying with lead arsenate, pyrethrum, or DDT is also effective.

Gall-forming insects sting the plant cells. Thereby they stimulate growth and cause the formation of gall-like structures of various sizes and shapes near the point of attack. Among them are the spruce gall aphids, the chrysanthemum gall midge, the beaked willow gall midge, and the dogwood club-gall midge.

The eastern spruce gall aphid occurs mostly in the eastern half of the United States. It causes small, conelike swellings or galls, which may develop on the base of the new shoots of Norway, white, black, and red spruce trees. The galls are usually about three-fourths inch long and resemble miniature pineapples. Many of the infested twigs die. The tree may be deformed and weakened by heavy or repeated infestations.

The tiny, bluish-gray, young aphids, or nymphs, spend the winter on the twigs, principally at the base of the buds. In the spring they develop into wingless adults, which are covered with a white cottony secretion and lay groups of eggs. The young begin feeding at the bases of the new needles, causing the development of galls, which enclose the insects. In August the galls turn brownish and open, permitting the emergence of the maturing aphids. These develop wings and lay groups of eggs on the needles, which soon hatch. The young aphids overwinter near the buds.

The Cooley spruce gall aphid causes galls on blue, Engelmann, and Sitka spruces in the West and East. The habits of the aphid resemble those of the eastern form except that the winged adults, upon emerging from the galls in July, migrate to Douglas-fir, where they lay groups of eggs on the needles and where the young pass the winter. In the spring they mature and produce a summer generation, at which time many of the winged adults return to the spruce trees.

Treatment: If only a few galls occur on small trees, the infestation can usually be controlled by cutting off and destroying the fresh galls before the insects emerge. In larger plantings, spray the terminals of the Norway, white, black, and red spruces and the Douglas-fir early in the spring before the buds begin to swell. Take care to wet the buds and twigs. A spray of 2 percent white-oil emulsion, nicotine sulfate, soap, and water is recommended.

The chrysanthemum gall midge, a fragile, orange-colored, two-winged fly, is common and persistent in greenhouses. Larvae or maggots, hatching from orange-colored eggs deposited on the surface of tender tips and new growth, bore into the plant tissue. Cone-shaped galls are formed by the plant as a result of the irritation. The fully developed galls are about one-twelfth inch long and occur on the leaf, stem, or flower head of the plant, projecting obliquely from the surface. Both larvae and pupae complete their development within the gall. Development from egg to adult takes about a month. There may be six generations in a year.

Heavily infested plants fail to bloom because of the dwarfed and gnarled condition of the growth. If the plants are attacked when the crown buds are forming, the flowers are not borne upright as normal flowers should be.

Treatment: Frequent fumigation at night with hydrocyanic acid gas or nicotine, supplemented by spraying with nicotine sulfate and soap solution, formerly was used to kill the adults. Spraying or dusting with DDT now is employed instead to kill the adults and immature stages within the galls. DDT aerosols also are effective.

TIP- AND STEM-INFESTING INSECTS include the larvae of certain beetles, moths, and flies. Their activity is more or less concealed and often not detected until considerable damage has been done. It consists mostly of hollowing out or tunneling the terminal buds, shoots, or main stems of flowers and shrubs. Examples are the pine tip and shoot moths, stalk borer, iris borer, lilac borer, dogwood twig borer, rose stem borers, rhododendron borer, and the flatheaded apple tree borer.

Pine tip moths, as small larvae or caterpillars, may hollow out and kill the tips of the new shoots, including the buds, of pine. The presence of short, dead needles near the apex of the new shoots, with partially developed or hollowed-out buds, is typical of this type of injury. Young pines, up to 12 feet tall, are most seriously affected and may become stunted and bushy from continued heavy infestation.

Several species of tip moths occur in different areas. The Nantucket pine moth is the common species through the East and South, east of the Mississippi. The larvae are yellowish and about one-half inch long when full-grown. There is one generation each season in the North, two in the Central States, and at least four in the South. The insects winter as pupae in the injured tips. In the northern Great Plains a variety of this moth winters in cocoons in litter or soil. Other species in the Southwest and West usually have one generation late in the spring and pass the remainder of the year in the ground.

Treatment: On a few trees, the Nantucket pine moth is controlled by cutting off infested tips and destroying the overwintering pupae before growth starts in the spring. In the northern Great Plains and the West, that should be done as soon as the dying needles become evident and before the larvae have left them, because the larvae pupate in the ground.

Considerable protection may be had by spraying the terminal branches with a DDT emulsion about the time the adult moths begin to emerge. Once the eggs hatch and larvae have penetrated the stem, the chemicals have little effect on them.

The European pine shoot moth is another species that causes serious injury to the terminal buds and stems of red, Mugho, and Scotch pines. It is controlled in much the same manner as the tip moths. In New England the best way is to make two applications—one about the last week in June and one the first or second week in July.

The stalk borer is the chief offender of the several species of caterpillars that bore and tunnel through the stalks of fleshy and thick-stemmed plants. Aster, cosmos, dahlia, delphinium, goldenglow, hollyhock, lily, peony, phlox, and zinnia are often attacked. Before the insect is discovered its attack usually has progressed to the point where wilting and breaking over the plants occur. An examination of affected plants will disclose a small, round hole in the stem. It is the entrance to the stalk borer's burrow and the opening from which the castings are expelled. By splitting the stalk lengthwise one may find the culprit, a slender caterpillar that is a little over an inch long when full-grown. It frequently moves from the stem of one plant to that of another and may cause considerable damage. The young caterpillar is brownish and bears a dark-brown or purple band around the middle of the body, with several conspicuous, lengthwise brown or purple stripes. The grayish-brown moths appear late in summer and deposit their eggs for the next season's brood on burdock, ragweed, and other plants.

Treatment: The best remedy is clean cultivation and the burning of all stems and all plant remains in and about the garden that may be likely to harbor the overwintering eggs. The growth of large weeds, especially the giant ragweed, should be prevented, or the weeds should be cut, raked together, and burned before the caterpillars in them can escape and migrate to garden plants. Individual plants in home gardens may be saved by splitting the infested stems lengthwise, removing the borers, and then binding the stem together again. Injecting pyrethrum, DDT, or chlordane into the burrows will kill the borers that can be reached by the insecticide. Application of DDT and chlordane sprays to the stems will help prevent the borers from entering them.

The iris borer injures the roots and crowns of iris, including the Japanese and the Siberian types. Decay and blackening, giving a tear-stain effect to the leaves of infested plants, usually indicate its presence. The injury becomes more evident during July and August. In heavy infestations entire plants are killed. The full-grown worm is usually pinkish, with a brown head, and about 2 inches long. Pupation takes place in the soil near the base of the plant. The adults, brownish moths that appear in the fall, lay overwintering eggs, preferably on dead or dry leaves. The young caterpillars, on hatching in the spring, gnaw their way into the leaves and then work down to the roots, which they hollow out completely.

Treatment: If only a few plants are concerned, watch for the tear-stained mines of the young larvae in the leaves and kill them by squeezing the infested portion between the thumb and forefinger, commencing at the ground and pulling upward. In the late fall or early spring cut off and destroy the old dried leaves so as to eliminate many of the overwintering eggs. Protect the new growth as it develops in the spring by spraying or dusting at weekly intervals with DDT. Older plants should be lifted in July and August and all unsound portions together with any larvae contained therein should be cut out and destroyed by burning.

The lilac borer often attacks lilacs, privet, and other ornamental shrubs. It tunnels under the bark and into the wood, weakening the stems or girdling them and causing the foliage to wilt. Roughened scars showing the old borer holes may occur on the larger stems at places where the borers have worked for several seasons. The caterpillar is creamy white and about three-fourths inch long when full-grown. It passes the winter in the tunnels in the stems. The adult, a clear-winged moth, emerges in the spring and early summer and usually lays its eggs on roughened or wounded places on the bark.

Treatment: Before spring, cut and burn any dying and unthrifty stems containing the borers. In summer, watch for evidence of fine boring dust being pushed from small holes in the bark by the young borers and cut these out with a sharp knife. Borers that have entered the wood can be killed by injecting a few drops of carbon disulfide into the tunnels. The openings should be closed immediately with some gasproof material, such as grafting wax, putty, or wet clay, and kept closed for a day or two to retain the fumes. The fumes are poisonous and inflammable, and care should be taken when handling the chemical to avoid inhaling it or bringing it close to an open flame. Further protection may be had by spraying the trunk of the tree with a 1 percent DDT or BHC emulsion just before emergence of the moths.

SOIL- AND ROOT-INFESTING INSECTS crawl on the surface of the soil or work through it to reach the underground portions of the plants, such as the roots, bulbs, corms, and tubers. They feed on the exterior surface or bore into and tunnel the parts they infest. Some of the insects begin their attack above ground, but the principal damage is caused below ground. Examples of the surface-infesting forms include ants, millipedes, slugs, and snails. The black vine weevil, strawberry root weevil, narcissus bulb fly, wireworms, and the white grubs are among the boring types.

Ants are annoying and occasionally injurious in flower gardens. Sometimes they damage plants by nesting among the roots and exposing them to drying. Some ants also may carry off newly planted seeds. Sometimes they are indirectly injurious through their habit of colonizing and protecting aphids, mealybugs, and certain scale insects. They are often merely annoying, being attracted to plants by the presence of aphids or other sucking insects which are excreting quantities of honeydew. Ants are also attracted by souring sap from tree and plant wounds and by sweet secretions of certain parts of the plants, such as the flower buds of peonies.

Treatment: Ants are difficult to control. No entirely satisfactory remedy is available that will serve under all conditions and for all species. Many species are controlled by chlordane, used as a wettable powder or emulsion spray or as a dust in the manner and dosage suggested by the manufacturer. Some species can be controlled with rotenone dust.

When honeydew attracts the ants, the insects producing the material should be gotten rid of.

Termites occasionally work in the roots of living plants, hollowing them out, extending their burrows up into the stems, and causing them to wither and die. Although the stems may be honeycombed, there is usually no external evidence of termites above ground because the outer surface of the stem is left intact. These termites are subterranean in habit and live in colonies in the soil. They normally feed on dead or decaying wood, form boards, stakes, or dead vegetable matter in contact with the ground. If the termites are numerous in the soil and this type of food becomes scarce, they are attracted to living roots of trees, shrubs, and flowering plants.

Treatment: Remove all infested

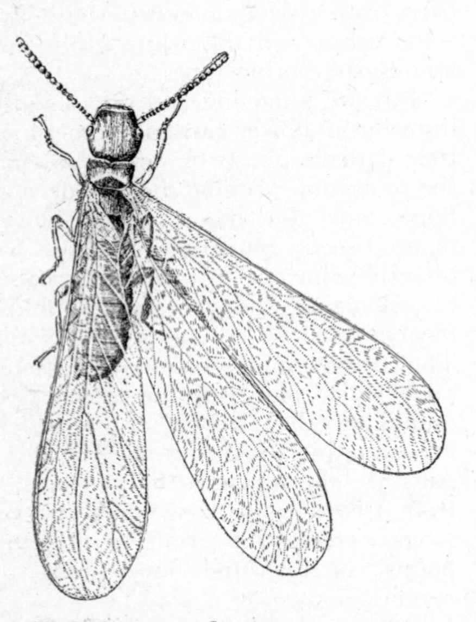

Reticulitermes flavipes, a termite.

wood and dying plants, and drench the soil with chlordane, using an emulsion or a wettable powder. The temporary substitution of commercial fertilizers for manure is often beneficial. Treatment of all plant stakes with suitable wood preservatives, as copper sulfate, zinc chloride, pentachlorophenol, and copper naphthenate will protect the wood from termite attack.

Millipedes, pillbugs, slugs, and snails are often troublesome to flowers and shrubs located in damp and shaded places where decaying vegetation is abundant. Millipedes often attack sprouting seeds or roots and bulbs. Pillbugs, sowbugs, feed on the tender roots and shoots. Slugs and snails feed on the leaves, stems, or roots of plants.

Treatment: Poisoned baits have been used extensively, but they are being replaced largely by the chlorinated compounds. For millipedes and pillbugs use DDT, toxaphene, or chlordane. For slugs and snails, baits containing calcium arsenate plus metaldehyde are most effective, especially with high temperature and low humidity. These recommendations apply outdoors and in greenhouses.

The black vine weevil is typical of snout beetles that attack stems and roots. The needles of yew, especially on the innermost branches, are bitten off at the tip along one side or eaten completely by the adults. They also feed on the bark of the stems and branches above ground. The young, white, grublike larvae feed on the rootlets, and later girdle or strip the bark from the larger roots. Arborvitae, astilbe, maiden-hair fern, gloxinia, hemlock, primrose, rhododendron, tuberous-rooted begonia, and wisteria are among the more than 75 greenhouse and outdoor plants this pest attacks. Outdoors, the insect usually breeds on strawberry, yew, rhododendron, or on such weeds as dandelion or broadleaf plantain. The adult is black with patches of yellowish hair scattered over its roughened body and is about two-fifths inch long. The winter is passed mostly as nearly full-grown larvae or as pupae. The wingless adult females emerge in June and July. There is one generation a year.

Treatment: Spray the above-ground parts of the plants with arsenate of lead, DDT, chlordane, or BHC in the form of emulsions or wettable powders late in June or early in July to kill the adults. This will prevent feeding on the bark and oviposition. Poison baits containing calcium arsenate, bran, and molasses are also useful. To control the ground-inhabiting grubs, the sprays or powders made of DDT or chlordane must be mixed with the soil.

Additional information on the biology and control of the insects mentioned in this article will be found in the publications cited, as well as in articles published on the subject by the various universities and agricultural experiment stations throughout the country.

THE INSECTS we have mentioned here are examples of a large number that infest flowers and shrubs. The measures we recommend against a specific insect often are effective against others of the same group. That they be controlled is of growing importance, just as the plants they infest are of increasing importance to home owners, gardeners, commercial florists, and nurserymen throughout the United States.

C. A. WEIGEL *is a senior entomologist in charge of the Beltsville laboratory of the division of truck crop and garden insect investigations, Bureau of Entomology and Plant Quarantine. He joined the Department in 1918 and has been associated with studies on insect problems of greenhouse and ornamental plants for more than 30 years. Dr. Weigel, a native of Massachusetts, is a graduate of the University of New Hampshire and holds advanced degrees from Ohio State University.*

R. A. ST. GEORGE *is an entomologist in the Bureau of Entomology and Plant Quarantine and is stationed at the Agricultural Research Center at Beltsville. He is a graduate of the University of Massachusetts and George Washington University. He has been associated with the division of forest insect investigations since 1918 and has specialized in research problems concerning insects that affect forest and shade trees and ornamental shrubs.*

For further reading on pests of ornamentals, the authors suggest:

Department of Agriculture publications—AIS–36, Longer Life for Poles and Posts, *1946; Farmers' Bulletin 1885,* Culture, Diseases, and Pests of the Box Tree, *by Freeman Weiss and R. A. St. George, 1947; Miscellaneous Publication 626,* Handbook on Insect Enemies of Flowers and Shrubs, *by C. A. Weigel and L. G. Baumhofer, 1948; Bureau of Entomology and Plant Quarantine publications E–759,* Parathion in Aerosols for the Control of Pests on Greenhouse Ornamentals, *by Floyd F. Smith, Paul H. Lung, and R. A. Fulton, 1948, and E–803,* Tetraethyl Dithiopyrophosphate in Aerosols for the Control of Greenhouse Insects, *by Floyd F. Smith and R. A. Fulton, 1950.*

State agricultural experiment station publications—California, Bulleint 713, California Greenhouse Pests and Their Control, *by A. Earl Pritchard, 1949; Connecticut (New Haven), Circular 173,* Control of Ants, *by J. C. Schread, 1949; Oregon, Bulletin 449,* Insect Pests of Nursery and Ornamental Trees and Shrubs in Oregon, *by Joe Shuh and Don C. Mote, 1948.*

University of Maryland Extension Service Bulletin 84, Common Insects of Lawns, Ornamental Shrubs and Shade Trees, *by George S. Longford and Ernest N. Cory, 1939.*

Eradication of Boxwood Leaf Miner and the Boxwood Psyllid, *by Lewis Pyenson, Journal of Economic Entomology, volume 39, page 264, 1946.*

1948 Experiments to Control Gladiolus Thrips, *by Floyd F. Smith and A. L. Boswell, Gladiolus Magazine, volume 13, number 2, pages 14–19, 1949.*

Use of DDT and H. E. T. P. as Aerosols in Greenhouses. I, II, *by Floyd F. Smith, R. A. Fulton, and Philip Brierley, Agricultural Chemicals, volume 2, number 12, pages 28–31, 62 (1947), and volume 3, number 1, pages 37, 39, 77 (1948).*

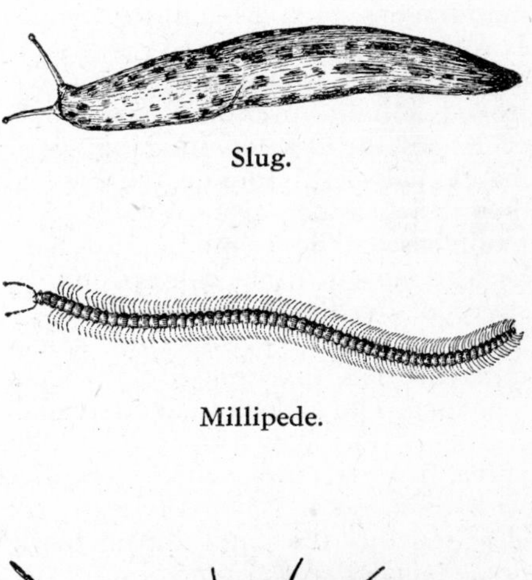

Slug.

Millipede.

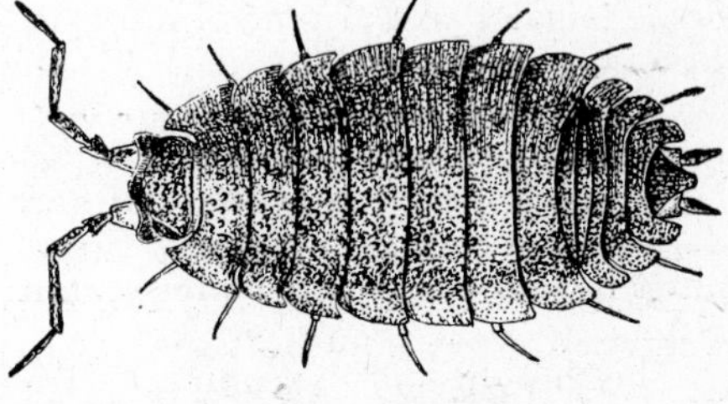

Sowbug, or pillbug.

Spider Mites and Resistance

Floyd F. Smith

Spider mites, or "red spiders," attack nearly all kinds of field crops, vegetables, orchard trees, weeds, and greenhouse plants. The mites often confine themselves to one kind of plant at first but move to other kinds when injury increases and food becomes scarce.

Several species, of similar habits but different morphological characters, are found out of doors.

Of six species that infest greenhouses, the two-spotted spider mite is predominant. It is a general feeder but it is almost constantly present on cucumbers, tomatoes, roses, carnations, chrysanthemums, violets, sweet peas, snapdragons, fuchsias, and ageratums. It is the major pest on roses and some other greenhouse crops. If it is not controlled it limits profitable production or makes the flowers unsalable. It is increasingly pestiferous in orchards and on other outdoor crops, especially if more susceptible related mites have been removed from competition by sprays or dusts.

Adult female two-spotted spider mites are less than one-fiftieth of an inch long. The males are much smaller. Bristles cover the oval body. The color varies from green or yellow to orange with dark spots. When the spots are close together the mites appear black. Some females are carmine or dark red. Mites generally become darker with age or in cool temperatures. Sometimes the progeny of green mites may be red, but in at least one strain the adults are dark red in all generations. Spider mites have a well-protected respiratory system.

The life history is complex. The newly hatched mite feeds for part of a day to nearly 2 days. Then it enters the resting stage. After a day or so it molts to a second active stage, which feeds and then becomes quiescent as in the first stage. The adult male emerges from the second quiescent stage, but the female passes through a third feeding and quiescent stage before becoming an adult. Mating usually occurs within a few minutes after the female becomes an adult. Only males develop from eggs of unmated females.

The developmental period varies widely with the temperature. The eggs hatch in 2 or 3 days at 75° F. or higher or after 21 days at 55°. The mites may reach the adult stage within 5 days at 75° or in 40 days at 55°. Under average greenhouse temperatures of 60° to 70°, the incubation period is 5 to 10 days and development to adult stage from 10 to 15 days. One female lays a few eggs daily and a total of 100 to 194 eggs during an average life of 3 to 4 weeks.

One female can give rise in one month, through succeeding generations, to a progeny of 20 mites at 60°, about 13,000 mites at 70°, and well over 13 million mites at 80° constant temperature. Multiplication therefore is rapid on hothouse crops, and control measures must be thorough and prompt.

The mites feed by piercing the epidermis of the leaf and drawing the liquid contents from the cells. The leaf turns pale and stippled around the injured part. When the infestation is severe the stippled areas coalesce and cause the leaf to appear sickly, turn rust-red, and then crumple and die. Affected plants are stunted and may be killed. The plant may become covered with fine silken webs, which the mites spin as they move from place to place.

Mites sharply reduce the average production of crops or flowers. The virtual elimination of red spiders with one of the organic phosphates has increased production of roses fivefold during the summer, when mite injury is most severe. Rose growers have reported an increase of 20 to 40 percent in production and better flowers with the newer pesticides. Growers of hothouse vegetables now can produce fall crops of tomatoes and cucumbers and maintain spring crops in high production until early summer or until field-grown crops become available.

Spider mites in greenhouses have been hard to control because they attack so many host plants. Their small size, rapid reproduction, and protection beneath webs on the lower leaf surface have increased the difficulty of combatting them.

Their well-protected respiratory system makes them resistant to the ordinary contact sprays and fumigants that their food plants tolerate. In the quiescent stages the mites are highly resistant to most chemicals and until recently no safe treatment was known that killed the eggs.

To meet those difficulties, greenhouse operators attempted to destroy all mites by cleaning out plant material at the end of the cropping season and by fumigating with burning sulfur before the new crop was planted. Sprays and dusts containing sulfur were applied to the young crop to reduce the mites to a minimum in the fall. When the crops were grown at cool temperatures, the mites did not increase markedly until late winter or early spring. Then productiveness of the crop was prolonged by spraying with 1 ounce of dry lime-sulfur in 3 gallons of water at 10-day intervals. Some used a spray containing 1 ounce of common salt in a gallon of water. Spraying with glue in water to stick the mites to the foliage was recommended. Syringing with water to wash the mites from the leaves was a general practice, but it damaged tender foliage and encouraged spread of such diseases as blackspot on roses, mildew on cucumbers, and carnation diseases.

Since about 1929 many acaricides—mite-killing compounds—have been reported on by research workers or made available by manufacturers. Fumigation with naphthalene flakes was the first new development, and special lamps were used for vaporizing required dosages. But only certain crops tolerated naphthalene fumigation, and high temperature and humidity had to be maintained. Sprays containing derris powder or rotenone extracts were followed by sprays containing a complex selenium compound—$(K\text{-}NH_4\text{-}S)_5Se$, known as Selocide. The latter was successful at first against spider mites but soon became ineffective despite repeated applications. We do not know why that happened because no specimens of the susceptible and resistant mites were preserved for later study. Another selenium compound, sodium selenate, applied in water to the soil at the rate of one-fourth gram per square foot to such crops as carnations and chrysanthemums, however, is still toxic to some strains of the spider mites. It is ineffective on roses or other plants with woody stems.

Sodium selenate, a systemic insecticide, is absorbed by the roots and translocated with the sap to the foliage and flowers of herbaceous plants. It poisons the mites as they feed. The material is highly toxic to humans. It should not be used on any food crops and is not recommended at all by the Department of Agriculture.

When azobenzene was found to be an effective acaricide, many rose growers and others fumigated with it at monthly intervals to control spider mites even though for several days the flowers developing from treated buds were faded in color and had to be discarded. Despite such losses, the fumigations controlled 95 to 99 percent of the mites and more salable flowers were produced than had been obtained with any previous treatment. Its use quickly declined, however, when the first of the aerosols containing the organic phosphate, hexaethyl tetraphosphate, became available in 1947. It eliminated or greatly reduced the spider mites and also controlled aphids, whiteflies, and mealybugs without injuring foliage or flowers.

Parathion, which became available in aerosols early in 1948, gave the same

970134°—52——43

Comparison of Toxicity of Several Organic Phosphates and Other Chemicals in Methyl Chloride Aerosols to Two Strains of Two-Spotted Spider Mites

Ingredient	*Percent mortality*	
	Nonresistant mites	*Resistant mites*
Parathion	99.9	5
Para-oxon	100	6
Methyl parathion	100	1
HETP	99.7	39
TEPP	97	12
Tetraisopropyl pyrophosphate	98	38
Sulfotepp	100	59
DMC	97	22
Aramite	100	2

NOTE: The following names and symbols were adopted in 1951: Para-oxon, for oxygen analog of parathion; methyl parathion, for methyl homolog of parathion; HETP, for hexaethyl tetraphosphate; TEPP, for tetraethyl pyrophosphate; sulfotepp, for tetraethyl dithiopyrophosphate; DMC, for di(*p*-chlorophenol)methylcarbinol; Aramite for 2-(*p-tert*-butyl phenoxy)-1-methyl ethyl-2-chloroethyl sulfite.

high degree of control of spider mites in most commercial greenhouses with less frequent applications than were required with hexaethyl tetraphosphate. Rose growers in Connecticut, New Jersey, and Pennsylvania, however, directed our attention to the poor results they got with parathion when they first used it in October 1948.

We learned that there are two strains of the two-spotted spider mite with respect to its resistance to parathion. No mites could be found in many greenhouses where parathion and hexaethyl tetraphosphate had been used to control them. In 33 other greenhouses in three States mites were collected on rose and other plants and were treated experimentally with parathion aerosols. Practically all the mites from 30 greenhouses were killed. Mites from one greenhouse in New Jersey and two in Pennsylvania survived the treatment. Twenty-four collections were made from various parts of the three establishments and the mites were found to be equally resistant to parathion when tested—an indication that mixed populations of susceptible and resistant mites were not present in those greenhouses. Because the houses had been repeatedly treated with parathion or hexaethyl tetraphosphate, it is possible that all susceptible mites, if formerly present, had been eliminated.

The three infestations of resistant mites in Pennsylvania and New Jersey, separated from one another by 50 to 100 miles, and the one in Connecticut apparently did not have a common origin through exchange of infested roses or other stock. Although one firm in Pennsylvania propagated roses for sale each year, none of the other three firms with resistant mites had procured stock from that source in recent years.

The results indicated that in the area surveyed in February 1949 resistant mites were restricted to the four firms. In June, however, for the first time, resistant mites were encountered in areas where only nonresistant mites had been previously collected, but they were definitely traced to introductions on rose plants recently purchased from the Pennsylvania firm. Thus the distribution of resistant mites was greatly extended in the late spring and summer of 1949 by these infested plants. By 1950 a large percentage of rose growers in the East, as far west as Illinois, had encountered resistant mites.

In many greenhouses, in which all roses are propagated from existing stocks and where other crops have been treated regularly with parathion or hexaethyl tetraphosphate for nearly 5 years, the progeny of surviving mites show no increased resistance. That finding does not support the theory that increased resistance generally follows repeated applications of the same insecticide. The evidence we had in 1952 was that resistant mites were limited at first to a few greenhouses and extended their range through commerce following the use of highly effective acaricides, which eliminated nonresistant strains of the same species and other nonresistant species as well.

In commercial greenhouses resistant

mites have been found on roses, carnations, chrysanthemums, cucumbers, tomatoes, snapdragons, ageratums, china asters, strawberries, beans, cannas, dahlias, and at least nine species of weeds, all of which are common hosts of nonresistant mites. Resistant mites have not been found on outdoor crops or weeds close to infested greenhouses. But resistant mites transferred to strawberries in the field in November 1950 survived winter temperatures of 8° F. and continued the infestation the following spring.

Resistant mites from roses were transferred to beans or the other host plants I mentioned and reared for 3 years. Samples taken from the colonies and tested periodically with parathion apparently did not lose their original resistance. These mites also did not lose their resistance when reared for several months on any of the hosts. Perhaps the mites in the original collections from single-plant colonies on roses were homozygous for resistance and their progeny did not lose this resistance through an estimated 50 generations regardless of the food plant. This thought, though, is not in agreement with statements of other investigators. I believe that their colonies were mixed with nonresistant strains and that the latter became dominant in the biological competition.

In view of the difference in resistance of mites from various sources, entomologists compared nonresistant mites with resistant mites and found no differences in the morphological characters. All were considered to be typical two-spotted spider mites. I have observed living mites for a long time, but have found no differences in coloration or other characters that will positively separate the two strains. Controlled tests have not been made to determine whether the two strains will interbreed.

In efforts to reduce the damage from resistant mites, some greenhouse operators returned to the use of some older remedies. Those who applied sprays containing derris extracts in water obtained good control of resistant mites but with considerable stunting and hardening of plant growth. Others went back to azobenzene, but discontinued it after obtaining poor control of resistant mites and injury to the flowers and succulent growth. Many syringed the plants with water and reduced the population, but foliage was severely injured, and black spot infection was encouraged.

In experiments on the resistant and nonresistant strains of mites, each of nine materials killed a higher percentage of the latter. It is evident that the one strain is resistant not only to parathion but to all other materials tested.

In further experiments, I discovered that aerosols containing *p*-chlorophenyl *p*-chlorobenzene sulfonate were toxic to hatching young of resistant mites but at a higher dosage than is required to kill nonresistant ones. The material can be used safely on roses only during the spring and summer because when days are shorter it is likely to cause the plants to drop their leaves. The material in sprays has also been effective against resistant spider mites but it causes leaf drop or other injury during short days. The material is also volatilized from heating pipes.

Sprays, aerosols, and smokes containing di(*p*-chlorophenyl) methyl-carbinol are highly effective against active stages of resistant mites. It has not been widely used because of the tendency for plant injury due to improper formulations and unavailability of the chemicals.

Sprays containing 2-(*p*-*tert*-butyl phenoxy)-1-methyl ethyl 2-chloroethyl sulfite are also effective against active stages of resistant mites and appear to be safe on greenhouse plants. This is one of several materials used successfully in commercial orchards in 1950 and greenhouse operators used it against resistant mites in 1951.

All three of these materials remained toxic to mites for 1 to 2 weeks after application. They are also sufficiently volatile to act as fumigants. These materials in aerosols or smokes are more convenient to the greenhouse operator than spray formulations.

Tetraethyl dithiopyrophosphate as a fumigant in aerosols kills a higher percentage of adult resistant mites than any of the organic phosphates and even more of the active stages of young mites. It was first used commercially in 1950 to combat this pest, but it has not been entirely satisfactory because of the frequency of applications required to keep resistant mites in check and occasional leaf distortion that follows continued usage.

In other experiments, the systemic insecticides octamethyl pyrophosphoramide and one of the trialkyl thiophosphates were applied in aerosols, in water as foliage sprays, or as soil applications. They killed both strains of mites in the active stages but killed the nonresistant mites 1 or 2 days earlier than the resistant ones. The materials resulted in the most satisfactory control of resistant mites in experiments conducted in commercial greenhouses. They are absorbed by the plant and render the sap toxic to feeding mites and aphids for 2 to 4 weeks or longer after they have been applied. Octamethyl pyrophosphoramide has no contact action of value for killing mites or aphids.

Outdoors, where spraying is practical and the crops have a higher tolerance than ornamentals, mites (including those that may be of the resistant strain) are being controlled by *p*-chlorophenyl *p*-chlorobenzene sulfonate, di-(*p*-chlorophenyl) methylcarbinol or 2-(*p*-*tert*-butyl phenoxy)-1-methyl ethyl 2-chloroethyl sulfite. In greenhouses until recently only a partial kill of mites was obtained by the inefficient acaricides if any were used at all. Predators and parasites could always be found and in some instances they practically killed out heavy infestations of mites but not until after severe damage had been caused to the plants. The predaceous mite *Iphidulus* sp. will destroy resistant as well as nonresistant mites but not rapidly enough to prevent extensive plant feeding.

The new, highly effective insecticides have nearly eliminated most insects and mites as well as their predators and parasites from many greenhouses. Freed of their pests, plants have greatly increased their production and quality of flowers or fruits. The higher standards thus established make it imperative to continue with the chemical methods of pest control in greenhouses. Because of the saving in cost of labor, the aerosol method of applying insecticides is preferable to spraying or dusting. Spraying and dusting leave conspicuous residues, and spraying encourages the spread of serious fungus and bacterial diseases.

To combat the resistant spider mite, the propagator of roses or other planting stock could assure against disseminating resistant mites by treatments with octamethyl pyrophosphoramide or other systemic acaracide that would poison the sap to feeding mites, and by killing the mites in all stages by fumigating with methyl bromide.

The commercial greenhouse operator may keep resistant mites in check by repeated applications of aerosol containing tetraethyl dithiopyrophosphate or carefully timed applications of *p*-chlorophenyl *p*-chlorobenzene sulfonate in aerosols, sprays, smokes, or fumigants to avoid plant injury. Sprays or aerosols containing 2-(*p*-*tert*-butyl phenoxy)-1-methyl ethyl 2-chloroethyl sulfite or di(*p*-chlorophenyl)-methylcarbinol, or smokes containing the latter, are effective alternates. The octamethyl pyrophosphoramide aerosols or sprays or even one of the newer systematic insecticides promise to give the desired control of the resistant spider mite as we recognize it in 1952.

FLOYD F. SMITH, *a senior entomologist in the Bureau of Entomology and Plant Quarantine, has devoted 28 years to the study of insects affecting greenhouse and ornamental plants. He has published more than 130 articles on the biology and control of these pests and on insects as vectors of plant diseases.*

Livestock and Insects

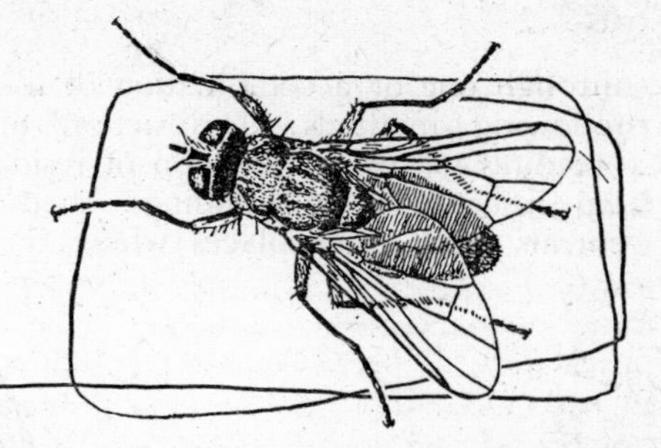

Flies on Livestock

Gaines W. Eddy

Horn flies are small black flies that somewhat resemble house flies but are only about half as large. They feed chiefly on cattle but may attack sheep, goats, horses, and a few other animals. Most of their adult life is spent on an animal. The horn fly lays its eggs only on fresh droppings. The larvae feed and develop in the manure. About 2 weeks are required for the horn fly to develop from egg to adult.

The cheapest and most effective way to get rid of horn flies is to apply an insecticide on the animals.

Methoxychlor is recommended for use on dairy animals at a concentration of 0.5 to 1.0 percent. To prepare the lower concentration, use 8 pounds of a 50-percent wettable powder to 100 gallons of water, or 16 pounds (2 gallons) of a 25-percent emulsion concentrate to 100 gallons of water. About 2 quarts is enough to spray an animal of average size. It will protect the animals for about 3 weeks. If a higher concentration is used, reduce the amount of spray proportionally.

Pyrethrum sprays also can be used effectively and safely on dairy animals to control horn flies, but more frequent treatments are necessary. DDT is not recommended for use on dairy animals.

Other insecticides as well as methoxychlor can be used safely for horn flies on beef or range cattle or on cows not being milked. DDT or TDE at 8 pounds of 50-percent wettable powder to 100 gallons of water are effective. Several different emulsifiable concentrates of toxaphene are also available. The manufacturer's directions for mixing and applying them should be followed closely. All four insecticides are effective. One spraying normally should protect the animals for about 3 weeks.

No special spray equipment is needed for applying insecticides to cattle to control the horn fly. High-pressure spraying is unnecessary. The number of animals to be treated largely dictates the type of sprayer. Small numbers can be treated satisfactorily with hand air-pressure sprayers of the cylindrical or knapsack type. For large numbers, a power sprayer with adjustable nozzle, operated at 100 to 200 pounds pressure, is suggested. Regardless of the sprayer used, the operator should make sure the insecticide always is well mixed.

Stable flies look like house flies and are of about the same size. Stable flies have long, piercing mouth parts, however, and the wings at rest are held at an angle to the body. Stable flies feed on several species of warm-blooded animals but cause the greatest annoyance and damage to cattle and horses. The flies bite mostly on the legs and lower parts. The females lay their eggs in moist fermenting organic matter. Manure, especially when mixed with straw, is a favorite breeding place. Development from egg to adult takes about 3 weeks.

The stable fly is usually controlled

through one or a combination of the following methods: Destruction of breeding places; application of residual insecticides to buildings, sheds, corrals, and other places where the flies rest; and application of insecticides to the animals.

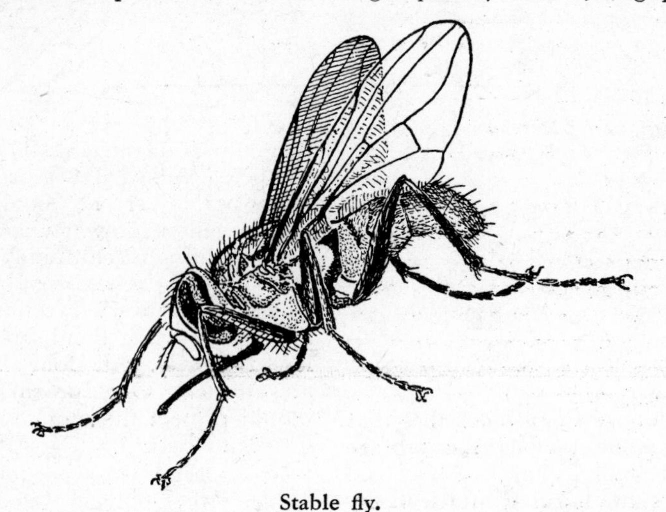

Stable fly.

Only methoxychlor, lindane, or pyrethrum sprays should be applied to dairy barns to control the stable fly. If a wettable powder of methoxychlor is used, a concentration of 2.5 percent is suggested. An emulsion may be used at a concentration of 2.5 to 5 percent. Lindane is recommended at a concentration of 0.25 to 0.5 percent. Pyrethrum sprays are not very effective as residual treatments against stable flies.

Those materials, as well as DDT and chlordane, may be used in or outside other types of buildings. DDT is recommended at the same concentrations as those I gave for methoxychlor. Chlordane is recommended at a concentration of 2 percent. The relative merits of the various materials as residual treatments against stable flies have not been determined. Residual sprays may not effectively reduce stable fly populations when used without other control measures, however.

The amount of spray to apply to barn surfaces depends on the type of surface. One gallon of spray will cover about 500 to 1,000 square feet. The surfaces should be wet with the spray just to the point of runoff. All buildings—poultry houses, hog pens, corrals, and such—should be sprayed at the same time. For treating barns or large buildings, power sprayers are most satisfactory.

Pyrethrum is one of the most effective materials against stable flies. It is used alone or in combination with other materials—activators, synergists, or antioxidants—that make pyrethrum more toxic or longer lasting. Among the better-known synergists used with pyrethrins are piperonyl butoxide and *n*-propyl isome. Pyrethrins are generally used against stable flies at concentrations of 0.05 to 0.1 percent. A concentration of 0.1 percent will protect animals from stable fly attack for 1 or 2 days. A combination of 0.1 percent of pyrethrins and 1.0 percent of piperonyl butoxide will usually give complete protection for 2 days and partial protection for 2 or 3 days longer.

The residual toxicity of pyrethrins is affected by weather conditions. Somewhat longer protection is had in the spring and fall than in summer. Pyrethrum sprays are rather expensive to use on range stock and generally are not considered practical for this purpose. They are widely used on dairy animals and around dairy barns, however.

A concentration of 0.5 to 1.0 percent of methoxychlor, the only chlorinated insecticide recommended in 1952 for the control of stable flies on dairy animals, will give some protection and cause a high mortality of the feeding flies during the first few days after treatment. DDT and methoxychlor can be used on beef or range animals. DDT is recommended at the concentration suggested for methoxychlor.

In treating animals for the control of stable flies, the lower half of the animal, especially the legs, should be sprayed thoroughly.

Farmers and ranchers are familiar with the large bloodsucking flies known as horse flies, but less familiar are the deer flies, which in some parts of the United States cause great annoyance to livestock. Horse flies and deer flies are members of the family Tabanidae.

As a group, the horse flies are more numerous, cause more trouble, and are considerably larger than deer flies. The several hundred kinds of horse flies have different breeding and feeding habits. Most of the species breed in moist places. Development from egg to adult may require only a few months or 1 to 2 years or more, depending on the species. Like stable flies, horse flies and deer flies feed on many different warm-blooded animals but cause the greatest annoyance and damage to cattle and horses.

For horse flies and deer flies, no satisfactory methods of control have been developed. Repellents in use in 1952 were not effective enough or were too costly for use on a large scale. The practical value of insecticides such as DDT or methoxychlor, which kill some of the feeding flies, was not fully determined in 1952.

Pyrethrum has been used often as a repellent against horse flies. Sprays containing 0.1-percent concentration of the pyrethrins will protect animals from fly attack for about 24 hours. The addition of piperonyl butoxide will extend the protection to about 48 hours.

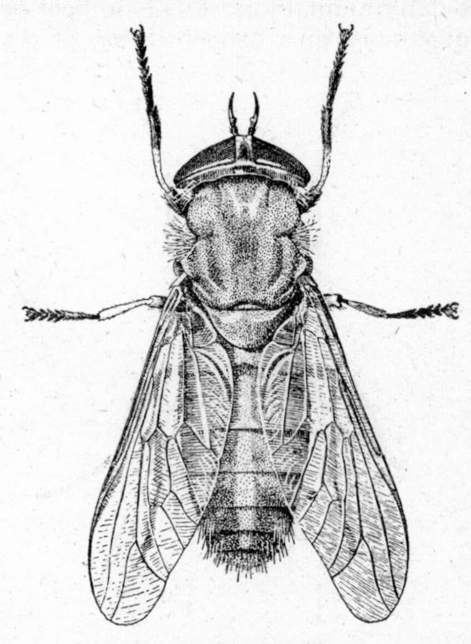

Striped horse fly.

Pyrethrum sprays do not kill many of the flies that alight or feed on the treated animals.

Results with some chlorinated insecticides have been extremely inconsistent. Some workers reported fair results with benzene hexachloride and protection for several days with a combination of benzene hexachloride and methoxychlor or DDT. I have observed little or no protection against one species of horse fly (*Tabanus abactor*), however, with rather high concentrations of DDT, methoxychlor, TDE, toxaphene, chlordane, benzene hexachloride, aldrin, or combinations of benzene hexachloride and DDT, or benzene hexachloride and methoxychlor. Practically all the materials caused some mortality to the feeding flies, the greatest resulting from DDT followed by methoxychlor. These materials caused fairly high mortality of the flies for the first 5 days after they were applied. The insecticides alone proved as toxic to the flies as the combinations tested, and some workers have reported a definite reduction in horse fly populations following the use of DDT alone.

I suggest that methoxychlor be used on dairy animals and DDT on beef or range stock at a concentration of 0.5

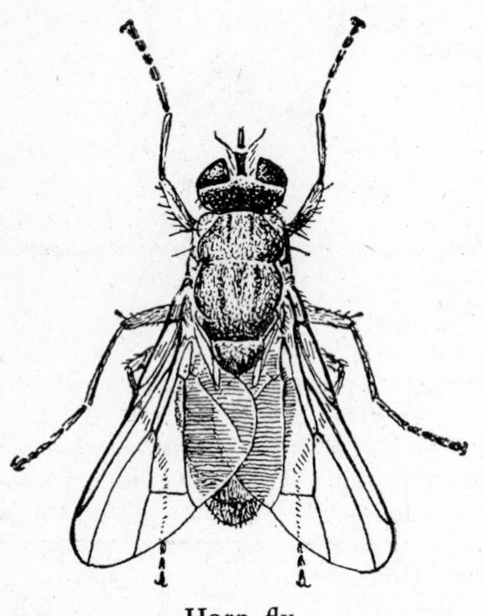

Horn fly.

to 1.0 percent. In areas where the fly season is relatively short, weekly applications of the insecticide should be feasible and worth while. Properly timed sprays should also be helpful even in areas where the horse fly season lasts 3 to 5 months.

Several compounds are relatively new. Neither their effectiveness against flies attacking livestock nor their toxicity to animals has been fully determined.

p-Aminophenol is used as an antioxidant for pyrethrins. It was reported to prolong greatly the residual toxicity of pyrethrins to stable flies. It has been tested in combination with pyrethrins against horn flies, stable flies, and horse flies. In laboratory, semifield, and field trials *p*-aminophenol was more effective than piperonyl butoxide. *p*-Aminophenol is apparently not highly toxic to cattle, but is known to be a photosensitizing agent. It stains or discolors light-colored animals if it is applied at concentrations much higher than 0.1 percent.

Tall oil was found to prolong the residual toxicity of pyrethrins in laboratory tests against stable flies. It was more effective at concentrations of 5 to 10 percent than at lower concentrations. In semifield tests against stable flies and in field tests against horn flies it was no more effective than a pyrethrum-piperonyl butoxide combination. However, against several species of horse flies a combination of tall oil and pyrethrum gave protection lasting 4 to 5 days, with 2 or 3 days' protection afforded by pyrethrum-piperonyl butoxide combination.

Allethrin is commonly referred to as allyl cinerin, or synthetic pyrethrins. Allethrin is as toxic (perhaps more toxic) to some insects as pyrethrins.

Against horn flies, stable flies, and horse flies, however, allethrin was considerably less effective or less toxic than pyrethrins. It showed little repellency to those insects in concentrations that normally are used for the pyrethrins.

RESEARCH ON THE CONTROL of flies attacking livestock has progressed considerably since 1945. Most progress has been made against horn flies—in 1940, for example, the control measures employed against them consisted of destruction of larvae in the manure and the use of fly traps and pyrethrum oil sprays against adults. The sprays usually afforded only a few hours of protection. About 3 weeks of protection can be obtained now with one application of several different insecticides.

Less striking advances have been made on the control of stable flies and horse flies than on horn flies, but the measures employed have been greatly improved. The protection afforded by pyrethrum against these flies has been increased from a few hours to 2 or 3 days by the use of synergists, activators, and antioxidants, which increase the toxicity and duration of effectiveness of the pyrethrins.

A NUMBER OF laboratory methods have been developed for evaluating materials as insecticides and repellents.

Tests on the toxicity of materials to biting flies are made by exposing flies to residual deposits of the insecticides. The materials are applied to glass, wood, or wire screen as solutions, emulsions, or as wettable powders. In routine tests, for example, pyrethrins are tested at 5 to 25 milligrams to the square foot; most organic compounds are tested at 25 to 200 milligrams to the square foot.

Small wire-screen cages 3.5 inches in diameter and 8 inches high are dipped in solutions of test insecticides, and flies are exposed in the cages. The insecticide residues on glass or wood are tested by confining flies under petri dishes on treated surfaces. Exposure is usually for a relatively short period (30 minutes to 2 hours) or for a continuous 24-hour period. Knock-down and kill of the flies are recorded for a 24-hour period or longer. The materials are then retested at intervals until they are no longer toxic. The relative toxicity of insecticides to flies can be determined easily by these methods.

White mice are utilized in the laboratory as test animals for determining the toxicity of insecticides to stable flies and deer flies. The mice are sprayed with the insecticide, usually in the form of an acetone solution, and then exposed to hungry flies. Mortality of the flies is recorded 24 hours after feeding. This method enables one to make tests with a small amount of insecticide, and the work can be done in winter when no field tests can be conducted. There is also a large saving in research cost when such preliminary tests are made on mice instead of on livestock.

Materials that show promise by those methods are sprayed on cattle, usually on only one or two animals at first, depending on what is known about the insecticide. For testing, the treated animals are placed inside large wire-screen cages (8 by 10 by 7 feet), and flies are released in the cages. The animals are tested at intervals until the treatments are no longer toxic to the flies. Preliminary tests against horn flies and stable flies on cattle are made in that manner. Laboratory colonies of the flies are maintained for this purpose. In many ways the results obtained are considered more accurate than those obtained in field tests where fly populations may fluctuate considerably or disappear entirely.

The materials that prove effective are then field-tested on larger numbers of animals. For tests against horn flies, the animals are usually sprayed with 1 to 2 quarts of the insecticidal preparation. When the fly population returns to an average of 25 flies per animal, the material is considered as having failed or lost its effectiveness, and the animals are resprayed or the test is ended. The toxicity of the insecticides to stable flies, horse flies, and deer flies under field conditions is determined through observations and collection of flies as they feed on treated animals. The flies are then observed to determine whether they die later as a result of contact with the insecticide during feeding.

GAINES W. EDDY *has been an entomologist in the Bureau of Entomology and Plant Quarantine since 1942. He is in charge of the research on flies affecting livestock at the Bureau's laboratory in Kerrville, Tex.*

Additional information on flies affecting livestock will be found in some publications of the Bureau of Entomology and Plant Quarantine: E–795, Control of House Flies in Barns with Different Insecticides, *by I. H. Gilbert, H. G. Wilson, and J. M. Coarsey, 1950; and E–762 (revised),* The New Insecticides for Controlling External Parasites of Livestock *(1949), Leaflet 270,* Horn Flies, Enemies of Cattle *(1950), Leaflet 283,* Fly Control on Dairy Cattle and in Dairy Barns *(1950), and Leaflet 291,* Horn Fly Control on Beef Cattle *(1950), all prepared in the division of insects affecting man and animals.*

In the Journal of Economic Entomology, volume 42: Residual Action of Organic Insecticides Against Stable Flies *(pp. 547–548) and* Use of White Mice for Testing Materials Used as Repellents and Toxicants for Stable Flies *(pp. 461–463), by Gaines W. Eddy and W. S. McGregor;* Tests to Control Horn Flies with New Insecticides, *by Gaines W. Eddy and O. H. Graham, pages 265–268. 1949.*

Ticks, Lice, Sheep Keds, Mites

E. F. Knipling

Lice, ticks, and mites annoy—and sometimes kill—animals and poultry. These external parasites are present the year around. They lower production of meat, milk, eggs, fiber, and leather. New insecticides can control them. There is little excuse any more for allowing some of them to exist.

TICKS must get blood from an animal in order to exist. Several species are important pests of farm stock—the cattle tick, Gulf Coast tick, lone star tick, fowl tick, and others. Some, like the cattle tick and winter tick, get on the animal in the seed-tick stage and remain on it until they mature in 2 weeks or longer. The mature tick drops to the ground and lays several thousand eggs, which hatch into the seed tick and start the life cycle all over. The Gulf Coast, lone star, and other ticks may feed on several hosts before they mature. The Gulf Coast tick usually gets on wild birds, such as meadowlarks and quail, in the seed-tick stage. The next stage, called the nymph, may again get on birds or on small animals such as rats and squirrels. The adult tick usually attacks larger animals, including cattle, sheep, and hogs.

The cattle tick, the worst of the ticks that affect livestock, has been eliminated from the United States except possibly in the extreme southern tip of Texas. It saps the strength of cattle. More important, it transmits the disease known as cattle fever or Texas fever. Early in this century scientists of the Department of Agriculture developed sufficient information about the life history and control of the parasite to attempt its complete elimination. Men in the Bureau of Animal Industry, cooperating with State workers, accomplished their objective, a great achievement.

The cattle tick and the disease it transmits still exist in South and Central America and other parts of the Tropics and take a heavy toll from the livestock industry there.

The elimination of the cattle tick from the United States was achieved by dipping in arsenical materials. The new tick-killing agents now available have been found to be more effective than the older arsenical dips. The new materials, which I describe later, can improve the livestock industry and over-all economy in Central and South America and in other parts of the world where the cattle tick is prevalent.

The Gulf Coast tick occurs along the Gulf of Mexico. It attacks all farm animals but is most serious on cattle. The tick usually attaches itself in and around the ears. Sometimes during July to September 100 ticks may be present on an animal. The bites cause severe inflammation and swelling of the ears. The annoyance due to the tick alone justifies efforts to eliminate it, but an even greater loss comes from the lesions caused by tick feeding, which are apt to become infested with the screw-worm, a destructive pest of livestock.

The newer insecticide sprays give the most effective and practical control. Sprays containing 0.5 percent of toxaphene destroy the ticks and protect animals from further serious attack for 2 to 3 weeks. A spray made of 0.025 percent of lindane (or gamma benzene hexachloride) and 0.5 percent of DDT is equally effective. Those treatments are also effective against flies and lice. Sprays containing DDT are not recommended for treatment of dairy cattle because the DDT will appear in the milk. Neither are toxaphene sprays recommended for dairy animals because of possible contamination of milk.

The lone star tick gets its name from the white spot on the back of the adult.

This tick attacks all kinds of livestock and many wild animals, especially deer. It may attach itself to any part of the animal. It is most abundant in the Southern and lower Midwestern States. It can be controlled with the same treatments used against the Gulf Coast tick.

The ear tick attaches itself deep in the ears of cattle, horses, sheep, and goats. A preparation of 5 parts of benzene hexachloride (12 percent gamma isomer), 10 parts of xylene, and 85 parts of steam-distilled pine oil will control it when applied in the ears of infested animals with a spring-bottom oiler. The toxaphene or lindane-DDT sprays described for use against the Gulf Coast tick are useful also against the ear tick. They should be applied inside and outside the ears and on the head and neck of the animal. To avoid possible injury to the ears, spray equipment developing low pressures of 30 to 50 pounds per square inch is recommended.

The winter tick is common in the Southwest, Midwest, and North Central States. It prefers to feed on horses but also attacks cattle. The sprays I have mentioned are effective against it. A single treatment in fall or winter often will protect animals against further attack for the season. Two treatments at intervals of 6 to 8 weeks may be necessary if the ticks are very numerous.

The fowl tick, also called the blue-bug, is one of the most injurious of the poultry parasites. It occurs in some Southern States, particularly in the Southwest. The blue-bug, light blue in color, remains well hidden in cracks in poultry houses or roosting places. If the farmer suspects infestations, he should examine cracks, loose boards, and boxes and other objects near the roosts.

Because the ticks may live for months or years, waiting for a chance to get blood, it is hard to control them once they infest the premises. Several chemicals may be used against them, but success depends on how thoroughly the materials are applied. Chickens and other poultry should not be permitted to roost in trees, livestock sheds, and other places, as they frequently do if good poultry houses are not provided. The houses should be kept clean and thoroughly treated with sprays about twice a year. All cracks, crevices, and other possible hiding places should be carefully treated. Creosote or carbolineum oils have been used successfully. Also effective are sprays containing 0.25 to 0.5 percent of lindane. Until more is known about the effects of lindane on poultry, I recommend that it not be used to treat the floors or litter where poultry, especially chicks, may have to remain in close contact with it for some time. Oil sprays containing 2.5 to 5 percent of DDT have given good results.

Every farm animal may become infested with one or more kinds of lice. Flies, ticks, and some other pests may attack various animals, but lice of a particular species usually live only on one kind of animal or fowl. There are two types of lice—those that suck blood (bloodsucking lice) and the kind that chew (biting lice). Sometimes lice may become so numerous that they kill animals or weaken them so much they die of exposure or become susceptible to other parasites and diseases.

Cattle in this country are attacked by four kinds of bloodsucking lice and one kind of biting louse. Horses can become infested with one bloodsucking louse and one or two species of biting lice. Two bloodsucking and three or four biting lice attack goats. Sheep may be attacked by two kinds of bloodsucking lice and one kind of biting louse. At least seven biting lice infest chickens. Hogs are subject to attack by only one kind, a bloodsucking species. The hog louse, the largest of all lice, measures about one-fourth inch in length and almost as broad.

All lice have a similar life history. The adult female lays its eggs on the animal, gluing them to the hair or feathers. The lice and eggs or nits may be present in unbelievable numbers on heavily infested animals. The eggs hatch in a few days to 2 weeks, depending somewhat on air temperatures. The young lice mature in about 2 weeks.

Although large numbers of lice plague livestock and poultry, research on methods for their control has been so successful that there is no longer any excuse for a lousy farm animal.

If all cattle, sheep, goats, horses, and hogs were treated three or four times at intervals of about 2 weeks with good insecticides, I believe all species of lice on our farm animals and the sheep-tick and sheep scab mite could be eradicated. The same treatment might also eradicate certain mange mites on hogs and cattle. Even the horn fly might be eliminated. Livestock men and organizations, I think, would do well to consider seriously the values of starting a coordinated program to accomplish this worth-while objective.

SPRAYS OR DIPS containing 1 pound of cube or derris (having 5 percent of rotenone) to each 100 gallons of water may be used for lice on dairy and beef cattle. Two treatments with an interval of about 2 weeks should be given. Pyrethrum sprays containing 0.025 percent of pyrethrins and 0.25 percent of another chemical called piperonyl butoxide, or other related materials, also are effective and safe for lice on dairy or beef cattle. Methoxychlor, used at a concentration of 0.5 to 1 percent, also is an excellent and safe spray for use on dairy or beef cattle.

On beef cattle, DDT, TDE, toxaphene, and chlordane can be safely used. Toxaphene and chlordane should be used at concentrations not exceeding 0.5 percent. DDT or TDE are also recommended for use at a concentration of 0.5 percent. Some stockmen, however, may prefer to use 1 to 1.5 percent of DDT or TDE and apply smaller amounts of spray than required when the 0.5-percent concentration is used. One thorough treatment with any of the four insecticides named, or with methoxychlor, will usually provide satisfactory control of lice, but a second treatment may be required about 14 to 18 days after the first.

In winter, especially on dairy animals, dusts may be preferred to sprays. Derris or cube dusts containing 1 percent of rotenone may be used. A dust containing 10 percent of methoxychlor or 1 percent of lindane may also be used. At least two thorough dust treatments with an interval of 14 to 18 days will be necessary to get satisfactory control of the lice.

DIPPING GOATS in water containing 0.25 percent of DDT, toxaphene, methoxychlor, TDE, or chlordane will eliminate all lice that attack those animals. The same treatments will also rid sheep of lice, except that for the foot louse on sheep, double the concentration is recommended. Derris or cube containing 5 percent of rotenone, used in dips at the rate of 1 pound per 100 gallons of water, are also effective against lice on sheep and goats. Lindane at a strength of 0.025 percent has also given good results in certain areas. Two treatments with lindane dips may be required or the strength of the dip may have to be doubled, especially when dipping is done immediately after shearing.

Many livestock men apply sprays to combat lice on sheep and goats. Dips are preferred because they assure the thorough treatment of the animals that is necessary to eliminate lice from the herds; sprays properly applied and containing a sufficient concentration of insecticide will give good results, however. If sprays are used it is recommended that twice the minimum strength recommended for dips be used. Animals should be sprayed thoroughly when the wool or hair is short. The best time for treatment usually is immediately after or within a few weeks after shearing.

THE HOG LOUSE may be controlled by DDT dips or by thorough treatment with DDT sprays. Complete eradication is often obtained with 0.5 percent DDT dips or sprays, but 0.75 percent is more likely to assure elimination of the parasite. Toxaphene, chlordane, methoxychlor, and TDE used as sprays at 0.5-percent strengths, and lindane at 0.05 to 0.06 percent, are also excellent against hog lice. One thorough treatment should give excellent results, but a second treatment 14 days after the first may be necessary.

To RID HORSES of lice, DDT has given good results. It should be used in the same way as for lice on cattle.

THE SHEEP-TICK, also called sheep ked, is not a true tick; it is a wingless fly. It is a common pest of sheep and will also attack Angora goats. It spends its whole life on the animal. The adult female deposits a round, whitish "egg," which is really the resting stage or pupa. It is glued lightly to the wool and turns to a dark brown in a day or so. The adult sheep-tick emerges in 2 or 3 weeks and begins to suck blood at regular intervals. It is controlled by insecticides. I think sheep-ticks could be completely eliminated by coordinated treatments of all sheep and Angora goats. Derris or cube dips are highly effective. As little as 8 ounces of a material containing 5 percent of rotenone used in 100 gallons of water makes a good dip. DDT, toxaphene, chlordane, TDE, methoxychlor, and lindane, used as described for controlling lice on sheep and goats, are equally as good. Sprays, if used, should be applied thoroughly at double the dip strength, preferably immediately or within a few weeks after shearing, when the wool is short.

POULTRY are often seriously affected by lice, mites, and fleas, as well as by the fowl tick, which has already been discussed. Heavy infestations of lice alone may reduce egg production of chickens by as much as 10 percent. A close examination of cracks, crevices, and other hiding places in poultry houses may reveal thousands of small red objects less than one-twenty-fifth inch in diameter—the red color is evidence that mites can sap a great deal of blood from the flocks. It is not unusual among neglected poultry flocks to see black rings around the eyes of young chicks or black spots on wattles and combs of chicks and older poultry. Close examination reveals that the rings and spots actually are hundreds of shining black fleas, engorged with blood. The chickens may be found to harbor hundreds of lice around the head, wing feathers, or vent. One may even note feathers on the vent glued together by literally thousands of small nits or eggs laid by one of the most common species, the body louse.

No longer need poultrymen tolerate infestations of these parasites on their poultry.

Thorough treatments of poultry houses with sprays containing 0.5 percent of lindane will usually control the mites. Sometimes DDT has given good results when used as a 5-percent emulsion or as a 5-percent oil solution. Creosote and carbolineum sprays, although somewhat objectionable to use because of the odor, have been used successfully. Whatever the material, however, it must be applied thoroughly. Proper clean-up to prevent accumulations of droppings, feathers, straw, and other refuse will eliminate some hiding places for the insects and mites and will make possible more thorough and effective treatments with insecticides.

Ordinary lard put on the heads of the fowls will destroy the fleas, but the aim should be to clean up and treat the infested places with a DDT dust or spray. Good results will be obtained if an emulsion, wettable powder, or oil spray containing from 2.5 to 5 percent of DDT is applied to the infested areas at the rate of about 2 gallons for each 1,000 square feet. Lindane sprays containing 0.5 percent of the insecticide can also be used with good success.

Lice on poultry can be destroyed by applying a pinch of sodium fluoride as a dust to various parts of the chicken, especially the head, back, under sides of wings, and the vent region. A 5 percent DDT dust can also be used with good results. Good control can be obtained without disturbing the chickens by applying a 1 percent lindane spray to the roosts or by painting it on with a brush. The lindane gives off sufficient vapor to kill the lice when the chickens perch on the roosts. Nicotine sulfate roost paint has also been used in that way.

E. F. KNIPLING *is in charge of the division of insects affecting man and animals, Bureau of Entomology and Plant Quarantine. Since 1931 he has conducted research on insects that attack livestock and man.*

Information on the role of insects in transmitting diseases and worm parasites to livestock will be found in the chapters "Carriers of Animal Diseases," page 161, and "Insects and Helminths," page 169. Some statistics on the losses caused by livestock pests will be found on page 144.

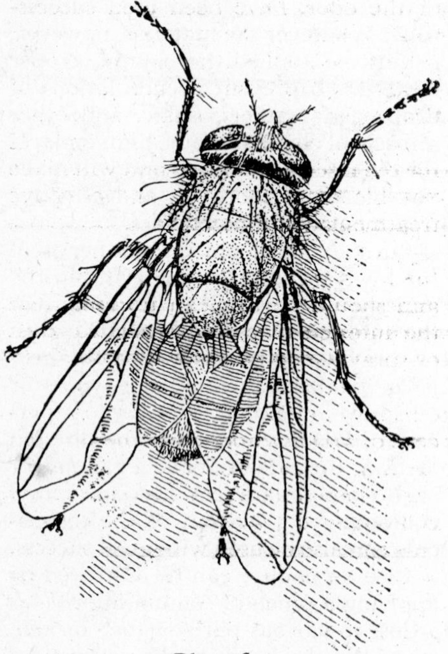

Blow fly.

Screw-worms

W. G. Bruce

Screw-worms, if they are not controlled, can wipe out entire herds of cattle, hogs, sheep, and goats. Good livestock management and prompt treatment of all infestations with an approved remedy are the ways to combat the parasites.

Screw-worms have been known in Texas since about 1842. Frequently in summer they have spread to adjoining States. Localized outbreaks have occurred occasionally in the Central and North Central States mainly because of the shipment of infested livestock into the areas. Screw-worms were unknown in the Southeastern States until 1933, when the first infestation was reported near Boston, Ga. By the end of 1933, infestations were reported in 30 counties in southern Georgia and in 18 or 20 counties in northern Florida. Infestations spread rapidly in Florida. By early 1935 screw-worms were found in every county of that State, and heavy losses of livestock were reported by hundreds of stockmen.

An extensive program was started in all Southern States in May 1935 by the Department of Agriculture and State agencies. The aim was to disseminate information on the control of screw-worms and to demonstrate the proper methods and materials for treatment. The program was discontinued in 1937 when it was believed the purpose had been served. Cases of screw-worms, all of them in Florida and southern Texas, were reduced then to a small number.

Severe screw-worm outbreaks occurred in Florida, Georgia, Alabama, and southern South Carolina. Less serious outbreaks occurred in Mississippi, Tennessee, northern South Carolina, and North Carolina. Infestations have also been found in Kentucky, Virginia, and New Jersey.

Surveys have been made each year since 1943 to determine the incidence and relative abundance of screw-worms, ascertain the amounts of critical insecticides needed for their control, aid in the proper distribution of the insecticides, and advise stockmen of the approved methods and materials for treatment and prevention.

THE SCREW-WORM FLY, bluish green in color, has three dark stripes on its back. The area below and between the eyes is reddish or orange. In size and coloration, the fly is almost identical to a species of common blow flies, which is the adult of another species known as the secondary screw-worm.

The female screw-worm fly lays her eggs—10 to 400 at a time—on the edges of wounds of warm-blooded animals. A female can lay 3,000 eggs, which she usually deposits in masses of 200 to 400 at 4-day intervals. The eggs of the screw-worm are placed in shinglelike masses and are cemented together. The eggs of ordinary blow flies are placed in haphazard fashion and are not securely cemented together.

The eggs hatch in 6 to 12 hours. The tiny whitish worms feed in clusters. They eat into the live flesh, in which they soon form a pocket. As they develop they assume a pinkish color. After about 3 to 10 days the screw-worms leave the wound, drop to the ground, and burrow into the soil. The outer skin hardens and forms a pupa. Seven to 14 days later the mature fly emerges. During cool weather the pupal stage may last 2 months. The flies are ready to mate and lay eggs 2 to 5 days after they emerge. The average life cycle from egg to egg is about 21 days. It may be shorter under favorable conditions or considerably longer under adverse conditions, especially in cool weather. If average daily temperatures lower than 54° F. prevail for 2 months or more, the pupae die in the soil. Therefore the screw-worm usually survives the winter only in Florida, southern Texas, and Mexico.

In the Southeast the overwintering area ordinarily is peninsular Florida, the northern limit of which is about 50 miles south of the Florida-Georgia line. In extremely mild winters, as in 1949–1950, the screw-worm has survived in Georgia, Alabama, South Carolina, and Florida.

In warm weather in spring and summer the screw-worm flies migrate at the rate of 35 miles a week. In the Southeast, the usual infested area in summer includes all of Florida, the southern two-thirds of Georgia, and the southeast corner of Alabama. In the Southwest the natural migration ordinarily encompasses most of Texas, southern New Mexico, southern Arizona, and southern California. When warm winters permit survival in a larger area, the subsequent migrations will extend over a proportionately greater area of the Southern States.

Screw-worm infestations frequently occur in the Central and Northern States, often in outbreak numbers. They are not due to the natural migration of screw-worm flies but to the importation of infested livestock. Severe and costly outbreaks, a direct result of the shipment of infested livestock to places where screw-worms were unknown and unrecognized and where stockmen were unprepared to combat them, have occurred as far north as South Dakota and New Jersey.

A NUMBER OF predatory beetles and ants destroy screw-worm larvae and pupae, but they do not effectively control screw-worms. No methods have been developed to propagate these beneficial insects in sufficient numbers so they can be utilized.

The screw-worm is a true parasite that lives only in the living flesh of warm-blooded animals. It is not found in cold-blooded animals or in decaying flesh or vegetable matter. The worms found in cold-blooded animals and decaying organic matter are common blow flies.

Any warm-blooded animal is subject to screw-worm attack. Infestations have been found on practically all kinds of wild and domestic animals, poultry, and man, but are more commonly found in cattle, hogs, sheep, and goats.

Occasional reports have been received that large numbers of wild animals, especially deer, were killed by screw-worms, but no intensive studies have been made and only a few of the reports have been verified. Outbreaks in wildlife apparently are associated with the development of large screw-worm populations in domestic animals.

Before an animal can become infested with screw-worms, some break must occur in its body surface. That may be a tick bite, the navel opening of a new-born animal, a scratch, a surgical operation, a cut, or some diseased condition of the skin or mucous membranes, especially around the natural openings. Any open wounds attract the female screw-worm fly, and around them she deposits the eggs. The worms cannot eat through the unbroken skin of a healthy animal.

An infested wound becomes increasingly attractive to the flies and constantly receives new batches of eggs. Screw-worms of different sizes and ages therefore are often found in a wound. As the larvae develop, there is a constant dropping of mature larvae from the wound to the ground, where they pupate and later emerge as flies, building up a population to infest new wounds and reinfest old ones.

INFESTED ANIMALS often stray from the herd and hide in the underbrush or palmettos or in some isolated place. They appear nervous and make frantic efforts to scratch or lick the infested wound.

Most untreated infestations result in the death of the animals. Death may be caused directly by the screw-worms in destroying tissues or by complications following an infestation. The screw-worm fly is a carrier of a joint disease in calves. It must be remembered that a wound is being continually reinfested, that old infestations are often more attractive than are fresh wounds, and that repeated reinfestation means death to the animal. If the infestation is in the navel, death very likely will result more quickly than if the infestation is in some meaty and less vulnerable part.

The infested wound has a watery discharge of bloody exudate and a bad odor. If one wipes the bloody discharge from the wound with absorbent cotton, he will see the worms crowded together in pockets, with only their rear ends exposed. The heads are embedded in the living flesh and have two hook-like mouth parts that tear the tissues and cause bleeding. In large wounds, where some flesh is decaying, there may also be maggots of ordinary blow flies. The maggots are not embedded in the flesh but crawl on the surface of the wound.

IN DOMESTIC LIVESTOCK screw-worms can be controlled by the proper and timely application of remedies that kill the worms but do not harm the animal.

The mistreatment of wounds and infestations often means more costly methods of control or the loss of the animal. Creosotes, coal tars, and similar preparations aggravate the wound by destroying tissues, enlarging the wounds, and retarding healing. They also invite reinfestations and impair the health of the animal.

Cooperative effort among all livestock owners is essential for effective control. One stockman can do a fairly good job by frequent inspections and treatment of his animals, but labor and materials would cost much less if everybody in a community did the same.

SEVERAL EXCELLENT REMEDIES are available. The most effective material for killing screw-worms and protecting the wound against reinfestation is a development by the Bureau of Entomology and Plant Quarantine, known as "EQ 335 Screw-worm Remedy." The figures 335 represent the concentrations of the two main active ingredients, lindane (3 percent) and pine oil (35 percent). EQ 335 does not

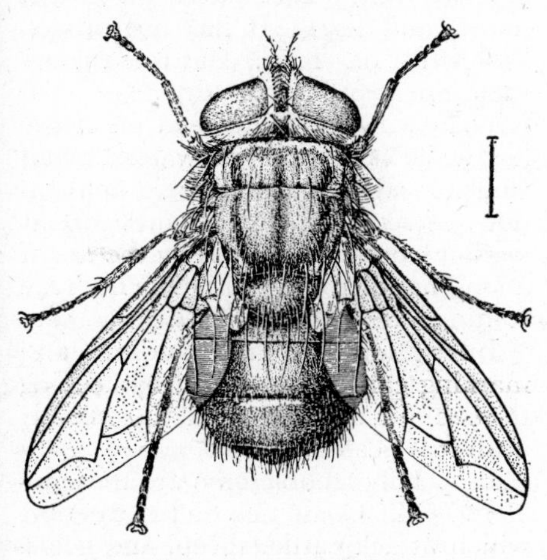

Screw-worm adult.

stain. It is not highly volatile. It will kill screw-worm flies that visit the terated wounds. It contains (in percentages by weight) lindane, 3; pine oli, 35; mineral oil, 40–44; emulsifier, 8–12; silica aerogel, 8–12.

EQ 335 is best applied with a 1-inch brush. It should be worked well into the wound. Special attention should be given any deep pockets. A coating should be applied completely around the wound and on areas contaminated with exudates.

Wounds should be treated at 7-day intervals until healed. Large suppurating wounds may require two treatments the first week. Frequently one or two treatments will protect the wound from infestation until it is completely healed.

Some stockmen prefer a liquid screw-worm remedy. Preparations containing a thickening agent usually provide a longer period of protection against attack than do liquids containing the same percentage of lindane. However, a liquid remedy can be prepared by omitting the thickening agent, silica aerogel, that is used in EQ 335 and increasing the percentage of mineral oil proportionately.

Smears 62 and 82 were also developed by Department entomologists and have been found to be good remedies for screw-worms. They should be used when the new smear EQ 335 is not available or when supplies of the older smears are on hand.

Smear 62 contains (in parts by weight) diphenylamine (the technical grade), 3.5; benzol (the commercial grade), 3.5; turkey red oil (sulfonated castor oil, pH 10 or neutral), 1; lampblack, 2.

Smear 82 was formulated as a substitute for smear 62 when one of the ingredients, turkey red oil, became scarce. It contains (parts by weight) diphenylamine, 35; benzene (benzol), 32; triton X–300 (sodium salt of an alkylated aryl polyether sulfate), 2; *n*-butyl alcohol, 10; lampblack, 21.

Most screw-worm infestations are due to man-made injuries or to injuries that man can prevent. Stockmen who know all about the screw-worm and practice good livestock management can prevent most infestations and greatly reduce losses. The stockman should be especially alert for screw-worms when the animals have experienced snags and scratches, surgical operations, tick bites, shear cuts, hog bites, dog bites, injuries to mouths of sheep and goats, wire cuts, warts, pink eye, and cancer eye.

Snags and scratches form a major group of predisposing conditions for infestation. The injuries may be due to the sharp horns of cattle and goats that hook one another; briers, thorns, or palmettos; the milk teeth of suckling pigs; and the rough handling of livestock—striking them with whips, sticks, or boards, or confining them in poorly constructed pens and chutes. Rushing cattle through gates and gaps and hurrying them through the woods cause many injuries. Most of the injuries can be prevented by handling livestock gently; removing rough edges from gates and gaps and protruding nails and slivered boards from fences, pens,

970134°—52——44

and chutes; avoiding the use of catch dogs; and by dehorning or tipping the sharp horns of cattle.

Dehorning, marking, registration tagging, branding, castration, lamb docking, and similar operations should be done when screw-worms are not present or during winter when they are least active. If those recommendations do not fit into the management program, the wounds should be treated with an approved remedy and the animals kept in a hospital pasture where they can be examined and treated until the wounds are healed.

All animals born during the screw-worm season are susceptible to navel infestations. Controlled breeding so that all calves are dropped in winter and careful inspection of all newborn animals and their dams will eliminate an important cause of attack. This type of infestation is the most common among all breeds of domestic animals. All animals born during the screw-worm season should be given extra care. A light application of EQ 335, or smears 62 or 82, will protect against infestation. In treating the navel of a newborn calf, it is advisable to tie off the umbilical cord, cut off the surplus, paint the cord with iodine, and apply the remedy to the area around the navel opening. It is wise also to make a light application of the remedy around the vulva of the mother before and after she gives birth. It is advisable to examine the mouths of cattle, sheep, and goats. They lick their wounds and often get some of the maggots into the mouth, where they become attached to the gums between the teeth. An examination of the mouths of the mothers of calves with navel infestations frequently discloses screw-worms in their gums. Screw-worm remedies should not be used in the mouths of livestock. The worms should be removed with blunt forceps and destroyed.

Dehorning should be done when calves are small because the horn cavities will heal more quickly, they are less apt to be infested, and the operation will not interfere with normal growth. The sharp horns of mature animals can be tipped at any time without danger of infestation.

Infestations following castration can be reduced or eliminated by the use of the bloodless emasculator on cattle, sheep, and goats. It has not proved successful on hogs. Castrated hogs should be kept in small, dry pens so the remedy will not be washed off if the hog wallows in mud and water. A convenient way to make frequent applications of screw-worm remedies to castration wounds in hogs is by the use of a long-handled mop while the hogs are feeding.

Infestations from branding and marking can be prevented by keeping the wound covered with the remedy until it is healed.

Especially troublesome are the bites of the Gulf Coast tick or the ear tick, which attack cattle, sheep, and goats. Dipping or spraying with one of the new insecticides, such as 0.5 percent of toxaphene or a mixture of 0.5 percent of DDT and 0.03 percent of lindane, will control those ticks.

Infestations after shear cuts can be avoided in sheep by shearing before the worms appear and by the application of an approved remedy to all cuts. Sheep that are badly cut should be kept in a hospital pen or holding pasture and treated until the wounds are healed. The use of the long-comb shearing equipment on goats greatly reduces the danger from shear cuts.

Many screw-worm infestations follow injuries suffered by swine in fighting. The teats of sows may be injured by the sharp milk teeth of suckling pigs. Often it has been necessary to extract the long tushes from hogs and the milk teeth of suckling pigs.

The use of dogs for catching hogs or driving other livestock results in many dog bites and subsequent infestations. Such injuries can be avoided by working livestock without dogs and destroying stray dogs that attack sheep and goats in the pasture. Infestations in the mouths of sheep and goats develop primarily in injuries suffered from eating pricklypears. This injury is being eliminated gradually by eradication of the pricklypear from grazing areas.

Many of the injuries and diseases I have mentioned cannot be avoided, but the protection of the wounds and the prompt treatment of infestations will prevent serious losses.

FIELD TESTS were conducted in 1951 of the use of radiant energy against the screw-worm. The new method involves the carefully timed liberation of laboratory-reared insects after exposing them to radiation that sterilizes them. A treated female fly lays infertile eggs that do not hatch. When a radiated male has mated with a normal female in the laboratory, the eggs from the female are deposited as usual, but do not hatch. The female fly mates only once, and if this mating is with a treated male, none of the eggs she lays will hatch.

Cage tests indicate that when there are 5 to 10 times as many radiated as normal males in a mating area, eggs from most females are infertile and there is only slight reproduction.

Entomologists developed a laboratory method for mass rearing of the flies. Because of the relatively small number of flies that survive the winter in Florida, the results of the cage tests indicated that it may be proved practical to rear and liberate the infertile-treated flies in numbers 5 to 10 times as great as the wild flies in the area. If field results compare with the laboratory results, the following generation in the field would then be much reduced below the number surviving the winter. The hope is that by continuing mass liberations of treated flies over two winters and the intervening summer, the complete elimination of the fly can be attained in the Southeast.

In the preliminary experiments that revealed this possibility, the radiation was with X-rays. The Bureau of Entomology and Plant Quarantine arranged with the Atomic Energy Commission for tests of atomic radiations as sources of sterilizing rays that might prove equally effective and less expensive for treatments. The research staff of the General Electric Company also became interested in the development and plans to provide irradiation with cathode rays for test groups of the pests. The laboratory work has indicated that close and accurate timing of treatment is necessary to make it effective. The pupal or resting stage of the pest lasts about 8 days. If the pupae are irradiated at 2 days of age the rays do not sterilize the males. Their sixth day has proved the most effective time.

The laboratory experiments suggested that an eradication campaign might proceed approximately as follows: Mass rearing laboratories would be set up ready for production of millions of the insects each week, starting early in the year. The insects would be irradiated on their sixth pupal day, and the flies when hatched would be distributed over the infested area from airplanes. Rearing and distribution would be continued through the normal season of the insects and into the following winter—unless the scientists found convincing evidence that the pest had been eradicated and that the campaign could be discontinued.

The original research was done at the Department's laboratory at Kerrville, Tex. X-ray equipment was used at a hospital near San Antonio. Small-scale field tests were conducted on an island off the west coast of Florida—a "pilot plant" test against wild flies designed to try the method under practical conditions and to give the scientists practical experience in the mass rearing, mass irradiation, and liberation of the treated flies.

Knowledge that X-rays can sterilize insects traces back to earlier genetic studies with fruit flies. Over-exposure, it was noted, left the flies sterile. The Kerrville experiments showed that with a heavy excess of X-rayed males, eggs from most female screw-worm flies failed to hatch.

W. G. BRUCE, *an entomologist, joined the Bureau of Entomology and*

Plant Quarantine in 1928. He has conducted research on insects affecting animals in many sections of the United States. He received his undergraduate and graduate training at Kansas State College. In 1951 he was named director of the southeastern region of the Bureau of Entomology and Plant Quarantine, with headquarters in Gulfport, Miss. He directs regulatory, control, and administrative functions in Alabama, Arkansas, Florida, Georgia, Louisiana, Mississippi, North Carolina, South Carolina, and Tennessee.

For further reading on screw-worms Dr. Bruce suggests three circulars of the Bureau of Entomology and Plant Quarantine—E–540, A New Remedy for the Prevention and Treatment of Screwworm Infestations of Livestock, *by Roy Melvin, C. L. Smith, H. E. Parish, and W. L. Barrett, Jr., issued in 1941; E–708,* A New Treatment for Screwworms in Livestock, *by C. S. Rude and O. H. Graham, 1947; and E–813,* EQ 335 and Other Wound Treatments for Screw-worm Control, *prepared in the division of insects affecting man and animals, 1951.*

Florida Agricultural Extension Bulletin 123, revised, Screw-worms in Florida, *by W. G. Bruce and W. J. Sheeley, 1944.*

Florida Agricultural Experiment Station Bulletin 407, "Swollen Joints" in Range Calves, *by M. W. Emmel, 1945.*

In the Florida Entomologist: Screwworm Survey in the Southeastern States in 1945, *by W. G. Bruce, A. L. Smith, and C. C. Skipper, volume 29, pages 1–4. 1946.*

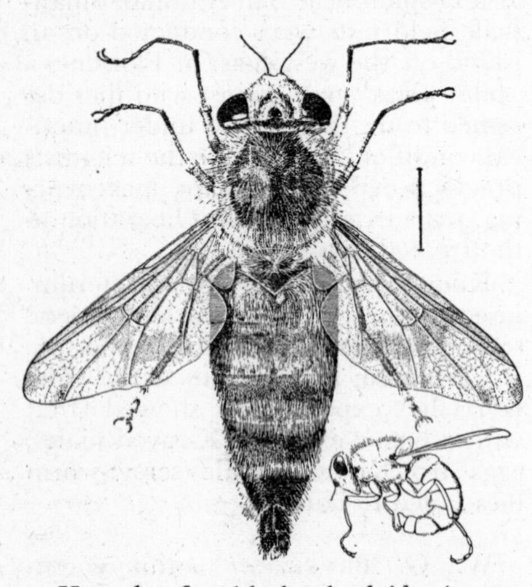

Horse bot fly with sketch of side view.

Cattle Grubs

Ernest W. Laake, Irwin H. Roberts

Cattle grubs, or heel flies, have been known to man from time immemorial. Few parasitic insects that attack man or domestic animal have received more attention from naturalists than these.

The introduction of the two species of cattle grubs we have in North America undoubtedly dates from the time of the first importation of European cattle. The spread of one, now called the common cattle grub, in the United States advanced with the progress of settlement to all parts of the country. The other, the northern cattle grub, has spread throughout the Eastern, Middle Northern, and Northwestern States. It is moving southward, but we doubt that it will ever invade the States farthest south.

The life history of the two species is similar. The eggs are securely fastened near the base of the hair on the host.

The adult of the northern species generally lays its eggs one at a time on the hind legs above the hocks, on the flanks, and on the sides of the abdomen. It is bold and vicious in its attack.

The adult of the common cattle grub lays its eggs in rows on the heel when the animal is standing or, when it is lying down, on any part of the body that touches the ground. It makes sneaking attacks. Often the animal is unaware of the fly. When the egg is 4 or 5 days old, the eggshell splits at the free end and the first-stage cattle grub emerges, crawls down the hair, and immediately bores into the skin. After migrating through and feeding on the host's tissues for a month or more, the young grub reaches the esophagus or the abdominal viscera, where it moves about for about 6 months to continue its development at the expense of the host animal. It then migrates on through the tissue under the skin to the back of the animal. The young larvae of the northern species do not invade the esophagus and abdominal viscera but migrate instead through the spinal canal on their way to the back of the animal. The grubs of both species usually locate along the median line of the back between the shoulders and hips and then cut holes through the skin in the choicest part of the hide.

After opening the hole through the skin, the grub molts to the second stage and becomes encysted under the hole. At this stage, small swellings on the back of the animal indicate the presence of the second stage of the heel fly grub. Having ample access to both food and air in the second stage, the grub grows rapidly for about 3 weeks and then molts again into the third, or last, stage. Up to this point the grub is opaque. As it goes through its third stage and completes its residence in the back of the animal it becomes dark brown or black in about 20 days, when maturity is reached, and it leaves the host animal through the hole in the skin.

Shortly before the mature grub leaves its host it partially dehydrates itself, shrinks considerably in size, and at the same time greatly enlarges the hole through the skin of the animal. These changes in the grub make possible a rapid and easy escape from the host and the dehydration keeps the grub from freezing after it leaves the body of the animal. The grub is not seriously affected by a sudden drop in temperature from around 103° F., the usual body temperature of cattle, to an outside air temperature of zero or lower. Few other insects can stand such drastic changes in their environments without suffering serious injury or death.

When the grub falls to the ground it crawls under nearby objects for protection and pupates for its transformation to the adult stage. The pupal period may range from 16 to 75 days, depending on prevailing temperatures. The adult fly does not feed. Its sole purpose is to reproduce. Mating is followed immediately by egg laying, which may take place within an hour after the adult emerges from the puparium.

The only method of control which has so far been successful in the United States has been to destroy the grubs by applying a larvicide during the time when the larvae, or grubs, inhabit the backs of animals. This method of treatment has been developed to the point where it is more effective than any other method known and is probably the only one that is practical and economical under our large-herd system of ranching.

Hundreds of materials have been tested, including such chlorinated hydrocarbons as DDT and benzene hexachloride, but rotenone is the only toxicant recommended for cattle grubs. Rotenone occurs in the roots of derris and cube plants; when the roots containing at least 5 percent rotenone are ground to a fineness that permits 90 percent or more to pass through a 200-mesh screen, the powder can be formulated so that it may be applied to the infested cattle as a dust, wash, spray, or dip.

Power spraying is the most rapid method of applying the powder in suspension to large herds of cattle. The dust or wash application usually is preferred by owners of small herds. The dust application is well adapted for use in very cold climates. If dipping vats are available and large herds are to be treated, the rotenone can be applied as a dip. Because the spray, dust, and wash are applied only to the grub-infested area of the animal, they are cheaper than the dip treatment, even for large herds.

Rotenone should be applied 30 to 45 days after the appearance of the first grubs in the backs of cattle and thereafter every 30 or 40 days during the grub season. Correct timing of the treatment, regardless of the method of application, is essential for satisfactory control.

Individual attempts to reduce cattle grub infestations are usually unsuccessful. If the grub population is to be satisfactorily reduced, control programs must be based on a community or area basis.

Time and again the value of organized community efforts to control cattle grubs has been proved. Grubs were practically eliminated on Clare Island, off the coast of Ireland, in 1920 after a 5-year program that involved the systematic destruction of grubs by all cattle owners working together. In Denmark, legislation in 1922 required that all cattle owners take measures to destroy the heel fly larvae in their herds; at the end of 3 years the percentage of infested hides in Denmark dropped from 20.5 to 2.5. In Prowers County in Colorado, a 6-year program, organized in 1928 and involving 22,500 head of cattle over 900 square miles, reduced the average infestations from 35 to 5 per head. Those programs were carried on largely without chemicals—cattlemen then had to squeeze the grubs out of their cysts in the backs of the cattle with the fingers, remove them with small forceps, or in limited trials to destroy them by inserting toxic materials into individual grub sacs.

Since 1932 control projects in the United States and Canada have been made simpler and more effective by the use of derris and cube root powders.

On Calumet Island in the Ottawa River, Canada, a cooperative program reduced the average numbers of cattle grubs in cattle from 16 to 2 between 1933 and 1936.

In Hughes County, S. Dak., a voluntary program effected an 80-percent reduction in grubs between 1947 and 1950; yearling calves harbored only an average of 15.5 larvae in the winter of 1950, while untreated cattle on farms outside the area were infested with an average of 78 grubs. In this program, as in similar work in New Mexico and Washington, the use of high-pressure spray equipment made it possible to treat large herds of cattle quickly, effectively, and inexpensively.

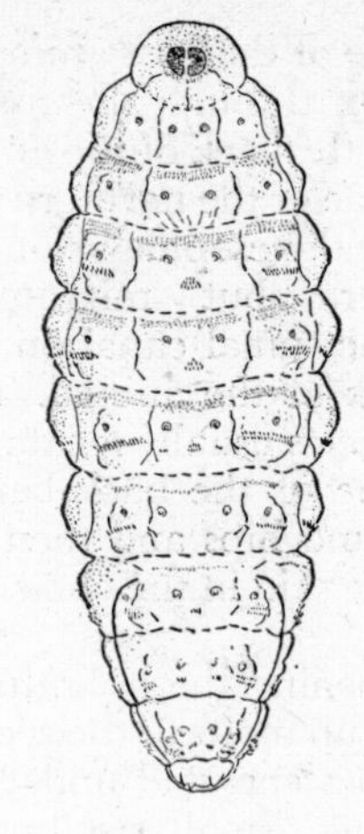

Common cattle grub.

A COMMUNITY PROGRAM can be organized successfully in almost any locality where cattlemen are willing to pool their efforts in a concerted attack on the grub. Between 1944 and 1949, projects were started in South Dakota, Montana, New Mexico, Oklahoma, Colorado, Washington, and California. Some were sponsored by Federal agencies and some by the State agricultural experiment stations. Several of the programs were assisted by such organizations as the National Live Stock Loss Prevention Board, State livestock sanitary associations, and the county cattlemen's associations.

Any group of stockmen or dairymen interested in a coordinated project against cattle grubs should seek the help offered by the county agent's office. They should first establish that cattle grubs are an economic problem in the locality. In a few sections infestations are sporadic and light and the expense and labor involved in community action would be of doubtful value.

The first step in outlining a grub-control project is to establish the boundaries of the area—not less than a

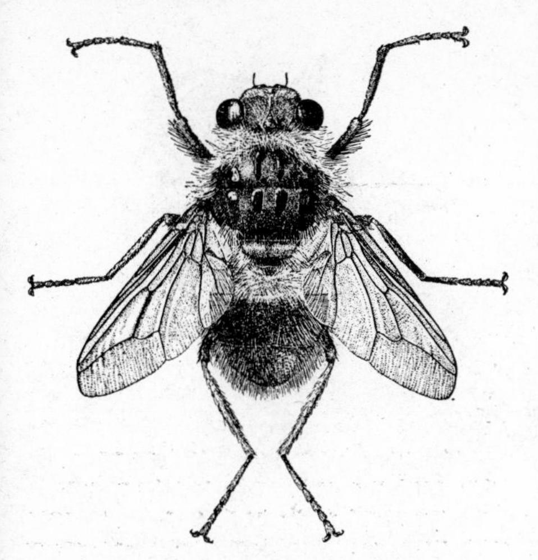

Common cattle grub adult.

township in extent—within which the work is to be conducted. A single township, in sections where dairy or feeder cattle are concentrated, may involve 100 or more owners and several thousand cattle, and will constitute therefore a satisfactory project. In regions where the carrying capacity of the range is low and there are no more than 300 or 400 cows in the township, the area selected should be much larger. In any case, the size of the area is important. The flight of the heel fly probably is limited to 3 miles or less. But even that limited movement is enough to permit flies from pastures on which untreated cattle are grazed to reinfest practically all cattle within a small grub-free area. In a larger area, flies from surrounding pastures can hardly make their way to the centrally located herds and would normally reinfest only the cattle at the periphery of the area.

It is also important that the area selected for grub control be as nearly square or circular as possible, rather than in the form of a long, narrow strip. In the latter case, flies from bordering pastures would be able to reach all farms in the area under control and quickly reinfest the grub-free cattle. Four or five townships are considered to be the optimum size for an initial project of moderate dimensions. Theoretically there is no limit in the size to which a program of this nature may grow.

Another factor to be considered is the existence of natural barriers against the return of the heel flies. The perfect place for a control project is an island. Heel flies apparently do not operate over large bodies of water, and grub-free cattle on an island a mile or more off the mainland apparently are not subject to natural reinfestation. In approximating such ideal circumstances, it is advisable to locate the area where natural barriers exist or to extend the area up to whatever barriers are at hand. Wide rivers and lakes discourage the activity of the heel fly. Mountains, forest, and even croplands from which cattle are absent are similarly effective. Less satisfactory are highways and railroad rights-of-way; the latter are not effective against the heel fly, but they may serve in many instances to define an area sharply.

Once the boundaries of the district have been established, all owners of dairy and beef cattle should be informed that 100-percent cooperation is desirable and that any untreated cattle within the area constitute a reservoir of infestation for the treated animals. Actually, if about 80 percent of the cattle can be included in the program the undertaking may be considered worth while. Participants in the project should be informed of the biology, pathology, economics, and therapeutics involved. A map should be prepared to show the boundaries, roads, and the location of farm and ranch units. A committee should be chosen to coordinate the activities.

The participant will find it useful to name an administrative head or group. If the program is a small one, the county agent or the local vocational agricultural instructor may serve in that capacity. If it is a large one, the duties may be assumed by a county cattlemen's association or a similar group.

Administrative duties will be many. Enough insecticide should be purchased for the treatment of all cattle within the project. Spray equipment must be provided for large herds. Some cattlemen's groups have found it expedient to purchase their own spraying equipment. Others have made use of county-owned machinery. Still others have contracted with commercial operators to conduct the work. The owners of small herds, who may want to treat their cattle by hand, must be provided with materials needed for the application of dusts and washes. When the time to apply treatment is determined, each neighborhood leader or committeeman should be prepared to see that work is coordinated on all farms and ranches within his district. Routes should be planned in advance for spraying crews, so that a minimum of time will be spent on each farm. Farmers who choose to apply insecticides by hand should be notified when treatment of their cattle is required. Groups of small operators might well pool facilities and labor. The work of the administrating or organizing body will be determined generally by the size of the project, the interest of the participants, the extent of cooperation, the kind of livestock management practiced, the nature of the terrain, and climate.

As WE STATED, the treatment of cattle every 30 or 40 days during the period when grubs are in their backs is essential if the grubs are to be destroyed. Two to four treatments a year therefore must be administered, depending on the section of the country. About three consecutive years of work may be required before one can appreciate the effectiveness of the program and its results in terms of sound hides, better beef, and more milk.

ERNEST W. LAAKE *is research adviser in entomology, Office of Foreign Agricultural Relations. He has been stationed in Costa Rica and Ecuador.*

IRWIN H. ROBERTS *is a parasitologist in the zoological division of the Bureau of Animal Industry.*

Engelmann spruce beetle.

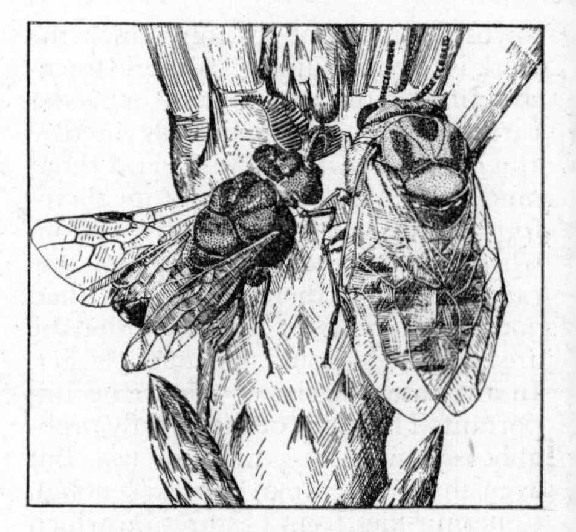

Introduced pine sawfly, male and female.

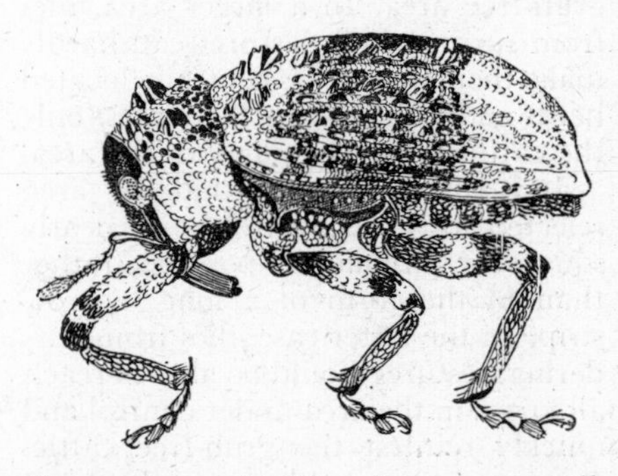

The poplar and willow borer, a weevil, whose cryptic coloration matches well the bark of its host trees.

Forests, Trees, and Pests

Insects and Spread of Forest-Tree Diseases

Curtis May, Whiteford L. Baker

Insects spread several important forest- and shade-tree diseases. Chief among them are the blue stain fungi, the Dutch elm disease fungus, and the virus of phloem necrosis of elms. The relation of insects to the spread of the blue stain fungi was the subject of early extensive investigations, and this relationship has been known for several years. Recently the large losses caused by the two elm diseases have stimulated intensive research, and much new information has been obtained on the insects that spread them and on their control. Additional investigations undoubtedly will disclose that insects are responsible for the spread of many other diseases of forest and shade trees.

The wind spreads the fungi that cause some forest-tree diseases—for example, the spores of the fungus that causes white pine blister rust. The same is true of the one that causes chestnut blight; insects have only a minor part in its distribution. At best, insects act only as accidental, secondary carriers when they happen to come in contact with spores of the fungus on a diseased chestnut tree and then move to a healthy one where the spores are dislodged from their bodies. No doubt the spores of many other parasitic fungi are thus carried from tree to tree and place to place by accidental insect carriers. The fortuitous relationship between insect and fungus in such instances offers practically no opportunity for the development of control measures through sprays or other treatments for the insects. But there are fungi and viruses that are spread primarily or entirely by insects. Then control of the disease may depend upon finding a satisfactory control for the insect carriers. The relation of insects to the spread of Dutch elm disease and phloem necrosis and their control is illustrative.

The Dutch elm disease is caused by the fungus *Ceratostomella ulmi*. Bark beetles carry the fungus from diseased trees and from dead elms or elm wood or logs in which it is growing to healthy trees or to other dead elms or elm wood. Were it not for these bark beetles, the disease would be relatively unimportant. By the same token, were it not for the destructiveness of the fungus, the bark beetles themselves would be relatively unimportant—before about 1930 they were so considered; only after the introduction of the Dutch elm disease into the United States in the late 1920's did they assume their present importance.

Two kinds of elm bark beetles are important in the spread of the disease. One, the smaller European elm bark beetle, is European in origin. The other, the native elm bark beetle, has been here right along. The European species was introduced 25 or 30 years before the Dutch elm disease fungus came in and, because it bred only in dying or recently dead elm or cut elm wood during the interval, it was relatively unimportant. When the fungus also was introduced, however, the combination of beetle and fungus produced a disastrous situation. This sequence of events emphasizes the importance of the need for constant vigilance to exclude dangerous or potentially dangerous parasites.

The story of how the elm bark beetles spread the Dutch elm disease fungus was brought to light through the research of many plant pathologists and entomologists in Europe and in this country. Workers in State agricultural experiment stations and divisions of agriculture, several colleges, and the Department of Agriculture have made contributions that have helped to fill out the picture.

The fungus that causes the Dutch elm disease lives in the water-conducting vessels and adjacent cells of the elm, where it grows and produces spores in the vessels. The spores are so small they can be transported rapidly in the sap stream in the trunk, branches, leaves, and roots. When the fungus has become established in the tree or a part of a tree, it causes wilting, yellowing, dying, and dropping of leaves. The symptoms may develop suddenly or slowly and may involve the whole tree or any part of it. The affected tree may be so severely diseased that it dies in a few weeks, or it may decline gradually for several years before it finally succumbs. Occasionally an infected tree may recover. The fungus can live for several years in standing trees; it can also live for a year or two in dead standing elms or in elm logs, wood, and branches broken off or partly broken off during storms. Without aid from elm bark beetles, however, the fungus has no effective way to reach other elms except through natural grafts of roots of diseased elms with nearby healthy elms. Unfortunately for those who wish to save their elms, the dying trees, broken branches, and recently cut logs and wood are soon invaded by the elm bark beetles, which may later carry the disease to the healthy trees.

The beetles bore into the bark where the females make egg galleries and lay eggs. The young larvae, when they emerge, eat the inner bark and make characteristic channels in it. After a period of feeding, they pupate and come out as adult beetles. The fungus may be carried into the original egg gallery made by the female beetles in the bark, or it may be present in the underlying wood if it was previously infected. The fungus can grow luxuriantly in the beetle galleries and produce spores in great abundance. When the adult beetle emerges from the bark it may be well seeded externally and internally with the fungus spores. It begins to feed soon after it emerges, either in living parts of the tree from which it has emerged, or after it has flown to another elm, which may be nearby or several miles distant.

The adult beetle feeds in the crotches of twigs or at the point of junction of a leaf and twig. While it does so, spores of the fungus may be rubbed off its antennae, mouth parts, feet, or body and become lodged in the feeding wound. Some of the spores, or indeed one of them, may start to grow in the feeding injury and infect the tree. That can happen only if the injury in which the spore is released reaches the wood, however; otherwise, no infection takes place. This limitation on the ability of the fungus to cause infection clinches the need for the assistance of the beetle in spreading the parasite from diseased to healthy trees. On its part, the fungus makes the tree suitable for invasion by egg-laying beetles.

Beetles may lay their eggs in dying elm of elm wood that has not previously been invaded by the Dutch elm disease fungus. If the invading beetles have emerged from diseased trees, however, they may carry the fungus with them into such wood, and it in turn becomes a source of danger for nearby healthy trees when the new brood of beetles emerges the following spring or later during the same season. The smaller European elm bark beetle therefore does not require the presence of the Dutch elm disease fungus to survive, although the fungus helps to provide it with the type of wood it needs for reproduction. Storms, drought, certain construction activities of man, and old-age decline of elm trees provide elm wood suitable for reproduction of the beetles. These alone would insure perpetuation of the species as it was perpetuated for years in Europe. With the additional assistance of the Dutch elm disease fungus in providing suitable wood there is little reason to hope that the beetle can ever be eradicated.

We have reason to hope, however, that it can be controlled. We know, for instance, that the beetle is highly susceptible to DDT sprays and that its numbers can be kept at a relatively low level by the systematic removal of all elm wood that might serve as breeding material. For weeks or months the beetles will not feed on individual trees that have been thoroughly sprayed with the correct formulation of DDT. If all breeding material is removed from a locality, the beetle population will be limited to migrants flying in from the outside, and will thus be held to a low level. If recommended spraying and sanitary measures are combined, it is likely that little loss from disease will result. Naturally, the larger the area in which sanitary measures are undertaken, the better the results will be.

The native elm bark beetle can also spread the Dutch elm disease fungus. Its life history is different from that of the European species and it has been a less effective carrier in the United States than the latter. The native beetle hibernates mostly as an adult in the bark of healthy elms, although occasionally it overwinters in the larval stage. An adult may carry the Dutch elm disease fungus into its hibernation chamber where the fungus will survive until the following spring. Before it emerges in early spring, the beetle feeds for a short time on the inner bark; it may then come in contact with the wood underlying its hibernation chamber. Elms are invaded by the fungus by way of these contact points, but they are often made so early in the spring that growth of new wood in the trees has not started and no new water-conducting vessels have been formed. When new growth does begin, therefore, it entombs the injury along with any spores that may be in it. Because the fungus has only weak power to penetrate cell walls, few infections can occur.

This beetle has not been an important carrier of the disease in the United States. Nevertheless, its habit of overwintering in healthy elms makes it impossible to eliminate as a source of disease transmission from an area, without at the same time eliminating all the elms of more than 1-inch trunk diameter. The beetle can be controlled, however, by the same spray program recommended for the European species.

In Canada the native elm bark beetle appears to be an important carrier of the Dutch elm disease fungus. We have no satisfactory explanation for the difference in its importance as a carrier in the two countries. We suspect that the seasonal history of the beetle may be more closely synchronized in that country with the development of the water-conducting vessels of elm in the spring. In our more northern and colder sections, therefore, it may prove to be a more effective carrier than it has been farther south. Just how effective the smaller European elm bark beetle will be in the more northerly regions we do not know, because it has only recently invaded these territories.

The importance of dead and dying elm wood, and of the breeding and overwintering habits of the beetles in the spread of the Dutch elm disease fungus, therefore, is apparent. Destruction of as much as possible of the beetle-infested material is of primary importance in any organized program to control the disease.

As a final word concerning the role

of insects in spreading Dutch elm disease, it might be well to emphasize that there is no obligate relationship between the two species of beetles and the fungus they distribute. Both kinds of beetles can survive without the fungus, but they and the fungus are complementary in their activities, and together they form a formidable coalition that is causing tremendous losses of elms. The destruction being wrought by the Dutch elm disease is serious enough in itself. Unfortunately, however, it is supplemented in the Midwest by the killing of scores of thousands of elms by another disease known as phloem necrosis, which is caused by a virus and spread by quite a different kind of insect.

THE VIRUS that causes phloem necrosis of elm cannot be transmitted by mechanical means. Healthy trees cannot be inoculated with the virus by grinding, extracting, or macerating infected tissue and then injecting or rubbing it into them. However, the virus can be transmitted experimentally to a healthy tree by grafting into it a small piece of bark from a tree infected with the virus. The virus does not seem to exist outside of living plant cells except when it is in the body of an elm leafhopper.

One kind of elm leafhopper, *Scaphoideus luteolus,* can transmit the virus of the disease from diseased to healthy trees. Only a short period of intensive research by entomologists and plant pathologists was required before proof was obtained of the role of the leafhopper in transmitting the virus.

The leafhopper overwinters as an egg in the bark of elms. The eggs are laid late in the summer. They hatch the following spring, about May 1, in the latitude of Columbus, Ohio. The young nymphs crawl immediately to elm leaves where they feed on the leaf veins. All through the nymphal period they continue to feed on the juice of elms. The beak is sunk into the phloem tissue of soft bark and leaf veins and the plant juices are sucked into the growing insect. The insect also feeds on elm as an adult. If feeding occurs on an elm infected with phloem necrosis, the insect may become infective. The virus does not seem to harm the insect.

The adult leafhopper, a capable flier, may move from elm to elm and feed for long periods during the summer. The virus is transferred to healthy trees during this process. Within a short time the virus can move from the point of injection by the insect to other parts of the elm tree where it may be picked up by other feeding leafhoppers.

As far as we know now, the virus does not live over winter in the eggs of the leafhopper. It must therefore survive from one year to the next in diseased elms, which become infected late enough in the season to escape death from the disease before winter. The trees that carry the virus over the winter leaf out weakly the following spring and die within a short time. However, they do not die soon enough to prevent the newly hatched leafhoppers from feeding on them and becoming infective. The relationship between the leafhopper and the virus disease is much more restrictive than that between the Dutch elm disease fungus and the bark beetles that transmit it from tree to tree. As a matter of fact, it would seem that without the leafhopper carriers, the virus causing phloem necrosis would soon cease to exist.

This leafhopper can be controlled by spraying elms with DDT, provided all leaf surfaces are covered thoroughly. Two applications of the spray are required—the first when elm leaves become full-grown and the second from 1 to 2 months later. The spray may be applied with hydraulic equipment or with a mist blower. For hydraulic equipment a 1 percent DDT emulsion spray is required. With the mist blower it is necessary to use a 6 percent DDT emulsion.

In certain sections of the Midwest both phloem necrosis and the Dutch elm disease occur. In such areas it may be desirable to control the insect vectors of both diseases at the same time.

That can be done by covering all elm bark and leaf surfaces thoroughly with DDT: A total of three separate spray applications are recommended. The first should be made early in the spring before elm leaves appear. It should consist of a 2 percent DDT emulsion if hydraulic equipment is to be used, or a 12½ percent emulsion if a mist blower is used. The second and third applications are made with the same formulations and at the same times as recommended for control of the vector of phloem necrosis alone.

THE ROLE OF the beech scale in the spread of nectria disease of beech represents a somewhat different kind of relationship between insects and forest-tree disease. The scale insect apparently reached the United States from Europe by way of Canada and is now fairly widespread in the Northeastern States. It establishes colonies on the lower trunks of beech trees, particularly on trees growing in cool, shady places. The colonies are small at first but enlarge and spread to new spots on the tree trunk within a few seasons. The scale inserts its beak into the bark and sucks up plant juices. As a result, there are many thousands of tiny punctures in the bark of infested beech trees. The injuries appear to be the entrance point through which the beech-bark canker fungus, *Nectria coccinea* var. *faginata,* invades the tree. Without these injuries, the fungus cannot invade the bark. Once it has gained entry through them, it rapidly kills the area of bark previously occupied by the scale, and produces a great abundance of spores on the affected bark. These are probably spread widely by the wind. Often the bright-red, spore-bearing structures on the surface of the bark can be observed in large patches from a distance.

The beech scale and the nectria disease can be controlled by spraying with lime-sulfur to eliminate the scale from infected trees. Such a direct method is not practical under forest conditions, although it may be used to protect ornamentals and trees in parks. In the forest, where spraying is not practicable, there is as yet no proved control for the trouble.

Bark beetle.

INSECTS ARE also responsible for spreading the destructive fungi that cause blue staining of standing coniferous trees, logs, and lumber. The stains do not weaken the wood, but they often cause a reduction in the value of wood products.

The relationship of insects to the spread of blue stain fungi resembles that of Dutch elm disease. The reason may be that the fungus causing that disease is closely allied to those causing blue stain. Again, as was true of the Dutch elm disease fungus, the insects that carry blue stain fungi from tree to tree are bark beetles. The habits of this group of beetles make them effective in transporting the spores of fungi from one tree and placing them in another.

Broods of the bark beetles develop between the bark and wood. That happens because adult beetles emerge from one tree and seek out another, alight on it, and bore through the bark, where they excavate tunnels and lay their eggs. Thus they carry the fungi into the bark with them. Once the fungi are implanted in the bark they begin to grow and produce spores in the tunnels and chambers occupied by the developing insects. When the beetles complete their development they bore their way out through the bark and, loaded both externally and internally with fungi, they seek out new trees to attack, thus starting the cycle over again.

All trees in a stand are not attacked equally by the bark beetles. We do not know why. We do know that fire-damaged trees are heavily attacked and that trees weakened by drought and root rot are more likely to be attacked than vigorous ones.

In logs and lumber, the beetles have a minor part in the spread of blue stain fungi. That is because wind and rain easily dislodge the spores of the fungi from the surface of the wood, where they are produced in abundance, and scatter them widely. Damage to logs and lumber can be prevented by the application of chemical sprays. When timber values are high, losses among standing trees can be offset considerably by the salvage and sale of the stained timber.

OTHER FOREST DISEASES are also carried by insects. It has been shown by J. G. Leach and his coworkers at the University of Minnesota that a definite relationship exists between the amount and rapidity of decay in Norway pine logs and the extent that two species of wood-boring insects tunnel into the wood.

The fungus causing persimmon wilt has been isolated from the wood immediately adjacent to insect-feeding injuries in otherwise healthy trees, indicating that some of the spread of this wind-borne fungus to healthy trees is related to the abundance of such insect-caused wounds.

A vascular disease of willow, caused by the bacterium *Pseudomonas saliciperda* is transmitted by the poplar and willow borer. The beetles become contaminated with the bacteria while feeding upon diseased willows. When they fly to healthy trees and resume their feeding, disease transmission takes place.

The fungus *Polyporus volvatus* is common in dead or dying trees of several species of conifers killed by bark beetles. It causes decay of the sapwood and is probably introduced into the trees by the beetles.

The pattern of occurrence of oak wilt suggests that the fungus causing it may be transmitted from tree to tree by insects, but experimental proof is lacking.

CURTIS MAY *is a principal pathologist in the division of forest pathology, Bureau of Plant Industry, Soils, and Agricultural Engineering. He has been engaged in research on the diseases of forest and shade trees for more than 25 years. He is a graduate of Ohio State University and was on the staff of the Ohio Agricultural Experiment Station before he joined the Department of Agriculture in 1933.*

WHITEFORD L. BAKER *is an assistant leader of the division of forest insect investigations, Bureau of Entomology and Plant Quarantine. He was graduated from Clemson Agricultural College in 1927 and, after graduate study at the University of Minnesota, joined the Department of Agriculture in 1929.*

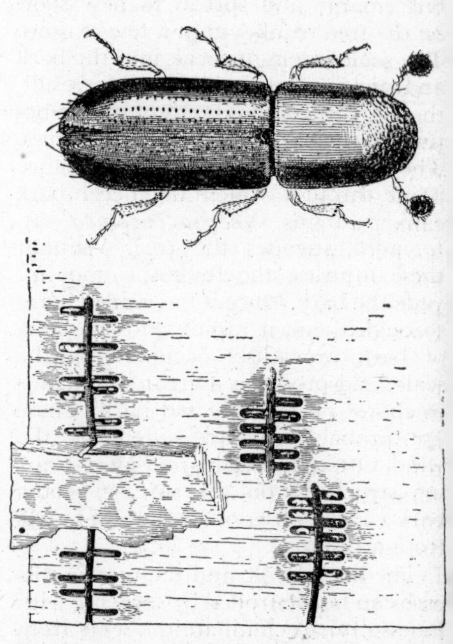

The western hemlock stainer is a very small beetle that constructs individual cells for rearing its young in timber trees.

The Spruce Budworm

R. C. Brown

The spruce budworm has destroyed thousands of square miles of coniferous forests in the United States and Canada.

An article in *Trees*, the Yearbook of Agriculture for 1949, discussed an outbreak in Canada and emphasized the importance of proper forest management as a way to alleviate the damage that the budworm inflicts on forests.

Since then the infestation has spread eastward over a wider area in Quebec, and tree mortality has greatly increased there and in Ontario. Noticeable defoliation of balsam fir and spruce is now evident over a quarter million acres in northern Maine. Heavily defoliated areas covering about 1.5 million acres have appeared in New Brunswick. Nearly 3 million acres of Douglas-fir have been severely defoliated in eastern Oregon since 1945, and severe outbreaks have occurred south of Mount Hood and near Eugene. Heavy outbreaks have started in Montana. In 1949, 1950, and 1951, nearly 2.5 million acres of Douglas-fir in Oregon were sprayed with DDT from airplanes in an attempt to save the forests from destruction.

The menace of the spruce budworm to the pulp, paper, and the lumber industries, the devastation already done in this country and Canada, and the threat of much greater damage has stimulated the Department of Agriculture to use every effort to combat it. Surveys are being conducted by the Department and State and private agencies to detect and appraise outbreaks. Where defoliation is sufficiently severe to cause trees to die, steps are taken to apply DDT to kill the feeding budworms. Foresters and entomologists are urging timberland owners to carry out cutting operations designed to lessen the impact of spruce budworm defoliation in threatened areas. Investigations are conducted on nearly every phase of the problem.

THE SPRUCE BUDWORM has worried timberland owners, foresters, and entomologists for 40 years. An investigation was conducted by J. M. Swaine and F. C. Craighead in eastern Canada in the early 1920's. It was primarily a study of post-outbreak conditions, for the heaviest defoliation had occurred in the preceding decade. But that did not detract from the value of the studies, for they permitted an appraisal of the damage under a wide variety of forest conditions and revealed the stands that best withstood the onslaught. They furnished information about ways to manage forests so as to minimize budworm damage. Their findings have been supported by later investigations in Canada. Observations in Ontario and Quebec have shown, for instance, that severe damage has occurred where balsam fir was the predominant species in the forest and that pure stands of black spruce have suffered practically no damage, while white spruce has been seriously injured. White spruce, however, is relatively unimportant as a component of the spruce-fir forests of the Northeastern States.

The studies are a basis for recommending three general methods for managing spruce-fir stands: To clearcut mature and overmature balsam stands; to operate balsam stands on a short rotation; to try to increase the proportion of red and black spruce in the stands.

Studies conducted by S. A. Graham and L. W. Orr in Minnesota in the late 1930's on the silvicultural aspects of the problem substantiated the findings of Swaine and Craighead and gave further support to the forest-management methods I have described. The investigations added another important suggestion: "To limit the size of individual tracts of susceptible types to the minimum size that can be economically handled as a unit, and either by cultural operation or by logging, to separate them from one another by nonsusceptible types or by stands that will not become susceptible until a later date."

The current outbreak in Canada, which reached epidemic proportions in Ontario in 1935, caused the Dominion Department of Agriculture to initiate a research program. With the backing of the pulp and paper industry, modern laboratories have been constructed where fundamental research work on the spruce budworm is being done. Field studies are conducted over large areas in the Canadian forests.

By 1944 the budworm infestation in Ontario and Quebec covered about 125 million acres. An enormous amount of timber had been killed. That and the memory of an earlier outbreak in Maine prompted the timberland owners of the Northeastern States to ask Congress for funds to study methods for combatting the spruce budworm. In 1944 the funds were made available to the Bureau of Entomology and Plant Quarantine and the Forest Service. Only a few specimens of the insect could be found then in New England, and plans were made to initiate studies in 1945 in Quebec in cooperation with Dominion entomologists. In that year an infestation was discovered in the Adirondacks of New York. Field studies were carried on there until 1948, when the infestation subsided. Meanwhile an increase in budworm population occurred in northern Maine, and field investigations were transferred there.

The research program in the Northeast has involved the following projects: The development of survey techniques; biological and natural control investigations; the application of biological information to silvicultural practices; control of the insect through the airplane application of insecticides; and the effect of the application of DDT on fish and wildlife.

One of the first problems was to develop a method for measuring the numbers of the insect in order to evaluate the effect of natural control factors and to measure the degree of control obtained from insecticide applications. Early investigations proved the futility of attempting to obtain records of the population of the insect on the entire tree because of its tiny size in its early stages, its concealed habit of feeding, and the labor and time involved in examining large volumes of foliage. Because only a small portion of the foliage from an individual tree could be effectively sampled, a 15-inch twig was adopted as the sampling unit. This sample could be used to obtain population records for larvae in all stages of development, for pupae, and also for egg masses of the insect. Although it did not provide a value for the total number of budworms on a tree or in an area, it served a useful purpose in comparing population densities from place to place or year to year. Reductions in population from stage to stage during a single generation could also be measured.

The 15-inch twigs taken with a pole pruner at a height of about 20 feet from the ground gave a fair measure of budworm populations when a number of representative trees were sampled. Thus, in conducting surveys to determine population trends, five 15-inch twigs taken from each of five trees at a sampling station was adopted as the standard procedure for measuring larval, pupal, and egg-mass populations. Estimates of percentages of defoliation are also recorded.

Much of the spruce-fir region of Maine cannot be reached by roads or navigable streams, and aerial surveys have been valuable in detecting defoliation. The Cessna 195 seaplane, a five-seated high-wing monoplane, with no struts to obstruct the view, is good for the survey work. By flying at an average speed of 95 miles an hour and at a constant elevation of 200 feet above the ground, an observer can detect defoliation in excess of 20 percent.

By following flight lines on a map and using an operation recorder, one can obtain a permanent record of defoliation. The records from the individual flight lines may then be transferred to a map in much the same manner that a type map is made up for a timber cruise. Such a system makes it possible to conduct aerial surveys annually along the same flight lines and thus obtain accurate information on the progress of the infestation. In areas where surveys had previously indicated the presence of an infestation of the budworm, flight lines were spaced 3 miles apart. When the observers could no longer detect defoliation along a line, the distance between flight lines was increased to 6 miles. If no defoliation showed up on those lines, the distance was increased to 10 miles. Ground checks made at several points revealed that the defoliation records obtained from the aerial survey were surprisingly accurate.

Emphasis has been given to studies of the biology and natural control of the spruce budworm. The studies have provided information on the seasonal development of the insect and its food-plant preferences. They indicated that the larvae prefer the foliage of balsam fir and develop readily on both old and current growth. When larvae emerge from hibernation they first mine the old needles. Then they enter the opening buds as soon as growth starts. The larvae develop readily on the new foliage of red and black spruce, but survival is poor on the old foliage of those species. The buds on red and black spruce open later than those on balsam; red and black spruce therefore are less favorable food plants than balsam fir. Such fundamental information on the biology and feeding habits of the budworm is a basis for formulating methods for its silvicultural control.

Also emphasized is the effect of natural factors of control—particularly measures of the controlling effect of egg, larval, and pupal parasites, diseases of larvae and pupae, predation by birds, and overwintering mortality.

970134°—52——45

Eleven quarter-acre plots representing different forest types were established in the Adirondacks in 1946 to get information on the degree of parasitization of the spruce budworm. Collections of eggs, hibernating larvae, small larvae in the buds, full-grown larvae, and pupae were made at each point and either dissected or reared to determine the percentage of parasitization. Aggregate percentages for all plots increased from 62 in 1946 to 72 in 1947 and to 75 in 1948.

Sixty-one species of parasites of the spruce budworm are known, but only about 12 of them were important in the Adirondack region. Disease apparently played an insignificant part in controlling the budworm. Mortality that occurred between the time the eggs hatched in late summer and the time the tiny larvae started mining needles in the spring accounted for a loss of 76 percent in 1946–1947 and 80 percent in 1947–1948. No quantitative measure of the effect of birds in controlling the budworm was obtained, but entomologists believe that the tremendous reduction in population during the late larval and pupal period in 1947 could be largely attributed to birds. That was possible because there were enough birds in the region almost to eliminate the budworms left after other natural factors had taken their toll.

The infestation that appeared in 1945 and threatened to attain outbreak proportions in 1946 was brought under control by 1948. Natural factors were responsible—the composition and characteristics of the forest in the Adirondack region were particularly favorable for the natural enemies of the spruce budworm. The spruce-fir stands in the area are relatively small and are interspersed with hardwoods, in contrast with regions farther north where large continuous areas of spruce and fir exist and where devastating outbreaks have occurred.

Studies in Maine have indicated that all the species of parasites reared in the Adirondacks exist there. Aggregate parasitization and winter mortality are nearly as high as in the Adirondacks. Birds are also important predators of the budworm in Maine.

Besides study plots, special techniques have been used in Maine to determine the role of natural control factors by artificially infesting trees with known numbers of spruce budworms. Some trees are caged to exclude parasites and birds. This method may permit a more precise evaluation of the natural enemies of the insect.

Although the area of noticeable defoliation in Maine has increased in size since 1949, the budworm population on individual trees in the older infestations has not shown a consistent increase; in fact, there are nearly as many instances where a decrease has occurred. Undoubtedly a gigantic struggle is in progress between the spruce budworm and its natural factors of control. The next few years will determine its outcome.

SEVERAL SPECIES OF PARASITES occur in the West but not in the East. Since 1945 the parasites have been reared and shipped to the East for colonization in the Adirondacks and Maine. It is too early to determine if they have become established in eastern infestations. As far as we know, all the eastern species of parasites exist in the West.

In 1950, studies were conducted in stands of Douglas-fir and white fir in three well-separated study areas in eastern Oregon to determine the effect of natural factors in controlling the spruce budworm. Aggregate parasitization there was 61, 52, and 32 percent.

In the third area, where parasitization was low, possibly because of the complexities of retarded seasonal development, however, 60 percent of the pupae died from what appears to be a disease. Aggregate mortality observed was, therefore, 73 percent in that area. No evidence of disease was noted in the other two. That is the only known record of appreciable mortality of the spruce budworm that may possibly be attributed to disease.

Studies to determine the application of biological information to silvicultural practices are being carried out. Sample plots have been established in areas that represent a wide variety of conditions of stand and site. If defoliation becomes sufficiently heavy to injure or kill trees, detailed studies will be undertaken to determine the effect of defoliation on spruce and fir in the sample plots. Defoliation in the Adirondacks was insufficient to damage trees and thus far no appreciable injury has occurred in Maine.

To demonstrate the cutting methods that I have described, 19 experimental areas covering 50 to 750 acres each have been established by the Forest Service, the Bureau of Entomology and Plant Quarantine, the States, and timberland owners in the Northeast. They are located in different parts of the region so that the influence of stand and site conditions may be observed if a budworm outbreak should occur.

Studies have been under way since 1945 to determine effective means for controlling the budworm by the aerial application of DDT. In that year field tests were initiated in the Province of Quebec, and three small plots were sprayed in the Adirondacks. Tests were continued in New York in 1946 and 1947, in Oregon in 1948, in Maine in 1949 and 1950, and in Quebec in 1951.

Undoubtedly the spruce budworm is highly susceptible to low dosages of DDT, but because of its concealed feeding habits it is much more difficult to control than free-feeding defoliators. Some of the tests made in 1945, 1946, and 1947 gave good results, but not all were satisfactory. Applications made when the insect was in the needle-mining stage and the early bud-feeding stage did not give a high degree of control. As the caterpillars became larger and were more exposed, the percentage of mortality from the spray applications increased. During the last 2 weeks of larval development, from about June 15 to July 1, many of the tests gave good control. Applications made for control of the budworm adults were ineffective. Most of the tests in the East were made in infestations of only light to medium intensity.

In 1948 a series of plots were treated with a small fixed-wing plane and a helicopter in a heavy infestation on Douglas-fir and white fir in eastern Oregon. The plots were sprayed with dosages of 1 and 2 pounds of DDT per acre during the last 2 weeks of larval development. The results were outstanding. In 10 of the 12 plots, more than 97 percent control was obtained. No appreciable difference was seen between the 1- and 2-pound dosages or between the airplane and helicopter applications. One of the two plots that gave lower control was inadvertently sprayed with a one-half pound dosage, and the other was treated late in the afternoon when thermal currents affected deposition of the spray.

The high percentage of control obtained in the tests in Oregon apparently was due largely to the extremely high larval population. The caterpillars were more active in their competition for food and were consequently more exposed than in the lighter infestations in the East, where an abundance of food was present and they were less active. The tests demonstrated that excellent control can be obtained by the aerial application of 1 pound of DDT in 1 gallon of spray per acre.

Experiments in Maine in 1949 and 1950 and in Quebec in 1951 were designed to obtain more precise information on the actual spray deposit on the foliage and the influence of such factors as droplet size and formulation of spray on deposit. The tests were made in relatively light infestations, and the control with a 1-pound dosage, measured as reduction in population, ranged from about 80 percent to more than 95 percent in the treated plots. The experiments showed that uniform coverage of the spray is a critical factor in obtaining a high measure of control. The amount of spray material, type of formulation, droplet size of the spray, weather conditions, and stand conditions are important mainly insofar as they influence the actual amount of DDT deposited on the foliage. Insuring a deposit of a lethal dosage is the primary problem of aerial application. A study of dosage-mortality relationships has shown that approximately 0.3 pound of DDT per acre is the minimum deposit for effecting 90 percent or more reduction of the budworm population in the late larval stages.

A HIGH DEGREE OF CONTROL of the budworm can be obtained but we have little information on the rapidity of build-up from the residual population left after spraying or the rate of reinfestation from the periphery of a treated area.

Spraying operations usually are carried on in the most heavily infested parts of a forest, and invariably there are more lightly infested adjacent areas that remain as a menace to the treated area. Some question exists as to the most effective time for applying treatment during the progress of an infestation. Should an area be sprayed in the early stages of infestation or should treatment be delayed until just before the time when defoliation is sufficiently severe to cause tree injury? We need to make further tests to determine the earliest stage in its life history at which the insect can be effectively controlled, with the hope that control operations may be carried out over a longer period during the season and greater protection afforded to the foliage of the current season. At present, spraying is restricted to about 2 weeks near the end of the feeding period—an exceedingly short time if vast areas need to be treated. Studies are needed to determine the effect on the natural enemies of the spruce budworm of spraying large areas with DDT.

In appraising infestations, it is desirable to determine the degree of control that natural factors exert. Perhaps under some conditions the infestation is actually subsiding from the activity of natural control factors and spraying may be unnecessary. The Adirondack infestation is a case in point.

Studies to determine the effect of DDT on birds, fish, and other wildlife have been conducted since 1945. Several forested areas have been sprayed specifically for those studies, and observations have been made in other areas sprayed to control forest defoliators.

In one locality sprayed experimentally with 5 pounds of DDT per acre, a population of more than three birds to the acre declined in 2 weeks to about one-sixth of the original population. In another place, sprayed for four consecutive years at the peak of the nesting period with 2 pounds of DDT per acre, no deleterious effect on birds was evident. In all experimental tests, birds were unaffected by a single application of 1 pound of DDT per acre.

All in all, the investigations have allayed many early fears of the use of DDT in the forest.

The greatest need in the future is an expansion of studies of the natural control of the insect. Such studies should be conducted throughout the country where the spruce budworm is a threat. We should try to determine under what forest conditions natural factors will keep the insect in check and why outbreaks develop in other areas. Studies should be undertaken to determine the effect of silvicultural practices on natural control as well as the effect of the widespread application of DDT on the natural enemies of the insect. That will call for the closest cooperation between those who conduct surveys, those who carry out control operations, and those who are working on basic research problems.

R. C. Brown *is an entomologist in the Bureau of Entomology and Plant Quarantine. He was graduated from the University of New Hampshire in 1922 and has been in the Bureau since 1925. In 1935 he was put in charge of the laboratory of the division of forest insect investigations in New Haven.*

Bark Beetles in Forests

F. P. Keen

The Engelmann spruce beetle in 1942 began to increase its numbers in wind-thrown spruce in the high mountains of western Colorado. From the windfalls, new beetle progeny emerged to attack living trees. With each generation, increasing hordes of beetles developed and attacked more and more spruce, until more than 4 billion feet has been killed.

During the flight period of 1949, the air was so full of beetles that the ones that happened to fall into a small lake in the infested area and washed ashore (although only a minor fraction of the total flight) were so numerous as to form a drift of dead beetles a foot deep, 6 feet wide, and 2 miles long. Those flying southeast over 18 miles of open country settled on a plateau of previously uninfested forest and killed 400,000 trees in one mass attack.

That is one example of the destructiveness of bark beetles, which, no bigger than small beans, can quickly bring about the death of a majestic pine, fir, spruce, or hemlock in its forest setting and can devastate extensive forests with much the same outcome as a forest fire.

Other species can be destructive, too: The Black Hills beetle often becomes epidemic in the Rocky Mountain region and kills hundreds of thousands of board feet of ponderosa pine. The mountain pine beetle has laid waste hundreds of miles of lodgepole forests in the Rocky Mountain and Pacific Coast regions and also kills valuable sugar pines in California. The western pine beetle killed 25 billion board feet of ponderosa pine saw timber in the Pacific Coast region between 1917 and 1943 and has been a serious competitor of lumbermen for available timber supplies.

Many others, such as the Douglas-fir beetle, the Sitka-spruce beetle, the southern pine beetle, the red turpentine beetle, the pine engraver, and the fir engraver, have added their toll of timber killed, to make this group of bark beetles one of the most destructive of forest enemies.

The association of bark beetles with dying trees has been known for a long time, but not until 1900, when the national forests were being created, was their seriousness as destroyers of forest trees fully realized. A timber-survey party under the direction of Gifford Pinchot then discovered bark beetles running rampant through the Black Hills forest reserve of South Dakota. A. D. Hopkins, then of the West Virginia University, found that this bark beetle was new to science. He named it the Black Hills beetle, *Dendroctonus ponderosa*. Before the epidemic waned, it had killed more than a billion board feet of ponderosa pine timber in the reserve.

Research on the habits and methods of controlling forest bark beetles has been unflagging since 1902. The results have been invaluable in developing methods of protecting forests from unnecessary damage by these native insects.

The usual picture of a researcher at work is that of a figure in white bending over his flasks and test tubes—but not so with the field-going forest entomologist. His garb is that of a woodsman or lumberjack. His laboratory most of the time is the forest and field. There he carries on his studies, using the native materials at hand. Through observation and experiments under woods conditions he tries to determine the role of forest insects. Sometimes, but not often, he brings his materials into the laboratory for special tests.

At first most attention was given to delving into the life histories and habits of the various species of bark beetles, in determining points they had in common and in determining differences. Because the beetles never seem to perform so well in the laboratory as in the woods, most of this biological work was carried out in the forest. Much of the information was obtained through careful observation. Periodically small sections of bark were removed from infested trees and the progress of gallery construction, egg laying, and larval development noted. Later, as the new broods neared maturity, screen cages were attached to the trees and the emerging adults collected.

The observations showed that adult bark beetles bore through the bark and into the cambial region between the bark and the wood. Here they construct egg galleries, tunnels, or cavities in which the eggs are laid. The only weapon of resistance the tree has is its pitch flow. If that is copious enough, the attacking beetles are drowned out. If not, they deposit their eggs.

Most species of bark beetles also introduce the spores of fungi, blue stains, or yeasts, which clog the cells in sapwood and hinder conduction. The beetles, by introducing fungi, sometimes cause such diseases as the Dutch elm disease, which in itself is fatal to the tree. The young, tiny larvae or grubs feed on the inner bark tissue and fan out to destroy more growing tissues. When they are plentiful enough they eventually girdle the tree. It takes several hundreds or thousands of attacking beetles to overpower a tree, but when they do they make short work of it and the tree is dead within 2 weeks or a month.

The *Dendroctonus* beetles, the most important group of tree killers, are monogamous—one male and one female to each gallery. Many others, such as the engraver beetles of the genera *Ips, Scolytus, Pityogenes,* and *Pityophthorus,* are polygamous; each female makes a separate egg tunnel from a central chamber, where the male beetle waits to serve her. When the larvae reach full growth, they transform to the pupa, or resting stage, and then to new adults, which emerge to carry on new attacks in other trees.

Beyond the discovery of these simple facts of behavior and life habits, important questions arose: Why do some species confine their attacks to specific host trees while others feed on a large number of forest tree species? What attracts them to the trees they attack? How far do bark beetles fly? How do they manage to kill trees so quickly? How are they controlled in nature? Cannot a natural parasite or predator be found to keep them in check? Those and other questions had to be answered by research as a basis for control strategy. Even today some of the questions are unanswered, although progress has been made in uncovering the essential points of behavior of the bark beetles.

A few examples of the type of studies carried out might be of interest. Bark beetles were brought into the laboratory, and many tests were run to find out what attracted them. An olfactometer, a Y-shaped tube through which air was passed, was used. The substance to be tested was placed at one prong of the Y and the beetles at the base of the Y. They then had their choice of the substance or fresh air, and the selection made by the beetles was determined and recorded. Another method was to place the attractant in one corner of a large cage in which the beetles were liberated. Thus they were given more freedom of movement than in the olfactometer. The studies showed that beetles were repelled by the oleoresins, first line of defense of the trees, and were attracted by the odors given off from fermenting inner bark—the deterioration of the tree in some way attracted the beetles.

The researcher who tried to develop large numbers of predators had quite a problem on his hands, for the predators of bark beetles are also cannibalistic and will quickly eat each other if they are not confined to individual quarters. It was found that this method of control was not practical. Nor was it worth while to import parasites from foreign countries, for practically all American bark beetles are native to this hemisphere and have a full complement of natural parasites and predators here with them.

It was discovered that extremely low winter temperatures kill some bark beetles, so experiments were made with the western pine beetle and mountain pine beetle to determine just how low temperatures had to be to prove fatal. Running tests under laboratory conditions was comparatively comfortable work, but the tests did not fully explain the effect of temperature on broods on forest trees as modified by wind, topography, elevation, bark thickness, and tree temperature. It was necessary therefore to take this study into the woods. In the forest, researchers took hourly bark-temperature readings while temperatures dropped to 26° F. below zero, and also skied over snow fields and climbed trees to read thermometers while temperatures hovered around 15° below.

THE CONTROL STRATEGY that first suggested itself was to destroy the developing broods of potentially destructive beetles before they could emerge and attack other trees. That could be done in a number of ways, such as felling the dead infested trees and peeling or burning the bark, or removing the infested trees to millponds where they could be stored until the wood could be cut into lumber. Such control work could be done in the fall, winter, and spring when low temperatures kept the beetles inactive and confined to the trees they had recently killed.

The first large-scale control project, following this control strategy, was started in northeastern Oregon in 1910 against an outbreak of the mountain pine beetle in lodgepole pine. The method was simple and effective enough in killing beetles, but the task of applying it to 2 million infested trees, scattered over 100,000 acres of rough forest land, presented many difficulties and the cost was high.

Much thought and effort has been devoted since to finding easier and less expensive methods of killing the bark beetles. Some that were tried and found wanting were electrocution, burying, and drowning. It was found that an electric current followed the pitch seams of the bark and left the beetles unharmed. Even though buried under 2 feet of soil, beetles emerged from infested bark and found their way to the surface. Beetles could be immersed in water for 6 weeks and still survive. Where logs were sent to millponds and then cut into lumber and the slabs burned, the beetles were destroyed either by drowning or burning.

Sun curing and tree injection have had limited success. In sun curing, trees are felled and laid where they will receive direct rays of the sun, or the bark is peeled and similarly exposed. The method is effective south of latitude 45°, in open timber on flats or southerly exposures where air temperatures reach 80° F. Trees that are not peeled have to be rolled after a few days of exposure. The method has limitations in that it cannot be used in dense shade, on north slopes, or in the cool northerly latitudes.

A great deal of research has been devoted to exploring the possibilities of injecting insecticides into infested trees so as to kill the broods. It can be done but not without girdling the tree so as to get the chemical uniformly distributed through the sap stream, so there is no hope of saving infested trees by use of this method. The method is tedious to apply and works effectively only when trees are still green and the sap is functioning.

A relatively cheap and effective way to destroy bark beetles is to use fuel or Diesel oil, to which a toxicant such as orthodichlorobenzene or DDT has been added. It is applied to standing or felled trees in such amounts as to soak and penetrate the bark. The method is particularly effective on such thin-bark trees as lodgepole pine, western white pine, and Engelmann spruce. When thoroughly applied, the oil treatment also is effective on trees with thicker bark, up to an inch in thickness, such as ponderosa pine and Coulter pine. The formula most frequently used is 1 part of orthodichlorobenzene to 6 parts of fuel oil. It is applied with power sprayers, ordinary garden sprayers, or stirrup pumps at the rate of 4 to 6 ounces per square foot of bark, or 6 to 8 gallons on a tree of average size.

DDT IS A NEW WEAPON. Its greatest value is its residual effect when it is applied as a surface deposit to prevent attack on threatened trees or to catch emerging beetles. In the campaign against the Dutch elm disease, a surface spray of 2 percent DDT in a water emulsion is effective in preventing attacks by the beetle that transmits the fungus causing the disease. To prevent piled ponderosa pine slash from becoming attacked by *Ips* engraver beetles, a 5 percent DDT spray in fuel oil is effective. Some success has been obtained in spraying infested ponderosa pine trees with a 5 percent DDT spray, which catches western pine beetles upon emergence.

Some of these methods of control were developed at first on a small scale or a "pilot plant" basis, but each had to be taken into the woods and applied under practical field conditions before cost and effectiveness could be determined. That was done on going control projects where labor for felling, burning, spraying, or other treatment of infested trees was available. The effectiveness of the method under test in killing broods could usually be determined by sampling the treated trees, but the effectiveness in reducing timber loss in the area treated could only be determined on an area sampling basis—sample plots or sample strips had to be established throughout the treated areas and on neighboring untreated ones. The timber mortality on the sample areas was determined by field crews, usually a compassman and two spotters who located the old and new infested trees. A comparison of timber loss before and after treatment and between treated and untreated areas gave the final answer as to the effectiveness of the control work.

Methods of forest sampling to determine amount and character of insect damage have also been developed and improved. The laborious work of field crews struggling up and down hill through dense underbrush to establish and check sample strips or plots on the ground may give way some day to the photographic sampling of plots from the air. Aerial reconnaissance of forest areas to determine the extent, status, and trend of outbreaks already has found an important place in the forest insect-survey program.

Direct methods of destroying beetles are still used to deal with outbreaks that cannot be handled in any other way. Forest entomologists, however, have come to realize that these "strong arm" methods are no permanent solution to the problem and that more attention should be given to preventing outbreaks rather than to the application of expensive control methods to suppress them after they have occurred. Detailed research work on the western pine beetle has pointed the way towards this objective.

Starting in 1921, a series of large projects directed towards controlling the western pine beetles in ponderosa pine forests of California, Oregon, and Washington were undertaken by the Federal Government and private timber owners. The fell-peel-burn method of destroying beetle populations was used. More than 1 million dollars was expended on these projects in the next decade, and yet the results left much to be desired. The control work reduced losses for the following year or two, but if left alone the bark beetles staged a prompt comeback and the effect of the control work was soon nullified.

Then in 1932 a natural phenomenon occurred that pointed up the futility of direct control measures as a permanent solution to the western pine beetle problem. A cold winter, with temperatures in some eastern Oregon forest areas dropping to 54° below zero, destroyed fully 80 percent of the beetles over extensive areas. The destruction of broods was more uniform and complete for large areas than could possibly be accomplished by the usual method of felling and burning infested trees. Yet despite this widespread mortality, it took only 2 years for the beetles to regain their position and go on killing more thousands of feet of ponderosa pine. Obviously direct control or the killing of the beetles themselves was not the answer.

In the meantime, scientists discovered another phase of beetle behavior. It was noted that certain types of pines were susceptible to western pine beetle attack and others were decidedly resistant. It was suspected, therefore, that if the susceptible trees could be removed from the stand, the resistant trees could ward off insect attacks. The problem was to be able to recognize these trees so they could be removed. Starting in 1927, tests and inventory studies were made to define as exactly as possible the more susceptible types of trees. It was found that they were slow growing—the crowded intermediate or suppressed trees, older and overmature trees, and those lacking in vigor.

On that basis a system of classification was set up in which ponderosa pine were classified in four relative age groups, from young to overmature; and in four vigor groups, from most vigorous to decadent. A sampling of 51,409 trees killed by bark beetles in eastern Oregon and northern California showed that this classification was sound, for the dead trees fell largely in the poor-vigor and older-age classes.

Further studies showed that it was not merely the slow-growing trees that were most susceptible but those declining in growth rate because of poor health. That being true, trees were now grouped in four degrees of risk, according to their current health, as indicated by short needles, dying twigs, declining vigor of top, poor color, and other characters.

In 1937, bark beetle control based on susceptibility of trees to attack was put to its first test on the Black's Mountain Experimental Forest of the California Forest and Range Experiment Station. From 15 to 20 percent of the stand, consisting of those trees of highest risk, were removed through logging, sent to the mill, and utilized. Subsequent results surpassed expectations. Bark beetle losses were reduced fully 90 percent on the treated areas during the first year following logging, even though the logged areas were surrounded with infested stands. Subsequent checks have shown over 70 percent less loss on the treated areas than on untreated areas for a period of 10 years or more following treatment.

This method of "bugproofing" ponderosa pine stands has been called sanitation-salvage logging. It has met with enthusiastic response on the part of timber owners, who have applied the method to several thousands of acres of high-hazard forest land. The recognition and identification of susceptible trees have also become an established part of the pine-marking rules on timber sales of the Forest Service, on Indian tribal lands, and on the holdings of many progressive timber owners.

The marked success of this method has given encouragement to the thought that similar methods might be applied to the control of other bark beetles. Studies along this line have been started, but it is already obvious that no two species of bark beetles follow the same rules and that what constitutes a susceptible tree for one may be a resistant type to another. The selective tendencies of each species of beetle will have to be determined through careful study.

For many species of bark beetles, the favorite breeding medium is not slow-growing or overmature trees but freshly felled slash. In such material they produce strong and abundant broods which can attack and kill large numbers of healthy trees. The *Ips* engraver beetles are characteristically of this type, and slash-bred *Ips* are the source of much damage to young pine stands in the vicinity. Prompt disposal of slash, therefore, is the clue to the prevention of this type of damage.

Windfalls are still another favorite breeding medium for many species of bark beetles. Many outbreaks, such as the Engelmann spruce beetle outbreak mentioned earlier, can be traced to this cause.

Forest fires, in killing and weakening large numbers of trees, have frequently resulted in subsequent bark beetle outbreaks. The Douglas-fir beetle, for example, bred in the fire-killed trees of the great Tillamook Burn of 1933 and developed such hordes of beetles that in 1935 some 300 million board feet of green timber surrounding the burn was attacked and killed.

Preventing outbreaks and damage from bark beetles that breed in slash, windfalls or fire-killed trees, as I mentioned, is not a matter of destroying beetle populations after they have developed in this material, but of avoiding development of beetles through prompt utilization or clean-up of their potential breeding places.

For the future, more and more effort will be given to finding ways through forest management of preventing bark beetle damage, rather than new ways of suppressing beetle populations after they have become epidemic. For example, control of the western pine beetle through sanitation-salvage logging is giving greater and more lasting reductions in bark beetle loss than suppressive measures ever did. Application of this preventive method is reducing the loss from this bark beetle in commercial stands of California, Oregon, Washington, and Idaho. Forest management of stands of lodgepole, western white, and sugar pine gives promise of solving the mountain pine beetle problem. More intensive forest practices in disposing of slash, salvaging fire-killed trees, and cleaning up windfalls will reduce the threat of many other potentially destructive bark beetles that find such material a favorite breeding medium.

Research in the future will study more intensively the relation of bark beetles to their forest environment, what causes them to become epidemic, why innocuous bark beetles sometimes suddenly become aggressive, and how beetles can be kept in their proper place through regulation of their host trees and environment, for we are dealing with native forest inhabitants that are just as much at home in the forest as the trees themselves. We must assume that Nature had a purpose in putting them there. Rather than upset the balance of Nature by attempting to eliminate them, we should try to find out what purpose they serve and work with Nature to keep them in their proper role. Foresters and timber owners will not object to bark beetles acting as Nature's caretaker in thinning the forest of a few old decadent trees to make room for new ones. All they ask is that the beetles not be allowed to go on a rampage and kill vast quantities of timber before it can be harvested and utilized. The job ahead challenges the insight and resourcefulness of research foresters and entomologists, who will need to work together to solve this forestry problem.

F. P. KEEN, *a graduate of the University of California, is principal entomologist of the Bureau of Entomology and Plant Quarantine in charge of the Forest Insect Investigations Laboratory at Berkeley, Calif. His experience with bark beetle problems in the western pine region covers 37 years. He is author of a number of technical papers and bulletins on forest insects. In 1947 he received the Department's Superior Service Award for his development of a ponderosa pine tree classification, which is used as an index to the susceptibility of pine stands to bark beetle damage and as a guide to tree selection on timber sales.*

An illustration of Ips *engraver beetles appears in the section of color drawings.*

The Gypsy Moth

John M. Corliss

The gypsy moth is a leaf-eating insect, native to Europe and Japan, that was accidentally introduced into this country in 1869. It was brought from France to Medford, Mass., by a French scientist for experimental purposes but escaped and became established there. It gradually spread through most of New England.

It feeds on many fruit, shade, forest, and ornamental trees. In epidemic outbreaks few species of trees are untouched. Evergreen trees, on which only the larger caterpillars feed, are particularly susceptible to attack and damage when grown near oak and other hardwood trees that the insect favors. Defoliation caused by the gypsy moth has retarded growth and killed trees over extensive areas.

The gypsy moth has four stages in its life history: The egg, larva or caterpillar, pupa or resting stage, and adult or moth. During late July and August the female moth deposits about 400 eggs in a cluster, and the insect overwinters in this stage. The eggs hatch in May and the caterpillars feed on foliage for about 6 weeks. This is the stage when the insect may be most effectively controlled. When full-grown, the caterpillars change into pupae, and the adult moths emerge from the middle of July until the middle of August. A new generation is then started. The male gypsy moth is brown with black wing markings and is a strong flier. The female is nearly white, with black wing markings, but cannot fly because of her heavy body.

In Europe and Japan the gypsy moth has many natural enemies, which contribute toward its control, but when it was introduced into this country none of these was present. In 1905 the State of Massachusetts and the Federal Government began to introduce parasites and other natural enemies of the gypsy moth. Much parasitized material has been received since then and several natural enemies have become established in this country.

But control of the gypsy moth by its natural enemies was less effective than people expected because some of the most important parasites from Europe could not be established—alternate host insects were not available here for the second or succeeding generations of the parasite. The wilt disease, caused by a polyhedral virus, attacks the gypsy moth in the larval stage and often kills large concentrations of caterpillars.

Congress first provided funds for Federal work on the gypsy moth in 1906 after the insect had spread through eastern Massachusetts and southern New Hampshire. The aim was to control and prevent the spread of the insect and eradicate outlying infestations. In 1923 a barrier zone was established where clean-up operations to prevent the further westward spread would be centered. The zone extended along the New England-New York State line from Canada to Long Island. The zone was replaced by a suppressive area in 1945 because the infestation had spread beyond the zone in New York after the hurricane of 1938.

Isolated infestations were found from time to time in New York, New Jersey, Pennsylvania, and Ohio. The smaller infestations were rapidly cleaned up.

In 1920 a well-established infestation was found in New Jersey near Somerville. It eventually covered some 1,450 square miles. Investigations traced the outbreak to blue spruce seedlings, which were imported from Europe and contained gypsy moth egg clusters. By 1935 complete eradication was effected by New Jersey and Federal cooperation, funds, and men. Spraying was done with hydraulic sprayers. Arsenate of lead was the insecticide.

In 1932 an infestation over 1,000 square miles was located near Pittston, Pa. In 1948 an infestation over 250 square miles was discovered at Quakertown, Pa. Both were sprayed with DDT by airplane. In 1951 only one isolation was known to exist in Pennsylvania. It was discovered near Pittston in August 1951, following the capture of male gypsy moths in two nearby traps.

The infested area in New England and New York is regulated by Federal Quarantine No. 45. The purpose is to prevent spread of the gypsy moth to uninfested sections of the country. Shipments of regulated plant material to points outside the infested area must be accompanied by a certificate of inspection.

Defoliation by the gypsy moth causes economic damage by ultimately killing the trees, retarding their growth, or creating other conditions that impair land value. The amount of defoliation varies from year to year.

The death of trees may be caused by single or repeated defoliations and is more extensive when partially developed deciduous foliage from primary buds has been killed by heavy frost earlier in the same season and when defoliation occurs during long periods of drought. White pine trees and some other conifers die almost always after a single stripping of the foliage.

Estimates based on a 20-year study of some 200 representative observation points in eastern New England put the value of all hardwood trees killed in those areas at 16 million dollars. Further estimates for the remainder of the infested area during that period placed the loss at 10 million dollars. No evaluation was placed on the accompanying mortality of young white pine trees, which has continued since the studies were made and is hard to estimate because the trees are usually killed before they have obtained sufficient growth to have any more than potential value.

A significant effect of defoliation is the loss in increment of tree growth.

Apparently the loss of growth in trees varies proportionately with the amount of defoliation—a tree defoliated 75 percent generally will put on only 25 percent of its annual normal growth. Estimates place the monetary loss of growth of trees from defoliation and consequent loss of lumber in the infested area at an average of 1.5 million dollars yearly.

The death of trees in woodland creates several problems. One is the opening of the forest stand, which affects the remaining growth so that the subsequently developing trees may be unsuitable or of inferior quality for timber. It also eliminates the good forest cover that helps to regulate stream flow and minimize floods. The loss of trees in recreation areas lowers land values and the production of wildlife. Heavy infestations of the caterpillars can make a place unpleasant to visitors and increase the hazard of spread of the pest by the traveling public.

EFFECTIVELY PLANNED spray operations must be preceded by surveys to delimit areas of infestation. Before establishing priorities for spraying one must know whether the growth is conducive to rapid build-up of infestation and determine whether the physical features of the forest are such as to increase the hazard of spread.

Special traps are an effective and economical way to survey extensive areas to find out if gypsy moth infestation exists and to check on the effectiveness of spraying operations. The traps are baited with a substance that attracts adult male gypsy moths in a radius of one-half mile or more. The substance is obtained by clipping the last two abdominal segments or tip of the virgin female adult and putting them in benzol, which extracts the material from the sex glands. The tips are then processed at Beltsville, Md., in order to stabilize and increase the potency of the attractant. They are then used at the rate of 15 tips to a trap. The material has been obtained by collecting large numbers of female pupae in heavily infested areas, but the spraying of extensive areas has reduced the numbers of pupae available in the United States.

The most satisfactory traps are made of salvaged cans, about 7 inches long and 4 inches in diameter, and are known as the Graham trap. The sex attractant is placed inside in a cardboard cartridge. The inside of the trap is lined with a sticky material that catches the moths. The ends of the can have cone-shaped screens with holes at the center to allow the moths to enter.

The traps are hung by wires to trees and spaced uniformly throughout the zone to be surveyed. They are placed in the field not later than early July, before the beginning of the moth flight, and removed the latter part of August or first of September. The traps are inspected every 7 to 10 days to remove moths in them and to renew the sticky material.

During the summer of 1950 trapping was done in New York, Pennsylvania, New Jersey, Vermont, Massachusetts, Rhode Island, and Connecticut. A total of 19,608 traps were placed in areas aggregating nearly 7,194,000 acres. No moths were caught in Pennsylvania and New Jersey.

In the fall and winter, scouting surveys are conducted in the vicinity of traps where moths were caught during the summer and in areas not trapped where infestation is known to occur in order to determine extent and intensity of infestation. Scouting is also carried on at points where infestation could be started by the importation of egg masses or living larvae by vehicles of all types. The latter work is largely confined to through highways, population centers, recreation areas, carrier terminals, State parks, and other locations of similar character. During the fall and winter of 1949–1950, more than 1,837,000 acres were scouted and 888 infestations were located.

SPRAYING IS DONE in spring. Priorities are given to areas where surveys

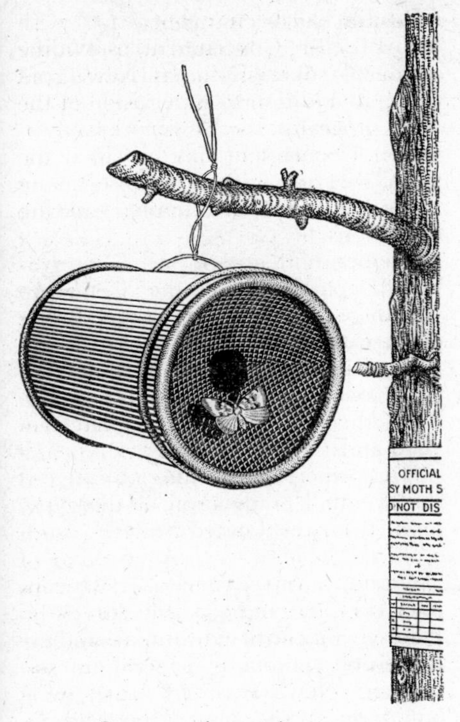

Gypsy moth entering trap.

have indicated the hazard of spread of the pest is greatest.

DDT has been used exclusively against the gypsy moth since 1946. The use of an oil solution of DDT at a concentration of 12 percent, applied at the rate of 1 gallon per acre, is most effective. During the spring of 1950 more than 600,000 acres of infested territory were sprayed by aircraft and specially designed ground mist blowers.

During the early years of the work, hydraulic sprayers were used to spray infested places with lead arsenate. Now Federal workers use the more effective and economical aircraft and blower equipment, but hydraulic equipment is still used in small commercial spraying operations. One Government-owned C–47 equipped for dispensing DDT solution can spray in an hour an area that formerly would take nine hydraulic units a whole season. Federal costs of operating hydraulic equipment averaged 25 dollars an acre. DDT-oil solution can be applied by airplane or mist blower for less than a dollar an acre. The gypsy moth is eradicated entirely when the solution is applied properly. Small single-engine biplanes of the N3N–3 type and multiple-engine types such as the C–47 have been adapted for the spraying.

The small biplanes are equipped with 90- and 110-gallon insecticide tanks located in the forward cockpit. The insecticide is pumped under pressure from the tank to the dispensing nozzle by a small gear-type pump hung beneath the fuselage just aft of the landing wheels. The pump is powered by a propeller connected with it which is mounted in suitable ball bearings and equipped with a braking mechanism. Forward motion of the plane turns the propeller at approximately 2,500 revolutions per minute, which in turn actuates the pump. The flow of insecticide is controlled by solenoid valves suitably located and operated electrically from a switch in the pilot's cockpit. The airplanes fly approximately 50 feet above the tree tops at about 80 miles an hour, pumping out insecticide solution at the rate of 20 gallons a minute and laying down a swath 100 to 110 feet wide.

The C–47 carries two cylindrical oil-resistant rubber-lined aluminum tanks with a capacity of 922 gallons of insecticide. A centrifugal-type pump and gasoline unit mounted aft of the tanks forces the insecticide solution out through aluminum piping and hose connections to streamlined booms mounted beneath the wings and fuselage. Electric motor-operated valves control the flow of insecticide to the booms. Nozzles with small check valves are spaced along the booms to deliver the proper amount of insecticide material. This plane flies 150 miles an hour at 150 to 200 feet above the trees. The output of insecticide is 150 gallons a minute. The effective swath width is about 600 feet. The dosage is applied at the standard rate of 1 gallon of solution per acre. In a normal operating season, 15,000 acres can be treated by a small biplane and 80,000 acres by a C–47.

In order to supply the aircraft with insecticide in large-scale spraying operations, large storage and mixing facilities are needed. Mixing tanks are equipped with heating units so that the insecticide can be heated to 80° F. to facilitate dissolving the technical grade DDT powder in the oil.

Ground mist blowers are effective for roadside spraying of woodlands. They are also used for spraying locations such as junk yards to prevent artificial spread of the insect. Blower units are mounted on trucks suitable for traveling along back roads and trails. The speed of the truck and the output of the blower are regulated so that the DDT-oil solution is applied at the rate of a gallon an acre.

Large-scale spraying operations require a great deal of planning. Maps are prepared showing areas to be treated. Just before the spraying season, windsocks are erected at specified locations for the guidance of aircraft. Property owners, as well as city, town, and other officials, including water commissioners, fish and game authorities, and the police are interviewed. Before and during the operations, radio stations and newspapers inform the citizens about the purpose and progress of the program.

Before the start of aerial spraying each day, small glass plates are placed on the ground in a line at right angles to the line of flight in order to check on the distribution of spray deposit. Plates not adequately covered give indication of areas that must be resprayed.

Six-foot-long helium-inflated dirigible-shaped balloons have proved effective as a guide for the large multiengine airplanes, as they are visible for 2 to 5 miles.

In New Jersey and Pennsylvania, funds and manpower were furnished to supplement Federal efforts. Since 1935, surveys in New Jersey have been conducted by the State. In Pennsylvania trapping has been cooperative, with the Federal Government providing technical supervision. In New York State, in addition to supervision of the work programs, the New York Conservation Department has provided the manpower and most of the insecticides and solvents used in extensive spraying operations.

Cooperation among the Conservation Department of the Commonwealth of Massachusetts, the counties of Barnstable and Plymouth, and municipalities therein, assisted by the Federal Government, made it possible to spray the two counties completely in 1949 and 1950.

The principal long-time objective is the eventual eradication of the gypsy moth from the United States.

Current objectives are: To conduct trapping and scouting surveys in Pennsylvania until extermination there is assured; eliminate general infestation in New York by 1953 with only mop-up of isolated incipient infestations remaining in succeeding years; reduce the intensity of infestation in western New England and minimize the hazard of westward spread of the pest; continue the large-scale coordinated cooperative eradication program in southeastern Massachusetts; and to furnish technical advice and limited assistance to States, counties, cities, and towns engaged in control in the New England States.

John M. Corliss *has been connected with plant-disease and insect-control projects since he joined the Department of Agriculture in 1917. In the program to prevent the spread of the white pine blister rust disease in 1928, he was in charge of transit inspection at Chicago. He was assigned to the division of gypsy moth control in 1943 and was in charge of the control measures against that insect in New Jersey, New York, and Pennsylvania until 1947, when he was made chief of the division of gypsy and brown-tail moth control.*

Insects and Wildlife

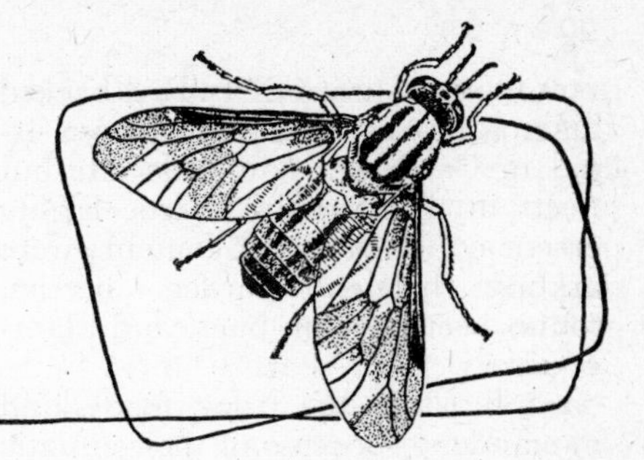

Insects and the Lower Vertebrates

Oliver B. Cope

Insects are so diverse in structure and habit and so widely distributed that they come into close contact with all other groups of living things, except the organisms that inhabit the sea. Through the contacts they have become involved in a variety of plant and animal relationships that bear all degrees of complexity and dependency. From one-celled protozoan to man, nearly every animal group has come to develop associations of one kind or another with the insects in the air, on the ground, or in fresh water. Some associations are quite casual. Others are so fixed that the existence of the insect or its neighbor would be gravely threatened by the removal of the other member.

The cold-blooded vertebrates—the fishes, amphibians, and reptiles—also have diversified habits. Aquatic, semiaquatic, subterraneous, terrestrial, and arboreal habitats put them close to many insect forms. Many specific relationships between the two animal groups have arisen through the ages. Perhaps no other classes can better illustrate the interrelationships between the insects and their neighbors in nature. It is also appropriate to consider the important economic implications of these associations of the lower vertebrates, especially the fishes.

The cold-blooded vertebrate animals depend on insects for their sustenance in varying degrees. Sometimes, as with the turtles, practically no insect material enters the diet. On the other hand, large groups of fishes could hardly exist without the benefit of abundant insect forage to sustain them. Between these extremes are vertebrate animals—toads, small snakes, lizards—which although usually not in the habit of eating insects to the exclusion of other kinds of foods, ingest them in great numbers when they are readily available.

Studies by E. M. Uhler, C. Cottam, and T. E. Clarke on Virginia snakes revealed that almost all of 15 species examined had insects in their stomachs. Large insects, such as grasshoppers, cicadas, and caterpillars, were most frequently taken. Smaller forms, such as ants and small beetles, also were found in abundance. Insect remains represented the total contents in some stomachs. In others less than 50 percent of the food was of insect origin. Only a few of the smaller species of snakes, such as green snakes, ground snakes, and ring-necked snakes, are essentially insect eaters; insects contribute moderately to the diets of other species of snakes.

Lizards are the most decidedly insectivorous of the reptile group. Many are vegetarians. Large species specialize in relatively bulky prey, such as crabs and mice, but most small lizards—fitted with tongues adapted for capturing insects by lapping them up or by striking at them heavily—subsist chiefly on insects. G. F. Knowlton found that beetles, ants, leafhoppers, and other terrestrial insects are staple items in many lizard diets. Red-backed alligator lizards from Santa Rosa Island in California had little else but insects in the digestive tracts. Eighty percent of the stomach contents were darkling beetles. Larder beetles, ground beetles, stink bugs, and plant-lice also were present.

Amphibians—the frogs, toads, and salamanders—because of their aquatic or semiaquatic habits, come into contact mostly with swimming or flying insects, although adult amphibians frequently seek crawling insects. Swimming or flying insects are readily taken as food by amphibians and in considerable quantities. Salamanders are not highly insectivorous but eat insects readily when they are available. In studies on the tiger salamander, D. S. Farner found that 74 percent of the stomachs examined had terrestrial arthropods, including ants, beetles, and flies. Thirty-seven percent of the stomachs contained aquatic beetles, flies, and caddisflies. Others have found mayflies, caddisfly larvae, and caterpillars in the food of salamanders.

Frogs are of minor importance as insect feeders, although certain species take insects in abundance. E. W. Jameson, Jr., in studying the western cricket frog, found beetles present as 55 percent of the total food volume, spiders as 24 percent, midge larvae and fly adults as 12 percent, and water boatmen as 7 percent. W. J. Hamilton, Jr., pointed out that the importance of insects in the diet of one species of frog varies with time and place. In summer and fall, when aquatic environments are usually restricted in area, grasshoppers become more important than in the spring. In both young and old frogs, beetles, flies, grasshoppers, and caterpillars were present as 60 percent of the bulk of the stomachs studied.

Toads are more dependent on the insects for nutrition than are other amphibians. The true toads, while omnivorous, taking only living or moving food and endowed with an extremely rapid digestive apparatus, consume large amounts of insect material. A. H. Kirkland determined that 77 percent of the food taken by *Bufo* throughout a season was of insect origin, authenticating the reputation of this toad for having a high economic value as a natural suppressor of insect populations. H. J. Pack pointed out that a large population of *Bufo woodhousii* in Utah in August 1921, was feeding exclusively on sugar-beet webworms. Each small toad had 24 to 40 worms in its stomach. There was a concentration of toads in the area, and they were eating webworms to the exclusion of their normal diet, a habit that contributed greatly to the control of the undesirable insects. The spadefoot toad, in its immature stages, is an active feeder on aquatic insects, particularly the larvae and pupae of mosquitoes.

The relationships between fish and insects as predator and prey are much better known and understood than are those of other cold-blooded vertebrates. Fish living in the ocean do not utilize insects as primary components of their diets, because insects are so poorly represented in the sea. Anadromous fish, which live in fresh water during portions of their life cycles, depend almost wholly on insect organisms during the fresh-water phase. There are fish, also, which inhabit brackish water, gleaning numbers of insects, among other organisms, in their search for food. It is in the true fresh-water haunts, however, that the ultimate in the use of insects as fish food is attained and the debt of fresh-water fish to the insects becomes obvious. Both herbivorous and carnivorous insects, either aquatic or terrestrial, are utilized.

The relationships between a population of insects and a particular population of adult fish can be direct or indirect. The fish may capture an aquatic insect in the water of the stream or lake or on the bottom. A flying insect whose habits are terrestrial may be snatched from the air or water surface. Herbivorous insects, such as midge larvae, may be devoured by carnivorous forms, like stonefly nymphs, which in turn may be eaten by fish in streams. Insects may contribute to the diet of a large fish by falling prey to a small fish, which is in turn captured by a larger one. Aquatic insects may be utilized by certain fish during the first part of the fish's development, before dietary habits are changed. For example, the largemouthed black bass ingests quantities of insects until it attains a length of a few inches. After that time, small fish replace insects as the dominant item in the bass diet. All these possibilities are everyday occurrences in the dynamics of food utilization.

Stream habitats used extensively by fish usually have a variety and abundance of aquatic insects. Streams considered suitable for trout and smallmouthed black bass have a good balance of pools and riffles. The bottom topography, aside from providing resting and feeding areas and incubation sites for the fish, makes for the support of a diversity of aquatic insects. Trout in most streams subsist principally on these, whereas terrestrial insects that fall onto the water usually form the second biggest portion of the diet.

The aquatic forms are associated with particular types of stream bottom. In riffles, where shallow water flows rapidly over gravel bottoms, insects with high oxygen requirements dwell—the early stages of stoneflies, mayflies, caddisflies, beetles, true flies, and other kinds. In most streams, riffles carry manyfold the amount of insect life that is present in pools. Pools, however, provide numbers of fly larvae and mayfly nymphs as fish food, and serve as temporary repositories for terrestrial insects that have fallen onto the water.

The insect types that dominate in stomach samples in stream fish usually follow a pattern, which varies only moderately according to the physical nature of the stream bottom and the chemical nature of the water. Mayflies or caddisflies usually occupy the most prominent place in the diet of trout and salmon. Of lesser importance are true flies, stoneflies, beetles, bugs, and nymphs of dragonflies and damselflies.

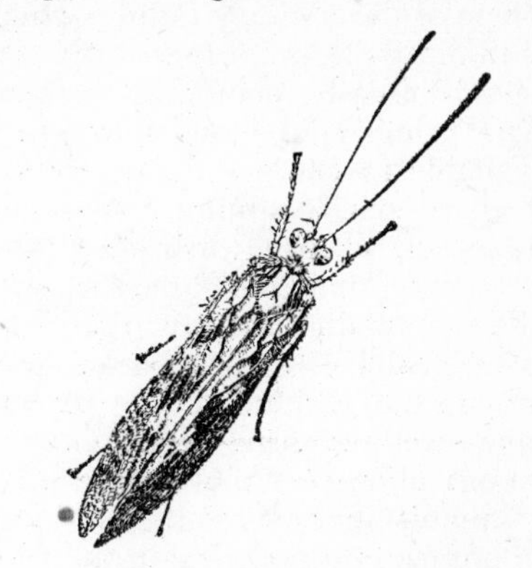

Phryganea vestita, a caddisfly.

Often trout will engorge great quantities of one particular kind of insect, no matter to what group it may belong, presumably because that insect is readily available as food. This occurrence is common at times of adult mayfly emergence, for instance. Adult smallmouthed bass have been found to prefer mayfly nymphs to other insects, with dragonflies, damselfles, and true bugs as second choices. Stoneflies, caddisflies, and beetles are used to some extent, and moths and nerve-winged species are taken in limited numbers. Fingerling smallmouthed bass prefer small organisms and ingest midge larvae almost exclusively in June from both riffles and pools. In July great quantities of mayfly nymphs are consumed, but fly larvae continue to serve as the chief food type. In August mayfly nymphs become the dominant item.

Fishes of sport or commercial importance in streams are not alone in their dependence upon insects for their food. The rough or trash fish—those that are not usually sought for their food or sport value and that often prey on or compete with valuable fish—take their share of insect material as food. Insects devoured by small rough fish, however, may ultimately help form flesh on a prized game fish; for example, a mayfly taken

970134°—52——46

by a young sucker, which migrates downstream to a lake, falls prey to a walleye. Stomach contents of several members of the minnow family, which serve in nature as important forage for game fish, usually include insect matter as a primary component, where it is available. Some members of this family are dace, minnows, roaches, chubs, blackfish, squawfish, and shiners. A few other nongame fish dependent upon insects to varying degrees are suckers, sticklebacks, topminnows, and sculpins.

Lake-dwelling fish utilize insects and bugs almost as much as do fish that inhabit streams. Forage fish assume immense importance in the diets of lake fish when adult size is reached, but before the advent of adulthood smaller organisms must form the bulk of the intake. Insects of various kinds fit into suitable size categories in this regard, and, where ecological conditions will support large enough insect populations, lake fish of the smaller sizes often are sustained almost completely by the insect fauna.

TROUT IN LAKES and ponds vary their diets from lake to lake and from season to season. While garnishing their food with assortments of crustaceans, mollusks, and spiders, trout are generally consistent in their use of two staple items—insects and smaller fish. Various studies on lake foods have shown many proportions between these two foods. J. W. and F. A. Leonard found 8- to 12-inch rainbow trout using aquatic insects as 40 percent of their diet and fish as 30 percent. Rainbow trout 12 to 22 inches long from the same lake had aquatic insects as 18 percent of their food and fish as 48 percent. Mackinaw trout from the same lake and during the same years contained 11 percent aquatic insects by volume and 83 percent fish. A. S. Hazzard and M. J. Madsen found that 5- to 23-inch cutthroat trout from Glacier Park lakes contained 54 percent insect food. The same species, 7 to 21 inches in length, from lakes of Teton Park, had 12 percent insect food and 68 percent fish in the stomach.

Other game fish in lakes and ponds use insects in substantial numbers, and, as with the trouts, smaller fish have a greater dependence on them than do fish of greater size. Bluegills at times may have insects as 90 percent of their stomach contents. Other spiny-rayed fishes, such as black crappie, yellow bullhead, yellow perch, pumpkinseed, long-eared sunfish, rock bass, and largemouthed bass, have been found to take insect food in large amounts. Some other species that consume insects in ponds, lakes, and reservoirs are sturgeon, suckers, whitefish, and cisco.

In streams and lakes, eaten by prized sport fish and lowly trash fish, young or old, bottom feeders or plankton eaters, insects enter into the nourishment of most fresh-water and anadromous fish. Diets vary from place to place and from time to time, but almost any given population of fish in fresh water, if deprived of insects for sustenance, would be forced to adopt new feeding habits or starve.

THE MOST COMMONLY recognized relationship between insects and the lower vertebrates, that of prey and predator, is frequently reversed in nature. Some insects make a habit of viciously attacking, killing, and feeding upon fish and their vertebrate relatives. The most prominent limiting factor in this type of behavior is that of size, but even overwhelming advantages in this regard are commonly disregarded by some types of insect predators that are especially well equipped for the attack. A pointed and long proboscis, as wielded by a toe-biter (Naucoridae), or a set of robust and sharp mandibles of the caliber flourished by many beetle larvae can be very effective in subduing victims many times the size of the attacking insect.

Among the best known of the fish-eating insects are certain aquatic beetles, some of whose adults habitually attack fish and others of which are predaceous as larvae. The carnivorous diving beetles probably rate foremost, both larvae and adults regularly preying upon fish, even when several times their size.

Two groups, *Dytiscus* and *Cybister,* are dreaded by pondfish culturists. Those beetles take fish of several species under normal conditions and represent a special threat to newly hatched fish. Under conditions where natural predators cannot keep the beetles in check, fish fry are sometimes killed about as often as they appear. Water scavenger beetle larvae habitually kill small fish, both in nature and in fish-cultural practices that bring large numbers of fish and beetles into close quarters. These beetles generally are omnivorous, but some species of *Hydrous* have the habit of taking fish in the diet. In fishponds, *Hydrous* larvae have reduced populations of buffalo fish and carp. Fish remains have been found in the stomachs of 12 out of 50 larvae examined in a series of studies.

One other noteworthy beetle family is that of the whirligig beetles. Both larvae and adults commonly devour fish under natural conditions, and fish culturists attempt to keep their ponds free from these predators. The genus *Dineutes* has species which, even in the presence of an abundance of other food, will choose to swarm about a fish until it succumbs.

The true water bugs hold a high rank among the insects that are destructive to fish. They are strong swimmers and fliers, often grow large, and are fitted wth formidable piercing and sucking mouth parts. The giant water bugs are so strongly associated with fish predation that they are often called fish killers. Fish of many species are overcome and fed upon in ponds and other types of water, and large specimens of giant water bugs, 4 inches or more in length, often assault foot-long trout. The vicious habits of two of these bugs, *Belostoma* and *Lethocerus,* account for the mortality of numerous fish of many species in nature. The back swimmers are renowned for their attacks upon young fish. Their relatives, the toe-biters, often overpower small fish.

The dragonflies and damselflies have been incriminated as destroyers of small fish. The nymphs of the larger kinds, especially *Aeschna* and *Anax,* are notorious; early fish culturists were ever on the alert for the presence of large dragonfly nymphs in their fishponds. All such nymphs are not guilty of attacking fish, and, indeed, the idea that even the most voracious habitually devour fish has been largely refuted. That fish populations ever suffer materially from their ravages is yet to be established conclusively.

Certain immature caddisflies will attack fish and kill them. Larvae of the seine-making caddisflies have been considered a minor menace in trout and salmon hatcheries. These net-spinning, predaceous larvae enter rearing troughs with the water supply and entangle and feed upon trout and salmon fry. Not until the fish have attained a size great enough to prevent entanglement do they attain relief from the larvae. The larvae habitually attack tiny fish in nature, as well. It is not uncommon, on digging into a salmon nest, to come upon one of these larvae in the act of grasping a newly hatched fry, which has just begun its ascent through the gravel to the flowing stream above. All in all, the significant reduction of fish populations in nature or in hatcheries through the action of insects is not frequent, and, when it occurs, is almost always done by water bugs or beetles.

The immature stages of frogs and salamanders are vulnerable to the attacks of some of the larger predaceous aquatic insects. Beetles and bugs will assault larvae and tadpoles under natural conditions, and may exert a degree of control over an amphibian population.

An example of successful biological control in the field is the suppression of obnoxious aquatic insects through the introduction of fish to waters in which insects breed. Mosquitoes have been controlled in their larval and pupal stages in tropical and subtropical areas by the method. Gnats whose immature stages are readily available to fish have also been brought under control through the planting of suitable fish in infested waters. A long history of difficulties and failures in trying to introduce fish for the purpose attests the fact that success is usually not attained without considerable thought and planning. When the right combination of fish and environment is discovered, however, the economic return of the effort may be extremely gratifying.

The practice of stocking mosquito-laden waters with appropriate fish for permanent control has become such an indispensable part of the well-rounded mosquito-abatement program in many tropical areas that specialists are retained just to raise and distribute the fish. The Rockefeller Foundation and the Brazilian Government, in developing an organization in Brazil for the fight against the yellow-fever mosquito, established a fish service for work in cities. The service maintains all the facilities necessary for the storage, transportation, and planting of fish, and has a staff to supervise their use. The service is set up on a businesslike, permanent basis and illustrates the importance attached to control through fish in that area. Many other programs in tropical regions hold fish to be of prime importance in the organization of control measures. In the United States, some States require that top-feeding fish be kept in all small reservoirs.

Two families of fishes, well adapted for the purpose, have been extensively used for the control of mosquito larvae. One group, the top minnows, family Poeciliidae, is native to the New World in temperate and tropical climates. The popularity of certain top minnows as mosquito killers has led to their introduction into other lands; indeed, in the case of a minnow known as *Gambusia,* there is probably no major region of the world to which these fish have not been carried for abatement purposes. In the United States, one species, *Gambusia affinis,* has been used in California, Texas, and in the Mississippi Valley; another species, *Gambusia holbrookii,* has been stocked on the Atlantic coast, from Virginia to Florida. Still other species have been used extensively for mosquito control in Central and South America, the West Indies and the Mediterranean region, those known as *Lebistes,* "millions," *Mollienesia,* mudfish, *Poecilia,* and *Heterandria* having been most popular. Short life cycles, abundance, small adult size suitable for penetrating vegetation, fecundity, surface-feeding habits, and ease of distribution make the fishes of this family readily usable for mosquito abatement.

The other family of fishes favored for mosquito-eating habits is that of the killifishes, family Cyprinodontidae. They are native to temperate and tropical regions. Like the top minnows, the killifishes are endowed with biologies and life cycles that are ideally suited to depredations on mosquito larvae and pupae, and they have been used both in their native waters and through introduction to remote areas. In North America, the killifish *Fundulus* has been encouraged in antimosquito practice on the salt marshes of the Atlantic coast. In Central and South America, another species, *Rivulus,* has served admirably in abatement work and is among the most widely used predators in those regions. In the Mediterranean region, *Fundulus* and still another, *Cyprinodon,* have contributed toward control.

Some other families of fishes have members that are effective in antilarval campaigns. In the minnow family, Cyprinidae, the well-known goldfish, often does an excellent job of suppressing mosquito larvae in garden pools and other artificial waters. The catfish, *Pygidium,* has been a success in its native South America, and various other fishes have been used there in the fight against mosquitoes.

A SECOND EXAMPLE of a fortunate combination in biological control involves an amphibian. A long history of economic loss to sugarcane in tropical areas through the ravages of June beetle larvae prompted an investigation into possibilities for control in Puerto Rico. The larvae had several natural enemies, including lizards and small tree toads, but those predators were too small to exert significant control. The importation of large, nocturnal toads to Puerto Rico was recommended as a feasible action against the white grubs. Accordingly, adults of the giant Surinam toad (*Bufo marinus*) were brought to the island and released. The white grubs were readily eaten by the toad, and *Bufo* saved the sugarcane holdings in Puerto Rico. Within 10 years, the grubs had become rare on the island.

The success of *Bufo marinus* in Puerto Rico occasioned its introduction to other tropical places. An importation into the Hawaiian Islands was aimed at control of another sugarcane pest, the oriental beetle, and the toad is doing a good job of controlling the beetles.

Another toad that has been suggested for use in insect control is the spadefoot toad, *Scaphiopus*. In this case, the tadpole rather than the adult has attracted attention, because of its appetite and equipment for capturing mosquito larvae. This tadpole has proved its efficiency in ridding borrow pits and other temporary ponds of mosquito larvae, and has been suggested for similar activities in more permanent waters.

Toads generally have a high value as exterminators of insects, especially in the Tropics. Indeed, in many places, they are maintained as substitutes for insecticides in suppressing garden pests. With their rapid digestive rates and their habit of choosing only living or moving food, toads can consume enormous quantities of insects in a day.

Among the reptiles, lizards are obviously the best potential controllers of insect populations because of their natural habit of using insects in the diet. In the Tropics, they approach birds as insect destroyers. Lizards are not usually encouraged to the point of introducing them to insect-infested areas, but they are given free run of most houses in many tropical regions.

THE FISHERY BIOLOGIST has many field techniques for helping the welfare of fresh-water fish populations. Many of his management practices consist of rather drastic modifications of the physical environment of the fish for the purpose of improving spawning conditions, reducing mortality, or promoting growth. Many techniques are initiated expressly to increase fish growth through the increase of insects for food. That is done through predictable changes in the insect habitat and is calculated to provide aquatic conditions that will promote rapid and sustained development of the insect fauna. In effect, therefore, a good deal of management of fresh-water fish through environmental change becomes the management of aquatic insects.

Lake management has many possibilities. The employment of the various methods may only indirectly affect fish through bettering conditions for insect existence, but often the results are rapid.

Changing the temperature of a lake usually directly affects the insect fauna. Lakes may be warmed by increasing shoal area, resulting in the increase of fish food. The control of pollution is usually aimed directly toward improving chemical conditions for the fish themselves, but often renders aquatic insects more abundant. The regulation of the water level, primarily initiated for the benefit of spawning conditions or to prevent stranding of fish, frequently brings about stabilized conditions favorable for insect organisms used as foods. Providing shelter in the form of logs and brush gives fish a feeding place where aquatic organisms will become readily available for them. When the fishery manager retards wave action in lakes, he often makes insect production greater by reducing silt in the water, thereby increasing the penetration of light. The management of competitors in a lake definitely involves the insect fauna; where the insects are competed for as food, the problem becomes one of making the best use of the insect material on hand. The regulation of plant growth in a lake directly concerns the insect fauna present, and represents a step in the promotion of food chains and anchorage for aquatic insects. The increase of natural food in lakes is thus brought about in various ways by the fishery manager—to repeat, by chemically fertilizing the water, by directly controlling turbidity and temperature, by creating widespread shoal areas, and by providing shelter for insect organisms.

Streams are susceptible to the same management techniques as lakes. Certain other mechanical changes often are used in stream management to achieve improved hydraulic conditions for fish and a better environment for the insects that fish eat. Chemical fertilization for the acceleration of food chains, control of pollution, regulation of competitors, promotion of plant growth, and provision of shelter can all be used to alter the stream environment in favor of its fish inhabitants. Somewhere along the way the aquatic insects are usually affected favorably and are in turn consumed by fish.

Building dams for the benefit of fish is a common stream-improvement practice. The check-dam, a low structure placed at the outlet of a mountain lake, checks excessive spring flows in the stream below, and maintains summer flows. The checking of spring runoff prevents the washing away of insect life, while the sustained summer flows provide a greater stream-bottom surface for the production of bottom insects. High dams, which impound deeper waters, sometimes serve as regulators of downstream water temperature. The high winter-water temperatures below such dams encourage insects to grow and multiply so that food conditions become favorable for fish.

Placing boulders or other obstructions in streams is another management tool that improves conditions for aquatic insects. Such obstructions change water-flow patterns by creating new areas of deep, quiet water that will support a new insect fauna. In fast water, the obstructions usually alter ecological conditions in favor of the fish and their chief food, the aquatic insects. Another structure, the deflector, is placed in running streams in order to change flow characteristics and form pools. Made of immovable logs or rocks, deflectors in streams often bring about marked improvement of productivity of stream life.

Even more drastic physical changes may be brought about in streams by changing the stream course. Usually that is done with a specific purpose in mind, but it generally results in a stream section that is better suited to fish life and food production. When new riffles appear through this means, food production increases accordingly.

Biologists concerned with fish and other cold-blooded vertebrates cannot avoid the implications of field treatments with almost any of the newer, more toxic insecticides. Fishery biologists particularly have had to be on the alert, since bodies of water have been the focal point for treatment against many insect pests. They must be aware of the effects of insecticides on the fish themselves through direct poisoning. They have also maintained interest in the effects of new insecticides on aquatic insects eaten by fish. Indirect damage to fish can come about in two ways—through the consumption by fish of insects that are saturated with a toxicant and by depriving the fish of the bulk of their food, if the food organisms have been destroyed by insecticides.

Large-scale insecticide treatments in the field are directed against mosquitoes. Many of the ecological situations frequented by mosquito larvae and pupae fortunately are not important as fish habitat. Mosquitoes generally utilize quiet, shallow waters, often of a temporary nature and not accessible to fish. In such places, the danger to fish is least when well-controlled methods of toxicant application are used. However, airplane spraying against mosquito larvae may be hazardous to fish in waters adjacent to the area being treated. In the San Joaquin Valley of California in 1950 toxaphene in kerosene solution, with an emulsifier, was deposited by airplane at rates up to 1 pound per acre of water, which was much in excess of the usual 0.2–0.3 pound per acre normally used. Biologists of the California Division of Fish and Game found numbers of black bass, sunfish, and catfish dead as a result of the insecticide treatment. Such instances are rare, however, and it is gratifying that the modern mosquito-abatement supervisor is aware of the ecological situation as he uses insecticides in the field.

Control of forest insects often entails the wide dispersal of potent toxicants over forest areas through which trout streams flow. In heavily forested places under airplane treatment, it becomes impractical to treat the woody areas without covering the streams. The problem is one of choosing the ideal insecticide in such strength that the forest insect pests will be destroyed, while harm to fish and fish food is kept at a minimum.

The control of black fly larvae and pupae in running streams has been attempted by chemical methods. The hazard then to other aquatic organisms is very obvious. Streams inhabited by black flies are almost always swiftly flowing and usually contain populations of trout or other prized fish, such as salmon, smallmouthed bass, or shad. Also in need of protection are the various minnows and other forage fish and the bottom-insect fauna so important as fish food. When chemicals are poured directly into the stream for action against the black flies, the problem again is principally one of choosing the most suitable insecticide—the one that will yield effective control while inflicting a minimum of damage on useful aquatic organisms.

Federal and State agencies have experimented with the new toxicants considered to be the most promising for field campaigns. Insecticides have been tested against many kinds of fishes and their foods, and toxicity thresholds have been established for various aquatic environments in the laboratory and in the field. Different formulations have been tested and different methods of insecticide dispersal have been tried, so that field biologists are now armed with facts that will guide them in the safe use of insecticides outdoors. Cooperative projects, in which entomologists and fishery biologists have worked together in the field on these problems, have been successful.

The new chemicals about which we know most in relation to their fish-killing properties are DDT, benzene hexachloride, chlordane, as well as toxaphene, TDE, methoxychlor, parathion, and tetraethyl pyrophosphate. Various formulations have been tested. The most popular mixtures have been xylene-triton emulsion, kerosene solution, fuel-oil solution, and acetone solution.

The choice of a field insecticide entails several considerations—cost, ease of handling, safety to humans, effectiveness in destroying the pest, and safety to wildlife. On those bases, DDT seems to be one of our safest all-around insecticides. TDE has shown promise against certain insect pests and is only mildly toxic to fish. Chlordane, methoxychlor, and benzene hexachloride have been used experimentally against some kinds of fish and might be all right to use under carefully controlled conditions. Toxaphene is very toxic to fish, and should be used only with extreme caution. The type of formulation can often affect the toxicity of these chlorinated hydrocarbons. In most instances xylene-triton emulsions of these toxicants are most toxic to fish, oil solutions are intermediate, and acetone solutions exhibit the least potency.

Fish are not alone among the cold-blooded vertebrates in their vulnerability to insecticides. Wartime tests by E. S. Herald in Florida showed that DDT-kerosene solutions, as sprayed routinely from aircraft, killed green water snakes, banded water snakes, coachwhips, black snakes, pine snakes, and king snakes, and one of the four cottonmouth moccasins that were exposed. Typical DDT tremors were observed in frogs and toads, although they appeared to be moderately resistant to its action.

As we accumulate new facts concerning the tolerances of fish and other cold-blooded vertebrates to the newer insecticides, we shall arrive at a better understanding of the possibilities for safe field treatments. The complex aquatic environment binds all of its members so closely that careful management becomes strictly necessary if the desirable components are to be perpetuated.

In the give-and-take struggle in which all animals are engaged, it is obvious that many kinds of animals are decidedly dependent upon the six-legged arthropods; certainly the cold-blooded vertebrates would have a most difficult time in discovering a suitable substitute for the insect link in the food chains leading to their subsistence.

OLIVER B. COPE *is chief of the Central Valley Fishery Investigations, Fish and Wildlife Service, Department of the Interior. He is a native of San Francisco and received a doctorate in biology at Stanford University. He has worked with the California and United States Departments of Agriculture, did mosquito abatement for the Navy in the southwest Pacific during the Second World War, and is now occupied with salmon and trout research in the Western States.*

Some Insect Pests of Wildlife

J. P. Linduska, Arthur W. Lindquist

Combining such contradictory qualities as "adaptability" and "specialization," insects hold a key position in the economy of most living things. There is scarcely a plant that does not contribute to the needs of one or more kinds of "bugs," and a considerable segment of the insect world has become adapted to making a living off the larger forms of animal life. Wildlife supports these pests in great variety. And, despite a remarkable diversity of habits among birds and mammals, few, if any, escape attack by insects or their near relatives.

Moles and other subterranean mammals, which seldom appear above ground, are hosts to a complement of these arthropods. Bats, alternating periods of sustained flight with retirement in the deep recesses of a cave, are not without some parasites—the little brown bat frequently carries two species of mites, one species of flea, and the bat bug, a form related to the common bed bug of humans. A semi-aquatic existence has not spared the beaver this "boring from without." Examination of 140 animals trapped in Minnesota produced one species of tick, one of mites, two types of beetles, and larvae of the screw-worm fly. Neither has the pelagic life of the northern fur seal entirely discouraged such parasitism. Young seals before their first oceanic crossing are host to two species of lice; two species of nasal mites affect young and old alike.

The distaste shown for some small mammals by their larger mammalian predators is not always shared by the lesser insect life. Short-tailed shrews, for instance, which may be commonly killed but seldom eaten by dogs, foxes, and cats, are entirely acceptable fare to several kinds of fleas, numerous species of mites, and occasionally ticks.

Among birds this relationship also appears to be practically universal. A survey of the ectoparasites of birds of the eastern United States yielded 198 species of lice, flies, ticks, and mites from 255 species and races of these animals. Such common songsters as the robin and song sparrow and also one of our commonest game species, the bobwhite quail, were found to harbor 15 species of external parasites. The rabbit tick, which was recorded from 46 of the 255 types of birds examined, belied its common name by appearing as the most widely distributed of the 198 types of parasites found. The ubiquity of such pests of birds is apparent from studies in many areas, and 33 species of biting lice (Mallophaga) alone have been recognized from 29 species of wild birds just in the Province of Alberta.

Indeed, it seems unlikely that any bird or mammal can claim complete freedom from insects or related air-breathing arthropods, such as ticks and mites. Whales and other cetaceans are possible exceptions, but even in this instance gill-breathing arthropods of several types appear in substitution. The large whale lice (Cyamus) aside from bearing a superficial resemblance to some of the true lice, functionally present the same problem to whales as do their smaller insect counterparts to land animals.

Obviously the endless kinds of animals falling within the definition of wildlife, in combination with unlimited types of known insect pests, prevent anything like a detailed consideration of interrelationships of the two. Accordingly, this discussion must be confined largely to a generalized account of the subject in which occasional examples, illustrative of certain points, will be given in more detail.

INSECTS AND THEIR CLOSE RELATIVES differ markedly in their relationships to wildlife. Some depend on the host during their entire span of life. And, as is the case with many lice and mites, some have reached a level of specialization that restricts them to a single species of animal. Others, including many ticks, experience intervals away from the host, and in the course of development a given individual may infest several species. Still others, such as adults of many of the biting flies and mosquitoes, are even less discriminating in the selection of hosts and are essentially free-living except for periodic visits for the purpose of obtaining a blood meal.

Additional differences are to be found in the way in which these pests attack wildlife and in the importance of such attacks to the welfare of the individual. While these innumerable relationships between insects and wildlife defy any logical classification, a few considerations of the characteristics and habits of the more important parasite groups will provide an insight into the nature of the problem. A number of insect-borne diseases of wildlife are capable of transmission by species of widely different parasite groups, and an account of this phase of the problem will be reserved for later discussion.

TICKS, which are closely related to insects, are distributed widely, and practically all mammals are attacked by one or more kinds. The habits of most wild birds are such that opportunities for infestation are not great. However, even among this group, many that nest or feed on the ground become parasitized, and one group of ticks, the soft-bodied ticks (Argasidae), are common pests of birds. Cliff swallows are known to be attacked by a species of this group and heavy populations of the so-called blue-bug frequently occur in the nests of barn swallows. Another species has been taken from several of the raptorial birds (hawks and owls) and others of the soft-bodied ticks are known to feed on a number of kinds of mammals. Ticks of this group are responsible for transmission of relapsing fever, a spirochete disease important to humans and fatal to laboratory animals in some strains, but of unknown consequence to the hosts in nature.

Ticks hold a special significance for wildlife in their capacity for disease transmission—a relationship we deal with later. Exclusive of this role, however, the mechanical effects of their feeding can be an important factor in predisposing animals to other pests and diseases. Through sheer numbers they frequently reduce the vitality of the host even to the point of occasionally being the direct cause of death.

The engorgement of female Rocky Mountain wood ticks has been recognized by William Jellison and Glen Kohls as being the cause of a noninfectious disease which they called tick-host anemia. After repeatedly producing this secondary anemia by heavy tick infestations on laboratory rabbits, these workers recognized the condition as being comparable to that previously observed in wild moose, jack rabbits, and foxes. They believed the disease occurred with some frequency in nature and that it could be the direct cause of death. Tick-induced anemia has been offered in explanation of a pronounced mortality among an island population of cottontail rabbits. This die-off, investigated by R. H. Smith and E. L. Cheatum, occurred on Fishers Island, N. Y., where a few dozen cottontails introduced in 1925 had reached near-plague proportions 13 years later. Ticks of the species *Ixodes dentatus* and the rabbit tick were abundant, and infestations on rabbits found dead were more than three times as heavy as those on live rabbits. Among dead animals suitable for autopsy the pathological conditions most consistently revealed were pale and watery-appearing blood and anemia, which, while generalized, was most apparent in the lungs and kidneys.

Feeding by ticks appears also to be an important underlying cause of subcutaneous abscesses reported in cottontail rabbits and wild hares. The condition, which has been termed lymphadenitis, or pyogenic disease, results from infection by one or more species of bacteria belonging to the genus *Staphylococcus*. The incidence or occurrence of the disease is not known, but among 84 cottontails examined from one area in New York State a rate of 17 percent was found. Likewise little is known of the disease as a mortality factor. Extensive involvement of the lymph nodes appears to be characteristic, however, and in some animals metastatic infections of the heart, lungs, kidney, and spleen have been noted. The rabbit tick and the species *Ixodes dentatus* have been associated with the disease in cottontails.

Tick paralysis, a disease of some consequence to humans in the Northwestern States and British Columbia, is known also to occur among a number of the wild mammals in that area. Engorging female Rocky Mountain wood ticks are associated with the disease, which is mainly of unknown causes. Most evidence favors the belief that a nerve poison, produced in the salivary glands and secreted by the tick during feeding, is responsible for the paralysis. Although removal of the offending tick is usually followed by rapid and complete recovery, it is likely that complete paralysis and death is more commonly the outcome in nature.

Ticks are believed to be of importance as a predisposing agent for such conditions as foot rot in deer and screw-worm common in many forms of wildlife. With other biting pests, they may serve to spread mechanically the disease, frequently fatal for rabbits, which is accompanied by so-called rabbit horns. This disease (rabbit papillomatosis) is caused by a filtrable virus. In the same way they probably carry the infectious agent responsible for fleshy "warts" on the feet and legs of rabbits.

Various degrees of blindness in birds are known to result from attachment and feeding by this pest in the region of the eyes, and occasional mortalities are reported wherein unusual tick infestations appeared to be the direct cause. F. C. Bishopp and Helen Trembley suspected that gross infestations of the lone star tick were responsible for mortality among wild turkeys on Bull's Island in South Carolina. Rabbits and other mammals occasionally are subject to massive subcutaneous infestations of ticks, and the appearance of these pests beneath the skin probably results from an allergic reaction by the host.

While comparatively little is known of the population relationships of ticks and wildlife, the widespread distribution, abundance of species, and immensity of numbers of ticks has led to some suspicions that population levels of one group may be regulated by the other. R. G. Green and his coworkers in Minnesota learned that cycles in numbers of the rabbit tick followed the population trend of the snowshoe rabbit and were related to it. In the fall of 1933, when snowshoes were at a cyclic peak, the estimated population of feeding ticks was 2,800,000 per square mile. With the hare population at a "low" in the fall of 1938, the numbers of ticks were at a corresponding low of 150,000 per square mile. The rabbit die-off was demonstrated to be independent of any immediate effects of the ticks, and due to "shock disease" in which hypoglycemia was the only definite finding.

MANY ADULT FLIES, such as black flies, horse flies, and deer flies are vicious biters and are more than a moderate annoyance particularly to larger forms of wildlife. There are few recorded observations of biting flies feeding on wild game and the effects of attacks of these bloodthirsty flies on wild animals can only be surmised from observations of distress caused domestic stock on mountainous or wooded ranges. In such locations black flies can be seen to issue from the ears of almost any large animal during the fly season, and such attacks must be massive, persistent, and continuous. Others, like the mosquitoes, that extract their blood meal by less painful means, make up in numbers what they lack in individual effect. Through constant harassment during the warm months these insects reduce the vigor of animals and, especially in the case of big game, discourage proper feeding and conditioning at a time when foods are bountiful. Animals kept poor through the summer and fall are scarcely prepared to face the adversities of deep snow and food shortages in winter.

One group of flies, the Hippoboscidae, are full-time residents on many species of wildlife. They occur on numerous songbirds and frequently are found on predatory birds as well as on a number of game species. The "sticky" fly of deliberate flight that scurries from the feathers of your pheasant or quail to settle on the kitchen window very likely is one of these louse flies.

Members of this family also infest mammals and at times are found on deer and other ruminants in considerable numbers. Species on mammals, which are commonly called ked flies, emerge from the quiescent pupal stage with wings, but these are shed a few days later. The remainder of their adulthood is spent in a wingless state, and they are frequently mistaken for ticks to which they bear a superficial resemblance. A number of these flies, together with some of the biting or sucking flies we mentioned, are important for their transmission of wildlife diseases. However, it has been through another attribute of these insects that the fly group has been of primary interest. This concerns the developmental habits of many species which require living animal tissue for completion of the larval, or maggot, stage.

MYIASIS is the term used for the condition in animals or man caused by the attack of the larvae of flies on the flesh. The screw-worm is one of the most important species causing myiasis. Its depredations on livestock are discussed elsewhere in this book.

Here we discuss its infestations of wild animals, which provide a constant reservoir of flies which infest domestic animals. The ranchman can systematically destroy screw-worms in livestock, but in some areas his efforts are partly nullified because of the great numbers of flies coming from wildlife. Game conservationists are directly concerned with the problem because the screw-worm takes a yearly toll of game animals, especially deer.

The screw-worm fly lays its eggs on any wound or broken skin of warm-blooded animals. The eggs hatch in a matter of hours, and the tiny larvae burrow into the flesh, creating holes or pockets. As the larvae grow, the suppurating wound is enlarged and becomes more attractive to flies. Usually more and more eggs are deposited in the wound, and the large number of larvae soon cause the death of the animal unless the wound is treated. The larvae mature in less than a week, drop from the wound, pupate in the soil, and adults emerge from a week to 6 weeks later, depending on temperature.

The secretive habits of deer and most wild species complicate obtaining reliable estimates of losses to these insects. In years of screw-worm abundance, the incidence among adult animals may run as high as 25 percent and even higher among young of the year. A bumper crop of these pests in 1949 and 1950 produced numerous reports of widespread infestations and deer losses in the Southeastern States, especially Georgia, Alabama, and the Carolinas. Screw-worms are one of the principal enemies of deer in Texas. In California 190 deer are known to have died from this cause in a limited area in one season.

Flesh flies belonging to the family Sarcophagidae are known to attack wild animals with telling effects. Mink, ferrets, foxes, and rabbits have been parasitized in confinement. There is a record of 100 percent mortality to the young in two cottontail nests. Adult flies of *Wohlfahrtia vigil* had apparently deposited their living larvae at the time the nestling rabbits were born or shortly thereafter. In the fox farms of the West, losses as high as 30 percent are frequent. F. X. Gassner and M. T. Jones have stated that the loss to the fur-farming industry in Utah and Idaho from this cause had amounted to about 4 million dollars by 1948.

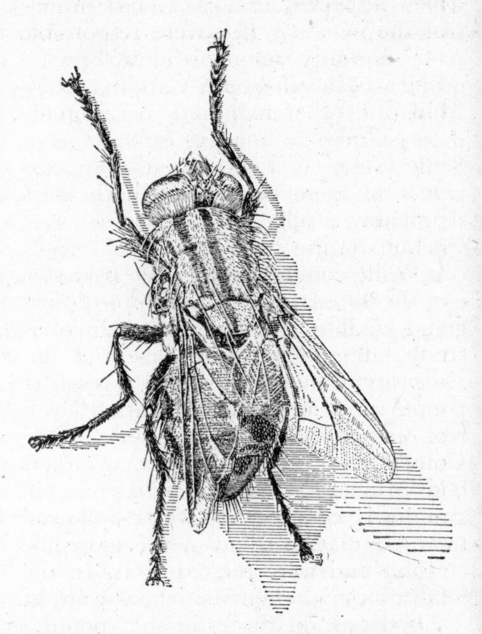

Sarcophaga haemorroidalis, a flesh fly.

Bot flies of the genus *Cephenomyia* are large, gray-brown, beelike creatures that have been reported to have the most rapid flight of any insect. They hover near deer, darting in and depositing living larvae in their nostrils. The process causes extreme terror. The animals react violently when attacked and jump, rear, and otherwise exhibit fear.

The tiny larvae of the bot fly crawl upwards over the mucous membrane of the nostrils and eventually enter the sinuses, where they remain until mature. Apparently they require several months to develop in the animal, maturing in the spring and early summer, when they drop to the ground and pupate. Deer seem to suffer greatly when the larvae crawl from the nasal passages.

These insects are widely distributed over the United States, Canada, and Alaska. They probably are one of the most injurious insect parasites of deer. S. C. Whitlock has estimated that 25 percent of the deer in Michigan carry the bots. In New York State, E. L. Cheatum found an incidence of 30 percent in deer found dead in winter and 21 percent in an apparently healthy group that had been collected for study.

As is true of most such types of parasitism, it is difficult to assess the real importance of nasal bot flies. I. M. Cowan states, "There is a considerable body of circumstantial evidence to suggest that the deer bot, if present in numbers greater than 30 per animal, can have serious consequences and may kill the host."

Elsewhere, outbreaks of bot infestations causing injury and death have been reported. One observer described the death of more than 60 deer from one herd in Colorado between February and April 1929. One deer had 54 bots, and its lower nasal passages were highly inflamed, with infestation in the sinus. However, otherwise healthy animals are known to tolerate nasal bots without critical effects. Whatever the immediate effects, such an infestation in the deer is recognized as a debilitating factor, which, when superimposed upon dietary inadequacies, inclement weather, and other basic influences, must surely reduce an animal's chances of survival.

Several species of bot flies of the genus *Cuterebra* are parasitic on rodents. The larvae of this fly are called simply bots and cause a skin myiasis. These bots have been collected from rabbits, squirrels, opossums, mice, pocket gophers, and other rodents. They are probably of minor importance as far as wildlife is concerned. Many times, however, people have discarded infested rabbits and squirrels as inedible, although the bots have no bad effect on the quality of the meat.

One instance is known where an effort was made to reduce this waste of game. In North Carolina, 30 percent of more than 2,000 gray squirrels examined from September 15 to January 1 were found to be infested with bots. In the following year, the State conservation department delayed the opening of the hunting season a month. Among animals taken during the later season, only 10 percent of 9,000 examined contained bots. The total kill for the State was estimated at 4.5 million squirrels, and because the later season reduced the apparent degree of parasitism by 20 percent, it is possible that as many as 800,000 animals were saved from discard.

The gross appearance of this type of parasitism would suggest rather critical consequences to the host, but apparently that is not usually the case. Studies involving the live trapping and recapture of marked cottontails, for instance, have not revealed losses due to the pest. However, these enormous warbles may be of greater importance to very small mammals. Studies on the woodland deermouse in Iowa by Thomas Scott and Edwin Snead showed that 42 percent of the adult mice and 17 percent of the young carried larvae of *Cuterebra* in September. Coincidentally with this period of maximum warble infestation, the mouse population, declined by 50 percent. Adult animals, having a greater percentage of infestation than the young, declined more appreciably in numbers.

A WARBLE FLY, *Oedemagena tarandi,* attacks reindeer in Alaska and northern Europe. The hides develop hundreds of holes; their usefulness is reduced as a source of leather for the Eskimos and other Arctic people. The migration of the grubs through the body is believed to cause injury and reduction of flesh and to affect its quality.

Nestling songbirds are rather commonly attacked by larvae of flies of the family Calliphoridae. Occasionally a high incidence of such parasitism is noted. At the Wharton bird-banding station in Massachusetts, Edwin Mason observed 162 songbird broods over the period 1936–1941 and found infestations by *Apaulina* (more commonly but incorrectly recorded as *Protocalliphora*) as follows: Bluebirds, 94 percent; tree swallows, 82 percent; and house wrens, 47 percent. The nesting success of these species in the same order was 78, 82, and 99 percent, possibly indicating the effects of the parasite burden. The area was being managed for songbirds and it is not unlikely that a heavier than normal population encouraged an unusually high incidence of parasitism. Elsewhere, however, under more natural conditions high rates of parasitism have been found. O. E. Plath examined 63 nests involving 6 species and found 61 percent infested with *Apaulina* larvae. In his studies on mourning doves in the San Joaquin Valley, Calif., Johnson Neff found over a 4-year period that parasitism by these blow flies involved about half of the nests. A high mortality among young doves was attributed largely to that cause. In one study area, where more than 100 nests were under observation, only 18 produced young that reached an independent age. Apparently that was not so much due to the actual killing of the nestlings by larvae as to their falling from the nest in efforts to escape the attacks of the parasites.

Subcutaneous infestations by these larvae are known. Very young larvae in particular occasionally find their way into the ears and nostrils of nestlings. However, the normal habit of the larger larvae is one of periodic feeding on feet, legs, and underparts of nestlings; afterwards they retreat into the inner structure of the nest. As might be expected from these habits, birds which nest in cavities or construct closely woven nests are most susceptible to attack. Loose nest construction in itself, however, does not always deter the pests—as is shown by their frequent presence in the makeshift nests of mourning doves.

Fleas occur widely. Birds are not frequently attacked, but most mammals support one or more species. Aside from their importance in the transmittal of murine typhus and plague (both chiefly in rodents), the importance of the group to wildlife is mainly of a nuisance nature. Extremely heavy infestations are occasionally encountered on mammals; these heavy populations undoubtedly have debilitating effects. During the winter marked increases occur in the number of the parasites on the skunk, cottontail rabbit, tree squirrels, and hibernating woodchucks and ground squirrels. Adult fleas live mainly in burrows, dens, and other situations frequented by the host. The developmental stages from egg to adult are passed in the litter of such sites.

The biting lice (Mallophaga) are among the commonest parasites of birds. Harold Peters, in his compilation for the Eastern States, lists 255 species and subspecies of wild birds known to carry ectoparasites. Of this total 239 were found to be infested with one or more species of biting lice. Such common birds as the robin and bobwhite were found to harbor six species.

The effects of the lice on wild birds are not considered to be of real consequence. Heavy infestations cause damage to the plumage. Superficial feeding may occasion some reduction in vigor. They are not known to be important from the standpoint of disease transmission.

Interesting accounts have been reported dealing with what may be a delousing effort on the part of some birds. Several species have the habit either of placing ants in their plumage or of spreading over an anthill with outstretched wings. Starlings, which frequently are lousy, have been observed to follow the first-mentioned procedure, and crows, another consistent host, the latter. If such a be-

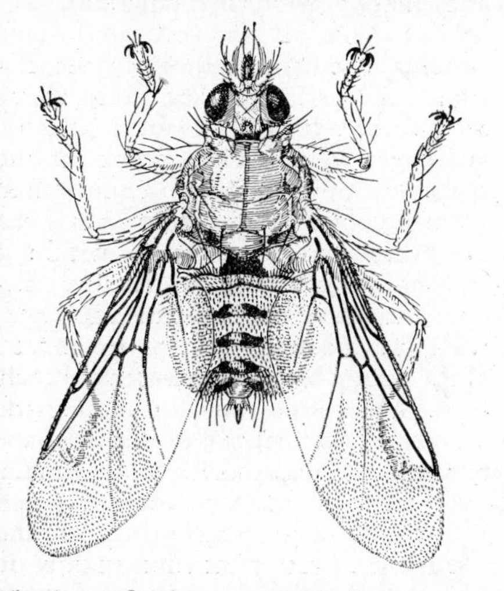

The louse fly that commonly infests song birds is provided with strong claws enabling it to cling to the feathers.

havior is effective in relieving these birds of the parasites, it has not been determined whether the ants accomplish this by preying on the lice or whether the formic acid which they produce has an insecticidal effect. In this regard it may be significant that, with a single exception, no mammal subsisting largely on ants is known as a host for lice.

Although both the biting and sucking lice infest mammals, it has been found that a wild host species seldom supports representatives of both groups regularly. Infestations of biting lice occur rather commonly on deer, elk, and other species, but their effect, as in the case of birds, is not of real consequence. The sucking lice, in addition to being of potential importance in the transmission of diseases also constitute a more serious parasite load than do the Mallophaga. Although biting lice hold significance for their transmission of disease in humans, this relationship in wildlife seems mainly to involve their participation in the transmission of endemic typhus.

MITES, which are relatives of ticks, make up a large group of diverse habits. Some, such as the mange mites and feather mites, are full-time parasites of wildlife and spend all stages of their life history on the host. Others belonging to the family Trombiculidae are parasitic on wildlife only during the larval stage. Several species are well known to inhabitants of Southern States. "Chigger" or "red-bug" are common names applied to those that frequently attack humans and cause intense itching and general annoyance.

Chiggers are numerous and widely distributed, but comparatively little is known of their importance and habits. That they occur commonly on wildlife and sometimes in considerable numbers may be exemplified by experiences of James M. Brennan, who took more than 4,000 chiggers from a single woodchuck in Bitterroot Valley of Montana. On other local rodents Dr. Brennan collected as many as seven species from one animal.

Practically all members of the mite group live externally on the host, but a few are adapted for an internal existence. The air-sac mite takes up residence in the respiratory passages and air sacs of pheasants and some domestic fowl, and other species are parasitic in the lungs and air passages of sea lions and other seals.

Mammals are attacked by a great variety of mites. Common forms like the muskrat may be parasitized by 5 species, the short-tailed shrew by 11 species, and the cottontail rabbit by 5 or more. In most instances mite parasitism seems to have but slight effect on the host. The mange mites, however, are capable of bringing severe consequences to infested animals, at times to the degree of being the immediate cause of death.

Fox squirrels are parasitized regularly by itch mites. It is not uncommon in late winter and early spring to see animals with bald patches on the head and neck and swollen and bleeding ears, which are the result of feeding by the mites. In severe cases animals are practically devoid of hair, and the skin becomes much thickened, rough, and of a characteristic grayish, lead-colored hue.

One of the mange mites (*Notoedres*) is claimed to have been responsible for a widespread die-off of gray squirrels in California. Animals infested with the mite were first noted in 1917; within 10 years gray squirrels were all but eliminated in the Yosemite region. In the Yellowstone Park area, elk have been observed infested with one of the psoroptic mange mites. During studies on this herd, Harlow Mills encountered one animal that very likely perished as a direct result of parasitism by a species of *Psoroptes,* probably the sheep scab mite. This individual had lost most of the hair from both sides of its body.

Birds are hosts to a considerable variety of mites including a few of importance to domestic birds. The chicken mite is known to occur on several wild species, and the northern fowl mite has been recorded even more commonly from wild birds. Little is known of the effects of these parasites on wild populations, but they do not appear to hold the same significance for wild birds as for domestic species.

An outbreak of an apparently fatal infestation of scaly-leg mite among ruffed grouse and California quail has been reported by I. M. Cowan. Birds with heavy infestations were found in which tissues of the feet and legs were greatly hypertrophied, and this stage was followed by ulceration and sloughing of the toes. The breast skin and the extremities were involved in some cases.

PREDACEOUS INSECTS hardly qualify for inclusion in this section concerned with ectoparasites. However, a discussion of insect pests of wildlife would not be complete without some mention of fire ants. Depredations by these insects are restricted both geographically and by species preyed upon—the bobwhite quail being the species primarily concerned, and the Southeastern States the region of principal losses.

Fire ants cause serious mortality of quail by entering the eggs as soon as they are pipped or attacking the young immediately after they have hatched. In the course of intensive life-history and management studies of the bobwhite in Georgia, Herbert Stoddard recorded in a year a 15-percent loss of quail nests to this insect. This occurred in spite of an intensive ant-control program involving fumigating with sodium cyanide all ant colonies within a 50-foot radius of the nests. In investigations extending over several years, Bernard Travis found that 4 to 16 percent of the young birds were destroyed each year. The studies developed methods for insecticidal control of ant colonies, but the cost was too high for general use.

THE TRANSMISSION OF DISEASES by insects has a significance for wildlife. Most of these insect-borne ailments are also infectious to humans, domestic animals, or both.

Tularemia, a bacterial disease, occurs as a natural infection in a variety of small mammals but primarily in rodents. Many wild mice, ground squirrels, gophers, and chipmunks are susceptible, and also larger rodents such as woodchucks, porcupines, muskrats, and beaver. Carnivores are not immune but apparently have a high natural resistance. The disease has been recognized in the coyote. On at least one occasion considerable losses among gray foxes were ascribed to it. Birds are also susceptible, the infection having been reported in ruffed grouse, sharp-tailed grouse, quail, the ring-necked pheasant, and sage grouse.

It is in populations of the cottontail rabbit, however, that the disease is of greatest consequence as far as wildlife is concerned. This animal, commonly involved in the passage of tularemia to human beings, is highly susceptible, and infected rabbits normally succumb. As early as 1932, studies in Minnesota demonstrated that the disease could decimate populations of the cottontail.

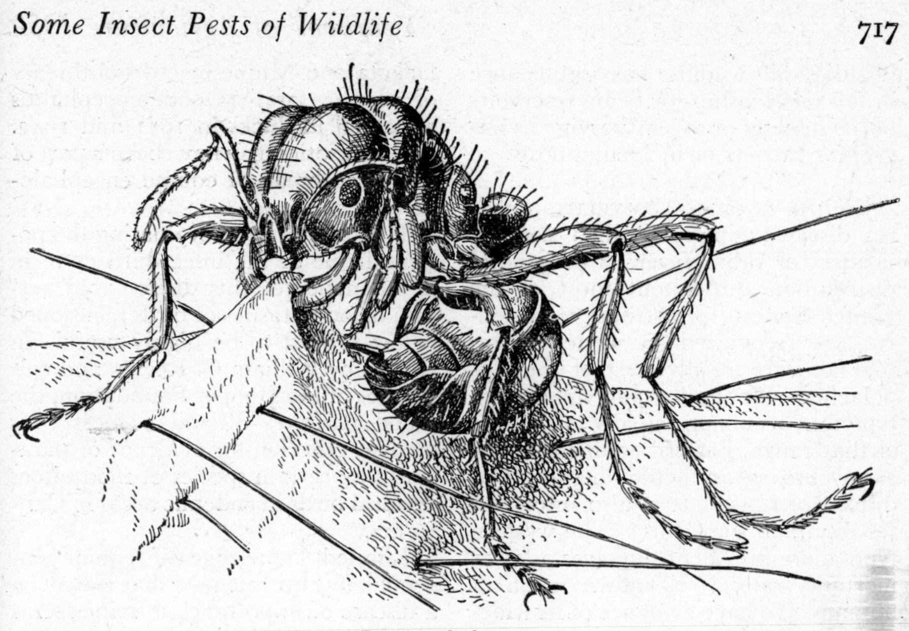

Imported fire ant.

Ticks, particularly the rabbit tick, are mainly responsible for the spread of the disease among rabbits. Fleas, deer flies, and probably other biting insects are other carriers of the infection.

Plague, responsible over the years for the death of millions of people, was first recognized in the United States in 1900. Numerous field surveys since then have shown that local areas of the infection among rodents are present in most of the Western and Southwestern States. The disease is highly infectious for a great variety of rodents. A number of epizootics (epidemics among animals) have testified to the importance of so-called sylvatic plague in regulating their population. In Park County, Colo., an outbreak among prairie dogs, first noticed in 1945, had spread over the entire county in 2 years, and in less than 4 years had practically eliminated this species on 625,000 acres.

Fleas of many species are the medium through which the malady is carried from animal to animal. The wide-spread travels of young rodents may serve to hasten the spread of the disease. During an outbreak in Kern County, Calif., the period of peak incidence among ground squirrels was associated with the time of emergence and dispersal of the young. The outbreak was checked when the shifting population again became sedentary.

Plague has not been observed in wild species of value as game or fur bearers, with one exception—a reported epizootic among cottontail rabbits in Lea County, N. Mex.

Virus encephalitides comprise a large group of viruses that show a special affinity or tropism for the central nervous system (neurotropic) and that characteristically cause an inflammation of the brain (encephalitis). Many of these maintain themselves in various species of wildlife, and are transmitted among wild forms, and to humans and domestic animals, by insects and other arthropods. For the most part these diseases are poorly understood and it is not unlikely that further investigation will show some to be of direct importance to wildlife. In any case, it appears that many have important implications as to public

970134°—52——47

health, and wildlife has significance in the relationship for being reservoirs of the diseases or at least serving as important carriers or incidental hosts.

EQUINE ENCEPHALOMYELITIS, a virus disease, popularly called sleeping sickness or brain fever, is of general distribution throughout most of the United States. Two strains of the virus are recognized—a western form that appears mainly west of the Appalachian Mountains and an eastern type that occurs principally to the east of that range. Eastern equine encephalomyelitis is an acute, highly fatal disease of horses. It is also infectious for man and some birds. The western type, more prevalent, involves a lower mortality rate. It is known to affect humans. We have evidence of its widespread occurrence in birds.

Experimentally a number of species of *Aedes* mosquitoes have been found to be capable of transmitting both the eastern and western strains. As to the western form, the virus has been isolated from mites, lice, several species of *Culex* mosquitoes, and assassin bugs (*Triatoma*). This virus has been transmitted experimentally by the Rocky Mountain wood tick.

The importance in nature of the disease to wildlife has not been established. However, the eastern virus has been identified from ring-neck pheasants under confinement in New Jersey and from a wild bird in Connecticut. From 1938, when the disease was first recognized in New Jersey pheasants, to 1946, 13 definite outbreaks occurred among confined birds. Coincidentally with an outbreak among horses in New Jersey in 1945, a severe die-off, presumably also due to this disease, was experienced in game-farm pheasant stock. In a total of 5,094 birds, 3,757 died in about 2 months.

Antibodies indicative of infection with western equine encephalomyelitis have been found commonly in a number of wild birds, and the virus has been isolated from a naturally infected prairie chicken and a deer. In North Dakota and Minnesota two outbreaks of a highly fatal epizootic encephalitis appeared in ducks in 1941 and 1942. The epizootics may have been a part of a vast outbreak of equine encephalomyelitis.

It is of interest in evaluating the potential role of the insect-bird cycle in maintenance of this disease that certain blood parasites of birds mentioned below proved to be highly useful. In studies by William C. Reeves and colleagues of the Hooper Foundation, the blood parasites offered a most convenient criterion for evidence of parasitism by certain species of mosquitoes on local birds in endemic areas in California.

Limited knowledge of equine encephalomyelitis suggests that it may be a disease of importance to some forms of wildlife. Studies in progress in 1951 by various organizations should uncover information showing more clearly the significance of the infection to wildlife and the relationship of wildlife to outbreaks of the disease in horses and humans.

A NUMBER OF BLOOD PARASITES (protozoa) invade and destroy the blood cells of wild animals. Three of these, which are known to infect wild birds commonly and with some pathogenic consequences, have at least one characteristic in common. All three are transmitted by insects and also have a complicated life history. Some of their developmental stages take place in the body of the insect carrier.

True bird malaria, caused by many species of *Plasmodium,* is of world-wide distribution. It is closely related to human malaria. Like that disease, it is carried by mosquitoes—a fact that was determined in the case of birds before mosquito transmission of the human form was established.

Numerous surveys involving the microscopic examination of blood smears from live-trapped birds have indicated a high rate of infection. This procedure is likely to detect the disease mainly during acute stages, which may last only a few days. Consequently many chronic infections escape detection; the true incidence of the disease probably is even greater than the already high rates (up to 25 percent) that have been reported. As an example, a group of song sparrows checked for the presence of malaria by blood-smear examination showed a 20-percent incidence. The actual rate was well over 50 percent as determined by more exacting studies involving the inoculation of blood samples into highly susceptible, malaria-free canaries. A still greater discrepancy was found in such a test of methods using eastern red-wings. In this case blood smears revealed an infection rate less than 5 percent whereas the actual incidence by inoculation of canaries was more than 60 percent.

The extent of mortality resulting from such an infection is not known. Judging from the high incidence and number of chronic infections, it is rather low. At the same time, the disease involves widespread destruction of red blood cells, with later involvement of the liver, spleen, and cells in the bone marrow. In this respect the disease could have important results as a condition predisposing the victim to other ailments.

Concurrently with losses among sharp-tailed grouse in the North Central States, a 40-percent incidence of infection with *Plasmodium* malaria was found in North Dakota. The organism produced acute symptoms and was quickly fatal to artificially infected birds. Chronic cases among naturally infected birds were observed to extend over several weeks.

Another type of malaria (*Haemoproteus*), similar to the one we described, is of widespread occurrence in birds. It also has been found in reptiles and amphibians. High rates of infection are known to occur in some waterfowl and also in California quail, which have received considerable attention as hosts of the infection. Over a 2-year period, E. C. O'Roke examined 312 California quail and found 45 percent of them parasitized by *Haemoproteus lophortyx*. Later studies on this bird in California by C. M. Herman and Ben Glading revealed an over-all incidence of 84 percent in 503 wild-trapped birds and a 100-percent incidence in late autumn. There is evidence that birds once infected with this blood parasite remain so for life. Although fatal infections have been observed in the wild, the mortality rate is not known. Mourning doves commonly carry infections of *Haemoproteus,* and in this species, as well as in quail, transmission of the disease is accomplished by hippoboscid flies. It is presumed that these flies also spread the infection in hawks, owls, songbirds, and other species known to be susceptible.

From studies started in 1930 and extending over 3 years, O'Roke discovered the cause and circumstances surrounding a mysterious and very destructive disease of both wild and domestic ducklings. The malaria-like disease, he found, was caused by a parasitic protozoan (*Leucocytozoan simondi* (=*L. anatis*)). The life cycle proved to be similar to that of the two malarial diseases mentioned above, and transmission was shown to be biological, involving a common black fly (*Simulium venustum*).

Investigations by O'Roke, and others since, have shown the disease to be both prevalent and deadly. In the case of ducks the infection occurs discontinuously over a wide area where black flies are found. Adult birds are resistant to the disease, and the mortality is usually less than 1 percent. It is highly fatal to young birds, however, and mortality rates found by O'Roke were 10 to 100 percent. Individuals surviving the malady can carry the infection indefinitely; these "carrier" birds perpetuate the disease and serve as a source of new infection on the breeding grounds. Studies in areas of heavy black fly activity in Maine revealed that black ducks with an incidence of 89 percent probably were more prone to *Leucocytozoan* infection than were several other species including the wood duck, American merganser, hooded merganser, American golden-eye, and green-winged teal.

For a number of years an effort has been made through releases of game-farm propagated mallards to establish local breeding populations of the bird in New York State. The program has been mainly unsuccessful, and known mortalities from *Leucocytozoan* infection have provided a possible explanation of the failure. Losses of young mallards were known to occur in black fly areas successfully occupied by black and wood ducks, an observation which led E. L. Cheatum to theorize a possible explanation based on the following facts: The natural breeding areas of black and wood ducks are wood-margined water areas frequently in the immediate vicinity of black fly producing streams. Logically the long-time association with such habitats might through selective survival lead to a high degree of tolerance to *Leucocytozoan* disease for these species. Mallards, on the other hand, are primarily a plains species and their breeding territory probably has evolved through a geographic range relatively free of black fly vectors of this infection. Consequently, the mallard on its ancestral breeding ground has not been closely associated with the disease, and evolutionary opportunities for establishing characteristics of survival value have been lacking.

In addition to its fatal characteristics in some waterfowl, *Leucocytozoan* disease has been credited with being of importance to other species. In Canada, C. H. D. Clarke noted during 1932–1934 that the decline of ruffed grouse was associated with the dying off of young birds. Investigation revealed nearly a 100-percent incidence of infection with a species of *Leucocytozoan* newly described as *L. bonasae*. During another cyclic decline 10 years later, 60–70 percent of the adult birds examined carried this blood parasite.

THE RELATIONSHIP OF INSECTS TO WILDLIFE has scarcely progressed beyond the "check-list" stage. The types of insect and other arthropod pests that one might expect to find on any given species of bird or mammal are reasonably well known. Also, there is some understanding of the potentialities of many of these parasites as disseminators of disease. There is little information, however, on the incidence of insect parasites and the diseases they transmit. And there is little to show how the numbers of these fluctuate seasonally and with the condition and population density of the host. The significance of parasite relationships to the individual and to populations of the host is a complex subject only vaguely understood. Until more basic facts are available on such points it is futile to speculate on the type of management programs that might be effective in dealing with problems involving these pests.

In some instances further research may demonstrate a justification for local programs of insect control. Referring to *Leucocytozoan* disease in ducks, we recall that on some areas a very high incidence of the disease was accompanied by a nearly 100-percent mortality among the young. Present methods of black fly control are both selective and economical. The elimination of this link in transmission of the disease undoubtedly could be profitable in some areas of concentrated duck nesting.

Principally, however, insect influences on wildlife are not of a nature to justify or require such direct methods. It is the common circumstance for wild animals to support their ectoparasites with only minor inconvenience to themselves. And when through unusual numbers, or transmission of a disease, these pests are responsible for widespread losses to their host species, it is usually a reflection of a more basic cause. In this connection we might consider briefly the present plight of big game herds throughout most of the United States.

Every winter tens of thousands of deer die in 30 of the 48 States that support populations of deer. The perennial inquiries following such die-offs reveal excessive parasitism, both internal and external, along with evidences of various infections and deficiency diseases. Autopsy reports routinely ascribe a share of the victims to infestations of bot fly larvae or other such parasites, some to pneumonia and similar ailments, and a proper percentage to plain starvation. As many investigators point out, the important consideration, of course, is that while the ultimate cause of many of these losses is disease, excessive parasitism, or a combination of such factors, the basic predisposing condition is malnutrition resulting from inadequate winter range. Obviously the solution to this widespread problem lies not in finding an economical direct means of insect or disease control, but in creating conditions which will insure for the animals concerned the high level of general health known to be effective in providing resistance to diseases, and to both the numbers and effects of parasites.

On a limited and local scale some partial alleviation of such winter food shortages has been accomplished in the West through dispersing and "moving" game concentrations. By placing salt at summer range elevations in Montana, elk herds have been encouraged to remain later in the fall and to return earlier in the spring. This has reduced the demands on limited winter ranges, and allowed some recovery of forage plants, as well as holding the animals in areas of abundant food supply. Considering the over-all problem, this procedure is of only very limited utility and has no application in the principal problem areas of the Eastern States.

The solution that has long been recognized by biologists is to reduce herds and maintain them at densities consistent with the forage supply. This can be readily accomplished through liberalized hunting and the taking of deer of any sex and age. Unfortunately there has been no widespread understanding of the problem, and public sentiment has opposed and prevented the adoption of this conservation measure. The alternative, now being followed in most States, is for natural forces to accomplish the reduction but only with further deterioration of the range and a deplorable waste of game.

Among other important species of wildlife, intervals of marked prosperity are observed to alternate with periods of acute population depression. The basic factors underlying these cyclic trends are not known. But the build-up in numbers of the host is observed to be accompanied by a corresponding increase in populations of ectoparasites, as well as in the variety and numbers of other "lesser life." The increased prevalence of these parasitic and infectious agents quite certainly is an *effect* of high host populations. To what extent they ultimately may function as a direct or indirect *cause* of the decline is not known. A clear understanding of such relationships would have far-reaching value. Besides providing a firm basis for the sound management of game populations, it is likely that such fundamental knowledge would find application in the field of human epidemiology and in other branches of science dealing with animal numbers. From these standpoints the problem is one to justify the concerted and coordinated attention of scientists of many specialties and interests.

J. P. LINDUSKA, *formerly assistant chief of the branch of wildlife research, and now chief of the branch of game management, United States Fish and Wildlife Service, is a graduate of the University of Montana and Michigan State College. Before joining the Fish and Wildlife Service in 1947, Dr. Linduska was employed as a wildlife biologist with the Michigan Department of Conservation, and as an entomologist with the Bureau of Entomology and Plant Quarantine.*

ARTHUR W. LINDQUIST, *a graduate of Kansas State College, has been an entomologist in the division of insects affecting man and animals, Bureau of*

Entomology and Plant Quarantine, since 1931. He has conducted and directed research on the biology and control of the screw-worm, blow flies, cattle grubs, horn flies, house flies, mosquitoes, tabanids, and other pests affecting livestock.

For further reference:

I. H. Bartlett: Whitetails, Presenting Michigan's Deer Problem, *Michigan Department of Conservation, Game Division Bulletin.* 1938.

F. R. Beaudette and J. J. Black: Equine Encephalomyelitis in New Jersey Pheasants in 1945 and 1946, *Journal of the American Veterinary Medical Association, volume 112, pages 140–147. 1948.*

J. F. Bell and W. S. Chalgren: Some Wildlife Diseases in the Eastern United States, *Journal of Wildlife Management, volume 7, pages 270–278. 1943.*

J. C. Bequaert: A Monograph of the Melophaginae, or Ked Flies, of Sheep, Goats, Deer, and Antelopes (Diptera, Hippoboscidae), *Entomologica Americana, volume 22, pages 1–210. 1942.*

John D. Beule: Cottontail Nesting-study in Pennsylvania, *Transactions of the Fifth North American Wildlife Conference, pages 320–327. 1940.*

F. C. Bishopp and Helen L. Trembley: Distribution and Hosts of Certain North American Ticks, *Journal of Parasitology, volume 31, pages 1–54. 1945.*

Bernard Brookman: Relation of Arthropods to the Epidemiology of Virus Encephalitis in Kern County, California, *CDC Bulletin, volume 9, pages 7–9. 1950.*

J. H. Brown and A. L. Wilk: Mallophaga of Alberta: A List of Species with Hosts, *Canadian Entomologist, volume 76, number 6, pages 127–129. 1944.*

E. L. Cheatum: Lymphadenitis in New York Cottontails, *Journal of Wildlife Management, volume 5, pages 304–308. 1941.*

C. H. D. Clarke: The Dying-off of Ruffed Grouse, *Transactions of the Twenty-first American Game Conference, pages 402–405. 1935.*

Ian McTaggart Cowan: Two Apparently Fatal Grouse Diseases, *Journal of Wildlife Management, volume 4, pages 311–312. 1940.*

Herald R. Cox, W. L. Jellison, and L. E. Hughes: Isolation of Western Equine Encephalomyelitis Virus from a Naturally Infected Prairie Chicken, *U. S. Public Health Reports, volume 56, pages 1905–1906. 1941.*

Wm. T. Cox: Snowshoe Rabbit Migration, Tick Infestation, and Weather Cycles, *Journal of Mammalogy, volume 17, pages 216–221. 1936.*

Gordon E. Davis: Ornithodoros parkeri: Distribution and Host Data; Spontaneous Infection with Relapsing Fever Spirochetes, *U. S. Public Health Reports, volume 54, pages 1345–1349, 1939;* Ornithodoros parkeri and Relapsing Fever Spirochetes in Southern Idaho, *U. S. Public Health Reports, volume 57, pages 1501–1503, 1942.*

Everett R. Doman and D. I. Rasmussen: Supplemental Winter Feeding of Mule Deer in Northern Utah, *Journal of Wildlife Management, volume 8, pages 317–338. 1944.*

J. R. Dymond: External Parasites of Bats, *Canadian Entomologist, volume 71, number 1, pages 20–21. 1938.*

Dean H. Ecke and Clifford W. Johnson: Sylvatic Plague in Park County, Colorado, *Transactions of the Fifteenth North American Wildlife Conference, pages 191–196. 1950.*

Arnold B. Erickson: Parasites of Beavers, with a Note on Paramphistomum castori Kofoid and Park, 1937, a Synonym of Stichorchis subtriquetrus, *American Midland Naturalist, volume 31, pages 625–630. 1944.*

F. C. Evans, C. M. Wheeler, and J. R. Douglas: Sylvatic Plague Studies. III. An Epizootic of Plague among Ground Squirrels (Citellus beecheyi) in Kern County, California, *Journal of Infectious Diseases, volume 72, number 1, pages 68–76. 1943.*

A. M. Fallis: Population Trends and Blood Parasites of Ruffed Grouse in Ontario, *Journal of Wildlife Management, volume 9, pages 203–206. 1945.*

John L. George and Robert T. Mitchell: Notes on Two Species of Calliphoridae (Diptera) Parasitizing Nestling Birds, *Auk, volume 65, pages 549–552. 1948.*

R. G. Green: A Ten-year Population Study of the Rabbit Tick, Haemaphysalis leporis-palustris, *with C. A. Evans and C. L. Larson, American Journal of Hygiene, volume 38, pages 260–281, 1943;* Shock Disease as the Cause of the Periodic Decimation of the Snowshoe Hare, *with C. L. Larson and J. F. Bell, American Journal of Hygiene, volume 30, section B, pages 83–102, 1939;* Progress Report of Wildlife Disease Studies for 1933, *with J. E. Shillinger, Transactions of the Twentieth American Game Conference, pages 288–297, 1934.*

John E. Guberlet and H. H. Hotson: A Fly Maggot Attacking Young Birds with Observations on its Life History, *Murrelet, volume 21, number 3, pages 65–68. 1940.*

Carlton M. Herman: Epidemiology of Malaria in Eastern Red-wings (Agelaius p. phoeniceus), *American Journal of Hygiene, volume 28, pages 232–243, 1938;* The Blood Protozoa of North American Birds, *Bird-Banding, volume 15, number 3, pages 89–112, 1944;* Hippoboscid Flies as Parasites of Game Animals in California, *California Fish and Game, volume 31, pages 16–25, 1945;* Deer Management Problems as Related to Diseases and Parasites of

Domestic Range Livestock, *Transactions of the Tenth North American Wildlife Conference, pages 242–246, 1945;* Blood Parasites of Birds from Kern County, California, *Journal of Parasitology, volume 34, section*

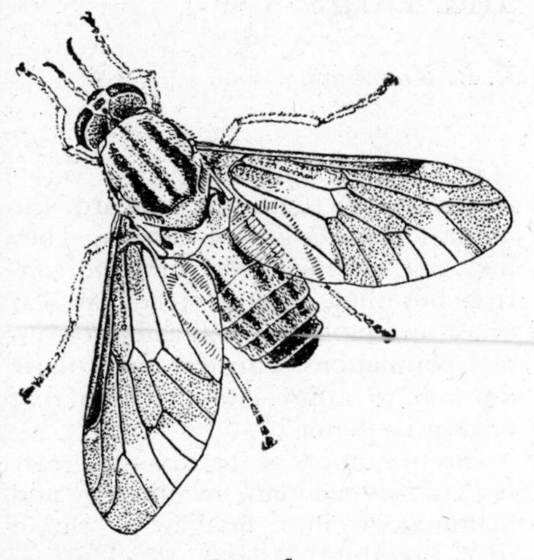

Deer fly.

2, pages 37–38, 1948; The Duration of Haemoproteus Infection in California Quail, *with Arthur I. Bischoff, California Fish and Game, volume 35, pages 293–299, 1949;* The Protozoan Blood Parasite Haemoproteus lophortyx O'Roke in Quail at the San Joaquin Experimental Range, California, *with Ben Glading, California Fish and Game, volume 28, pages 150–153, 1942.*

Redginal Hewitt: Bird Malaria, *The Johns Hopkins Press, Baltimore. 1940.*

Harold M. Hill and Telford H. Work: Protocalliphora Larvae Infesting Nestling Birds of Prey, *Condor, volume 49, number 2, pages 74–75. 1947.*

G. H. E. Hopkins: The Host-Association of the Lice of Mammals, *Proceedings of the Zoological Society of London, volume 119, part 2, pages 387–604. 1949.*

E. W. Jameson, Jr.: The External Parasites of the Short-tailed Shrew, Blarina brevicauda (Say), *Journal of Mammalogy, volume 31, pages 138–145. 1950.*

Wm. L. Jellison: Host Distribution of Lice on Native American Rodents North of Mexico, *Journal of Mammalogy, volume 23, pages 245–250, 1942;* Tick-host Anemia: A Secondary Anemia Induced by Dermacentor andersoni Stiles, *with G. M. Kohls, Journal of Parasitology, volume 24, number 2, pages 143–154, 1938.*

Glen M. Kohls: Notes on the Tick, Ixodes howelli Cooley and Kohls, with Descriptions, *Journal of Parasitology, volume 33, pages 57–61. 1947.*

C. L. Larson, J. E. Shillinger, and R. G. Green: Transmission of Rabbit Papillomatosis by the Rabbit Tick, Haemaphysalis leporis-palustris, *Proceedings of the Society for Experimental and Biological Medicine, volume 33, pages 536–538. 1936.*

Aldo Leopold, Lyle K. Sowls, and David L. Spencer: A Survey of Over-populated Deer Ranges in the United States, *Journal of Wildlife Management, volume 11, pages 162–177. 1947.*

Arthur W. Lindquist: Myiasis in Wild Animals in Southwestern Texas, *Journal of Economic Entomology, volume 30, pages 735–740. 1937.*

Vernon B. Link: Plague Epizootic in Cottontail Rabbits, *U. S. Public Health Reports, volume 65, page 696. 1950.*

Donald D. McLean: The Screw-Worm Fly, *California Conservationist, volume 6, number 2, pages 11, 20, and 21. 1941.*

Edwin A. Mason: Parasitism by Protocalliphora and Management of Cavity-nesting Birds, *Journal of Wildlife Management, volume 8, pages 232–247. 1944.*

Harlow B. Mills: Observations on Yellowstone Elk, *Journal of Mammalogy, volume 17, pages 250–253. 1936.*

Johnson A. Neff: Maggot Infestation of Nestling Mourning Doves, *Condor, volume 47, number 2, pages 73–76. 1945.*

Clifford E. Nelson and Jay S. Gashwiler: Blood Parasites of Some Maine Waterfowl, *Journal of Wildlife Management, volume 5, pages 199–205. 1941.*

E. C. O'Roke: The Morphology, Transmission, and Life History of Haemoproteus lophortyx O'Roke, a Blood Parasite of the California Valley Quail, *University of California Publications in Zoology, volume 36, pages 1–51, 1930;* A Malaria-like Disease of Ducks Caused by Leucocytozoan anatis Wickware, *University of Michigan School of Forestry and Conservation Bulletin 4, 1934.*

Harold S. Peters: A List of External Parasites from Birds of the Eastern Part of the United States, *Bird-Banding, volume 7, number 1, pages 9–27. 1936.*

Cornelius B. Philip: Ticks as Vectors of Animal Diseases, *Canadian Entomologist, volume 71, number 3, pages 55–65. 1939.*

O. E. Plath: Parasitism of Nestling Birds by Fly Larvae, *Condor, volume 21, pages 30–39. 1919.*

Edward Rosenow: Studies on the Relation of a Neurotropic Streptococcus and Virus to Epizootic Encephalitis of Wild Ducks, *Cornell Veterinarian, volume 33, number 3, pages 277–304. 1943.*

Morris Schaeffer: Encephalitis, *CDC Bulletin, volume 9, pages 1–2. 1950.*

Thos. G. Scott and Edwin Snead: Warbles in Permyscus leucopus noveboracensis, *Journal of Mammalogy, volume 23, pages 94–95. 1942.*

M. S. Shahan and L. T. Giltner: A Review of the Epizootiology of Equine Encephalomyelitis in the United States, *Journal of the American Veterinary Medical Association, volume 107, pages 279–288. 1945.*
R. H. Smith and E. L. Cheatum: Role of Ticks in Decline of an Insular Cottontail Population, *Journal of Wildlife Management, volume 8, pages 311–317. 1944.*
Leroy C. Stegeman: Some Parasites and Pathological Conditions of the Skunk (Mephitis mephitis nigra) in Central New York, *Journal of Mammalogy, volume 20, pages 493–496. 1939.*
Ernest Swift: A History of Wisconsin Deer, *Wisconsin Conservation Department Publication 323, page 96. 1946.*
Walter P. Taylor and Henry C. Hahn: Die-offs Among the White-tailed Deer in the Edwards Plateau of Texas, *Journal of Wildlife Management, volume 11, pages 317–323. 1947.*
Bernard V. Travis: Fire Ant Problem in the Southeast with Special Reference to Quail, *Transactions of the Third North American Wildlife Conference, pages 705–708. 1938.*
Ernest E. Tyzzer, Andrew W. Sellards, and Byron L. Bennett: The Occurrence in Nature of "Equine Encephalomyelitis" in the Ring-necked Pheasant, *Science, volume 88, pages 505–506. 1938.*
H. Van Roekel and Miriam K. Clarke: Equine Encephalomyelitis Virus (Eastern Type) Isolated from Ring-necked Pheasant, *Journal of the American Veterinary Medical Association, volume 47, pages 466–468. 1939.*
H. L. Van Volkenberg and A. J. Nicholson: Parasitism and Malnutrition of Deer in Texas, *Journal of Wildlife Management, volume 7, pages 220–223. 1943.*
N. E. Wayson: Plague—Field Surveys in Western United States During Ten Years (1936–1945), *U. S. Public Health Reports, volume 62, pages 780–791. 1947.*
Psyche W. Wetmore: A Species of Plasmodium from the Sharp-tailed Grouse Infective to Other Birds, *Journal of Wildlife Management, volume 3, pages 361–365, 1939;* Blood Parasites of Birds of the District of Columbia and Patuxent Research Refuge Vicinity, *Journal of Parasitology, volume 27, pages 379–393. 1941.*
S. C. Whitlock: The Prevalence of Disease and Parasites in White-tail Deer, *Transactions of the Fourth North American Wildlife Conference, pages 244–249. 1939.*
Ralph B. Williams: Infestation of Raptorials by Ornithodoros aquilae, *Auk, volume 64, number 2, pages 185–188. 1947.*
Martin D. Young and Arne V. Hunninen: Blood Protozoa of Birds at Columbia, South Carolina, *Journal of Parasitology, volume 36, pages 258–260. 1950.*

Birds, Beasts, and Bugs

E. R. Kalmbach

Birds, mammals, and other vertebrates work constantly toward the natural suppression of insects. They may not always effect complete control, but they exert a steady and at times an emphatic local effect on insect populations. Farmers particularly do well to appreciate the help that birds give them.

Circumstances of the times led early research in economic ornithology and mammalogy into qualitative rather than quantitative channels. Most of the problems were approached with the idea of disclosing through stomach analysis the character of the food of birds and mammals; through a process of deduction an appraisal was made of the economic status of the creature involved. By far the greater part of our knowledge still is of this character, but keen observers through the years have encountered and appraised in the field instances of insect suppression that have been recorded quantitatively. Usually these recitals deal with local or temporary conditions, yet their frequency of occurrence under many diversified conditions gives indication of the possibilities.

To present this information one must resort to a compilation of published reports and in doing so I avail myself to a large extent of the contributions of W. L. McAtee, who more than anyone else has assembled information of this kind and whose philosophies with respect to bird-insect relations are classical.

McAtee always took pains to preface his dissertations on avian economics with words of caution regarding the nature and extent of benefits to be expected, as for instance:

"The general utility of birds in checking the increase of injurious animals and plants is well understood. It must be admitted, however, that while birds constantly exert a repressive influence on the numbers of the organisms they prey upon and even exterminate certain pests locally, they are not numerous enough to cope successfully with widespread invasions.

"Birds are prone to feed upon things that are abundant and easily accessible, for instance, in elderberry season a very large number of birds take elderberries; if May-flies swarm in a locality, practically all of the birds there devour May-flies. Thus, under unusual conditions, such as attend outbreaks of insects or other pests, birds may very naturally turn their attention to the plentiful and easily obtained food, and the attack on a particular pest often is intensified also by the flocking of birds from surrounding areas."

THE INSTANCES of insect suppression that I recite here are mere fragments from an abundant literature. I make no attempt to include illustrations even from all the major groups of insects or all the species of birds whose good work is on record.

Plagues of grasshoppers (locusts) have been recorded throughout the history of mankind. In our country one frequently encounters a recital of what was considered providential aid rendered by gulls in the control of the Mormon cricket in the early days of settlement in the Salt Lake Valley. Less heralded but no less significant have been the instances of grasshopper suppression by birds in the Midwest. An example was reported by Samuel Aughey in Nebraska.

He stated: "No Nebraskan will forget the countless number of young locusts that hatched out in the spring of 1875. Only where they were removed by causes known or unknown were crops produced during this season over the infested region. Among the few causes operating in the destruction of locusts during that period was the work of insectivorous birds. Among the spots that birds frequented was one on the west side of Salt Creek, not more than 2 miles from Lincoln. There was a small area of about 320 acres that harbored an immense number of locusts. The birds, however, made it one of their feeding grounds, and the locusts lessened daily in numbers. Within a month hardly a locust was left. Similar instances of the work of birds were observed farther down on Salt Creek and on Middle Creek.

"In the spring of 1877 . . . on Middle Creek and its tributaries, and in various other places, I could see that the birds sensibly and radically diminished their numbers. One notable point was a few miles down Salt Creek from Lincoln. In May I visited the spot owing to the reported great numbers of locusts there. I estimated the number when I visited the place to be about 135 to a square foot. Already the birds had discovered it, and within sight were quail, larks, bobolinks, yellowheads (blackbirds), plovers, curlews, and a few prairie chickens. With my glass I could see them picking up these insects. In a month hardly a locust was left in this place."

A more recent occurrence of bird control of an orthopterous insect closely related to the Mormon cricket was recorded by A. C. Burrill. He stated: "The State of Washington with the aid of agents of the United States Department of Agriculture, has been attempting to control the Coulee cricket, which devastates large areas in the vicinity of Adrian, Washington. According to Mr. Max Reeher, scientific assistant in the United States Bureau of Entomology, western meadowlarks appeared in great numbers in the Dry Coulee last fall and began eating the newly hatched crickets. So efficient were these birds in controlling the situation that arrangements for a 1919 control campaign were abandoned. The meadowlarks were almost entirely responsible for the complete cleanup of the area."

Appraisal of the effect of birds on insect populations often has been done by computing the amount of food eaten by the individual bird and then prorating this for the number of birds involved. Such an approach was used in judging the worth of the lowly English sparrow in Utah at a time when the alfalfa weevil was rising to ascendancy as a pest of this forage crop.

To quote from my comments on observations made in 1910 and 1911 in the Salt Lake Valley: "Parent birds (English sparrows) were timed for a period, usually an hour, and at the end of this time the incoming bird was captured and the contents of its bill and throat recorded. By taking the average of a number of such observations a fair idea was obtained of the amount of food brought daily to a brood of these young birds. . . . From this series of observations it appeared . . . that 15 larvae (of the alfalfa weevil) or their equivalent in bulk of other insects was a fair estimate of the amount of food brought in at each trip by the adult birds. It frequently greatly exceeded this amount."

On the basis of this amount of food being brought in on each of 11 trips an hour and on the assumption that the young were fed 12 hours a day, a single brood of English sparrows would account for 1,980 larvae or their equivalent of other insect food. At that time it was not uncommon to find farmyards with straw-thatched cattle sheds, which supported 100 or more nests of English sparrows. Such a colony of birds would devour a daily total of 198,000 alfalfa weevil larvae or other insect food. As the young remained in the nest for at least 10 days, they would have eaten insect food equal to the volume of 1,980,000 weevil larvae during their nestling life. Inasmuch as these birds were feeding on the larvae of the alfalfa weevil to about one-fourth of their food, it would appear that they were accounting for about 500,000 larvae. And this activity was representative of what occurred on a number of farms.

Were it possible to restrict the insect eating of wild birds to particular areas and to compare the results with other areas not frequented by birds, appraisal of the benefits would not be so difficult. At times, however, circumstances make it possible to measure visually the effect of insect destruction by birds.

Such an opportunity arose in connection with the earlier study of the relation of bird life to the alfalfa weevil. In that case, however it was not a wild but a domestic species, the chicken, that yielded the information. It came about in the following manner. Farmers in the Salt Lake Valley early became aware of the beneficial work done by young chickens and turkeys through their feeding on weevil larvae. By placing brooder houses for these birds in or near badly infested fields, not only were the insects reduced but the birds in turn acquired a substantial amount of needed food. After cutting the first crop of hay in a field of 15 acres, one farmer near Kaysville, Utah, set out three colony houses containing 100 chicks that were 8 weeks old, 90 that were 5 weeks old, and 160 that were 2 weeks old. The broods were moved from place to place in the field as the areas about the houses were cleaned of larvae. On June 29, 1911, the field was inspected; in the areas where the brooder houses had been removed, the second crop had responded rapidly and was from 9 to 10 inches high. At other points, far from the feeding chicks, there was no evidence of the second crop. At one point, where two brooder houses had been located for some time at a distance of several rods apart, circles of bright green indicated the area over which the young birds had removed enough of the larvae to permit growth of the second crop. Were it possible to restrict the feeding activities of wild birds in a like manner I have no doubt but that the benefits of their work would be equally apparent.

Woodpeckers long have been recognized as archenemies of wood-boring insect pests, and much has been written of these defenders of our forest resources. It is difficult, however, to appraise with certainty the benefits of this type of work in large forest areas to which the birds have unrestricted access. Yet some significant appraisals have been made locally.

Tom T. Torrel, of the Bureau of Entomology and Plant Quarantine, had this to say regarding an infestation of Engelmann spruce beetles in the Kootenai National Forest in Idaho:

"In 1937 a severe infestation of the Engelmann spruce beetle was reported to be depleting stands of spruce in the Pinkham Creek drainage on the Kootenai National Forest. . . . During the time of the second examination in June 1938, rather large groups of infested spruce were found with overwintering brood. Woodpecker activity, however, had destroyed the brood to such an extent that the source of potential reinfestation was reduced to the protected brood below the snow line and it was predicted that very little reinfestation would occur."

Later comments on the same situation pointed out: "Woodpeckers had removed a large part of the bark from all trees above the snow line and it is believed that perhaps 75 to 80 percent, or even more, of the broods above snow line have been destroyed. We have observed that woodpeckers concentrate upon the most heavily infested trees, which allows the greatest returns for their labor. . . ."

More recent reports of the beneficial work of woodpeckers in the suppression of spruce beetles have come from the White River National Forest in Colorado, where field representatives of the Department of Agriculture were quick to detect evidence of the good work. C. L. Massey and Frank T. Hutchison were convinced that "during the summer of 1947, woodpeckers were the most important natural enemy of the Engelmann spruce beetle in the area." Three species of woodpeckers were involved; many of the heavily infested trees were completely stripped of bark; and in those instances the "mortality of the brood approaches 100 percent. Even a slight amount of woodpecker work reduced the beetle population by more than half." It is hoped that such observations on an insect pest that is threatening much of the stand of Engelmann spruce may be continued and the full story of the role of the woodpeckers recorded.

McAtee has given us a thorough summary of the recorded instances of caterpillar control by birds, and from it I select a few citations.

"The tussock moth caterpillar is generally supposed to be too hairy for birds, but this is another strained assumption. When they are common in Washington, D. C., nearly every robin seen carrying food to its young shows a telltale white fluff at the end of its bill. . . . Mr. Alan G. Dustan . . . in Canada . . . found that birds and ants are responsible for holding the insect at par in forests. When he exposed larvae to birds, the supply disappeared regularly and he credits birds with destroying half of the larvae hatching in forests. He further says that 'practically every egg mass laid above the snow line (and over 90 percent of them are) had been either partially or wholly destroyed by birds.' Cases of local extermination of tussock moths are recorded for the English sparrows in Massachusetts and the hairy woodpecker in Ohio."

McAtee goes on to report a case in which "starlings had locally extirpated a mixed infestation of brown-tail and gypsy moth larvae, and when E. H. Forbush was in charge of the gypsy-moth campaign for the State of Massachusetts, birds were observed to so hold the gypsy moth in check at one locality for several years that work by the State force was suspended. . . . It was almost impossible to complete certain experiments with larvae protected by netting bags because so many caterpillars were taken from the nets by birds. Sixty percent of the gypsy moth larvae used in these experiments were destroyed by birds."

The appleworm, larva of the codling moth, has also come in for attention by numerous birds. Even before the turn of the century, M. V. Slingerland at the Cornell Agricultural Experiment Station asserted that "by far the most effective aids to man in controlling the codling moth are the birds." This conclusion was reached by reason of the scarcity of intact hibernating cocoons and by the abundance of empty ones which apparently had been attacked by birds.

In New Hampshire, E. D. Sanderson reported: "Only 5 to 20 percent of the larvae survived the winter. An examination of seven trees . . . showed but 5 percent alive in the spring, 87 percent having been killed by birds, 4 percent by disease and 3 percent by cold. . . . It is quite evident that the birds, particularly the downy woodpeckers and nuthatches, are the most important enemies of the codling moth in New England. . . ."

And so the story continues. There are on record instances of commendable work by birds in the suppression of many other species of caterpillars, flies, beetles, ants, true bugs, plant-lice, and scale insects. Outstanding as these accomplishments are, they still may not represent the most important contribution by birds to man's battle against destructive insects. The cases I have cited, from the very nature of things, are conspicuous examples of the utility of birds; they are the high lights that have attracted attention. Their recital has been used to punctuate a story which may have its greatest significance, not in the spectacular, but in the day-by-day pressure exerted by birds. This effect is difficult if not impossible of measurement, yet nevertheless certain to be there.

Another consideration that has raised doubts in the minds of some who attempt to interpret the utility of birds is the realization that they feed not exclusively on insects injurious to man but (within certain limits) rather indiscriminately on whatever insects may be present and available to capture. Thus, both injurious and beneficial insects may be reduced.

An answer to that puzzling situation was well phrased by the late F. E. L. Beal in an article in the Yearbook of Agriculture for 1908: "Whoever expects to find in birds beneficent organisms working with a sole view to the benefit of the human race will be doomed to disappointment. Birds eat food to sustain life, and in their selection are guided entirely by considerations of their own. If all species of insectivorous birds be considered as a whole, it is found that they eat insects of the various species in about the proportions in which these species exist in nature. . . . It would appear that the true function of insectivorous birds is not so much to destroy this or that insect pest as it is to lessen the numbers of the insect tribe as a whole—to reduce to a lower level the great flood tide of insect life."

To that statement I add that flexibility of food habits and a tendency to prey on what is most abundant and easiest to capture make the bird world a highly mobile and responsive force for the reduction of any insect that may be inordinately abundant—significantly, the destructive insects are as a rule the most abundant ones.

One encounters fewer records of insect destruction by mammals than by birds—a reflection, no doubt, of conditions as they exist. As a group, mammals do not exert the pressure on insect life that birds do. That is true notwithstanding the fact that North American bats are largely if not exclusively insectivorous; that moles, shrews, and certain small rodents, particularly grasshopper mice, skunks, and the armadillo, feed extensively on insects; and that many other species partake of insects frequently. Availability and abundance play an important part in determining the extent of insect destruction by the casual feeders on insects among mammals. Those same considerations, however, often determine the abundance or even survival of bats, shrews, moles, and the armadillo, which are highly dependent on arthropod food.

Relatively little is known statistically of the over-all or even local effect of mammalian predation on insects. The feeding of highly insectivorous bats is essentially indiscriminate in character. That I must stress despite the frequently proclaimed (yet unproved) prowess of these winged mammals in mosquito control. No doubt many a mosquito falls as prey to these nocturnal aviators, but a few moments spent in observing their flight maneuvers will convince one that moths, beetles, ephemerids, and other high-flying forms are more likely to be caught than the low-flying mosquitoes. Stomach examination likewise has demonstrated this fact.

Shrews and moles feed to a large extent on subterranean invertebrates, among which are the larval and pupal forms of numerous destructive beetles and lepidopterans. Earthworms, because of their abundance, also are a staple item of food. Mice of various kinds, particularly grasshopper mice and deer mice, eat many insects. They were conspicuous in their destruction of the range caterpillars in New Mexico in 1913. That insect appeared in nearly half of 56 stomachs of deer mice collected on open range lands and, in bulk, they formed nearly a fifth of the food. Grasshopper mice collected under the same conditions indicated an even better performance, for, besides the consumption of an equal portion of range caterpillars, they had consumed even larger quantities of grasshoppers; the only vegetable food they had eaten were the seeds of Russian-thistle.

Skunks also rendered yeoman service against the range caterpillar in New Mexico at that time. On the basis of examined droppings, fully 85 percent of their food was comprised of the pupae of this insect. Late in the pupal season, the localities that showed signs of the presence of skunks would be largely free of pupae. Frequently areas of 4 to 5 acres would have two-thirds of the silken cocoon webs empty. In a section near Maxwell it was reported that only 5 percent of the pupae remained undamaged. This, no doubt, was the result of attacks by mammals, including several species of mice, skunks, badgers, and even coyotes.

Without doubt the nine-banded armadillo present in considerable numbers in Texas, Louisiana, and Florida is our most insectivorous medium-sized mammal. Stomach examination has revealed that more than 92 percent of its food is insects and other invertebrates, a performance that places it closely behind the bats in its relation to insects. In volume of food consumed, it greatly exceeds the latter; in diversity of items eaten, the armadillo probably has no peer among mammals. One specimen, found near Ingram, Tex., had ingested at least 87 different food items (mainly insects) aggregating more than 3,100 individuals.

Among the armadillo's insect food are numerous outstanding agricultural pests. Nearly 28 percent of the diet consists of the adults and larvae (white grubs) of scarab beetles. Termites, ants, and caterpillars (cutworms) constitute appreciable portions, and earthworms, millipedes, and crawfishes round out a regimen that is distinctly subterranean in origin. The location of the armadillo's food—beneath the surface—tends to offset somewhat the benefits derived from its consumption. In its energetic search for subsurface food, the 'dillo pays little concern for the welfare of young plants. The result is that sprouting corn may be destroyed immediately by the armadillo in its removal of wireworms, which may kill the plant at a later time. In general, however, the character of the armadillo's food indicates an influence for good.

In approaching the subject of birds and mammals in relation to insects, one naturally thinks in terms of direct predation, the effect wrought on insect populations by reason of the food habits of the predators. That process of reasoning has prevailed ever since serious consideration has been given to the three-cornered relationship between man and injurious insects at opposing points and those natural factors that tend to lessen the intensity of this struggle. Research aimed at demonstrating and recording the effect of such predation has characterized the sciences of economic ornithology and mammalogy in this country and in Europe for more than a century.

As early as 1858 J. W. P. Jenks was examining the stomachs of robins in Massachusetts to learn something of their food habits and economic relations to agriculture, and, on the basis of that work, he may be considered the American pioneer in that method of research. Some 20 years later, Professor Aughey of Nebraska published his *Notes on the Nature of the Food of the Birds of Nebraska,* based on studies over a period of 13 years on 90 different species and on an examination of more than 630 stomachs. Then followed the work of S. A. Forbes in Illinois, F. H. King in Wisconsin, B. H. Warren in Pennsylvania, and C. M. Weed in New Hampshire. Others, many of whom were entomologists, contributed to the early knowledge of the relation of birds to insects and their control. All of this served to create an early and growing appreciation in State and Federal legislative halls of the significance of biological control and led directly, in the 1880's, to the enactment of Federal legislation implementing such studies. The first appropriation ($5,000) authorized specifically for such research was allocated in 1885 to the entomologist of the Department of Agriculture, who had "declared that the interrelation of birds and insects was a subject which he long had desired to make a part of the work of his division," and stated that the food-habits phase of the work was of chief interest to the farmer.

It is particularly significant that, although the stimulus for this early effort to determine the economic status of birds in the United States came from the American Ornithologists Union, it had the aggressive support of entomologists who long had recognized, probably more clearly than any other group, the importance of natural enemies in the control of insect pests. From that modest beginning the science of economic ornithology and mammalogy in the United States grew rather steadily during the following three decades. McAtee, who rightfully may be considered the dean of American economic ornithologists, in 1913 published an index of papers dealing with the food and economic relations of birds prepared by members of the Biological Survey, the predecessor of the Fish and Wildlife Service. The report, published by the Department of Agriculture, involved 131 documents discussing 401 native and 59 foreign or introduced birds. Between that date and 1933 (the point of last summarization), 84 additional species of birds were formally reported upon and others mentioned in briefer statements. Since 1933 there has been less study of food preferences revealed through stomach analysis and greater emphasis placed on field appraisal. Nevertheless, the desirability and necessity of stomach examination will remain as long as wildlife administration is to be based on facts.

Although the study of the economics of birds and mammals in the United States has been more extensive than that carried out in Europe, the science has not been neglected there and its history is even older. The names and writings of Prevost in France, Schleh and Rörig in Germany, and Gilmour and Collinge in Great Britain attest to the wide recognition given in Europe to the importance of the vertebrate controllers of insect pests. Of utmost significance is the work conducted abroad on species later introduced to this country, notably the English sparrow and the starling.

In 1883 Schleh published on the food of the house sparrow in Germany and, although he did not use the volumetric method of computing food in vogue today, the results he obtained compare favorably with current procedures. More recently, Walter E. Collinge in England has given us an appraisal of the English sparrow in that country and direct comparisons can thereby be made of a species which, in the one case, has been with us for about a century with the same bird in an environment where it has existed for many centuries. Further comparisons of the economics of the English or house sparrow also are available from Turkestan, where D. Kashkarov and others appraised its direct influence on the production of grain and other crops.

Even a more precise comparison of the economics of an introduced species according to its performances here and abroad is available by reason of the studies carried out in England and in this country on the starling, which was brought to this country late in the last century and now is generally abundant in the Eastern States and found in limited numbers on the Pacific coast. A comparison of the data obtained in these two studies left "not a shadow of doubt as to the marked economic superiority of the American bird based on a study of food habits at this time."

One might continue with such recitals at length and give citations of notable research carried out in economic ornithology in Europe, North America, South Africa, Australia, and elsewhere. All point to the fact that recognition of the influence of birdlife on the affairs of man is world-wide.

As one delves through the literature on the subject, he is impressed also by the fact that recognition of insect destruction by birds has come more frequently from the entomologists directly concerned with matters of insect suppression than from the ornithologists whose interest in the welfare of birds might at times bias deductions. In fact, the entomologists, confronted as they are with the problem of seeking every possible means toward achieving pest insect control, have ample reason for recognizing biological help from whatever source it may stem.

Much remains to be learned regarding the influence of birds and mammals on insect populations. Quantitative information, local, widespread, and current, of the effect of vertebrate predation on economically important insect pests is needed. Much of this will have to be acquired through intensive field observations and appraisal. Estimates need to be made on a substantial and representative scale of insect populations in the presence and the absence of vertebrate enemies; from them tangible data should be forthcoming on the present-day economics of such predation on the insect world.

In the meantime, it behooves us to retain and encourage to the utmost all of those natural elements whose suppressive effect on insect pests, be it great or small, is so sorely needed.

E. R. KALMBACH, *a biologist in the Fish and Wildlife Service, Department of the Interior, is in charge of the Wildlife Research Laboratory at the Denver Federal Center. Before joining the Biological Survey, predecessor of the Fish and Wildlife Service, he was engaged in museum work in Michigan.*

For further reading:

F. E. L. Beal: The Relations Between Birds and Insects, *Yearbook of Agriculture 1908, pages 343–350. 1909.*

Walter E. Collinge: The Starling: Is It Injurious to Agriculture? *Journal of the Ministry of Agriculture, volume 27, pages 1114–1121, 1921:* The Food of Some Wild British Birds: A Study in Economic Ornithology, *edition 2, revised and enlarged, York, England, 1927.*

Clarence Cottam and Francis M. Uhler: Birds as a Factor in Controlling Insect Depredations, *U. S. Fish and Wildlife Service Wildlife Leaflet 224. 1950.*

E. R. Kalmbach: Birds in Relation to the Alfalfa Weevil, *U. S. D. A. Bulletin 107, 1914;* A Comparison of the Food Habits of British and American Starlings, *Auk, volume 39, pages 189–195, 1922;* The Armadillo: Its Relation to Agriculture and Game, *Austin, Tex., Game, Fish and Oyster Commission in cooperation with the U. S. Fish and Wildlife Service, 1943;* Economic Value of the Starling in the United States, *with I. N. Gabrielson, U. S. D. A. Bulletin 868, 1921.*

U. S. Entomological Commission: First Annual Report . . . for the Year 1877 Relating to the Rocky Mountain Locust and the Best Methods of Preventing its Injuries and of Guarding Against its Invasion. . . .

Bibliography and Appendix

A Selected list of Publications

Compiled by
Ina L. Hawes, J. S. Wade

GENERAL ENTOMOLOGY

General

Annals of the Entomological Society of America, volume 1–, Columbus, Ohio. 1908–. Published by the Entomological Society of America.

Brues, C. T., and Melander, A. L.: *Classification of Insects; A Key to the Known Families of Insects and Other Terrestrial Arthropods,* Harvard College Museum of Comparative Zoology Bulletin, volume 73, 672 pages, Cambridge, Mass. 1932, reprinted 1945.

Brues, C. T.: *Insect Dietary; An Account of the Food Habits of Insects,* 466 pages, Cambridge, Mass.; Harvard University Press. 1946.

Chamberlin, W. J.: *Entomological Nomenclature and Literature,* edition 2, 135 pages, Ann Arbor, Mich.; Edwards Bros., Inc. 1946.

Chapman, R. N.: *Animal Ecology with Especial Reference to Insects,* edition 1, 464 pages, New York; McGraw-Hill Book Co., Inc. 1941.

Chu, H. F.: *How to Know the Immature Insects; An Illustrated Key for Identifying the Orders and Families of Many of the Immature Insects with Suggestions for Collecting, Rearing and Studying Them,* 234 pages, Dubuque, Iowa; William C. Brown Co. 1949.

Clausen, C. P.: *Entomophagous Insects,* 688 pages, New York; McGraw-Hill Book Co., Inc. 1940.

Comstock, J. H.: *An Introduction to Entomology,* edition 9 revised, 1,064 pages, Ithaca, N. Y.; Comstock Publishing Co., Inc. 1940.

Essig, E. O.: *College Entomology,* 900 pages, New York; Macmillan Co. 1942.

Essig, E. O.: *Insects of Western North America,* 1,035 pages, New York; Macmillan Co. 1926, reprinted 1938.

Felt, E. P.: *Plant Galls and Gall Makers,* 364 pages, Ithaca, N. Y.; Comstock Publishing Co., Inc. 1940.

Folsom, J. W., and Wardle, R. A.: *Entomology with Special Reference to Its Ecological Aspects,* edition 4 revised, 605 pages, Philadelphia; Blakiston's Son & Co., Inc. 1934.

Frost, S. W.: *General Entomology,* 524 pages, New York; McGraw-Hill Book Co., Inc. 1942.

Howard, L. O.: *The Insect Book,* 429 pages, New York; Doubleday, Page & Co. 1910. Reprint: New York; Doubleday Doran & Co., Inc. 1937.

Johannsen, O. A., and Butt, F. H.: *Embryology of Insects and Myriapods; The Developmental History of Insects, Centipedes, and Millepedes from Egg Deposition to Hatching,* 462 pages, New York; McGraw-Hill Book Co., Inc. 1941.

Kellogg, V. L.: *American Insects,* edition 3 revised, 694 pages, New York; Henry Holt & Co., Inc. 1914.

Matheson, Robert: *Entomology for Introductory Courses,* edition 2, 629 pages, Ithaca, N. Y.; Comstock Publishing Co., Inc., 1951.

Michener, C. D., and Michener, M. H.: *American Social Insects; A Book About Bees, Ants, Wasps, and Termites,* 267 pages, New York; Van Nostrand Co. 1951.

Oman, P. W., and Cushman, A. D.: *Collection and Preservation of Insects,* U. S. D. A. Miscellaneous Publicaton 601, 42 pages, Washington, D. C.; Government Printing Office. 1946.

Peterson, Alvah: *A Manual of Entomological Equipment and Methods,* edition 5, 2 parts in one volume, Ann Arbor, Mich.; Edwards Bros., Inc. 1947.

Ross, H. H.: *A Textbook of Entomology,* 532 pages, New York; John Wiley & Sons, Inc. 1948.

Snodgrass, R. E.: *Principles of Insect Morphology,* 667 pages, New York; McGraw-Hill Book Co., Inc. 1935.

Steinhaus, E. A.: *Principles of Insect Pathology,* 757 pages, New York; McGraw-Hill Book Co., Inc. 1949.

Steinhaus, E. A.: *Insect Microbiology; An Account of the Microbes Associated with Insects and Ticks, with Special Reference to the Biological Relationships Involved,* 763 pages, Ithaca, N. Y.; Comstock Publishing Co., Inc. 1946.

Torre-Bueno, J. R. de la: *A Glossary of Entomology,* 336 pages, Lancaster, Pa.; Science Press Printing Co. 1937.

Ward's Natural Science Establishment, Inc.: *How to Make an Insect Collection,* 32 pages, Rochester, N. Y. 1945.

Wheeler, W. M.: *The Social Insects, Their Origin and Evolution,* 378 pages, New York; Harcourt, Brace & Co. 1928.

Wheeler, W. M.: *Social Life Among the Insects,* 375 pages, New York; Harcourt, Brace & Co. 1923.

Wigglesworth, V. B.: *The Principles of Insect Physiology,* edition 3, 434 pages, London; Methuen & Co., Ltd. 1947.
American edition: New York; E. P. Dutton & Co., Inc. 1939.

Historical

Essig, E. O.: *A History of Entomology,* 1,029 pages, New York; Macmillan Co. 1931.

Hatch, M. H.: *A Century of Entomology in the Pacific Northwest,* 43 pages, Seattle; University of Washington Press. 1949.

Howard, L. O.: *A History of Applied Entomology (Somewhat Anecdotal),* Smithsonian Institution Miscellaneous Collection, volume 84, 564 pages, Washington, D. C. 1930.

Osborn, Herbert: *Fragments of Entomological History, Including Some Personal Recollections of Men and Events, 2 parts,* Columbus, Ohio; published by the author. 1937, 1946.

Weiss, H. B.: *The Pioneer Century of American Entomology,* 320 pages, New Brunswick, N. J.; published by the author. 1936.

ECONOMIC

Baerg, W. J.: *Introduction to Applied Entomology,* edition 3 revised, 191 pages, Minneapolis, Minn.; Burgess Publishing Co. 1948.

Brues, C. T.: *Insects and Human Welfare; An Account of the More Important Relations of Insects to the Health of Man, to Agriculture, and to Forestry,* revised edition, 154 pages, Cambridge, Mass.; Harvard University Press. 1947.

Campbell, F. L., and Moulton, F. R., editors: *Laboratory Procedures in Studies of the Chemical Control of Insects,* American Association for the Advancement of Science Publication 20, 206 pages, Washington, D. C. 1943.

Chamberlin, W. J.: *Insects Affecting Forest Products and Other Materials,* 159 pages, Corvallis, Oreg.; published by the O. S. C. Cooperative Association. 1949.

Craighead, F. C.: *Insect Enemies of Eastern Forests,* U. S. D. A. Miscellaneous Publication 657, 679 pages, Washington, D. C.; Government Printing Office. 1950.

Cotton, R. T.: *Insect Pests of Stored Grain and Grain Products,* revised edition, 244 pages, Minneapolis, Minn.; Burgess Publishing Co. 1950.

Doane, R. W., Vandyke, E. C., Chamberlin, W. J., and Burke, H. E.: *Forest insects; A Textbook for the Use of Students in Forest Schools, Colleges and Universities, and for Forest Workers,* 463 pages, New York; McGraw-Hill Book Co., Inc. 1936.

Ebeling, Walter: *Subtropical Entomology,* 747 pages, San Francisco; Lithotype Process Co. 1950.

Ewing, H. E.: *A Manual of External Parasites,* 225 pages, Springfield, Ill.; Charles C. Thomas. 1929.

Fernald, H. T., and Shepard, H. H.: *Applied Entomology; An Introductory Textbook of Insects in Their Relations to Man,* edition 4, 400 pages, New York; McGraw-Hill Book Co., Inc. 1942.

Graham, S. A.: *Principles of Forest Entomology,* edition 2, 410 pages, New York; McGraw-Hill Book Co., Inc. 1936.

Herms, W. B.: *Medical Entomology with Special Reference to the Health and Well-being of Man and Animals,* edition 4, 643 pages, New York; Macmillan Co. 1950.

Herms, W. B., and Gray, H. F.: *Mosquito Control; Practical Methods for Abatement of Disease Vectors and Pests,* edition 2 revised, 419 pages, New York; Commonwealth Fund. 1944.

Herrick, G. W.: *Insect Enemies of Shade Trees,* 417 pages, Ithaca, N. Y.; Comstock Publishing Co., Inc. 1935.

Herrick, G. W.: *Insects Injurious to the Household and Annoying to Man,* revised edition, 478 pages, New York; Macmillan Co. 1926.

Isely, Dwight: *Methods of Insect Control,* 2 parts, Minneapolis, Minn.; Burgess Publishing Co. 1946, 1947.
Part 1, edition 3 revised, 6th printing. 1949; part 2, edition 4 revised, 4th printing. 1947.

Journal of Economic Entomology, volume 1–, Menasha, Wis. 1908–. Published by the American Association of Economic Entomologists.

Keen, F. P.: *Insect Enemies of Western Forests,* U. S. D. A. Miscellaneous Publication 273, revised, 210 pages, Washington, D. C.; Government Printing Office. 1939.

Langford, G. S., editor: *Entoma, A Directory of Insect and Plant Pest Control,* edition 9, 448 pages, College Park, Md.; American Association of Economic Entomologists Eastern Branch. 1951–52.

970134°—52——48

Leach, J. G.: *Insect Transmission of Plant Diseases,* 615 pages, New York; McGraw-Hill Book Co., Inc. 1940.

Mallis, Arthur: *Handbook of Pest Control; The Behavior, Life History and Control of Household Pests,* 566 pages, New York; MacNair-Dorland Co., Inc. 1945.

Matheson, Robert: *Medical Entomology,* edition 2, 612 pages, Ithaca, N. Y.; Comstock Publishing Co., Inc. 1950.

Maxson, A. C.: *Insects and Diseases of the Sugar Beet,* 425 pages, Fort Collins, Colo.; Beet Sugar Development Foundation. 1948.

Metcalf, C. L., and Flint, W. P.: *Destructive and Useful Insects; Their Habits and Control,* edition 3, revised by R. L. Metcalf, 1,071 pages, New York; McGraw-Hill Book Co., Inc. 1950.

Muesebeck, C. F. W.: *Common Names of Insects Approved by the American Association of Economic Entomologists,* College Park, Md. 1950.

Reprinted from the Journal of Economic Entomology, volume 43, No. 1. April 1950.

Needham, J. G., Frost, S. W., and Tothill, B. H.: *Leaf-mining Insects,* 351 pages, Baltimore; Williams & Wilkins Co. 1928.

Newcomer, E. J.: *Orchard Insects of the Pacific Northwest and Their Control,* U. S. D. A. Circular 270, revised, 63 pages, Washington, D. C.; Government Printing Office. 1950.

Painter, R. H.: *Insect Resistance in Crop Plants,* 520 pages, New York; Macmillan Co. 1951.

Peairs, L. M.: *Insect Pests of Farm, Garden and Orchard,* edition 4, 549 pages, New York; John Wiley & Sons, Inc. 1941.

Pyenson, Louis: *Pest Control in the Home Garden, Reissued with Additional Material,* 108 pages, New York; Macmillan Co. 1945.

Quayle, H. J.: *Insects of Citrus and Other Subtropical Fruits,* 583 pages, Ithaca, N. Y.; Comstock Publishing Co., Inc. 1938.

Westcott, Cynthia: *The Gardener's Bug Book; 1,000 Insect Pests and Their Control,* 590 pages, New York; American Garden Guild, Inc., *and* Doubleday & Co. 1946.

Williams, F. X.: *Handbook of the Insects and Other Invertebrates of Hawaiian Sugar Cane Fields,* 400 pages, Honolulu; Hawaiian Sugar Planters' Association. 1931.

Insecticides

De Ong, E. R.: *Chemistry and Uses of Insecticides,* 345 pages, New York; Reinhold Publishing Corp. 1948.

Dethier, V. G.: *Chemical Insect Attractants and Repellents,* 289 pages, Philadelphia; Blakiston Co. 1947.

Frear, D. E. H.: *Chemistry of Insecticides, Fungicides and Herbicides,* edition 2, 417 pages, New York; D. Van Nostrand Co., Inc. 1948.

Shepard, H. H.: *The Chemistry and Action of Insecticides,* 504 pages, New York; McGraw-Hill Book Co., Inc. 1951.

POPULAR

Curran, C. H.: *Insects in Your Life,* 316 pages, New York; Sheridan House. 1951.

Duncan, C. D., and Pickwell, Gayle: *The World of Insects,* 409 pages, New York; McGraw-Hill Book Co., Inc. 1939.

Fabre, J. H. C.: *The Insect World of J. Henri Fabre; with Introduction and Interpretive Comments* by Edwin Way Teale, 333 pages, New York; Dodd, Mead & Co. 1949.

Several of the most famous of Fabre's studies are included.

Howard, L. O.: *The Insect Menace,* 347 pages, New York; Century Co. 1931.

Jaques, H. E.: *How to Know the Insects; An Illustrated Key to the More Common Families of Insects, with Suggestions for Collecting, Mounting and Studying Them,* edition 2, 205 pages, Dubuque, Iowa; William C. Brown Co. 1947.

Lutz, F. E.: *Field Book of Insects of the United States and Canada,* edition 3, rewritten, 510 pages, New York; G. P. Putnam's. 1935.

Lutz. F. E.: *A Lot of Insects; Entomology in a Suburban Garden,* 304 pages, New York; G. P. Putnam's Sons. 1941.

National Geographic Society: *Our Insect Friends and Foes and Spiders,* 232 pages, Washington, D. C. 1935.

Needham, J. G.: *Elementary Lessons on Insects,* 210 pages, Springfield, Ill.; Charles C. Thomas. 1928.

Pierce, G. W.: *The Songs of Insects,* 329 pages, Cambridge, Mass.; Harvard University Press. 1948.

Reinhard, E. G.: *The Witchery of Wasps,* 291 pages, New York; Century Co. 1929.

Standin, Anthony: *Insect Invaders,* 228 pages, Boston; Houghton Mifflin Co. 1943.

Swain, R. B.: *The Insect Guide; Orders and Major Families of North American Insects,* 261 pages, Garden City, Doubleday & Co., Inc. 1948.

Teale, E. W.: *Grassroot Jungles; A Book of Insects,* revised edition, 240 pages, New York; Dodd, Mead & Co. 1944.

Urquhart, F. A.: *Introducing the Insect,* 287 pages, New York; Henry Holt & Co. 1949.

Wellhouse, W. H.: *How Insects Live; An Elementary Entomology,* 435 pages, New York; Macmillan Co. 1926.

Juvenile

Jones, M. P.: *4–H Club Insect Manual,* U. S. D. A. Miscellaneous Publication 318 revised, 63 pages, Washington, D. C.; Government Printing Office. 1949.

Needham, J. G.: *Introducing Insects; A Book for Beginners,* 129 pages, Lancaster, Pa.; Jaques Cattell Press. 1940.
Available from Ronald Press Co., New York.

Patch, E. M.: *Dame Bug and Her Babies,* 126 pages, Orono, Maine; Pine Cone Publishing Co. 1913.

Patch, E. M.: *A Little Gateway to Science,* Hexapod Stories, 178 pages, Boston; Atlantic Monthly Press. 1920.

Phillips, Mrs. Mary (Geisler): *Honey Bees and Fairy Dust,* 213 pages, Philadelphia; Macrae Smith Co. 1926.

Schackelford, Frederick: *Insect Stories,* 236 pages, San Francisco; Harr Wagner Publishing Co. 1940.

Teale, E. W.: *The Boy's Book of Insects,* 237 pages, New York; E. P. Dutton & Co., Inc. 1939.

Whitney, R. C.: *Six Feet,* 288 pages, St. Louis, Mo.; Webster Publishing Co. 1939.

INSECT GROUPS

Coleoptera
(Beetles)

Bøving, A. G., and Craighead, F. C.: *An Illustrated Synopsis of the Principal Larval Forms of the Order Coleoptera,* 351 pages, New York; Brooklyn Entomological Society, 1931.
Reprinted from Entomologica Americana, new series volume 11.

Leng, C. W.: *Catalogue of the Coleoptera of America, North of Mexico,* 470 pages, Mount Vernon, N. Y.; John D. Sherman, Jr. 1920.
Five supplements 1927–47.

Diptera
(Flies and Mosquitoes)

Aldrich, J. M.: *A Catalogue of North American Diptera (or Two-winged Flies),* Smithsonian Institution Miscellaneous Collections, volume 46 in part, 680 pages, Washington, D. C. 1905.

Hall, D. G.: *The Blowflies of North America,* Entomological Society of America, Thomas Say Foundation Publication, volume 4, 477 pages, Baltimore. 1948.

Matheson, Robert: *Handbook of the Mosquitoes of North America; Their Anatomy and Biology, How They Can Be Studied and Identified, How They Carry Disease and How They Can Be Controlled,* edition 2 revised, 314 pages, Ithaca, N. Y.; Comstock Publishing Co., Inc. 1944.

See also economic list *under* Herms, W. B.

Hemiptera, Homoptera
(Aphids, Scale Insects, Etc.)

Fernald, Mrs. Maria E. (Smith): *A Catalogue of the Coccidae of the World,* Massachusetts Agricultural College Hatch Experiment Station Special Bulletin 88, 360 pages, Amherst, Mass. 1903.
For supplemental lists, *see:* U. S. Bureau of Entomology Technical Series 12, part 1, 18 pages. 1906; Series 16, part 3, pages 33–60. 1909; Series 16, part 4, pages 61–74. 1911; Series 16, part 6, pages 83–97. 1912; Entomological Society of Washington Proceedings, volume 17, pages 25–38. 1915.

Ferris, G. F.: *Atlas of the Scale Insects of North America.* Series 1–5, Stanford University; Stanford University Press. 1937–1950.
Series 1–4, Armored scales; Series 5, Pseudococcidae, Part 1.

MacGillivray, A. D.: *The Coccidae,* 502 pages, Urbana, Ill.; Scarab Co. 1921.

Patch, E. M.: *Food-plant Catalogue of the Aphids of the World, Including Phylloxeridae,* 431 pages, Maine Agricultural Experiment Station Bulletin 393, Orono. 1938.
Supplement, Bulletin 393–S. 1945.

Van Duzee, E. P.: *Catalogue of the Hemiptera of America, North of Mexico, Excepting the Aphididae, Coccidae and Aleurodidae,* University of California Publication Technical Bulletins Entomology, volume 2, 902 pages, Berkeley. 1917.

Wilson, H. F., and Vickery, R. A.: *A Species List of the Aphididae of the World and Their Recorded Food Plants.* Wisconsin Academy of Sciences, Arts and Letters Transactions, volume 19, part 1, pages 22–355. 1918.

Hymenoptera
(Ants, Wasps, Bees)

Creighton, W. S.: *The Ants of North America,* Harvard University Museum of Comparative Zoology Bulletin, volume 104, 585 pages, Cambridge, Mass. 1950.

Muesebeck, C. F. W., Krombein, K. V., Townes, H. K., and others: *Hymenoptera of America North of Mexico—A Synoptic Catalog,* U. S. D. A. Agriculture Monographs, No. 2, 1,420 pages, Washington, D. C.; Government Printing Office. 1951.

Rau, Philip, and Rau, Nellie: *Wasp Studies Afield,* 372 pages, illus., Princeton University Press, Princeton. 1918.

Wheeler, W. M.: *Ants; Their Structure, Development and Behavior,* 663 pages. New York; Columbia University Press. 1910, reprint 1926.

See also: General, Popular *under* Reinhard, E. G.

Bees and Bee Culture

Grout, R. A., editor: *The Hive and the Honeybee; a New Book on Beekeeping to Succeed the Book "Langstroth on the Hive and the Honeybee"*, revised edition, 652 pages, Hamilton, Ill.; Dadant & Sons. 1949.

Maeterlinck, Maurice: *The Life of the Bee,* translated by Alfred Sutro, 427 pages, New York; Dodd, Mead & Co. 1901. Various editions.

Pellett, F. C.: *American Honey Plants; together with Those Which are of Special Value to the Beekeeper as Sources of Pollen,* edition 4, 467 pages, New York; Orange Judd Publishing Co. 1947.

Root, A. I.: *The ABC and XYZ of Bee Culture; An Encyclopedia Pertaining to Scientific and Practical Culture of Bees,* revised by E. R. Root, H. H. Root, and M. J. Deyell, 703 pages, Medina, Ohio; A. I. Root Co. 1950.

Snodgrass, R. E.: *Anatomy and Physiology of the Honeybee,* 327 pages, New York; McGraw-Hill Book Co., Inc. 1925.

Teale, E. W.: *The Golden Throng; A Book About Bees,* 208 pages, Dodd, Mead & Co. 1940.

Isoptera

(Termites)

Kofoid, C. A., editor: *Termites and Termite Control,* edition 2, 795 pages, Berkeley, University of California Press. 1934.

Snyder, T. E.: *Catalog of the Termites (Isoptera) of the World,* Smithsonian Institution Miscellaneous Collections, volume 112, 490 pages, Washington, D. C. 1949.

Snyder, T. E.: *Our Enemy the Termite,* revised edition, 257 pages, Ithaca, N. Y.; Comstock Publishing Co., Inc. 1948.

Lepidoptera

(Butterflies, Moths)

Holland, W. J.: *The Butterfly Book; A Popular and Scientific Manual, Describing and Depicting All Butterflies of the United States and Canada,* new edition, 424 pages, New York; Doubleday, Doran & Co., Inc. 1931. Available Doubleday & Co., New York.

Holland, W. J.: *The Moth Book; A Popular Guide to a Knowledge of the Moths of North America,* 479 pages, New York; Doubleday, Page & Co. 1913.

Klots, A. B.: *A Field Guide to the Butterflies of North America, East of the Great Plains,* 349 pages, Boston; Houghton Mifflin Co. 1951.

Macy, R. W., and Shepard, H. H.: *Butterflies; A Handbook of the Butterflies of the United States for the Region North of the Potomac and Ohio Rivers and East of the Dakotas,* 247 pages, Minneapolis; University of Minnesota Press. 1941.

McDunnough, J. H.: *Check List of the Lepidoptera of Canada and the United States of America,* 2 parts, Southern California Academy of Sciences Memoirs, volume 1; volume 2, No. 1, Los Angeles. 1938, 1939.

Orthoptera

(Cockroaches, Grasshoppers, Etc.)

Blatchley, W. S.: *Orthoptera of Northeastern America, with Especial Reference to the Faunas of Indiana and Florida.* 784 pages, Indianapolis, Ind.; Nature Publishing Co. 1920.

Hebard, Morgan: *The Blattidae of North America, North of the Mexican Boundary,* Entomological Society of America Memoirs, No. 2, 284 pages, Philadelphia. 1917.

Morse, A. P.: *Manual of the Orthoptera of New England,* Boston Society of Natural History Proceedings volume 35, No. 6, pages 203–556, 1920.

Uvarov, B. P.: *Locusts and Grasshoppers; A Handbook for Their Study and Control,* 352 pages, London; Imperial Bureau of Entomology. 1928.

Siphonaptera

(Fleas)

Fox, Irving: *Fleas of Eastern United States,* 191 pages, Ames; Iowa State College Press. 1940.

Holland, G. P.: *The Siphonaptera of Canada.* Canada Department of Agriculture Publication 817 (Technical Bulletin 70), 306 pages, Ottawa. 1949.

Hubbard, C. A. F.: *Fleas of Western North America; Their Relation to the Public Health,* 533 pages, Ames; Iowa State College Press, Inc., 1934.

Smaller Groups

Berner, Lewis: *The Mayflies of Florida,* 267 pages, Gainesville; University of Florida Press. 1950.

Betten, Cornelius, and others: *The Caddis Flies or Trichoptera of New York State,* New York State Museum Bulletin 292, 576 pages, Albany; University of the State of New York. 1934.

Frison, T. H.: *Studies of North American Plecoptera, with Special Reference to the Fauna of Illinois,* Illinois Natural History Survey Bulletin, volume 22, article 2, pages 235–355. September 1942.

Maynard, E. A.: *A Monograph of the Collembola or Springtail Insects of New York State,* 339 pages, Ithaca, N. Y.; Comstock Publishing Co., Inc. 1951.

Mills, H. B.: *A Monograph of the Collembola of Iowa,* 143 pages, Ames, Iowa; Collegiate Press, Inc., 1934.

Needham, J. G., and Claasen, P. W.; *A Monograph of the Plecoptera or Stoneflies of America North of Mexico,* Entomological Society of America. Thomas Say Foundation Publication, volume 2, 397 pages, LaFayette, Ind. 1925.
Needham, J. G., and Heywood, H. B.: *A Handbook of the Dragonflies of North America,* 378 pages, Springfield, Ill.; Charles C. Thomas. 1929.
Needham, J. G., Traver, J. R., and Hsu, Y.-C.: *The Biology of Mayflies,* 759 pages, Ithaca, N. Y.; Comstock Publishing Co. 1935.
Ross, H. H.: *The Caddis Flies, or Trichoptera of Illinois,* Illinois Natural History Survey Bulletin 23, article 1, 326 pages, Urbana. 1944.
Watson J. R.: *Synopsis and Catalog of the Thysanoptera of North America,* Florida Agricultural Experiment Station Bulletin 168, 100 pages, Gainesville.

INSECT RELATIVES
(Mites, Ticks, Spiders)

Baker E. W. and Wharton, G. W.: *An Introduction to Acarology,* 465 pages, New York; Macmillan Co. 1952.
Comstock, J. H.: *The Spider Book,* revised and edited by W. J. Gertsch 740 pages, New York; Doubleday, Doran & Co., Inc., 1940. Reprint, Ithaca, N. Y.; Comstock Publishing Co., Inc. 1948.
Gertsch, W. J.: *American Spiders;* 285 pages, New York; D. Van Nostrand Co., Inc. 1949.

BIBLIOGRAPHICAL SOURCES

Bibliography of Agriculture, volume 1–, Washington, D. C. 1942–. Issued by the U. S. Department of Agriculture Library.
Biological Abstracts, volume 1, December 1926–, Philadelphia, 1927–.
Chemical Abstracts, volume 1–, Washington, D. C. 1907–. Published by the American Chemical Society.
Hagen, H. A.: *Bibliotheca Entomologica; die Litteratur über das ganze Gebiet der Entomologie bis zum Jahre 1862,* 2 volumes, Leipzig; Verlag von Wilhelm Engelmann. 1862–63.
Horn, Walther, and Schenkling, Sigmund: *Index Litteraturae Entomologicae, Serie I: Die Welt-literatur über die gesamte Entomologie bis inklusive 1863,* 4 parts, Berlin-Dahlem; Erschienen im Selbstverlag von Dr. Walther Horn. 1928–29.
Index to the Literature of American Economic Entomology, American Association of Economic Entomologists Special Publication 1–7. 1917–48.
Index 7 issued at College Park, Md.
Preceded by: Bibliography of American Economic Entomology, parts 1–8, Washington, D. C.; Government Printing Office. 1889–1905.

How To Get Further Information on Insects

Compiled by
David G. Hall

The kind of information a person might need about insects determines largely the place he should turn to for it. He might, for example, want to know more about the identification of a particular insect, control measures for a pest, the regulations governing shipment of plants, the labeling of insecticides, the sources of insecticides, textbooks about insects, or beekeeping.

No one person can give full information on all those items. But in practically every county in the United States there is an agricultural extension agent, who usually is referred to as the county agent, parish agent, or county extension director. Because he is close at hand and knows most about local conditions, he might be the first person to consult for further information. If he cannot give an answer to the problem, he can give the name and address of the proper person to whom to write or telephone. The extension agents usually have their offices in the county courthouse or the post office in the county seat and often are listed in the telephone book under the name of the county with other county officials.

Listed below are the addresses of the State extension directors. The staff of most State extension services includes an entomologist, who is well equipped to give information on the identity, habits, and control of insects, beekeeping, and available publications. Similar information can be had from the entomologist on the staff of the State experiment station. Plant quarantine officials are in the best position to give information on State and Federal regulations governing the movement of plants and the labeling of insecticides.

Agricultural Experiment Stations

(Unless otherwise indicated, the station should be addressed: Agricultural Experiment Station—at the post office indicated.)

State or Territory	*Address*
ALABAMA	Auburn.
ALASKA	Palmer.
ARIZONA	Tucson.
ARKANSAS	Fayetteville.
CALIFORNIA	Berkeley 4.
COLORADO	Fort Collins.
CONNECTICUT	Connecticut Agricultural Experiment Station, New Haven 4.
	Storrs Agricultural Experiment Station, Storrs.
DELAWARE	Newark.
FLORIDA	Gainesville.
GEORGIA	College of Agriculture, Athens.
	Georgia Agricultural Experiment Station, Experiment.
	Coastal Plain Experiment Station, Tifton.
HAWAII	Honolulu 14.
IDAHO	Moscow.
ILLINOIS	Urbana.
INDIANA	Lafayette.
IOWA	Ames.
KANSAS	Manhattan.
KENTUCKY	Lexington 29.
LOUISIANA	University Station, Baton Rouge 3.
MAINE	Orono.
MARYLAND	College Park.
MASSACHUSETTS	Amherst.
MICHIGAN	East Lansing.
MINNESOTA	University Farm, St. Paul 1.
MISSISSIPPI	State College.
MISSOURI	Columbia.
MONTANA	Bozeman.
NEBRASKA	Lincoln 1.
NEVADA	Reno.
NEW HAMPSHIRE	Durham.
NEW JERSEY	New Brunswick.
NEW MEXICO	State College.
NEW YORK	State Agricultural Experiment Station, Geneva.
	Agricultural Experiment Station at Cornell University, Ithaca.
NORTH CAROLINA	State College Station, Raleigh.
NORTH DAKOTA	State College Station, Fargo.
OHIO	Ohio Agricultural Experiment Station, Wooster.
	Ohio State University, Columbus 10.
OKLAHOMA	Stillwater.
OREGON	Corvallis.
PENNSYLVANIA	State College.
PUERTO RICO	Rio Piedras.
RHODE ISLAND	Kingston.
SOUTH CAROLINA	Clemson.
SOUTH DAKOTA	Brookings.
TENNESSEE	Knoxville 16.
TEXAS	College Station.
UTAH	Logan.
VERMONT	Burlington.
VIRGINIA	Blacksburg.
WASHINGTON	Pullman.
WEST VIRGINIA	Morgantown.
WISCONSIN	Madison 6.
WYOMING	Laramie.

United States Department of Agriculture

Agricultural Research Administration

Bureau of Entomology and Plant Quarantine

(Unless otherwise indicated, the address is: Washington 25, D. C.)

Chief of Bureau.
Assistant Chief of Bureau (Administration).
Assistant Chief of Bureau (Control).
  Staff Assistant (Plant Disease Control).
Assistant Chief of Bureau (Insecticides-Chemistry).
Assistant Chief of Bureau (Regulatory).
Assistant Chief of Bureau (Research).
Division of Accounting and Auditing.
Division of Administrative Services.
Division of Budget and Administrative Management.
Division of Bee Culture and Biological Control, Agricultural Research Center, Beltsville, Md.
Division of Cereal and Forage Insect Investigations.
Division of Cotton Insect Investigations.
Division of Forest Insect Investigations, Agricultural Research Center, Beltsville, Md.
Division of Fruit Insect Investigations.
Division of Insect Detection and Identification.
Division of Information.
Division of Insecticide Investigations, Agricultural Research Center, Beltsville, Md.
Division of Insects Affecting Man and Animals.
Division of Personnel Management.
Division of Plant Quarantines.
Division of Stored Product Insect Investigations.
Division of Truck Crop and Garden Insect Investigations.
Director of Region 1 (Northeastern States), 20 Sanderson Street, P. O. Box 72, Greenfield, Mass.:
  Golden Nematode Control Project, P. O. Box 104, Hicksville, N. Y.
  Gypsy and Brown-Tail Moth Control Project, 20 Sanderson Street, P. O. Box 72, Greenfield, Mass.
  Japanese Beetle Control Project, P. O. Box 461, Hoboken, N. J.
  White-Pine Blister Rust Control Project, 20 Sanderson Street, P. O. Box 72, Greenfield, Mass.
Director of Region 2 (Southeastern States), 25th Avenue, City Limits, P. O. Box 989, Gulfport, Miss.:
  Phony Peach and Peach Mosaic Diseases Eradication Project, 25th Avenue, City Limits, P. O. Box 989, Gulfport, Miss.
  Sweetpotato Weevil Control Project, 25th Avenue, City Limits, P. O. Box 989, Gulfport, Miss.
Director of Region 2—Continued
  White-Fringed Beetle Control Project (Gulf Coast), 25th Avenue, City Limits, P. O. Box 989, Gulfport, Miss.
  White-Fringed Beetle Control Project (South Atlantic Coast), 632 Mulberry Street, Macon, Ga.
Director of Region 3 (Southwestern States), P. O. Box 2300, 571 Federal Building, San Antonio 6, Tex.:
  Citrus Blackfly Control Project, Room 212 McClendon Building, 305 East Jackson Street, Harlingen, Tex.
  Mexican Fruit Fly Control Project, Room 212 McClendon Building, 305 East Jackson Street, Harlingen, Tex.
  Pink Bollworm Control Project, P. O. Box 2300, 571 Federal Building, San Antonio 6, Tex.
Director of Region 4 (Western States), 2288 Fulton Street, Berkeley 4, Calif.:
  Hall Scale Eradication Project, 336 Broadway, Chico, Calif.
  White-Pine Blister Rust Control Project, 2288 Fulton Street, Berkeley 4, Calif.
Director of Region 5 (North Central States), 301 Metropolitan Building, Minneapolis 1, Minn.:
  Barberry Eradication Project, 301 Metropolitan Building, Minneapolis 1, Minn.
  Grasshopper Control Project, Building 85, Federal Center, P. O. Box 1056, Denver 1, Colo.
  White-Pine Blister Rust Control Project, 301 Metropolitan Building, Minneapolis 1, Minn.
  Aircraft and Special Equipment Center, P. O. Box 7216, Oklahoma City, Okla.

Federal Insecticide, Fungicide, and Rodenticide Law Enforcement Officials

United States Department of Agriculture

Production and Marketing Administration

Administrator:
  Director, Livestock Branch:
    Chief, Insecticide Division:
      Chief, Bacteriological Section.
      Chief, Chemical Section.
      Chief, Entomological Section.
      Chief, Fungicide and Herbicide Section.
      Chief, Investigation and Case Development Section.
      Chief, Pharmacological and Rodenticide Section.
      Chief, Registration Section.

National Association of Commissioners, Secretaries, and Directors of Agriculture

ALABAMA: Commissioner of Agriculture and Industries, 515 Dexter Avenue, Montgomery 1.
ARIZONA: Chairman, Commission of Agriculture and Horticulture, Phoenix.
ARKANSAS: Director, Resources and Development, Little Rock.
CALIFORNIA: Director of Agriculture, State Office Building No. 1, Sacramento 14.
COLORADO: Commissioner of Agriculture, 20 State Museum, Denver 2.
CONNECTICUT: Commissioner, Department of Farms and Markets, State Office Building, Hartford.
DELAWARE: Secretary, State Board of Agriculture, Dover.
FLORIDA: Commissioner of Agriculture, Tallahassee.
GEORGIA: Commissioner of Agriculture, State Capitol, Atlanta 3.
HAWAII: President, Board of Agriculture and Forestry, Honolulu 1.
IDAHO: Commissioner of Agriculture, Room 206 State House, Boise.
ILLINOIS: Director of Agriculture, State Fairground, Springfield.
INDIANA: Commissioner of Agriculture, Lieutenant Governor, 332 State House, Indianapolis.
IOWA: Secretary of Agriculture, State House, Des Moines 19.
KANSAS: Secretary, State Board of Agriculture, State House, Topeka.
KENTUCKY: Commissioner of Agriculture, Frankfort.
LOUISIANA: Commissioner of Agriculture and Immigration, P. O. Box 951, Baton Rouge 1.
MAINE: Commissioner of Agriculture, Augusta.
MARYLAND: Executive Officer of the State Board of Agriculture, University of Maryland, College Park.
MASSACHUSETTS: Commissioner of Agriculture, 41 Tremont Street, Boston 8.
MICHIGAN: Director, State Board of Agriculture, State Office Building, Lansing 13.
MINNESOTA: Commissioner of Agriculture, Dairy and Food, State Office Building, St. Paul 1.
MISSISSIPPI: Commissioner of Agriculture and Commerce, Jackson 5.
MISSOURI: Commissioner of Agriculture, Jefferson City.
MONTANA: Commissioner of Agriculture, Labor and Industry, Helena.
NEBRASKA: Director of Agriculture and Inspection, Lincoln 9.
NEVADA: Director, Division of Plant Industry, State Department of Agriculture, Box 1027, Reno.
NEW HAMPSHIRE: Commissioner of Agriculture, Concord.
NEW JERSEY: Secretary, State Department of Agriculture, Trenton 8.
NEW MEXICO: A & M College, State College Post Office.
NEW YORK: Commissioner of Agriculture and Markets, State Office Building, Albany 1.
NORTH CAROLINA: Commissioner of Agriculture, Temple of Agriculture, Raleigh.
NORTH DAKOTA: Commissioner of Agriculture and Labor, Bismarck.
OHIO: Director of Agriculture, Columbus 15.
OKLAHOMA: President, State Board of Agriculture, State House, Oklahoma City.
OREGON: Director of Agriculture, Agriculture Building, Salem.
PENNSYLVANIA: Secretary of Agriculture, South Office Building, Harrisburg.
RHODE ISLAND: Director of Agriculture and Conservation, Providence 2.
SOUTH CAROLINA: Commissioner of Agriculture, Wade Hampton Office Building, Columbia.
SOUTH DAKOTA: Secretary of Agriculture, Pierre.
TENNESSEE: Commissioner of Agriculture, Nashville 3.
TEXAS: Commissioner of Agriculture, Austin 14.
UTAH: Chairman, Board of Commissioners, State Department of Agriculture, Salt Lake City 1.
VERMONT: Commissioner of Agriculture, Montpelier.
VIRGINIA: Commissioner of Agriculture and Immigration, Richmond 19.
WASHINGTON: Director of Agriculture, 213 Old Capitol Building, Olympia.
WEST VIRGINIA: Commissioner of Agriculture, Charleston 5.
WISCONSIN: Director of Agriculture, Madison 2.
WYOMING: Commissioner of Agriculture, 310 Capitol Building, Cheyenne.

Plant Quarantine Officials of the States, Territories, District of Columbia, Canada, and Mexico

ALABAMA: Chief, Division of Plant Industry, State Department of Agriculture and Industries, 515 Dexter Avenue, Montgomery 1.
ALASKA: Commissioner of Agriculture, Box 1101, Fairbanks.
ARIZONA: State Entomologist, Commission of Agriculture and Horticulture, P. O. Box 6246, Phoenix.
ARKANSAS: Chief Inspector, State Plant Board, Capitol Avenue and Center Street, Little Rock.

CALIFORNIA: Chief, Bureau of Plant Quarantine, State Department of Agriculture, Sacramento 14.

CANADA: Chief, Division of Plant Protection, Department of Agriculture, Ottawa, Ontario.

COLORADO: Chief, Division of Plant Industry, 20 State Museum, Denver 2.

CONNECTICUT: State Entomologist, Agricultural Experiment Station, Box 1106, New Haven 4.

DELAWARE: Nursery Inspector, State Board of Agriculture, Dover.

DISTRICT OF COLUMBIA: Bureau of Entomology and Plant Quarantine, United States Department of Agriculture, Washington 25.

FLORIDA: Plant Commissioner, State Plant Board, Gainesville.

GEORGIA: Director of Entomology, State Capitol, Atlanta 3.

HAWAII: Plant Quarantine Inspector In Charge, Board of Commissioners of Agriculture and Forestry, P. O. Box 2520, Honolulu 4.

IDAHO: Commissioner, State Department of Agriculture, Boise.

ILLINOIS: Division of Plant Industry, State Department of Agriculture, Room 300, Professional Arts Building, Glen Ellyn.

INDIANA: State Entomologist, 311 West Washington Street, Indianapolis 9.

IOWA: State Entomologist, 311 Science Building, Iowa State College, Ames.

KANSAS, NORTH: State Entomologist, State College of Agriculture and Applied Science, Manhattan.

KANSAS, SOUTH: State Entomologist, University of Kansas, Lawrence.

KENTUCKY: State Entomologist, College of Agriculture, University of Kentucky, Lexington 29.

LOUISIANA: State Entomologist, State Department of Agriculture and Immigration, Box 4153, Capitol Station, Baton Rouge 4.

MAINE: Chief, Division of Plant Industry, State Department of Agriculture, Augusta.

MARYLAND: State Entomologist, University of Maryland, College Park.

MASSACHUSETTS: Assistant Director, Division of Plant Pest Control and Fairs, 41 Tremont Street, Boston 8.

MEXICO: Director General of Agriculture, San Jacinto, D. F., Mexico.

MICHIGAN: Chief, Bureau of Plant Industry, State Department of Agriculture, Lansing 13.

MINNESOTA: Director, Bureau of Plant Industry, State Department of Agriculture, Dairy and Food, University Farm, St. Paul 1.

MISSISSIPPI: Entomologist, State Plant Board, State College.

MISSOURI: State Entomologist, State Department of Agriculture, Jefferson City.

MONTANA: Chief, Division of Horticulture, State Department of Agriculture, Labor and Industry, Missoula.

NEBRASKA: State Entomologist, Bureau of Plant Industry, State Department of Agriculture and Inspection, Lincoln 9.

NEVADA: Director, Division of Plant Industry, State Department of Agriculture, P. O. Box 1027, Reno.

NEW HAMPSHIRE: State Entomologist, Insect and Plant Disease Suppression and Control, State Department of Agriculture, Durham.

NEW JERSEY: Director, Division of Plant Industry, State Department of Agriculture, Trenton 8.

NEW MEXICO: Deputy Inspector, College of Agriculture and Mechanic Arts, State College.

NEW YORK: Director, Bureau of Plant Industry, State Department of Agriculture and Markets, Albany 1.

NORTH CAROLINA: State Entomologist, State Department of Agriculture, Raleigh.

NORTH DAKOTA: State Entomologist, Department of Entomology, North Dakota Agricultural College, Fargo.

OHIO: Chief, Division of Plant Industry, State Department of Agriculture, Columbus 15.

OKLAHOMA: Director, Division of Entomology and Plant Industry, Oklahoma State Board of Agriculture, Oklahoma City 5.

OREGON: Chief, Division of Plant Industry, State Department of Agriculture, Agricultural Building, Salem.

PENNSYLVANIA: Director, Bureau of Plant Industry, State Department of Agriculture, Harrisburg.

PUERTO RICO: Director, Plant Quarantine Service, Department of Agriculture and Commerce, San Juan.

RHODE ISLAND: Administrator, Division of Entomology and Plant Industry, State Department of Agriculture and Conservation, State House, Providence 2.

SOUTH CAROLINA: Entomologist, State Crop Pest Commission, Clemson.

SOUTH DAKOTA: Director, Division of Plant Industry, State Department of Agriculture, Pierre.

TENNESSEE: State Entomologist and Plant Pathologist, 312 Cotton States Building, Nashville 3.

TEXAS: Chief, Division of Plant Quarantine, State Department of Agriculture, Austin.

UTAH: State Supervising Inspector, State Department of Agriculture, Salt Lake City.

VERMONT:
Vermont Nursery Inspector, 230 Loomis Street, Burlington.
Director, Division of Plant Pest Control, State Department of Agriculture, Montpelier.

VIRGINIA: State Entomologist, State Department of Agriculture and Immigration, 1112 State Office Building, Richmond 19.

WASHINGTON: Supervisor of Horticulture, State Department of Agriculture, Olympia.

WEST VIRGINIA: Entomologist, State Department of Agriculture, Charleston 5.

WISCONSIN: State Entomologist, State Department of Agriculture, State Capitol, Madison 2.

WYOMING: State Entomologist, State Department of Agriculture, Powell.

Associations

American Association of Economic Entomologists,
Office of the Secretary-Treasurer,
University of Maryland,
College Park, Md.

Entomological Society of America,
University of Minnesota,
University Farm,
St. Paul 1, Minn.

National Agricultural Chemicals Association,
Barr Building, 910 Seventeenth Street NW.,
Washington 6, D. C.

National Association of Insecticide & Disinfectant Manufacturers, Inc.,
110 East Forty-second Street,
New York 17, N. Y.

National Pest Control Association, Inc.,
30 Church Street,
New York 7, N. Y.

National Canners Association,
1133 Twentieth Street, NW.,
Washington 6, D. C.

National Sprayer and Duster Association,
4300 Board of Trade Building,
Chicago 4, Ill.

For private agencies, see:

National Research Council Bulletin 115: *Handbook of Scientific and Technical Societies and Institutions of the United State and Canada.* 1948. (2101 Constitution Avenue NW., Washington, D. C.)

National Research Council Bulletin 113: *Industrial Research Laboratories of the United States.* 1946. (2101 Constitution Avenue NW., Washington, D. C.)

State Extension Directors

ALABAMA: Alabama Polytechnic Institute, Auburn.

ARIZONA: University of Arizona, Tucson.

ARKANSAS: College of Agriculture, University of Arkansas, Fayetteville.

CALIFORNIA: College of Agriculture, University of California, Berkeley 4.

COLORADO: Colorado Agricultural and Mechanical College, Fort Collins.

CONNECTICUT: Associate Director, University of Connecticut, Storrs.

DELAWARE: University of Delaware, Newark.

FLORIDA: Agricultural Extension Service, Horticultural Building, Gainesville.

GEORGIA: Georgia State College of Agriculture, Athens.

IDAHO: College of Agriculture, University of Idaho, Moscow.

ILLINOIS: College of Agriculture, University of Illinois, Urbana.

INDIANA: Purdue University, Lafayette.

IOWA: Iowa State College of Agriculture and Mechanic Arts, Ames.

KANSAS: Kansas State College of Agriculture and Applied Science, Manhattan.

KENTUCKY: College of Agriculture, University of Kentucky, Lexington 29.

LOUISIANA: Louisiana State University and Agricultural and Mechanical College, University Station, Baton Rouge 3.

MAINE: College of Agriculture, University of Maine, Orono.

MARYLAND: University of Maryland, College Park.

MASSACHUSETTS: University of Massachusetts, Amherst.

MICHIGAN: Michigan State College of Agriculture and Applied Science, East Lansing.

MINNESOTA: Dept. of Agriculture of the University of Minnesota, University Farm, St. Paul 1.

MISSISSIPPI: Mississippi State College, State College.

MISSOURI: College of Agriculture, University of Missouri, Columbia.

MONTANA: Montana State College of Agriculture and Mechanic Arts, Bozeman.

NEBRASKA: College of Agriculture, University of Nebraska, Lincoln 1.

NEVADA: Agricultural Extension Service, University of Nevada, Reno.

NEW HAMPSHIRE: University of New Hampshire, Durham.

NEW JERSEY: State College of Agriculture and Mechanic Arts of Rutgers University, New Brunswick.

NEW MEXICO: New Mexico College of Agriculture and Mechanic Arts, State College.

NEW YORK: New York State College of Agriculture, Ithaca.

North Carolina: North Carolina State College, State College Station, Raleigh, North Carolina.
North Dakota: North Dakota Agricultural College, State College Station, Fargo.
Ohio: College of Agriculture, Ohio State University, Columbus 10.
Oklahoma: Oklahoma Agricultural and Mechanical College, Stillwater.
Oregon: Oregon State Agricultural College, Corvallis.
Pennsylvania: Pennsylvania State College, State College.
Rhode Island: University of Rhode Island, Kingston.
South Carolina: Clemson Agricultural College of South Carolina, Clemson.
South Dakota: South Dakota State College of Agriculture and Mechanic Arts, Brookings.
Tennessee: College of Agriculture, University of Tennessee, Knoxville 7.
Texas: Agricultural and Mechanical College of Texas, College Station.
Utah: Utah State Agricultural College, Logan.
Vermont: College of Agriculture, Burlington.
Virginia: Virginia Polytechnic Institute, Blacksburg
Washington: Box 328, College Station, Pullman.
West Virginia: College of Agriculture, West Virginia University, Morgantown.
Wisconsin: Associate Director, College of Agriculture, University of Wisconsin, Madison 6.
Wyoming: College of Agriculture, University of Wyoming, Laramie.

Territories:

Alaska: University of Alaska, College.
Hawaii: University of Hawaii, Honolulu.
Puerto Rico: University of Puerto Rico, Rio Piedras.

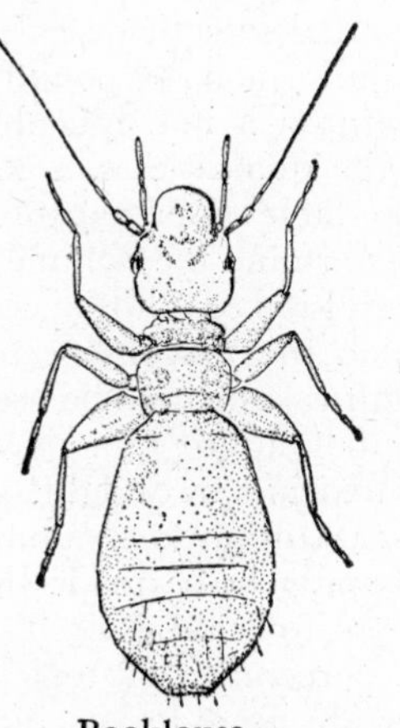

Booklouse.

Conversion Tables and Equivalents

Compiled by R. H. Nelson

It is sometimes convenient to use a measuring cup and measuring spoons in making up sprays for dooryard or small-garden applications. The following equivalents are of use in this connection:

3 teaspoonfuls = 1 tablespoon.
2 tablespoonfuls = 1 fluid ounce.
16 tablespoonfuls, 2 gills, ½ pint, 8 fluid ounces = 1 cup.

Dilution of Insecticides

Some insecticides, such as certain of those intended for household use, are purchased ready for use. In general, however, it is necessary to dilute the material with water to form a spray or with a dry powdered material to form a dust. The labels placed on the packages by manufacturers should be carefully read and followed.

The discussion which follows is intended to assist users in the proper dilution of various types of insecticides.

Sprays

Powdered Insecticides. Recommendations for the use of powdered insecticides in sprays are often given on the basis of pounds per 100 gallons. The quantities necessary to produce the same dilutions in smaller quantities of water are tabulated on the next page.

Several of the more recently developed insecticides, such as DDT, are made up into wettable powders which contain only a stated percentage of the toxicant. The recommendations may, however, be on the basis of pounds of actual insecticide per 100 gallons. The

Quantity of water in gallons	*Quantity of insecticide*				
100	1 lb.	2 lb.	3 lb.	4 lb.	5 lb.
25	4 oz.	8 oz.	12 oz.	1 lb.	1¼ lb.
12.5	2 oz.	4 oz.	6 oz.	8 oz.	10 oz.
2.5	0.4 oz	0.8 oz.	1.2 oz.	1.6 oz.	2 oz.

dilution table above may be used by finding the desired quantity in the table and multiplying it by the proper factor as given below. The answer will be the quantity of the wettable powder to be used.

Example: A recommendation calls for applying a spray containing DDT at the rate of 3 pounds per 100 gallons, and you wish to make up 2.5 gallons of spray using a DDT wettable powder known to contain 25 percent of DDT. The dilution table above indicates that 1.2 ounces per 2.5 gallons is equivalent to 3 pounds per 100 gallons. You therefore multiply 1.2 ounces by 4, the factor indicated below for a material containing 25 percent of toxicant, and find you must use 4.8 ounces of the DDT wettable powder.

	Percent insecticide in wettable powder				
	20	25	40	50	75
Factor	5	4	2½	2	1⅓

These wettable powders are also recommended for use on a percentage basis in sprays and dips, the recommendation usually specifying a certain percentage of the toxicant. Equivalents for use in making up such suspensions are given here.

Percent toxicant in wettable powder	*Pounds of wettable powder to make 100 gallons of spray with toxicant content of—*		
	0.25 percent	0.5 percent	1 percent
20	10.4	20.9	41.7
25	8.3	16.7	33.4
40	5.2	10.4	20.9
50	4.2	8.3	16.7
75	2.8	5.6	11.1

The number of pounds of any wettable powder to be used in any given quantity of spray or dip of a given percentage toxicant can be calculated by the use of the following formula. This formula can also be used for powdered Derris or cube root where the rotenone content is known.

$$\frac{\text{Number of gallons of spray} \times 8.345 \times \text{Percent toxicant desired in spray}}{\text{Percent toxicant in the wettable powder}} = \text{Pounds of wettable powder to be used.}$$

Example: 500 gallons of dip containing 0.25 percent DDT is needed. The wettable powder to be used contains 50 percent DDT.

$$\frac{500 \times 8.345 \times 0.25}{50} = 21 \text{ lb. wettable powder.}$$

Water is then added to make 500 gallons of dip.

Liquid insecticides. Insecticides in the form of solution or emulsion concentrates are most readily handled by liquid measure. However, since spray recommendations are generally on the basis of weight of the toxicant per volume of water, or percent by weight, or weight of the toxicant to be applied to a given area, dilution of these concentrates is often confusing. If the label states that the concentrate contains so much actual insecticide by weight per unit volume, such as 1 pound per quart, then dilution is not difficult and proportionate quantities can be obtained from the table on page 746.

To determine the volume in gallons of an emulsion or solution concentrate, for which the percentage of toxicant by weight is known, to be used in making up an emulsion of a given percentage of toxicant by weight, proceed as follows: Multiply the number of gallons of spray to be made by the percentage of toxicant desired and divide by the percentage of toxicant in the concentrate times its specific gravity.

Conversion Tables

In the dilution and application of insecticides it is often necessary to determine the equivalents of various weights and measures. The following tables are intended for such use. The tables are set up so that equivalents may be found by reading across from either side.

Weight

United States avoirdupois units	*Metric units*
1 ounce (oz.)—16 drams (dr.)	28. 35 grams (gm.).
1 pound (lb.)—16 ounces	453. 59 grams.
1 short ton—2,000 pounds	0. 91 metric ton.
1 long ton—2,240 pounds	1. 02 metric tons.

Liquid Measure

United States units	*Metric units*
1 fluid ounce (fl. oz.)	29. 57 milliliters (ml.).
1 gill—4 fluid ounces	118. 29 milliliters.
1 pint (pt.)—4 gills	0. 47 liter (l.).
1 quart (qt.)—2 pints	0. 95 liter.
1 gallon (gal.)—4 quarts	3. 79 liters.

Dry Measure

United States units	*Metric units*
1 pint	0. 55 liter.
1 quart—2 pints	1. 1 liters.
1 peck (pk.)—8 quarts	0. 88 dekaliter.
1 bushel (bu.)—4 pecks	0. 35 hectoliter.

Measure of Length

United States units	*Metric units*
1 inch (in.)	25. 4 millimeters (mm.).
1 foot (ft.)—12 inches	30. 48 centimeters (cm.).
1 yard (yd.)—3 feet	0. 91 meter (m.).
1 rod (rd.)—5.5 yards	5. 03 meters.
1 mile—320 rods	1. 61 kilometers (km.).

Area Measurement

United States units	*Metric units*
1 square inch (sq. in.)	6. 45 square centimeters ($cm.^2$).
1 square foot (sq. ft.)—144 square inches	9. 29 square decimeters ($dm.^2$).
1 square yard (sq. yd.)—9 square feet	0. 84 square meter ($m.^2$).
1 square rod (sq. rd.)—30.25 square yards	25. 29 square meters.
1 acre—160 square rods	0. 4 hectare (ha.).

Cubic Measurement

United States units	*Metric units*
1 cubic inch (cu. in.)	16. 39 cubic centimeters (cc.).
1 cubic foot (cu. ft.)—1,728 cubic inches	28. 32 cubic decimeters ($dm.^3$).
1 cubic yard (cu. yd.)—27 cubic feet	0. 76 cubic meter ($m.^3$).

Example: 100 gallons of spray containing 2 percent chlordane by weight is to be prepared from an emulsion concentrate containing 40 percent chlordane having a specific gravity of 1.02. The amount of the concentrate that will be needed is

$$\frac{100 \times 2}{40 \times 1.02} = 4.9 \text{ gallons.}$$

Sufficient water is added to make 100 gallons of spray.

Recommendations for field application of insecticides are often given in pounds of toxicant per acre. The weight of the toxicant in a gallon of emulsion concentrate is readily determined, when the percentage of toxicant and the specific gravity are known, by the following relationship:

Quantity of water in gallons	*Quantity of material*				
100	½ pint	1 pint	1 quart	½ gallon	1 gallon
25	2 fl. oz.	4 fl. oz.	8 fl. oz.	1 pint	1 quart
12.5	1 fl. oz.	2 fl. oz.	4 fl. oz.	½ pint	1 pint
2.5	0.2 fl. oz.	0.4 fl. oz.	0.8 fl. oz.	1.6 fl. oz.	3.2 fl. oz.

$$\frac{8.345 \times \text{specific gravity} \times \text{percentage of toxicant}}{100}$$

=pounds of toxicant.

Example: A chlordane emulsion concentrate containing 45 percent of chlordane by weight and having a specific gravity of 1.07 is to be used. Each gallon of the concentrate contains

$$\frac{8.345 \times 1.07 \times 45}{100} = 4 \text{ pounds of chlordane.}$$

The quantity of water to be added depends upon the method of application. If 1 pound of chlordane is required per acre, 1 quart of the concentrate should be used in the quantity of spray that the apparatus at hand will deliver per acre.

Specific gravity is often unknown to the average user. The above formulas can be used, leaving this factor out and the results will be approximately correct.

Dusts

Insecticides are also applied in the form of dusts. Generally a noninsecticidal material such as talc is used as the diluent. Such dusts are on the market ready for use. If, however, further dilution is necessary or if it is desirable to make up the finished dust from the various ingredients the following formula will be of use.

To determine the weight of insecticidal material to be used in preparing a dust containing a given percentage of toxicant, multiply the percentage of toxicant desired by the pounds of dust to be made and divide by the percentage of toxicant in the insecticidal material to be used.

Example: One hundred pounds of dust containing 0.5 percent of rotenone is to be prepared. The powdered root to be used contains 4 percent of rotenone. The quantity of powdered root necessary is

$$\frac{0.5 \times 100}{4} = 12.5 \text{ pounds.}$$

Sufficient diluent is then added to make 100 pounds.

Rates of Application

The recommendations for use of insecticides on row crops are often given in gallon of spray or pounds of dust per acre. Approximately equivalent rates of application for use in connection with less than acre areas are tabulated below. The figures are based on rows 3 feet apart.

Sprays

Rate per acre	*For 100 feet of row*	*1 gallon will cover*	
Gallons	*Pints*	*Feet of row*	*Square feet*
5	¼	2, 904	8, 712
10	½	1, 452	4, 356
25	1½	581	1, 742
50	2¾	290	871
75	4	194	581
100	5½	145	436
200	11	73	218

Dusts

Rate per acre	*For 100 feet of row*	*1 pound will cover*	
Pounds	*Ounces*	*Feet of row*	*Square feet*
5	0. 6	2, 904	8, 712
10	1. 1	1, 452	4, 356
15	1. 7	968	2, 904
20	2. 2	726	2, 178
25	2. 8	581	1, 742
50	5. 5	290	871

Summary of Federal Plant Regulatory Legislation

Ralph W. Sherman

Insect Pest Act of 1905 (33 Stat. 1269, 7 U. S. C. 141). This was the first plant pest legislation enacted by the Congress, having been approved March 3, 1905. It prohibits the importation or interstate movement, by any means of transportation, of any living insect that is notoriously injurious to cultivated crops. A heavy fine is provided for violation of the act. This act is still of considerable importance since it is applicable to the entry of insects by airplane.

The Plant Quarantine Act of 1912 (37 Stat. 315, 7 U. S. C. 154). This act, approved August 20, 1912, is the most important of all Federal legislation enacted to protect the United States against the entry of dangerous insects and plant diseases and to prevent the widespread distribution of such pests if they accidentally gain a foothold here. This act gives the Secretary of Agriculture broad authority to prevent the entry of plant pests that might infest or infect imported plants or plant products and to prevent the spread of an introduced pest of limited distribution in the United States.

Sections 1 to 5 of the act authorize the Secretary of Agriculture to establish conditions and regulations governing entry into the United States of nursery stock and other plants and plant products, and to require that permits be secured for such importations. Section 7 authorizes the Secretary to prohibit the entry of nursery stock and other plants and products from a country or locality where a plant disease or injurious insect exists. In addition, section 8 authorizes the Secretary to promulgate quarantines and regulations restricting interstate movement of plants or plant material, or any other article of any character whatsoever, capable of carrying any dangerous plant disease or insect infestation that may be specified in a quarantine as "new to or not heretofore widely prevalent or distributed within and throughout the United States." Penalties are provided for violation of the act.

Amendments to the act were approved March 4, 1913; March 4, 1917; May 31, 1920; April 13, 1926; May 1, 1928; and July 31, 1947. In order of their approval, these amendments have, among other items, authorized (1) the importation for experimental or scientific purposes by the Department of Agriculture of plants and plant products, (2) the promulgation of an interstate quarantine without the necessity for determining that the area involved is actually infested, (3) the regulation of the movement of plants and plant products into the District of Columbia, (4) the several States to quarantine, in the absence of an applicable Federal quarantine, against the shipment through or into their environs of plants, plant products, and other articles from other States in which a dangerous plant disease or insect infestation exists; (5) the halting and without warrant, inspection, search, and examination of persons, vehicles, receptacles, boats, ships, or vessels, and seizure and destruction or other disposition of plants or other articles found to be moving in violation of the act or any regulation issued thereunder; and (6) the added condition for the importation of nursery stock under permit that, when deemed necessary, such stock must be grown in post-entry quarantine for the purpose of determining its freedom from infestation or infection.

Mexican Border Act (56 Stat. 40, 7 U. S. C. 149). This act, approved January 31, 1942, authorizes the Secretary of Agriculture to regulate the entry from Mexico of all vehicles, freight, express, baggage and other materials which may carry insect pests and plant diseases. The Secretary is also authorized to provide facilities for inspection, cleaning, and disinfection of such vehicles and materials, and to collect fees for such services.

Export Certification Act (58 Stat. 735, 7 U. S. C. 147a (b)). This act, included as Section 102 (b) of the "Department of Agriculture Organic Act of 1944," approved September 21, 1944, authorizes the Secretary of Agriculture to provide for the inspection of domestic plants and plant products to meet the phytosanitary requirements of foreign countries.

Terminal Inspection Act (38 Stat. 1113, 7 U. S. C. 166). This act, approved March 4, 1915, provides, under specified conditions, for inspection by State plant pest officials at mail terminals of plants and plant products moving interstate. This permits the States, in cooperation with the Post Office Department, to protect themselves against the entry of infested or infected plants or plant products through the mails.

Pickleworm.

Insecticides

The following list of names and symbols was compiled by a committee of the American Association of Economic Entomologists and issued January 10, 1952. The terms designated by two asterisks are common names approved by the Interdepartmental Committee on Pest Control. Those designated by one asterisk are trade names; sometimes they are followed by a letter or a number or both, which indicate a product of specific composition.

Name	*Definition*	*Other designations*
aldrin**	not less than 95 percent of 1,2,3,4,-10,10-hexachloro-1,4,4a,5,8,8a,-hexahydro-1,4,5,8-dimethano-naphthalene.	compound 118.
allethrin**	*dl*-2-allyl-4-hydroxy-3-methyl-3-cyclopenten-1-one esterified with a mixture of cis and trans *dl*-chrysanthemum monocarboxylic acids.	allyl homolog of cinerin **I.** synthetic pyrethrins.
Aramite*	product containing 2-(*p*-*tert*-butyl-phenoxy)-1-methylethyl 2-chloroethyl sulfite.	88R (alkyl aryl sulfite).
BHC	1,2,3,4,5,6-hexachlorocyclohexane, consisting of several isomers and containing 12 to 14 percent of the gamma isomer.	benzene hexachloride. 666. Gammexane.*
chlordane**	1,2,4,5,6,7,8,8-octachloro-2,3,3a,4,-7,7a-hexahydro-4,7-methanoindene.	Velsicol 1068.* Octachlor.* Octa-Klor.*
bis(*p*-chloro-phenoxy)-methane.		K–1875. Neotran.* di(4-chlorophenoxy)-methane.
p-chlorophenyl *p*-chlorobenzene sulfonate.		K–6451. Ovotran.*
compound 923	2,4-dichlorophenyl ester of benzene sulfonic acid.	Genitol 923.
compound 22008	3-methyl-1-phenyl-5-pyrazolyl dimethylcarbamate.	G–22008.
CS–645A*	1,1-bis(*p*-chlorophenyl)-2-nitro-propane.	Prolan.*
CS–674A*	1,1-bis(*p*-chlorophenyl)-2-nitro-butane.	Bulan.*
CS–708*	mixture of 1 part 1,1-bis(*p*-chloro-phenyl)-2-nitropropane (CS–645A) and 2 parts 1,1-bis(*p*-chlorophenyl)-2-nitrobutane (CS–674A).	Dilan.*

Name	*Definition*	*Other designations*
D-D mixture	mixture of 1,2-dichloropropane and 1,3-dichloropropene.	D-D.*
DDT	Commercially available dichloro-diphenyl-trichloroethane, the principal constituent of which is 1,1, 1-trichloro-2,2-bis(*p*-chlorophenyl)-ethane.	chlorophenothane (U. S. Pharmacopoeia 14:136. 1950).
DFDT	1,1,1-trichloro-2,2-bis(*p*-fluorophenyl)ethane.	fluorine analog of DDT.
dieldrin**	not less than 85 percent of 1,2,3,4,-10,10-hexachloro-6,7-epoxy-1,4,-4a,5,6,7,8,8a-octahydro-1,4,5,8-dimethanonaphthalene.	compound 497.
diisopropyl *p*-nitrophenyl thiophosphate.	O,O-diisopropyl O-*p*-nitrophenyl thiophosphate.	compound 3456.
dimethyl carbate	dimethyl ester of cis-bicyclo(2.2.1)-5-heptene-2,3-dicarboxylic acid.	
DMC	4,4-dichloro-alpha-methylbenzhydrol.	di(*p*-chlorophenyl)methylcarbinol. 1,1-bis(*p*-chlorophenyl)-ethanol. Dimite.*
E-1059	O-[2-(ethylmercapto)ethyl] O,O-diethyl thiophosphate.	a trialkyl thiophosphate. see Systox.
EPN*	O-ethyl O-*p*-nitrophenyl benzenethiophosphonate.	
2-ethyl-1, 3-hexanediol.	....	Rutgers 612.*
ferbam**	ferric dimethyl dithiocarbamate	Fermate.* Kerbam.*
heptachlor**	1 (or 3a),4,5,6,7,8,8-heptachloro-3a, 4,7,7a-tetrahydro-4,7-methanoindene.	Velsicol 104.* E-3314.
HETP	mixture of ethyl polyphosphates containing 12 to 20 percent of tetraethyl pyrophosphate.	hexaethyl tetraphosphate.
Indalone*	butyl ester of 3,4-dihydro-2,2-dimethyl-4-oxo-2H-pyran-6-carboxylic acid.	*n*-butyl mesityl oxide oxalate. Butopyronoxyl (U. S. Pharmacopoeia 14:91.1950).
lindane**	gamma isomer of benzene hexachloride of not less than 99 percent purity.	
malathon**	O,O-dimethyl dithiophosphate of diethyl mercaptosuccinate.	compound 4049. S-(1,2-dicarbethoxyethyl) O,O-dimethyl dithiophosphate.
Metacide*	product containing methyl parathion and parathion.	
methoxychlor**	1,1,1-trichloro-2,2-bis(*p*-methoxyphenyl)ethane.	Marlate.* DMDT.

970134°—52——49

Name	*Definition*	*Other designations*
methyl parathion	O,O-dimethyl O-*p*-nitrophenyl thiophosphate.	methyl homolog of parathion.
4-methylumbelliferone O,O-diethyl thiophosphate.	....	O,O-diethyl thiophosphoric acid ester of 7-hydroxy-4-methylcoumarin. Potasan.* E-838.
MGK-264*	N-(2-ethylhexyl)bicyclo(2.2.1)-5-heptene-2,3-dicarboximide.	N-octylbicyclo (2.2.1)-5-heptene-2,3-dicarboximide. Octacide 264.* Van Dyk 264.*
nabam**	disodium ethylene bisdithiocarbamate	Dithane.*
para-oxon	diethyl *p*-nitrophenyl phosphate	oxygen analog of parathion. E-600.
parathion**	O,O-diethyl O-*p*-nitrophenyl thiophosphate.	E-605. compound 3422.
piperonyl butoxide	product containing as its principal constituent alpha-[2-(2-butoxyethoxy)ethoxy]-4, 5-methylenedioxy-2-propyl toluene.	(butyl carbitol) (6-propylpiperonyl) ether. compound 312.
piperonyl cyclonene.	mixture of 3-alkyl-6-carbethoxy-5(3, 4-methylenedioxyphenyl)-2-cyclohexen-1-one and 3-alkyl-5(3,4-methylenedioxyphenyl)-2-cyclohexen-1-one.	piperonyl cyclohexenone.
Q-137	1,1-dichloro-2,2-bis(*p*-ethylphenyl)-ethane.	
R-242	70 percent of *p*-chlorophenyl phenyl sulfone plus 30 percent of related sulfones.	Sulphenone.*
schradan	octamethyl pyrophosphoramide	bis(bis-dimethylamino)-phosphonous anhydride. OMPA. Pestox III.*
sulfotepp	tetraethyl dithiopyrophosphate	dithione.
Systox*	product containing E-1059.	
TDE	commercially available dichlorodiphenyl-dichloroethane, the principal constituent of which is 1,1-dichloro-2,2-bis(*p*-chlorophenyl)ethane.	DDD. Rhothane.*
TEPP	tetraethyl pyrophosphate	TEP.
thiram**	tetramethylthiuram disulfide.	
toxaphene**	chlorinated camphene having a chlorine content of 67-69 percent.	compound 3956.
zineb**	zinc ethylene bisdithiocarbamate.	
ziram**	zinc dimethyl dithiocarbamate.	

Index[1]

[1] In this index, common names of insects approved by the American Association of Economic Entomologists are indicated by asterisks. Italic page numbers refer to line drawings.

970134°—52——50

Some Important Insects

The colored picture sheets that follow illustrate a selected group of insects that are commonly found in the United States. Some are of great economic importance. Information is provided on the distribution, habits, nature of damage caused, and methods of preventing or controlling the infestations.

It is hard here to give recommendations that will apply equally well throughout the country: Variations in crop practices, soils, and weather conditions cause insect problems to be much more acute in one area than another, and frequently different control measures and timing therefore are required. Accordingly it is often wise to consult county agents, State officials, or other authorities to ascertain which methods and procedures would be most satisfactory to use locally. Their addresses are given in the appendix. Although greatest reliance is placed upon insecticides for the control of injurious insects today, one should remember that other methods of control are important.

The primary aim today, however, should be the development of practices that will prevent insects from causing damage to crops.

Our hope is that these pictures will enable the reader to recognize the most destructive insects and stimulate him to apply effective control measures promptly. Such action results in economical control. Cooperative community and widespread control programs have an important place in safeguarding our people's health and supply of food and fiber. Insect control is also an integral part of the increased food production that is vitally needed during emergency periods for our own welfare and to fulfill commitments made to other free countries of the world.

All the insecticides here recommended to control the insects pictured are poisons. Handle them with caution. Follow carefully the directions and warnings given on the containers. Store insecticides in plainly labeled, closed containers, in a dry place away from food products, and where children or animals cannot reach them.

When mixing or applying insecticides, avoid inhaling dusts or sprays. Protect the hands with leather or rubber gloves. Keep the hands away from the mouth and wash them thoroughly before eating. Bury any waste material. Thoroughly wash out containers that have been used in mixing insecticides.

Oils used in making insecticide solutions are inflammable. Do not mix or apply them near an open flame.

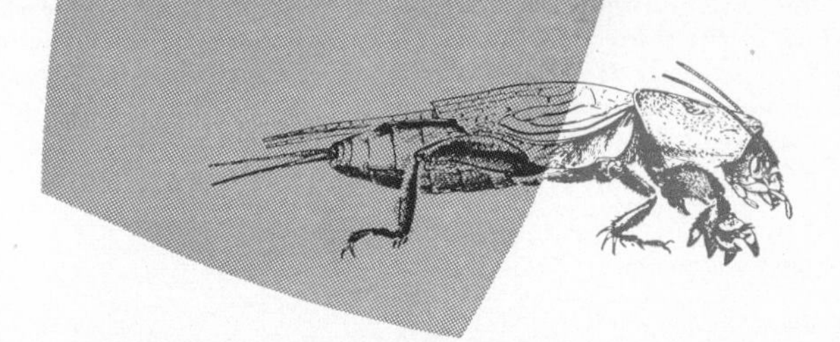

BOLL WEEVIL

Boll weevils pass the winter as adults in woods trash or other protected places near cottonfields. They return to cottonfields in the spring and remain there until frost. Boll weevils prefer to feed on and to lay their eggs in squares, but they also attack bolls. Eggs are laid singly in deep punctures within the squares or bolls. After 3 to 5 days they hatch into white larvae, or grubs. The grubs feed for 7 to 14 days within the squares or bolls in which they hatch and then change into pupae. The adults emerge from the pupae in 3 to 5 days and cut their way out of the squares. After feeding on blooms, squares, or bolls for 3 to 4 days, the females are ready to lay eggs. The cycle from egg to adult weevil takes about 3 weeks. There may be seven generations a year.

The leaflike bracts at the base of squares punctured by boll weevils open up, or flare, and the squares turn yellow and die. Most of the punctured squares and small bolls are shed. Large punctured bolls are not shed, but the lock in which a grub feeds fails to develop properly, and the lint is cut, stained brown, and decayed.

Low winter temperatures and hot, dry summers help control the boll weevil. Watch for a rapid increase of weevils and severe damage during rainy periods.

Farming practices that help set bolls quickly will help control weevils. The practices are: Plant cotton on good land that has been well prepared. Use fertilizer recommended for your locality. Select an early-maturing variety suited for growing in your locality. Plant early, space closely, and cultivate frequently. Pick early and cleanly. After the cotton has been picked, stop further fruiting by plowing out, cutting, or grazing the cotton stalks as early as possible in the fall, to reduce the number of weevils in next year's crop.

Control with dusts and sprays: Benzene hexachloride, calcium arsenate, toxaphene, aldrin, and dieldrin can control the boll weevil, but when they are so used, other insect problems must be considered; infestations of the cotton aphid, the bollworm, and spider mites may develop when some of them are used alone.

The following dusts have been approved for use in some areas: (1) Benzene hexachloride to give 3 percent of the gamma isomer in the finished dust plus 5 percent of DDT (sometimes referred to as "3–5–0"); (2) calcium arsenate applied alternately with calcium arsenate plus 2 percent of nicotine; (3) calcium arsenate applied alternately with a mixture of benzene hexachloride (3 percent gamma isomer) and 5 percent of DDT; (4) lime-free calcium arsenate plus 1 percent of parathion; (5) lime-free calcium arsenate plus 1 percent of parathion and 5 percent of DDT; (6) toxaphene 20 percent; (7) aldrin 2.5 percent; (8) aldrin 2.5 percent plus 5 percent of DDT; (9) dieldrin 1.5 or 2.5 percent; (10) dieldrin 1.5 or 2.5 percent plus 5 percent of DDT; (11) chlordane 10 percent plus 5 percent of DDT. (This mixture is recommended only in areas where it has given good control. It has given erratic results in some areas, perhaps because of high temperatures and humidity.)

In areas where spider mites are a problem, dust formulations of organic insecticides should contain sulfur or some other suitable miticide.

The following treatments with sprays made from emulsion concentrates have given favorable results and are approved where recommended: (1) Toxaphene at the rate of 2 to 3 pounds of the technical material per acre; (2) toxaphene and DDT in the ratio of 2 to 1 applied at the rate of 2 to 3 pounds of technical toxaphene per acre; (3) a mixture to give 0.3 to 0.5 pound of the gamma isomer of benzene hexachloride and 0.5 pound or more of technical DDT per acre; (4) aldrin at the rate of 0.25 to 0.5 pound of the technical material per acre; (5) a mixture to give 0.25 to 0.5 pound of technical aldrin and 0.5 pound or more of technical DDT per acre; (6) dieldrin at the rate of 0.15 to 0.4 pound of technical material per acre; (7) a mixture to give 0.15 to 0.4 pound of technical dieldrin and 0.5 pound or more of technical DDT per acre. In areas where it has proved satisfactory and where it is recommended, a mixture of 1 pound of technical chlordane and 0.5 pound or more of technical DDT per acre may be used.

Control measures directed against the boll weevil should be applied when definite need is indicated. Except where early-season control measures are practiced, insecticides should be applied at intervals of 4 to 5 days until the infestation is brought under control. Thereafter the fields should be inspected weekly and applications made when necessary.

{PLATE I

BOLL WEEVIL

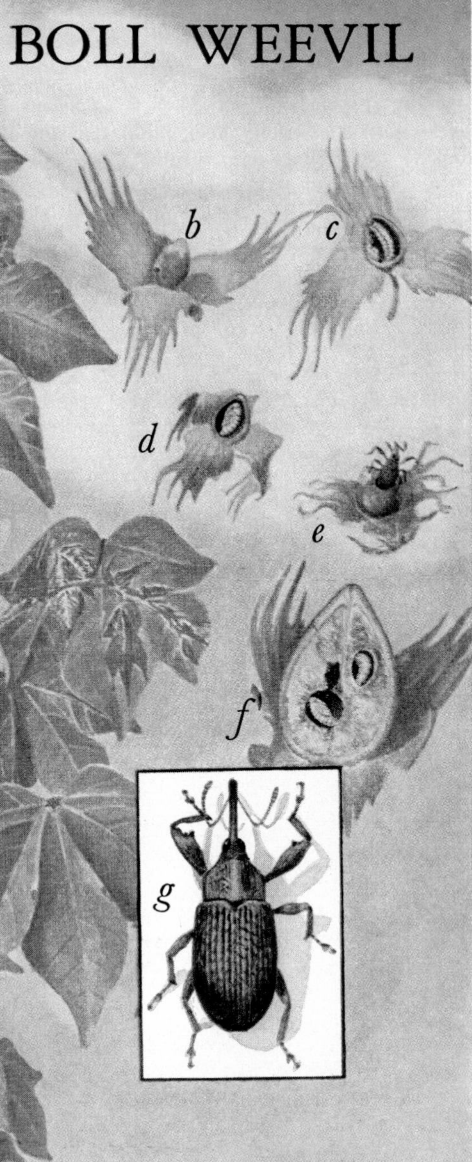

Cotton plant showing *a*, punctured squares on ground; *b*, square showing egg puncture; *c*, larva in square; *d*, pupa in square; *e*, adult emerging from square; *f*, larva and pupa in boll; *g*, adult. (*a*, one-fourth natural size; *b*, *c*, *d*, *e*, and *f*, natural size; *g*, six times natural size.)

THE BOLLWORM

The bollworm, also known as the tomato fruitworm and the corn earworm, damages cotton wherever it is grown in the United States, but the losses are usually greatest in Texas, Oklahoma, and Louisiana. It also feeds on many plants besides cotton, especially corn and tomato. Cotton is not the preferred food plant. Bollworm infestations usually develop rather late in the season.

Each bollworm destroys a large number of squares and bolls. When bollworms are numerous a crop of cotton can be ruined in a short time. Damage often occurs so late in the season that the plants do not have time to mature another crop of bolls.

The bollworm moths prefer rapidly growing, succulent cotton in which to lay their eggs. The eggs are laid singly on the tender growth and newly formed squares. They are smaller than the head of an ordinary pin, and pearly white when first laid, but change to a dark color before hatching. The small larvae, or "worms," feed for a few days on the tender buds or leaves and on the outside of squares before burrowing into squares or bolls, usually near the base. Large worms feed almost entirely inside the bolls, so that it is very difficult, if not impossible, to control them. Full-grown larvae enter the soil and change to the pupal, or resting, stage. There are several broods a year. The last brood passes the winter in the underground pupal cells.

Control: When it is about time for bollworms to appear, examine the tops of the plants frequently for eggs and small worms. When 20 to 25 eggs that are beginning to hatch (or that number of eggs and very small worms) are found per 100 plants, it is time to begin applying insecticides. *Successful control of bollworms requires heavy applications of dusts or sprays while the eggs are hatching and before the worms enter the bolls.*

At 5-day intervals apply 10 to 15 pounds per acre of a 10 percent DDT dust or the equivalent in spray form; a dust containing 5 percent of DDT plus sufficient benzene hexachloride to give 3 percent of the gamma isomer; or a 20 percent toxaphene dust. Calcium arsenate, lead arsenate, and cryolite are less effective. Whenever the spider mites must also be controlled, any mixture containing organic insecticides should include at least 40 percent of sulfur or some other suitable miticide. Use more pounds per acre when the infestation is heavy and the plants are large. Two or three applications will usually control a brood of bollworms, but there may be more than one brood or a steady movement of egg-laying moths to cotton from other crops, with no distinct broods. In such cases several additional applications may be needed to keep the plants covered with insecticides to kill the newly hatched worms. Lady beetles and other natural enemies or extremely hot, dry, windy weather often destroy enough eggs and young bollworms to control a threatening infestation without the use of insecticides. Nicotine or benzene hexachloride may be added to the insecticides to prevent aphids from becoming injurious.

[PLATE II

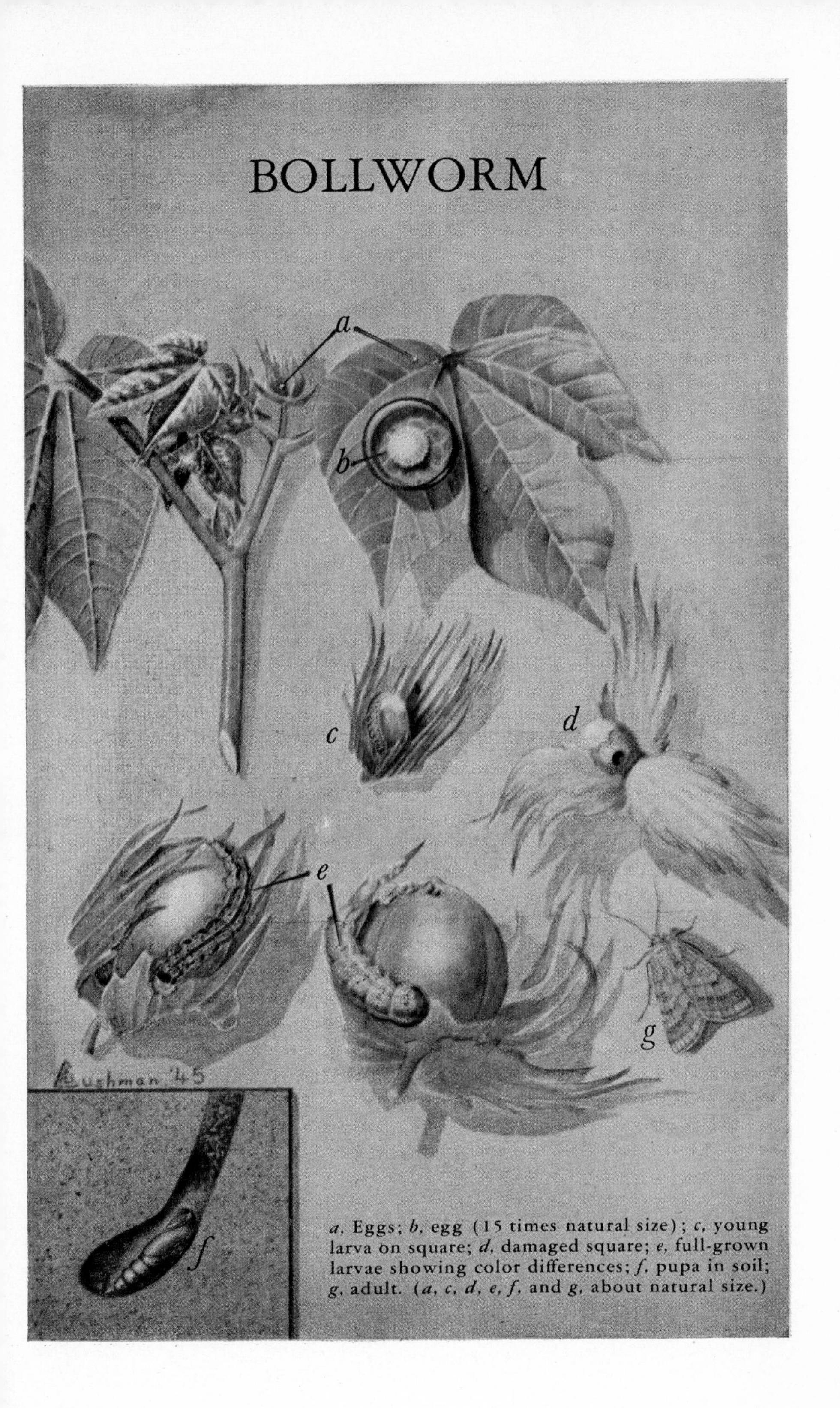

a, Eggs; *b*, egg (15 times natural size); *c*, young larva on square; *d*, damaged square; *e*, full-grown larvae showing color differences; *f*, pupa in soil; *g*, adult. (*a*, *c*, *d*, *e*, *f*, and *g*, about natural size.)

COTTON

APHID

The cotton aphid, also known as the cotton louse and the melon aphid, is found all over the United States. It is a general feeder on cotton, okra, melons, squash, cucumbers, and other cucurbits. It is a small, soft-bodied, sucking insect. Its color is light yellow to dark green or almost black. In Northern States, both sexes occur and eggs are laid; in the South only females that give birth to living young are known. Some adults are winged; others are wingless. The aphids spend the winter on various weeds, from which they spread to cotton in early spring. Reproduction is continuous in the South and becomes rapid during warm weather. There are no distinct broods; aphids of all sizes are present on the under side of the leaves and on the stems of plants. Lady beetles and other predators, parasites, diseases, and unfavorable weather are natural factors that help control aphids.

Aphids are present in almost every field of growing cotton. During cool, wet springs they often cause curling of the leaves, stunting of growth, or death of cotton seedlings. They do more damage later in the season by causing the leaves to curl and fall from the plants before the bolls are mature, thereby reducing the yield and grade of cotton. Aphids secrete a sticky substance known as honeydew, which drops on the leaves and bolls and gives the plants a glossy appearance. Honeydew falling on the open bolls makes the lint gummy and difficult to gin. A fungus often develops in the honeydew, which causes the plants to appear black or sooty.

Control: Heavy infestations of the cotton aphid often occur on cotton after the use of certain insecticides. Infestations may also be severe on seedling cotton where no insecticides have been applied.

The following dust treatments, which are recommended for general use against cotton insects, will usually prevent a build-up of aphids:

1. A mixture containing 3 percent of the gamma isomer of benzene hexachloride and 5 percent of DDT in every application at the rate of 10 to 12 pounds per acre.
2. A mixture containing 3 percent of the gamma isomer of benzene hexachloride and 5 percent of DDT at the rate of 10 to 12 pounds per acre in alternate applications with calcium arsenate.
3. Nicotine 2 percent in regular calcium arsenate at the rate of 10 to 12 pounds per acre alternated with calcium arsenate alone.
4. Parathion 1 percent in lime-free calcium arsenate at the rate of 10 pounds per acre.
5. Toxaphene at the rate of 2 to 3 pounds of the technical material per acre in every application (where toxaphene is not formulated with DDT).

When heavy infestations of the cotton aphid occur and if the need for rapid kill is indicated, the following treatments are effective:

1. Benzene hexachloride, applied as either a dust or spray, to give 0.5 pound of the gamma isomer or an equivalent amount of lindane per acre.
2. A 1 percent parathion dust applied at the rate of 12 to 15 pounds per acre.
3. Nicotine 3 percent in hydrated lime applied as a dust at the rate of 10 to 15 pounds per acre.

Another insecticide which will give quick control of heavy infestations of the cotton aphid, but which is not generally recommended because of its toxicity and low residual action, is 0.5 pint per acre of 40 percent tetraethyl pyrophosphate, or its equivalent, applied as a spray.

{PLATE III

a, Curled infested leaves; *b*, aphids on under side of leaf; *c*, aphids on stem; *d*, honeydew on leaf; *e*, winged female; *f*, wingless female; *g*, young. (*a*, *b*, *c*, and *d*, natural size; females and young, about 14 times natural size.)

COTTON FLEAHOPPER

The cotton fleahopper infests cotton throughout the Cotton Belt. It causes the greatest damage in Texas, Oklahoma, and Louisiana, but in some years losses are also serious in other States. This pest often becomes sufficiently numerous on cotton to cause almost complete loss of the crop.

The cotton fleahopper lays eggs in the fall in the stems of croton (goatweed), other weeds, and to some extent in cotton. The eggs hatch early in the spring, and the population builds up rapidly on certain tender weeds, such as horsemint, croton, and evening primrose. The movement to cotton increases as the weed hosts become tough. Rainfall is favorable to the breeding on cotton, which continues as long as the plants are succulent. When the squaring season is over, the leafhoppers return to weeds to feed and to lay their eggs. A generation of fleahoppers spans 2 to 3 weeks.

The winged adults and the wingless young fleahoppers alike are very active and are hard to see. Both stages feed on the juices of the tender parts of the cotton plants, especially the terminal buds and small squares. The leaves become deformed and somewhat ragged in appearance, but the greatest damage is caused to the small squares. Many of the squares are killed when they are no larger than a pinhead; they turn brown or black and fall from the plants. Because they are so small they are frequently overlooked; the failure of the plants to bloom is sometimes attributed to weather or other unfavorable conditions. The infested plants grow taller and more whiplike; they have fewer large branches than normal plants and usually produce only a few bolls near the tops.

Control: If cotton is not squaring properly, or if young cotton fails to set small squares, the terminal buds should be examined for fleahoppers. Dusting should be started when 15 to 25 fleahoppers are found per 100 terminal buds.

The cotton fleahopper can be controlled by any one of the following dusts: DDT 5 percent; toxaphene 10 percent; dieldrin 1.5 percent; aldrin 2.5 percent; benzene hexachloride (gamma isomer 1 percent); chlordane 2 percent. When spider mites are likely to be a problem, 40 percent or more of sulfur or a suitable miticide should be added to organic insecticide formulations. Less effective control of the cotton fleahopper may be obtained with sulfur alone or with a 1 : 1 or 2 : 1 mixture of calcium arsenate and sulfur.

Any of the following materials applied as low-gallonage sprays at the rates indicated per acre will give good control of the cotton fleahopper: 0.5 pound of DDT; 1 pound of toxaphene; 0.5 pound of toxaphene plus 0.25 pound of DDT; 0.1 pound of dieldrin; 0.2 pound of aldrin; 0.5 pint of 40 percent tetraethyl pyrophosphate.

Sometimes cotton aphids develop after the use of DDT dust or spray.

{PLATE IV

COTTON FLEAHOPPER

b

a

b

c

Cotton Fleahoppers

Adult

Nymph

Cotton fleahopper damage: *a*, blasted square; *b*, whiplike plant and lack of fruit resulting from blasted squares; *c*, injured leaf. (*a* and *c*, natural size; *b*, about one-fourth natural size; adult and nymph, 15 times natural size.)

COTTON LEAFWORM

The cotton leafworm is a tropical insect not known to survive the winters in the United States. New infestations are started each spring by moths that fly in from the south and lay their eggs on cotton. The first leafworms generally appear in April, May, or June, usually in southern Texas but sometimes in Florida. As the leafworms increase in numbers, the moths fly to other areas, and in some years invade all the cotton States except California. The moths often reach the Northern States and Canada and feed on ripe fruit, such as peaches or grapes. The larvae, or "worms," feed only on cotton. The small leafworms feed on the under side of the leaves and do not cut through the upper surface. The larger worms eat the entire leaves. When abundant they completely strip, or "rag," the leaves and then gnaw on the squares, bolls, and bark until the field looks as if it had been swept by fire. The brown pupae are found within folded leaves or are attached by silken cords to the stems and ribs of the leaves.

The spread of the leafworm varies greatly from year to year. Damage usually is greater west of the Mississippi River, but control often is needed in the Eastern States. Early ragging of the plants prevents bolls from maturing and reduces the yield and quality of the cotton. The stripping of the leaves by leafworms after most of the bolls are mature may be beneficial; by admitting more sunlight to the plants and permitting better circulation of air, the stripping may prevent boll weevils from increasing and keep the bolls from rotting on rank cotton.

Control: Small cotton leafworms can be controlled easily by dusting or spraying with any of the arsenical insecticides. Large worms are harder to control and may cause considerable stripping before they are killed. Dusting with calcium arsenate or lead arsenate at the rate of 5 to 7 pounds per acre will control leafworms. Other effective formulations are a 20 percent toxaphene dust; a mixture of 20 percent toxaphene dust and 5 percent DDT; a benzene hexachloride dust containing 3 percent of the gamma isomer; and a mixture containing 5 percent of DDT plus sufficient benzene hexachloride so that the dust contains 3 percent of the gamma isomer. These formulations are equally effective in spray form. If a quick kill of large worms is needed to prevent stripping, add 7 or 8 pounds of paris green to each 100 pounds of calcium arsenate, or use 8 to 10 pounds of paris green plus 100 pounds of lime.

{PLATE V

COTTON LEAFWORM

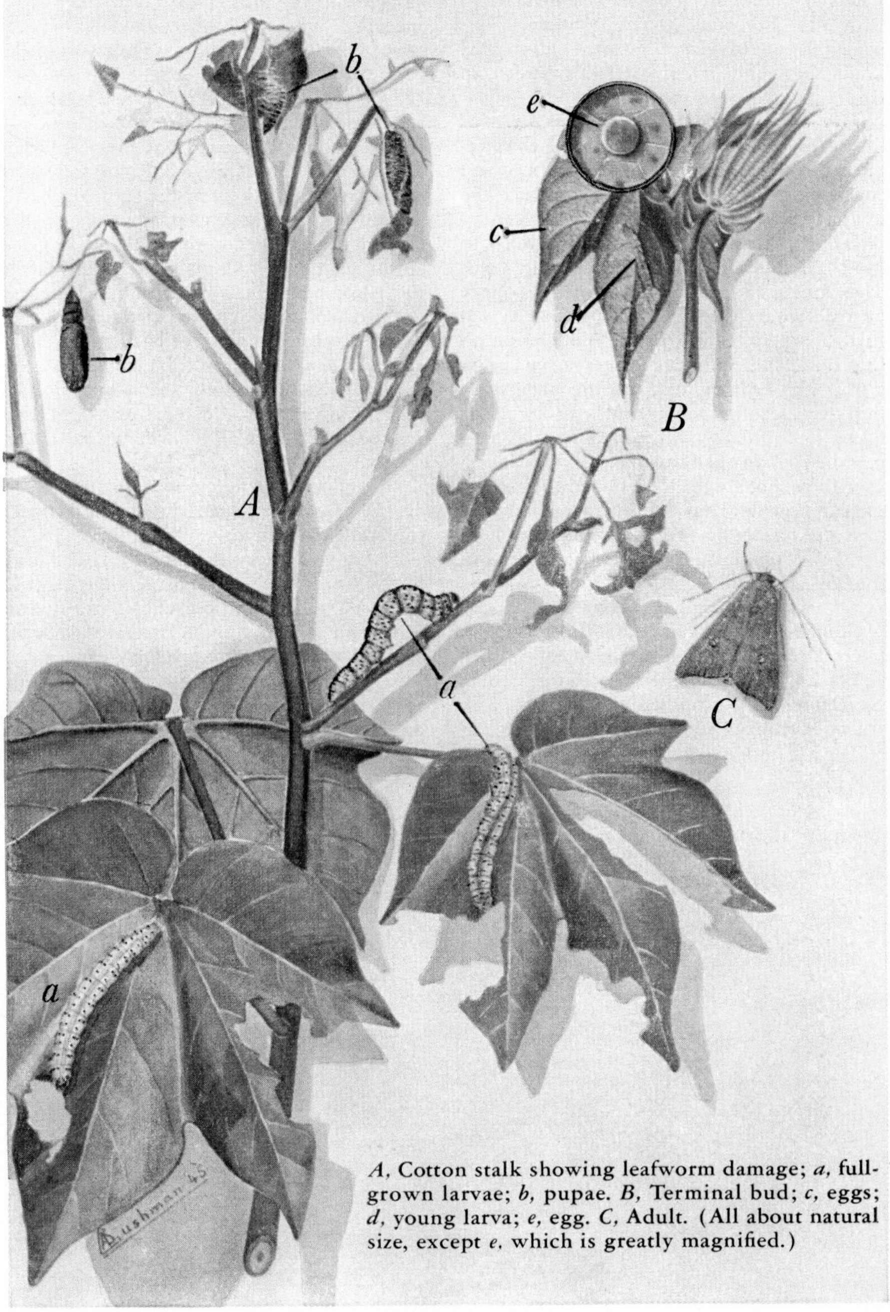

A, Cotton stalk showing leafworm damage; *a,* full-grown larvae; *b,* pupae. *B,* Terminal bud; *c,* eggs; *d,* young larva; *e,* egg. *C,* Adult. (All about natural size, except *e,* which is greatly magnified.)

PINK BOLLWORM

The pink bollworm is a serious pest of cotton in many parts of the world. It was first discovered in the United States in Texas in 1917. In 1951 it was present in 6 of the 20 cotton-growing States—Arizona, New Mexico, Texas, Oklahoma, Louisiana, and Florida. Infestations in Georgia have been eradicated.

The small pinkish caterpillars eat out the seeds of the cotton plant and thus reduce the yield, weight, vitality, and oil content of the seeds. They also reduce the quantity and quality of the lint. Severe infestations cause squares and small bolls to shed. The female lays 100 to 200 tiny eggs. The young caterpillar bores into a square or boll, where it feeds 10 to 14 days. When full-grown, it cuts a round hole through the boll and either changes to a pupa within the boll or drops to the ground to pupate. Development from egg to adult takes 25 to 30 days in midsummer. There may be as many as four to six generations a year in sections with long growing seasons. Larvae that develop late in the season may pass the winter in seed, old bolls, trash in the fields or at the gins, and in cracks in the soil.

Control: Methods of controlling the pink bollworm include destruction of cotton stalks immediately after the harvest; heat treatment of cottonseed; burning of gin waste; compression of lint; and the application as a dust or spray of 1.5 to 2 pounds of technical DDT per acre. In southern Texas, pink bollworm infestations early in any season are in proportion to the number of insects that survive the period between crops. The longer this period the fewer insects will survive. Therefore the number of overwintering insects may be reduced by destroying cotton stalks at the earliest possible date. The best procedure is to cut the stalks with a stalk cutter, which crushes them to the ground. If this operation is carried out early enough, a high mortality of pink bollworms results from exposure to heat of the sun. The roots should be plowed out promptly and the crop debris plowed under. All seedlings or sprouted cotton plants developing after the plowing should be eliminated before fruiting so as to create a long host-free period between crops. For best results these cultural practices should be carried out on an area-wide basis with the cooperation of all cotton growers. Cultural practices used to control the pink bollworm will also control the boll weevil.

In regions where temperatures of 10° F. or lower are expected during the winter the stalks should be left standing.

If you find an insect resembling the pink bollworm in areas thought to be free of it, you will help in the ceaseless fight against it if you place it in a bottle of diluted alcohol and send it to the Bureau of Entomology and Plant Quarantine, Washington 25, D. C., with full information as to date and place of collection and your name.

{PLATE VI

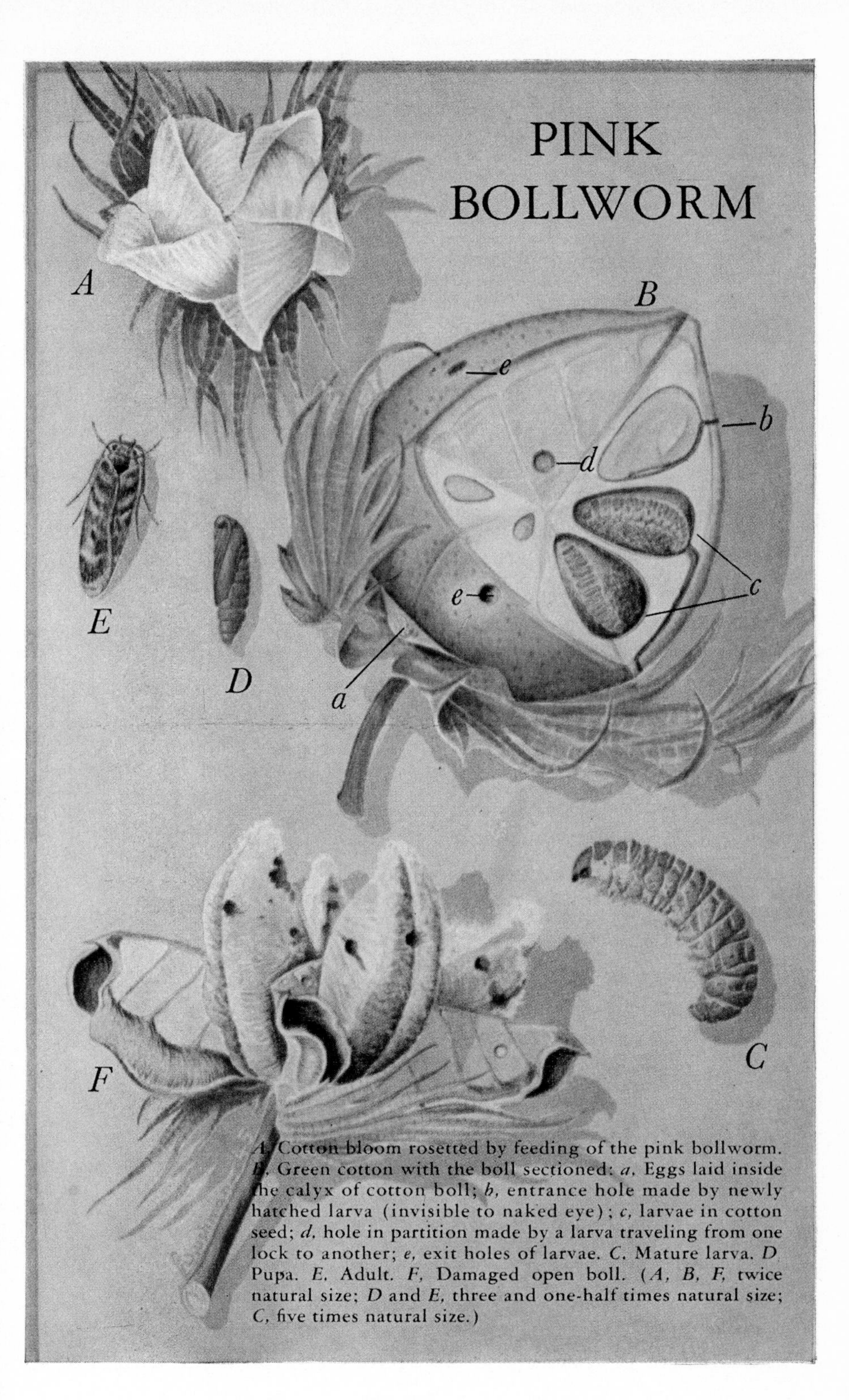

A. Cotton bloom rosetted by feeding of the pink bollworm. B. Green cotton with the boll sectioned: *a*, Eggs laid inside the calyx of cotton boll; *b*, entrance hole made by newly hatched larva (invisible to naked eye); *c*, larvae in cotton seed; *d*, hole in partition made by a larva traveling from one lock to another; *e*, exit holes of larvae. *C*. Mature larva. *D*. Pupa. *E*. Adult. *F*, Damaged open boll. (*A*, *B*, *F*, twice natural size; *D* and *E*, three and one-half times natural size; *C*, five times natural size.)

SPIDER MITES

Spider mites are so small that they can hardly be seen without a magnifying glass. At least seven species are known to attack cotton. They may be greenish or yellowish in color, but the females are usually reddish to carmine and the smaller males reddish yellow. Spider mites multiply rapidly. There may be as many as 17 generations a year. Hot, dry weather is most favorable for rapid multiplication. A heavy rain often checks an outbreak. They are found throughout the Cotton Belt. They feed on almost 200 kinds of plants, including many garden and field crops, ornamentals and weeds. In the South they pass the winter on leaves that remain green, such as wild blackberry, Jerusalem-oak, wild vetch, and violet. They move to cotton early in the summer. When cotton is no longer suitable for food they return to weeds or other plants. They crawl on the ground and are carried by wind or rainwater.

Spider mites live on the under side of the leaves, where they lay their eggs and spin delicate webs. They suck the sap from the leaves causing the under surfaces to become thickly dotted with whitish feeding punctures. Spider mite injury, often called rust, is first indicated when blood-red spots appear on the upper surface of the leaves. The entire leaf then reddens or turns rusty brown (as in the case of potash deficiency), curls, and drops from the plant. The loss of leaves causes shedding of small bolls and may prevent the lint from developing properly in large bolls.

Control: The spread of spider mites to cotton may be prevented by destroying weeds around the fields and by controlling the pest on dooryard plants. An infestation can often be stamped out by pulling out and destroying the first few cotton plants that become infested. Dusting cotton with finely ground sulfur at the rate of 10 to 25 pounds per acre is the most practical direct-control measure. A second application a week later is necessary to kill the spider mites that hatch after the first application. The under side of the leaves should be covered thoroughly with the dust.

In areas where spider mites are a pest, dust mixtures of organic insecticides used against cotton insects should contain at least 40 percent of sulfur, or 1 percent parathion, or some other organic phosphorus compound, to prevent spider mite increase.

TEPP at the rate per acre of 0.5 pint of 40 percent concentrate in a spray, or its equivalent, effectively controls heavy populations of spider mites.

{PLATE VII

a, Spider mites (natural size) on under side of leaf showing typical type of injury; *b,* adult and young (40 times natural size); *c,* leaf showing both spider mite injury and potash deficiency.

JAPANESE BEETLE

Japanese beetles are destructive to the leaves, blossoms, and fruits of more than 275 plants, shrubs, and trees. In 1952 they were widely distributed in States along the Atlantic seaboard from Massachusetts to South Carolina. They occurred also at scattered points in adjoining States and through much of the Midwest east of the Mississippi. The grubs feed in the ground on the roots of various plants and often cause serious damage to turf in lawns, parks, golf courses, pastures, and other turf areas.

Japanese beetles spend about 10 months as grubs in the soil. In late May or early June the grubs stop feeding and go through a short resting, or pupal, stage, after which they become beetles. The adults dig their way out of the soil. By early July they are flying about in numbers and feeding on trees and plants. During July and August the females periodically go into the ground and lay eggs.

Control: The foliage of trees, shrubs, and flowering plants can be protected from beetle attack with the following sprays:

1. DDT (50 percent wettable powder), 3 ounces (16 tablespoonfuls); water, 10 gallons (for fruit and shade trees, shrubs, and flowering plants).
2. Lead arsenate, 10 ounces (30 tablespoonfuls); wheat flour, 6 ounces (24 tablespoonfuls), or light-pressed fish oil, 2½ fluid ounces (5 tablespoonfuls); water, 10 gallons (for shade trees and shrubs).
3. Powdered derris (4 percent rotenone), 5 ounces (30 tablespoonfuls); water, 10 gallons (for apple, plum, cherry, and peach trees, grapes, and small fruits when fruit is about to ripen, and flowering plants).

If spray equipment is not available, apply a 5 percent DDT dust or hydrated dusting lime. Apply the spray or dust when the beetles first appear. Repeat as needed to maintain a protective coating on all parts of the plant subject to attack, until the beetles disappear. Dusts must be applied more often than sprays.

Lawns can be protected from injury by the grubs for at least 6 years with one application of DDT, for at least 3 years with one application of chlordane, and indefinitely with one application of milky disease spore dust. If enough grubs are present to cause noticeable turf injury, use one of the insecticides. They are faster in action than milky disease, which usually takes two or more years to become fully effective. Use 6 pounds of a 10 percent DDT powder or 2¼ pounds of a 10 percent chlordane powder to each 1,000 square feet of lawn. Mix the material with several times its volume of slightly moist sand, soil, or other inert material, and apply evenly to the lawn with a garden-type fertilizer distributor or by hand. Wash the material in with a hose.

Do not spray fruits with DDT or lead arsenate later than 4 weeks before picking. Scrub or peel sprayed or dusted fruits or vegetables before eating them.

{PLATE VIII

A, Mature grub in spring feeding on roots in underground burrow. *B,* Pupa in underground cell. *C,* Adult beetle emerged from earth. *D,* Beetles feeding on smartweed. *E,* Beetles feeding on grape leaves. *F,* Beetles feeding on apple leaves. *G,* Female beetle depositing eggs in soil at bottom of shallow burrow. *H,* Egg. *I,* Egg hatching and young grubs. *J,* Partly grown grub in fall.

MILKY DISEASE

The milky disease of grubs of the Japanese beetle has caused marked reductions in the abundance of the pest in the older infested areas. The disease is caused by germs, which the grubs take in as they work their way through the soil and feed on plant roots. The germs multiply rapidly within the grubs and form tiny bodies known as spores. The spores are long-lived and can stand dryness, heat, cold, and other unfavorable conditions. Billions of spores are produced in the blood of the grubs, which is normally clear but then becomes milky in appearance—hence the name "milky disease." Under favorable conditions the disease kills a high percentage of the grubs of the Japanese beetle and some of the grubs of closely related insects. It has no effect on other insects, warm-blooded animals, earthworms, plants, or human beings. Once established it protects treated areas indefinitely and spreads to new areas. Milky disease spores are processed with talc to make a spore-dust powder that is available commercially.

Milky disease usually works slowly, and its full effect may not be evident for several years. The first noticeable effect will be a reduction in the grub population in the treated area; adult beetles will not be affected by it nor prevented from flying in from an untreated area.

Application: The spore dust may be applied to lawns or other grass areas (comparatively small numbers of grubs are found in cultivated soil, unless sod or turf has recently been turned under for garden purposes) in spots spaced at regular intervals or broadcast. In the spot-treatment method, apply 1 level teaspoonful (about 2 grams) at intervals of 3 feet (at 3-foot intervals in rows 3 feet apart), 5 feet, or 10 feet, depending on the degree of infestation. A teaspoon or an ordinary hand corn planter with a rotary disk seeder, adjusted to deposit the desired amount of material each time it is tripped, may be used to apply the spore dust. The 3-foot intervals will require about 20 pounds of material to treat 1 acre; the 5-foot intervals about 7½ pounds, and the 10-foot intervals about 1¾ pounds. The broadcast method of treatment is less effective. If it is used, apply at least 10 pounds of spore-dust material to treat 1 acre and spread it by hand or with a fertilizer distributor. In either case mix the spore dust with several times its volume of topsoil, fairly coarse sand, or commercial fertilizer before spreading the dust.

{PLATE IX

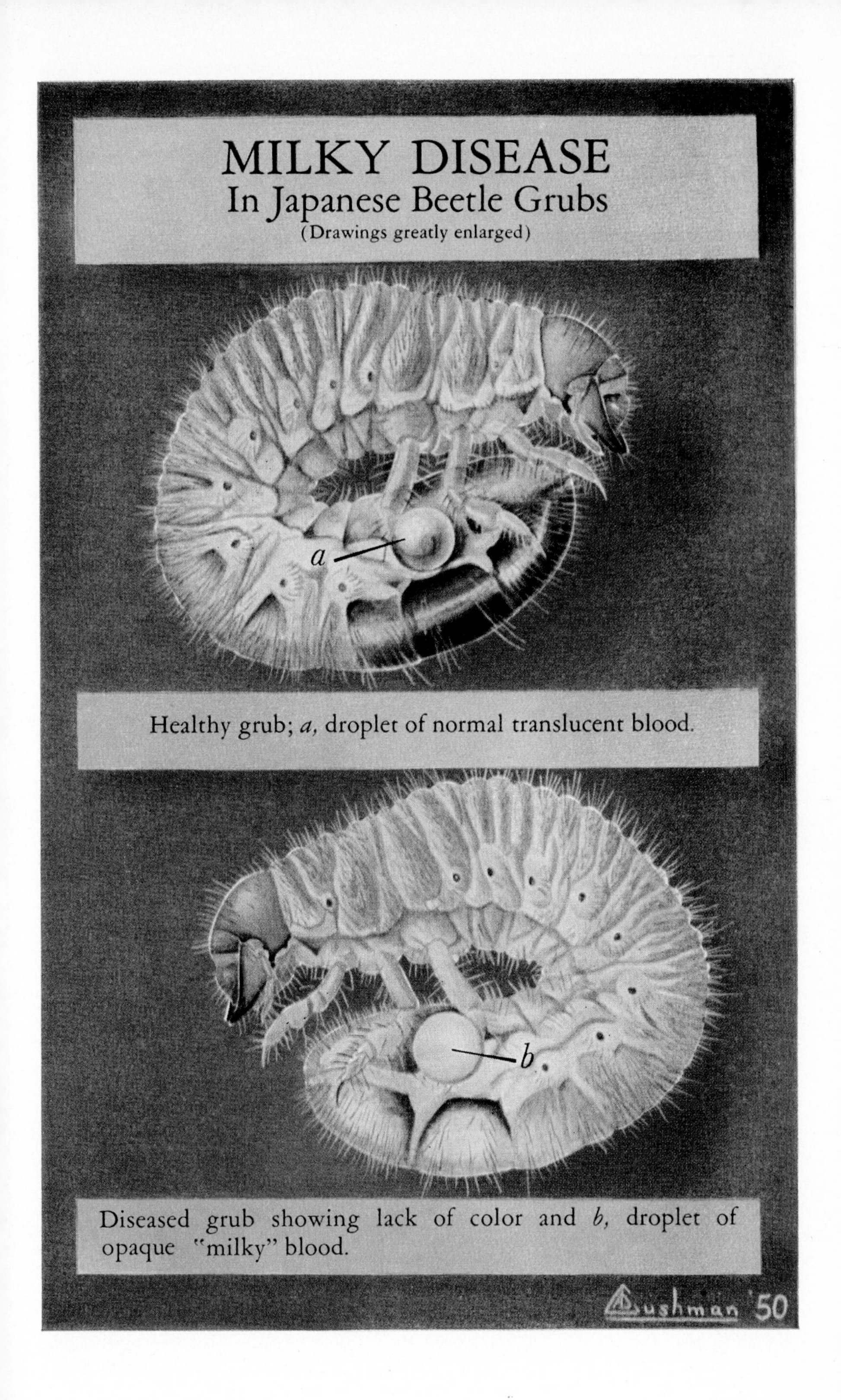
MILKY DISEASE
In Japanese Beetle Grubs
(Drawings greatly enlarged)
a
Healthy grub; a, droplet of normal translucent blood.
b
Diseased grub showing lack of color and b, droplet of opaque "milky" blood.
Cushman '50

ORIENTAL FRUIT MOTH

The oriental fruit moth occurs generally throughout the United States. But it is most destructive in the East and Midwest. It favors peaches and quinces but may attack other deciduous fruits. In the larval stage the insect injures both twigs and fruit. Early in the season the larvae, or worms, bore into the tips of tender twigs and cause them to wilt and dry up. Later, as the twigs harden and the fruit nears maturity, most of the worms bore into and injure the fruit. Moths first appear about the time peach trees are in bloom. The females usually lay their eggs on the leaves.

The newly hatched worms feed in twigs or fruit until mature and then spin cocoons in a protected place on the tree or ground. Usually there are four or five generations each year. The insect passes the winter as a full-grown worm in a cocoon in a protected place on the tree or ground.

Control: Sprays containing 2 pounds of 50 percent DDT or 1½ to 2 pounds of 15 percent parathion wettable powder per 100 gallons of water are effective in protecting twigs and fruit. Apply three applications at 10- to 12-day intervals beginning at the petal-fall or shuck-split stage of fruit development to prevent injury from first-brood larvae. To control injury from second- and third-brood worms, apply one spray 7 to 8 weeks and another 3 to 4 weeks before harvest. Control of the first brood may give control for the entire season in orchards not subject to reinfestation from nearby untreated orchards. Many growers have protected their fruit from injury by making only the applications suggested for controlling the second and third broods.

Do not spray fruits later than 3 weeks before picking. Scrub or peel sprayed or dusted fruits before eating them. Parathion is especially dangerous to handle; when you use it, follow all safety precautions printed on the package.

{*PLATE X*

ORIENTAL FRUIT MOTH

B

d

A

c

a

b

C

e

D

A, Life stages: *a*, young larva; *b*, mature larva; *c*, pupa; *d*, adult. *B*, Damage to tender new tips. *C*, External evidence of fruit moth damage to ripe peach. *D*, Internal damage with *e*, larva and frass next to the stone. (*A*, six times natural size; *B*, *C*, and *D*, natural size.)

A. Cushman '49

APPLE MAGGOT

The apple maggot, or railroad worm, causes brown tunnels or burrows inside the apple. After an infested apple has fallen or is picked from the tree, the flesh usually breaks down and becomes a brownish, pulpy mass. The adult apple maggot is a fly, about the size of a house fly. It appears in the largest numbers in July in orchards throughout the Northeastern States and northern part of the Midwest. The flies lay their eggs in the flesh of apples, preferably sweet and subacid varieties that ripen during the summer or fall. The legless white maggots, or worms, develop in the flesh of the fruit. The insect passes the winter in the resting, or pupal, stage in the soil.

Control: Keep the foliage and fruit covered with lead arsenate or DDT during July to destroy the flies before they lay their eggs. Make two applications of 3 pounds of lead arsenate alone or with an equal amount of hydrated lime, or three applications of 2 pounds of a 50 percent DDT wettable powder per 100 gallons of water (for small quantities of either material this strength equals 8 tablespoonfuls per 5 gallons) 10 to 14 days apart. Spray thoroughly all trees, including any that may not have a crop. In a season when the flies appear late, an additional application is sometimes required. The timing of the sprays is important. In the small home orchard, gather and promptly destroy wormy, fallen fruit; pick up fruit of early-maturing varieties every 3 or 4 days, and later-maturing ones every 7 to 10 days. Ask your State experiment station, Extension entomologist or county agricultural agent for information on when the apple maggot flies are expected to appear in your locality and the best time to apply the first spray.

Do not spray fruits later than 4 weeks before picking. Scrub or peel sprayed or dusted fruits before eating them.

A, Life stages: *a,* adult; *b,* pupa; *c,* larva, or maggot. (All about three times natural size.) *B,* Adult female making egg puncture in an apple. *C,* Exterior evidence of maggot damage. *D,* Halved apple showing damage to flesh and *d,* maggots feeding inside. (*B, C,* and *D,* about natural size.)

CODLING MOTH

The codling moth, or appleworm, is the dirty-white or pinkish caterpillar or worm that is so often found in apples in all sections of the United States. It causes the worm holes on the sides and blossom ends of apples that lead to the core. The holes are often filled with dark-colored masses, coarse brown or black pellets, which sometimes project out of the hole. The codling moth is also a pest of pears, quinces, English walnuts, and occasionally other fruits. The worms pass the winter in cocoons in crevices under the bark and in other protected places, usually on or beneath the tree. The moths begin to appear about the time apple trees bloom and some moths are present most of the rest of the growing season. The tiny white eggs are usually laid on leaves near fruit or on the fruit. The first worms normally begin to enter the small apples 3 to 4 weeks after the blossom petals have fallen. The number of generations in a season ranges from one (with a small part of a second) in the northern apple-growing areas to three nearly complete generations (and a part of a fourth) in the southernmost producing areas.

Control: Spray the trees thoroughly with 50 percent DDT wettable powder, 2 pounds per 100 gallons of water or 8 level tablespoonfuls per 5 gallons, (a) just after the blossom petals have fallen, (b) 3 weeks later, (c) 3 weeks later, and (d) 5 weeks later. Lead arsenate, 3 pounds per 100 gallons of water or 8 level tablespoonfuls per 5 gallons, plus an equal amount of hydrated lime, may be substituted for DDT but will be less effective. DDT and lead arsenate can be used in combination with most other insecticides and fungicides needed to control other insects and diseases of apples. Spray schedules vary widely according to local conditions; therefore, consult your State experiment station or Extension entomologist for such a schedule for your own locality.

Do not spray fruits with DDT or lead arsenate later than 4 weeks before picking. Scrub or peel sprayed or dusted fruits before eating them.

{PLATE XII

CODLING MOTH

A

a

d

c

b

B

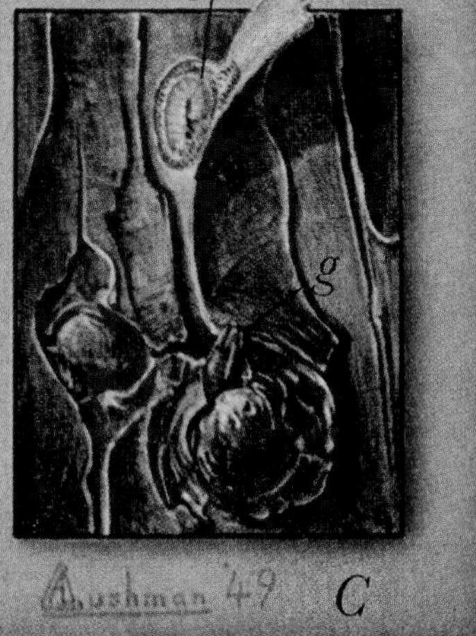

A, Adult moth (about three and one-half times natural size). *B*, Twig and fruits showing *a*, eggs on under side of leaves; *b*, larva and internal damage; *c*, "sting"; *d*, surface breakdown and frass from internal feeding; *e*, frass-plugged emergence hole. *C*, Section of bark from trunk or large branch showing *f*, hibernating larva and *g*, pupal skin from which adult has emerged. (*B* and *C*, about natural size.)

PLUM CURCULIO

The plum curculio is a common and serious pest of peaches, plums, cherries, and apples in the States east of the Rocky Mountains. The surface of the fruit is scarred or distorted by the feeding and egg-laying punctures of the adult curculios. The inside is injured by the burrowing of the larvae or grubs. The adults are small, hump-backed, and brownish snout beetles about one-fourth inch long that spend the winter in protected places on the ground in and near orchards. They move to the trees about the time peaches bloom or a little later and feed on the leaves and blooms. They attack the fruit soon after it sets and attack it intensively for about 3 weeks. The feeding punctures are small circular holes. The eggs are laid in crescent-shaped cuts, which the females make in the fruit. Eggs hatch in about a week. The yellowish-white grubs become full-grown in 2 weeks or more. The mature grubs leave the fruit and go into the ground, where they complete their development into adult beetles. Two generations are often completed in the southern range of the insect, but there is only one in the northern range. In an intermediate zone (latitude of Delaware to Virginia) there may be a partial second generation. The second generation develops in maturing fruit. Most of the fruit injured early in the season falls to the ground or is scarred, dwarfed, and deformed. Fruit injured later remains on the tree, but is scarred and wormy.

Control: On apples, spray the trees with lead arsenate, 3 pounds, or with a combination of lead arsenate, 2 pounds, and 50 percent DDT wettable powder, 2 pounds, per 100 gallons of water, (a) at petal fall, (b) 7 to 10 days later, and (c) about 2 weeks later.

On peaches and other stone fruits, spray the trees with lead arsenate, 2 pounds, plus hydrated lime, 8 pounds, or with 15 percent parathion wettable powder, 2 pounds per 100 gallons of water, (a) at shuck split, (b) 7 to 10 days later, (c) 7 to 10 days after (b), and (d) if parathion is used, 12 to 14 days later. In areas where a second brood occurs, spray (a) just after the petals have fallen, (b) when the shucks are shedding, (c) 7 to 10 days after (b), and (d) about 1 month prior to harvest. If parathion is used, put on application (d) 5 weeks before harvest and (e) 3 weeks before harvest.

Do not spray fruits with lead arsenate or DDT later than 4 weeks before picking. Do not spray them with parathion later than 3 weeks before harvest. Scrub or peel sprayed or dusted fruits before eating them. Parathion is especially dangerous to handle; follow all the safety precautions printed on the package.

{PLATE XIII

A, Life stages (greatly enlarged): *a,* larva; *b,* pupa; and *c,* adult. *B,* Peach "mummy" with larva inside. *C,* Small apple showing curculio scar. *D,* Small peach with gum oozing from curculio puncture. *E* and *F,* Mature apple and plum showing appearance of curculio scars at time of harvest. (*B, C, D, E,* and *F,* natural size.)

ORCHARD MITES

Tiny, eight-legged sucking pests, closely related to insects, known as mites and often called spider mites because of their resemblance and relationship to spiders, cause major damage to orchard trees throughout the United States. Many kinds of mites suck the sap from the leaves of deciduous fruit trees (apples, pears, peaches, plums, and cherries), causing them to become bronzed or brown and dry. When injury is extensive, many of the leaves drop off and the fruit is small and poorly colored.

The habits and life history of most such mites are much the same. The most important differences are that some spin webs on the leaves and about the twigs and some do not. Some (like the clover mite, which attacks many kinds of plants as well as fruit trees) and the European red mite overwinter in the egg stage on the trees. Others (like the two-spotted spider mite and the Pacific mite) overwinter as adult females in protected places, mostly on the ground. Mites may develop from egg to adult in a week or 10 days. There are several generations a year. Hot, dry weather speeds up development and favors a rapid increase to outbreak numbers. Mites are usually most numerous in July and August.

Control: Application of a 3 percent lubricating oil emulsion late in the dormant season will destroy the overwintering eggs of the European red mite and of the clover mite. Mites may be controlled during the summer with the following insecticides (per 100 gallons of spray): 1 pound of 15 percent parathion wettable powder; ½ pint of 40 percent tetraethyl pyrophosphate (TEPP) liquid; 1½ to 2 pounds of 15 percent 2-(*p*-*tert*-butylphenoxy)-1-methylethyl 2-chloroethyl sulfite (Aramite) wettable powder; ½ pound of 27 percent O-ethyl O-*p*-nitrophenyl benzene-thiophosphonate (EPN) wettable powder; or 1 pint of 25 percent 1,1-bis(*p*-chlorophenyl)ethanol (DMC) liquid. The summer mite-control program may be preventive (if you include a recommended material in two or three early-season sprays applied for other pests) or it may be corrective—if you delay until mites begin to increase noticeably, usually the last of June or later but before injury reaches the bronzing stage. In a corrective program at least two applications, 7 to 10 days apart, are usually necessary. Occasionally, if infestation persists, a third application may be needed. The spraying must be thorough.

Parathion and TEPP are especially dangerous to handle; the safety precautions on the package must be followed. EPN is also dangerous to handle. Be careful with it. Do not spray fruits later than 3 weeks before picking. Scrub or peel sprayed or dusted fruits or vegetables before eating them.

[PLATE XIV

TWO-SPOTTED SPIDER MITE
EUROPEAN RED MITE

A, Peach twig showing typical "russeting" of foliage by mites. *B*, Life stages of two-spotted spider mite: *a*, egg; *b*, young (note 6-legged at this stage); *c*, half grown; *d*, adult male; *e*, adult female; and *f*, overwintering female. *C*, "Russeting" of apple foliage. *D*, Stages of European red mite: *g*, egg; *h* and *i*, nymphs; and *k*, adult female. (*B* and *D*, very greatly magnified.)

SAN JOSE SCALE

The San Jose scale is a tiny insect that sucks the sap from the wood, leaves, and fruit of apple, pear, peach, and other fruit trees. It occurs throughout the United States. Large numbers of scales lower the vitality of the tree and may gradually kill individual branches or even the tree itself. The mature female insect is yellow and about the size of a pinhead. It lives under a protective covering that is formed over it as it grows. Small reddish discolorations often are found at the point of feeding, particularly on new, tender wood and fruit. Heavily infested trees have a roughened appearance. The insect remains in one place except during the first few hours of its life and the short time adult males are active. The tiny, newly emerged young, called crawlers, move around on the tree and are sometimes blown or carried to trees some distance away. Partly grown scales survive the winter better than very young or mature ones. The generations, which overlap greatly, number one or two in northern fruit areas and three or four or more farther south.

In some areas, particularly the Midwest, another insect—the Forbes scale—may be confused with San Jose scale. The general appearance, seasonal history, and habits of the two scales are similar.

Control: Spray the trees early in the spring, before the buds open, with a petroleum oil emulsion. Dilute it to provide 4 percent oil in a spray for use in the Pacific Northwest and 3 percent oil in other areas. Parathion, one-half pound of 15 percent wettable powder per 100 gallons, in two or three or more summer spray applications will also control San Jose scale effectively and do away with need for the early spring application of oil.

Forbes scale, if present, can be held in check by the treatments used for San Jose scale.

Parathion is a dangerous poison; all safety precautions noted on the label should be observed in using it.

{PLATE XV

A and *B*, Infestation on fruit; *C*, typical damage to new growth; *D*, a small cluster of scales (greatly magnified).

GYPSY MOTH

The gypsy moth is a serious foe of forest and shade trees in New England and eastern New York State. The caterpillars, or larvae, of these moths eat the leaves. The defoliation retards the growth and otherwise weakens the trees. Repeated complete defoliation may kill the trees.

This moth was accidentally introduced into this country in 1869. It spread rapidly through several Northeastern States. For many years the infested area has been under Federal quarantine. In part of the area suppressive measures have been carried out by State, local, and Federal agencies.

The gypsy moth larvae usually appear about the first of May. By the middle of June they are about 2 inches long. They have several pairs of red and blue dots on their backs. Late in June or early in July they become mature and seek shady places, such as on trees or rocks, in which to pupate and transform into moths. The moths emerge about a month later. The males are strong daytime fliers, but the females cannot fly and so lay their eggs close to the place where they issued as moths. The eggs are laid in clusters of 400 or more, which are covered with brownish hairs. The winter is passed in the egg stage.

Control: The gypsy moth can be controlled most effectively with DDT. An oil solution or an emulsion containing this insecticide is applied as a spray while the insect is in the caterpillar stage.

Large forested areas usually are sprayed from aircraft. For use along highways and residential areas, mist blowers or hydraulic sprayers are suitable. For treating low growth along stone walls and fences, sprayers of the knapsack type can be employed. Early in the season the spray should be applied at the rate of 1 pound of actual DDT per acre; after the foliage has developed, three-fourths pound per acre is sufficient.

Because of the many difficulties involved in formulation, it is best to obtain proprietary DDT insecticides and prepare them according to the manufacturers' instructions. Concentrated DDT solutions for use in blowers or aircraft are available on the market in 9- and 12-percent solutions. Apply at the rate of 1 gallon per acre to give, respectively, either the three-fourths or 1 pound dosage of actual DDT. If emulsion concentrates are used they should be diluted with water in the amounts suggested on the package to produce the desired three-fourths or 1 pound per acre coverage.

{PLATE XVI

GYPSY MOTH

Close-up of *a,* ovipositing female; *b,* male; *c,* female pupa; *d,* male pupa; *e,* old egg mass. Larvae on oak leaf: *f,* First instar; *g,* second instar; *h,* fourth instar; *i,* sixth instar, or mature larva. Egg masses, *k,* under branches and on rock; *l,* young larvae spinning down. (*a* to *i,* about natural size; *k* and *l,* reduced.)

ELM LEAF BEETLE

The elm leaf beetle feeds on all species of elms. Repeated defoliations cause a weakening or death of the trees. The beetle lives over winter as an adult. In the spring it eats holes in the young leaves and lays its eggs on the under sides of them. The eggs hatch in about a week, and the young larvae skeletonize the foliage, causing it to dry, turn brown, and fall to the ground. Full-grown larvae pupate in the ground or in crevices in the bark of the lower trunk. In about a week they become adults and emerge. Around Washington, D. C., there are two generations a year; in Oregon there may be three.

The beetle occurs in the United States from Maine to North Carolina and westward to Arkansas and Michigan. It occurs also in Idaho and along the Pacific coast from Washington to California.

Control: Pupae and young beetles can be killed by soaking the ground and the trunk of the tree with a spray containing nicotine sulfate. For small amounts, mix 1 pint of summer oil and 4 tablespoonfuls of nicotine sulfate (40 percent) in 6¼ gallons of water. For larger amounts, mix 2 gallons of the oil and 1 quart of nicotine sulfate in 100 gallons of water.

The foliage of elms can be protected by spraying the under side of the leaves, when they are about two-thirds grown, with either lead arsenate or DDT. Lead arsenate spray is prepared by mixing 1½ level tablespoonfuls of the powder in 1 gallon of water (or 3 pounds in 100 gallons) and adding three-fourths teaspoonful of linseed oil per gallon, or three-fourths pint (12 ounces) per 100 gallons of the spray mixture. DDT spray is prepared by mixing 2 teaspoonfuls of a 25 percent DDT emulsion concentrate, or three-fourths teaspoonful of a 50 percent DDT wettable powder per gallon of water. To make 100 gallons, use 1 quart or 1 pound, respectively. These sprays are applied with hydraulic equipment.

For mist-blower applications, a concentrated lead arsenate spray is made up of the following materials: Lead arsenate, 1½ pounds; cottonseed oil or fish oil, 4½ ounces; and enough water to make 1 gallon. A DDT spray is prepared for application by mist blowers by formulating the following: DDT 1 pound, xylene 2½ pints, Triton X–100, 1½ ounces (3 tablespoonfuls), and water to make 1 gallon; or DDT 50 pounds, xylene 15⅔ gallons, Triton X–100 ⅝ gallon, and water to make 100 gallons. The Triton X–100 acts as a spreader. Only 2 quarts of a 6-percent emulsion of DDT are needed to treat a 50-foot elm tree with a mist blower.

{*PLATE XVII*

ELM LEAF BEETLE

A, Undamaged elm leaf. *B*, Elm leaf showing typical feeding damage, skeletonization, and perforation; *a*, egg mass; *b*, larvae; *c*, pupa; and *d*, adult elm leaf beetle. (All about two and one-half times natural size.)

BARK BEETLES

Ips engraver and turpentine beetles are occasional pests of pines and other coniferous trees grown in the vicinity of dwellings, summer-home sites, and in recreational areas in various parts of the country. These bark beetles are usually found only in trees weakened by drought, mechanical injury, severed roots, sunscald, or like condition. Sunscald is caused by excessive exposure to the sun following sudden removal of many of the surrounding trees. The beetles seldom attack and kill healthy trees, but may do so when they are present in large numbers. If only a few turpentine beetles are present in a tree, it may survive through its ability to secrete sufficient resin to drown the adult beetles or their young in their tunnels. Such wounds heal over later. If engraver or turpentine beetles attack and make holes in the bark entirely around the trunk of a tree, the tree is killed.

Turpentine beetles emerge from infested trees in the spring, fly to green, uninfested ones and bore holes in the bark on the lower part of the trunk. The female beetles deposit their eggs in groups in the inner bark. The eggs hatch in a few days and the larvae feed side by side on the soft inner bark, leaving a cavity behind them. In about 8 weeks the larvae are full-grown, and a month later the adult beetles emerge. Soon after the beetles bore into the bark, large globules of resin flow from the holes and harden on the bark surface.

In the Bay region of California, Monterey pines are frequently infested by the red turpentine beetle. It also occurs over much of the rest of the country. The most prevalent species in the South is known as the black turpentine beetle. The number of generations varies from two or more a year, to one every 2 years, depending upon the locality and climate.

The adult *Ips* engraver beetles are smaller than turpentine beetles and attack the entire trunks of trees. Sometimes they attack the upper parts of trees that are infested lower down with turpentine beetles. Tunnels made for egg-laying by *Ips* are elongate and generally in the direction of the grain of the wood. When the eggs hatch, the larvae make galleries at right angles to the tunnels. The tunnels and galleries give the inner bark and outer surface of the wood an engraved appearance.

Control: Small infestations of turpentine beetles—only three or four attacks in a large-size tree—can be disregarded. But if five or more attacks occur per square foot of bark, the tree may be killed. To save it, remove the resinous masses and flood each tunnel with a 2 percent chlordane emulsion or with ethylene dichloride. Or one can inject into each tunnel about a teaspoonful of carbon disulfide, which is highly inflammable and dangerous to inhale. Household insect sprays in which 2 tablespoonfuls of naphthalene flakes per half pint of spray are dissolved are also effective.

Danger from bark beetles is great in droughty periods. Weakened trees should be watched closely for signs of beetle activity. A spray containing 0.5 percent of the gamma isomer of benzene hexachloride prepared from either lindane or benzene hexachloride emulsion or wettable powder, applied to the trunk, may help to prevent further attack for 2 to 3 months. The bark should be sprayed until it begins to drip.

Trees which are heavily attacked by engraver beetles and from which comes brownish boring dust should be felled and the bark removed to destroy the brood before it emerges as adult beetles. This should be done while the foliage is green or pale yellow. Usually the beetles have already left trees whose foliage is brown or red.

[PLATE XVIII

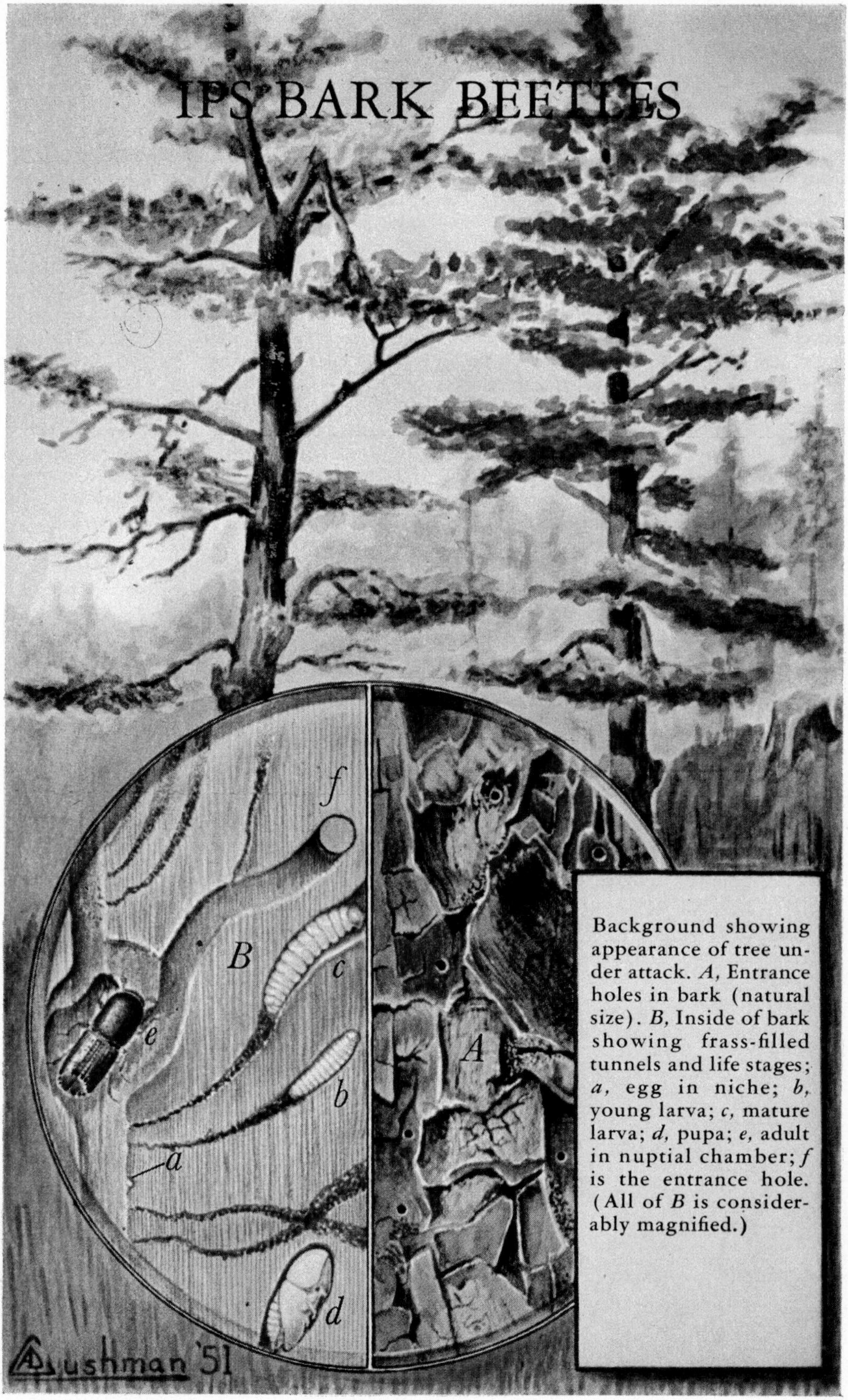
IPS BARK BEETLES
A
B
a
b
c
d
e
f
Cushman '51

Background showing appearance of tree under attack. *A*, Entrance holes in bark (natural size). *B*, Inside of bark showing frass-filled tunnels and life stages; *a*, egg in niche; *b*, young larva; *c*, mature larva; *d*, pupa; *e*, adult in nuptial chamber; *f* is the entrance hole. (All of *B* is considerably magnified.)

POWDER-POST BEETLES

Powder-post beetles attack the woodwork of buildings and reduce the wood to a powderlike condition. One of them is the old house borer. Powder-post beetles cause extensive damage in this country in sills, floor joists, studs, doorjambs, flooring, siding, and rafters of buildings.

Some powder-post beetles infest only the sapwood portion of flooring made of seasoned hardwoods, such as oak or maple. Others attack the sapwood of such soft woods as pine, fir, and hemlock used for the under structure and roofs of buildings. Some infest only wood with the bark still intact—the females lay their eggs in crevices on the surface of the bark or deposit them in the inner bark through slits they make. Some deposit their eggs in pores or crevices in wood devoid of bark. Others bore holes directly into the wood and place their eggs in tunnels.

Wood infested by powder-post beetles can be detected readily by the presence of powder or pellets coming from holes leading to the surface. Sometimes also one can hear rasping or scratching sounds made by grubs of the beetles as they cut channels through the wood. Little or no powder may be observed then on the surface of the infested wood. By probing with a sharp-pointed instrument, however, one can detect the powder at once. Such activity is characteristic of the old house borer, an introduced pest that is becoming well established in many buildings in this country. Frequently lumber is infested by this insect before it is used in construction. Such attacks are difficult to locate at the time the house is built.

Most powder-post beetles mature in a year's time. The old house borer takes 3 to 7 years. It is confined largely to the eastern half of the United States, but most of the others are generally distributed over the country.

Control: Replace with sound material all wood so badly damaged as to impair its structural strength. Wood lightly infested may be sprayed heavily or brush-coated with a penetrating insecticide, such as a 5 percent solution of pentachlorophenol. For best results make two or three applications in order to permit the chemical to be carried into the wood. Also effective for short periods are straight kerosene and a mixture of 9 parts of turpentine to 1 part of kerosene.

The best way to control severe infestations, especially in wood behind plaster-covered walls or in detached houses, is by fumigation with lethal gases. A good fumigant is hydrocyanic acid, but because of the great danger involved in its use only licensed fumigators should apply it.

Pentachlorophenol is irritating to some persons and it should be handled carefully. If it comes in contact with the body, wash it off shortly afterward with warm, soapy water. It should not be used near an open flame.

[PLATE XIX

OLD HOUSE BORER

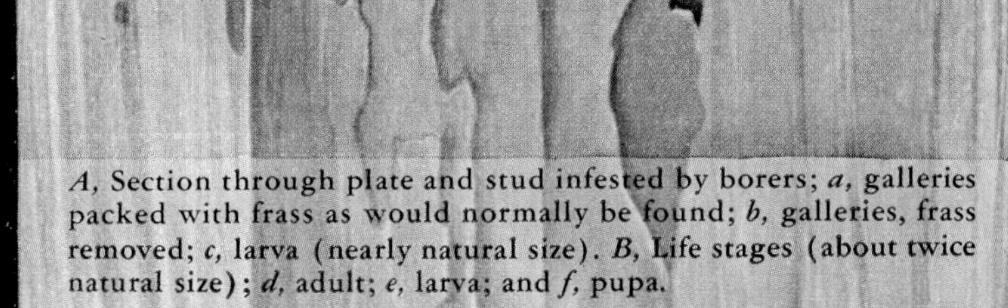

A, Section through plate and stud infested by borers; *a,* galleries packed with frass as would normally be found; *b,* galleries, frass removed; *c,* larva (nearly natural size). *B,* Life stages (about twice natural size); *d,* adult; *e,* larva; and *f,* pupa.

SUBTERRANEAN TERMITES

Subterranean termites can cause extensive damage to the woodwork and other cellulose-containing products stored in buildings or used in the construction of buildings.

Usually they get the water they need to live from the soil where their colony is established. Their food they get from wood. A termite colony comprises winged reproductive adults, mature workers, soldiers, and young nymphs. Each has specific duties to perform.

Winged adults often emerge in the early spring. They fly away to establish new colonies or else shed their wings and die if they cannot find their way back to the ground. This kind of termite cannot become established in the seasoned woodwork or furniture in a building. It dies if it cannot get to moisture. There is only one flight each year from a particular colony.

The workers do the damage to wood. They excavate it, making channels that run parallel with the grain. The sides of the galleries are stained with grayish excrement, which is characteristic only of termites. Their galleries are free of powdered wood dust. This distinguishes their work from that of powder-post beetles, whose feeding tunnels are filled with it. Termites occur in every State but are more prevalent in the southern half of the country.

Control: One can control subterranean termites by blocking them off from soil. To do that, foundations must be made impervious to their attack; masonry walls must be free of voids; and expansion joints must be filled with coal-tar pitch. The subfloor space of unexcavated buildings must have proper clearance (18 inches from soil to wood), adequate ventilation, and drainage. If wood supports are necessary, they must rest on poured concrete bases at least 6 inches above the ground level. Enclosed porches should have access panels to permit periodic inspections and chemical treatments if necessary. After such structural modifications are made as are necessary to block the entry of termites, the soil next to foundation walls and piers must be poisoned to kill termites already present in it and to set up a toxic barrier to prevent others from entering.

Trenches for holding soil poisons must be dug 1 foot wide and 15 inches deep along the foundations of buildings having shallow footings and no basements. The trenches should be dug twice as deep along foundation walls of buildings having full basements and deep footings. Soil poisons generally are applied at the rate of one-half gallon per lineal foot in the shallow trench and at twice that rate in the deeper one. They are applied by mixing them with the soil as it is replaced in the trench.

These chemical mixtures are effective: 10-percent solution of sodium arsenite; 5-percent solution of DDT in No. 2 fuel oil; 5-percent solution of pentachlorophenol in fuel oil; one part orthodichlorobenzene diluted with 3 parts of fuel oil; one part trichlorobenzene diluted with 3 parts of fuel oil; one part coal-tar creosote diluted with 2 parts of fuel oil. All those mixtures are poisonous.

{*PLATE XX*

SUBTERRANEAN TERMITES

A, Section through foundation, floor, and wall of house and *a,* concrete slab porch with no termite protection; *b,* shelter tubes on basement wall. The red lines indicate common sources and routes of infestation. (Note wood scraps in backfill.) *B,* Some castes of termites; *c,* soldier; *d,* winged reproductive form; and *e,* worker (all greatly enlarged).

CARPENTER ANTS

Carpenter ants nest in wood. They are a pest in dwellings, utility poles, posts, and tree cavities. In most sections their damage is restricted to minor parts of buildings; thus their injury is less important than that caused by termites.

Carpenter ants seek soft wood (particularly wood that has weathered and begun to decay) to make cavities in which to rear their young. They may be found in porch columns and roofs, window sills, foundation plates, and logs of cabins. The ants do not eat wood. They simply eject it in fibrous shreds as they remove it while constructing their chambers. They feed on honeydew obtained from aphids and scales and on animal remains and plant juices.

The chambers of carpenter ants are clean and are cut across the grain of the wood. Piles of shredded fibers also occur on the outside of infested wood. Wood damaged by termites is characterized by stained, grayish chambers running with the grain. Also, termites eat the wood as they remove it in extending their galleries.

A colony of carpenter ants consists of workers of various sizes, of reproductive forms, and immature individuals. It takes 9 weeks for them to develop from the egg to the adult stage and 3 to 6 years for them to produce a well-developed colony.

Carpenter ants are distributed over most of the country.

Control: Carpenter ants are controlled by applying poisonous dusts, sprays, or fumigants to their nests or the places they frequent.

Sanitation measures: Remove and destroy logs and stumps that harbor colonies. Seal crevices present in foundation walls to prevent their entry. Repair leaks in porch roofs.

Chemical applications: (1) *For buildings,* dust with 5 percent chlordane; 4 percent rotenone (derris powder); 10 percent DDT; or with sodium fluoride. Use about a tablespoonful per crevice. These are most effective if applied in warm, dry weather. If colonies occur in decaying wood in porches and columns, soak the wood with a 5-percent solution of pentachlorophenol (a wood preservative as well as an insecticide). (2) *For tree cavities or stumps near shrubbery,* stir 8 teaspoonfuls of 50 percent chlordane wettable powder into 1 gallon of water and soak the infested wood with it. Do the same with the 48-percent emulsion made from this chemical. The dusts mentioned for use in buildings can also be employed. (3) *For poles and posts,* introduce any one of the following materials into the cavities: A mixture composed of equal parts coal-tar creosote and gasoline; a 5-percent solution of pentachlorophenol; a mixture of either orthodichlorobenzene or trichlorobenzene and kerosene (1 to 4 parts by volume); one of the sprays made from chlordane; or fumigate with carbon tetrachloride after sealing all openings except the one being used. The latter also should be sealed as soon as the chemical is applied.

{PLATE XXI

CARPENTER ANTS

Background shows a common site for damage by this pest. Insert depicts the insects and their damage (natural size); *a*, larvae; *b*, pupa, cocoon removed; *c*, worker; *d*, winged female; *e*, shredded frass which is pushed from the galleries.

RED-HEADED PINE SAWFLY

The red-headed pine sawfly attacks young pine trees in nurseries, plantations, areas of natural reproduction, parks, and ornamental plantings. It occurs throughout the eastern half of the United States, in eastern Canada, and perhaps in Missouri and Arkansas.

The adults are robust and four-winged. Their name comes from the sawlike egg-laying apparatus that the female uses to make slits in the needles in which to deposit her eggs. The larvae mature in 25 to 31 days. The winter is passed in the prepupal stage in capsule-shaped cocoons in the duff or topsoil under infested trees.

This sawfly feeds on many kinds of pines and some other conifers. It prefers the hard pines. The young larvae prefer the old needles as food, but the maturing larvae will eat the new foliage and the tender bark of young twigs.

Its life history is rather complicated. There may be one, one and one-half, or two generations a year. Some adults of each generation emerge the year the eggs are laid, but the rest go over until the following year. As a result, broods of larvae may be found feeding nearly the entire season; the length of the period depends somewhat on the climate.

Control: Lead arsenate or DDT applied to the foliage will kill any larvae present. Small infestations on a few trees around residences can be destroyed by hand-picking the larvae or by dislodging them with a stream of water from a hose. They can then be crushed or otherwise destroyed.

In nurseries, plantations, or areas of natural reproduction, sprays can be applied with hydraulic equipment or mist blowers. (1) For hydraulic sprays use either 1½ tablespoonfuls of the 50 percent wettable DDT powder or 3 level tablespoonfuls of arsenate of lead in a gallon of water, or 2 and 4 pounds respectively in 100 gallons. To increase the stickiness of this spray add three-fourths teaspoonful of linseed oil per gallon, or three-fourths pint (12 ounces) per 100 gallons of the spray mixture. (2) For mist blowers use a 6-percent concentrated emulsion or suspension at 2 gallons per acre. Quantities to make up 1 gallon of DDT concentrate emulsion consist of: DDT, one-half pound; xylene, 1¼ pint; Triton X–100, three-fourths ounce (1½ tablespoonfuls); and water to make 1 gallon. Materials needed for 1 gallon of the suspension are: Arsenate of lead, three-fourths pound; cottonseed or fish oil, 4½ ounces; white mineral oil, 1½ ounces (3 tablespoonfuls); and water to make 1 gallon.

A careful survey of sprayed areas should be made up to 14 months following treatment because some of the larvae may have formed cocoons and may have been protected at the time of application of the chemical. Another treatment therefore may be necessary.

[PLATE XXII

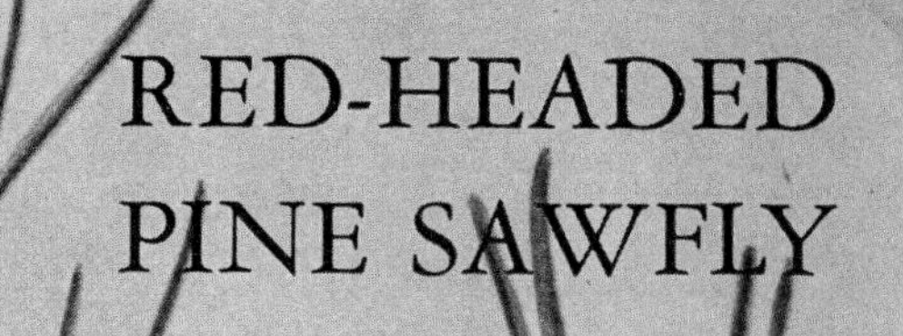

a shows a cluster of larvae feeding on a pine twig; *b*, adult male. (*a* and *b*, about natural size.) *c* and *d* are the female and egg niches in a needle, respectively. *e*, Mature larva. *f*, Cocoon. (*c*, *d*, *e*, and *f*, all greatly enlarged.)

THE ROACHES

Roaches sometimes become extremely abundant in houses, restaurants, and stores. They destroy or contaminate food. They may leave an offensive odor, excretions, and disease or food-poisoning organisms on dishes and cooking utensils. Several roach eggs are enclosed in each egg capsule from which the young roaches escape when the eggs hatch. The young are very small at first but otherwise look very much like the adults, except that they do not have wings.

Adults of the German cockroaches and brown-banded roaches are about one-half inch long. There are two or three generations a year in houses and other warm places. They live mostly inside buildings and are usually troublesome right in the area where they develop, as in the kitchen or bathroom. The brown-banded roach may also live all through the house. It will be found on the under side of tables, chairs, and upholstered furniture, behind pictures on the wall, or inside television and radio cabinets, bookcases, desks, dressers, and linen closets.

Adults of the American and oriental cockroaches are 1¼ to 2 inches long. They complete one generation in about a year. In warm climates they can live outdoors the year around, inhabiting barns, outbuildings, rubbish piles, and other places where they can hide. They constantly invade homes from these sources. In colder climates they cannot survive the winter outside, but continue to grow and be active during cold weather in heated buildings. These roaches usually do not develop in kitchens or the living portions of homes. They may wander there during the night when they are foraging, but they come from such places as basements, furnace rooms, storage areas, steam tunnels, sewers, alleys, yards, or around foundations and porches. During the day most of them go back to the place in which they developed.

Control: A 2 percent chlordane spray is effective and practical for use under ordinary conditions. It may be sprayed or applied with a small paint brush to the proper surfaces. It will remain effective for several weeks. Chlordane powder, DDT spray or powder, pyrethrum spray or powder, sodium fluoride powder, and phosphorus paste have varying degrees of effectiveness.

To control roaches satisfactorily, it is necessary to get the insecticide into the places where they hide or develop, as well as on surfaces where they will walk when they wander around at night. It is important therefore to know which kind of roach is involved, because of the different habits of the various species.

Good housekeeping and thorough sanitation are helpful in controlling roaches by reducing the available food supply, although an infestation may become established in the cleanest of houses.

{PLATE XXIII

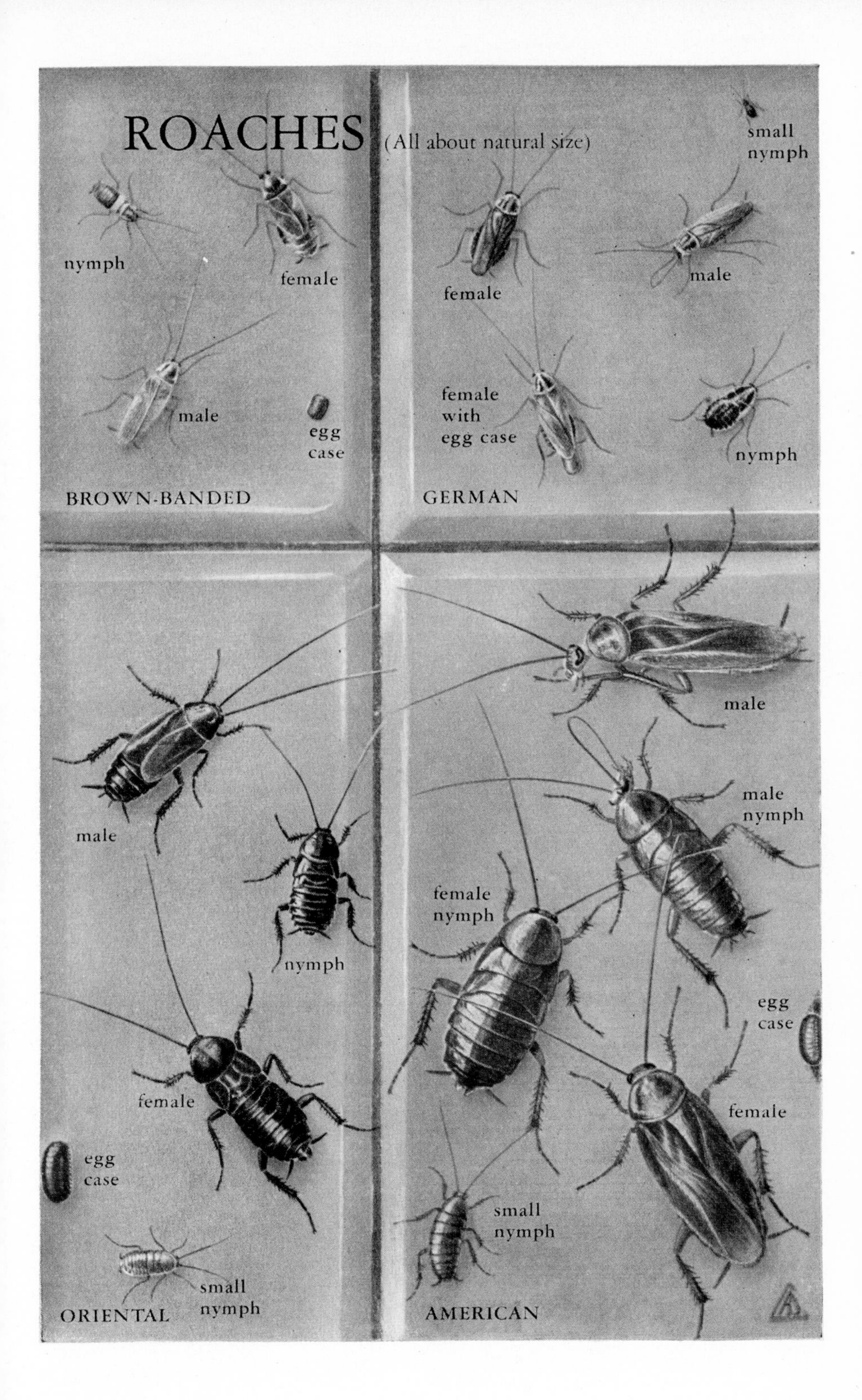
ROACHES (All about natural size)
nymph
female
male
egg case
BROWN-BANDED
small nymph
female
male
female with egg case
nymph
GERMAN
male
nymph
female
egg case
small nymph
ORIENTAL
male
male nymph
female nymph
egg case
female
small nymph
AMERICAN

CATTLE GRUB

The cattle grubs in the backs of cattle are the larvae of two species of heel flies. One, the common cattle grub, is found in most parts of the United States. The other, the northern cattle grub, occurs in the northern half of the country. It appears in the backs of cattle later than the common species. If both species are present the period from the first appearance of grubs in the backs of cattle until the last one has emerged from the tissues of the host may last about 5 months or longer. In some of the southern localities the grub season begins in late summer or early fall. In the northernmost States the season does not begin until in the winter or early spring.

The adults, or heel flies, lay their eggs on the animal during the spring and summer. The young grubs hatching from the eggs burrow through the body of the animal for about 9 months and finally become located under the skin of the back. They cut a hole through the skin, become encysted, and complete their development in the cyst in 5 to 7 weeks. The mature larvae drop to the ground and form a pupal case from which the heel flies later emerge. The cattle grubs have one generation a year.

The adults also injure cattle. The attacks of the heel flies frighten animals; often they cause stampedes that result in loss of flesh and milk and in mechanical injury. The grubs bore large holes in the choicest part of the hide and produce irritation, inflammation, subnormal development of young animals, and considerable loss of beef, milk, and leather.

Control: Rotenone is the only insecticide recommended for the control of cattle grubs. Finely ground cube or derris containing 5 percent of rotenone may be applied to the backs of cattle in the form of a spray, dust, or wash. Power spraying is the fastest way to treat cattle and is generally preferred for large range herds. The spray should contain 7½ pounds of the cube or derris powder per 100 gallons of water. It should be applied at the rate of 1 gallon per animal. One should use a driving nozzle and a pressure of 400 pounds per square inch. Dusts are preferred by owners of small herds of cattle and are desirable for use in cold weather. Three ounces of a dust containing 1 part of derris or cube and 2 parts by weight of a suitable diluent should be used per grown animal. The dust must be well rubbed into the grub cysts by hand. The use of derris or cube wash when thoroughly applied with a stiff fiber brush gives excellent control of grubs. The wash should contain 12 ounces of derris or cube powder and one-fourth ounce of a wetting agent per gallon of water. From 1 to 2 pints per animal is needed for each treatment.

The correct timing of treatment, whatever method of application is used, is essential for good cattle grub control. The precise time of treatment in any given locality can be determined by the county agent or other experienced advisers.

[PLATE XXIV

Background, section of tanned hide showing grub damage. *A,* Calf being chased by heel flies. *B,* Life cycle diagram showing *a,* eggs attached to hair (greatly enlarged); *b,* small larvae; *c,* encysted larva and the hole in the hide; *d,* puparium under litter, *e,* adult heel fly. (*b, c, d,* and *e,* all about natural size.)

HORN FLY

The horn fly is a small, bloodsucking fly about one-half as large as the house fly. It lives on cattle, usually resting and feeding on the back and shoulders. During hot, sunny days the flies may concentrate on the under parts to escape the heat. Despite their name, they are seldom seen on horns. Occasionally on cool days hundreds of the flies may concentrate near the base of the horns.

The horn fly breeds only in fresh cattle droppings. Flies will dart from the cattle and quickly deposit several reddish-brown eggs on fresh droppings and then fly back to rest on the animal. In summer the eggs hatch in about 16 hours. The small maggots, or larvae, feed on the manure for 5 days or so and then change to the resting, or pupal, stage. The pupae are usually found in the lower part of the droppings or on or in the soil beneath the droppings. After 4 to 5 days the flies emerge and seek cattle on which to feed. Within a few days they are ready to repeat the life cycle, which, from egg to egg, is completed in about 2 weeks in warm weather. The horn fly lives through the winter in the pupal stage.

The horn fly entered the United States about 1890 and quickly spread. It is found yearlong on cattle in southern Texas and Florida. Early in the spring in the more southern areas and in late spring in the central and northern parts of the country, the adults begin to appear. They quickly increase in numbers as the warm season advances.

If control measures are not taken, horn flies commonly become so abundant that each animal may be attacked by 3,000 to 4,000 flies. Such large numbers cause extreme annoyance and are a constant drain on the blood supply of the animals. Large numbers of the flies can reduce milk production of dairy cattle by 10 to 20 percent and prevent weight gains of beef cattle by as much as one-half pound a day.

Control: Sprays containing toxaphene or at least a 0.5 percent concentration of TDE, methoxychlor, or DDT are recommended for controlling the insect on beef cattle. Apply about 2 quarts of the spray per animal; if the concentration is increased up to 1.5 percent, one needs to apply correspondingly less spray. Spray the backs, sides, and bellies of the animals. When toxaphene is used, do not exceed a concentration of 0.5 percent so as to avoid possible harm to cattle, especially calves. One treatment with any of the insecticides will control the flies for 3 to 4 weeks.

Methoxychlor is recommended as most economical and effective on dairy cattle. Use as suggested for beef cattle. DDT, toxaphene, and TDE are not recommended for use on dairy cows because the chemicals may appear in milk. Pyrethrum sprays that have been fortified with piperonyl butoxide, *n*-propyl isome, or similar synergists are also recommended for horn flies on dairy cows. Oil-base pyrethrum sprays can be applied in small amounts (not exceeding 1 ounce) to dairy cows at each milking or pyrethrum water-base sprays may be applied at the rate of 1 or 2 quarts per animal for protection up to a week. Oil-base sprays containing lethane and thanite may also be used as a light mist spray at milking time for controlling flies on dairy cattle. Do not soak the animal with oil-base sprays, as the oil alone can be harmful.

{*PLATE XXV*

HORN FLY

A, Cow being attacked by horn flies showing almost solid patch of flies on shoulder. *B,* Life stages in cow dropping; *a,* adult; *b,* eggs; *c,* larvae; and *d,* pupa. (Life stages all about three times natural size.)

IRRIGATION-WATER MOSQUITOES

Several species of mosquitoes breed in irrigation ditches, rice fields, and pastures. On thousands of acres in the West that have become valuable because of irrigation, mosquitoes reproduce so abundantly as to be a menace to man and beast. Beef cattle held on summer pasture lose weight, milk flow drops, a serious labor turn-over occurs during haying and fruit harvesting operations, and frequently otherwise desirable property loses value.

The irrigation-water mosquitoes overwinter in the egg stage. Eggs are laid singly on the damp soil in late summer and hatch the following summer when covered with the irrigation water. The number of eggs per acre may be as high as 20 million. The larvae, or wrigglers, reach the pupal stage and emerge as adults in from 5 days to 2 weeks, according to species and weather. One to eight broods may occur during the season or after each flooding. Little is known about their flight habits, but they have been observed several miles from their breeding grounds.

Control of larvae: Because the wrigglers cannot live without water, the simplest way to keep them from developing into adults is to have the water soak into the fields or drain off before the wrigglers have had enough time to develop. The problem of furnishing an adequate supply of water to the fields and drying them up within a week's time is therefore the important consideration in the reduction of the pest about irrigated fields. The border method solves the problem and is economical of water.

If larvicides can be used, DDT formulations applied at the rate of 0.02 to 0.4 pound of DDT per acre and toxaphene or TDE applied at the same rate destroy wrigglers.

Control of adults: Adult mosquitoes that have migrated over large areas may be killed economically by spraying DDT from ground equipment or aircraft. A spray made of 1 pound of 50 percent DDT wettable powder in 2 gallons of water can be applied with hand-operated garden-type sprayers to shrubbery around homes. The use of a 5 percent DDT oil solution in a fine spray will give relief to fruit pickers and lumber crews and in recreational areas for several hours.

Repellents: The best materials for use on the skin and on clothing for repelling mosquitoes and other biting flies are dimethyl phthalate, dimethyl carbate, Indalone, and Rutgers 612. The materials may be used alone or in combination. They are safe to use and are effective for several hours.

Do not apply overdosages of DDT, TDE, or toxaphene in places where fish and animals are present. Do not pasture milk cows on treated fields for about a month after treatment. Use repellents with caution near synthetic cloth and plastic watch crystals, since they are solvents of plastics.

[PLATE XXVI

IRRIGATION-WATER MOSQUITOES

Background shows irrigated area in which low spots in fields and pastures and seepage from ditches combine to create a mosquito problem (x). *A*, Life stages of *Aedes dorsalis*, a typical mosquito that breeds in irrigation water; *a*, egg, which is laid on dry land in areas subject to periodic flooding; *b*, adult female; *c*, young larva; *d*, full-grown larva; *e*, pupa. (Life stages all about five times natural size.)

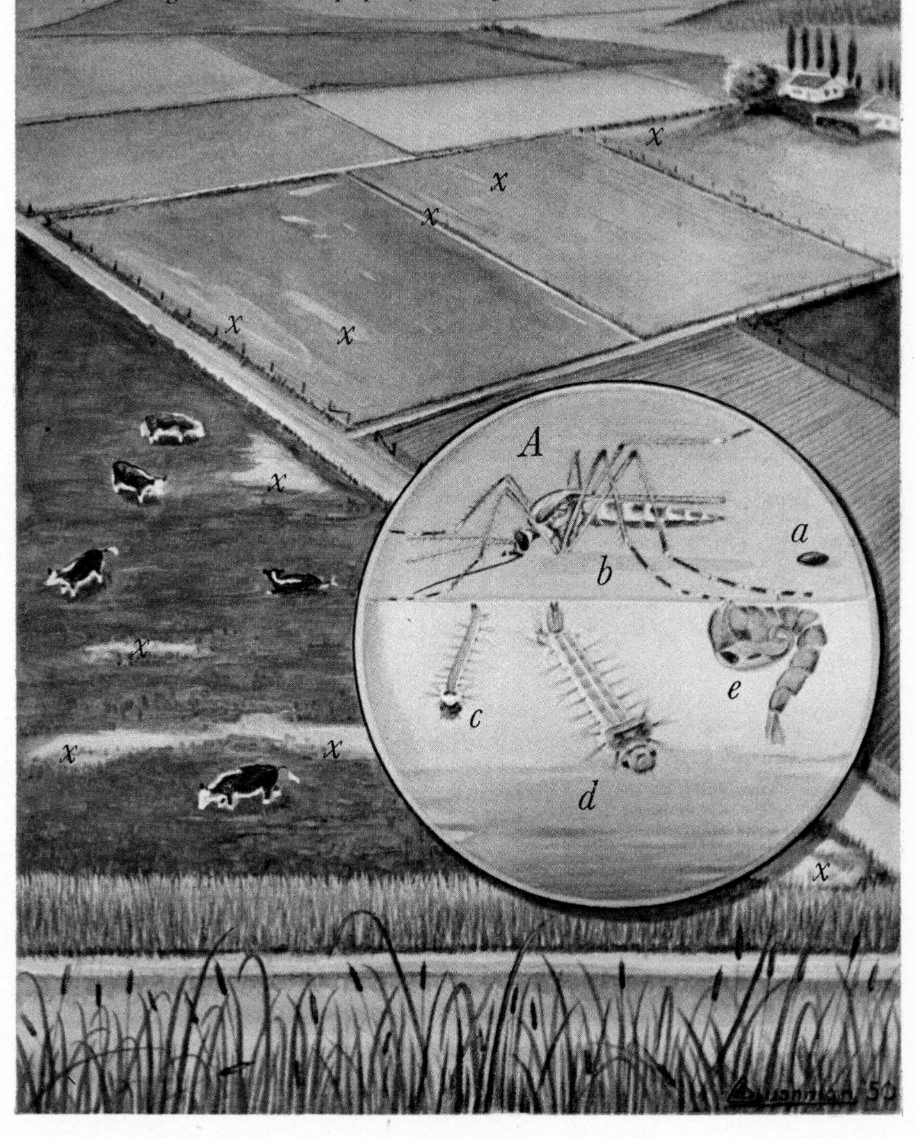

THE SCREW-WORM

The screw-worm, a very destructive livestock pest, is the larva of a fly that is about two or three times larger than the house fly. From eggs laid on wounds of livestock and other warm-blooded animals hatch maggots that feed on the flesh. Bites by ticks and flies also promote infestations. Newborn animals are susceptible to attack on the navel.

An adult fly deposits 200 to 300 eggs, which hatch in about 12 hours. The maggots reach maturity in about 5 days, when they are about one-half inch long. They crowd together in the wound with their heads (the small end) down. One hundred mature maggots will cause a wound about an inch in diameter and almost an inch deep. Infested wounds develop a straw-colored or bloody discharge, which smells bad. An infested wound is more attractive than a fresh wound. So in a few days several flies may have deposited eggs, which may have hatched; instead of the 200 or more maggots from the first fly, there then may be a thousand or more maggots of all sizes in the wound. Unchecked, the feeding by hundreds or thousands of maggots will soon kill the animal.

Mature maggots leave the wound, drop to the ground, enter the soil, and transform into the pupal or resting stage. The flies emerge from the pupae in 8 to 30 days, depending on the temperature. The adult flies mate a few days after they emerge, and the females seek an animal with a wound in which to repeat the life cycle.

The screw-worm can survive most winters only in the southern parts of Texas, Florida, or California. In spring it spreads northward. The adults are strong fliers and may spread as much as 25 to 35 miles per week. Thus before frost the pest usually spreads through parts of Texas, Oklahoma, Arizona, New Mexico, California, Florida, Georgia, and Alabama. The insect often is transported also into other parts of the country through shipments of infested livestock; if that happens in the spring, the insect may increase to outbreak proportions before fall.

Control: An animal must have a wound before it is susceptible to screw-worm attack. Any measures that will reduce the number of wounds in animals will therefore reduce the number of screw-worm cases. Handle animals carefully at all times. Take measures that will reduce chances for accidental wounds. Avoid surgical operations if possible during screw-worm seasons. Control ticks and flies.

Examine all livestock carefully twice each week. Treat any wound, whether infested or not, promptly with a good screw-worm remedy. EQ 335, which contains lindane and pine oil, is excellent. If wounds are infested, use EQ 335 to destroy the maggots; keep the animal available for re-treatment at least once each week until the wound is healed. Other screw-worm remedies such as Smear 62 and similar preparations containing diphenylamine and benzol have been used successfully for many years.

{*PLATE XXVII*

A, Life-history group showing *a*, egg mass; *b*, young larva; *c*, mature larva; *d*, pupa; *e*, adult female fly laying eggs. *B*, Part of an infested wound showing egg masses, very small larvae, and the posterior ends of mature larvae. (All about twice natural size.)

FABRIC PESTS

Several kinds of clothes moths and carpet beetles cause damage to clothing, blankets, rugs, and furniture. They feed on articles containing wool, mohair, feathers, down, hair, or fur. The black carpet beetle can also live on cereal products and other organic matter.

The carpet beetles, or buffalo moths, are more common than clothes moths in some localities. Much of the damage attributed to clothes moths is actually caused by carpet beetles.

Only the larvae, or immature stages, of fabric pests feed and cause damage. The adults can fly and go to new places to lay eggs and start infestations. In homes and heated buildings the insects continue to develop and feed the year around. The black carpet beetle goes through about one generation a year. The other carpet beetles may have two or three generations a year. In homes there are usually two to four generations of clothes moths a year.

Control: The control of fabric pests should be directed along three lines:

Thorough cleaning and good housekeeping; killing the insects in the home; protecting articles susceptible to damage.

Housekeeping. Fabric pests, especially the carpet beetles, can live on the lint and other material that collects in corners, in cracks in the flooring, behind baseboards, in attics, on closet shelves, in dresser drawers, or behind radiators. Thorough cleaning to remove as much as possible of this food supply helps to control the insects. It also disturbs or removes many of the insects.

Killing fabric pests. A spray containing 2 percent of chlordane or ½ percent of lindane should be applied in the places where fabric pests may live in the house. The sprays can be put on with an ordinary household sprayer, or with surface sprayers that operate on the same principle as aerosol dispensers. This spraying helps kill out any lingering infestation that might spread to clothing, rugs, furniture, or other susceptible articles. These sprays should not, however, be applied on such articles.

The true aerosol sprays, which are of no value for the kind of treatment just mentioned, are for releasing insecticides into the air and can be used to spray in closets at frequent intervals to kill any clothes moth adults that might be flying around. This treatment, however, has no lasting effect and should be supplemented by other methods of control or protection.

Carpet beetles are more difficult to control than clothes moths because they wander around more, tend to be more generally distributed all over the house, and are more resistant to most insecticides. Control measures will have to be carried out more thoroughly and more extensively, therefore, against carpet beetles.

Protection against damage. Wool clothing, blankets, rugs, draperies, and upholstery can be protected in several ways from fabric pests. Effective mothproofing products are 5-percent solutions of DDT or methoxychlor in a refined oil. Those insecticides are also available in pressure sprayers similar to aerosol containers. A number of commercial mothproofing solutions contain some of the silicofluorides.

Articles to be stored for a season or longer can be placed in a tight storage closet, garment bag, trunk, or box, with paradichlorobenzene crystals or naphthalene flakes. One pound of crystals or flakes is adequate for a trunk. Use 1 pound for each 100 cubic feet in a storage closet. The storage space must be tight enough to hold the gas formed by the slow evaporation of the crystals. The mere odor is not any protection. The gas must build up to a concentration high enough to kill the insects.

Articles may also be protected by placing them in cedar chests or in commercial storage, where fumigation, cold storage, or a combination of the two is used.

Dry cleaning kills all stages of fabric insects, but gives no protection against reinfestation. Mothproofing services, however, are offered by many cleaning establishments. Frequent sunning and thorough brushing are also an effective way to rid articles of an infestation. Frequent and thorough vacuum cleaning is helpful in preventing damage to rugs; it is well to apply a mothproofing solution to places that are hard to clean.

{PLATE XXVIII

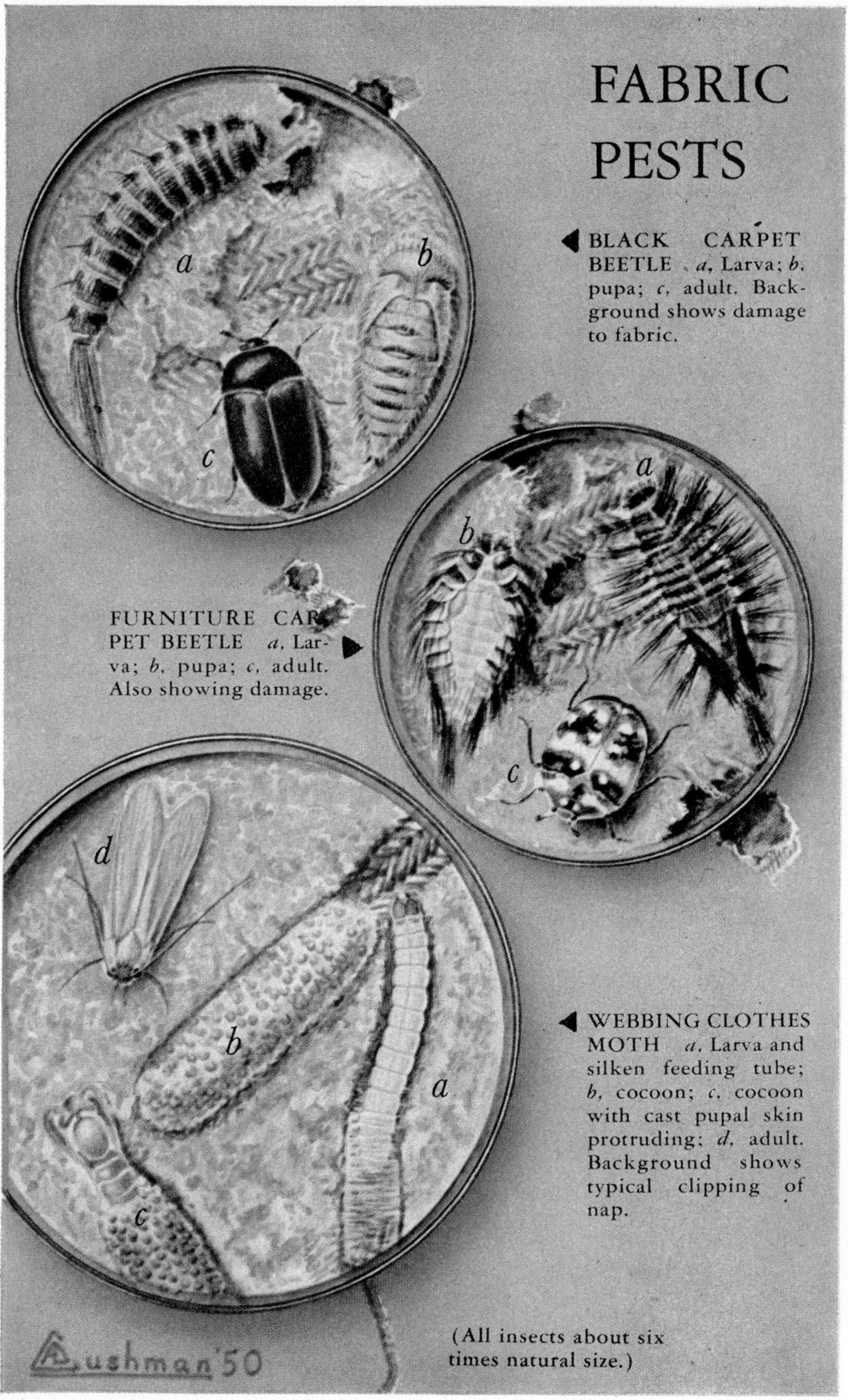

FABRIC PESTS

◀ BLACK CARPET BEETLE *a*, Larva; *b*, pupa; *c*, adult. Background shows damage to fabric.

FURNITURE CARPET BEETLE *a*, Larva; *b*, pupa; *c*, adult. Also showing damage. ▶

◀ WEBBING CLOTHES MOTH *a*, Larva and silken feeding tube; *b*, cocoon; *c*, cocoon with cast pupal skin protruding; *d*, adult. Background shows typical clipping of nap.

(All insects about six times natural size.)

Cushman '50

HOUSE ANTS

House ants are common pests in homes, restaurants, hotels, stores, bakeries, and many other places. They are not known to carry disease, but they are a nuisance and often get into food.

Colonies containing queens, young, and workers live within walls or partitions, behind baseboards, or beneath flooring. There may be several scattered colonies and they readily move from one place to another. A nest may suddenly turn up in a dresser drawer or on clean sheets in a linen closet.

Sometimes these ants are not attracted to food but seek sources of water in the kitchen or bathroom. They may wander around aimlessly and individually or in small numbers or there may be a solid stream of them from food or water to a place where they are coming out of the walls. This may be around a window or door frame, from behind the baseboard or a kitchen cabinet, or around pipes or electrical outlets.

Ants may also invade the house from outside. They will come in through cracks in foundations or basement and ground-level floors, around porches and chimneys, or through windows and doors.

At intervals ant colonies produce swarms of winged forms which leave to establish new colonies. Flying ants from colonies around the foundation may accidentally find their way inside the house. This flight may be over in a day or a few days at the most. The queens and wingless workers remain at the original site of the colony.

Control: A 2 percent chlordane spray is effective against house ants. It should be sprayed into cracks or openings from which ants enter the room. A small surrounding area may also be sprayed so the ants will have to crawl over the insecticide deposit when they come out. The deposit remains effective for several weeks.

House ants are not always easy to control, especially when they are numerous or several colonies are present. One or more small colonies may be killed and others may remain or move in. This often happens in apartments or row houses. In such instances better results will be obtained if several neighbors work together on the problem.

Do not apply the insecticide to tables, kitchen cabinets, or other places where it will contaminate food. If ants are troublesome in such places, apply the insecticide to openings in walls or floors of the room where they will come in contact with it.

Poison ant baits, either sirup or jelly, are available commercially and are sometimes effective. They should be kept where children or pets cannot reach them. Ants will sometimes go for long periods without paying any attention to a bait or they may not be attracted at all to the particular bait offered them.

{PLATE XXIX

A, Life stages (greatly enlarged): *a*, eggs; *b*, larva; *c*, pupa; *d*, adult worker; *e*, winged queen; *f*, queen after shedding wings. *B*, Section of wall cut away to show nest inside. *g*, Point where ants are entering the room through a crack in the plaster.

PANTRY PESTS

Several kinds of insects get into the dry food products that are kept in kitchens. Among them are weevils, grain and flour beetles, and larvae of the meal and flour moths. These pantry pests are the same kinds of insects, common throughout the country, that attack stored grains on farms and in elevators and food products in mills, food plants, warehouses, railway cars, and retail stores. They cause tremendous losses.

The adults of most of them can fly into houses and start infestations, or the insects or their eggs or larvae may be brought in with dry foods that are infested because a container is improperly sealed or broken. They spread from one container to another on pantry shelves.

Control: Infestations in houses usually can be controlled easily by following five steps.

Clean the shelves. Cereals and other dry foods get spilled, and particles sift out of packages. Pantry pests can live on the food that stays on shelves or lodges in corners or cracks. Brush the shelves and then scrub them with warm water and a cleanser.

Spray with DDT. After the shelves are dry and before the food is replaced, spray a 5 percent DDT solution on the inside surfaces of cupboards or cabinets. The tiny crystals of DDT left after the spray dries will remain effective for several months. Insects that crawl over the crystals will be killed before they have a chance to lay eggs and start new infestations. Wait until the spray dries before putting packages back on the shelves. The dry DDT deposit will not harm food inside packages.

Inspect food packages. While the spray is drying carefully examine all packages of food. You may find insects in flour, meal, cereals, crackers, breakfast foods, macaroni, spaghetti, and noodles. Some of the beetles develop in large numbers in chili powder, red pepper, paprika, and other spices. Do not overlook such things as nut meats, chocolate, cocoa, dehydrated foods, dried fruits, dry soup mixes, dog biscuit, and bird seed. The meal and flour moth larvae produce webbing in or on the product where they are feeding. Flour or meal sticks to the webbing and it is easy to detect an infestation by the stringy masses of material.

Destroy heavily infested products or feed them to birds, pets, chickens, or livestock. Food is not ruined just because one or two beetles may have crawled into it. A few beetles or larvae in flour, for instance, can be picked out or the flour sifted through a fine sieve. Sterilize food that will not be used right away and store it in tight containers.

Sterilize with heat. Most dry food products can be freed of insect life by heating them in the oven at 140° F. for about one-half hour. Small packages can be heated just as they are. The contents of larger packages should be spread on cake or pie pans or on cookie sheets, so the heat can penetrate more easily. If insects or their eggs are in food, they will continue to develop even in a tight container—if you think the product might be infested, give it the heat treatment.

Store food in tight containers. Store sterilized or insect-free foods in clean metal or glass containers with tight covers. Lard buckets, fruit jars, or coffee cans are good to use. If a container has previously held infested food, heat it in boiling water or in the oven. Use up the contents of one package before opening another. Store the unused remainder of a newly opened package in a container with a tight-fitting cover to keep insects out.

{*PLATE XXX*

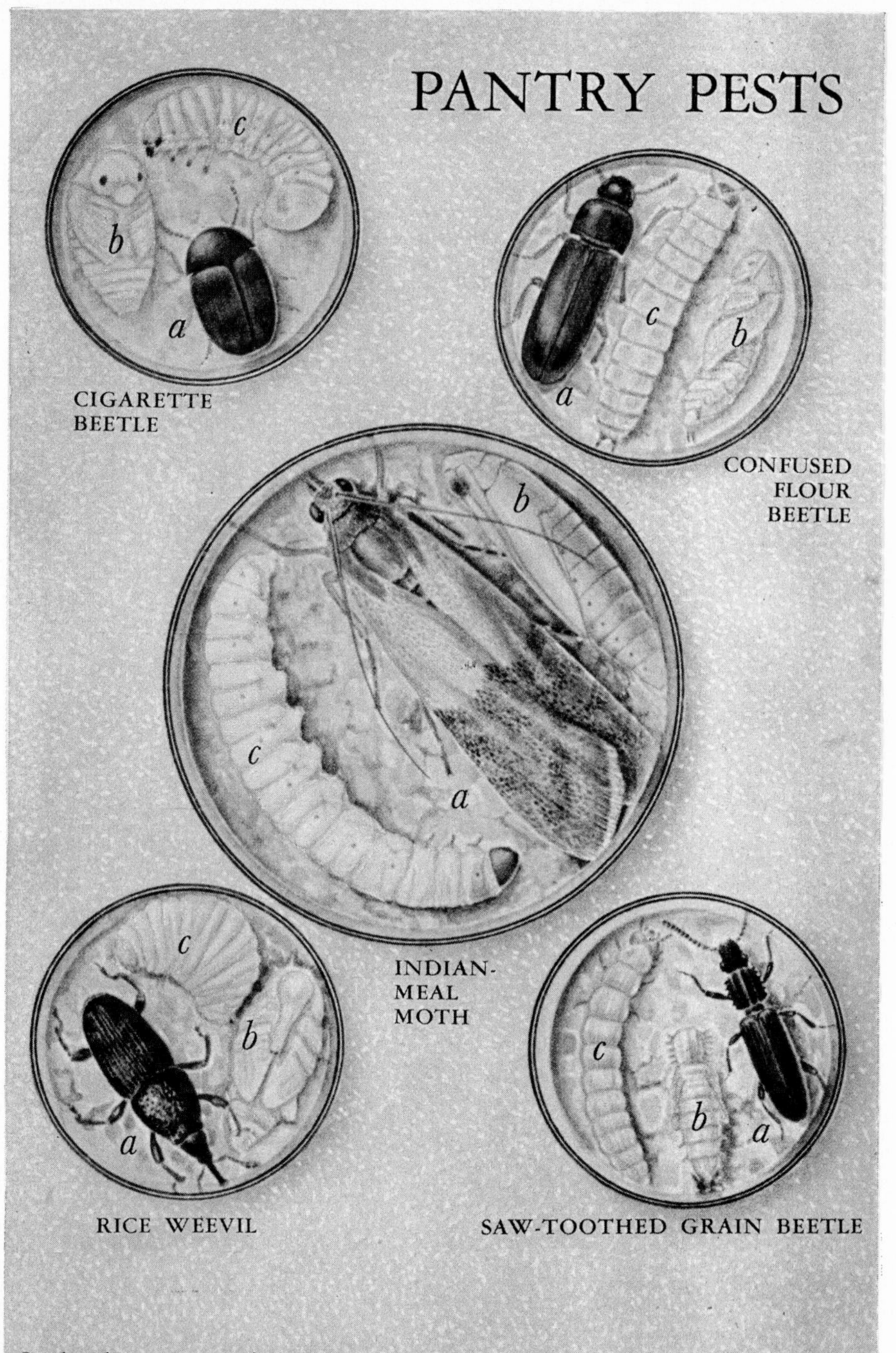

In the above group of illustrations all adults are designated *a;* all pupae, *b;* and all larvae, *c.* (All are greatly enlarged.)

HORNWORMS ON TOMATO

The moths of the hornworms that feed on tomato lay eggs on the under side of the leaves. The eggs hatch in 6 to 8 days or so.

The resulting larvae feed on the leaves and sometimes the fruits. The larva passes through five or six stages and reaches full growth in 3 or 4 weeks. The full-grown larva then burrows several inches into the ground and changes to a pupa. The pupa may remain in the soil all winter and transform to the moth stage in the spring, or, if weather conditions are suitable, the moth may emerge from the pupa after 2 to 4 weeks. In any event, the emerging moth makes its way to the soil surface and deposits eggs on tomato plants for the next brood of hornworms.

Control: Hand-pick the hornworms from infested plants in gardens. Dust field plantings with 10 percent TDE or with a mixture of equal parts of calcium arsenate and hydrated lime. The dusts should be applied directly to all parts of the plants at 30 pounds per acre. The treatments should begin early in the season and be repeated at weekly or 10-day intervals until the earliest formed fruits on the plants are about half-grown. TDE and calcium arsenate may leave a poisonous residue on the fruit; it should be removed by washing before the fruit is marketed or eaten.

{*PLATE XXXI*

a, Tomato hornworm moth (or adult) with wings spread; *b,* egg; *c,* larva, dark form; *d,* pupa (or resting stage); *e,* tobacco hornworm larva, light form. (*a,* about three-fourths natural size; *b,* about four times natural size; *c, d,* and *e,* about one-half natural size.)

MEXICAN BEAN BEETLE

Mexican bean beetles overwinter in the adult or beetle stage, usually in woodlands near bean fields. They leave their winter quarters in the spring, and the female beetles lay their eggs on the under side of the bean leaves. These eggs hatch in 5 to 14 days into larvae that feed principally on the under side of the bean leaves. The larvae grow rapidly, passing through four stages. Each stage is larger than the preceding one. They reach full growth in 20 to 35 days. The full-grown larva attaches itself to the under surface of the leaf on which it has been feeding or to some nearby plant or object, and changes to the pupa, or inactive stage. After 10 days or so the adult beetle emerges from the pupa. Within 2 weeks the female beetle is ready to deposit eggs for another brood.

Control: Spray or dust with derris, cube, or cryolite. Any of the following insecticides applied to the beans so as to *cover the under side of the leaves thoroughly* will protect the plants. (Spraying has given better results than dusting.)

To prepare a derris or cube spray, use finely ground derris or cube root (4 percent rotenone content) at the rate of one-half ounce (3 level tablespoonfuls) to 1 gallon of water; or 1½ pounds to 50 gallons.

To prepare a cryolite spray, use 1 ounce (3 level tablespoonfuls) of cryolite to 1 gallon of water; or 3 pounds to 50 gallons.

To prepare a derris or cube dust, containing 0.5 percent of rotenone, use 10 ounces of finely ground derris or cube root (4 percent rotenone content) to 4 pounds 6 ounces of diluent (finely ground talc, clay, sulfur, tobacco, gypsum, or other powder, except lime); or 12½ pounds to 87½ pounds of the diluent.

To prepare a cryolite dust, use 3 pounds of cryolite to 2 pounds of diluent (finely ground talc or sulfur); or 60 pounds of cryolite to 40 pounds of the diluent. Cryolite should not be applied to beans after the pods begin to form.

The first application of insecticide (spray or dust) should be made when Mexican bean beetles are found in the field when eggs become numerous on the under side of the leaves. Repeat every week or 10 days if the insects are numerous.

{*PLATE XXXII*

MEXICAN BEAN BEETLE

A, leaves skeletonized by bean beetle feeding. *a,* Egg cluster; *b,* larva; *c,* pupa with larval skin still attached; *d,* adult. (All about twice natural size.)

COLORADO POTATO BEETLE

The eggs of the Colorado potato beetle are laid in bunches on the under sides of the leaves. The eggs hatch in 4 to 9 days. The larvae (or slugs) feed on the plant. The larva grows rapidly, passing through four stages, similar in appearance except that each stage is larger than the stage that preceded it.

It becomes full-grown in 10 to 21 days after hatching. It then burrows into the ground and changes to a pupa, or resting stage. After 5 to 10 days the adult beetle emerges from the pupa, crawls up out of the ground, and, after feeding on the plants for a few days, may lay eggs for another brood of larvae.

Control: Dust the foliage thoroughly with a 3 percent DDT dust. Sprays are also effective if applied with a good sprayer that throws a fine mist. To each gallon of water, use 3 level tablespoonfuls of 50 percent DDT wettable powder or 2 level teaspoonfuls of 25 percent DDT emulsion concentrate. To make 100 gallons of spray, use 3 pounds of the 50 percent wettable powder or 2 pounds of the 25 percent DDT emulsion concentrate. If sprays are to be used for disease control, either of these DDT preparations may be added to the fungicidal spray rather than to water, and both materials applied with one operation.

Begin spraying or dusting when the beetles first appear. Spray or dust for the slugs when eggs are hatching, and repeat the treatment as often as necessary.

{PLATE XXXIII

a, Adult beetle; *b,* eggs; *c,* larvae (or slugs); *d,* pupa (or resting stage). (*a, c,* and *d,* about natural size; *b,* about twice natural size.)

HARLEQUIN BUG

The harlequin bug (also known as the fire bug, the collard bug, and the calico bug) is a pest in vegetable gardens in the South. Its favorite food plants are cole crops like broccoli, cabbage, turnip, horse-radish, and kale.

In early spring the bugs come out of their winter quarters and invade the fields. On the under side of the leaves they lay eggs, which hatch 4 to 15 days later. The young, or nymphs, feed by sucking the sap from the leaves and stems. White or yellowish blotches soon appear where the insect feeds. When the insects are abundant, the plants may wither and die quickly. The bugs become full-grown 6 to 8 weeks after hatching, Another brood may start 2 or 3 weeks after the first one matures.

Control: Practice clean cultural methods throughout the season. Disk and plow under all stalks and other refuse as soon as the crop has been harvested.

Against the adult or nearly mature bug, control by insecticides is not wholly effective. Dusts or sprays containing sabadilla, rotenone, or pyrethrum will control the insect in the younger stages.

For dusting, use a dust containing 10 to 20 percent of sabadilla-seed powder, 1 percent of rotenone, or 0.3 percent of pyrethrins. Apply at the rate of about 30 pounds per acre, or 1 to 2 ounces to 50 feet of row. Begin dusting or spraying as soon as the bugs appear and repeat every week if necessary. Hand picking the adult bugs when they first appear in the garden area often will keep the pests in check. Dropping the bugs as they are picked from the plant into a container partly filled with soap and water is a convenient way of destroying them.

[PLATE XXXIV

a, Adult; *b*, eggs; *c* to *g*, young, or nymphs; *h*, damaged cabbage leaf with nymphs, adult bug, and eggs. (*a* and *c* to *g*, about three times natural size; *b*, about four times natural size; *h*, about natural size.)

GLADIOLUS THRIPS

Gladiolus thrips overwinter and may reproduce on the stored gladiolus corms. During the growing season the adults and larvae attack the foliage and flowers of the growing plant. The eggs are inserted into the plant tissue. In the summer a generation of the thrips may be completed in 2 weeks.

The gladiolus thrips can be controlled by applying DDT to the stored corms or the growing plants.

On dormant corms use a 5 percent DDT dust. Apply 1 ounce of dust per bushel of corms in trays or 1 teaspoonful per 100 corms in paper sacks. Apply the dust with a duster over the top of filled trays soon after the corms are harvested or after cleaning. It is important to destroy the thrips before they penetrate beneath the protecting scales.

Watch the growing plants for evidence of thrips feeding. If you observe such feeding, spray or dust with DDT at once and continue at weekly intervals until the flowers appear. If infested plants are not treated until they bloom, the flowers cannot be saved from disfigurement.

Apply the spray as a fine mist, and avoid runoff. For spraying a few plants use 1 ounce, or 6 tablespoonfuls, of 50 percent DDT wettable powder to 3 gallons of water; for larger quantities use 2 pounds to 100 gallons of water.

If you use a dust, it should contain 5 percent of DDT. Apply it lightly and evenly over the plant.

{PLATE XXXV

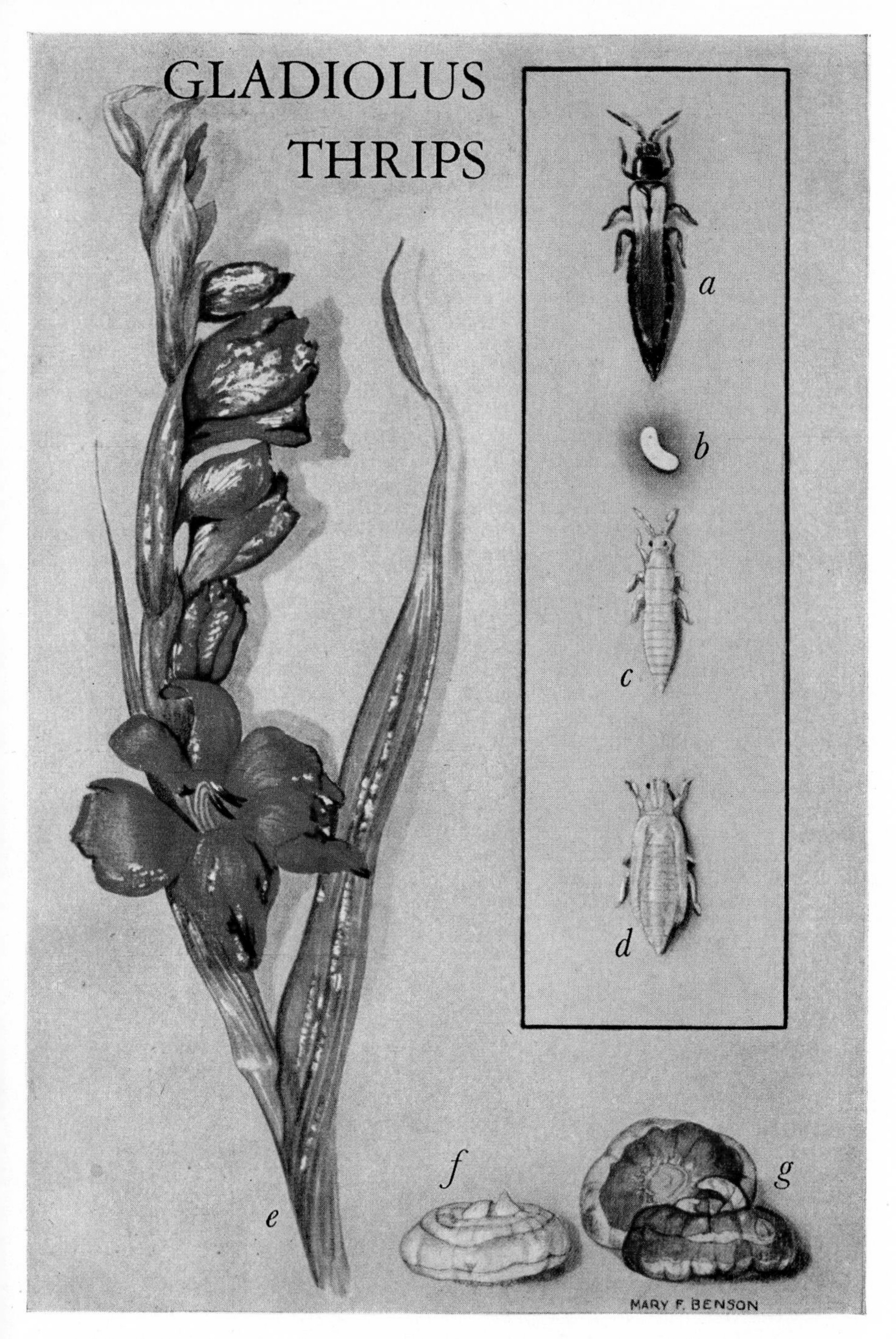

a, Adult thrips; *b,* egg; *c,* larva; *d,* pupa (or resting stage); *e,* foliage and flower spike showing typical feeding injury; *f,* uninjured gladiolus corm; *g,* corms injured by feeding of thrips, showing characteristic russeted appearance. (*a, b, c,* and *d,* about 20 times natural size; *e, f,* and g, about one-half natural size.)

STRIPED CUCUMBER BEETLE

The striped cucumber beetle is familiar and troublesome in gardens in the Eastern and Central States. The beetles invade cucumber, squash, and melon plantings almost overnight and may destroy the tiny seedlings before they push through the soil. They girdle stems of older plants and eat parts of the leaves. They also transmit bacterial wilt and mosaic disease from plant to plant. The grubs, or larvae, live on the roots and reduce the vitality of the plants.

The adult beetles spend the winter in uncultivated areas, protected by plant debris. In spring they become active, feeding on some wild plants about the time apple trees are in bloom. As soon as the first melon, cucumber, squash, or pumpkin seedlings push through the soil, the beetles attack them. Here they feed first on the stems and cotyledons, oftentimes killing the plants. There may be an influx of beetles into the field for several weeks. As the plants grow, the beetles collect under the vines and feed on the lower surfaces of the plants. Females crawl into cracks in the soil and deposit eggs. The young larvae, or grubs, that hatch from these eggs feed on the plant roots for about a month, pupate in the soil, and emerge as adults of the next generation.

Control: Several insecticides are effective, provided they reach the beetles in time. Derris or cube and cryolite are recommended. They may be applied as dusts or sprays to prevent plants from becoming infected by wilt.

The derris or cube dust should contain 0.75 to 1 percent of rotenone. The cryolite dust should contain 40 to 50 percent of sodium fluoaluminate. They are usually obtainable at those strengths from local dealers.

Sprays can be prepared from undiluted powdered derris or cube, which contains from 3 to 5 percent of rotenone, or from a rotenone-containing extract. Use enough powder to give a spray containing 0.02 percent of rotenone. This requires 5½ pounds of a powder containing 3 percent of rotenone (or 4 pounds of one containing 4 percent) in 100 gallons of water. Use the rotenone-containing extract at the strength recommended by the manufacturer. To prepare a cryolite spray use 5 pounds of cryolite containing 90 percent of sodium fluoaluminate or its equivalent in 100 gallons of water.

Apply the dusts at 15 to 30 pounds per acre and the sprays at 75 to 100 gallons per acre, the rate depending on the size of the plants. To be effective the applications must be timely, thorough, and frequent. Keep in mind the following points: Protect the young seedlings. Apply the dust or spray to the plants as soon as the beetles appear. Apply a light, even coating over the entire plant, especially at the point where the stems emerge from the soil. Repeat the applications after rains and as often as necessary to keep the plants free from the beetles.

{PLATE XXXVI

STRIPED CUCUMBER BEETLE

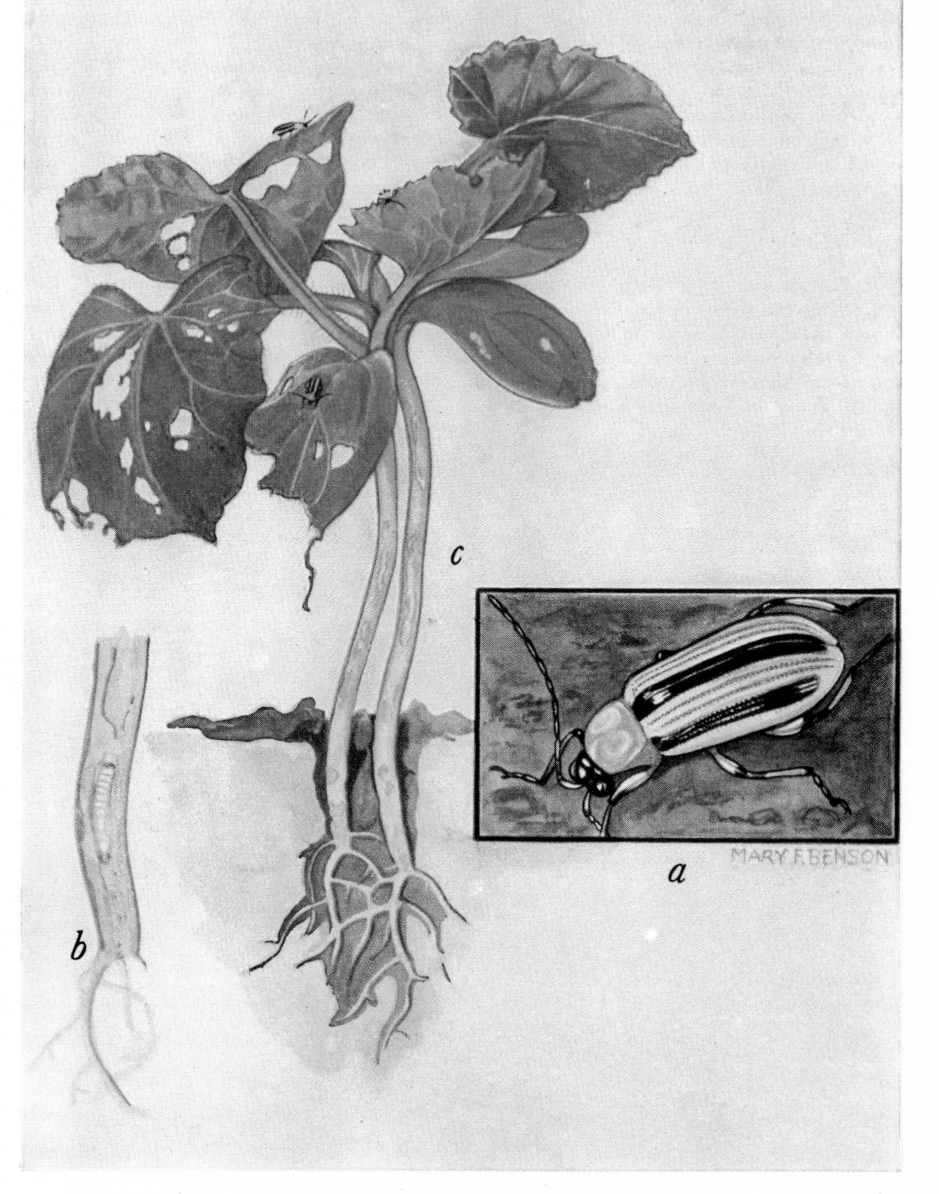

a, Adult beetle; *b,* underground stem of cucumber seedling cut open to show larva (grub, or "worm") feeding within; *c,* small cucumber plants showing characteristic feeding by adult beetles on leaves and stems. (*a,* about seven times natural size; *b,* about twice natural size; *c,* about three-fourths natural size.)

POTATO LEAFHOPPER

The potato leafhopper injures potatoes, beans, and many other plants in the Eastern States. Young and adult forms feed on the under surface of the leaves by sucking the plant juices. The adults fly when disturbed and the tiny nymphs scamper for cover, traveling sidewise. This leafhopper transmits to the plant a substance that causes a disease condition known as hopperburn, the first symptom of which is a triangular brown spot at the tips of the leaflets. Later the entire margins may curl upward and turn brown as though scorched. Badly affected plants die early and the yield of potatoes is reduced.

In Florida and other Gulf States the leafhopper breeds throughout the year. In the North the adults appear in April or May. As they have never been found there in the winter, they probably migrate from the South. Early in June they move in large numbers to potato fields and deposit eggs in the tissue of the plants. In about a week the eggs hatch into wingless nymphs. The nymphs pass through five stages and become winged adults in 10 to 14 days. They begin laying eggs 5 or 6 days later. The period from egg to adult is about 1 month.

Control: Dust the foliage thoroughly with a 3 percent DDT dust. For a spray, use two level tablespoonfuls of 50 percent DDT wettable powder or two level teaspoonfuls of 25 percent DDT emulsion concentrate per gallon of water. Apply with a good sprayer that throws a fine mist. To make 100 gallons of spray use either 2 pounds of the 50-percent wettable powder or 2 pints of the 25 percent DDT emulsion concentrate. If spray is to be used for disease control, add either of these DDT preparations to the fungicidal spray rather than to water, and apply at once.

Begin spraying or dusting when the insects first appear and repeat the treatment as often as necessary.

[PLATE XXXVII

a, Adult leafhopper; *b,* nymphs; *c,* potato leaflets, showing upcurled brown tips and margins, known as hopperburn, caused by the feeding of leafhoppers. (*a* and *b,* about 14 times natural size; *c,* about three-fourths natural size.)

IMPORTED CABBAGEWORM

The imported cabbageworm is the larva, or caterpillar, of a yellowish white butterfly with several black spots on the wings. The velvety-green caterpillars feed on the leaves of cabbage, collards, cauliflower, broccoli, and related crops.

In the Northern States the insect passes the winter in the chrysalis, or pupal stage, from which the butterflies emerge early in the spring. In the Southern States the caterpillars may be found from March until December, or even throughout the winter.

The eggs are laid usually on the under side of the leaves. In warm weather they hatch within a week, and the caterpillars take about 15 days to mature. The change from mature caterpillar through the chrysalis to the butterfly takes place in about 10 days to 2 weeks. There are several broods each year.

Control: The imported cabbageworm can be controlled with derris, cube, or other powders containing rotenone. Apply a dust containing 0.75 to 1 percent of rotenone at the rate of 20 to 30 pounds per acre or a spray containing 0.025 percent of rotenone at 100 gallons per acre. For small plantings use 1 to 1½ ounces of the dust or 1 to 1½ quarts of the spray to each 50 feet of row. Begin the applications when the caterpillars appear and repeat every 7 to 10 days until the insects are brought under control. For best results apply when the air is calm, as in early morning or late afternoon. Direct the dust or spray onto the buds, or heads, of the plants and the under sides of the leaves.

Pyrethrum insecticides are less effective than those containing rotenone. But frequent and thorough applications of a dust containing 0.2 percent of pyrethrins or a spray containing 0.006 percent of pyrethrins usually give satisfactory results.

DDT will control the imported cabbageworm and most other caterpillars that attack cabbage and related plants, but should not be applied to any leafy vegetable after the edible portion of the plant can be seen. Use a 3 percent DDT dust or 2 pounds of 50 percent DDT wettable powder per 100 gallons of spray (2 level tablespoonfuls to each gallon). Do not apply DDT on cabbage after the heads begin to form or on cauliflower after the curds begin to form (about 30 days before harvest in each case) or to any leaves that are to be eaten.

{PLATE XXXVIII

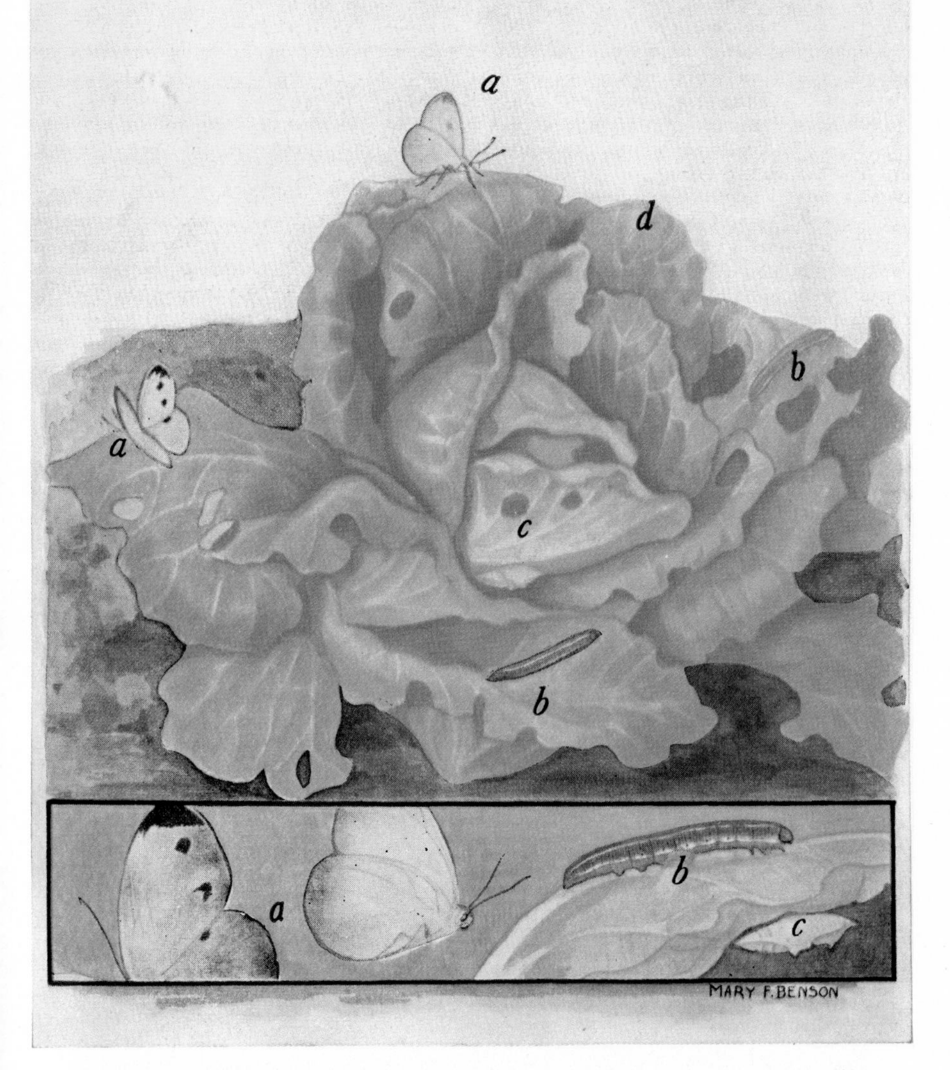

a, Butterflies (or adults) with wings in natural positions; *b,* larvae (caterpillars, or "worms"); *c,* pupae (chrysalids, the resting stage); *d,* cabbage plant showing typical feeding injuries. (Upper illustration: *a, b,* and *c,* about one-half natural size; *d,* slightly less than two-thirds natural size. Lower illustration: *a, b,* and *c,* about natural size.)

SQUASH VINE BORER

A gardener might discover one morning that his squash vines have wilted suddenly. Usually the wilting is due to the squash vine borer, a caterpillar that bores into the stem near the ground. Its presence may escape notice until piles of yellow, sawdustlike excrement, which falls from holes in the stem, become evident.

The adult is called a clear-winged moth because the hind wings are transparent, like those of a wasp. The female moth lays eggs on the stems in June or July in the North and in April and May in the South. The minute young larvae, or caterpillars, on hatching from the eggs, bore into the stem, grow rather rapidly, and are full-grown in about 4 weeks, when they are about 1 inch long. There is one generation a year in the North, two in the South, and a partial second generation in intermediate regions. The winter is spent in the soil as mature larvae or as pupae.

When the borers are numerous they cause severe injury. They bore throughout the interior of the stems near the base and may travel up the stems, even to the petioles of the leaves. Sometimes vines are almost severed. The fruits are sometimes attacked. As the larvae become larger the excrement, which is pushed out of holes in the stems, becomes visible. While most serious on squashes, especially the Hubbard, the borers also attack pumpkins, cucumbers, gourds, and other cucurbits.

Control: Although control is difficult, insecticides have been helpful. Apply a dust containing 1 percent of rotenone to the stems and basal parts of the vines three or more times at 10-day intervals. A spray composed of 1 part of 40 percent nicotine sulfate to 100 parts of water has been reported as effective in reducing infestations.

Apply the spray to the stems near the base of the plant and repeat the application at least weekly during the egg-laying period.

The success of any insecticidal treatment depends on early and repeated treatment, because after the young larvae have reached the inside of the stem the insecticides will not affect them.

The practice of covering the stems with soil to induce rooting beyond injured portions has long been followed with success, especially on heavy soils in humid areas.

After the borers have entered the stems and their presence becomes evident, the only known remedy is to slit the stems lengthwise with a thin knife or razor blade and remove the borer. The injured part should then be covered with soil.

{PLATE XXXIX

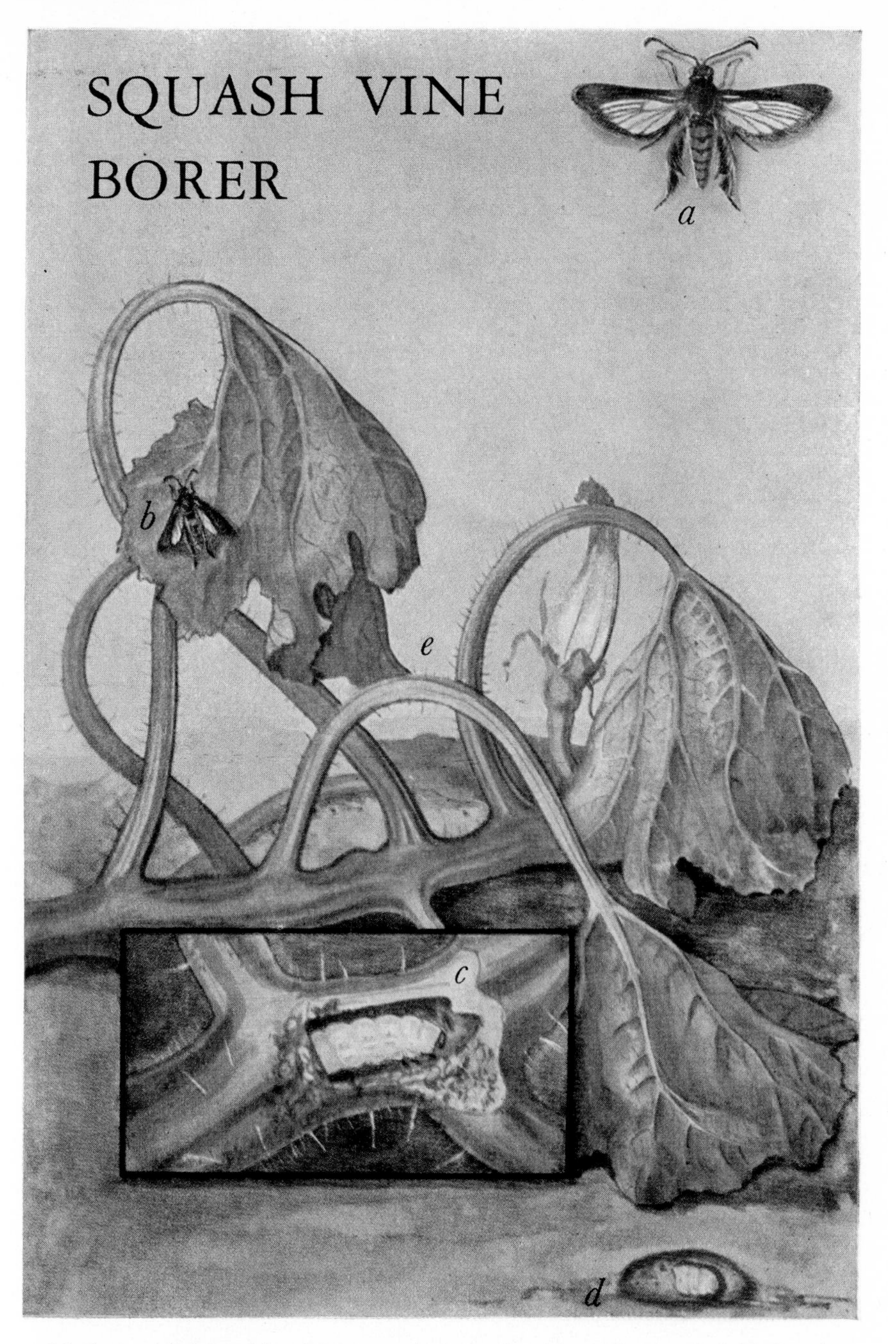

a, Moth (or adult) with wings spread; *b,* moth with wings partly folded; *c,* part of squash stem (enlarged) cut open to show borer (or larva) feeding within; *d,* pupal cell in soil cut open to show pupa (or resting state) inside; *e,* part of squash plant showing typical appearance of wilting caused by feeding of squash vine borer inside the stem. (*a, c,* and *d,* about one and one-fourth times natural size; *b,* about two-thirds natural size; *e,* about one-third natural size.)

TOMATO FRUITWORM

The tomato fruitworm, also known as the corn earworm and the bollworm, occurs all over the United States. It feeds on several crops, including tomatoes, cotton, and corn. In the Southern States and in California it is a serious pest of tomatoes every year. In the extreme South moths may emerge as early as January from their pupal cells, although most of them appear later in the spring. The female moth begins to lay eggs soon after she emerges. The eggs are somewhat smaller than a pinhead. She lays them singly on the leaves. As the larvae hatch they crawl over the leaves, feeding sparingly. They eventually find their way to the fruits, into which they cut holes or burrow, usually at the stem end. A worm may feed until full-grown upon a single tomato, or it may move from one tomato to another, injuring several before it completes its growth. The full-grown worm leaves the fruit and enters the soil, where it transforms into the pupal or resting stage. There may be two or more broods a season.

Control: Apply a dust containing 10 percent of either TDE or DDT. A corn-meal bait containing 10 percent of cryolite, scattered evenly over the leaves of the plants, will also give satisfactory control. In localities where the tomato russet mite occurs, the TDE or DDT dust should also contain at least 25 percent of sulfur, thus providing for the control of the mite as well as the tomato fruitworm.

Best results with either dusts or bait will be had if three applications are made—the first when the plants are about 1 to 2 feet across and are beginning to set fruit, and the second and third applications after intervals of 14 days. The dusts should be applied at 30 pounds per acre, and the corn-meal mixture at 60 pounds per acre per application. The entire foliage should be covered, especially the growing tips and outer leaves of the plants. The dust should be applied with hand or power dusters. The corn-meal mixture may be scattered by hand. Remember that DDT, TDE, and cryolite are poisons. They may leave a residue, which should be removed by washing or wiping.

{PLATE XL

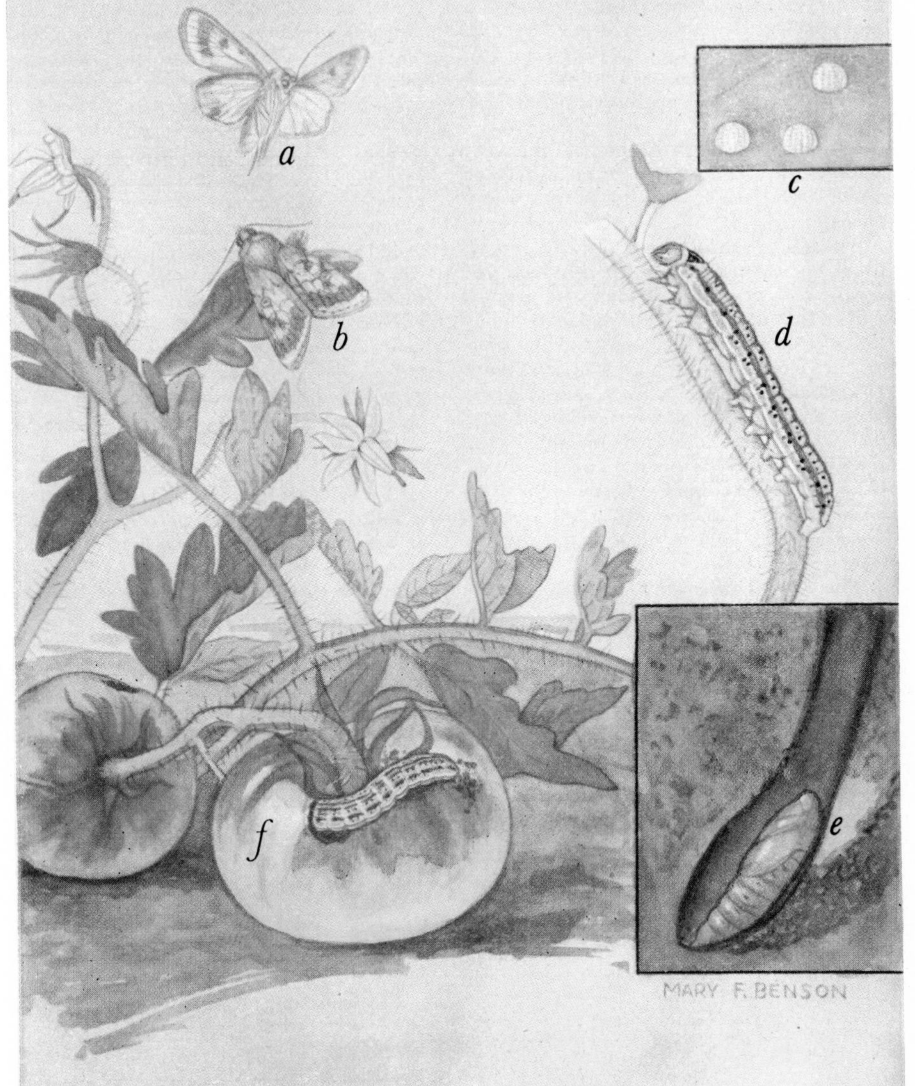

a, Female moth (or adult) with wings spread; *b*, male moth with wings in natural position; *c*, eggs; *d*, larva; *e*, pupa (or transformation stage) in its cell in the soil; *f*, larva feeding on tomato fruit, showing typical injury. (*a*, *b*, and *f*, about two-thirds natural size; *c*, about seven times natural size; *e*, about one and one-third natural size.)

SWEETPOTATO WEEVIL

The sweetpotato weevil lays its eggs in small holes that it makes in the stems of sweetpotato plants or directly in the potatoes. In about a week the eggs hatch into small, white grubs, which feed and grow in the vines or in the potatoes. In 2 or 3 weeks the grub reaches its full growth.

While in the stem or potato, the grub changes into the pupa, or resting stage, which lasts 7 or 8 days before the weevil emerges.

The adult weevils injure the sweetpotato plant by feeding on the leaves, vines, and roots. The grubs do damage by feeding within the stems, roots, and potatoes. Small holes in groups on the surface of the potatoes are either feeding marks or holes made by females in laying their eggs. Larger holes are made by newly developed weevils when they emerge from the sweetpotatoes. If weevily potatoes are cut open, the grub-made tunnels can be seen, often with grubs or pupae in them. Infested sweetpotatoes have a bitter taste and are unfit for food.

The weevil is known to exist in Alabama, Florida, Georgia, Louisiana, Mississippi, South Carolina, and Texas.

Control: If infestations are light, the pest can be eradicated if it is deprived of its food for about 1 year. The procedures are:

1. Plant no sweetpotatoes for 1 year in a zone extending ½ to 1 mile from any known infestation.

2. On infested farms: (a) Dispose of all remaining sweetpotatoes by February 1 or earlier by dehydration, feeding to livestock, or burning. (b) Immediately after cleaning up the storage place, dust it with 10 percent DDT dust at the rate of 1 pound to each 1,600 square feet of surface area. If a spray is desired, add 8 pounds of 50 percent DDT wettable powder to 100 gallons of water. Apply the spray at the rate of 1½ gallons to each 1,000 square feet. (c) At harvest remove all sweetpotatoes from the field and do not store infested potatoes. Destroy all roots, crowns, small sweetpotatoes, scraps, and volunteer plants. Graze livestock on the field after harvest if possible. Plow old sweetpotato fields at least twice during the winter.

In commercial areas where fields are generally infested with the weevil, effective control may be had by the following practices:

Use State-certified seed sweetpotatoes. If seed is selected locally at harvesttime, treat it thoroughly with 10 percent DDT dust at the rate of 1 pound to 6 to 8 bushels of seed.

Follow clean-up practices given for light infestations (2, b and c).

Destroy plants and tubers in seedbeds as soon as you have produced enough plants.

Rotate field plantings. Do not follow sweetpotatoes with sweetpotatoes.

Plant the new crop as far away as possible from the crop of the previous year.

{PLATE XLI

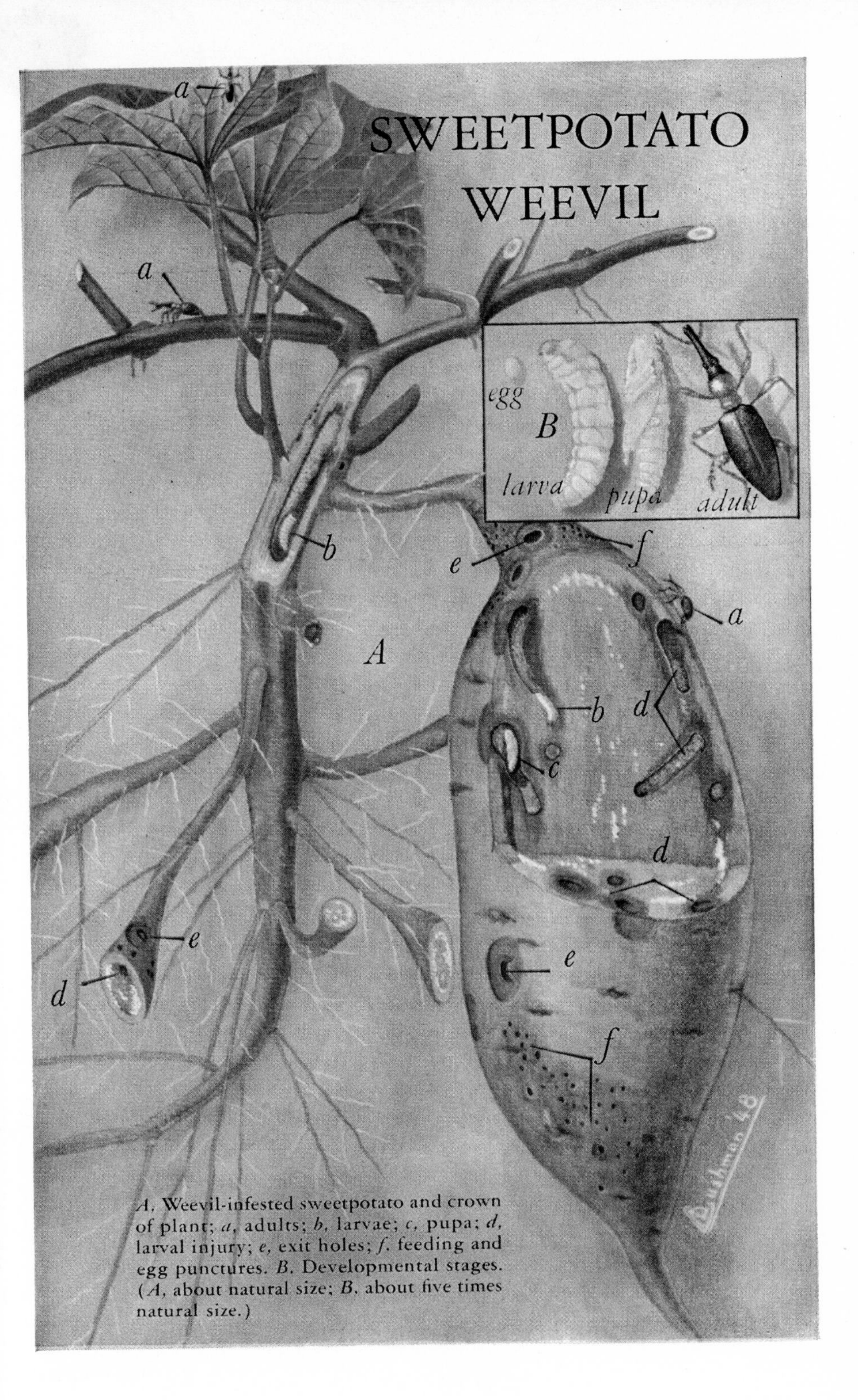

A, Weevil-infested sweetpotato and crown of plant; *a*, adults; *b*, larvae; *c*, pupa; *d*, larval injury; *e*, exit holes; *f*, feeding and egg punctures. *B*. Developmental stages. (*A*, about natural size; *B*. about five times natural size.)

SEED-CORN MAGGOT

The seed-corn maggot attacks the sprouting seeds of beans, peas, and corn and potato seed pieces. The adults look like small house flies. They lay their eggs in the soil on or near the food plants. The white, legless maggots hatch in 2 or 3 days and feed on decaying plants or seed or on the soft sprouting seed. They usually destroy the germ of the seed so that no plants are produced. Damaged beans often have root systems that develop and push the seeds out of the soil as ballheads with no foliage. In 2 to 3 weeks the maggots become full-grown and pupate. After another week or two the adults emerge to repeat the cycle. The insect is distributed throughout the United States and attacks a wide variety of plants.

Control: As soon as maggot injury is discovered, replant. Avoid organic fertilizer in the seeded row. Partly decayed vegetable matter attracts the flies; soils containing such material are likely to become infested with maggots. Plant seed shallow in such lands, and prepare the seedbed so as to promote rapid germination. Plant the seed when the soil is warm. Cool, wet periods retard seed germination and promote injury by maggots.

Damage may be prevented by delaying planting until the maggots of the first generation have become full-grown and are entering the pupal stage. The plants will then have time to come up before maggots of the next generation appear.

Seed-corn maggot damage to potato seed pieces is prevented by allowing the cut seed pieces to heal before planting. The maggot attacks the sound pieces of potato only where the skin is broken or the surface is injured.

The treatment of seed with insecticides like chlordane has given promising results, but the method has not been perfected.

{PLATE XLII

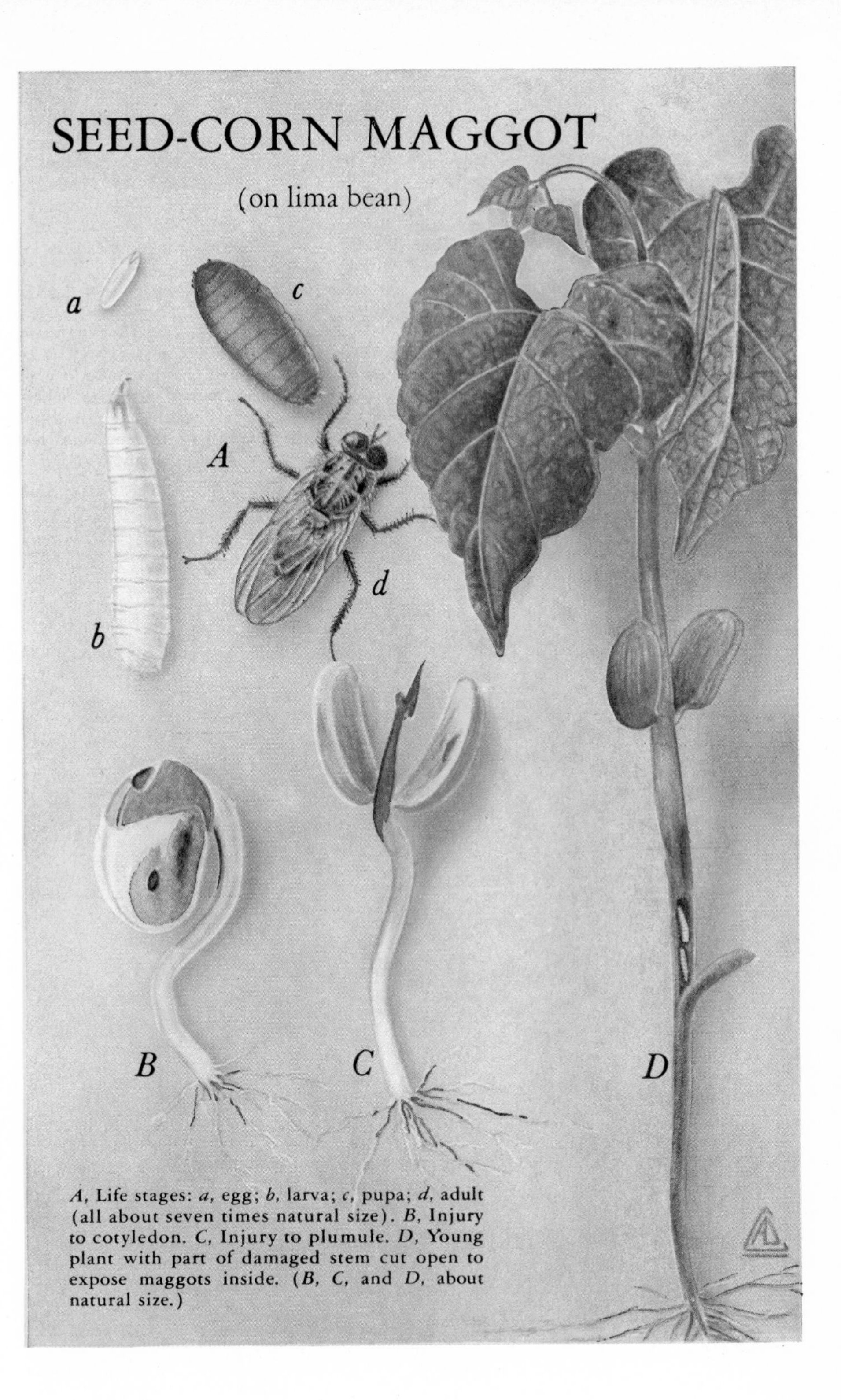

A, Life stages: *a*, egg; *b*, larva; *c*, pupa; *d*, adult (all about seven times natural size). *B*, Injury to cotyledon. *C*, Injury to plumule. *D*, Young plant with part of damaged stem cut open to expose maggots inside. (*B*, *C*, and *D*, about natural size.)

PEA WEEVIL

The pea weevil is a hazard in the production of all peas whenever extensive acreages are harvested as dry peas. The adult weevils fly into the pea fields when the plants begin to bloom. The eggs are laid on the living green pods only. The tiny grubs that hatch from the eggs burrow into the green peas, where they develop as the pea develops. As a result, they are found in green peas harvested for canning. The grubs become full-grown some time after the normal crop matures. If they are allowed to continue feeding, the seed will not germinate. The adult weevils emerge from the seed in late summer and fall and seek a protected place to pass the winter. They do not attack mature seed. There is only one generation a year.

Control: Dust the infested parts of the fields with insecticides during the early-bloom stage before the eggs of the weevils are laid. Use an insect net to determine where the weevils occur. The insecticide dusts should contain not less than 0.75 percent of rotenone or 5 percent of either DDT or methoxychlor. Apply at 20 pounds per acre. Repeat in 3 or 4 days if necessary. Do not feed pea plants treated with DDT to milk animals or to meat animals being finished for slaughter.

Plant only weevil-free seed. Reduce to a minimum the shatter of dry peas at harvest. Destroy harvest refuse. Do not allow rubbish to accumulate around the pea fields and farm buildings for weevils to overwinter in.

{*PLATE XLIII*

A, Life stages (greatly enlarged): *a*, adult; *b*, pupa, *c*, larva; *d*, egg. *B*, Stem of pea vine with life-size adult in bloom, *e*. *C*, Small pod with several eggs attached. *D*, Larva in seed (considerably enlarged).

BEET LEAFHOPPER

The beet leafhopper, commonly called the whitefly in the West, is the only known carrier of curly top, a destructive virus disease of sugar beets, beets, beans, tomatoes, cantaloups, some ornamental flowering plants, many weeds, and other crops. The insect occurs in the arid and semiarid regions of the western United States, northern Mexico, and southwestern Canada.

The beet leafhopper passes the winter in the adult stage, chiefly in uncultivated and overgrazed areas where there are mustards or other suitable host plants. The insects are active and feed during the winter whenever the temperature permits. The female usually begins to lay eggs about the time the overwintering host plants begin their spring growth. The eggs are laid inside the tissues of the leaves and stems of plants. They hatch in 5 to 40 days, depending on the temperature. The young leafhoppers, or nymphs, emerge from the eggs and immediately begin to feed by inserting their beaks into the plant tissue and sucking the juices. As they grow, they shed their skins five times, becoming larger after each molt. After the fifth molt, they become adults and have wings. Development of the insect from egg to adult takes from 1 to 2 months. The generations overlap considerably. All stages may be found in the same breeding area at the same time in the summer. In the northern areas three generations are produced each season. In the warmer regions in Arizona and California, five or more generations may develop.

Control: Reducing curly-top infection in susceptible crops by controlling its carrier, the beet leafhopper, with insecticides is a difficult problem, because there might be continuous reinfestation. Applications of DDT will reduce beet leafhopper numbers but will not prevent the feeding of all leafhoppers that reinfest the fields. Weekly applications of 1 pound of actual DDT per acre for 3 or 4 weeks during the spring movement have reduced curly-top infection.

Chemical control of the beet leafhopper in weed-host areas that contribute large populations to the cultivated areas has proved practical. An oil solution or an emulsion containing DDT is applied as a spray from aircraft or mist blowers to the large breeding areas. The spray should be applied in the spring at the rate of 1 pound of DDT in 2 gallons of spray per acre before the leafhoppers begin to move to cultivated areas.

The control of weed-host plants of the leafhopper in the major breeding areas by proper land management is practicable. The replacement of weed hosts by perennial grasses that are not breeding hosts of this leafhopper may best be accomplished by reseeding the abandoned and burned areas; if native perennial grasses are still present, protection against overgrazing will accomplish the same purpose.

{PLATE XLIV

A, Life stages: *a,* adult; *b,* nearly mature nymph; *c,* young nymph (all about eight times natural size). *B, C,* and *D* show the effect of curly top disease on tomato, sugar beet, and bean, respectively.

PACIFIC COAST WIREWORM

The Pacific Coast wireworm is one of the most destructive of the many kinds of wireworms in the United States. It is generally distributed in the irrigated lands west of the Rocky Mountains. The shiny, tough, yellow-to-orange insects feed only on the underground parts of plants. They have a long life cycle—2 to 5 years in the soil. They injure crops by destroying seeds, cutting off small underground stems, and boring holes in the larger stems, roots, and tubers. No vegetable or field crop is immune to the damage they do. Such crops as potatoes, onions, corn, lettuce, beans, sugar beets, tomatoes, peas, carrots, and melons are particularly susceptible to their attacks.

The Pacific Coast wireworm hatches from tiny white eggs laid in the soil by the parent click beetles early in the spring. The beetles die soon after. The small wireworms grow to about one-fourth inch in length by fall. Most of them become full-grown, about three-fourths inch long, in 3 years. They change to pupae during midsummer. The pupae change to adults in about 3 weeks, but the adults remain in the soil within earthen cells until spring, when they emerge to lay eggs.

Control: To control wireworms in irrigated lands, treat the soil with 10 pounds of DDT per acre after harvest in the summer or fall or before planting in the spring. Spray or dust the insecticide on the soil surface and thoroughly mix it into the soil 6 to 9 inches deep. The Pacific Coast wireworm is killed by this insecticide in 6 to 8 weeks after application, but the material will remain in the soil and prevent new infestations for several years.

{PLATE XLV

PACIFIC COAST WIREWORM

Showing damage to carrot, potato, and onion; *a*, larva (natural size) on potato. *A*, eggs; *B*. larva; *C*, pupa in underground cell; *D*, adult click beetle. (*A*. *B*. *C*. and *D*. about three times natural size.)

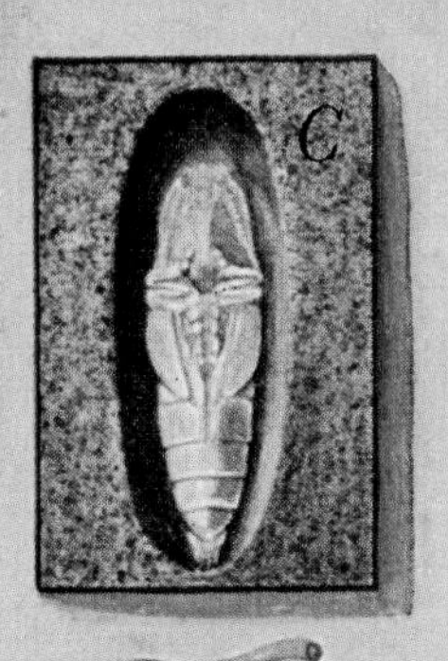

TUBER FLEA BEETLE

The tuber flea beetle is one of several kinds of flea beetles that attack potatoes. Its grub prefers to feed on the tubers; other flea beetles feed mostly on the roots. The flea beetles look alike. Some are destructive to other crops. The tuber flea beetle, however, is a pest only in Washington, Oregon, Colorado, and Nebraska, and causes little damage to crops other than potatoes.

The flea beetle jumps like a flea and quickly disappears when disturbed. The adult tuber flea beetle eats small round holes in the leaves—a type of injury characteristic of all flea beetles. The adult female enters the soil near the base of the plant to lay her eggs, which hatch in 5 to 8 days into slender white grubs, or larvae, which feed on the roots and in the tubers. Injury to the latter may take the form of roughened trails on the surface or tiny brown tunnels, extending as far as three-quarters of an inch into the tuber. After feeding for 2 or 3 weeks, the mature larva enters the inactive, or pupal stage, which lasts 10 to 14 days. At the end of this time the young beetles emerge to begin a second generation. Sometimes a second generation is completed and a third begun during the season. The insect passes the winter as an adult in the soil and emerges in May or June to begin feeding on the next season's crop.

Control: Apply a 5 percent DDT dust at 20 to 35 pounds per acre. This will also control most of the other insects which attack potato foliage. When power dusters are used, attach a lightweight canvas apron, 12 to 20 feet long, to the boom of the duster to help prevent the dust from drifting away. If sprays are preferred, apply 2 pounds of 50 percent DDT wettable powder per acre. With ordinary spray equipment the wettable powder should be applied in 80 to 125 gallons of water at a pressure of at least 250 pounds per square inch, preferably with three nozzles to the row.

{PLATE XLVI

TUBER FLEA BEETLE

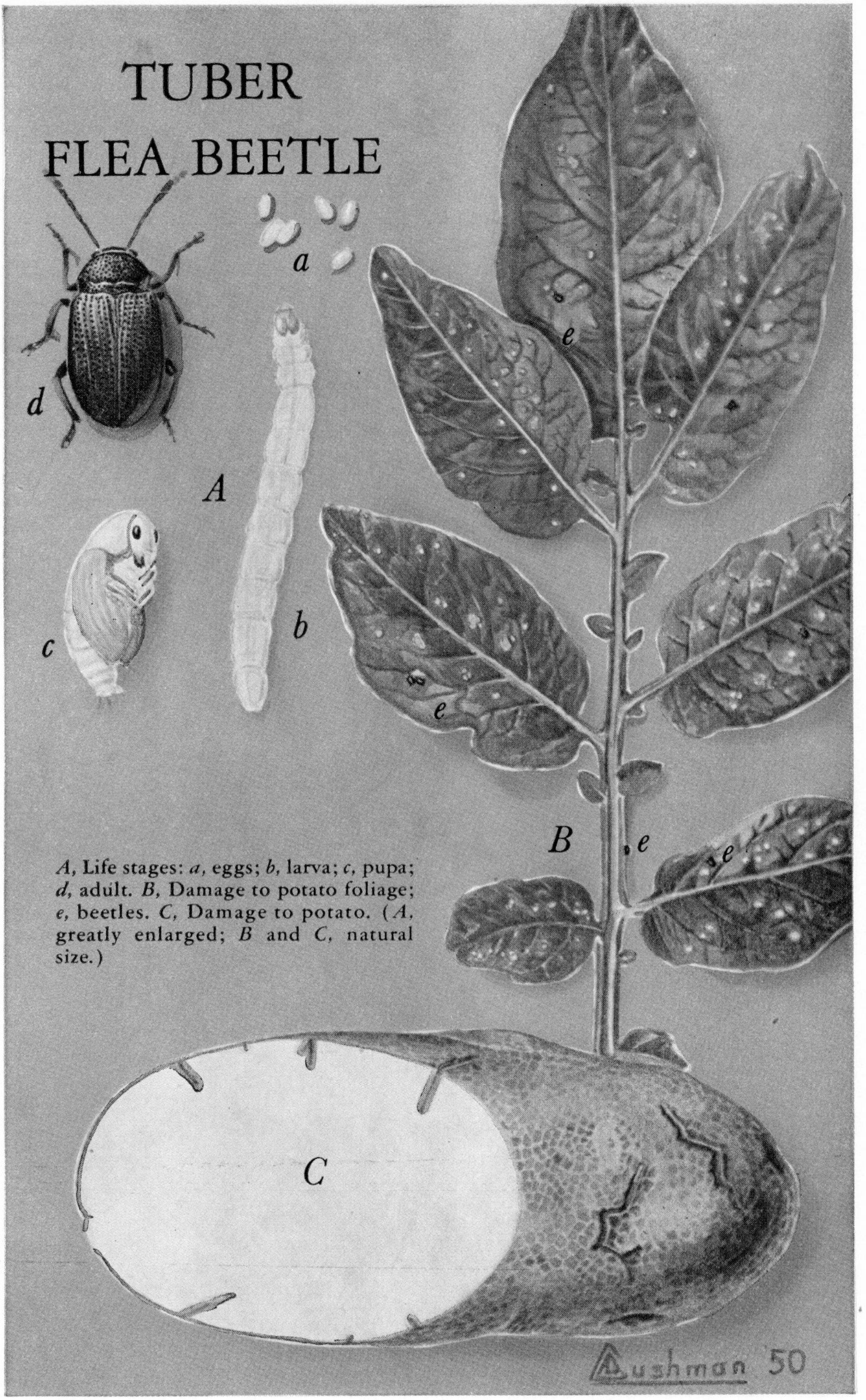

a

d

A

b

c

e

e

B

e

e

C

A, Life stages: *a*, eggs; *b*, larva; *c*, pupa; *d*, adult. *B*, Damage to potato foliage; *e*, beetles. *C*, Damage to potato. (*A*, greatly enlarged; *B* and *C*, natural size.)

Cushman

ONION THRIPS

The onion thrips occurs wherever onions grow. It attacks many cultivated crops and weeds. Its damage varies with seasons, localities, and the variety of onions.

In the South the onion thrips feeds on onions and other host plants throughout the winter. In the North they pass the winter in both the adult and larval stages on onion plants left in the fields and in the crowns of alfalfa and clover. They overwinter in discarded onions and sometimes in stored onions. The female lays her small whitish eggs in the more tender tissues of the leaves of the host plants. The eggs hatch in 4 to 10 days. The tiny white larvae emerge from the eggs and immediately begin to feed upon the growing tender points of the center leaves, where they are well protected. The larvae pass through two stages while feeding upon the plants and complete their growth in about 5 days. Then they enter the soil, where they pupate. The pupal stage lasts about 4 days if conditions are favorable. Thus a generation is completed in about 2 weeks. Generations overlap considerably. All stages may be in fields at the same time during the summer. Thrips often build up large populations on alfalfa, other cultivated crops, or weeds, and migrate to onion fields when the hosts mature or are harvested.

Control: Apply a dust containing 10 percent of DDT or a spray containing 2 pounds of 50 percent DDT wettable powder per 100 gallons of water. Use 20 to 25 pounds of dust, or 150 gallons of spray, per acre for each application. Repeat applications every 7 to 10 days. The spray should be applied as a fine mist so as to cover all parts of the plants thoroughly. Do not apply DDT to onions if the tops are to be eaten. If the onion tops are to be eaten, use a spray containing 1 quart of 40 percent nicotine sulfate per 100 gallons of water.

[PLATE XLVII

ONION THRIPS

Onion plant showing severe thrips damage. Insert, adult thrips (about 40 times natural size).

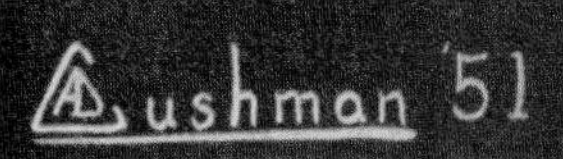

CLAY-BACKED CUTWORM

Cutworms cut off and eat young transplants. They are the young of dull-colored, night-flying moths. Each female moth may lay 200 to 1,500 eggs in sod, weedy land, or cultivated fields. The eggs hatch in a few days. The young cutworms feed greedily. When mature they burrow into the soil and change through the pupal stage to adult moths. There are several dozen common kinds of cutworms. Some have only one generation a year. Others have as many as three or four. Some overwinter as pupae. Others overwinter as cutworms. They differ widely in feeding habits. Some feed like other caterpillars in armies or alone, but most kinds prefer to hide in or near the soil during the day and feed at night. Generally they eat almost any kind of tender plant.

The clay-backed cutworm is generally distributed east of the Rocky Mountains. It has only one generation a year and passes the winter as a partly grown caterpillar. When the first plants are set out in the spring it cuts them off just above the soil surface at night and drags them to its burrow nearby for later feeding. The clay-backed cutworm reaches maturity in late spring, remains inactive during the hot summer, and pupates during the early fall. The adult moths emerge in the fall and lay eggs in grassy fields.

Control: Apply poison bait prepared by thoroughly mixing 1 pound of sodium fluosilicate with 25 pounds of wheat bran and moistening with water. Paris green may be substituted for the sodium fluosilicate. Prepare the bait in the morning and apply it late in the day so that it will be moist and attractive when the cutworms begin to feed in the evening. Scatter the bait lightly and evenly on the soil surface or around the transplants.

Dusting with 5 percent DDT is often effective, particularly if the dust is worked into the surface of the soil.

{PLATE XLVIII

A, Cabbage plant damaged by cutworm. *B,* Tomato with *a,* adult moth; *b,* larva feeding on stem; *c,* larva in ground; *d,* pupa. (All about natural size.)

PEA APHID

The pea aphid injures garden peas by sucking the sap from the leaves, stems, blossoms, and pods. Even a few aphids may kill small plants and stunt larger ones. The pea aphid may also spread virus diseases, thus causing further damage to the plants. Damage by the pea aphid may occur wherever garden peas are grown.

The adult is a light-green, soft-bodied insect that may or may not have wings. The winged aphids fly into the pea fields early in the spring and produce living young, which look like the wingless adult aphids. A single adult produces each day 10 to 14 young, which themselves begin to produce additional young in 1 to 2 weeks. When food is plentiful, most of the adult aphids are wingless. When food conditions are unfavorable, winged forms develop and fly to other fields of peas, alfalfa, or clover. In the South this cycle continues throughout the year. In the North, egg-laying adults develop in the fall; the black, shiny eggs are laid on alfalfa or clover. In some climates only the eggs survive the winter.

Control: Dust or spray with rotenone or DDT. Dusts should contain either 1 percent of rotenone or 5 percent of DDT and should be applied at 35 to 40 pounds per acre. Sprays should contain either 3 pounds of a 4 percent rotenone powder or 2 quarts of a 25 percent DDT emulsifiable concentrate to 125 gallons of water per acre.

DDT leaves poisonous residues on the foliage. Do not feed pea plants treated with DDT to milk animals or to meat animals being finished for slaughter.

{*PLATE XLIX*

A, Aphid-infested pea plant showing damage and many aphids on leaves and stems. *B,* Undamaged pea plant. *C,* Aphids (greatly enlarged); *a,* winged adult; *b,* wingless adult; and *c,* half-grown nymph.

CITRUS MEALYBUG

The citrus mealybug is one of the common mealybugs that damage garden flowers and potted plants. Among the plants most frequently attacked are coleus, fuchsia, cactus, fern, begonia, gardenia, poinsettia, citrus, ageratum, and dracaena. The mealybugs feed on the juices of plants and may cause loss of color, wilting, and eventual death of the affected parts. They also coat the foliage with sticky "honeydew," on which an unsightly black mold grows and which is the natural food for certain ants that care for the mealybugs and spread them to other plants.

Mealybugs are usually found in clusters along the veins on the under sides of leaves and crevices at the base of the leaf stems. Since they multiply rapidly all stages may be present at the same time. Mealybugs accidentally get into the home, conservatory, or garden on infested plants brought in from other sources.

The female has an amber-colored body and short, waxy filaments along the margin. The eggs are laid in a protective cottony mass or sac resembling a small puff of cotton. Each mass may contain 300 or more eggs. The eggs hatch in 10 to 20 days. The nymphs crawl away, start feeding, and produce a waxy white covering over their bodies. From 6 weeks to 2 months are required for the young females to reach maturity. The males form a cottony cocoon 2 or 3 weeks after hatching, in which they transform to small, rarely seen midgelike winged adults.

Control: The first step in the control of mealybugs on garden flowers is to eliminate ants in and about the garden. This is done by thoroughly drenching all nests with a suspension of chlordane, prepared by adding 3 level tablespoonfuls of 50 percent chlordane wettable powder to 1 gallon of water.

Potted plants should be sprayed thoroughly and with as much force as possible. Use either two level tablespoonfuls of 50 percent DDT wettable powder per gallon of water or three level tablespoonfuls of white oil emulsion plus 1½ teaspoonfuls of 40 percent nicotine sulfate per gallon. Make a second application in about 2 weeks. Potted plants may be dipped in a pail of the insecticidal mixture, then laid on the side to permit the excess to run off.

On plants that are not damaged by frequent watering, partial control may be obtained by syringing the infested plants frequently with as forcible a stream of water as the plants can stand without injury.

{PLATE L

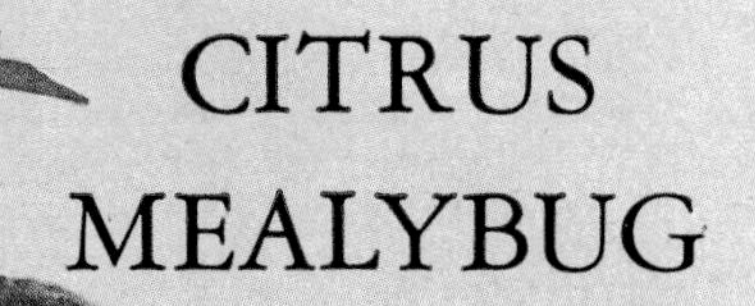

A, Coleus stunted by mealybugs; *a,* cottony masses surrounding the insects. *B,* Healthy coleus plant. *C,* Life stages; *b,* female surrounded by "cotton" and eggs; *c,* small "crawlers"; *d,* "crawler" somewhat larger; and *e,* adult male. (*A* and *B,* about natural size; *C,* greatly enlarged.)

THE PICKLEWORM

The pickleworm is a serious pest of squash, cucumber, and muskmelon in the South Atlantic States and Gulf Coast States. It frequently causes considerable damage in adjoining States and occasionally occurs as far west as Texas, Kansas, Missouri, and Iowa and as far north as the tier of States extending from Illinois eastward to Connecticut. Summer squash is its favorite host.

The pickleworm is active throughout the winter in extreme southern Florida, where its cultivated or native hosts are continuously available. From this and similar subtropical areas the insect gradually spreads northward each year, usually appearing later in the spring than most insects.

The eggs are laid singly and in small clusters among the hairs on flower and leaf buds, small fruit, and young leaves. They hatch in about 3 days. The young pickleworms feed on the surface of the areas where the eggs are laid, but soon tunnel into and mutilate flowers, terminal buds, stalks, vines, and fruits. The fruits are made unfit for food and the plants are injured or killed. The pickleworms mature in 6 to 28 days and pupate in partially folded leaves or in trash under the plants. The pupal stage is from 5 to 31 days.

Control: It is not easy to prevent pickleworm injury. In some areas damage can largely be avoided by planting susceptible crops as early as possible in the spring.

Early and frequent application of an insecticide is necessary when susceptible crops, especially squash and cucumber, are grown in the summer and fall in areas where the pickleworm is abundant. The larvae must be killed before they enter the fruits. A satisfactory control program free of the hazard of poisonous residues and off-flavor has not been developed.

Weekly use of the fungicide zineb for disease control will aid in the prevention of pickleworm injury.

Beginning when the pickleworm first shows up, which may be within 2 weeks after a crop is seeded, apply at weekly intervals a dust containing either 1 percent of lindane or at least 50 percent of cryolite. Use 15 to 25 pounds per acre application or 1 to 1½ ounces to each 50 feet of row. Lindane should also give adequate control of cucumber beetles and the melon aphid and be of value against the squash vine borer.

Lindane and cryolite are poisonous. Do not apply them on any part of the plant that is to be marketed or used as food unless it is known that the residue will be adequately removed by washing, brushing, or other means. Use of lindane until harvest may impart a slight off-flavor to the fruits. Until additional information is obtained on the effects of lindane residues in the soil, do not use lindane in fields to be planted to potatoes or other root crops.

At least partial control can be obtained after fruits appear by weekly use, at a rate of 20 to 30 pounds per acre, of a dust containing either 1 percent of rotenone, 20 percent of sabadilla, or 0.3 percent of pyrethrins (0.2 percent if impregnated form). These materials will be more effective if preceded by applications of lindane (before the fruits appear) and accompanied by use of zineb.

{PLATE LI

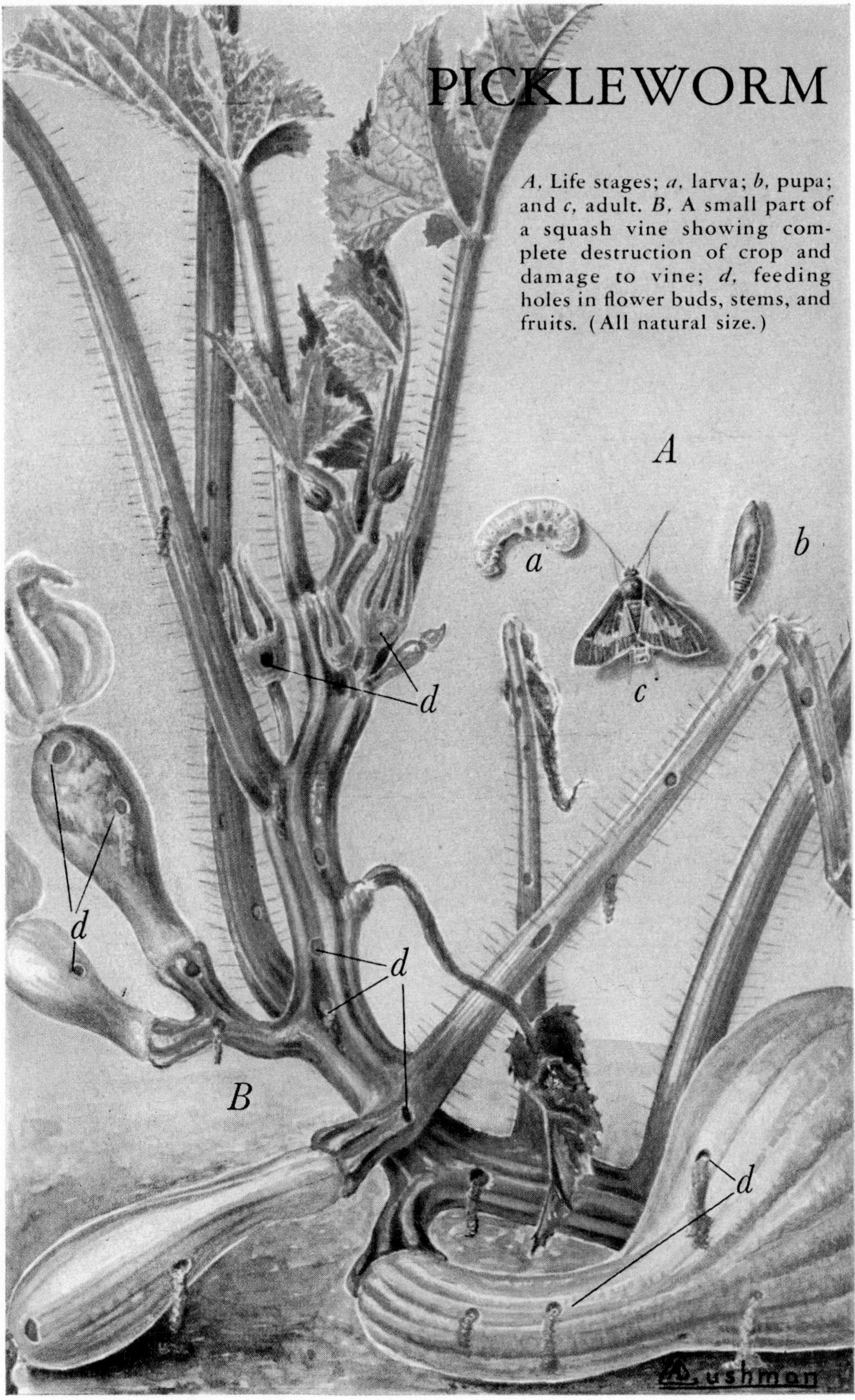

PICKLEWORM

A, Life stages; *a*, larva; *b*, pupa; and *c*, adult. *B*, A small part of a squash vine showing complete destruction of crop and damage to vine; *d*, feeding holes in flower buds, stems, and fruits. (All natural size.)

ALKALI BEES

Alkali bees inhabit the salty valleys west of the Continental Divide. In places where the soil meets their requirements, they may form great aggregations of nest burrows that number a million nests and occupy an acre or more of ground. Even the smaller nesting sites generally contain thousands of nests. Such sites, housing populations of wild bees comparable to hives or whole apiaries of honey bees, are valuable pieces of real estate to the grower of legume seeds. Wherever alfalfa seed is grown close to good nesting sites of alkali bees, yields are exceptionally high if other factors in seed production are properly handled. Some districts in central Washington and central Utah, which are becoming famous for their consistently high yields of alfalfa seed, depend largely on these bees for pollination.

Alkali bees locate their nests in fine-grained soils with high moisture and low organic content. They avoid areas where water stands for extensive periods. They tolerate only short, sparse vegetation. Consequently most nesting sites are found on low hummocks and gentle slopes where soil moisture is held close to the surface and where a high evaporation rate has left salty conditions and scanty vegetation.

In recent years alkali bees have been increasing throughout most of their range, very likely because of expanding acreages of their favorite forage plants and favorable man-made changes in soil conditions. Some progressive farmers now are protecting the nests rather than plowing them up. In some places farmers have undertaken to create new nesting sites.

Alkali bees are highly gregarious but are classified as solitary bees in the sense that they have no caste system or division of labor. Each female constructs, provisions, and seals her own nest. After laying her eggs in separate cells, she has no further contact with her offspring. Adult males and females emerge from the soil in the summer. Males emerge first and divide their time between sipping nectar from nearby plants and zigzagging over the fields and nesting sites in search of females. Soon after emerging, the females mate and begin digging their nests. Before bringing back her first load of pollen from the field, a female bee must construct her main burrow, rough in a few cells, and polish one ready for occupancy. Three or four loads of pollen are formed into a rough ball which is then mixed with a load of nectar and troweled into a smooth, flattened spheroid. An egg is laid on the pollen ball before the cell is sealed and plugged. A completed nest usually contains from 8 to 15 cells.

Within a few weeks the larval bees consume their provisions. Some of them pupate and emerge as a partial second generation. The others and the progeny of the second generation overwinter as mature larvae, which do not pupate until a few weeks before emergence time the next summer.

Most nesting sites are active for about 2 months. The peak of activity, which lasts for about a month, usually falls in the latter part of July and early August but may be advanced or retarded by early or late development of high soil temperatures. To get maximum benefit from alkali bees, seed growers must properly time the blossoming period of their crop. On sites with vegetation it is possible to advance the emergence date of the bees by applying a weed killer in the spring.

{PLATE LII

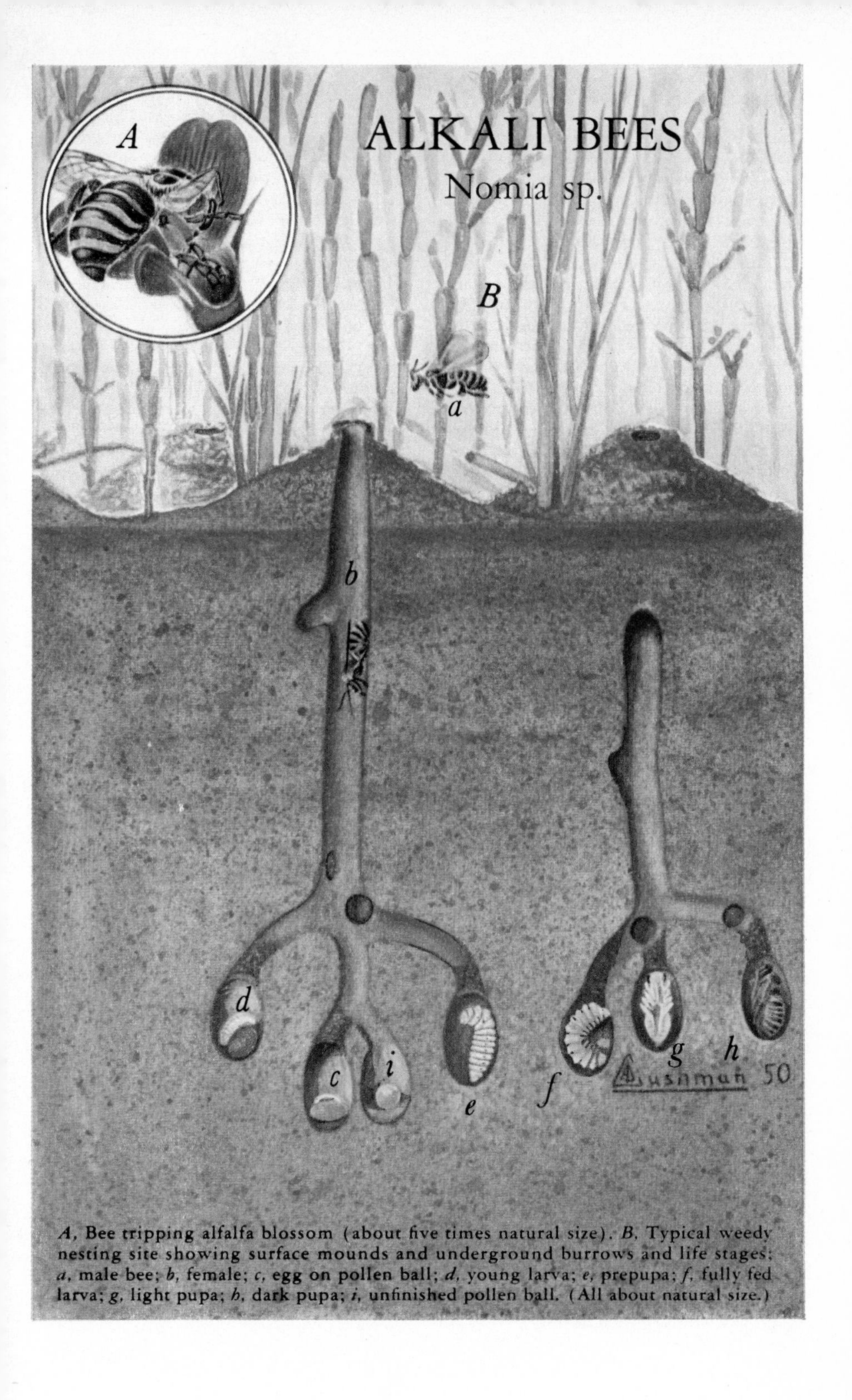

A, Bee tripping alfalfa blossom (about five times natural size). *B*, Typical weedy nesting site showing surface mounds and underground burrows and life stages: *a*, male bee; *b*, female; *c*, egg on pollen ball; *d*, young larva; *e*, prepupa; *f*, fully fed larva; *g*, light pupa; *h*, dark pupa; *i*, unfinished pollen ball. (All about natural size.)

TOBACCO HORNWORM

The tobacco hornworm, like the tomato hornworm, which it closely resembles, feeds voraciously on the leaves of tobacco, tomato, and related plants. Because of its large size and appetite, even a few hornworms can destroy the plants.

The parent of the tobacco hornworm is a large hawk-moth, which in flight is sometimes mistaken for a hummingbird. The eggs are laid on the under side of the leaves. In about a week a tiny hornworm emerges from the egg. It feeds on the leaves until it reaches full growth in about 3 or 4 weeks. The mature hornworm burrows several inches into the soil and enters the pupal, or resting, stage. It ordinarily remains inactive 2 to 4 weeks, although this stage may last until the following spring. When the moth emerges from the pupal cell, it leaves the soil to mate and lay eggs for the next brood.

Control: Despite its large size and formidable-appearing horn, the hornworm is an easy prey to its natural enemies. The half-grown hornworm is the victim of a tiny wasp (*Apanteles congregatus*), which hunts it down and lays its eggs within the hornworm's body cavity. As many as 377 grubs of this wasp have been found feeding within a single hornworm. The grubs mature in a week or two and form white cocoons attached to the back of the weakened hornworm, giving it an appearance of being covered with tiny eggs. The parasitized hornworm becomes weaker and more sluggish and soon dies. The mature grubs of the wasp usually remain in the cocoon for 3 or 4 days, and then enter the pupal stage, which also lasts 3 or 4 days, after which the adult wasp emerges. Some of the grubs, however, do not pupate until the following spring, but remain in cocoons that have fallen to the soil and become protected by debris.

The wasp and other natural enemies do much to reduce hornworm numbers, but they cannot be depended on to prevent damage to tobacco or tomato. When control measures are necessary, one of the following should be used:

Destroy tobacco plants as soon as the crop is harvested.

Hand-pick the hornworms from infested plants in small plantings.

Apply 10 percent TDE dust at 30 pounds per acre per application.

{PLATE LIII

TOBACCO HORNWORM AND AN ENEMY

A, Parasite cocoons and adult on hornworm (greatly magnified); *a,* hornworm eggs; *b,* young larva; *c,* mature larva; *d,* pupa; *e,* adult moth. (All stages of hornworm about natural size.)

PRAYING MANTID

Several kinds of praying mantids flourish in the United States. Two large, conspicuous species of Asiatic and European origins came into this country more than 50 years ago, presumably on nursery stock. Now they are quite commonly found in the Northeast. The Asiatic form, the larger, is about 3 inches long when full-grown.

Praying mantids have curious habits and odd structures. They got their name from the unusual way they hold up the forepart of the body and stout forelegs as if in prayer. They have no sting. The dark-colored saliva they eject from their mouths is harmless.

The species in the Northeast have one generation a year. The eggs are deposited during the fall in a soft mass about 1 inch or more in diameter on brambles, stems of grass, or the branches of low bushes. This braided-appearing, frothy mass hardens into a fibrous substance and becomes darker in color. Each female can deposit several egg masses, each containing about 50 eggs. Shortly after laying the eggs, she dies.

Hatching occurs the following spring when insect material is available for food. The mantid sheds its skin several times before it becomes mature in late summer. It is usually light-colored during the early stages and becomes darker with age. The full-grown females are larger and more robust than the males and have large, distended abdomens.

The mantids, their forelegs raised in front of their heads, are to be found on foliage and flowers frequented by various insects. They resemble somewhat the color of the foliage or flowers around them. Quietly they await the approach of any insect. Then with a quick movement they grasp the prey with their forelegs, which have rows of sharp teeth for holding the insect, and devour it. The young stages feed on aphids, small caterpillars, flies, and other soft-bodied insects. The older mantids are able to capture larger insects; when they are full-grown they can kill and devour beetles, caterpillars, wasps, and other large insects.

Mantids usually are considered beneficial insects because they destroy many insect pests. They do capture and devour honey bees and other beneficial insects, however. Mantids are not abundant enough in any one locality to be of any great value in the control of insect pests.

{*PLATE LIV*

PRAYING MANTID

b

b

a

c

d

Some of the developmental stages of a common mantid: *a*, egg mass attached to stem; *b*, newly hatched nymphs; *c*, large nymph; *d*, adult female feeding on grasshopper. (All stages about natural size.)

SQUASH BUG

The squash bug feeds by sucking the sap from the leaves of squash, pumpkin, and related plants. The leaves it attacks wilt rapidly and become black and crisp, as if the flow of the sap had been cut off or poisoned. Small plants may be killed outright. In older plants only some leaves or runners may be killed.

Only the unmated parent bugs can live through the winter. They hibernate in all kinds of protected places but prefer to hide under piles of boards or in buildings. In the spring, when the plants begin to develop runners, the bugs fly into the garden and lay eggs on the under sides of the leaves. The young, wingless nymphs emerge from the eggs in a week or two and begin feeding. They require about 4 to 6 weeks to reach maturity. There is one generation a year.

Control: Dust with 10 to 20 percent sabadilla seed powder. In small plantings, hand-pick the adults, nymphs, and eggs. Trap adults under small pieces of board laid on the soil around the plants. Collect and kill trapped bugs each morning.

A tiny tachinid fly (*Trichopoda pennipes*) preys on the squash bug and eventually causes its death. The fly deposits its eggs on the mature or nearly mature squash bug. In 3 or 4 days a maggot hatches from each egg. The maggot bores into the squash bug, where it begins to develop when the squash bug matures. Only one maggot develops in each bug. In summer 2 to 3 weeks is required for the maggot to become full-grown. During that time the squash bug continues to live but gradually becomes unable to produce eggs. When it is mature, the maggot bores its way out, finds its way to the ground, and enters the soil to pupate. The squash bug is killed by the emergence of its parasite. The pupal stage of the tachinid maggot ordinarily lasts about 2 weeks. There are several generations a year. If winter sets in, however, the fly passes the winter as a maggot within the body of the squash bug, and does not mature until spring.

{PLATE LV

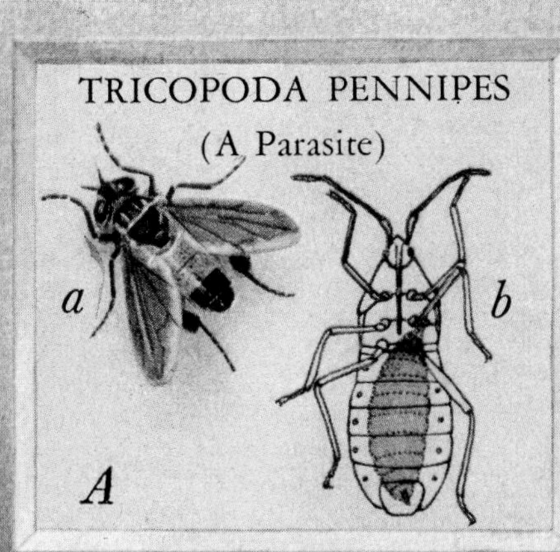

SQUASH BUG

A, a, the parasite fly; *b,* diagram of a squash bug showing relative size and location of parasite larva in the host. *B,* Some of the life stages of squash bug; *c,* eggs; *d,* newly hatched nymph; *e,* half-grown nymph; *f,* adult. *C,* Damaged plant; *g,* egg mass; *h,* nymphs a few hours old; *i,* adult. (*A* and *B,* about twice natural size.)

STINK BUGS

Stink bugs attack a wide variety of plants. Several species seriously damage cotton in all areas where cotton is grown. They feed largely on bolls and seldom invade the cotton fields in large numbers until the plants are fruiting. They insert their needlelike beaks into the bolls and suck the juice from the immature seed. The punctures may cause the shedding of young bolls. Small bolls become soft, turn yellowish, and fall off. Punctured bolls not thrown off by the plants may show injury varying from a slight stain in one lock of the mature boll to what is termed an "unpickable" boll or a boll in which every lock has been punctured. Severe injury results in a mummified, prematurely half-opened boll in which the lint in every lock is stained, short, weak, and of little marketable value. If populations are heavy and uncontrolled, the yield might be reduced more than half and the grade of lint and seed lowered greatly.

The southern brown stink bug occurs in all the cotton-growing States as far west as New Mexico. The closely related Arizona brown stink bug attacks cotton in New Mexico, Arizona, and California. The range of the southern green stink bug covers the extreme southern portion of the United States, although at times it occurs north of this area. The most serious damage to cotton has been noted in the Southeastern States. The Say stink bug occurs most abundantly in Texas, Oklahoma, New Mexico, Arizona, and California. The conchuela occurs most often on cotton in Texas and New Mexico.

Control: Stink bugs can be controlled on cotton by dusts containing enough benzene hexachloride to give 3 percent of the gamma isomer plus 5 percent of DDT and 40 percent of sulfur, or sufficient benzene hexachloride to give 2 percent of the gamma isomer plus 10 percent of DDT and 40 percent of sulfur. Also, a dust containing 15 percent of toxaphene plus 5 percent of DDT and 40 percent of sulfur may be used. These dusts should be applied at the rate of 10 to 15 pounds per acre.

Two treatments with sprays made from emulsion concentrates have given effective control: Benzene hexachloride to give 0.4 pound of the gamma isomer per acre; and benzene hexachloride to give 0.3 pound of the gamma isomer plus 0.75 pound of DDT per acre.

{PLATE LVI

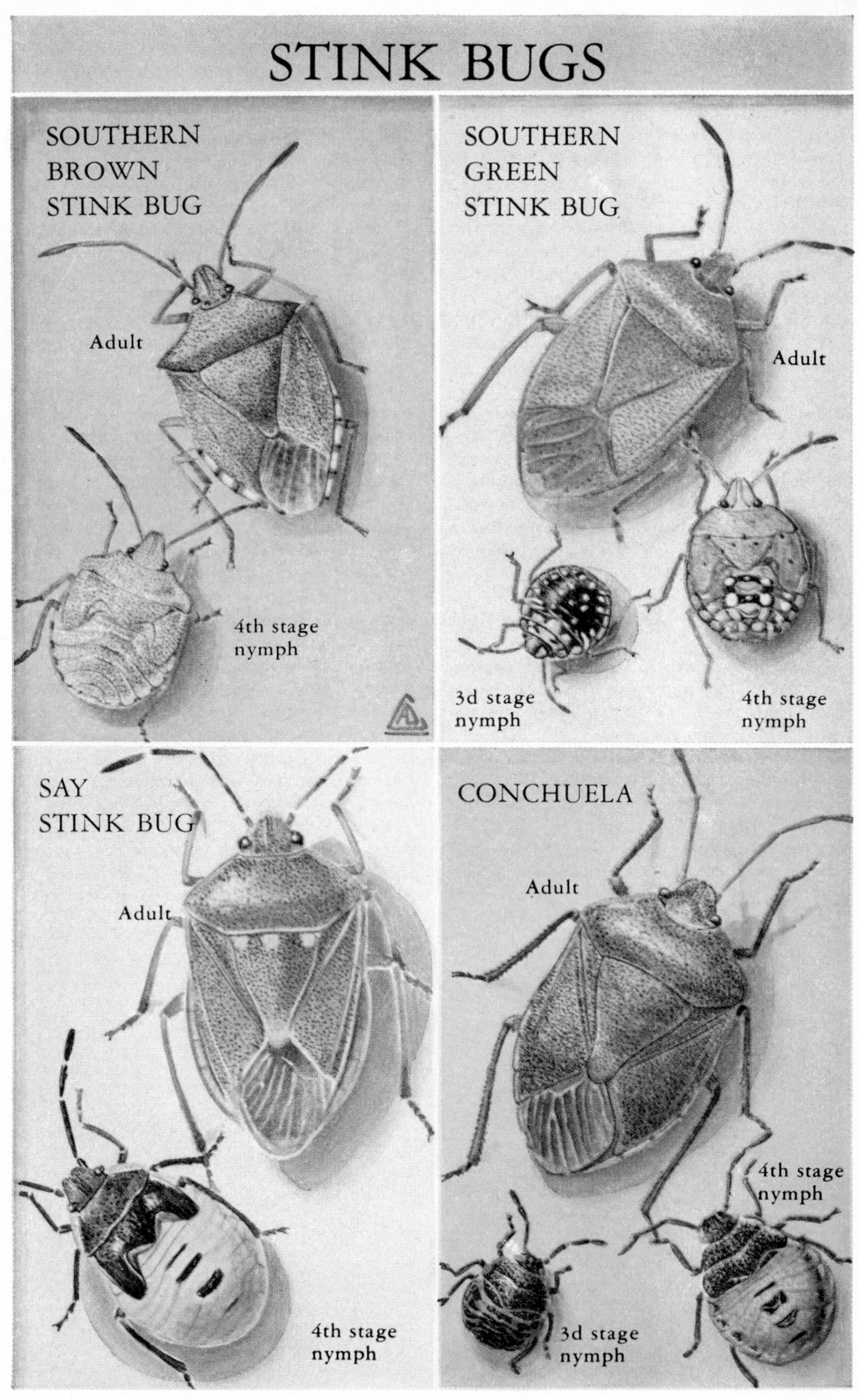

(All stages about three times natural size.)

CORN EARWORM

The corn earworm, also known as the tomato fruitworm and the bollworm, attacks many cultivated crops. It is discussed here only as an enemy of corn. The moth lays its eggs usually on the corn silks. The eggs hatch in 2 to 8 days. The tiny larvae or caterpillars feed downward, following the silks into the ear tip. Serious damage to the ear frequently results from their feeding and from the fermentation or molds that follow. The full-grown larva leaves the ear, enters the soil, and becomes a pupa; from it the moth emerges. The development from egg to adult takes about 30 days in midsummer. Pupae produced in late summer or in fall may pass the winter in the soil and become moths the following spring or early summer. Usually two generations are developed annually in the North, but in the South there may be five generations or more.

Control: Injury to field corn can be reduced by growing strains with long, tight husks and, in the South, by planting early.

Sweet corn can be protected by spraying. Prepare an emulsion by mixing 3 quarts of 25 percent DDT emulsifiable concentrate (obtainable commercially) and 2½ gallons of white mineral oil of 65 to 95 seconds Saybolt viscosity thoroughly with water to make 25 gallons. For a smaller quantity use one-fourth pint of the DDT emulsifiable concentrate and three-fourths pint of the oil with water to make 1 gallon of spray. Apply the spray to the ears 1 day after silks appear in the field and again 2 days later. A third application 2 days after the second usually increases the control. Spray only enough of the mixture onto the silks to wet them. Twenty-five gallons of the spray is enough for 1 acre of corn; 1 gallon will take care of a plot about 17 by 100 feet.

A spray similarly prepared, but including only 1¼ gallons of mineral oil in a 25-gallon lot, can be applied to the entire plant to reduce "budworm" damage by the earworm to sweet corn before tasseling and silking.

Any good hand sprayer is satisfactory for treating garden plots of sweet corn. For commercial acreage use a high-clearance power sprayer with hollow-cone nozzles adjusted to give adequate but not excessive coverage of the ears. Shake the emulsion well so that the oil will not separate.

The earworm can also be controlled in small plantings of sweet corn by injecting into the silk at the tip of each ear about one-fourth teaspoonful of refined white mineral oil. If obtainable, use a ready-mixed oil containing 0.2 percent of pyrethrins. Apply with a pump-type, long-spouted oilcan, or use a glass medicine dropper filled about half full of oil for a small ear and three-fourths full for a large ear. Do not apply until the silks have wilted and have begun to turn brown at the tips. Earlier treatment will interfere with pollination and result in poorly filled ears.

Because of the danger of poisonous residues, husks or other parts of corn plants treated with DDT should not be fed to dairy animals or to meat animals being finished for slaughter.

[PLATE LVII

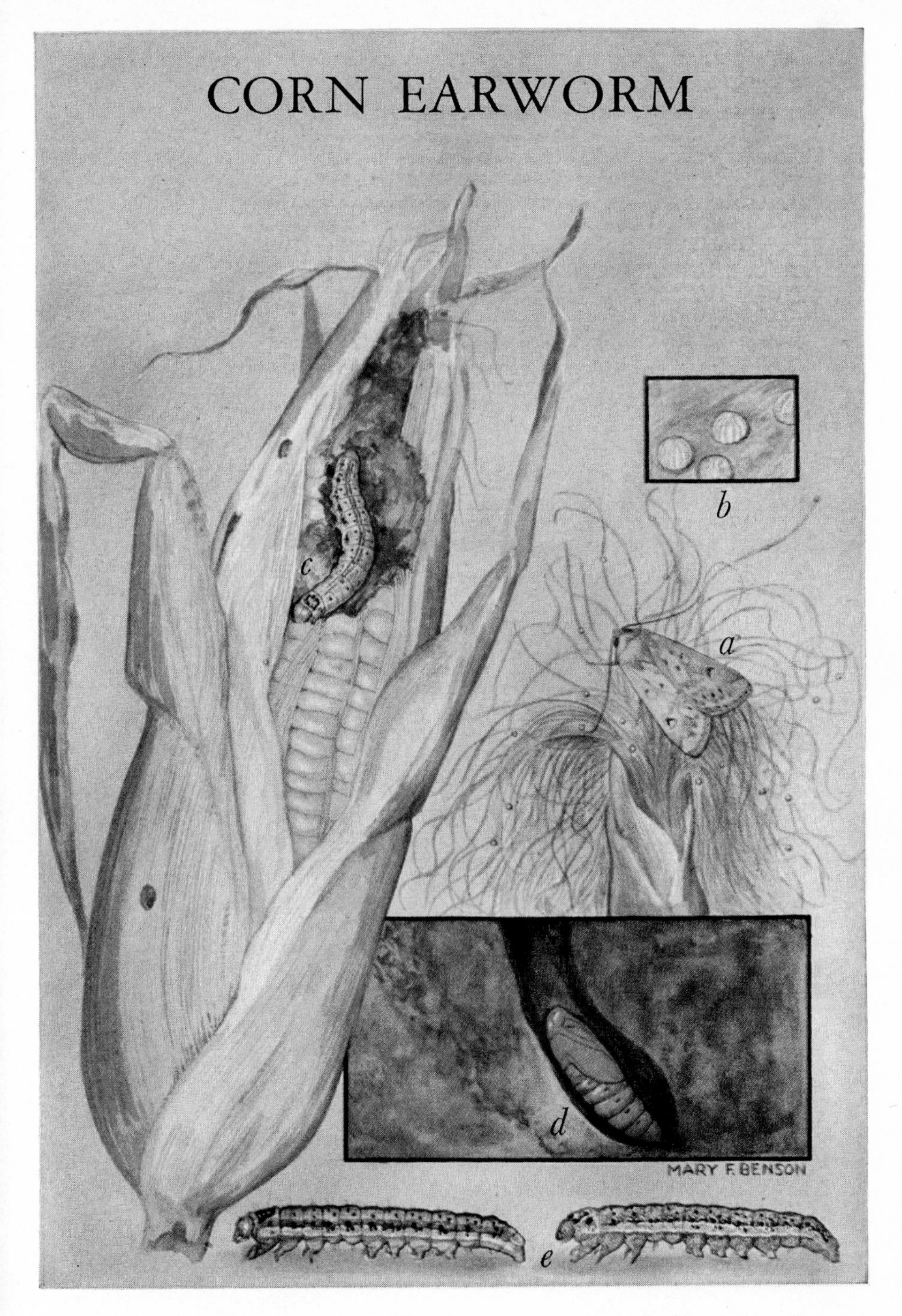

a, Moth (or adult) and eggs on silks; *b,* eggs; *c,* earworm feeding in ear of corn; *d,* pupa in a cell; *e,* color phases of the earworm. (All except *b,* about natural size; *b,* five and one-half times natural size.)

FALL ARMYWORM

The fall armyworm is known mainly as an enemy of growing corn, but it feeds on many other cultivated crops (alfalfa, cotton, peanuts, grasses) and wild plants. The eggs are laid at night on grasses or other plants and hatch in about 5 days. The young larvae (caterpillars or "worms") feed at first near the ground, become full-grown in about 20 days, and then enter the soil for a few inches and change into pupae. The inactive pupal stage lasts about 10 days. After the moths emerge from the pupal cases they often fly many miles before the females lay eggs. The fall armyworm may have as many as six generations a year in the Gulf States but does not survive the winter farther north. Besides eating the blades of corn and boring into the stalks, the larvae may bore into the ears, particularly the shanks of the ears, and feed extensively therein.

Control: The fall armyworm can be controlled with the following sprays: (1) 2 pounds per acre of a wettable powder containing 50 percent of either DDT or TDE, mixed with 40 gallons of water. (2) A toxaphene emulsifiable concentrate, applied by aircraft at the rate of 1½ to 2 pounds of toxaphene in 2 gallons of spray per acre.

A dust containing 5 percent of DDT, toxaphene, or TDE, at the rate of 40 pounds per acre and a 20 percent toxaphene dust at 10 to 15 pounds per acre also give good control.

To control "budworm" damage in sweet corn, caused by the feeding of the worm deep in the whorls of the corn plant, spray with an emulsion made with 3 quarts of a 25 percent DDT emulsifiable concentrate, 5 quarts of a white mineral oil of 65 to 95 seconds Saybolt viscosity, and enough water to make 25 gallons of spray. Apply the spray at the rate of 25 gallons per acre.

When the worms are crawling over the ground in large numbers they may be destroyed by broadcasting a poisoned bait thinly over the infested fields, and moderate infestations in corn may sometimes be controlled by light sprinklings of the bait in the leaf whorls. To prepare this bait mix 50 pounds of wheat bran with 2 pounds of paris green, and then add 6 gallons of water to make a damp mash. This amount is enough for 2 to 3 acres.

Hay or forage that has been treated with DDT, TDE, or toxaphene should not be fed to dairy animals or to meat animals being finished for slaughter.

{PLATE LVIII

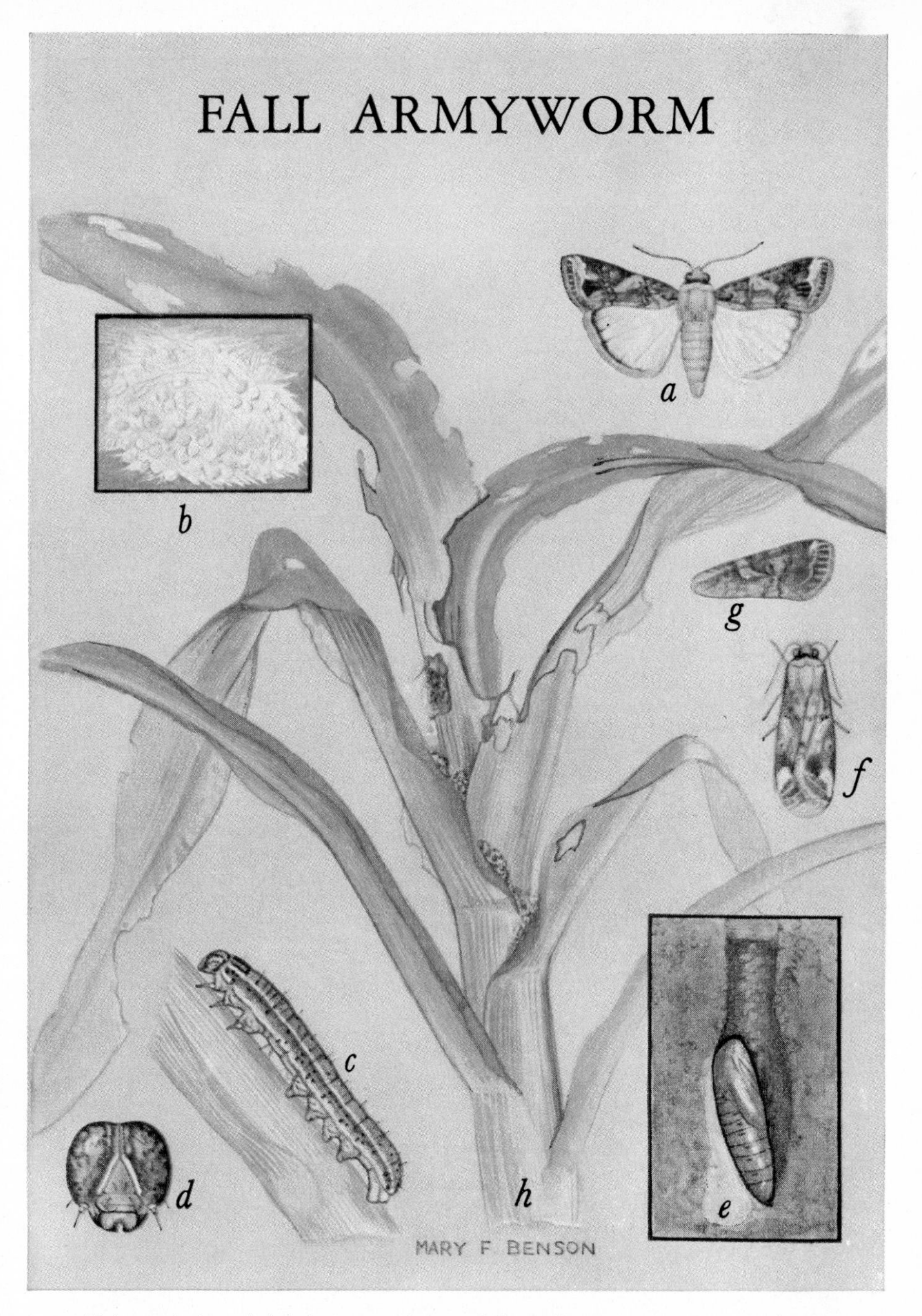

a, Male moth (or adult); *b,* eggs; *c,* larva; *d,* face of larva; *e,* pupa in a cell; *f,* moth in resting posture; *g,* wing of female moth; *h,* feeding injury to corn plant. (*a, c, e, f, g, h,* about one and one-third times natural size; *b,* twice natural size; *d,* eight times natural size.)

EUROPEAN CORN BORER

The European corn borer attacks many cultivated crops and weeds. Its favorite host plant is corn. The eggs (laid overlapping one another like fish scales in masses of 15 to 20 or more on the under sides of the corn leaves) hatch in 4 to 9 days. The tiny borers immediately crawl to protected places on the plants, where they feed on the tissues of the immature leaves and tassels. Eventually they bore into the stalks and ears. They mature in about a month and, after providing an exit for the adult moth, change to pupae inside the burrows, either at once or after an inactive period. In 10 to 14 days the adult moths emerge from the pupal cells and lay about 400 eggs each on corn or other plants that they may find in an attractive stage of growth. The moths live from 10 to 24 days. They are active fliers during the evening or night and may migrate several miles. The insects pass the winter in the borer stage inside infested stems of corn or other plants, where they change to moths late in the spring or early in the summer. There are one or more generations a year, depending on the length of the growing season in different latitudes.

Control: A. Destroy the overwintering borers by disposing of the infested cornstalks—by feeding to livestock direct or as silage or in finely cut or shredded form; by plowing under clean in the fall or in early spring before the moths emerge, using attachments such as trash shields, wires, or chains to insure burial of all stalks; or by burning infested plants completely, where other methods of disposal cannot be used.

B. Plant as late as practicable, but only within the normal planting period adapted to the locality. Moths of the first brood lay their eggs on the earliest planted corn.

C. Plant resistant or tolerant kinds of hybrid corn. No immune strains are available, but hybrids differ in their resistance and tolerance. Select types that will mature when planted moderately late. Consult your county agent or your State experiment station on the best hybrids to plant in your locality.

D. Modify cropping practices: Avoid sowing fall wheat or other small grain in standing corn or corn stubble. Plow the cornstalks under clean or cut them at ground level and remove them before seeding small grain. Dispose of all early sweet cornstalks in fields and gardens immediately after harvesting the ears, by feeding, ensiling, or plowing them under. Dispose of cobs and other remnants from the cannery in the same manner.

E. Use insecticides where profitable. Consult your county agent or State experiment station for current recommendations.

[PLATE LIX

EUROPEAN CORN BORER

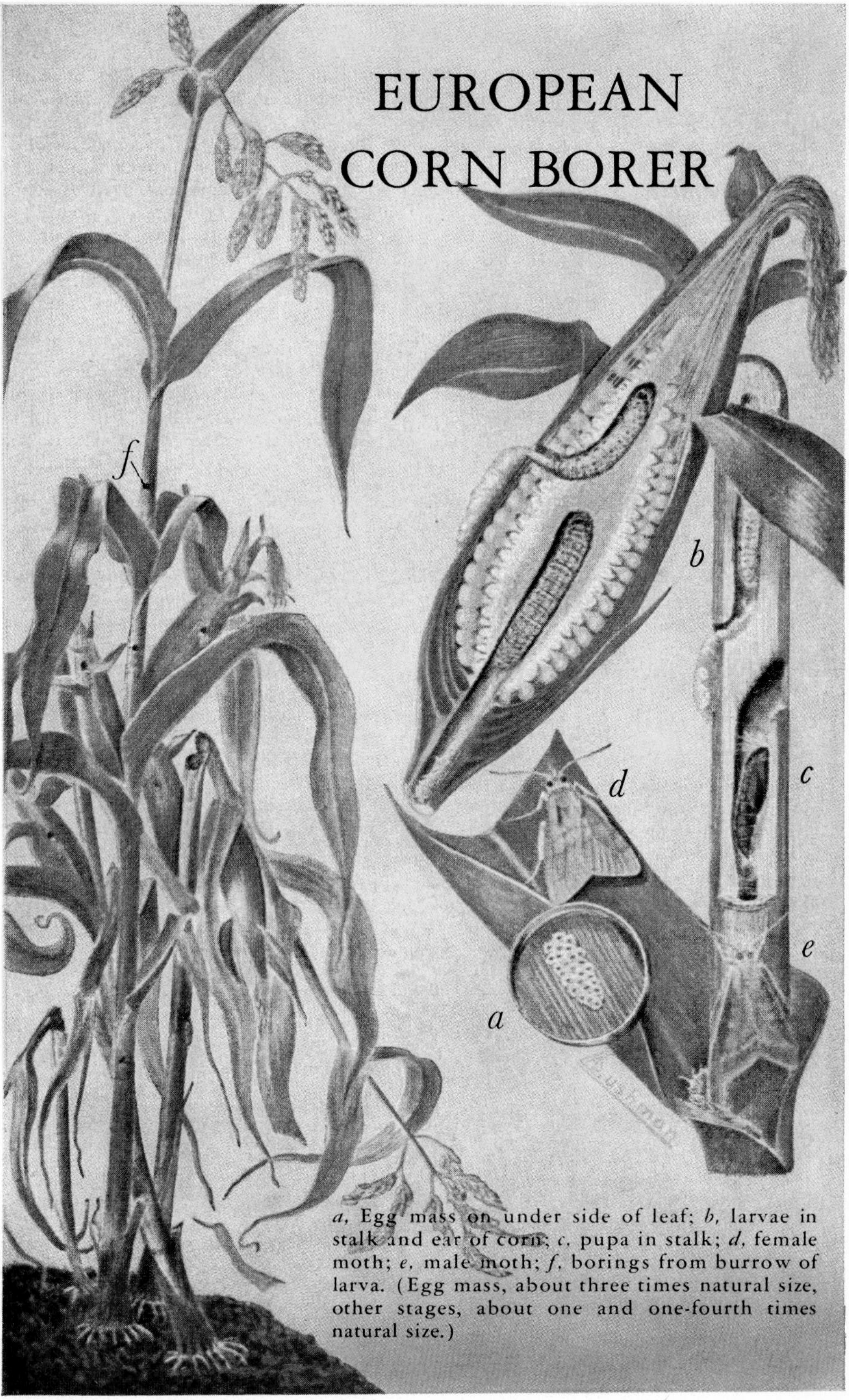

f

b

d

c

e

a

a, Egg mass on under side of leaf; *b,* larvae in stalk and ear of corn; *c,* pupa in stalk; *d,* female moth; *e,* male moth; *f,* borings from burrow of larva. (Egg mass, about three times natural size, other stages, about one and one-fourth times natural size.)

WHITE-FRINGED BEETLE

White-fringed beetle grubs live in the soil and feed on the roots of many kinds of plants, including beans, cotton, corn, peanuts, potatoes, various weeds, and ornamentals. They feed most heavily in the spring when nearly full-grown.

The three species and several races of white-fringed beetles are similar in appearance and habits. The one illustrated is *Graphognathus leucoloma striatus.*

About 310,000 acres of land in Alabama, Florida, Georgia, Louisiana, Mississippi, North Carolina, South Carolina, and Tennessee were known to be infested with beetles in 1951.

The insects pass the winter as grubs. In spring or early summer most of the grubs change to adults in little cells, which they form in the soil. The adults—all of them wingless females—normally emerge from the soil during the summer. They lay their eggs in small masses, usually attached to plant stems, sticks, or pebbles at or just below the soil surface. A single beetle may live 2 or 3 months and lay 600 to 700 eggs. The eggs hatch in about 2 weeks in warm, moist weather, and the grubs immediately enter the soil, where they remain until full-grown. There is usually one generation a year.

Control: The Department of Agriculture is cooperating with State agencies in the control of white-fringed beetles and the maintenance of quarantines to prevent their spread.

Control of larvae by soil treatment. Apply 10 pounds of DDT per acre uniformly to the soil surface as a dust (example, 200 pounds of a 5 percent DDT dust) by hand or with a mechanical distributor, or apply as a spray. Disk or cultivate immediately into the top 3 inches of soil.

Control of adults by foliage applications. Spray yards, vacant lots, idle fields, shrubs, flowers, or other plants not used as food for man or animals with ½ to 1 pound of DDT per acre in a water suspension or an emulsion. Apply the spray every 10 to 15 days throughout the beetle season. For a suspension spray use 2 pounds of a wettable powder containing 50 percent of DDT in 100 gallons of water, or, for small quantities, ⅓ ounce of this powder in 1 gallon of water. DDT emulsions have greater residual value than suspensions. Ready-prepared emulsions are obtainable and should be used according to directions on the container.

In gardens, pastures, or on crops to be used as food, apply 8 to 10 pounds of cryolite in 100 gallons of water per acre at intervals of 7 to 10 days throughout the season.

Control by cultural practices. Legume crops are favored by white-fringed beetles. Keep infestations low by the following practices: Plant oats or other small grains in heavily infested fields. Do not plant more than one-fourth of the cropland in annual legumes each year, and do not plant the same land to these crops more than once in 3 or 4 years. Do not intercrop corn with peanuts, soybeans, crotalaria, or velvetbeans. Practice clean cultivation. Fertilize corn or cotton heavily with commercial fertilizer or by turning under a winter cover crop.

{PLATE LX

WHITE-FRINGED BEETLE

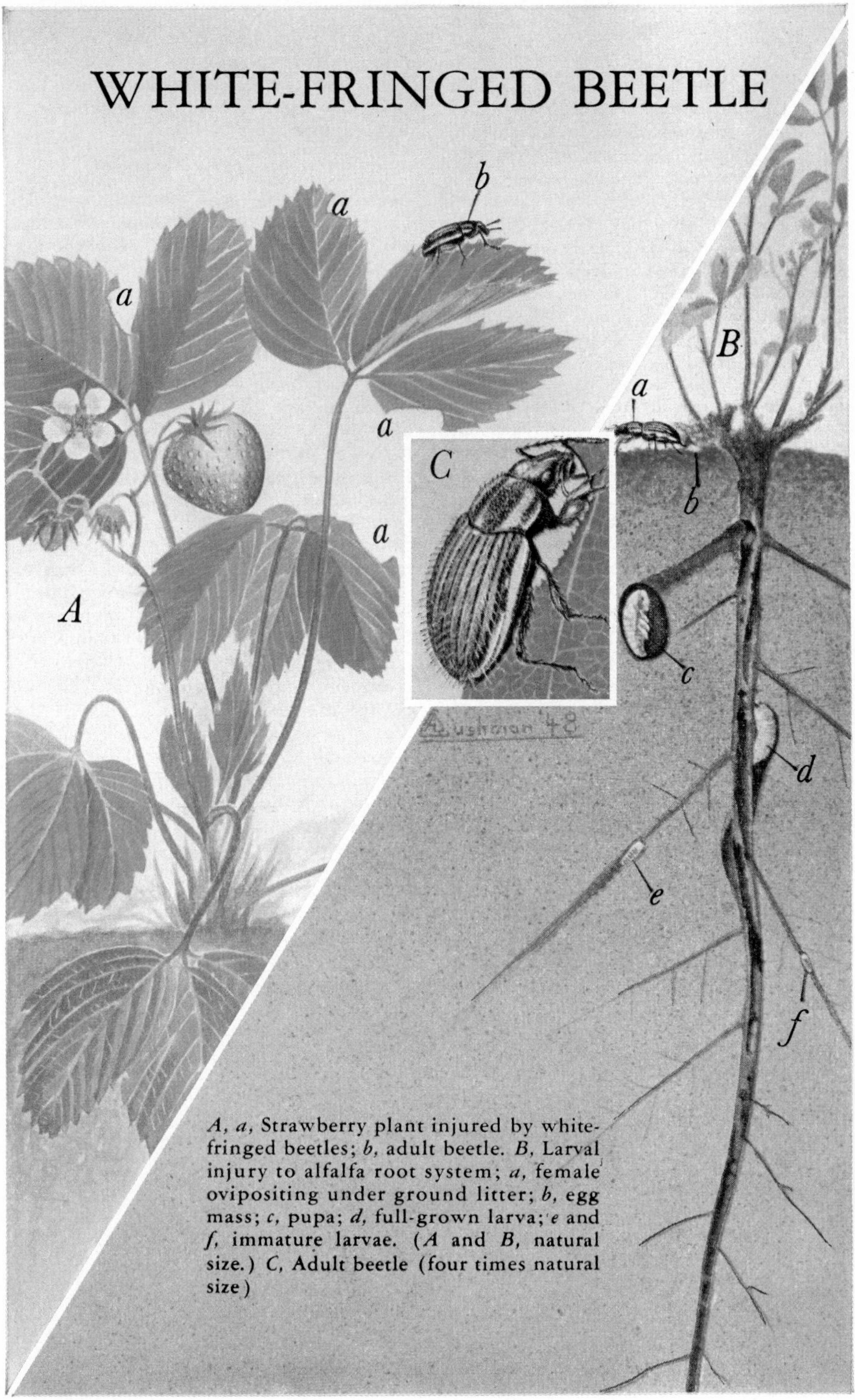

A, a, Strawberry plant injured by white-fringed beetles; *b,* adult beetle. *B,* Larval injury to alfalfa root system; *a,* female ovipositing under ground litter; *b,* egg mass; *c,* pupa; *d,* full-grown larva; *e* and *f,* immature larvae. (*A* and *B,* natural size.) *C,* Adult beetle (four times natural size)

ALFALFA WEEVIL

The alfalfa weevil was brought to Utah from Europe about 1900 and has since spread into Arizona, California, Colorado, Idaho, Montana, Nebraska, Nevada, Oregon, South Dakota, and Wyoming. The larvae feed on the growing tips, leaves, and buds of alfalfa and may destroy most of the feed value of a hay crop or prevent the profitable production of seed. The weevil is essentially a pest of first-growth alfalfa. When the first growth is cut for hay, however, weevil larvae feed upon the basal shoots and retard the second growth for a few days to several weeks. This is especially serious in dry-land farming or second-crop seed production.

The insects winter chiefly as adults, mostly in the alfalfa fields. Soon after the snow melts, the females lay their first eggs in fragments of dead stems on the ground. After the spring growth of the alfalfa is about 6 inches high, the weevils gradually shift their egg laying to the growing plant stems. The number of eggs per female averages about 400, most of which are laid in April and May. Hatching generally begins in April, but larvae do not become numerous enough to cause economic crop damage until late May or early June, about the time the first growth of alfalfa produces buds. Meanwhile, almost all of the early larvae and many of the later ones have become parasitized by a tiny wasp, *Bathyplectes curculionis,* commonly called the weevil parasite. Starting about May 15, the weevil larvae complete their growth, drop to the ground, and spin lacelike cocoons, usually attaching them to fallen leaves. Parasitized larvae die after they spin their cocoons. Healthy larvae pupate inside their cocoons and change to adults in from 7 to 10 days. Weevil adults then leave their cocoons but remain sexually immature until fall or spring. Consequently there is only one generation of weevils each year.

Control: Alfalfa for hay—maintain a dense, vigorously growing stand of alfalfa. Cut the first and second crops when most plants are in the bud stage. Mow the field clean and remove the hay as soon as it is cured. Do not irrigate the field for 7 to 10 days after cutting. *Early spring treatment to kill the adults:* Apply one-fourth pound of dieldrin or 1.5 to 2 pounds of chlordane per acre as a spray when the spring growth of alfalfa is 1 to 2 inches tall. This application will usually be made between March 15 and April 15, depending on the locality and the season. *May or June treatment to kill the larvae:* Dust or spray the crop as soon as plants become noticeably riddled but before many have turned gray, with 2 pounds of calcium arsenate, 1 to 2 pounds of methoxychlor, or one-fourth pound of parathion per acre. Do not cut hay treated with calcium arsenate or methoxychlor for 7 to 10 days after treatment. Leave parathion-treated hay uncut for at least 14 days.

Alfalfa for seed—apply the dieldrin or chlordane treatment as for hay crops to kill adults in the early spring. When the plants reach the bud stage of development, treat with 2 pounds of DDT as a dust or 1.5 pounds as a spray per acre. This treatment is prescribed to control lygus bugs and several other pests of seed alfalfa as well as alfalfa weevil.

Do not feed alfalfa treated with DDT to dairy animals, animals being finished for slaughter, or poultry.

{PLATE LXI

ALFALFA WEEVIL

A, Larva feeding on tip of alfalfa plant. *B*, Area at ground level showing *a*, eggs in living and dead stems; *b*, pupa in cocoon; *c*, adult weevil. (*A* and *B*, about three times natural size.) Upper left shows general feeding damage and *d*, larvae. Lower right shows adults, *e*, in lower portions of plant (all natural size)

LYGUS BUGS

Lygus bugs thrive on a wide range of cultivated and uncultivated plants. They cause severe damage to seed alfalfa. They are active from early spring to late fall. The adults fly freely from one host to another and from farm to farm. They breed continuously during the growing season. In the latitude of Utah there are three to four generations a year, each taking 6 to 7 weeks; in more southern regions, such as Arizona, a generation requires from 20 to 30 days, and the insects breed most of the year.

During cold weather the adults find protection among dormant alfalfa plants or in various crop debris. With the coming of warm weather they seek early-flowering weeds. The females insert their eggs singly in the plant tissues. Later they also deposit their eggs in alfalfa. The eggs hatch in 10 to 15 days. The hatch is usually concentrated during the period when alfalfa plants are budding or blooming. The insects become full-grown and change to adults in about 3 weeks. The new adults usually fly to more succulent alfalfa or other plants and begin to lay eggs in about 10 days.

The young lygus bugs, or nymphs, feed extensively on the buds of alfalfa, causing them to wilt and die. Sometimes such destruction by a large population of nymphs is severe enough to prevent flowering of the plants. At other times the bugs feed on the flowers and cause them to drop. They will also feed on the pods, causing the injured seeds to shrivel and turn brown. Vegetative growth of the plant is also impaired and distorted. The nymphs feed more constantly than the adults and are thus more destructive.

Control: Alfalfa grown for seed can often be adequately protected from lygus bugs by a single application of DDT as soon as the plants begin to bud. Use 20 to 25 pounds of 10 percent DDT dust per acre or a spray containing at least 1.5 pounds of actual DDT per acre.

Sometimes the crop is reinfested during the bloom period to an extent that a second application of insecticide is needed. Generally, excessive reinfestation occurs when the first growth is left for seed or when pollination is deficient and slow. If a second treatment is desirable, toxaphene may be applied to the blooming plants before 7 a. m., or after 7 p. m., when bees are not working in the field. Dust with 20 pounds of 10 percent toxaphene per acre or spray with 1.5 pounds of actual toxaphene per acre. The best time for this application is 3 to 4 weeks after the bud stage treatment with DDT.

Forage or chaff treated with DDT or toxaphene should not be fed to dairy animals, animals being fattened for slaughter, or poultry.

[PLATE LXII

A, Normal alfalfa plant; *a*, undamaged blooms; *b*, well-developed seed pods; *c*, nymphs; *d*, adult lygus bugs. *B*, Badly damaged plant showing *e*, relatively short internodes and *f*, completely blasted flower buds. *C*, *g*, Normal alfalfa seeds; *h*, lygus-damaged seeds. (*A* and *B*, about three times natural size; *C*, greatly enlarged.)

CHINCH BUG

The chinch bug is mainly a pest of corn and sorghums, but it may injure small grains and other grass crops. As adults the bugs hibernate chiefly in clump-forming native prairie grasses or, lacking them, in hedgerows, bushy and grassy fence rows, and the south and west edges of woodlands. The spring flights of overwintering bugs occur on sunny days when the temperature remains at 70° F. or more for several hours. They usually fly to fields of small grains but in some years may go directly to early-planted corn or sorghums. Each female lays an average of 200 eggs over a period of 3 to 4 weeks. The eggs are deposited behind the leaf sheath, in the ground around the plants, or on the roots. They hatch in 7 to 14 days.

As the small grains ripen, the young bugs move into adjacent fields of young corn, sorghum, or other grass plants. In the northern section of their habitat, the migration is on foot; in the southern area the adults may fly. Mating takes place again, and the eggs of a second generation are deposited on the host plants. During the warm fall afternoons the chinch bugs fly to their winter quarters. There are two or more generations a year, depending on the length of the growing season.

Control: Grow immune or resistant crops. Plant nongrass crops adjacent to fields of small grains. Growing of legumes among small grains and corn often helps to produce shade and dampness in which the chinch bugs thrive. Plant strains of corn and sorghums that are resistant to the attacks of chinch bugs. No immune strains are available, but strains differ in their resistance and tolerance. Consult your county agent or your State agricultural experiment station on the best hybrids to plant in your locality. Modify farm practices to reduce infestation. Chinch bugs will reproduce faster on barley than other small grains and the planting of this crop (especially spring barley) should be avoided when there is a prospect of an abundance of chinch bugs. Anything that can be done to produce a thick, vigorous growth of small grain such as thorough tillage, ample fertilization, and timely seeding helps to reduce injury from the bugs. In the South, plant sorghums as early as practical; if possible, do not plant corn until after the chinch bugs have migrated from winter quarters. Several types of barriers are effective in preventing the chinch bugs from crawling from small grain into adjacent corn and sorghums. The best barriers include a narrow band of either a repellent such as coal-tar creosote oil or insecticidal dusts containing DDT or dinitro-*o*-cresol. Detailed instructions for building chinch bug barriers may be obtained from your State agricultural experiment station. Use insecticides on lawns, valuable grasses, grains or where the bugs are confined to the border rows of corn or sorghums. Insecticide formulations containing nicotine, rotenone, sabadilla, DDT, chlordane, and toxaphene have given good results.

Consult your county agent or State agricultural experiment station for current recommendations for your locality.

{PLATE LXIII

CHINCH BUG

Background shows chinch bugs leaving maturing wheat to feed on young corn. *A,* Life stages of the insect (greatly enlarged); *a,* eggs in wheat sheath; *b,* adult bug; *c,* red nymph; and *d,* black nymph.

WHITE GRUBS

White grubs are the young or immature stage of the common brown May beetles, of which there are more than 100 species. The grubs feed on the roots of bluegrass, timothy, corn, soybeans, and several other crops, and on the tubers of potato. They sometimes ruin bluegrass pastures in the Northeastern and North Central States and may be serious pests of nursery plantings. The adult beetles eat the leaves of oak, ash, hickory, poplar, elm, willow, locust, blackberry, pine, walnut, and other trees. Most of the injurious species have a 3-year life cycle and cause serious outbreaks in certain years.

The pearly-white eggs are deposited in the spring 1 to 8 inches deep in the soil. They hatch 3 or 4 weeks later into young grubs, which feed on decaying vegetation and even on living roots. The grubs do their greatest injury in their second year but in their third year may sometimes damage early plantings.

Control: Populations of white grubs can be reduced by planting the deep-rooted legumes such as sweetclover, alfalfa, and various clovers, which are unfavorable to these insects, in rotation with more susceptible crops, such as timothy and small grains. The use of legumes is most effective if they are planted in the years of major beetle flights. A system of renovating bluegrass pastures badly infested with white grubs has proved beneficial. The sod is thoroughly torn up during the late fall or early spring, treated with lime and fertilizer as needed, and sown in the spring with a seed mixture consisting mainly of legumes. These soon provide good pastures and are gradually replaced by the original bluegrass.

Lawns and golf courses infested with white grubs may be treated with 10 pounds of lead arsenate per 1,000 square feet of area. Chlordane has also given satisfactory control when applied to turf on golf courses at a dosage of 10 pounds of the technical material per acre in the form of a 5-percent dust, or as a spray preparation.

The inclusion of other crops, such as the clovers or alfalfa, in the rotation is recommended to combat white grub damage to soybeans or to corn following soybeans.

A spray prepared by mixing 2 pounds of lead arsenate, 1 pound of wheat flour or 8 fluid ounces of raw linseed oil, and 25 gallons of water has been used successfully to destroy the adult beetles feeding on tree foliage.

Keep small children and domestic animals away from turf treated with lead arsenate or chlordane until the insecticide has been washed into the soil.

{PLATE LXIV

WHITE GRUBS

A, Adult beetles feeding on white oak leaf. *B*, Grub feeding on roots of young corn plant. *C*, Life stages including *a*, eggs in earth cells; *b*, fully developed grub; and *c*, pupa in earth cell. (All about natural size.)

A

b

a

C

B

c

WHEAT STEM SAWFLY

The wheat stem sawfly is a serious pest of wheat in the northern Great Plains, particularly in Montana and North Dakota. It also attacks rye and to a lesser extent barley, oats, and flax. Several large-stemmed native grasses, such as the wheat, rye, and bromegrasses, are favored host plants.

The adult sawflies emerge from the stubble fields and native grasses in June and July. They fly to the young growing wheat plants, where the females deposit eggs singly in the hollow centers of the stems. The eggs hatch within a week. In the worm stage the insect mines up and down within the growing wheat stem. When full-grown, it cuts a groove around the inside of the stem at about ground level, and makes its overwintering cell in the base of the stem. Winter is spent by the mature larva just beneath the surface of the ground in the cell. Pupation takes place during May and June, resulting in the next generation of adults. There is but one generation of the sawfly annually.

Wheat losses from the sawfly occur in two ways: By shrinkage of the kernels in the heads of tunneled stems, and by total loss of the grain in the heads when infested stems break over in the wind and fall to the ground so that many of the heads cannot be picked up by the harvester.

Control: The sawfly cannot be controlled by the application of an insecticide. Crop losses can be reduced by using certain cultural practices.

Start harvesting as early as possible and before many of the stems have fallen. Where swathers and binders are used, cut the grain before it is quite ripe. In areas where straight combining is practiced, pick-up equipment on combines will salvage many fallen stems.

Cultivate infested wheat stubble in the fall by either deep plowing with a moldboard plow or by extremely shallow tillage. If shallow tillage is practiced, leave as much of the stubble on the surface as possible. Confine spring cultivation to deep plowing. In areas where soil blowing or washing is serious, follow the practice of extremely shallow cultivation.

Do not seed heavily infested fields to sawfly-susceptible wheat. Seed such fields to barley, oats, flax, corn, mustard, or other resistant crops. In Montana the sawfly-resistant wheat variety Rescue should be used if wheat is to be grown on infested fields. Crop rotations, if they provide for the seeding of wheat on sawfly-free fields, will help hold the sawfly in check.

{PLATE LXV

WHEAT STEM SAWFLY

A, Stubble showing cutting by larvae; *a*, larva in cell within wheat stem; *b*, pupa in stem. *B*, Growing wheat plants; *x*, stem split to show tunneling of larva inside; *c*, young larva and frass in stem; *y*, adult sawfly; *d*, adult female depositing eggs inside stem, with stem cut away to show egg within. (*a*, *b*, *c*, and *d*, all about three times natural size.)

HESSIAN FLY

In the winter-wheat region, the hessian fly injures wheat chiefly, but it may also attack barley and rye. The flies lay their eggs in the grooves of the upper surface of the leaves of young wheat. One female may deposit several hundred eggs and infest many plants as she flies over the grain field. The eggs hatch in 3 to 12 days, and the small red maggots make their way down the leaf and behind the sheath, where they begin feeding on the tender tissues of the plant. The maggots are full-grown in 2 to 4 weeks. They are then glistening white, but they soon turn brown, forming puparia or "flaxseeds." Adults emerge from the overwintering "flaxseeds" in early spring to lay their eggs. Small tillers of infested plants die; jointed tillers often break over and fall to the ground before harvest. Adults that emerge from "flaxseeds" in stubble and in volunteer plants of harvested fields infest early fall-seeded fields, with resultant stunting and death of tillers and plants.

Control: The control of the hessian fly in wheat depends on good farm management and community cooperation. The methods that have proved to be the best are as follows: Plow under the stubble of the last crop, where practicable, soon after harvest. Destroy volunteer plants so far as possible before the seeding period of the next crop. Prepare a good seedbed and maintain a high fertility in the soil. Use only the varieties of wheat recommended by your State agricultural experiment station or county agent, and sow at recommended "safe" dates for your locality. Cooperate with neighboring farmers in following approved practices.

[PLATE LXVI

A, Infested wheat plant. *B*, Uninfested. *C*, Infested stubble with puparia exposed. *a*. Puparium; *b*, larva; *c*, adult male; *d*, egg-laying female and eggs; *e*, puparia in base of stubble. (*a*, *b*, *c*, and *d*. about six times natural size; all others, natural size.)

MORMON CRICKET

Mormon crickets, a wingless form of grasshopper, are bad pests in the Western States. Their range extends from the Missouri River west to the Cascade and Sierra Nevada Mountains and from the Canadian line south to northern California, Nevada, Utah, and Colorado. Most of the crops grown there are susceptible, but the greatest damage has been done to range grasses as well as to dry-land wheat and alfalfa.

The eggs are laid during the late summer and fall in well-drained, light sandy-loam soil. They are inserted just under the soil surface in bare spots between clumps of grass or sagebrush. Unlike grasshopper eggs, which are in a pod, cricket eggs are laid singly. Each female lays about 150 eggs. The young crickets start hatching early in April and reach maturity about 6 to 8 weeks later. There is one generation a year.

Mormon crickets persist in small numbers year after year in rough foothill and mountainous country remote from farm lands. When weather conditions over a period of years are favorable for maximum reproduction, their numbers increase rapidly and they start migrating. One to 3 years usually elapse after migrations start before croplands are invaded.

Control: Mormon crickets can be easily killed in all stages by application of wet bait made according to either of the following formulas: (1) Standard wheat bran (no shorts or middling), 100 pounds; sodium fluosilicate, 4 pounds; water, 12 to 15 gallons. (2) Mill-run bran, 25 pounds; sawdust, 3½ bushels; sodium fluosilicate, 4 pounds; water, 8 to 10 gallons.

Mix the dry ingredients thoroughly, add the water slowly, and continue mixing until a moist crumbly mash is attained. The bait should be spread at about 20 pounds an acre in the forenoon while crickets are migrating. It should be broadcast at right angles to the direction of migrations.

The following dry-bait formula is well adapted to spreading by aircraft: Standard bran (no shorts or middlings), 100 pounds; toxaphene, 1 pound, or chlordane, one-half pound; fuel oil or kerosene, one-half gallon.

Dissolve toxicant in oil and spray onto bran while mixing. This bait can be applied at any time of day at the rate of 10 pounds per acre. It is not recommended for spreading by hand or with ground equipment.

[PLATE LXVII

MORMON CRICKET

a, Adult female with ovipositor thrust into ground; *b*, egg in soil; *c*, nearly mature female nymph; *d*, young nymph; *e*, nearly mature male nymphs. (All about natural size.)

WHEAT JOINTWORM

The wheat jointworm does damage that in some years amounts to millions of bushels of wheat. It is widespread throughout most of the wheat-growing regions east of the Mississippi River and in Missouri, Iowa, and parts of Utah, Oregon, and California.

Heads of infested wheat plants have fewer and smaller kernels and heavily infested fields show many broken straws and much lodging.

The adult jointworm looks like a small black ant with wings. It lays eggs early in the spring in the succulent plant stems. The larvae, small footless grubs, soon hatch and form cells in the wall of the stem, usually just above the second or third joint from the ground. By harvest the larvae are yellowish in color and about one-fourth inch long. Their cells or "galls" have now become hard and woody. Sometimes they appear as wartlike swellings, and the wheat stems are badly twisted and bent. In winter the larvae change to pupae, which are pale yellow at first but turn black later. In the spring the adults emerge through small circular holes which they gnaw through the walls of their cells. Mating soon takes place and the females leave the old stubble fields to find and infest green wheat fields in the vicinity. There is only one generation a year.

Control: The wheat jointworm may be controlled by plowing under the infested stubble, preferably late in the summer or early in the fall, to prevent the emergence of the adults during the following spring. When this is done the wheat should be cut as high as practicable so that most of the jointworms will be left in the standing stubble to be plowed under. Objections to control by plowing, because of its interference with the growing of red clover and other crops useful in soil conservation may be met by the temporary substitution of soybeans, sweetclover, and other crops for forage and green manure. For those areas infested with jointworm in Oregon it is recommended that winter barley or Winter Turf (Oregon Gray) oats be substituted for wheat as a nurse crop for red clover.

In Southern and Southeastern States, where double-cropping systems are in general use, and in Western States, where summer fallowing is practiced, it would be desirable to plow the stubble under throughout large areas and thus secure effective community control.

Where infested stubble has not been plowed, the wheat should be sown as far as practicable from such stubble fields. This will make it more difficult for the jointworm adults emerging from the old stubble to reach the new crops.

In areas where severe losses from the jointworm have occurred during the preceding season, land sown to wheat should be top-dressed only with manure containing straw that has been well rotted or thoroughly trampled. This helps to insure the death of jointworms that might otherwise emerge from the straw to reinfest the field.

If jointworm attacks are especially threatening it may be advisable to substitute temporarily other crops such as rye, barley, oats, or buckwheat for wheat. This can be done safely because the wheat jointworm attacks no other crops except wheat.

Insecticidal control of the wheat jointworm is not practical.

{PLATE LXVIII

WHEAT JOINTWORM

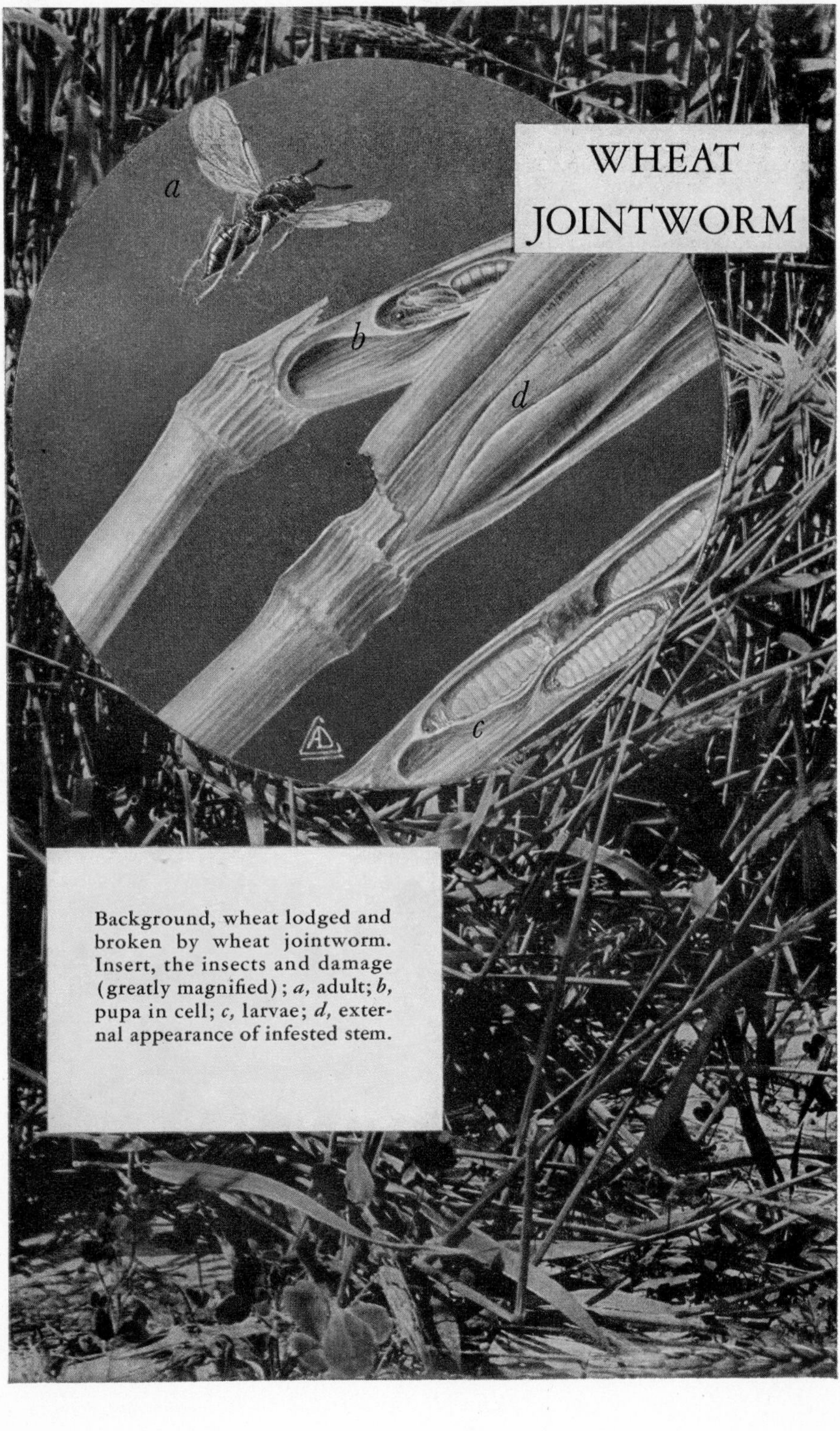

a

b

d

c

Background, wheat lodged and broken by wheat jointworm. Insert, the insects and damage (greatly magnified); *a,* adult; *b,* pupa in cell; *c,* larvae; *d,* external appearance of infested stem.

VELVETBEAN CATERPILLAR

The velvetbean caterpillar is frequently a serious pest in the Southeastern States where it attacks soybeans, velvetbeans, and peanuts, and also feeds on kudzu, alfalfa, horsebeans, and other plants. The insect is a tropical species which does not survive the winter in continental United States except perhaps in the most southerly tip of Florida. The moths fly into this country sometime in June or July and may produce as many as three generations during the season. The insect does not usually become very abundant until late summer or early fall. However, a heavy infestation of caterpillars may completely strip the plants in a field within a few days. The small white roundish eggs are laid singly on the lower surfaces of the leaves and hatch in from 3 to 5 days. The caterpillars feed for about 3 weeks. They are very active and will spring into the air wriggling rapidly when disturbed, at the same time spitting a brownish liquid. After completing feeding, the caterpillars enter the soil to pupate at depths of 1/4 to 2 inches. The adult moths emerge about 10 days later.

Control: The velvetbean caterpillar on soybeans, peanuts, and other crops may be controlled with a 3 percent DDT dust, a good dusting sulfur, or cryolite, applied at the rate of 15 pounds per acre, when the caterpillars are starting to hatch. A second application of cryolite may be necessary about 10 days later to destroy the newly hatched caterpillars. The dust should be applied in the late afternoon when the air is quiet.

If a crop is treated with DDT, it should not be fed to dairy animals, poultry, or meat animals being finished for slaughter.

[PLATE LXIX

Plant showing general feeding damage, *a; b,* larvae; *c,* pupa; *d,* moth. (All about natural size.)

POTATO LEAFHOPPER ON ALFALFA

The potato leafhopper is an important pest of alfalfa in the eastern half of the United States, as far west as Kansas. It also attacks many other plants. It is wedge-shaped, pale greenish-yellow, and about one-eighth inch long when full-grown. The females deposit their eggs in the petioles and in the larger veins of the leaves. In about a week the eggs hatch into wingless nymphs, which pass through five stages and become winged adults in 8 to 14 days. The period from egg to adult under most favorable conditions is about 3 weeks. The adults and nymphs are extremely active and feed on the petioles and lower surface of the leaves by sucking the plant juices. This leafhopper probably does not overwinter in the North but breeds throughout the year in Florida, and during most winters in other Gulf States. In the latitude of Washington, D. C., adults usually appear about May 3 to 10 and gradually become more abundant, causing yellowing and dwarfing of the second and third crop of alfalfa during July, August, and September. A severe attack causes the plants to wilt. Under favorable conditions, the leafhopper can build up its populations rapidly and cause important losses to both the quality and quantity of alfalfa. When young stands are injured, weeds and grass crowd out the alfalfa. Alfalfa is often so severely weakened by this leafhopper during the summer that it is unable to survive the following winter.

Control: The potato leafhopper can be controlled effectively on alfalfa with methoxychlor. Prepare a spray by mixing 1 quart of the 25-percent emulsifiable oil (one-half pound of methoxychlor) with 5 gallons of water and apply this amount per acre with sprayer at about 40 pounds pressure per square inch. Make the application midway in the development of the crop or earlier if the insect becomes abundant.

A delay of 10 days to 2 weeks in cutting the first crop, if this does not lower the quality of the hay, will destroy large numbers of eggs and young leafhoppers which otherwise would mature to adults and infest the next alfalfa crop.

{PLATE LXX

POTATO LEAFHOPPER ON ALFALFA

A, Damaged plant showing discolored leaves, short internodes, and lack of bloom. *B,* The insect (greatly enlarged); *a,* nymph; *b,* adult.

TWO GRASSHOPPERS

The two grasshoppers illustrated are among the most important and injurious species. The control measures recommended are useful against them and other species.

The differential grasshopper attacks crops over most of the United States but is seldom found north of the southern boundaries of Minnesota and North Dakota. It prefers heavy soil and rank-growing vegetation. Females deposit large egg pods, containing 50 to 75 yellow eggs, just below the ground surface in heavy sod along roadsides, fence rows, and field margins. Eggs are sometimes laid throughout alfalfa fields but seldom in grain or cultivated crops. They are laid during the summer and fall and hatch in the spring. There is only one generation each year.

The lesser migratory grasshopper attacks crops and range vegetation throughout the United States. Females deposit egg pods containing about 20 cream-colored eggs just below the ground surface in grain stubble, alfalfa fields, ditch banks, and weedy field margins. In Northern States eggs are laid in the summer and fall and hatch in the spring. In the South there are two or more generations each year. Adults sometimes gather in swarms and fly long distances.

Control: Sprays are more effective than dusts. Less material is needed and they kill over a longer period. Prepared oil solutions, emulsifiable concentrates, wettable powders, and dusts in various strengths are available at local dealers and may be diluted to suit available equipment. The insecticides may be applied with hand sprayers or dusters, power ground equipment, or airplanes. Take great care in diluting insecticides and adjusting equipment to insure application at the acre-dosages recommended.

In tall or dense succulent crops and in range grass use the following per-acre dosages—Aldrin sprays, 2 ounces; dusts, 3 ounces. Chlordane sprays, ½ to 1 pound; dusts, ¾ to 1½ pounds. Toxaphene sprays, 1 to 1½ pounds; dusts, 1½ to 2½ pounds.

Use the lower rate of chlordane and toxaphene for young grasshoppers when long-continued killing action is not essential. Use the higher dosages for older grasshoppers or when kills over a longer period are needed. When it is necessary to kill young grasshoppers before hatching is completed, the higher quantities may extend residual action long enough to kill the rest of the hatch and save the cost of a second treatment.

In dry vegetation and short, fall-seeded grain, bait is usually more effective than a spray or dust. Bait is also useful in gardens and on crops where insecticides applied to foliage might create health hazards. Oil concentrates are best for making dry baits. Measure out enough concentrate to obtain the active ingredient in one of the following quantities: Aldrin, 2 ounces; chlordane, one-half pound; or toxaphene, 1 pound; add kerosene to make one-half gallon of solution. Apply as a finely divided spray to 100 pounds of coarse bran.

To prepare a wet bait, use emulsifiable concentrates, employing the same quantity of active ingredient used in making dry bait. Add water to make 10 gallons of diluted emulsion and mix thoroughly with the bran. Distribute 5 pounds of dry bait or 20 pounds of wet bait per acre. Dry bait is best for airplane application but does not scatter well from wet-bait broadcasting machines. It can be stored and used when needed.

Do not feed forage or chaff contaminated with aldrin, chlordane, or toxaphene to dairy animals, to animals being finished for slaughter, or to poultry. If these insecticides are used on fruits or vegetables, do not apply them to the parts of the plants that will be eaten or marketed. If grasshoppers must be controlled on legumes for seed production while in bloom, spray with toxaphene in the early morning or late evening when bees are not active in the field.

Cultivation after harvest discourages egg laying by the lesser migratory grasshopper in fields of grain stubble. Do not drill grain into unworked stubble. Tillage before seeding will destroy many of the eggs.

{*PLATE LXXI. PLATE LXXII overleaf*

LESSER MIGRATORY GRASSHOPPER

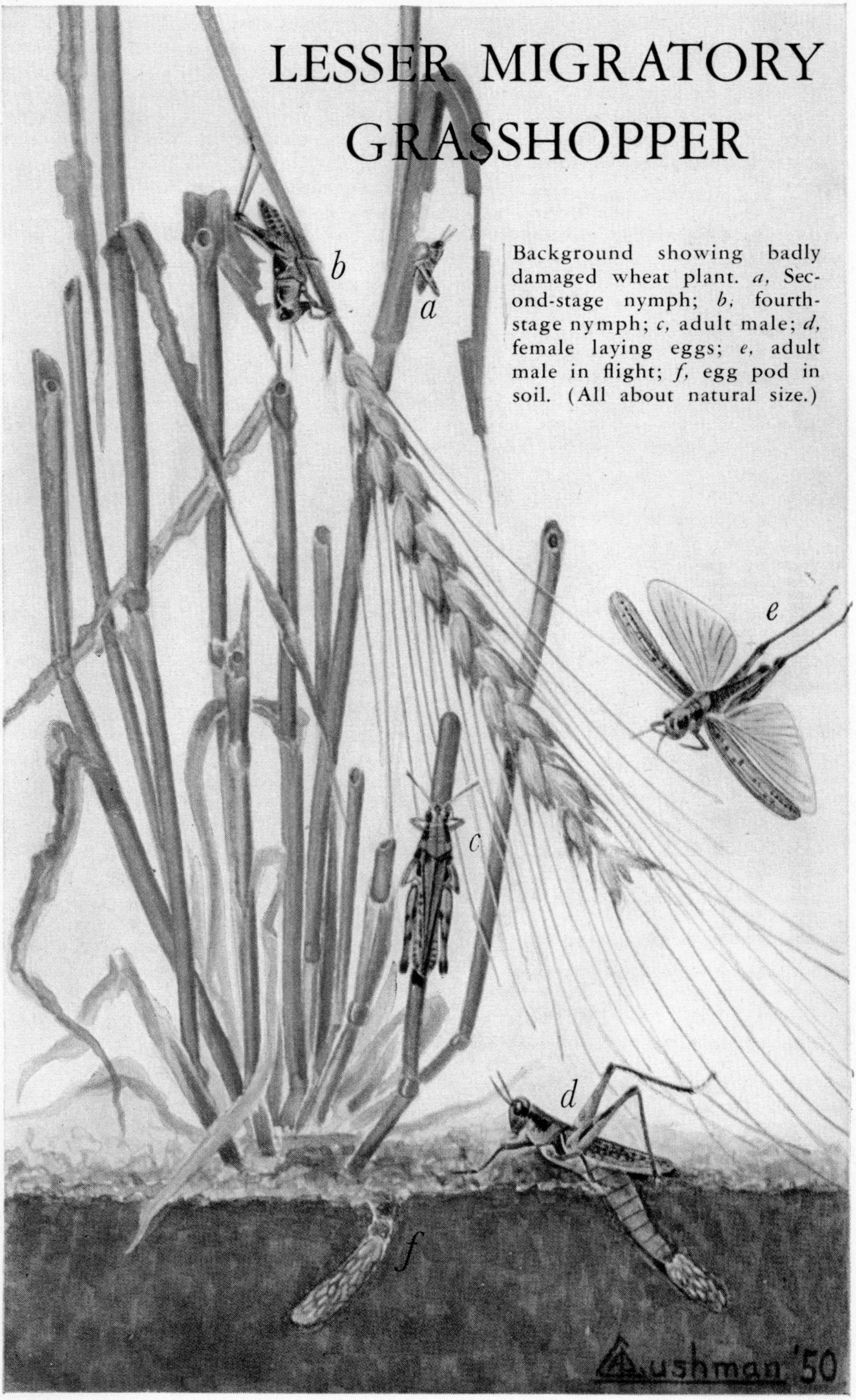

Background showing badly damaged wheat plant. *a,* Second-stage nymph; *b,* fourth-stage nymph; *c,* adult male; *d,* female laying eggs; *e,* adult male in flight; *f,* egg pod in soil. (All about natural size.)

DIFFERENTIAL GRASSHOPPER

A, Damage to leaves and ear of corn; *a*, small nymph; *b*, half-grown nymphs; *c*, male adult. *B*, Female adult laying eggs in the soil; *d*, egg pod. (All about natural size.)